D1621946

McGraw-Hill Modern Men of Science
Volume II   ☆ ☆

McGraw-Hill

McGRAW-HILL BOOK COMPANY

NEW YORK   ST. LOUIS   SAN FRANCISCO   DALLAS   TORONTO   LONDON

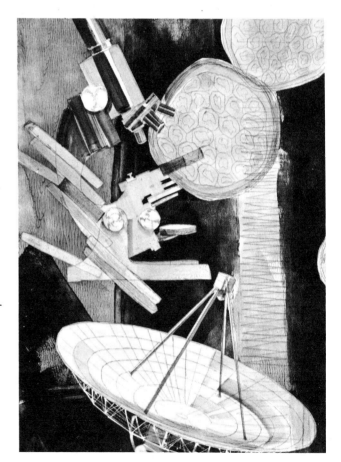

Volume II

Modern Men of Science

420 MORE LEADING CONTEMPORARY SCIENTISTS

PRESENTED BY THE EDITORS OF THE

McGRAW-HILL ENCYCLOPEDIA OF SCIENCE AND TECHNOLOGY

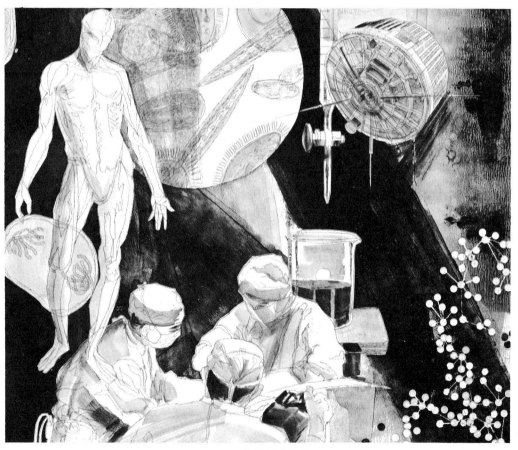

Preface

This second volume of the *McGraw-Hill Modern Men of Science* carries forward the objective of the first, published in 1966: to present extended biographical data on contemporary leaders of science around the world in a form possessing reference value for the librarian and educational value for the student. The articles contained in the two volumes are, in a very real sense, "science biographies." They describe not only *what* each man did but *why* and *how* as well. In addition, they include the conventional biographical chronologies offered by professional and other directories. For the student, no other volumes afford comparable insights into the workings of today's best scientific minds. For the reference librarian, there is no comparable compendium about contemporary scientists.

The subjects of the 420 articles in this second *McGraw-Hill Modern Men of Science* are in no sense of secondary stature when compared to those in the first volume. In selecting the subjects for the present volume, the editors employed the same criteria that they used in the first—receipt of major science prizes from, and membership in, the world's leading scientific societies. Space limitations prevented us from inviting many outstanding scientists to participate in the creation of the first volume; happily, in many cases these men are now represented in the second. Many men who were unable to contribute to the first volume were invited again to contribute to the second, and a number of them did so. In this second volume, 380 articles (identified by black stars beside their titles) are autobiographical. Twenty-two other articles (identified by open stars beside their titles) were written by persons other than their subjects but were reviewed by their subjects before publication. Articles written by persons other than their subjects and not read by their subjects (usually deceased) have no stars beside their titles.

The two volumes of the *McGraw-Hill Modern Men of Science* are conceived as a single reference tool. Each is separately indexed, but the second volume contains a combined table of contents. Furthermore, the second volume updates articles in the first volume in cases where the subjects of those articles have died or have been awarded Nobel Prizes since that volume was published. Although it can be used quite independently, the two-volume *McGraw-Hill Modern Men of Science* is intended as a biographical supplement to the *McGraw-Hill Encyclopedia of Science and Technology*. Every article in the *McGraw-Hill Modern Men of Science* concludes with references to articles in the *McGraw-Hill Encyclopedia of Science and Technology* that will give the reader "in-depth" background information on scientific areas touched upon in the biography.

The editors want especially to thank Sir Gavin de Beer for his article on Sir Julian Huxley and Professor John G. Trump of the Massachusetts Institute of Technology for his article on Robert Jemison Van de Graaff.

THE EDITORS

Editorial Advisory Board

Combined Table of Contents
McGRAW-HILL MODERN MEN OF SCIENCE
VOLUMES I and II

Articles preceded by ★ are autobiographical; those preceded by ☆ were
staff-written but reviewed by their subjects. Roman numerals indicate volume numbers.
Occasionally a biography of Volume I is updated by a note in Volume II.

McGraw-Hill Modern Men of Science
Volume II ☆ ☆

★ ABELSON, Philip Hauge

American geochemist
Born Apr. 27, 1913, Tacoma, Wash., U.S.A.

ABELSON MADE contributions to the fields of nuclear physics, chemistry, microbiology, organic geochemistry, and to studies of the origin of life. He also wrote many items on science policy.

As a graduate student in 1939 at the Radiation Laboratory, University of California, Berkeley, he was the first American scientist to identify products of uranium fission. These included three radioactive isotopes of antimony, six of tellurium, and four of iodine. In 1940 Abelson's attention focused on some work that E. M. McMillan had done the previous year on neutron irradiation of thin layers containing uranium. McMillan had found that most of the fission products escaped from the layer, but that a nonrecoiling 2.3-day beta emitter remained. Emilio Segrè had postulated that the activity followed the chemistry of the ordinary rare earths and that the substance was not a transuranic. An alternative explanation occurred to Abelson. He felt that the activity was due to element 93, but that instead of being an eka-rhenium, element 93 was a member of a new rare-earth series. Pointing out that cerium could exist in two valence states, Abelson thought that the easiest way to demonstrate the existence of element 93 might be by its response to oxidizing and reducing agents. He conducted some experiments at the Department of Terrestrial Magnetism of the Carnegie Institution of Washington with encouraging but not clear-cut results. The intensities there did not permit use of thin-foil technique. He went to Berkeley and discussed his ideas with McMillan. The two scientists then collaborated in the discovery of element 93 (neptunium). McMillan prepared and irradiated some of his thin-layer material. Within a day

Abelson demonstrated that the 2.3-day activity could exist in at least two valence states. In the reduced state the fluoride was precipitated with a cerium carrier. However, in the presence of fluoride and bromate in acid solution, the activity remained in solution while fission-product rare earths precipitated. Abelson also learned that element 93 is more readily reduced than uranium. Thus he was able to show by repeated precipitations that the 2.3-day activity is the daughter of a 23-min uranium activity. The total duration of the research plus preparation of a letter to the editor of the *Physical Review* was 5 days.

In 1940 nuclear physicists were already talking of the possibility of nuclear reactors and atomic weapons. There was uncertainty whether a chain reaction could be established using natural uranium. Uranium enriched in U^{235} seemed the key to many possibilities; partial enrichment of U^{235} would guarantee a successful chain reaction. One application advocated by Ross Gunn of the Naval Research Laboratory was as a source of power for submarines.

The prospects for large-scale isotope separation were dim. At that time only microgram quantities of uranium had been fractionated. Few uranium chemicals were available. Abelson devised a method for large-scale synthesis of UF_6 from UF_4 and produced the first 100 kg of the substance. He discovered that the uranium isotopes could be partially separated by liquid thermal diffusion. The process was conducted in an annular space with cold wall at 70°C and hot wall at 286°C, with columns 14 m long. In a single column a maximum enrichment from 0.7% U^{235} to 1.4% U^{235} was obtained. By mid-1943 more than 100 kg of partially fractionated U^{235} had been obtained, by far the largest amount of fractionated uranium available at that time. A small pilot plant at the Naval Research Laboratory, then a larger pilot plant at the Philadelphia Naval Base, and finally a 2100-column plant at Oak Ridge, Tenn., were built. The partially enriched uranium (0.85% U^{235}) was used as feed for the electromagnetic separation plant, which in turn produced the U^{235} employed in one of the first atomic bombs.

After World War II Abelson led a small group that prepared a feasibility report (dated Mar. 28, 1946) on the atomic submarine. The group showed that a nuclear reactor, shielding, and associated propulsion equipment could be substituted for the then conventional equipment and that a very useful submarine might result. Among the advantages cited for an atomic submarine was long range at high speed under water. The report also stated that "this fast submarine will serve as an ideal carrier and launcher of rocketed atomic bombs."

In 1946 Abelson began a new scientific career

in biophysics. The new venture was a consequence of discussions involving M. A. Tuve, then recently appointed director of the Department of Terrestrial Magnetism of the Carnegie Institution of Washington. Abelson and Tuve concluded that one of the great future frontiers lay in the application of physical methods and theory to biological problems. Subsequently, Abelson was appointed chairman of a Biophysics Section, which soon included four physicists and a biologist. The group exploited opportunities created by availability of radioactive tracers, notably C^{14}. Using tagged glucose and other tagged compounds, including amino acids and CO_2, and employing the technique of isotopic competition, Abelson outlined many of the pathways of the biosynthesis of amino acids in microorganisms.

In 1953 Abelson became director of the Geophysical Laboratory of the Carnegie Institution of Washington and embarked on still another career as one of the nation's pioneers in organic geochemistry. Among his discoveries was the identification of original amino acids preserved in fossils, especially shells. He found alanine, glutamic acid, glycine, leucine, and valine in many old fossils. Subsequently, with T. C. Hoering and Patrick Parker, Abelson isolated fatty acids in old rocks, including some more than a billion years old. Abelson also contributed to the study of the origin of life. He pointed out in 1966 that most model experiments, such as that of S. L. Miller and H. C. Urey, employ assumptions not consonant with the realities of geochemistry. Abelson advanced evidence to support the hypothesis that the Earth's primitive atmosphere consisted largely of CO, N_2, and H_2. Solar irradiation of this mixture produced HCN, which polymerized in the primitive ocean, giving rise to amino acids. Abelson further pointed out that the nature of the environment limited the number of compounds available for life, which began in a thin rather than a thick soup.

In 1962, in addition to his work at the Carnegie Institution, Abelson accepted the editorship of *Science*, America's leading scientific weekly. In more than 100 editorials and scores of lectures, he treated many aspects of the interaction of science and public policy. He joined J. S. Huxley in the view that man now has the power to control his own destiny. Abelson felt that at least some scientists should attempt to build bridges between science and society, and that such efforts might be the most significant which responsible scientists could engage in during the foreseeable future.

Abelson entered what is now Washington State University in 1930 and received a B.S. in chemistry in 1933 and an M.S. in physics 2 years later. He then entered the University of California at Berkeley, working with Ernest O. Lawrence and the cyclotron in the Radiation Laboratory. After receiving the Ph.D. in physics in 1939, Abelson became associated with the Department of Terrestrial Magnetism of the Carnegie Institution of Washington. Except for wartime work at the Naval Research Laboratory, he remained with the Institution. For his wartime service Abelson was given in 1945 the Navy's highest civilian recognition—the Distinguished Civilian Service Medal. He was elected to the National Academy of Sciences in 1959.

For background information *see* AMINO ACIDS; BIOSPHERE, GEOCHEMISTRY OF; ISOTOPE; RARE-EARTH ELEMENTS; REACTOR, SHIP PROPULSION in the McGraw-Hill Encyclopedia of Science and Technology.   □

★ **AGNEW, Harold Melvin**

American physicist
Born Mar. 28, 1921, Denver, Colo., U.S.A.

AFTER THE *Enola Gay* was airborne on its way to Hiroshima on Aug. 6, 1945, the final assembly of the nuclear weapon aboard took place. The weapon used at Nagasaki, however, was fully assembled before it left Tinian. Had there been an accident on takeoff, it is conceivable that all of the installations, aircraft, and personnel on the north end of the island would have been lost. Agnew flew on the Hiroshima mission and was present during the Nagasaki takeoff. He later engaged in activities related to the United States weapons development program. Since those first days concerted effort has been directed to guaranteeing that the nation's nuclear weapons will be used only when properly authorized and will not produce a nuclear yield if they are involved in an accident. For his contribution to the development of nuclear weapons and for his success in working with the armed services to assure the maximum safety and effectiveness of atomic weapons systems, Agnew received the U.S. Atomic Energy Commission's Ernest O. Lawrence Award in 1966.

In 1942 Agnew joined the Metallurgical Laboratory at the University of Chicago. He worked with Enrico Fermi and Herbert Anderson and was with them at Stagg Field when the first nuclear reaction went critical. When it was decided that weapon design would take place at Los Alamos, Agnew and his wife moved there in 1943. He became involved in measuring needed basic nuclear cross sections in a group with John Manley, Bernard Waldman, and Heinz Barshall. However, the field of applied nuclear physics proved more interesting to him, and he became involved in a program with Luis Alvarez to measure the yield of the Hiroshima weapon. This experiment, conducted over Hiroshima at the time of the explosion, proved successful. In 1946 Agnew returned to the University of Chicago to obtain his doctorate but went back to Los Alamos in 1949. There he collaborated with Richard Taschek and Arthur Hemmendinger in measuring the light particle reaction cross sections necessary to develop the thermonuclear weapons.

These studies led directly into weapon design work. It became apparent that the scientific developments were outpacing the military concepts and plans for utilizing them. Agnew became involved in helping the military establishment anticipate future developments by the Atomic Energy Commission. With the development of new weapon delivery systems and United States membership in NATO, new problems of command and control arose. AEC Commissioner James T. Ramey, then staff director of the Joint Committee on Atomic Energy of the U.S. Congress, and Senator Clinton P. Anderson of New Mexico called upon Agnew to join them in studying these problems. As a result of their work, systems were conceived and developed which allowed the government to have better command and control over its nuclear stockpile without inhibiting rapid utilization by the military.

Agnew majored in chemistry at the University of Denver, obtaining an A.B. in 1942. He received an M.S. in 1948 and a Ph.D. in physics under Fermi from the University of Chicago in 1949. He worked at Los Alamos from 1943 to 1946 and again from 1949 except for a period in 1961–64, when he served as scientific advisor to the Supreme Allied Commander in Europe. As the first senator from Los Alamos County, Agnew served in the New Mexico State Senate from 1955 to 1961. In addition to serving on several other government panels, he was appointed chairman of the Army Scientific Advisory Panel.

For background information *see* NUCLEAR EXPLOSION; NUCLEAR REACTION in the McGraw-Hill Encyclopedia of Science and Technology. □

★ AIGRAIN, Pierre Raoul Roger

French physicist
Born Sept. 28, 1924, Poitiers, Vienne, France

AFTER THE discovery of minority carrier injection in semiconductors by William Shockley, John Bardeen, and W. H. Brattain in 1948, Aigrain studied various connected phenomena related to the simultaneous presence of electrons and holes in semiconductors. This led him in sequence from a study of the photoelectromagnetic (PEM effect) phenomena, to injection electroluminescence and its use as a spectroscopic tool in solid-state physics and its application to semiconductor lasers, to finally the problem of electromagnetic wave propagation in semiconductors showing a Hall effect.

Bardeen and his co-workers had shown that minority carriers could be injected in semiconductors either through *p-n* junctions as in transistors or through light. It was thus important to understand the mechanisms of recombination of these minority carriers with those already present in the semiconductors. This study could be pursued in two main directions, one relatively global in which the time necessary for a carrier to disappear was studied without detailed reference to the mechanisms for its recombination, and one more analytic in which emphasis was put on the physical mechanisms for recombination and the detection of the corresponding energy could be detected.

Pursuing the second line, Aigrain showed that this energy can in some cases appear in the form of light. The study of the emitted spectrum can give information on the energy level in semiconductors of comparable accuracy and detail as that obtained in gases through optical spectroscopy. The same line was being pursued at the same time by W. Haynes and later by many others. In 1958 Aigrain proposed at the Brussels Conference on Semiconductors that this light emission in semiconductors can take the form of stimulated emission, thus opening the possibility for semiconductor lasers.

The other line of study had first led Aigrain to study the photoelectromagnetic phenomenon discovered some 25 years earlier by Kikoin and Noskov, but the explanation of which could not be given accurately before the discovery of minority carrier motion. In this phenomenon a plate of semiconductor illuminated with a magnetic field parallel to the surface is the seat of a voltage perpendicular to the magnetic field. The study of this voltage, which is due to the separation by the magnetic field of unlike charges diffusing perpendicular to the surface where they have been produced, can lead to a large amount of detailed information on recombination mechanisms in semiconductors. The PEM effect can also be used for practical purposes, for example, light detectors. There are some connected phenomena, such as the photomagnetomechanical effect (appearance of a torque due to light in certain geometries) or the photoparamagnetic effect (increased apparent paramagnetism of an illuminated semiconductor). Further experimental studies in other laboratories of this last phenomenon apparently indicated unexpectedly large diffusion lengths for injected carriers. Although these phenomena were later explained on the basis of trapping of charged carriers, reflection about these effects led Aigrain to consider possible long-lived excitation in semiconductors placed in a magnetic field. He was thus led to reconsider the problem of the century-old Hall effect. When the electric field is rotating around the magnetic field, the Hall effect behaves as a nonreciprocal reactance. This opens the way to propagation of circularly polarized electromagnetic waves, even of low frequencies. Aigrain dubbed these waves helicons, and they were later discovered both in semiconductors and in metals. Through their interactions with various other excitations (magnons, phonons, and so forth), helicons have become a powerful tool for the study of solids.

Aigrain started his career as a naval officer; he spent 3 years at the Carnegie Institute of Technology in Pittsburgh, where he obtained a D.Sc. in 1948. He obtained a D.Sc. from the University of Paris in 1950 and taught at the University of Lille from 1952 to 1954. In that year he became a professor at the University of Paris and, from 1965, served also as director general of higher education. In 1961 he was elected a foreign member of the American Academy of Arts and Sciences.

Aigrain was coauthor of two books on semi-conductor physics, *Les Semi-conducteurs* (1958) and *Electronic Processes in Solids* (1960).

For background information *see* SEMICONDUCTOR; TRANSISTOR in the Mc-Graw-Hill Encyclopedia of Science and Technology.   □

★ ALLER, Lawrence Hugh

American astronomer
Born Sept. 24, 1913, Tacoma, Wash., U.S.A.

THE CHEMICAL compositions of the stars may offer important clues to their history and to nuclear processes occurring within their interiors, and may even shed light on the evolution of the galaxy. Following application of the Saha ionization theory in the 1920s and recognition of special excitation mechanisms, it became obvious that most of the differences between the spectra of stars could be explained by differences in their temperatures and atmospheric pressures. Attempts were made to explain in this way even stars whose spectra were rich in heavy metals (those of spectral class S), but the explanation failed for the cool carbon stars. As late as 1945 distinguished astrophysicists asserted that chemical composition differences between stars did not exist.

Quantitative studies of the spectra of hot stars with broad bright lines (Wolf-Rayet stars) convinced Aller that well-known differences in their spectra could be explained only as arising from actual chemical composition differences. The elements involved—helium, carbon, nitrogen, and oxygen—include those characteristic of the carbon-nitrogen energy generation cycle. Later, in collaboration with Joseph W. Chamberlain, Aller undertook a quantitative spectroscopic analysis of two examples of subdwarf stars. Superficially their spectra resembled those of stars with surface temperatures of the order of 8000–9000°K with prominent hydrogen lines and weak metal lines. The character of the metallic line spectrum indicated a temperature more nearly comparable with that of the Sun, 5700°K, a conclusion subsequently verified by color measurements of these stars. The stars were metal deficient; later more detailed studies by J. L. Greenstein and Aller showed the metal-hydrogen ratio to be about 0.01 that of the Sun. Presumably these very ancient stars were formed when the metal-hydrogen ratio was very much smaller in the galaxy than it is now.

High-temperature stars recently formed from the interstellar medium were studied by Aller, who pioneered in applying model atmosphere methods to the star Gamma Pegasi (1949). Aller, Elste, and Jugaku in 1955 applied the modern theory of hydrogen line broadening, due to Kolb and Kolb and Griem, to the interpretation of stellar spectra. Instead of assuming that the stellar spectrum could be interpreted as though it were formed at a constant temperature and pressure, they took into account the stratification of the atmosphere and the change of the shape of the line intensity–abundance curve (curve of growth) from one type of ion to another, for example, singly ionized silicon to trebly ionized silicon.

In the late 1950s Leo Goldberg, Edith Müller, and Aller undertook a comprehensive spectrochemical analysis of the Sun. Further refinements were developed by Aller and his associates; these included abundance determinations by reproducing by theoretical calculations small sections of the solar spectrum. John Ross and Aller applied this method to lines of silver and lead.

At Harvard in 1937 D. H. Menzel initiated a theoretical study of physical processes in gaseous nebulae, attempting to establish quantitative interpretations of observable spectroscopic features in terms of electron temperature, density, radiation field, and chemical composition. Aller undertook a prominent role in these investigations and supplemented theoretical insights with spectroscopic observations. After he left Harvard, he continued this work at the McDonald, Mount Wilson, and Lick observatories. In 1949 Aller, C. W. Ufford, and J. H. Van Vleck noted that the relative intensities of the 3726 A and 3729 A "forbidden" lines of ionized oxygen are sensitive indicators of the densities of gaseous nebulae.

Realizing the importance of accurate spectrophotometric measurements to theoretical interpretations of stars and gaseous nebulae, Aller and his co-workers emphasized the combination of photoelectric and photographic photometry. Working in collaboration with W. Liller, O. C. Wilson, I. S. Bowen, R. Minkowski, D. J. Faulkner, J. B. Kaler, and S. Czyzak, he attempted to secure accurate spectral measurements of gaseous nebulae. M. F. Walker and Aller used the electronographic camera to measure extremely weak spectral lines that lie below the practical limit of conventional photographic spectroscopy. This wealth of observational material illustrated the great range in density concentration, excitation, structure, and chemical composition in the so-called planetary nebulae, which surround certain stars in advanced evolutionary stages. Aller carried out extensive studies of the spectra of these residual stars, which appear to be objects on the verge of becoming white dwarfs. Temperatures derived from their spectra are often in sharp disagreement with those inferred from the spectrum of the nebula itself.

Other investigations were concerned with the interstellar medium, the material out of which stars are formed. Liller and Aller studied the chemical composition of the diffuse Orion Nebula. Other investigations were concerned with the composition of the nebulosities in the Magellanic Clouds, the nearest of all external galaxies, which appear to have a chemical composition closely similar to that of our own galaxy.

Additional researches concerned "A-type" stars of peculiar composition—stars with surface temperatures of 10,000–15,000°K and excess amounts of manganese, gallium, strontium, and occasionally iron and titanium. Other studies included measurement of the energy distributions in the spectra of southern stars (with Faulkner); combination variables believed to be stars near the end of their evolution; exploding or temporary stars—notably the mysterious object Eta Carinae; the rotation of the Triangulum galaxy, Messier 33 (with N. U. Mayall); and the nature of the particles comprising the zodiacal cloud.

Aller was taken out of school at the age of 15 to serve his father's chimerical ambitions to find gold. He was rescued from a poverty-stricken mining camp by his elder sister, Jane Kegg, and D. H. Menzel, later director of Harvard Observatory. Although Aller had not finished high school, Menzel arranged for him to enter the University of California as a special student. He was transferred to regular status after a semester, and received his A.B. in 1936. In 1943 Aller took his Ph.D. in astronomy at Harvard University, where he was a junior fellow in the Society of Fellows during 1939–42 and instructor in physics in 1942–43. He was assistant professor of astronomy at Indiana University from 1945 to 1948. In 1948 he went to the University of Michigan as associate professor, and became full professor in 1954. He served as visiting professor at the Australian National University and at the University of Toronto before going to the University of California, Los Angeles, in 1962. He was elected to the American Academy of Arts and Sciences in 1961 and to the National Academy of Sciences in 1962.

Aller wrote *Astrophysics* (2 vols., 1953–54), *Gaseous Nebulae* (1956), and *Abundance of Elements* (1961).

For background information *see* ASTRONOMICAL SPECTROSCOPY; NEBULA; STAR in the McGraw-Hill Encyclopedia of Science and Technology.   ☐

★ ANDERSON, Charles Alfred

American geologist
Born June 6, 1902, Bloomington, Calif., U.S.A.

ANDERSON WAS introduced to the problems of volcanic rocks in 1928, when he studied a cinder cone and its associated lava flows east of Lassen Peak in northern California. Throughout his professional career volcanic rocks were a major interest, with emphasis on field studies leading to the preparation of geologic maps illustrating the sequence of events, followed by microscopic and chemical studies of the rocks.

The basaltic lava flows east of Lassen Peak contain scattered broken crystals and fragments of quartz, SiO_2, whereas no quartz is present in the fine crystal matrix of the lava, but bright green olivine crystals, $(Mg, Fe)_2SiO_4$, are conspicuous. Olivine is an orthosilicate and can crystallize only from lava that is deficient in SiO_2, so the quartz cannot be in equilibrium with the olivine; the association, together with the absence of quartz in the olivine-bearing matrix, indicates that the quartz is foreign and must have been picked up by the molten lava as it rose in the volcanic vent. Later studies by Anderson in the Clear Lake area north of San Francisco revealed foreign quartz in other olivine basaltic flows, as well as the reverse relationship of scattered olivine crystals in rhyolitic obsidian, which has a high SiO_2 content; the magnesian-rich olivine is obviously not in equilibrium with the obsidian and is another example of the mixing of foreign material in rising molten lava.

West of Lassen Peak extensive bouldery plains are striking features of the landscape, and in 1929 Anderson made a study of the volcanic rocks exposed in the canyons cut into the plains. He found that mudflows originating from old volcanoes to the east were responsible for the spreading out of thick accumulations of unsorted angular lava fragments in a matrix of volcanic ash. As the fine ash was washed out of the matrix, the boulders lagged behind and were concentrated on the surface. The concept of mudflows for the origin of these kinds of volcanic deposits has been widely accepted. In 1930 Anderson studied the decomposition of lava fragments immersed in hot springs near Lassen Peak, and he found fragments with an unaltered core grading outward to a soft powdery exterior. The progressive leaching of the iron, aluminum, magnesium, calcium, sodium, and potassium from the fragments leaves a residue of high silica content, similar to altered rocks found in some ore deposits.

Spectacular obsidian flows, about 1000 years old, in the Medicine Lake Highland in northeastern California attracted Anderson's attention in 1932, and his detailed geologic mapping proved that one of the flows began with the eruption of dacite, continued with the simultaneous eruption of rhyolitic obsidian mixed with the dacite, and ended with the eruption solely of rhyolitic obsidian. A single lava flow composed of two dissimilar rock types is rare, and the preservation of the flow top and margins is so clear at Medicine Lake as to leave no doubt that this is a composite flow, an interpretation that has been helpful in understanding older but similar composite flows. Anderson then prepared a geologic map of the entire Medicine Lake Highland, which documents a complex volcanic history starting with the building of a broad-shield volcano and culminating in the central collapse to form an oval-shaped caldera. New volcanic vents formed along the caldera margins, erupting a series of lava flows that buried the caldera walls. The obsidian flows 1000 years of age mark the final episode of the volcanic history.

In 1939 Anderson joined C. W. Merriam in the mapping of the Roberts Mountains in central Nevada, which documented the existence of a low-angle thrust fault in which Ordovician lava flows and tuffs, black shales, and bedded cherts were thrust eastward over limestones of Ordovician and Devonian age. Subsequent geologic studies have demonstrated that the Roberts thrust is an impressive and widespread tectonic feature in central Nevada, marking the close of an important orogenic disturbance. The mapping of the Tertiary volcanic rocks in the Roberts Mountains revealed that they were erupted on an erosion surface that existed prior to the normal faulting that displaced the thrust plate and lava flows. Chemical studies showed that these central Nevada lavas have a high potassium content, unlike the lava in California and Oregon, but similar to many of the lavas in Utah and New Mexico.

The Scripps Institution of Oceanography sponsored a scientific cruise to the Gulf of California in 1940, and Anderson was invited to participate in land surveys on some of the islands in the Gulf, as well as in selected areas in Sonora and Baja California. Volcanic rocks are important elements in land geology, and sufficient evidence was gathered to indicate that the Gulf of California originated in early Pliocene time and that the dislocation along the western margin of the Gulf coincided in part with a chain of older volcanic vents. Only one island represents a volcanic cone built on the Gulf floor.

During World War II Anderson joined the U.S. Geological Survey and made an intensive study of the copper deposit at Bagdad, Ariz. The geologic mapping revealed that the copper deposit is localized in a central stock of granodiorite porphyry at the intersection of two dike swarms. Structural disturbances produced a number of intersecting fractures in this stock, which served as a sponge for rising, hot, mineralizing solutions to react with the granodiorite porphyry. Some of the calcium, sodium, and magnesium were removed, and potassium, sulfur, and copper were added to form new K-feldspar, pyrite, and chalcopyrite.

After the war Anderson was involved in a long-term study of Precambrian volcanic rocks in central Arizona. He and his associates, S. C. Creasey, P. M. Blacet, and M. H. Krieger, were successful in recognizing original textures and structures in the old volcanic rocks, and by patient geologic mapping they were able to portray the distribution of the diverse volcanic rocks and to determine their sequence. The rocks have been metamorphosed by the addition of 5 to 6% (by volume) of water during a period of increased heat flow and crustal deformation about 1,700,000,000 years ago. Chemical studies show that migration of sodium and potassium was important during metamorphism, indicating that recrystallization in part took place in an open system. The unraveling of the folded and faulted structure of these old volcanic rocks is of value for mineral exploration in the area, since the known ore deposits can now be related to particular segments of the volcanic sequence and to particular structural environments.

Anderson received his A.B. from Pomona College in 1924 and his Ph.D. from the University of California, Berkeley, in 1928. He taught geology at the University of California until 1942, when he joined the U.S. Geological Survey. He was chief of the Mineral Deposits Branch from 1953 to 1958 and chief geologist of the Survey from 1959 to 1964. He was elected to the American Academy of Arts and Sciences in 1956 and to the National Academy of Sciences in 1957.

Anderson wrote *The Tuscan Formation of Northern California* (1933), *Volcanoes of the Medicine Lake Highland, California* (1941), and articles on his studies in Nevada, the Gulf of California, and Arizona.

For background information *see* PETROLOGY; VOLCANO; VOLCANOLOGY in the McGraw-Hill Encyclopedia of Science and Technology. □

★ ANDRADE, Edward Neville da Costa

English physicist
Born Dec. 27, 1887, London, England

ANDRADE'S RESEARCHES in physics were concerned with the mechanical properties of matter in the solid and liquid states. A law concerning the creep of metals and a law governing the variation of the viscosity of liquids with temperature are particularly associated with his name. In his first papers on the flow of metals under large stresses, Andrade emphasized the advantage of measuring the movement under conditions of constant stress rather than under the then prevalent conditions of constant load, which means continuously increasing stress. A device now in general use for the maintenance of constant stress is the Andrade-Chalmers bar, an improvement on the one first used by Andrade. In these early papers he established the existence of a transient flow with strain proportional to $t^{1/3}$ (Andrade's law) and of a quasi-viscous flow with strain proportional to t for a variety of metals, including solid mercury. He also showed that the very different behavior of the different metals at atmospheric temperature was determined by the relation of this temperature to the melting point. This work, carried out at University College, London, before World War I, was the foundation of the study of metallic creep as a precise science. It was interrupted by a year at Heidelberg devoted to work on the electrical properties of flames.

In 1913 Andrade went to work with Ernest Rutherford at Manchester. They carried out the first measurements of the wavelength of the gamma rays from radium, which had an important bearing on the question of radioactive isotopes. The outbreak of war in 1914 cut short Andrade's collaboration with the founder of the modern theory of the atom.

After the war, having no opportunity to work on atomic themes, Andrade turned his attention to the viscosity of liquids. In 1930 he put forward a simple formula, usually known by his name, expressing the variations of viscosity with temperature, and a more precise version of the formula, which has been shown to represent experimental results very accurately. With student collaborators he worked out an experimental method, depending upon the damping of oscillations of a suspended sphere containing the liquid, for measuring the viscosity of liquid metals, which, being monomolecular, are the simplest form of liquid. Andrade was able to determine the viscosity of many metals in liquid form over a range of temperature with this method. The viscosity at melting point was found to obey a simple law. The effect of an electric field on the viscosity of normal, nonconducting liquids was established for the first time by the use of alternating fields, since there is no effect for nonpolar liquids, but a very small increase of viscosity proportional to the square of the field with polar liquids. Very large effects recorded by previous workers were shown to be spurious.

Andrade also took up work on single crystals of metals, which he had prepared accidentally before World War I. With Robert Roscoe he elaborated a method, which has since been widely used, of preparing single-crystal rods of metals of low melting point. Later, with Cyril Henderson, Andrade developed a method for metals of high melting point. The deformation of single-crystal rods of metals of hexagonal and face-centered cubic structure under stress was investigated in detail, and the differences of behavior were explained in terms of crystal structure. With single crystals of gold and silver, the phenomenon known as "easy glide" was discovered and elaborated.

A variety of problems in the field of sound were also solved during the period between the wars, including that of the remarkable behavior of particles in Kundt's tube. The behavior of the sensitive flame was analyzed and explained.

After World War II Andrade devised the method of studying the flow of polycrystalline metals under simple shear stress. With the appropriate apparatus this method has great advantages over the usual procedure of measuring the increase of strain under tension. The mechanical conditions are simpler; the sense of the stress can be reversed at will; and the visible surface of the metal remains plane and of constant area, so that the behavior of the crystal grains accessible to microscopic or x-ray examination is typical of those throughout the metal. Andrade, in collaboration with K. H. Jolliffe, carried out a detailed investigation of the flow of the typical face-centered cubic metal lead by this method, which resulted in the discovery of new types of flow. In particular, they found a deformation strictly proportional to $t^{1/2}$, which takes place at small strains before the $t^{1/3}$ regime is established. Also, at large shear strains, exceeding 30%, they found a non-Newtonian viscous behavior, the rate of flow at constant stress being constant and the same for forward or reversed direction of stress. At lower strains, before the grain structure of the metal is thoroughly broken up, the behavior under forward and reversed stress is quite different and very informative. With D. A. Aboav, Andrade investigated the flow of the typical hexagonal metal cadmium under simple shear, which showed differences of behavior from lead, explicable in terms of the crystal structure. In general, the complicated flow behavior of polycrystalline metals under the simple conditions of stressing in question could be explained in terms of intragranular behavior and grain boundary adjustment and migration. With Aboav he also investigated grain growth in metals, with results that threw new light on the problems.

Andrade became an authority in certain areas of the history of science, in particular the work of Newton, Hooke, and their contemporaries, as well as the early days of the Royal Society. From its inception he was chairman of the Royal Society committee dealing with the publication of Newton's letters.

Andrade's scientific career was not without its difficulties. The period of World War I, much of which he spent at the front, broke off his work with Rutherford. It was not until his appointment as Quain Professor of Physics in the University of London in 1928 that he had facilities for experimental research, and those very exiguous. Until the outbreak of war again in 1939, he built up a research school in which, with very simple apparatus, the work on viscosity, metal single crystals, and sound problems was carried out. During World War II, when he was employed in government work, his laboratory was destroyed by bombs. With it went all his notes, a collection of valuable books, and manuscript letters from great figures in the world of science, including Lord Rutherford, Sir James Frazer,

Sir Charles Sherrington, Charles Barkla, and S. Arrhenius, with whom he was on terms of intimate friendship until the latter's death in 1927. After the war, then, there was nothing left of Andrade's laboratory but one or two bare rooms and some sand, with which he carried out, in collaboration with J. W. Fox, research on the mechanism of dilatancy. In 1950 Andrade was appointed director in the Royal Institution of Great Britain and director of the Davy Faraday Research Laboratory, posts from which he resigned in 1952. The work on the flow of metals under simple shear and on grain growth was carried out at the Imperial College of Science, where he became senior research fellow. Andrade was elected a fellow of the Royal Society in 1935 and later received the Society's Hughes Medal. He was elected Membre Correspondant de l'Académie des Sciences, Institut de France, in 1950 and was awarded many honors in France. He was Chevalier Légion d'Honneur, Membre d'Honneur of the Société Française de Physique, and recipient of the Grande Médaille Osmond and the Holweck Prize.

His contact with Rutherford inspired Andrade to write *The Structure of the Atom* (1923; rev. 3d ed. 1927), which was for a time the standard work on the subject. For the general reader he wrote *The Mechanism of Nature* (1930), translated into six foreign languages. Andrade was the author of other popular works on aspects of physics; of books on Newton, Rutherford, and the history of the Royal Society; and of accounts of Doppler and his work, and of Benjamin Franklin's life in London.

For background information *see* CREEP OF MATERIALS; METAL, MECHANICAL PROPERTIES OF; SINGLE CRYSTAL; VISCOSITY OF LIQUIDS in the McGraw-Hill Encyclopedia of Science and Technology. ☐

★ ANDREWES, Christopher Howard

British virologist
Born June 7, 1896, London, England

ANDREWES'S LIFE-LONG interest in natural history—birds, insects, and plants—greatly influenced his approach to viruses, the main subject of study throughout his career. He was fortunate in beginning a life of work in medical research at a time when viruses were first becoming the object of serious interest to laboratory workers. He was thus "in the swim" throughout a period of tremendous advances in this field. Though he worked at different times with many viruses infecting animals, including those causing tumors, his main contributions were in three areas: influenza, common colds, and virus classification.

In 1933, working with Wilson Smith and P. P. Laidlaw, he first transmitted the virus of human influenza to an experimental animal, the ferret, and thus laid the foundations of present knowledge of this virus infection. He continued to study it for many years. In 1947 it became clear to him that the antigenic changes which the virus periodically underwent needed to be studied on a worldwide basis. The World Health Organization was readily persuaded to take an interest, and Andrewes, rather to his surprise and dismay, found himself in charge of a World Influenza Center, with an associated network of influenza laboratories throughout the world. The chief function was to collect and compare influenza viruses from different countries; and it soon appeared that new variants, when they appeared, tended to spread rapidly around the world, displacing older ones. This knowledge was a matter of importance for manufacture of flu vaccines, for vaccines against out-of-date strains were of little or no use against new ones, and early information concerning changes in the antigenic composition of the virus was greatly valued. Later, networks of reference centers for viruses of other kinds were set up by WHO, and these networks followed the pattern originally laid down for influenza study.

The other most troublesome infection of temperate climes is the common cold. By 1946 almost all the important viruses affecting man, other than colds, had been transmitted to animals or cultivated in fertile hens' eggs, so Andrewes undertook the formidable task of trying to do something about colds. No other approach being possible, it was necessary to use volunteers to test for the presence of virus in materials under investigation, by drops up the nose and a wait to

see whether a cold developed. The Medical Research Council supported Andrewes by setting up a common cold research unit at Salisbury. Here volunteers came, two dozen or so at a time, every fortnight, prepared to be given common colds in the cause of science; mostly they enjoyed the experience. The primary objective was to find a way to make a common cold virus accessible to quantitative study in the laboratory. But while an attack of influenza had yielded results 14 days after the opening shot of the campaign, it took 14 years before a similar success attended work on the common cold. Attempts to infect animals or to grow the virus in eggs were unsuccessful, so in 1952 Andrewes concentrated the attack, in which a number of colleagues were concerned, on attempts to grow the virus in tissue culture. A glimmering of success came in the following year, but it was not until 1960 that David Tyrrell and colleagues, working in the Salisbury laboratory, found a way of regularly growing cold viruses—now known as rhinoviruses—in culture. Unfortunately it later appeared that there are so many serological types of these that specific prophylaxis will not be easily achieved.

In 1949 Andrewes and Dorothy Horstmann, who was visiting his laboratory from Yale, showed that some viruses were readily inactivated by ether while others were not. When ether sensitivity and size were taken together, the first indications of a rational classification of viruses began to appear. A classification of viruses published about that time seemed to Andrewes to be on wholly wrong lines, laying too much stress on the symptoms produced and neglecting more fundamental characteristics. He contacted the International Committee for the Nomenclature of Bacteria, which then set up a subcommittee, with Andrewes as its chairman, to deal with viruses. At the first meeting in Rio de Janeiro in 1950, at subsequent international congresses in Rome, Stockholm, Montreal, and Moscow, and by means of correspondence and questionnaires, the matter was bit by bit hammered out. Most virologists were long apathetic, but finally much interest was engendered and the acquisition of new facts, particularly about virus morphology, led to general agreement as to the basis on which virus classification should proceed.

Andrewes studied medicine at St. Bartholomew's Hospital in London, qualifying in 1921. He then spent a few years combining clinical medicine and laboratory work: two of them, 1923–25, were at the hospital of the Rockefeller Institute in New York. In 1927 he opted for a laboratory career and joined the staff of the National Institute for Medical Research at Hampstead, moving with it later to Mill Hill. He remained at the Institute for 34 years, until his retirement in 1961, becoming head of the Division of Bacteriology and Virus Research in 1940 and deputy director of the Institute in 1952. Andrewes was elected a fellow of the Royal Society in 1939 and knighted in 1961; he was

elected a foreign associate of the U.S. National Academy of Sciences in 1964.

Before retiring he had accumulated an enormous mass of records about viruses, and this was distilled into a textbook, *Viruses of Vertebrates* (1964), which brought together, on a taxonomic basis, the viruses affecting man and other vertebrates. Two other books, *The Common Cold* (1965) and *The Natural History of Viruses* (1967), were less technical, being directed to lay as well as medical readers.

For background information *see* ANIMAL VIRUS; COLD, COMMON; INFLUENZA; VIRUS in the McGraw-Hill Encyclopedia of Science and Technology.   □

★ ANFINSEN, Christian Boehmer

American biochemist
Born Mar. 26, 1916, Monessen, Pa., U.S.A.

ANFINSEN BEGAN his studies on the amino acid sequences, biosynthesis, and three-dimensional structures of proteins in 1948, focusing on what might be called the "evolutionary design" of proteins. His work helped establish that the so-called primary structure of proteins—that is, the amino acid sequence—contains all the information necessary to determine the complex and unique three-dimensional structure that characterizes each protein molecule in living cells.

During 1954–55, as a recipient of the Rockefeller Public Service Award, Anfinsen worked in the laboratories of Kai Linderstrøm-Lang at the Carlsberg Laboratory in Copenhagen. His work in this stimulating environment led him to appreciate the potentialities of research on proteins as organic chemicals, stripped of their classical mystique as large, amorphous macromolecules. He wrote, with Robert Redfield, a review article on the relationships between protein structure and function that strongly colored his later research activities. The attitudes developed during this period—that proteins are like other organic molecules, only larger and more complex—led directly to the studies on the spontaneous folding of polypeptide chains.

Although Anfinsen's work was mainly of a purely biochemical nature, its implications may be more important in evolutionary theory. The information content of living cells appears to be encoded exclusively in the linear arrangement of nucleotides within the enormously large strands of deoxyribonucleic acid (DNA) molecules that constitute the genetic material of the cell nucleus and of certain other cellular organelles. This information is translated, through the mechanisms of protein biosynthesis, into linear polypeptide chains. Three-dimensional structure first appears when these linear polypeptides undergo a transition that converts them into the highly coiled and folded form that characterizes the enzymes, hormones, and structural proteins of living cells. At the same time these biologically inert polypeptides assume their characteristic biological function.

Biological function, therefore, may be thought of as a series of problems in the geometry of protein molecules, in which amino acid residues that may be quite distant from one another in a linear sense are brought into close proximity to create an "active center" that facilitates the performance of a unique biological function. Thus, at the molecular level, the process of evolution may be envisioned as the "selection" of protein molecules possessing amino acid sequences determined by the nucleotide sequences of the particular portions of DNA that code for them and that can fold into three-dimensional forms compatible with the function in question. Anfinsen's experimental studies make it possible to predict that computer programs can be devised which will permit the computation of protein geometry without the laborious application of crystallographic analysis so elegantly applied by M. F. Perutz, J. C. Kendrew, D. C. Phillips, and their colleagues.

Anfinsen and his colleagues showed that a variety of native proteins, particularly those containing rigid, covalent cross linkages in the form of disulfide bonds, could be converted by reduction of these bonds in denaturing solvents into random linear chains. These randomized protein chains, after purification and after exposure to oxidizing conditions at neutrality, were found to reform the same disulfide bonds and to assume three-dimensional conformations indistinguishable from the original native protein.

The son of a Norwegian engineer, Anfinsen received a B.A. from Swarthmore College in 1937. He studied organic chemistry at the University of Pennsylvania (M.S., 1939) and, after a year of fellowship at the Carlsberg Laboratory in 1939–40, studied in the department of biological chemistry at Harvard Medical School, receiving his Ph.D. in 1943. He left Harvard Medical School in 1950 to become chief of the Laboratory of Cellular Physiology and Metabolism in the National Heart Institute of the National Institutes of Health. He was again at Harvard Medical School as professor of biological chemistry in 1962–63, then went to the National Institute of Arthritis and Metabolic Diseases in 1963 as chief of the Laboratory of Chemical Biology. In addition to his research activities, he served as director of the Research Associate Program at the National Institutes of Health and as a member of the board of governors of the Weizmann Institute of Science in Rehovoth, Israel. He was elected to the American Academy of Arts and Sciences in 1958, to the National Academy of Sciences in 1963, and to the Royal Danish Academy in 1964.

Anfinsen wrote *The Molecular Basis of Evolution* (1959).

For background information *see* AMINO ACIDS; PROTEIN in the McGraw-Hill Encyclopedia of Science and Technology.   □

★ ARNON, Daniel Israel

American biochemist and physiologist
Born Nov. 14, 1910, Warsaw, Poland

A RNON'S EARLY research was mainly concerned with inorganic metabolism of plants, especially with the role of inorganic micronutrients (trace elements). His main contributions in this area were the discovery of vanadium as an essential micronutrient for the growth of algae and the discovery, with P. R. Stout, of molybdenum as an essential micronutrient for the growth of higher plants and algae. His interest in the function of micronutrients in plant metabolism led him eventually to shift his main research activity to photosynthesis, especially the biochemistry of the photochemical phase. He began his work on the premise that the biochemistry of energy conversion in photosynthesis, like the biochemistry of fermentation in an earlier period, would be elucidated only when the process was removed from the functional and structural complexity of whole cells. This approach led Arnon, with M. B. Allen and F. R. Whatley, to the achievement of complete, cellfree photosynthesis and the discovery of photophosphorylation.

R. Hill showed in 1937 that when chloroplasts (the chlorophyll-containing organelles of plant cells) were isolated from the cell and illuminated, they produced oxygen but were incapable of assimilating carbon dioxide. In 1954, using different methods, Arnon and his co-workers obtained with isolated spinach choloroplasts an assimilation of carbon dioxide to the level of carbohydrates (including starch) with a simultaneous evolution of oxygen, at physiological temperatures and with no energy supply except visible light. The attainment of complete photosynthesis by chloroplasts was accompanied by the discovery of photosynthetic phosphorylation. or photophosphorylation. This discovery revealed a new process for the formation of adenosinetriphosphate (ATP), a compound known to serve as an energy carrier in all living cells. In photophosphorylation the chlorophyll-containing particles of photosynthetic cells convert solar energy into the pyrophosphate-bond energy of ATP independently of carbon dioxide assimilation. Photophosphorylation differs from the well-known processes of ATP formation in fermentation and respiration in that it does not consume any energy-rich chemical substrate (the only "substrate" consumed is light quanta).

In the early type of photophosphorylation, later renamed cyclic photophosphorylation, the only product formed was ATP. In 1957 Arnon and his associates discovered a second type of photophosphorylation, named noncyclic photophosphorylation, in which ATP formation was stoichiometrically coupled with oxygen production and reduction of triphosphopyridine nucleotide (TPN). Noncyclic photophosphorylation accounted, aside from oxygen evolution, for all the reduced TPN and most of the ATP—two substances known to be required for the assimilation of carbon dioxide. The additional ATP needed for carbon dioxide assimilation could come from cyclic photophosphorylation. Jointly, cyclic and noncyclic photophosphorylation seemed to represent the "light phase" of photosynthesis that generates the assimilatory power, made up of ATP and reduced TPN, that is required for carbon dioxide assimilation by reactions independent of light. Arnon, with A. V. Trebst and H. Y. Tsujimoto, substantiated the validity of this concept of photosynthesis by experimentally separating its light and dark phases in isolated choloroplasts. First, chloro-

plasts were allowed to form ATP and reduced TPN in the light and in the absence of carbon dioxide. Next, radioactive carbon dioxide was added in the dark and was found to be converted to carbohydrates at the expense of the ATP and reduced TPN formed previously in the light.

In 1962 Arnon, with K. Tagawa, found that illuminated chloroplasts did not reduce TPN directly but first reduced an iron-containing protein, present in all photosynthetic cells and in certain anaerobic bacteria and now called ferredoxin. They found that ferredoxin has an oxidation-reduction potential about 100 millivolts more electronegative than TPN, and is therefore the most electronegative electron carrier known in cellular physiology. Ferredoxins from different organisms are at least partly interchangeable in catalyzing TPN reduction by illuminated chloroplasts. In further experiments, with M. Shin, the "photoreduction" of TPN was resolved into three reactions: (a) a photochemical reduction of ferredoxin, followed by two dark reactions; (b) a reduction of a flavoprotein enzyme by reduced ferredoxin; and (c) a reduction of TPN by the reduced flavoprotein. The flavoprotein enzyme native to chloroplasts was crystallized and named ferredoxin-TPN reductase.

Photoreduced ferredoxin thus emerged as the most electronegative, chemically characterized substance that has been isolated from the photosynthetic apparatus. The recognition of the importance of ferredoxin in the energy conversion reactions of photosynthesis was greatly enhanced when Arnon, with Tagawa, Tsujimoto and B. D. McSwain, found that, apart from TPN reduction, ferredoxin is also involved in the formation of ATP and in the evolution of oxygen. Ferredoxin acts as a catalyst of cyclic photophosphorylation; in noncyclic photophosphorylation the photoreduction of ferredoxin is coupled with a stoichiometric formation of ATP and evolution of oxygen. Thus it became clear that oxygen evolution, photophosphorylation, and the photoreduction of ferredoxin are key events in the conversion of radiant energy into chemical energy by chloroplasts. All subsequent photosynthetic reactions in chloroplasts are chemical events which consume ATP and reduced ferredoxin and proceed independently of light.

In later research Arnon, with B. B. Buchanan, M. C. W. Evans, and R. Bachofen, uncovered a new, direct role of ferredoxin in the assimilation of carbon dioxide. They found in photosynthetic bacteria two enzyme systems that can use directly, without mediation by TPN, the strongly electronegative potential of ferredoxin for reductive incorporation of carbon dioxide: pyruvate synthase, which uses reduced ferredoxin to form pyruvate from acetyl coenzyme A and carbon dioxide, and α-ketoglutarate synthase, which uses reduced ferredoxin to form α-ketoglutarate from succinyl CoA and carbon dioxide. The two ferredoxin-dependent carboxylation reactions, together with two other known carboxylation reactions, phosphopyruvate carboxylase and isocitric dehydrogenase, form a new cyclic pathway for carbon dioxide assimilation in photosynthetic bacteria. One complete turn of the cycle incorporates four molecules of carbon dioxide and results in the synthesis of oxalacetate. Oxalacetate may then be further metabolized through the cycle to provide intermediates with 2, 3, 4, 5, and 6 carbons for the synthesis of amino acids, lipids, and other cell constituents. The new cycle, named the reductive carboxylic acid cycle, appears especially well adapted to the synthesis of lipids and amino acids, which are the main products of bacterial photosynthesis.

Arnon received his B.S. in 1932 and his Ph.D. in 1936 at the University of California, Berkeley, where Professor D. R. Hoagland aroused his interest in plant biochemistry and strongly influenced his choice of a scientific career. Arnon joined the staff of the University of California in 1936 and remained there continuously, except for military service during World War II. He became professor of plant physiology in 1950, professor of cell physiology and biochemist in the Experiment Station in 1960, and chairman of a newly established department of cell physiology in 1961. He was a Guggenheim fellow twice in the Molteno Institute and department of biochemistry at Cambridge University, England, in 1947–48 and in the Hopkins Marine Station of Stanford University in 1962–63. He was a Fulbright research fellow at the Max Planck Institut für Zellphysiologie in Berlin-Dahlem in 1955–56. He was elected to the National Academy of Sciences in 1961 and the American Academy of Arts and Sciences in 1962.

For background information *see* CHLOROPHYLL; PLANT, MINERALS ESSENTIAL TO; PLANT METABOLISM; PHOTOSYNTHESIS in the McGraw-Hill Encyclopedia of Science and Technology. □

★ ASTWOOD, Edwin Bennett

American physician
Born Dec. 29, 1909, Bermuda

Astwood PROBABLY became best known for his elucidation of the mechanism whereby certain chemical compounds lead to enlargement of the thyroid. Experiments in rats (1942–43) indicated that the compounds interfere with the synthesis of the thyroid hormone, and that goiter is due to a compensatory oversecretion of thyrotropin from the pituitary. The compounds (thiourea and thiouracil) were given to patients with overactive thyroids, and eventually a workable treatment for hyperthyroidism was developed. Later more effective compounds were found.

One of the most telling arguments that these compounds act in this way was the finding that treatment with thyroid hormone prevents or reverses a goiter. Patients with thyroid enlargement without hyperthyroidism were treated with thyroid hormone, and in many of them the thyroid enlargement regressed. The concept that goiter is, in most instances, a compensatory adaptation to thyroid deficiency gradually gained acceptance over the years, and operations upon simple or nodular goiter for cosmetic or cancerophobic reasons declined.

His earliest work was concerned with the effects of sex hormones on the development of the mammary gland in the rat. This led to an interest in the rat's estrous cycle and its control by the follicle-stimulating and luteinizing hormones of the pituitary. His experiments showed clearly that neither of these hormones can account for the function of the corpora lutea. A third gonadotropin, labeled luteotropin, was characterized for this species and was subsequently identified with prolactin—the substance responsible for the secretion of crop milk in the pigeon and for the initiation of lactation in most mammals. Later work also showed that the corpora lutea of other species are controlled in quite other ways. It was further found that the extended functioning of the corpora lutea during pregnancy in the rat is sustained by a hormone secreted by the placenta.

Studies on luteotropin led to work on corticotropin (ACTH). As early as 1942, Astwood had prepared crude extracts which were more potent than the described protein hormone. The hormone was found to be readily destroyed in fresh pituitary tissue, so the glands were dried in acetone and then extracted with glacial acetic acid. In 1951 oxidized cellulose was used as an ion-exchange medium for purification, and a product was obtained which was 100 times as active as the originally described protein. This preparation had wide clinical application, and was used by others to elucidate the structure of further purified hormone.

Astwood received his B.S. at Washington Missionary College in 1929 and his M.D. and C.M. at McGill University Medical School in 1934. At McGill he gained his first interest in endocrinology from serving as a laboratory helper under J. B. Collip and, later, from discussion with J. S. L. Browne while Astwood was an intern at the Royal Victoria Hospital, Montreal (1934–35). At the Johns Hopkins Hospital in 1935–37, he had the opportunity to work with rats, and it was there that experimental experience was first gained. His research work was furthered by a Rockefeller Foundation fellowship to the biology department of Harvard University, under F. L. Hisaw. This stimulating experience led to his Ph.D. in 1939 and a thesis on the control of the function of the corpus luteum of the rat. After a return to Johns Hopkins Hospital as an associate obstetrician in 1939, he set up a laboratory for the study of reproduction. In 1940 he was appointed to the department of medicine at the Peter Bent Brigham Hospital, and was given research laboratories in the department of pharmacology at Harvard Medical School. He moved in 1945 to the New England Medical Center Hospitals and Tufts University, where he had much improved laboratory and clinical facilities. Studies on human thyroid function, using the new iodine-131, were initiated, several pituitary factors were purified, studies were carried out on the substances causing mobilization of fat from the adipose depots, and, in association with numerous able, young researchers, he was involved with work on most of the endocrine systems. He became professor of medicine at Tufts University School of Medicine, senior physician at the New England Medical Center Hospitals, and director of the Endocrine Service and Clinical Research Ward of these hospitals. He received a number of honors, including the Ciba Award of the Endocrine Society in 1944, the Cameron Prize of the University of Edinburgh in 1948, the Philips Medal of the American College of Physicians in 1949, the Borden Award of the Association of the American Medical Colleges in 1952, the Lasker Award of the American Public Health Association in 1954, and the Koch Award of the Endocrine Society in 1967. He was elected to the National Academy of Sciences in 1957. In 1967 he was given an honorary D.Sc. by the University of Chicago.

For background information *see* ENDOCRINE GLAND; ENDOCRINE MECHANISMS; HORMONE in the McGraw-Hill Encyclopedia of Science and Technology.   □

★ AUGER, Pierre Victor

French physicist
Born May 14, 1899, Paris, France

FROM THE outset of his work in 1922 Auger interested himself in the cloud chamber method discovered by C. T. R. Wilson and applied it to studying the photoelectric effect produced by x-rays on gas atoms. The Wilson method provided him with the most direct means of obtaining detailed information on the photoelectrons produced, since their trajectories could be followed as soon as they left the atom that had absorbed the quantum of radiation. Auger aimed to simplify the phenomenon and to obtain the photoelectric effect on a single category of atoms, rather than on all those of the mixture of air and water vapor used hitherto. He filled the chamber with hydrogen, which has a very low x-ray absorption coefficient, and a small proportion of highly absorbent and chemically neutral heavy gases, such as krypton and xenon.

While providing information on the directions in which the photoelectrons were emitted, this method revealed the effect of the radiations emitted by the positive ion left behind after the departure of the electron. Thus, if the photons of fluorescence (that is, the characteristic x-rays emitted by atoms ionized in their inner, or K and L, layers) were reabsorbed in the gas of the chamber, they should show up in the form of short electron trajectories.

Auger was able to observe some instances of this reabsorption in the gas, but usually found that the expected electron trajectory started from the same point as the electron trajectory attributable to the first photoelectron, that is, the two tracks started from the positive ion itself.

The common source of the tracks meant that an internal conversion of the photon of fluorescence had to be taking place when it became reabsorbed among the electrons of the very ion from which it had sprung. Such reabsorption would diminish the fluorescence correspondingly, since the photon was not emitted outside, a fact that could be checked by global methods.

Numerous experiments enabled Auger to show that the phenomenon is a general one and amounts, in fact, to "nonradiating" transitions among the electrons of atoms ionized in depth; the fall of peripheral electrons toward the free places in the inner levels is directly accompanied by the emission of electrons that carry away the liberated energy in kinetic form. This phenomenon was named the Auger effect, and the corresponding electrons Auger electrons. The ionization of the positive remainder increases with each repetition of the effect. N. Perrin later proved that certain heavy atoms can, by a series of Auger effects, attain a positive charge as high as 28 elementary charges. The effect thus discovered is similar to the internal conversion of gamma rays and Klein and Rosseland's collisions of the second kind.

Shortly after James Chadwick's discovery of neutrons in polonium-beryllium source radiations, Auger established their energy spectrum, and was able to demonstrate the existence of a group forming a continuous band of low energies. He explained the emission of such neutrons as a peculiar mechanism of disintegration of the beryllium nucleus by alpha particles without the latter being captured.

Much of Auger's work was devoted to cosmic rays. He was able to reveal the tracks of penetrating corpuscles in a double expansion chamber before and after their passage through half a meter of lead. The nonelectronic nature of these particles thus became a certainty (1935), and was finally demonstrated in 1938, when C. D. Anderson discovered the muon.

Auger next studied the cosmic showers in the form of photoelectron cascades and sought the existence of very-high-energy particles by looking for the very extensive showers which they ought to produce in passing through the atmosphere. By means of high-speed-resolution coincidence-counting equipment (10^{-6} sec in 1938), built with the help of Roland Maze, Auger demonstrated the existence of enormous atmospheric showers, which he called "grandes gerbes" and which are also known as extensive air showers or extensive Auger showers (EAS). The great size of these showers, which contain tens of millions of electrons and photons spread over areas of thousands of square meters, enabled Auger to attribute energies exceeding 10^{15} electron volts to the initial particle from which these showers originate. Later estimates raised the figure to 10^{20} ev, giving the extensive Auger showers the highest known energy of any natural phenomenon. It is a billion times that which the most powerful proton accelerator can attain. How corpuscular radiations with this amount of energy are created in the universe is still an unsolved problem of cosmic physics, though partial explanations have been suggested by various physicists, in particular Enrico Fermi.

Auger studied at the Ecole Normale Supérieure and the Faculty of Sciences at the University of Paris, where he obtained his doctorate in 1926. He remained associated with the university throughout his career, becoming a full professor in 1937. His research work was carried out first at Jean Perrin's laboratory there and then at the Ecole Normale Supérieure. He played an important role in the establishment of both French and international scientific research bodies. After taking part during World War II in the work of the Anglo-Canadian Atomic Energy Research group in Montreal, he returned to France in 1945 to help found the Commissariat a l'Energie Atomique. In 1952, as director of the Department of Sciences at UNESCO, he was responsible for setting up the European Nuclear Research Organization (known as CERN). After organizing the Centre National d'Etudes Spatiales (National Space Study Center) in France, he spent the years from 1960 to 1964 in bringing about the establishment of the European Space Research Organization (ESRO), of which he became director-general in 1962.

Auger wrote works on cosmic rays; a book of scientific philosophy, *L'Homme Microscopique*; and *Main Trends in Scientific Research*, prepared for the United Nations and UNESCO (1961).

For background information *see* AUGER EFFECT; CLOUD CHAMBER; COSMIC RAYS in the McGraw-Hill Encyclopedia of Science and Technology.   □

AVERY, Oswald Theodore

American physician and biologist
Born Oct. 21, 1887, Halifax, Nova Scotia, Canada
Died Feb. 20, 1955, Nashville, Tenn., U.S.A.

WHILE INVESTIGATING the transformation of one strain of pneumococcus (the bacterium causing pneumonia) into another, Avery discovered that the substance responsible for the hereditary alteration of the cell is deoxyribonucleic acid (DNA). This established the specificity of DNA in biological reactions, and ultimately served as the initial rung in the ladder of

genetic studies further extended by the work of such Nobel laureates as George Wells Beadle, Arthur Kornberg, Severo Ochoa, and Maurice Hugh Frederick Wilkins.

In 1928 Frederick Griffith, a British pathologist, reported that, when he inoculated mice with a mixture of a harmless strain of living pneumococci and the killed remains of a virulent strain, the mice died from an infection with live organisms of the virulent variety. He further reported that subsequent generations of the bacteria retained the new-found virulence. Since it was logical to assume that the dead organisms had not come to life, Griffith theorized that something in their bodies had transformed the living harmless strain into an infectious one. At first his report was viewed with skepticism by many authorities, including Avery, who believed strongly in immunological specificity. However, Avery asked an assistant, Martin H. Dawson, to try to duplicate Griffith's experiments. Dawson not only did so but in 1931, working at Columbia University with Richard H. P. Sia, succeeded in causing killed pneumococci to transform living organisms in laboratory glassware instead of in mice. A year later James L. Alloway, a member of Avery's group at the Rockefeller Institute, succeeded in using a cellfree extract rather than whole dead cells as the transforming agent, indicating that the agent involved is a chemical substance.

These results caused Avery to enter the investigation personally. He decided that the best approach would be to separate from capsulated pneumococci a soluble fraction capable of bringing about the change in vitro. Working at the Rockefeller Institute in New York City, first with Colin M. MacLeod and later with Maclyn McCarty, Avery grew large quantities of the virulent type III capsulated pneumococcus. From these cultures Avery extracted the chemical constituents of the organisms and tested the transforming power of each fraction. By 1944 he

had arrived at a practically pure substance that could transfer to noncapsulated variants and their subsequent generations the hereditary property to produce the capsular polysaccharide of the strain used for preparation of the extract. This fraction proved to be identical with one of the nucleic acids, DNA.

However, Avery felt that at this point he could still not be certain that the active agent is the DNA in the fraction or a small amount of protein contaminant. To verify the result, first McCarty and then Moses Kunitz prepared a quantity of DNase, an enzyme that would destroy the DNA without affecting any protein that was present. When upon treatment with the DNase the fraction lost its transforming power, Avery and his co-workers had demonstrated that DNA is the effective agent in inducing an inheritable change in a living organism. This finding provided the impetus for a major change in the thinking of geneticists. While the nucleic acids had previously been thought of as biologically inert substances, the work of later researchers, notably Alfred E. Mirsky, demonstrated that DNA is present in all animal organisms and, hence, that a similarity exists in the mechanism of heredity among all animal species, from the smallest bacterium to the largest mammal.

Avery's lifelong work with pneumococci began in 1913 in collaboration with A. Raymond Dochez. The two investigated the types of pneumococci present in pneumonic patients and in carriers. This investigation, which was to exert a great deal of influence on the evolution of medical microbiology, had as one result the discovery of specific soluble substances of pneumococcus origin in the blood and urine during lobar pneumonia.

Among his other studies was that of the role played by the capsular polysaccharides in determining the immunological specificity and virulence of pneumococci. This investigation permitted the development of sensitive and specific diagnostic procedures: serological typing and a skin test for the demonstration of a circulating antibody. More important, it proved that virulence and immunity can be analyzed apart from the parasite as a whole in terms of some highly specialized cellular component—in the case of pneumococci, the polysaccharide capsule.

The son of a clergyman, Avery moved to New York City with his family in 1887. He received his A.B. from Colgate University in 1900 and his M.D. from the College of Physicians and Surgeons of Columbia University in 1904. After serving as an assistant to a New York City physician for several months, he decided that he found little pleasure in the practice of medicine. He became interested in the pathogenesis of infectious diseases and, with the aid of a research fund, began a study of the phagocytic index in respiratory disease. Avery obtained a permanent position in the Hoagland Laboratory in Brooklyn in 1906 and remained there until 1913. In that year he joined the Rockefeller Institute Hospital as a bacteriologist, remaining at the Institute for 43 years before retiring to Nashville, Tenn., in 1947. Among the honors and awards he received were the John Phillips Memorial Award of the American College of Physicians in 1932, the Copley Medal of the Royal Society of London in 1945, and the Kober Medal of the Association of American Physicians in 1947. Avery was elected to the National Academy of Sciences in 1933, and was made a foreign member of the Royal Society of London in 1944.

For background information *see* DEOXYRIBO-NUCLEIC ACID; NUCLEIC ACID; PNEUMOCOCCUS in the McGraw-Hill Encyclopedia of Science and Technology.   □

★ **BABCOCK, Horace Welcome**

American astronomer
Born Sept. 13, 1912, Pasadena, Calif., U.S.A.

Babcock's main research interest related to the magnetic fields of stars and of the Sun. It originated as early as 1934, when he recognized the importance of polarization as a property of radiation from astronomical objects. Prior to that time other properties of stellar radiation—its direction, magnitude, intensity as a function of wavelength, variability, and coherence—had been exploited in astronomical observations, but polarization had been almost neglected except for George E. Hale's discovery of the strong magnetic field in sunspots and for his attempt to measure the "general magnetic field" of the Sun.

When the 100-in. telescope with its high-dispersion grating spectrograph became available at Mount Wilson in 1946, Babcock provided a differential analyzer for circular polarization with the aim of investigating rapidly rotating sharp-line stars. His hope was to detect coherent magnetic fields in the stars through the Zeeman effect in their spectra, the magnetic splitting of spectrum lines into characteristically polarized components. He expected that stars rotating much more rapidly than the Sun might well have far stronger general magnetic fields in their atmospheres, sufficing to bring the Zeeman effect within the range of measurability notwithstanding the weakness of the radiation. The earliest tests resulted in the discovery of a polar magnetic field of about 1500 gauss in the star 78 Virginis. (The Earth's magnetic field has a strength of about 0.6 gauss.) This was soon followed by the discovery of a regularly reversing magnetic field in the peculiar A-type star HD 125248; its effective field varied between the approximate limits +2100 and −1900 gauss in a

period of 9.3 days. The search for other magnetic stars and the investigation of their magnetic phenomena were carried forward first with the 100-in. and, after 1951, mainly with the 200-in. Hale telescope at Palomar. In 1958 the observational results were collected in a catalog that listed 89 sharp-line stars definitely showing the presence of strong magnetic fields. By 1966 the number had been increased to 129. Of these stellar magnetic fields, the strongest is 34,000 gauss, in the star HD 215411. Most of the stars listed show fields in the range from a few hundred gauss to about 5000 gauss.

Babcock provisionally classified the magnetic stars of spectral type A (and late B), which are in the majority, into three groups: α-variables, showing periodic magnetic variations; β-variables, showing irregular magnetic fluctuations with reversal of polarity; and γ-variables, showing irregular magnetic fluctuations always with the same polarity. Most of the α-, β-, and γ-stars are also known to be "peculiar" in that their spectra show an abnormal strength of such elements as Sr, Si, Cr, or the rare earths; the α-stars, in addition, are spectrum variables, the outstanding example being 53 Camelopardalis, which displays magnetic variations ranging between +3700 gauss and −5100 gauss in a period of 8.03 days. Other magnetic variables have periods as short as 4 days or less, but some are much longer. The period of magnetic and spectrum variation is 226 days for HD 188041 and about 2350 days for HD 187474.

Two physical models were considered in accounting for the periodically changing stellar fields: the oblique rotator, in which the line of sight is oblique to the axis of rotation of a star that carries an asymmetrically distributed magnetic-field pattern on its surface, and the magnetic oscillator, in which the star, observed nearly "pole-on," undergoes an intrinsic hydromagnetic oscillation. The latter model is conceptually based on the far weaker and slower 22-year magnetic cycle of the Sun, which shows a reversal of the characteristic magnetic polarity near the north and south heliographic poles. At present, the evidence is preponderantly in favor of the oblique rotator model for the magnetic α-variables, but this would seem to require for confirmation the discovery of an oblique rotator viewed nearly parallel to its rotational axis. Such a star would show either a constant magnetic field or a sinusoidally varying field of small amplitude *without* reversal of magnetic polarity. No such star has yet been discovered.

The observations of stellar magnetism stimulated the development, by other authors, of the theory of magnetohydrodynamics in astrophysical context. According to the theory, stellar magnetic fields are either generated *de novo* within a star, or they are primeval, having condensed with the gas from the interstellar medium when the star was formed. Magnetic fields are important in modifying activity in the convective layers of stars and in generating flares. Around rotating stars the magnetic field may be vital in coupling the star to a circumstellar ionized medium; such coupling results in the transfer of angular momentum, braking the rotation of the star and accelerating the rotation of the external medium. This concept, coupled with the ubiquity of magnetic fields, forms much of the basis for the current opinion that a great many stars besides the Sun probably have planetary systems.

From 1952 to 1958 Babcock collaborated with his father, Harold D. Babcock, in the development and use of the solar magnetograph, an electrooptical system for measuring and recording the strength, polarity, and distribution of magnetic fields (and velocity fields as well) over the surface of the Sun. Primary innovations included an electrooptic birefringent crystal used with a powerful grating spectrograph and an ac amplifier with synchronous demodulation, as well as techniques for scanning the Sun's image and conformally mapping the data. The magnetograph, now in use at several observatories, is capable of measuring fields as weak as a small fraction of 1 gauss. The instrument provided much new data on the systematics of the Sun's surface features and resulted in the discovery of weak ($\sim$1 gauss), persistent magnetic fields near the Sun's poles of rotation (the elusive "general field") and of the reversal of the Sun's polar fields that is linked with the sunspot cycle.

In 1961 Babcock advanced a theory of the Sun's 22-year magnetic cycle, based on T. G. Cowling's idea of subsurface amplification by differential rotation. Involving a systematic pattern of circulation of the plasma in the outer convection zone, the model accounts for the reversal of the Sun's polar magnetic fields, for Spörer's law of sunspot distribution, and for several other solar phenomena. The observations and the theory required severing and reconnection of lines of force, with a resultant outflow of tenuous plasma (now commonly referred to as the solar wind).

Babcock's early interests were developed by his father and by association with the astronomical group of the Mount Wilson Observatory, as well as by an uncle, Ernest B. Babcock, professor of genetics at the University of California. Horace Babcock received a B.S. at the California Institute of Technology in 1934 and a Ph.D. at the University of California in 1938 after completing at the Lick Observatory a thesis on the rotation of the spiral galaxy in Androm-

eda, showing that the mass of the spiral galaxy is 10^{11} suns. After experience at the Yerkes and McDonald observatories, he engaged in wartime research on radar and rockets. He joined the staff at Mount Wilson in 1946 and became director of the Mount Wilson and Palomar observatories in 1964. Babcock was awarded the Draper Medal of the National Academy of Sciences in 1957 and the Eddington Medal of the Royal Astronomical Society in 1958. He was elected to the National Academy of Sciences in 1954, to the American Academy of Arts and Sciences in 1959, and to the American Philosophical Society in 1966.

Most of Babcock's scientific publications appeared in the *Astrophysical Journal* and other journals.

For background information *see* Astronomical spectroscopy; Stellar magnetic field; Sun; Zeeman effect in the McGraw-Hill Encyclopedia of Science and Technology.   □

★ BADGER, Richard McLean

American physical chemist and molecular spectroscopist
Born May 4, 1896, Elgin, Ill., U.S.A.

B ADGER WORKED in several fields of physical chemistry, though his predominant scientific interest over many years was the application of spectroscopy to the solution of chemical problems. These included particularly the structures of polyatomic molecules, both the very small and the very large, especially the proteins and simpler related substances; the problem of hydrogen bonding; and the relation of potential constants to internuclear distances. While Badger was a graduate student, his interest was directed toward spectroscopy through his association with Richard C. Tolman and with Paul S. Epstein. Tolman was engaged in one of the earliest attempts to calculate thermodynamic properties of simple molecules by the application of quantum statistical mechanics, then in a very elementary state, and was using internuclear distances roughly estimated from gas kinetic data. At Tolman's suggestion Badger became involved in checking the calculations and saw the possibility of improvement by the use of the spectroscopic moments of inertia, just then becoming available. Shortly thereafter he became aware of the possibilities which infrared spectroscopy offers to the chemist through a lecture presentation by Epstein of the remarkable high-resolution work being done at the University of Michigan.

For very practical reasons Badger's first experimental work in spectroscopy was in the far infrared. Diffraction gratings were very difficult to obtain, but coarse gratings suitable for the long-wave regions could be made with the relatively primitive facilities available. These made possible the discovery of the pure rotation spectrum of ammonia, the first rotation spectrum of a polyatomic molecule to be interpreted. This work confirmed the symmetrical pyramidal structure of ammonia and cleared up a former misinterpretation of the $10-\mu$ band, then so interesting as the first example of inversion doubling. At this time the development of new photographic sensitizers was making the near infrared available for convenient investigation, and Badger turned his attention in this direction. He continued work on ammonia with R. Mecke in Bonn, but unfortunately theory was not yet developed for the interpretation of vibration-rotation bands of symmetrical rotors with degenerate vibrations. However, a number of papers followed on overtone and combination bands of simple polyatomic molecules that directed attention to the great variability of the OH group frequency, most puzzling until correlated with the hydrogen bonding tendency of this group. This subject proved to be a continuing interest and was the basis for 17 papers directly or indirectly bearing on the subject of hydrogen bonding. Badger was also struck by regularities in the potential constants of simple molecules. He formulated an empirical rule, commonly known as Badger's rule, that expresses a periodic relation between the distance and force constant of diatomic molecules. This systematization of experimental data resulted in disclosing several errors in the literature. The rule is less accurate for polyatomic molecules, but has frequently been used to estimate distances in the absence of precise data.

World War II diverted Badger's research activities to other fields, including a side interest in the physical chemistry of high polymers and ultimately in proteins and related substances, which were the subject of later spectroscopic studies. The war interval was not without compensation, since the important advances in techniques and instrumentation enormously facilitated infrared spectroscopy. With his student coworkers, Badger investigated the spectra of a series of simple polyatomic molecules with interesting structural problems. In particular, nitrous acid offered an unusual case of the double minimum problem and ozone presented a dilemma of long standing. A reasonable interpretation of the infrared spectrum had seemed impossible, until the discovery by M. Kent Wilson and Badger of a new band attributable to the ν_1 symmetrical stretch. This resolved the difficulty and established spectroscopically the obtuse angled model for the ozone molecule.

Badger's secondary education began in Brisbane, Australia, and continued at the Elgin Academy, in Illinois. His college career, begun at the Junior College of the Elgin Academy and continued at Northwestern University, was interrupted by World War I. He finally received his B.S. (1921) and Ph.D. (1924) from the California Institute of Technology. He remained there, with some interruptions, and was active in teaching and research until his retirement as emeritus in 1966. In 1928–29 Badger was Rockefeller International fellow at the universities of Göttingen and Bonn, and in 1931 he was lecturer at the University of California, Berkeley. During World War II he was engaged in work for the Army Air Force, the National Defense Research Committee, the Manhattan District, the Office of Scientific Research and Development, and the Office of Naval Research. He was elected a member of the National Academy of Sciences in 1952 and a fellow of the American Academy of Arts and Sciences in 1961. He was John Simon Guggenheim Memorial fellow in 1960–61. In 1961 he was awarded the medal of the Manufacturing Chemists Association for excellence in college teaching in chemistry.

Badger wrote or coauthored 85 publications in scientific journals.

For background information *see* Hydrogen bond; Molecular structure and spectra; Protein; Spectroscopy in the McGraw-Hill Encyclopedia of Science and Technology.   □

★ BAKER, William Oliver

American chemist
Born July 15, 1915, Chestertown, Md., U.S.A.

In studies with C. P. Smyth at Princeton stimulated by the theories of molecular dipoles of P. J. W. Debye, Baker began a new phase in solid-state science. He showed that the rotation of molecules in crystals reduced the

entropy of fusion to a ratio of about 2 and drastically raised the melting point and reduced the liquid range of a variety of compounds. This explained, among other things, the belief in organic chemistry that highly symmetrical molecules, such as tertiary butyl compounds, camphor, and many others, would have high melting points and sublime readily. This work was extended to solid solution formation by symmetrical structures, where both thermal and dielectric studies of polar components, such as mixtures of tertiary butyl chloride in carbon tetrachloride, yielded new insight into eutectics and other multiphase crystallizations. It was also applied to the alipathic chain systems, such as cetyl alcohol and stearic and palmitic esters, whose unsuspected mobility in the solid state (around the long-chain axis) explained curious plastic as well as thermodynamic properties of these components of natural waxes and other biological substances.

In 1939 Baker joined the research program at Bell Telephone Laboratories devoted to a basic understanding of the chemistry and physics of high polymers, which then promised to provide major mechanical and insulating materials for new electronics and telecommunications. Working to this end, he studied a variety of simple polyamides and polyesters based on the syntheses of W. H. Carothers. By x-ray, dielectric, dynamical, and chemical studies, he discovered the thermal conditioning of microcrystalline plastics through which all present processes for assuring fiber, film, and bulk rigidity and tenacity are derived. Principles were developed for determining the structural quality in the solid state of not only the linear condensation polymers, but also of natural systems such as regenerated cellulose. The x-ray line-width techniques that Baker found to express lateral ordering of parallel chains were widely applied in manufacturing control of such commercial processes as rayon tire cords and nylon extrusions.

During World War II his principal tasks were preparation of strong and stable polymer dielectric radiators for the earliest shipborne radar and application of new principles of polymer science to the national synthetic rubber program. This latter work resulted in a rapid optical method for control of composition of the synthetic rubber and discovery of a new kind of molecule still widely used in controlling the critical processing and viscoelasticity of rubbery systems. Instead of the typical chainlike molecules of most synthetic polymers, these new molecules were globular or loose molecular networks. Discovery of these molecules, called microgels, the largest discrete synthetic molecules known, stimulated development of modern light-scattering techniques for molecular weight determination as based on the work of Albert Einstein and Debye.

In the postwar period Baker broadened his particular interest in the structure of molecular solids into what was to become known as materials science. With his co-workers he found that the new microcrystalline polymers, such as polyethylene, could be made with such control of average chain length, structure, and crystallinity that rather massive structural functions could be achieved, for example, the replacement for lead in heavy communications and power cable. This caused a great advance in the economy of cable production and usage. The scientific base studies revealed that, under multiaxial stressing, microcrystalline polymers—now extensively used in all sorts of containers, films, tubings, plumbing, and so forth—were subject to destructive cracking, especially in the presence of certain common liquids, unless the molecular weight was adjusted specifically to minimize this mechanical effect. Such chemical controls are now used worldwide to assure the quality of modern polymers.

In another phase of his contribution to the development of materials science, Baker collaborated with W. P. Mason and J. H. Heiss in the application of high-frequency piezoelectric transducers to the study of viscoelastic properties of macromolecular solids, liquids, and solutions. By simultaneous use of compressional and shear waves over a wide range of frequencies extending into hundreds of megacycles, the general pattern of elasticity and flow of many model structures was revealed. The first work on shear relaxations in dilute solutions of polymers indicated the processes of chain configuration and chain entanglement as causes of the vital technical qualities of flexibility and resilience in fibers and plastics.

Baker's work on electrical properties of

molecular solids continued over several decades. He discovered the large temperature-induced direct-current conductivity of polyamides, which also was analyzed in association with the remarkable dielectric properties of these analogs of natural polypeptides. The unsuspected electronic, as well as quasi-ionic, conductivity in hydrogen-bonded organic systems was subsequently extended, in collaboration with F. H. Winslow, in a wide range of densely cross-linked polymers composed of carbon, hydrogen, and oxygen. Using the techniques of solid-state electronics, including electron paramagnetic resonance and Hall effect, Baker found that by chemical variation of the proportions of carbon and hydrogen in highly conjugated, densely cross-linked polymers (polydivinyl benzene and so on), it was possible to create a continuous transition between paramagnetic but insulating solids and highly semiconducting systems of rather low charge mobility but high carrier concentration. This led eventually to a highly refractory form of pyrolytic-type graphite, forming a system called polymer carbons. Studies of the chemistry of these transformations and of these highly cross-bonded structures led to an interesting by-product—the realization that a particular shape of polymer network would be maintained macroscopically even during the intense energy absorption of hydrogen and oxygen dissociation during very high temperature exposure. Hence, in 1954–55, when Baker was chairman of the National Research Council Subgroup on Synthetic Materials for Missile Nosecones and Satellite Heat Shields, the use of an organic ablating structure was proposed. Such composite, netted polymers have subsequently been developed in a number of federal contract laboratories, and are the basis for most reentry protection of intercontinental missiles and Earth satellites, including all of the known manned satellite recoveries. Another earlier application of Baker's interest in cross-linking of polymers was the invention of the first polyester casting and laminating resins which contain little or no residual unsaturation. These were "cured" by the peroxide- or other radical-catalyzed catalysis associated with the abstraction of hydrogens from the main polymer chain, especially from methylene groups on the alpha carbons relative to the ester linkages.

From 1955, Baker was responsible for the research programs of Bell Telephone Laboratories. In this period his associates created Earth satellite communications, the microwave maser, the optical laser, and the superconducting solenoid, among other physical facilities for modern science and electronic communications. In his department extensive discoveries were made of principles for organizing and programming high-speed digital computers, which are based on the solid-state diodes and transistors earlier produced in the physical sciences research of the Laboratories. Hence, Baker's interests turned to the broader fields of telecommunications and information processing, which benefit from the various facilities derived from materials science and the chemistry and physics of solids. He worked also for the federal science offices, serving as an original member of the President's Science Advisory Committee when it was established in the White House, where he was chairman of the initial panels on scientific and technical information and on materials research and development. First chairman of the National Science Information Council, he also was a member of the National Science Board from 1960 to 1966.

Baker received his B.S. (1935) from Washington College and his Ph.D. (1938) from Princeton University. Author of more than 80 scientific and technical papers, he contributed to nine books and obtained 14 patents. In 1963 he received the Perkin Medal, which is the international award for applied chemistry, and in 1966 the American Chemical Society's Priestley Medal. He was elected to the National Academy of Sciences in 1961 and to the American Academy of Arts and Sciences in 1965.

For background information see CRYSTAL STRUCTURE; POLYESTER RESINS; POLYMER PROPERTIES; POLYMERIZATION in the McGraw-Hill Encyclopedia of Science and Technology.   □

★ BALL, Eric Glendinning

American biochemist
Born July 12, 1904, Coventry, England

LACKING FUNDS to undertake graduate training in physical chemistry, Ball accepted a position in 1926 as a research assistant in the department of physiological chemistry at the University of Pennsylvania. Fascinated by the opportunities afforded by this rapidly growing area of investigation and encouraged by D. Wright Wilson, head of the department, he entered graduate school there and embarked upon a career in biochemistry. After he completed his Ph.D. work, his earlier interest in physical chemistry led him to seek postdoctoral work with W. Mansfield Clark at the Johns Hopkins Medical School. There, first as a National Research Council fellow and then as a staff member, he carried out investigations on the oxidation-reduction potentials of a number of biological systems. This led to an interest in the mechanisms of biological oxidations and the enzymes related to these processes.

In 1937–38 Ball spent a year as a Guggenheim fellow in the laboratories of Otto Warburg at the Kaiser Wilhelm Institut für Zellphysiologie in Berlin-Dahlem. There he purified xanthine oxidase and showed that it contained flavin adenine dinucleotide. He also estimated the oxidation-reduction potentials of the cytochromes and deduced that the order of reaction within the cell of these components must be a, c, b. His work on xanthine oxidase won for him the Eli Lilly Award in biochemistry in 1940. In the fall of that year he became a member of the department of biological chemistry at the Harvard Medical School. During the war years he carried on investigations first on the mustard gases and then on the malarial parasite. The team of researchers under his supervision achieved the first in vitro cultivation of the malarial parasite. At war's end he returned to studies in the field of biological oxidations and intermediary metabolism. Working with his students, he conducted investigations leading to the recognition of cytochrome c and b_5, the high content of phospholipids in the electron transmitter system, and other discoveries.

In 1958 Ball's attention was directed to adipose tissue, brown and white. White adipose tissue had long been regarded as relatively inert metabolically and was looked upon mainly as a storehouse for fat. Work in a number of laboratories indicated that this was a misconception, at least for certain species, and that various metabolic processes in this tissue could be made to proceed apace when stimulated by the addition of certain hormones. For example, the addition of minute amounts of insulin to adipose tissue in vitro resulted in a marked acceleration of glucose uptake with its conversion primarily to fat. Consideration of the known events that occur in this lipogenic event led Ball and his students to devise a simple manometric procedure to measure the carbon dioxide evolved and in turn to study the action of insulin. The procedure was also useful for the assay of minute quantities of insulin and of substances that mimic or inhibit the action of insulin. He and his students also elucidated the quantitative details of the enzymatic processes by which glucose is converted to fat in adipose tissue. This led to the recognition of a new pathway for the production of reduced triphosphopyridine nucleotide, a coenzyme essential for fat synthesis.

During these studies on adipose tissue a new role for insulin as an antilipolytic agent was found. This new function of insulin was shown to be due to its ability to suppress the formation of cyclic 3′,5′-adenosinemonophosphate. This compound, first described by E. W. Sutherland and his co-workers as important in the control of cellular glycogen mobilization, is rapidly becoming recognized as a key substance in the control of a number of other metabolic processes. Various investigators showed that the rate of cyclic adenosinemonophosphate formation is increased by a number of hormones. Insulin now appears to be able to exert a counterbalancing effect upon this action of these hormones, besides regulating glucose uptake by certain tissues.

Brown adipose tissue is a special type found most abundantly in hibernators and in newborn fur-bearing animals. Its color is largely due to its high content of cytochromes, and it is capable of unusually high rates of oxygen consumption. Work in Ball's laboratory and in other laboratories suggested that this tissue serves as a furnace to supply heat to the animal during arousal from hibernation or at times of excessive heat loss, as during cold exposure or before fur has developed.

Long interested in marine biology and the comparative biochemistry of marine forms, Ball spent his summers at the Marine Biological Laboratory at Woods Hole and served as a member of the Corporation of this institute and of the Bermuda Biological Station. He became a member of the national advisory board for the operation of the *Alpha-Helix*, the oceangoing vessel for biological studies operated by the Scripps Institution of Oceanography at La Jolla.

Son of an Episcopal minister, Ball was born in England, but received nearly all of his education in the United States. He received a B.S. in 1925, M.A. in 1926, and D.Sc. (honorary) in 1949 from Haverford College in Pennsylvania, a Ph.D. in 1930 from the University of Pennsylvania, and an M.A. (honorary) in 1942 from Harvard University. After a year as National Research Council fellow at Johns Hopkins Medical School, he became a staff member there in 1930. He moved to Harvard in 1940, where he became associate professor in 1942 and full professor in 1946. In 1952 he was appointed chairman of the

Division of Medical Sciences, a part of the Faculty of Arts and Sciences established in 1908 to train Ph.D. candidates in the medical school. Ball was awarded the Cruzerio du Sol by the Brazilian government in 1945 and the Certificate of Merit by the United States government in 1948. He was elected a member of the American Academy of Arts and Sciences in 1945 and of the National Academy of Sciences in 1948.

For background information *see* ADIPOSE TISSUE; ENZYME; METABOLISM; OXIDATION-REDUCTION in the McGraw-Hill Encyclopedia of Science and Technology.   □

★ **BARKER, Horace Albert**

American biochemist
Born Nov. 29, 1907, Oakland, Calif., U.S.A.

MOST OF Barker's research was on the degradation of organic compounds by anaerobic bacteria and the chemistry of these fermentations. His interest in bacterial metabolism was first stimulated by C. B. van Niel and A. J. Kluyver. At that time knowledge of the pathway of carbohydrate degradation by the glycolytic path and tricarboxylic acid (TCA) cycle was developing rapidly, but little was known about the chemistry of most bacterial fermentations. Barker's first significant contribution to this area resulted from studies of the bacterial formation of methane. He developed methods for the isolation of methane-producing bacteria and obtained purified cultures of several species. One of the cultures was shown to couple the oxidation of ethanol to acetic acid with the reduction of carbon dioxide to methane, thus apparently confirming the hypothesis of van Niel that all biological methane is formed by carbon dioxide reduction. T. C. Stadtman and Barker later showed that methane is also formed from carbon dioxide in the fermentations of propionate and butyrate, whereas in fermenta-

tions of acetate and methane, methane is derived entirely from the methyl group of these substrates. Their observations led to the proposal of a more general theory of the chemistry of methane formation.

During studies of the methane fermentation of ethanol by enrichment cultures, a massive anaerobic conversion of ethanol to butyric acid and caproic acid was observed. *Clostridium kluyveri*, the bacterium responsible for the synthesis of these volatile fatty acids, was isolated and was shown by Barker, M. D. Kamen, and B. T. Bornstein to convert ethanol and acetate to C_4 and C_6 fatty acids by the successive condensation of C_2 units. Subsequent studies by E. R. Stadtman and Barker demonstrated that these reactions can occur in cellfree enzyme preparations. Acetylphosphate, a product of ethanol oxidation, was shown to be reversibly reduced to butyrate. Since none of the previously considered C_4 intermediates in butyrate synthesis were active in this system, it was postulated, and later demonstrated, that the true intermediates are linked to F. Lipmann's coenzyme A. A very active phosphotransacetylase was discovered in *C. kluyveri* extracts. This enzyme, which catalyzes a reversible transfer of acetyl groups between phosphate and coenzyme A, was later used by E. R. Stadtman to demonstrate enzymatic synthesis of acetyl coenzyme A.

C. kluyveri was also used to investigate the synthesis of amino acids from C_2 compounds and carbon dioxide. About 25% of the carbon in the cell materials is derived from carbon dioxide, and the remainder from C_2 substrates. By the use of ^{14}C-labeled acetate or carbon dioxide, Neil Tomlinson and Barker showed that C_3 amino acids (alanine, serine) are formed by a C_2-C_1 condensation, and the C_4 amino acid (aspartic) by a C_3-C_1 condensation, with the carboxyl groups being derived from carbon dioxide. The origin of the carbon atoms of glutamate was inconsistent with its formation via the usual TCA cycle reactions. Later enzymatic studies by G. Gottschalk and Barker proved that glutamate is synthesized from oxalacetate and acetyl coenzyme A via the TCA cycle reaction, but the enzyme that forms citrate is unusual in the stereospecificity of the reaction it catalyzes.

Barker and his associates carried out a series of investigations of the anaerobic decomposition of amino acids, purines, and related compounds by soil bacteria isolated after enrichment in media containing single nitrogenous substrates. Several species so obtained were highly specialized with respect to the compounds fermented. Thus, one species fermented glycine preferentially, another used alanine, serine, or threonine, a third decomposed uric acid and other purines, and a fourth attacked glutamate with special facility. The sequence of chemical reactions and the specialized enzymatic systems in some of these bacteria were studied. The path of glutamate fermentation by *C. tetanomorphum* was shown to involve the formation of several branched chain compounds. The key reaction is the reversible conversion of glutamate to 3-methylaspartate by glutamate mutase. This reaction was found to require a new, light-sensitive cofactor that was isolated and identified as a coenzyme form of pseudovitamin B_{12}.

H. Weissbach, J. I. Toohey, and Barker subsequently isolated the analogous vitamin B_{12} coenzyme from *C. tetanomorphum* and other anaerobic bacteria. Toohey and Barker showed that the coenzyme is present in the livers of man and animals. Weissbach and others established that the corrinoid coenzymes contain an adenine nucleoside moiety not present in vitamin B_{12}; this was later shown by P. G. Lenhert and D. C. Hodgkin to be a 5'-deoxyadenosyl group attached to the cobalt atom of the vitamin by a novel cobalt-carbon bond. These developments stimulated interest in the biochemical role of corrinoid compounds. R. L. Blakley and Barker found that the vitamin B_{12} coenzyme was required for the enzymatic conversion of ribonucleotides to deoxyribonucleotides by the ribonucleotide reductase of *Lactobacillus leichmannii*.

While investigating the metabolism of anaerobic bacteria, Barker and his associates found that acetic acid synthesis from carbon dioxide is a rather common process. This was first observed by use of $^{14}CO_2$ in *C. thermoaceticum*, which couples the oxidation of glucose to acetate and carbon dioxide with the reduction of carbon dioxide to acetate. A similar process was later observed in fermentations of purines and of glycine.

In collaboration with M. Doudoroff, W. Z. Hassid, and N. O. Kaplan, Barker participated in the first demonstration of enzymic sucrose synthesis from fructose and glucose-1-phosphate by sucrose phosphorylase from *Pseudomonas saccharophila*. The enzyme was shown to function as a glucosyl-transferring agent using phosphate, fructose, and certain other sugars as glucosyl acceptors. This study substantially broadened the concept of enzymatic group transfer.

The son of a public school teacher, Barker studied at Stanford University and the University of Chicago, receiving both his A.B. (1929) and his Ph.D. in chemistry (1933) at Stanford. He spent 2 years as a postdoctoral fellow at the Hopkins Marine Station with T. Skogsberg and C. B. van Niel, and 1 year at the Technical University in Delft, Netherlands, with A. J. Kluyver. He later studied with F. Lipmann at Massachusetts General Hospital and with A. Kornberg at the National Institutes of Health.

He joined the staff of the department of plant nutrition, University of California, as a soil microbiologist in 1936, transferred to the department of plant biochemistry in 1950, and to the biochemistry department in 1959. He was honored with the Sugar Research Award with M. Doudoroff and W. Z. Hassid (1945), the Neuberg Medal (1959), the Borden Award in Nutrition (1962), the California Museum of Science and Industry Award (1966), and the Gowland Hopkins Medal (1967). He was elected to the National Academy of Sciences in 1953.

Barker wrote some 190 papers and *Bacterial Fermentations* (1957).

For background information *see* BACTERIAL METABOLISM; COENZYME; ENZYME; FERMENTATION in the McGraw-Hill Encyclopedia of Science and Technology.   ☐

★ BARTLETT, Sir Frederic (Charles)

British experimental psychologist
Born Oct. 20, 1886, Stow-on-the-Wold, England

THE EXPERIMENTAL psychological study of memory was initiated by Hermann Ebbinghaus in 1885. He used lists of nonsense syllables, each member of which could be regarded as equivalent in difficulty to any other member. The lists had to be learned or partially learned under prescribed conditions and then recalled by the learner after a given lapse of time in varied orders with or without prompting. This model treated memory as a kind of receptacle or storehouse, into which whatever was memorized disappeared for a time, to be recovered later with more or less accuracy. It became the accepted model for the great bulk of psychological experiments on recall. After taking part in, and directing, many investigations in this conventional form, Bartlett became convinced that the results threw little light upon how remembering takes place in the course of everyday behavior.

In this case, the material which is recalled has only rarely been given careful or prolonged preliminary study, and the recall itself is prompted by immediate environmental demands and is carried out to answer the challenges of these demands.

Accordingly, he set to work to devise experiments for the investigation of remembering as distinct, though not entirely different, from the more conventional sense of "the memory." Preliminary experiments on perception demonstrated that what is perceived at any moment is partially determined by earlier experiences, though these are rarely specifically reinstated. Then Bartlett embarked upon a large series of experiments on remembering as an event of everyday occurrence. He used material consisting of short connected stories of a familiar form, of descriptive prose, of arguments, and of pictures. His observers read, heard, or looked at this material, but were never required to "learn it by heart." At determined and recorded intervals later, the observers were asked to "remember" what they had read, heard, or seen, or were given conditions by the experimenter such that the material could be used to help or hinder their response. It soon became apparent that as the "remembered" material was made use of from interval to interval, and particularly as it was passed on from person to person within a group, it was in constant and often radical process of change. Especially where groups of socially related members were involved, the recorded versions approached or assumed forms of accepted conventions. Bartlett was therefore led to a study of the social determining factors in remembering. He himself made field studies in Africa, and he obtained many results from students in other countries.

The theories of remembering to which all these experiments led treated recall as a thoroughly active process. What is claimed to be reinstated is in constant but ordered change, and is organized, coded, and controlled by its relation to current demands on behavior. These ordered changes were clarified, and the likelihood of their occurrence considered.

This work on remembering was begun before World War I. When the war came, Bartlett's attention was officially diverted to investigations of skills as a consequence of his appointment to organize and develop psychological studies on the selection of naval ratings and officers enlisted for antisubmarine work. After the war the remembering experiments and their analysis were completed and published. The British Medical Research Council, of which he then became a member, was interested in various personnel problems as they affected the military services, and Bartlett was appointed a member of the personnel committees, first of the Royal Air Force and then of the navy and army. When World War II broke out, he became the leader of a research group, mainly working at Cambridge University, whose concern was to develop new methods for the study of human skills, particularly of those involved in flying and the ground control of flight. In prescribing and proving these methods, leading parts were also played by Kenneth Craik, a most brilliant student whose death by accident closely following the war was an irreparable loss, and by G. C. Drew, who became professor of psychology in the University of London.

Bartlett's investigations into remembering had led him to the view that human thinking processes were a further development in the same directions, but relatively free from temporal and spatial control. The work on skill had convinced him that the achievements of bodily skills were precursors, on a more elementary level, of the processes which lead from perception, through remembering, to thinking proper. It further appeared that, by utilizing the methods which had been successfully explored in the investigation of bodily skills, more objectively based information could be obtained about the conditions and nature of the higher-level skills of thinking.

Bartlett's experimental work was thus along three main lines, regarded as closely related: the leading characteristics of remembering, those of bodily skills, and the nature and conditions of the thinking processes.

Bartlett graduated from the University of London and from St. John's College, Cambridge, of which he became a fellow. He was made a Commander of the Order of the British Empire in 1932 and was knighted in 1941, both mainly for his work for the Royal Air Force and the Admiralty. A fellow of the Royal Society of London, he was elected a foreign member of the Philosophical Society of Philadelphia, the U.S. National Academy of Sciences, and the American Academy of Arts and Sciences as well as of the psychological societies of France, Italy, Belgium, Sweden, Spain, Switzerland, and Turkey. He was awarded the Baly Medal of the Royal College of Physicians, the Huxley Medal of the Royal Anthropological Society, a Royal Medal of the Royal Society, the Longacre Award of the Aero Medical Association, and the Gold Medal of the International Academy of Aviation and Space Medicine.

His best-known books are *Remembering, an Experimental and Social Study* (1932), *The Mind at Work and Play* (1951), and *Thinking, an Experimental and Social Study* (1956).

For background information *see* MEMORY in the McGraw-Hill Encyclopedia of Science and Technology.   ☐

★ BARTLETT, Neil

British chemist
Born Sept. 15, 1932, Newcastle-upon-Tyne, England

WHILE INVESTIGATING the fluorides of the platinum metals, Bartlett in 1962 prepared the first chemical compound of a noble gas. The noble gases were discovered by Lord Rayleigh and by Sir William Ramsey and his co-workers in the 1890s. The first gas to be discovered and the most abundant, argon, was quickly subjected to intensive chemical and physical examination and found to be chemically inert. Henri Moissan, the first to prepare fluorine, attempted to prepare an argon fluoride in 1895, and his failure impressed him and his friend Ramsey with the inertness of the gas. Several perceptive chemists pointed to the greater likelihood of the heavier (and much rarer) gases, krypton and xenon, entering into chemical combination. L. C. Pauling, in particular, suggested in 1933 that xenon and krypton fluorides should be preparable, and in the same year an abortive attempt was made to prepare a xenon fluoride. The failure to sustain claims to noble gas compounds, together with the inability of experienced investigators to carry out the most favorable syntheses, contributed to an acceptance of the complete inertness of the gases, but it was probably not the most important contributing factor. Undoubtedly, the popularity of the simple electronic theories of valence, which emphasize the special stability of the noble gas configurations, had a major influence. The scarcity of the most favorable gas, xenon, and the instability of radon, which should be the most chemically active gas, were also contributing factors.

Bartlett started his independent research with the intention of better defining the factors which limit the oxidation states of the elements. The noble metals, in particular, attracted his interest because of the promise of a greater range of oxidation states. Investigation of these elements also promised to be of value in his concern to define more clearly the relationship of the ligand geometry of molecules and crystals to the valence electron configurations of the central atom. The synthetic work, which involved fluorides and oxyfluorides, was therefore accompanied by structural studies. This combination was to prove vital to the discoveries which followed.

The compound of prime importance in the discovery of xenon chemistry was investigated initially in the belief that it would prove to be an oxyfluoride of 6-valent platinum. The compound was first observed as a sublimable red solid produced when platinum or platinum compounds were treated with fluorine in glass apparatus at moderate temperatures. The red solid was marked by great chemical reactivity, and it proved necessary to develop special techniques to analyze it. In 1961 Bartlett, with D. H. Lohmann, established the empirical formula as PtO_2F_6. Extensive chemical and physical characterization clearly indicated the compound to be a salt, dioxygenyl hexafluoroplatinate, $O_2{}^+[PtF_6]^-$. This was the first example known to represent either of the ions. It was particularly remarkable for its oxidized oxygen cation. This formulation implied that the molecular fluoride, platinum hexafluoride, which had been reported by Bernard Weinstock and J. G. Malm in 1958, should be capable of oxidizing molecular oxygen. This proved to be so, the two gases combining spontaneously at ordinary temperatures and pressures:

$$O_2(g) + PtF_6(g) \rightarrow O_2{}^+[PtF_6]^-(s)$$

Although the salt formulation had seemed appropriate early in the research, it posed the difficulty that the electron affinity of platinum hexafluoride,

$$\Delta E(PtF_6(g) + e \rightarrow PtF_6{}^-(g))$$

needed to be greater than −160 kcal/mole (that is, approximately twice the value for atomic fluorine or atomic chlorine), so that oxidation of molecular oxygen should proceed spontaneously. The proof of the salt formulation, therefore, pointed to platinum hexafluoride as the most powerfully oxidizing molecular species recognized so far. Bartlett noted that the ionization potentials of the heavier noble gases (xenon, 12.2 ev; radon, 10.5 ev) were as low as, or lower than, molecular oxygen (12.2 ev), and hence he concluded that these gases should also be oxidizable. In his investigations in 1962 xenon gas proved to be as easy to oxidize as molecular oxygen. The orange-yellow solid formed in the spontaneous gas-gas reaction was designated xenon hexafluoroplatinate, $Xe^+[PtF_6]^-$. The work on xenon hexafluoroplatinate stimulated investigation of the other noble gases in a number of laboratories, and compounds of krypton, xenon, and radon are now well characterized chemically and physically. Major consequences of the discovery of the chemical activity of the heavier noble gases have been the development of a greater awareness of the limitations of simple valence theory and the focusing of attention on the nature of bonding in these and related compounds.

Bartlett was an undergraduate and graduate student at King's College, Newcastle-upon-Tyne, from 1951 to 1957; his Ph.D. work was done with P. L. Robinson. He was senior chemistry master at the Duke's School, Alnwick, for 1 year, and in 1958 moved to the University of British Columbia, where he served on the faculty for 8 years. In 1966 he was appointed a professor of chemistry at Princeton University. Among the honors awarded Bartlett were the 1962 Corday-Morgan Medal and Prize of the Chemical Society of Great Britain, the 1965 Research Corporation Award, and the 1965 E. W. R. Steacie Prize.

For background information *see* INERT GASES; VALENCE in the McGraw-Hill Encyclopedia of Science and Technology.   □

★ BATCHELOR, George Keith

British applied mathematician
Born Mar. 8, 1920, Melbourne, Australia

THE NEEDS of World War II threw Batchelor into research connected with the design and operation of aircraft and led to a sustained interest in fluid dynamics, which has dominated his work as an applied mathematician. He has made contributions to a number of problems, including the motion of suspended particles in streams, the stability of jets, trailing vortices from wing tips, the scattering of sound or radio waves in a nonuniform fluid, heat transfer by convection in enclosed regions, and flow through resisting sheets. The topic to which he has devoted most of his research time is the permanently fluctuating and irregular motion called turbulent flow. A proper understanding of turbulence and a means of predicting its effects have been sought for more than 50 years, but it remains the outstanding unsolved problem in fluid dynamics. The theoretical difficulties are those encountered in the statistical mechanical treatment of any system of strongly interacting components, such as the group of molecules making up a liquid. The pioneering studies of G. I. Taylor in the 1930s showed what conceptual and mathematical framework was needed for the description of turbulence, and other work of Taylor, together with the penetrating contribution of A. N. Kolmogoroff in 1941, indicated some universal features of the small-scale components of the motion. Batchelor was one of the first to recognize the value of Kolmogoroff's theory, and much of his work on turbulence during 1945–53 was devoted to extensions of the work of these two men and its application to a variety of physical problems involving turbulence.

Many of Batchelor's later papers on turbulence concern diffusion and dispersion in fluids. Molecular diffusion takes place through the movement of molecules over a large number of random steps, each of which is of very short duration and length, and the cumulative average effect can be represented by a diffusion equation with a certain value of the diffusivity. In the case of turbulent diffusion, the random steps are of the same size as the eddies in the turbulent motion, only a few steps are taken, and the simplifying features of molecular diffusion arising from the "law of large numbers" are absent. Batchelor realized that there is a significant difference between problems in which material is being diffused relative to a fixed point and those in which different portions of the fluid are diffusing relative to each other. The former type involves only the statistics of a typical marked element of the fluid which originates at the fixed point. For example, the average concentration of smoke at positions downwind of a chimney or fire can be calculated if one knows the statistical properties of the path of a typical smoke-bearing element of fluid which has passed near the source of smoke. This brings in the properties of wind turbulence, which are known to be dominated by proximity to a boundary and to depend on distance from it in a simple way. Batchelor was able to account for several features of the observed concentrations, including the strange tendency for a smoke-bearing element to migrate upward at a constant average velocity (indicating an accelerating character of the diffusion, which arises from the continually increasing size of the relevant eddies).

The more difficult concept of relative diffusion of marked fluid elements involves the joint probability distribution of the velocities of different elements, and there are interesting connections with the tendency for material lines and surfaces (that is, those which coincide always with the same fluid particles) continually to increase in size in a turbulent flow. The way in which the linear dimensions of a cloud of marked fluid increases, on the average, can be analyzed, provided the cloud is small enough for the relative diffusion to be dominated by those small eddies of the turbulence to which the Kolmogoroff local-equilibrium theory applies. One of the results agrees with an inference from observations in the atmosphere made many years ago, namely, that the cloud width increases as time to the power 3/2, but, in general, experimental information about relative diffusion is lacking. Another related piece of work was concerned with the spatial distribution of some quantity such as temperature or dissolved salt which is being convected by a turbulent motion and diffused by molecular transfer. By devising a suitable model of the way in which neighboring level surfaces of concentration are being extended and brought closer together (on the average), he was able to determine the functional form of the small-scale end of the spectrum of concentration. There is promise here of some useful information about the increased rate of molecular mixing of two different fluids due to the presence of turbulence.

On the whole Batchelor found theoretical research on turbulence frustratingly difficult and liable to make a man too conscious of his limitations, since the worthwhile developments seem to be out of reach of all but the outstanding minds. Nevertheless, the appeal of the subject is strong, and Batchelor has not wanted to give up the pursuit, agonizing though it has been for much of the time. He felt he probably made a more valuable contribution to science through his other activities, which have been varied in nature although mostly motivated by a simple urge to create something which improves on what exists.

After taking a degree in mathematics and physics at the University of Melbourne in 1940, Batchelor worked on a variety of aerodynamical problems at the Aeronautical Research Laboratory at Melbourne. In 1945 he went to Cambridge, England, as a research student to work on turbulent flow and had the good fortune to be supervised by Sir Geoffrey Taylor, who has remained an inspiring influence. He was elected a fellow of Trinity College in 1947 for this research

and was appointed to the staff of the university in 1948. In 1964 he became the first professor of applied mathematics at Cambridge. He took an active part in the establishment in 1959 of the department of applied mathematics and theoretical physics and became the administrative head of it. The form of the department corresponds with his conviction that theoreticians in different branches of physical science and engineering can profit by close association with one another. He was elected a fellow of the Royal Society in 1957 and a foreign honorary member of the American Academy of Arts and Sciences in 1959.

Batchelor has written *The Theory of Homogeneous Turbulence* (1953) and *An Introduction to Fluid Dynamics* (1967), and he has edited *Surveys in Mechanics* (1956) and the four volumes of *Scientific Papers* (1958–68) by G. I. Taylor. He has been editor of the *Journal of Fluid Mechanics* since its inception in 1956.

For background information *see* FLUID DYNAMICS; FLUID MECHANICS; FLUID-FLOW PRINCIPLES; FLUID-FLOW PROPERTIES; TURBULENT FLOW in the McGraw-Hill Encyclopedia of Science and Technology.   □

★ BATES, Leslie Fleetwood

British physicist
Born Mar. 7, 1897, Kingswood, Bristol, England

EITHER BY accident or design, some scientists are moved at an early age to take a main and an abiding interest in a particular branch of a great subject. When Bates had barely turned 17, he found himself, almost by accident, acting as a student assistant in a minor research in magnetism at the University of Bristol. World War I interrupted his academic career, and for some 4 years he served as a commissioned radiographer with the British army in India before returning to Bristol to do research on magnetism in earnest. There he came under the influence of A. P. Chattock and collaborated with him in the first of a series of measurements of the gyromagnetic ratio, which started with the direct determination for iron and nickel and eventually culminated in Willie Sucksmith's brilliant determination of the ratios for many paramagnetic ions. These measurements were most opportune, for they almost coincided with the publication of papers on the inner quantum number and the Landé *g* factor.

Bates spent a 2-year interlude, 1922–24, in the Cavendish Laboratory, Cambridge, working under the supervision of Ernest Rutherford on a series of experiments in radioactivity. These included the determination of the ranges of α-particles in the rare gases, later used by others in cloud chamber work. Bates was then appointed to the staff of University College, London. He regarded the Cambridge interlude as very valuable to him—for did not the great Rutherford himself say that it did nobody any harm to follow another branch of experimental work for a time? It was nevertheless only an important break in the orderly development of his magnetic work, to which he soon returned.

In London he became interested in the properties of manganese and its alloys. In those days pure manganese was a rarity, and Bates made his material by electrolyzing manganese into mercury and then boiling off the mercury in vacuo. With such starting material he made several manganese compounds and, in particular, investigated the unusual electrical, magnetic, and thermal properties of MnAs. This material is still of considerable magnetic interest, and the original measurements have value after nearly 40 years. The method of preparing a pure metal by electrolysis into mercury was also used to prepare chromium, which was found to exhibit a small magnetic change, in the region of 40°C, of interest in the study of antiferromagnetism.

When, in 1936, he was appointed Lancashire-Spencer Professor in University College, Nottingham, he continued to study the electrical and magnetic properties of metals in dilute concentrations in mercury—in particular, iron, nickel, and cobalt. Some remarkable properties of nickel amalgams were thus discovered. It was unfortunate that these experiments were curtailed by the outbreak of World War II, as otherwise the production of iron particles for compressed powder magnets might have been started earlier.

Wartime work for the Interservices Research Bureau brought him into contact with special uses of permanent magnet materials. He devised methods for the measurement of their energy of magnetization relationships and measured the change in electrical resistivity caused by the application of magnetic fields either longitudinal or transverse to the axis of a specimen when carrying an electric current. The resistivity of every modern high-coercivity alloy so investigated always decreased on the application of a magnetic field in marked contrast to the behavior, for example, of cobalt, where a longitudinal field produced an increase and a transverse field produced a decrease in resistivity.

A keen interest in hysteresis phenomena caused Bates to start a series of direct measurements of the very small heat changes which accompany step-by-step changes of magnetization in ferromagnetic materials in low and moderate magnetic fields. His object was to obtain information concerning the magnetization processes which actually take place. In such experiments the temperature changes are of the order of 10^{-6} °C, and usually reversible and irreversible changes are superimposed. It was found that by using special techniques and highly sensitive apparatus the reversible changes could be measured separately. From the Leeds school came another, indirect method of measurement: the temperature of a specimen was changed quickly by some 2°C or so, and the accompanying change in magnetization was recorded. A theory of E. C. Stoner and Philip Rhodes showed a means of allowing for heat changes due solely to changes in spontaneous magnetization. Hence, experiment and theory could be successfully compared over higher-field regions where the magnetization process was probably that of domain vector rotations whose heat changes could be calculated from a knowledge of anisotropy constants. But in very low fields where vector rotation is very unlikely to be a principal magnetization process, several different processes are likely to occur simultaneously. A graphical method of examination of a wealth of experimental data was developed by Bates and A. J. Pacey, and this permitted consideration of the data in the light of a number of modern theories of coercivity for soft magnetic materials. It was found that each coercivity formula could be separated into two parts. One of these, denoted by β, was temperature dependent, so that information concerning it might be derived from the magnetothermal measurements. In the case of nickel, it emerged that within certain field ranges $\beta = \gamma =$ the energy per unit area of a domain wall.

The need for detailed knowledge of magnetization processes engendered a keen interest in their possible visualization by powder, electron microscope, and polarized light techniques. Consequently, in Nottingham new colloids with new techniques and methods of surface preparation of materials were developed. Emphasis was always placed on quantitative aspects of domain study. Numerical data were found for well-known closure domain systems—for example, for the echelon pattern discovered by D. H. Martin, for spike and tube systems, and for domains of reverse magnetization. The techniques were successfully applied to permanent magnet materials and to many ferrites.

Attempts were made to correlate domain powder patterns with corresponding magnetothermal measurements. Using a single-crystal specimen of silicon-iron, it was shown that in a state of technical saturation small spikes and domains of reverse magnetization gave rise to thermal changes which were indistinguishable from those due to vector rotations. In fact, the Bitter figure studies and the magnetothermal measurements provided evidence that very dissimilar domain structures often have essentially the same energy values. Many of the results of these researches were reviewed in the Guthrie Lecture which was delivered at the Nottingham International Conference on Magnetism, 1964.

Postwar developments in atomic energy produced a happy collaboration with Harwell in measuring the electric, magnetic, and thermal properties of pure uranium and thorium and their alloys with metals such as Nd, Ce, Pd, Nb, Zr, and Mo. This resulted in the collection of data which formed a basis for informed discussion of the valency behaviors and the electron band configurations of these metals.

Bates held strongly that a university instructor should be actively associated with the administration, teaching, and the general conduct of university affairs. He was for considerable periods a member of the governing bodies of the institutions he served. He was for many years a member of council of the Physical Society and president in 1950–52. He was actively concerned with the Association of University Teachers (England and Wales) and was president in 1937–38. He was awarded the Holweck Prize of the English and French Physical Societies in 1949, was elected a fellow of the Royal Society of London in 1950, and was created Commander of the Order of the British Empire in 1966 for work in civil defense.

Bates wrote *Modern Magnetism* (1939; 4th ed. reprint 1963).

For background information *see* HYSTERESIS, MAGNETIC; MAGNETIZATION; MANGANESE COMPOUND in the McGraw-Hill Encyclopedia of Science and Technology.   □

★ BEAMS, Jesse Wakefield

American physicist
Born Dec. 25, 1898, Belle Plaine, Kans., U.S.A.

B EAMS STARTED his research with an investigation of the initial stages of the electrical breakdown in gases and, principally, the initiation of the electric spark in air. He soon found

that in order to proceed properly, methods with much higher time resolving-power capability had to be developed for observing the light emitted, as well as the potential and current in the initial stages of the breakdown. For measuring the potential and current during the breakdown, he developed transmission line techniques, but later employed the cathode-ray oscillograph. For observing the light emitted in the breakdown, he improved and modified the Kerr cell light shutter, previously used by G. Abraham and A. N. Lemoine and by Lord Rayleigh, until it could be made to open and close in less than 10^{-9} sec at any desired time. He modified and stabilized the air-supported, air-driven turbine of Henriot and Huguenard, and used it to spin a high-speed rotating mirror, with which optical phenomena occurring in less than 10^{-9} sec could be observed. With these devices it was possible to photograph the light emitted in the initial stages of the electrical spark in gases at various pressures and in a high vacuum. In some cases it was possible to measure the propagation of luminosity in the discharge, as well as the first appearance of the various spectral lines in the discharge. With the same techniques he found that the time lag in the fluorescence in some substances was very small ($\sim 10^{-8}$ sec).

In the mid-1920s many physicists believed that the light quantum had a finite length of at least 3 m. In collaboration with Ernest O. Lawrence, Beams used the Kerr cell and rotating mirror techniques to show that if the light quantum had a finite length, it was less than about 10 cm. They showed that photoelectrons were emitted from a metal surface in less than 10^{-9} sec after the light quanta struck the surface—that is, any time lag in the photoelectric effect was less than 10^{-9} sec. Later these phenomena became under-

standable from the new quantum mechanics and the Heisenberg indetermination principle.

Soon after returning to the University of Virginia from Yale, Beams became interested in the production and use of high-energy particles, and in collaboration with his colleague L. B. Snoddy and students W. T. Ham and H. Trotter, he developed a new type of linear particle accelerator. The ions were accelerated down a long tube by an electrical field, which was made to move with the same speed of the ions, like a surfboard riding an ocean wave. Both ions and electrons with energies in excess of 10^6 ev were produced, but the work was terminated by the approach of World War II.

In the late 1920s he became interested in the physical properties of some of the proteins which T. Svedberg had recently shown to consist of very large molecules by means of his ultracentrifuge. Most of these large-molecular-weight substances existed in dilute solutions and were mixed with many other substances. Calculations indicated that a centrifuge mounted on the air-supported, air-driven turbine previously developed for spinning the rotating mirror should be able to purify all of these substances. However, Beams found that in many cases even though the centrifugal field was greater than 10^6 times gravity, true molecular sedimentation did not occur because of convection currents induced by thermal gradients on the centrifuge. Fortunately, however, even in these high centrifugal fields, the substances studied were not deactivated or harmed in any observable way. The thermal gradients in the centrifuge were traced to the effect of air friction on the rotor, which in 1934 led Beams and his student E. G. Pickels to develop the first centrifuge which spun in a high vacuum (10^{-6} torr). In this ultracentrifuge the residual air pressure surrounding the rotor was so low that air friction was negligible and true molecular sedimentation was obtained. Many of the substances of importance in biology, medicine, and chemistry have been purified and characterized by ultracentrifuges based upon this original prototypal vacuum-type ultracentrifuge. By adapting the vacuum-type ultracentrifuge to the separation of gases and vapors, Beams and his students A. V. Masket and C. Skarstrom obtained in 1935 the first separation of isotopes by centrifuging. Soon after the discovery of uranium fission, Beams, Snoddy, and their students employed the centrifuge for the successful separation of the uranium isotopes.

With F. T. Holmes, Beams magnetically suspended and spun a small steel rod inside a sealed vacuum chamber. Immediately following World War II, this magnetic suspension method of freely supporting and spinning ferromagnetic bodies was further developed and stabilized by Beams's group at the University of Virginia, and it became the essential element in his magnetically suspended vacuum-type ultracentrifuge. There are two principal centrifuge methods for determining the molecular weights of substances in solution. In the first method the rate of sedimentation is measured, and in the second method the density gradient across the centrifuge cell is determined after equilibrium between sedimentation and diffusion has been obtained. This second, or equilibrium, method is much more reliable, but it requires the centrifuge rotor to be free of fluctuation in speed and temperature variations to a much greater extent than in the first method. The magnetically suspended vacuum-type ultracentrifuge solved these problems and became an ideal equilibrium ultracentrifuge. In collaboration with D. W. Kupke and his students, Beams was able to determine the molecular weights of a large number of substances, including many proteins and heavy viruses, with an absolute precision of between 1 and 0.1% over the molecular weight range from 10^2 to 10^8.

In order to determine the absolute value of the molecular weight of a substance by centrifuging, it is necessary to know its partial specific volume. Also, the partial specific volume itself is of importance in characterizing a molecule. Unfortunately, standard methods of measuring the partial specific volume require more of the pure material than is usually available in the case of most of the interesting, biologically important compounds. Beams solved this problem by devising the magnetic densitometer, with which the partial specific volumes are routinely determined with a precision of 0.1%, and the solution densities are determined to one part in 10^5 with less than 1% solutions 0.3 ml in volume. With this precision interesting variations in partial specific volume were found with changes in pH and with pressure.

The magnetically suspended centrifuge provides an excellent method of testing the tensile strengths of materials, because the clamps on the test specimen, which may produce stress concentrations, are eliminated. With this method, in collaboration with his students, Beams discovered that very thin films of metals become much stronger than the bulk material. They were able to measure the absolute value of the adhesion between the film and the rotor. Furthermore, they measured the tensile strength of a number of fine fibers and so-called iron whiskers from room temperature down to liquid helium temperature with increased reliability. In some of these experiments the rotor speed exceeded 1,500,000 revolutions per second and produced centrifugal fields of over 10^9 times gravity. The almost negligible friction in the magnetically suspended rotor in a high vacuum enabled Beams and his students to measure with increased precision the pressure of light, the angular momentum of light, and the gravitational constant G in the Newton gravitational relation in Eq. (1).

$$F = G \frac{m_1 m_2}{d^2} \tag{1}$$

Born on a farm in Kansas, Beams received an A.B. from Fairmount College (now Wichita State University) in 1921, an M.S. in mathematics from the University of Wisconsin in 1922, and a Ph.D. in physics from the University of Virginia in 1925. He was an instructor in physics and mathematics at the present Auburn University in 1922–23. He held a National Research fellowship at Virginia in 1925–26 and at Yale in 1926–27, after which he was an instructor at Yale during 1927–28. He then returned to the University of Virginia, where he served as associate professor, professor, department chairman, and Smith Professor of Physics. He served as president of the American Physical Society, vice-president of the American Philosophical Society, and vice-president and chairman of Section B of the American Association for the Advancement of Science. He was elected to the National Academy of Sciences in 1943 and the American Academy of Arts and Sciences in 1949. Beams received the Potts Medal in 1942, the Thomas Jefferson Award in 1955, the John Scott Award in 1956, and the Lewis Award in 1958 for his work with ultracentrifuges. During World War II he served as a principal investigator with the Office of Scientific Research and Development and did research on isotope separation, military weapons, and ramjets. He later served on several government committees, including the General Advisory Committee of the Atomic Energy Commission.

For background information *see* CENTRIFUGATION; QUANTUM MECHANICS; SPARK, ELECTRIC; ULTRACENTRIFUGE in the McGraw-Hill Encyclopedia of Science and Technology. ☐

★ BELOZERSKY, Andrei Nikolaevitch

Soviet biochemist and molecular biologist
Born Aug. 29, 1905, Tashkent, Russia

THE MAIN fields of Belozersky's research were nucleic acids and nucleoproteins of higher and lower plants, including the bacteria. He started his research in the early 1930s. At that time nucleic acids were considered to be no more than one of the numerous groups of substances of biological origin. No one could then think that nucleic acids, according to their biological importance, could stand on a level with such important and highly specific components of living matter as proteins. It was even considered that the animal organisms had their own peculiar thymonucleic acid or, as it is called today, deoxyribonucleic acid (DNA), and that the plant organisms had their own yeast nucleic acid or, in modern terminology, ribonucleic acid (RNA). As far back as 1924 R. Feulgen and H. Rossenbeck with the aid of the cytochemical reaction, which they had worked out, demonstrated the presence of DNA in the nuclei of plant cells. At that time, however, the literature contained no authentic data on the isolation and identification of DNA from plants.

The first cycle of Belozersky's work was devoted to the proof of the presence of DNA in higher plants. In a number of researches the presence of DNA was proved by the thymine-pyrimidine base, so typical for DNA, found in plant nucleoproteins. In 1936 DNA was first isolated in the pure state and identified by studying the products of its hydrolysis. These experiments finally established the unity of the chemical structure of nuclear material of the plant and the animal cells. RNA was always found together with DNA. Therefore it was evident that DNA and RNA are always present in higher plants.

The next cycle of Belozersky's research was closely connected with that in higher plants. It was necessary to establish the presence and the type of nucleic acids in microorganisms, the representatives of the "lower" realm of living organisms, and particularly in bacteria. The very first analysis performed in 1939–41 showed that nucleic acids of both types (DNA and RNA) are always present in bacteria. In conjunction with the earlier data on higher plants, these researches established the universal distribution of both types of nucleic acids in plants of different phylogenetic groups.

This research showed, furthermore, that bacteria deserve special attention because the content of the nucleic acids in the bacterial cell is particularly high: over 20% of the dry weight of

the bacteria. The large amount led, as far back as the late 1930s, to the conclusion that this weight factor is probably connected with a higher biological activity of the bacterial cell, intensive reproduction, and wonderful adaptability to the environment. In 1941 the weight changes of nucleic acids during bacterial cell development were studied, and it was concluded that there is a great variability in the amount of nucleic acids depending on the age of the bacterial culture. Thus, a correlation between the age and the biological activity of the cell on the one hand and the age and the amount of nucleic acids in the cell on the other hand was established.

Belozersky was the first to establish the presence of nonbasic proteins in the nucleoproteins of the nucleus (1936). Thus he modified the then existing conception that only basic proteins of the histone and protamine types were present in the nucleoproteins of the nucleus. While the work of E. and E. Stedmann and later that of A. E. Mirsky established the presence of higher (nonbasic) proteins together with histones in animal nucleoproteins of the nucleus, there was no direct experimental data concerning histones in plants. Belozersky and G. T. Abelev filled in that gap. They isolated a histone from a "structural" nucleoprotein of the wheat embryo and identified and analyzed it. That research demonstrated the unity of general principles of organization of the nuclear apparatus of animals and higher plants.

Although repeated attempts to isolate histone were not successful, Belozersky assumed that bacterial chromatin generally has no histones and contains only higher proteins. This assumption was later confirmed and is now considered one of the most important differences between bacterial chromosomes, in which the greater part of DNA is not covered with protein, and those of higher organisms with a typical nucleus, in which the DNA threads are bound with histones throughout their length. Simultaneously the existence of different types of bonds between the proteins and the nucleic acids in nucleoproteins was established, and it was shown that the interrelation between the proteins and the nucleic acids may change during the ontogenesis.

The situation radically changed in the early 1950s, when Erwin Chargaff developed new methods for nucleic acid analysis, and the specificity of these biologically important compounds was shown. In this connection Belozersky's laboratory had studied for many years the nucleotide composition of DNA and RNA in higher plants, fungi, algae, actinomycetes, and bacteria and also in vertebrate and invertebrate animals. That vast experimental material led to the important conclusion that DNA of the whole organic world, of all representatives of higher and lower forms, is in the main composed of only four deoxynucleotides. Thus the DNA macromolecule of every organism is built to the same pattern and

to the same nucleotide ratio; these principles, established in the early 1950s and known as the Chargaff rules, underlie the DNA structure. The DNA of different phylogenetic groups of organisms is undoubtedly of taxonomic importance. A comparative study of DNA and RNA nucleotide composition in a large group of bacteria established a positive correlation between the composition of DNA and a certain fraction of RNA in the cell (A. S. Spirin and Belozersky, 1957). Already in 1957 this fact predicted the existence of messenger RNA, which was later (1961) isolated in several laboratories.

A series of studies was devoted to the exchange of polyphosphates—a special group of phosphorus compounds, polymers of phosphoric acid, which apparently play an important role in the activity of some lower organisms and are the sources of energy and phosphorus in various biosynthetic processes. New data were obtained on the formation of polyphosphates in lower organisms and also on their interrelation with other biologically active compounds. As to polyphosphates, research was conducted on the chemical nature of the volutin cell inclusion, typical for some microorganisms. According to Belozersky, the base of volutin is a complex consisting of polyphosphates and RNA.

In the late 1940s Belozersky investigated antibiotics. In collaboration with T. S. Paskina, Belozersky was the first to study the amino acid composition of gramicidin S.

Belozersky completed his undergraduate studies at Tashkent University in 1927; from 1927 to 1930 he stayed on doing postgraduate work. In 1930 he was appointed assistant in the plant biochemistry department of Moscow University; he became associate professor in 1932, full professor in 1947, and head of the department in 1960. In 1965 Belozersky set up and headed a research laboratory of organic biochemistry. In 1958 he was elected corresponding member and in 1962 full member of the Academy of Sciences of the U.S.S.R.

For background information *see* BACTERIAL CELL CHEMISTRY; NUCLEIC ACID; NUCLEOPROTEIN in the McGraw-Hill Encyclopedia of Science and Technology.   □

★ BENZER, Seymour

American biologist
Born Oct. 15, 1921, New York, N.Y., U.S.A.

A SIGNAL achievement in genetics was the demonstration that genes are ordered in a one-dimensional array in chromosomes. Classically, genes were regarded as the "atoms" of heredity, acting as indivisible units when parts of chromosomes undergo recombination. Benzer's

work showed that a single functional gene can be split into hundreds of smaller recombining elements. Furthermore, these elements are themselves arranged in a strictly linear array. This splitting of the gene and unraveling of its internal structure has forced a reexamination of classical concepts of the elementary units of heredity.

Benzer began his career as a physicist, receiving his Ph.D. at Purdue University in 1947. As a graduate student, he worked under the direction of Karl Lark-Horovitz in a group developing germanium semiconductor devices for application to radar. Out of this work came a number of discoveries concerning solid-state diodes, *p-n* junctions, and photodiodes that helped set the stage for the development of the transistor. On reading Erwin Schrödinger's book, *What Is Life?* (1945), however, he was captivated by the possibilities of applying physical concepts to biological problems and of using viruses as model systems for gene replication. Taking a leave of absence from Purdue to learn biology, he spent a year at Oak Ridge National Laboratory, a summer with Cornelius van Niel at Pacific Grove, 2 years with Max Delbrück at the California Institute of Technology, and 1 year as a Fulbright scholar at the Institut Pasteur in Paris, where he was associated with André Lwoff, Jacques Monod, and François Jacob. He returned to Purdue in 1952 and undertook work with phage T4, a virus that infects bacteria and makes a hundred copies of itself in about 20 min.

At that time Alfred Hershey had just shown that the part of the phage that carries its hereditary information is its deoxyribonucleic acid (DNA). Shortly thereafter, J. D. Watson and F. H. C. Crick announced their discovery of the molecular structure of DNA. Their conception of a gene was a certain length of the (double-stranded) coil of DNA, comprising perhaps a thousand paired nucleotides, the specific sequence of nucleotides containing the information to determine, say, the amino acid sequence of a particular enzyme. This concept suggested that a gene should be topologically linear, should have well-defined beginning and end points, and should be divisible into many smaller parts. However, to demonstrate this experimentally was very difficult. The problem was that as two points on a chromosome are closer together, the probability of a chance event that splits the structure between those points is less. In ordinary organisms popular in genetics, such as the fruit fly, *Drosophila*, the probability of observing a split between two points within a single gene is extremely small.

The key was discovered in 1954, when Benzer found that a certain type of mutant of phage T4, the *r*II mutant, was unable to multiply on a certain host strain of bacteria, whereas the normal phage T4 could multiply. Thus, if a cross was made between two *r*II mutants, each having a mutation at a different site in the length of DNA constituting the *r*II gene, it would be easy to detect any progeny in which a recombination event had occurred such that two nonmutated portions of the gene (each contributed by one of the mutants) were joined to form a normal gene. If even one such progeny particle arose in as many as 10^8 offspring from the cross, it could be detected by its activity on the selective bacterial strain. A calculation showed that this easily was enough sensitivity to permit the detection of recombination between two mutants even if their respective mutations were located only one nucleotide apart in the DNA. Thus, using this system, the gene could be split into its ultimate parts.

By isolating thousands of *r*II mutants and crossing them in appropriate combinations, it was possible to construct a detailed map of the region of the chromosome of phage T4 that controlled the *r*II function. This was greatly facilitated by the discovery of mutants in which segments of the structure had apparently been deleted (the ends being rejoined so that the DNA remained continuous). Given two such mutants in which the deleted portions overlapped, it was impossible to generate a normal gene by recombination of the two. Conversely, if recombination was obtained when two mutants were mated, it could be concluded that their mutations did not overlap. If the topology of the gene is really linear, crosses between various such mutants should give results compatible with a map in which each deletion is represented as a segment in a one-dimensional jigsaw puzzle. That result was found for hundreds of deletion mutants, confirming the topological prediction from the Watson-Crick model.

Thus, the hereditary structure needed by the phage to multiply on the selective bacterial strain consists of many parts distinguishable by mutation and recombination. Is this region to be thought of as one gene (because it controls one characteristic) or as hundreds of genes? Although a mutation at any one of the sites leads to the same observed physiological defect, this effect may be due to blocks in a series of separate functions that combine to give a particular end result. To define a functional unit, a test known in genetics as the *cis-trans* comparison was applied to the *r*II mutants. That test showed that the *r*II region could be divided into two functional segments; each segment could function independently, regardless of what defect might be contained in the other. The term "cistron" was coined to denote such a functional unit. Each of the cistrons had sharp boundaries, as expected from the DNA structure. Some years later, Benzer and his student Sewell Champe showed that, if the space between the two cistrons is deleted, thus joining the remaining segments, the two formerly independent units became functionally joined. This outcome implied that the normal structure contains elements to indicate the end of one cistron and the start of the next.

By mapping the locations at which point mutations arose, it was shown that there are enormous differences in spontaneous mutability at various sites, as might be expected from different local sequences of nucleotides. Working with Ernst Freese, Benzer showed that specific chemical substances—for example, 5-bromouracil, which enters DNA in place of thymine—induce mutations specifically at certain points and that those points are different from the ones at which spontaneous mutations most frequently occur. This finding suggested the feasibility of understanding the genetic map in chemical terms. In order to better understand the molecular basis of mutation, Benzer spent the year 1957–58 at the Cavendish Laboratory of the University of Cambridge, England, working on nucleic acid and protein structure with Crick, Sydney Brenner, and Vernon Ingram.

Returning once more to Purdue, Benzer and Champe extended the studies involving nucleotide base analogs to work with 5-fluorouracil, which enters messenger RNA, thereby causing errors not in the hereditary information of the genes, but in the transcribed information which determines the phenotype. They showed that it was possible thus to reverse certain mutant defects in an individual without altering its inheritance. This kind of study made it possible to obtain information concerning the identity of the nucleotides at the various points in the genetic structure. They also found that certain mutations in phage could be reversed by "suppressor" mutations of the host bacterium. Further analysis showed that the mechanism at play in certain suppressors was an actual modification of the genetic code. A code word that constituted nonsense when read according to the code of one bacterium became meaningful when read by the code of a suppressor strain. They speculated that the suppressor mutation operated by altering one of the elements of the cell's machinery for translating messenger RNA into amino acid sequences. The prime candidates were transfer RNA and the amino acid–activating enzymes, which act together in the translation process.

Investigation revealed that these substances were indeed subject to genetic modification, showing considerable differences in properties from one species to another. Collaborating with Bernard Weisblum, Robert Holley, and Gunther von Ehrenstein, Benzer showed that for a given amino acid there could be several versions of transfer RNA, each responding to a different messenger-RNA code word. This demonstration established a physical basis for degeneracy in the genetic code. It also showed, as Crick had predicted years before, that once an amino acid is attached to transfer RNA, it is the RNA and not the amino acid that determines the specificity for incorporation of the amino acid into protein. This was also shown in another way, in collaboration with F. Chapeville, F. Lipmann, Weisblum, von Ehrenstein, and W. Ray, by attaching an amino acid A to its normal transfer RNA and then changing it, while still attached, to another amino acid B. When transferred into protein, amino acid B went into the position where A normally belonged.

Inspired partly by the possibility of applying the new knowledge of molecular biology to problems of brain function and partly by curiosity as to the genetic control of behavior, Benzer turned his attention to behavioral biology. He spent the years 1965–67 at the California Institute of Technology working in Roger Sperry's psychobiology laboratory and remained at Caltech as professor of biology to investigate behavior of the fruit fly, *Drosophila*.

Benzer received his B.A. in 1942 from Brooklyn College and his M.S. in 1943 and Ph.D. in physics in 1947 at Purdue University, where he was an assistant professor in 1947–48. He was a biophysicist at the Oak Ridge National Laboratory in 1948–49, a research fellow in biophysics at the California Institute of Technology in 1949–51, and a Fulbright research scholar at the Pasteur Institut, Paris, in 1951–52. Returning to Purdue, he was assistant professor of biophysics in 1952–53, associate professor in 1953–58, professor in 1958–61, and Stuart Distinguished Professor of Biology from 1961. He received the Ricketts Award (1961) from the University of

Chicago and the Gairdner Foundation Award of Merit (1964). He was elected to the American Academy of Arts and Sciences in 1959 and to the National Academy of Sciences in 1961.

For background information *see* GENE ACTION; MUTATION; NUCLEIC ACID in the McGraw-Hill Encyclopedia of Science and Technology.   □

★ BERG, Paul

American biochemist
Born June 30, 1926, New York, N.Y., U.S.A.

IN THE course of studies on the mechanism of acetyl coenzyme A (acetyl CoA) synthesis in certain microbial cells, Berg, while still a research fellow in Arthur Kornberg's laboratory, discovered a new mechanism for activating carboxyl groups with adenosinetriphosphate (ATP). This type of reaction was subsequently shown to be the prototype for a variety of reactions involving acyl group activation, particularly the activation of amino acids for protein biosynthesis. It was during the investigation of amino acid activation that Berg and his associates recognized the existence of discrete enzymes and ribonucleic acid (RNA) molecules specific for activating each amino acid for protein assembly. For these contributions Berg received the Eli Lilly Prize in 1958 and the California Scientist of the Year Award in 1963.

After receiving the Ph.D. in biochemistry at Western Reserve University in 1952 for studies on the metabolism of one-carbon compounds and the synthesis of the labile-methyl group of methionine, Berg traveled to Copenhagen for a year's study in H. Kalckar's laboratory. There, with W. K. Joklik, he discovered a new enzyme involved in nucleoside polyphosphate metabolism; this enzyme, nucleoside diphosphokinase, is a transphosphorylase which forms nucleoside triphosphates from the corresponding diphosphates. As is now recognized, this is a key enzyme in forming the nucleoside triphosphate precursors for RNA and deoxyribonucleic acid (DNA) biosynthesis.

In 1953 he joined Kornberg's new department of microbiology at Washington University in St. Louis. There his experiments led to the deduction that acetyl CoA formation proceeds via an enzyme-bound intermediate, an acetyl adenylate, formed in the reaction of ATP, acetic acid, and the enzyme protein. This enzyme-bound acyl adenylate reacts with the sulfhydryl group of coenzyme A to form acetyl CoA, thereby regenerating the free enzyme. Work in other laboratories has now established the existence of the predicted enzyme-acyl-adenylate complex and shown that this type of mechanism is the first step in the metabolic utilization of the higher fatty acids as well.

In 1955 during the studies of fatty acid activation Berg showed that there are enzymes which catalyze the same partial reaction with the amino acids, that is, the formation of enzyme-amino acyl adenylates. During his search for the naturally occurring amino acyl acceptor, he independently discovered the existence of RNA molecules to which the activated amino acids become esterified. Such amino acyl RNAs were later proved to be an integral component of the machinery for translation of genetic messages into protein molecules; the amino acyl RNAs interact specifically with the nucleic acid triplets which code for each amino acid.

Berg's work helped clarify how the specificity of amino acyl RNA synthesis is achieved. Studies in his laboratory established that a single enzyme protein activates each amino acid and then transfers the activated amino acyl group to a specific attachment site on a special class of RNA molecules. Because the accuracy with which each amino acid is attached to its corresponding RNA is crucial for ensuring correct translation of genetic information, Berg's laboratory concentrated on the problem of the structure and the specificity of both the individual enzymes and RNA species. Later, in collaboration with Charles Yanofsky's laboratory, it was established that mutations which affect the specificity of the amino acid activation process can alter the accuracy of translation of the genetic message.

In 1962 Berg's laboratory announced the isolation of an enzyme which synthesizes RNA from nucleoside triphosphates and uses DNA to direct the order of assembly of the RNA nucleotides. In a series of investigations over the next few years, strong emphasis was placed on clarifying the way DNA directs RNA synthesis and the way the enzymically synthesized RNA directs protein formation. These studies provided a firm foundation on which to mount an attack on the problem of how these two processes might be regulated.

Berg completed his undergraduate training in biochemistry at Pennsylvania State University (B.S., 1948) after military service in 1943–46. After receiving his Ph.D. from Western Reserve University in 1952, he spent 2 years in postdoctoral training as a United States Public Health Service fellow, first at the Institute of Cytophysiology in Copenhagen and later at Washington University in St. Louis. He remained in the microbiology department at Washington University during 1954–59 as scholar in cancer research and then as assistant and associate professor of microbiology. In 1959 Berg became professor of biochemistry at Stanford University. In 1966 he was elected to both the American Academy of Arts and Sciences and the National Academy of Sciences.

For background information *see* AMINO ACIDS; CARBOXYLIC ACID; ENZYME; NUCLEIC ACID in the McGraw-Hill Encyclopedia of Science and Technology.   □

★ BERKNER, Lloyd Viel

American physicist and engineer
Born Feb. 1, 1905, Milwaukee, Wis., U.S.A.
Died June 4, 1967, Washington, D.C., U.S.A.

DURING THE early years of long-distance radio transmission, it was not clear why radio waves of short wavelength travel almost unattenuated for very long distances around the Earth. By the early 1920s the theories of O. Heaviside and A. E. Kennelly, calling for an ionized layer some 100 km (about 60 mi) above the Earth, had been shown to account for the transmission of very long wavelengths. But these theories could not explain the even better performance of the shorter radio wavelengths.

Berkner became interested in these phenomena as a high school student at Sleepy Eye, Minn. Using an amateur radio station, in 1923 he established records in relaying messages by short-wave radio between the East Coast and Hawaii. After graduating from the University of Minnesota in 1927, he continued his studies of high-frequency radio transmission in the Antarctic on the first Byrd Antarctic Expedition in 1928–30. There he showed that high-frequency waves from antipodal points change their direction of travel following the night hemisphere preferentially. Upon his return to the United States, he continued his studies in physics at the George Washington University.

Following the work of G. Breit and M. A. Tuve, who showed that short radio pulses are discretely reflected from the ionized regions above, Berkner, working at the Carnegie Institution of Washington, devised the first instrument to map the height, distribution, and ionic density of the ionized layers of the outer atmosphere, or the ionosphere. Thousands of these complex instruments, known as ionosondes, are now employed over the Earth to describe the three major ionized layers—the E, F_1, and F_2—and their variation with time. Employing this method in Washington, Peru, Australia, and Alaska, Berkner showed how these layers varied diurnally, seasonally, and geographically; their critical dependence on sunspot activity; and their disruption by magnetic storms and solar chromospheric eruptions. Out of this work of Berkner (and related work of others) emerged not only the complete explanation of the propagation of high-frequency radio waves, but also the daily prediction service of the National Bureau of Standards, which forecasts high-frequency radio performance at varying distances.

Because the ionized layers showed an interrelationship with meteorology of the Earth's outer atmosphere, Berkner became interested in the origin and development of the atmosphere as early as 1935. Success in obtaining relevant measurements and scientific data required space vehicles, and this necessity resulted in his interest and leadership in space activities. The need for worldwide measurements of our planet on an organized basis led to his proposal in 1950 for the International Geophysical Year (IGY), the most comprehensive study of the Earth ever undertaken. This study was organized under the International Council of Scientific Unions, of which Berkner became president during the IGY, 1957–59. He also coordinated international planning for scientific research in space during the period in which the first spacecraft were launched by the Soviet Union and the United States.

Berkner's interest in the atmospheres of the planets led to the formulation in 1963 with L. C. Marshall of a general theory of the origin and historical development of the atmospheres of the inner planets. This theory shows that on the Earth oxygen has appeared in significant quantities only in the last one-eighth of its history. The appearance of oxygen in significant concentrations is dependent wholly on the presence of primitive photosynthetic life over sufficient areas. The rise of oxygenic pressures and the advance of evolution toward more complex organic forms constitute an intimately related interaction. More advanced and widespread photosynthetic life produces the atmospheric oxygen required for further evolution of even more advanced forms of organisms, and so on. Only a planet of just the right size and temperature regime can ever acquire an oxygenic atmosphere, and with it the more advanced forms of life.

In engineering, Berkner's initial work with electromagnetic pulses put him in the forefront of development of aircraft radar and navigation devices. As a Naval aviator from 1926 (rising to the grade of rear admiral, USNR), he took charge of all engineering of electronics for Naval aircraft during World War II. Subsequently, under Vannevar Bush he organized the Research and Development Board of the Department of Defense (now Directorate of Defense Research and Engineering). Later, acting directly under Secretary of State Dean Acheson, Berkner organized the military program under NATO and, following his extensive study, the Science Office of the Department of State in 1950. He was active in the studies establishing the Distant Early Warning System and was one of the co-discoverers in 1951 of ionospheric scattering propagation.

Berkner received a B.S. in electrical engineering from the University of Minnesota in 1927. After his return from the Byrd Expedition in 1930, he joined the National Bureau of Standards in Washington, moving in 1933 to the Carnegie Institution, where he remained until 1951. In that year he became president of Associated Universities, Inc., and in 1960 he was named president and later chairman of the board of trustees of the Southwest Center for Advanced Studies in Dallas. In addition to numerous government decorations and honorary degrees, Berkner received the John A. Fleming Medal and the William Bowie Medal of the American Geophysical Union, the Cleveland Abbe Award of the American Meteorological Society, and the Public Service Medal of the National Aeronautics and Space Administration. He was elected to the National Academy of Sciences in 1948 and to the American Academy of Arts and Sciences in 1956.

The author of more than 100 scientific and engineering papers, Berkner wrote, among other books, *Rockets and Satellites* (1958), *Science in Space* (1961), and *The Scientific Age* (1964).

For background information *see* AERONOMY; ATMOSPHERE; IONOSPHERE; RADIO-WAVE PROPAGATION in the McGraw-Hill Encyclopedia of Science and Technology.   □

☆ BERNAL, John Desmond

British physicist
Born May 10, 1901, Nenagh, Ireland

O NE OF the pioneer investigators in x-ray crystallography, Bernal contributed to the discipline both by his own investigations and by the guidance given to his students. He developed a very powerful, simple graphic method, based on the concept of the reciprocal lattice, for the indexing of crystal planes. He also put forward a theory of the structure of water and, later, proposed a model of the structure of liquids in general.

X-ray diffraction studies began about 1912 with the investigations of Max von Laue. Hearing of his efforts, William Henry Bragg and his son, William Lawrence Bragg, worked out the mathematical details involved in the investigation and derived the equation that bears their name. About 1921 the German crystallographer Paul P. Ewald proposed the concept of the reciprocal lattice to facilitate visualization of the crystal lattice which Bernal independently developed.

About 1926, while conducting research at the Davy-Faraday Laboratory of the Royal Institution under the direction of William Henry Bragg, Bernal undertook the preparation of a chart for indexing x-ray diffraction photographs from single crystals. Now known as the Bernal chart, it included two sets of curves, from which could be read the radial and axial cylindrical coordinates of the point in reciprocal space that corresponded to any particular x-ray reflection. The two coordinates were ζ, the distance of any reciprocal-lattice point from the equatorial plane, and ξ, the distance of the point from the axis of rotation. To construct his chart, Bernal worked out ζ and ξ for all positions on a cylindrical film. By drawing on a transparent surface two sets of curves through the positions that he had calculated, Bernal created a tool that necessitated only placing a rotation photograph on the chart and reading off the ζ and ξ coordinates for every spot on the film, thus saving many tedious hours of calculation.

In 1933 Bernal and R. H. Fowler published the results of their study of the structure of water and ionic solutions. The x-ray patterns they discussed suggested that water retains in part a hydrogen-bonded structure similar to that of ice. They pointed out that, as temperature increases, more and more of these bonds are ruptured. The oxygen molecules may then arrange themselves in a manner approximating more and more closely the closest packing in spheres. There would be a significant increase in density for such a packing compared with the open packing of the completely hydrogen-bonded structure of ice. They suggested that this might explain the increase in density of water as its temperature increases from 0 to 4°C.

Bernal investigated many areas of crystallography. With Dorothy Crowfoot (later Crowfoot-Hodgkin), he investigated liquid crystals and made significant contributions to the crystallography of the mesomorphic state. During 1932–34 Bernal, Crowfoot, and I. Fankuchen collaborated on a crystallographic analysis of sterols and discovered the common structure of their nucleus. During the 1930s, also, Bernal realized that use might be made of a particular property of proteins, namely, that many of them form crystals. He took the first x-ray photograph of a protein crystal, pepsin, in 1934; later he joined with Fankuchen, Max F. Perutz, and Crowfoot to take the first x-ray diffraction photographs of crystals of hemoglobin, chymotrypsin, and insulin.

In 1935 he studied the structure of tobacco mosaic virus solutions. This virus was shown to be a nucleoprotein, whose structure was finally solved by his pupil, Rosalind Franklin, as were several other viruses of a crystalline nature by A. Klug and his co-workers.

During the late 1950s Bernal attempted to make a model of a liquid structure that would give a better approximation to the distribution function than does the hard-sphere model. He began by assuming that a liquid consists essentially of a set of molecules similarly—but never identically—placed with respect to one another. He also restricted himself to the simplest case of spherical molecules and assumed that liquids are essentially homogeneous. He built a number of physical models and found that in each the molecules tended to show five-fold symmetry, which was unusual in that crystals do not exhibit such a symmetry. To check his results and eliminate the human factor involved in building the physical models, Bernal used a computer at the University of London (employing a program devised by his son, M. J. M. Bernal) to produce a mathematical model. The computer produced a dense but random distribution of points (representing molecules) with the one condition that there be a minimum distance between them. This equidistance model, in which each molecule is surrounded by a limited number of others at equal distances, corresponds to the structure of a model with rigid molecules without attractive forces. This work is still continuing. Although not yet commonly accepted, Bernal's model may lead to a rigorous theory of the liquid state. More recently, Bernal directed a team of workers investigating the structure of proteins, liquids, viruses, magnetic materials, and corrosion products. This latter work, in conjunction with J. W. Jeffery and H. F. W. Taylor, was directed to solving the structure of portland cement and related materials. Bernal had been for many years very interested in the origin of life, especially chemical evolution, and developed an explanation of biogenesis, published in his book *Origin of Life* (1967).

Bernal was educated in England, studying at Stonyhurst College, Bedford School, and Emmanuel College, Cambridge (M.A., 1922). After performing crystallographic research at the Davy-Faraday Laboratory from 1923 to 1927, he became a lecturer in structural crystallography at Cambridge. He retained the post until 1934, when he was named assistant director of research in crystallography. In 1938 Bernal left Cambridge to become a professor of physics at Birkbeck College, University of London. During World War II he worked for the Ministry of Home Security on protection against bomb damage, and he was later adviser to the Air Ministry and scientific adviser to the Chief of Combined Operations. In 1963 he was named professor of crystallography at Birkbeck. Among his prizes and awards was the Royal Medal of the Royal Society (1945), of which he had become a fellow in 1937.

Bernal wrote several books of social significance, such as *The Social Function of Science* (1939), the concepts of which were expanded in *Science of Science* (1964), and *World Without War* (1958). His technical works included *The Physical Basis of Life* (1951) and *Science and Industry in the Nineteenth Century* (1953).

For background information *see* LIQUID; X-RAY CRYSTALLOGRAPHY; X-RAY DIFFRACTION in the McGraw-Hill Encyclopedia of Science and Technology.   □

BETHE, Hans Albrecht

American physicist

Bethe received the 1967 Nobel Prize in physics. See *McGraw-Hill Modern Men of Science*, Volume I.

★ BLEANEY, Brebis

British physicist
Born June 6, 1915, London, England

BLEANEY BEGAN his research in physics in 1937 in the Clarendon Laboratory, Oxford, under the guidance of F. E. Simon. Bleaney's measurements of the thermal and magnetic properties of potassium chromium alum suggested that the then current vapor pressure scale of liquid helium was in error near 1°K. In 1939 Simon, who had already criticized this scale on thermodynamic grounds, led the calculation of a fresh scale, which was verified by measurements of Bleaney and R. A. Hull, using the susceptibility of paramagnetic salts as an intermediate standard thermometer.

In January, 1940, Bleaney became the youngest member of a group working for the British Admiralty in the Clarendon Laboratory on centimeter waves. In collaboration with J. H. E. Griffiths, Bleaney successfully built small klystrons to oscillate at 3-cm wavelength. About 200 reflex klystrons were supplied to act as local oscillators in experimental radar systems at this wavelength in 1941–42. A reflex klystron of novel design for 1.25-cm wavelength (which later became the 2K50 tube) was then developed with D. Roaf. Measurements on the inversion spectrum of ammonia, NH_3, at wavelengths between 1 and 2 cm were begun as a fundamental study of pressure broadening; with R. P. Penrose, Bleaney analyzed the rotational structure of the inversion band in 1945–46. This work, the first

application of wartime microwave techniques to high-resolution spectroscopy, initiated a fertile field of investigation in microwave gas spectroscopy.

The discovery in 1945 of ferromagnetic resonance by Griffiths and the realization that level splittings of order 0.1 cm^{-1} in paramagnetic salts (such as the chromium alums) could be measured by centimeter wave spectroscopy led to a rapid development of electron spin resonance in the Clarendon Laboratory. Detailed and extensive measurements by D. M. S. Bagguley showed the power of this method of investigation and the need for measurements to be carried out at low temperatures to avoid broadening through spin-lattice relaxation. A simple cavity spectrometer, operating down to 14°K, was designed by Bleaney and Penrose in 1946–47, and it revealed the temperature dependence of the splitting of the spin quartet ground states of the chromium alums. Hyperfine structure in a diluted copper salt was discovered by Penrose during a visit to the Kamerlingh Onnes Laboratory, Leiden, in 1949. In the following years detailed experimental studies of hyperfine structure were made by Bleaney and a number of collaborators in salts of the iron (3d), the lanthanide (4f), and the actinide (5f) groups. During this period the importance of covalent effects and of ligand hyperfine structure, particularly in the palladium (4d) and platinum (5d) groups, was demonstrated by the parallel work of J. Owen and Griffiths. At the same time the theory of the magnetic resonance spectrum, based on the earlier work of J. H. Van Vleck, was worked out in the Clarendon Laboratory by M. H. L. Pryce, A. Abragam, K. W. H. Stevens, R. J. Elliott, and others. Most of the basic features of the theory, including the use of an "effective spin" Hamiltonian, resulted from this work, and day-by-day collaboration between theoreticians and experimentalists ensured particularly rapid progress.

Paramagnetic substances form the "working fluid" in the method of magnetic cooling for obtaining temperatures well below 1°K. Much of the work in electron spin resonance was directed toward finding the best "coolants" and providing exact data on paramagnetic salts of interest in low-temperature physics. The determination of spin-spin interactions from the resonance spectrum of "pairs" of ions in semidilute salts was initiated in 1953, and this has become an invaluable tool in the study of exchange interaction. Measurements of hyperfine structure, during which the correct values of a number of nuclear spins were established, proved particularly valuable in furthering work on oriented nuclei. Methods of producing spatially oriented nuclei, which could be detected through the anisotropy in their radioactive emissions (particularly gamma rays) had been discussed by N. Kurti and Simon in the 1930s. Following the arrival of H. Halban in Oxford in 1946, as well as the rapid development of the low-temperature school in Oxford after World War II, preparations were made for specific experiments on nuclear orientation. At a meeting in Simon's office to discuss the best type of experiment, Bleaney suggested that the local anisotropy of a paramagnetic ion due to interaction with its ligand field could be used as the mechanism producing orientation. This simplified the experimental problem, since adiabatic demagnetization of a suitable paramagnetic salt to zero field should be sufficient, eliminating the need (in the Gorter-Rose method) for an external field to define an orientation axis (in fact, such a field often acts in competition with the internal fields). The first successful nuclear orientation experiment, based on this suggestion, was carried out in 1951, and the method has since been extensively exploited. In later work Bleaney explored the correlation between hyperfine structures in salts and metals of the rare-earth group and examined the importance of ligand field effects in intermetallic lanthanide compounds.

Bleaney went to Westminster City School, London, and then to Oxford University, where he took his B.A. in physics in 1937 and his D.Phil. in 1939. He was lecturer in physics at Oxford University from 1945 to 1957. In 1957 he was appointed Dr. Lee's Professor of Experimental Philosophy and head of the Clarendon Laboratory, Oxford, in succession to Sir Francis Simon. He became a fellow of the Royal Society in 1950, and was awarded the Charles Vernon Boys Prize of the Physical Society of London in 1952 and the Hughes Medal of the Royal Society in 1962.

Bleaney wrote *Electricity and Magnetism,* with his wife, Betty Bleaney (1957; 2d ed. 1965).

For background information *see* ELECTRICITY; KLYSTRON; PARAMAGNETISM in the McGraw-Hill Encyclopedia of Science and Technology.   □

★ BLINKS, Lawrence Rogers

American botanist
Born Apr. 22, 1900, Michigan City, Ind., U.S.A.

B LINKS CONTRIBUTED to plant physiology through the study of the simplest plants, the algae, his interest in them being aroused by his teacher at Harvard, W. J. V. Osterhout. With the latter he went to Bermuda in 1923, working on the giant-celled marine alga *Valonia,*

and he continued to utilize this genus and other such coenocytes throughout the next 40 years.

His first experiments dealt with the electrical resistance of the protoplasm—a measure of the ease with which ions enter or leave the cell. It had long been appreciated that living cells interpose a considerable resistance to current flow, but Blinks was the first to assign a value to it. This value ranged from 10,000 ohms/cm² of cell surface in *Valonia* to 100,000 ohms/cm² in the freshwater plant *Nitella.* Considering the extremely thin structures involved (the plasma and vacuolar membranes), this was the resistance to be expected from an oily rather than aqueous layer.

One of the most important of his early findings was on the action potential of *Nitella.* When a low stimulating potential is applied to the cells, such an action can be initiated and will then pass at about 1 cm/sec down the cell. As the cell's potential falls toward zero, so does the electrical resistance. Both then recover in 10–15 sec. Such fall of resistance was later found in the squid axon and other nerve cells by K. S. Cole.

The resistance in large algal cells had to be measured with direct current, since even at 1000 cycles the impedance fell to much lower values. This fall is due to the high capacitance of the membranes, spread as they are in single or double uninterrupted layers. The capacitance was found to be about 1 microfarad/cm² of cell surface—a value also displayed by many other living cells. In addition to the static capacitance to be expected of a thin, oily layer, there appeared to be a "polarization" component as well, dependent on frequency and probably due to the

differential mobility of ions (such as K and Cl) in the membrane.

There occurs in Bermuda another large algal cell, the sea bottle, which, contrary to the high potassium content of the sap of *Valonia,* displays no accumulation (even partial exclusion) of this element. Blinks recognized it as the genus *Halicystis* (now regarded as the sexual generation of *Derbesia*), and he spent many years on its study, both in Bermuda and California. Curiously enough, the California species accumulates potassium fairly well. Yet both plants display almost the same potential (emf) across the protoplasm: about 70–75 millivolts (mv). Furthermore, the vacuole can be perfused with seawater, so that there is no solute gradient across the protoplasm as a whole; yet the potential remains almost unchanged. These factors necessarily threw the emphasis on gradients *within* the cytoplasm and on asymmetrical properties of the membrane systems. Substitution of various anions (such as nitrate, sulfate, acetate, formate, lactate, and glutamate) for the chloride of seawater caused a very large change of potential, reversing the positive emf to some 40 mv negative. This great change was due to the much lower mobility of these anions in the outer surface of the protoplasm; on the other hand, a substitution of such anions in the vacuole (by perfusion) produced a much smaller effect. It could hence be postulated that there was a rather large potential across the outer (plasma) membrane, and a much smaller one across the vacuolar membrane (tonoplast), because of the presence of indiffusible anions (organic acids, amino acids, proteins, and others) in the cytoplasm and a negligible concentration of them in the seawater or sap. The observed potential was the algebraic sum of the larger plasma and the smaller tonoplast potentials. If either of the membranes was altered, the potential would be increased, decreased, or reversed.

One of the simplest ways to alter one membrane (probably the tonoplast) was by exposure of *Halicystis* to dilute ammonia or other weak bases: At a certain threshold value the potential reversed, in a sigmoid time course. The reverse in potential seemed to have been caused by the entrance of the undissociated weak base, since the effect was increased by higher pH and decreased by lower. Light also favored such emf reversal, since photosynthesis increased the pH (due to CO_2 utilization). Curiously, however, the potential often increased before falling and reversing, as if the first effect of light was an increased acidity. This unexpected result demanded independent measurement, which was supplied by glass electrodes in direct contact with the cells or other algal tissues. On illumination the pH was indeed found often to decrease before it rose in the expected fashion— the first evidence of an initial "acid gush" (later identified by Robert Emerson as caused by CO_2 evolution).

Influenced by this electrical measurement, Blinks developed an electrode measurement for oxygen based on the polarographic method. Instead of dropping mercury, however, in 1938 Blinks and R. K. Skow applied a polarized platinum electrode directly to the tissue. The diffusion distance was reduced to a minimum, and the responses to light were extremely rapid; the method also directly indicated rates rather than absolute amounts. It showed many previously unsuspected parts of the photosynthetic induction period, such as an "oxygen gush" immediately after an anoxic period. The speed of the response was utilized by Blinks and F. T. Haxo in 1949 to study the photosynthetic action spectra of a large number of marine algae. Although green and brown algae showed good correspondence between absorption spectra and photosynthetic activity (indicating the participation of most pigments), red algae showed remarkable deviations, with very high efficiency in green light (absorbed by the accessory pigment phycoerythrin) but much lower activity in red or blue light. Since red or blue light is absorbed by chlorophyll, the function of this important pigment was thrown into considerable question.

The electrode method also was the first to indicate chromatic transients—changes in the steady-state photosynthetic rate when the wavelength of light is suddenly changed (for example, from red to green). Both of these effects found their explanation shortly afterward when Emerson discovered photosynthetic enhancement —an increased efficiency resulting from light absorption by *two* pigment systems: chlorophyll *a* and accessory pigments, such as carotenoids, phycobilins, or other chlorophylls.

Blinks recently introduced the giant-celled alga *Boergesenia* into physiological study. It resembles *Valonia* in many respects, but its normal potential is larger and can be reversed readily by a variety of agents. Light is especially effective upon its potential.

Blinks graduated cum laude from Harvard in 1923. He received his M.A. in 1925 and his Ph.D. in general physiology in 1926, both from Harvard. After 7 years on the staff of the Rockefeller Institute for Medical Research, in 1933 he was appointed associate professor of plant physiology at Stanford University, being promoted to professor of biology in 1936. He was director of Stanford's Hopkins Marine Station from 1943 to 1965. He became professor emeritus in 1965, and was then appointed professor of biology at the new Santa Cruz campus of the University of California. He was elected to the American Academy of Arts and Sciences in 1949 and to the National Academy of Sciences in 1955.

For background information *see* ALGAE; CELL MEMBRANES AND MONOLAYERS; CELL-SURFACE

IONIZATION; CHLOROPHYLL; PHOTOSYNTHESIS in the McGraw-Hill Encyclopedia of Science and Technology.   ☐

☆ BOHR, Aage

Danish physicist
Born June 19, 1922, Copenhagen, Denmark

WHILE ATTEMPTING to explain why in certain instances calculations of the quadrupole moment of the nucleus based on the nuclear-shell model are very much smaller than the observed value, Bohr—in collaboration with Ben R. Mottelson—proposed the collective, or unified, model of the nucleus. In their model Bohr and Mottelson retained the essential features of the nuclear-shell model, but also brought out the analogy between the surface of the nucleus and that of a liquid drop. Thus, the collective model reconciled the nuclear-shell model with its predecessor, the liquid-drop model.

In 1936 the Danish physicist Niels Bohr advanced the liquid-drop theory of the nucleus. On this basis the fission of uranium discovered a few years later could be understood in terms of the analogy between an unstable atomic nucleus and a rupturing water drop. In the liquid-drop model the form of the nucleus is determined by a balance between Coulomb repulsive forces between like charges (protons) and inward-directed forces of surface tension. In 1949 J. Hans D. Jensen, working in Germany with O. Haxel and H. E. Suess, and Maria Goeppert Mayer, working independently in the United States, advanced the shell model of the nucleus. In their model the nucleus, like the electron shells of the atom, displays all the properties of a quantum-mechanical system of particles.

About 1950, working at the University of Copenhagen and at Columbia University in New York, Aage Bohr began to study those phenomena that did not seem to fit the nuclear-shell

model, whose validity had been generally established, to determine in what way the model could be refined. The calculation of the quadrupole moments of nuclei of odd mass number on the basis of the nuclear-shell model involved the assumption that the nuclear core, consisting of all the nucleons except the odd one, was spherical. Bohr made the assumption—first proposed by the American physicist James Rainwater—that the odd nucleon, regardless of whether it was a neutron or a proton, would distort the core. This distortion, Bohr realized, would make an additional contribution to the quadrupole moment.

Based on this assumption, Bohr and Mottelson developed the collective model of the nucleus, which they announced in 1952. The fundamental postulate of the model is that, because of the collective action of the nucleons, the surface of the nucleus behaves like that of a liquid drop. The deformation caused by the odd nucleon moves across the surface of the nuclear core in the form of waves, which are equivalent to surface oscillations and rotations. Near closed shells, the nuclear equilibrium shape is spherical and the models of excitation correspond to vibrations about equilibrium in addition to the single-particle excitations of the shell model. When the shells are partially filled, the nucleus may acquire a permanent distortion, usually of spheroidal shape. For such deformed nuclei, the low energy modes of excitation involve a new degree of freedom corresponding to rotational motion. Although the nucleus does not rotate like a rigid structure, the resulting spectrum of states could be treated by quantum-mechanical methods previously developed for the study of molecules. As a result, Bohr and Mottelson were able to calculate the energies and other properties of nuclear states for the various values of the rotational quantum number. The results thus derived have been found to be in excellent agreement with the empirical evidence.

Although his principal investigations dealt with the structure of the nucleus and with its rotational states, Bohr made contributions to other areas of physics. Among these were his researches in superconductivity, in which he attempted to explain the stability of permanent currents, and his studies of elementary particles.

One of four sons of Niels Bohr, Aage Bohr studied at the University of Copenhagen (M.Sc., 1946; Dr.Phil., 1954). He became a research assistant at the Institute of Theoretical Physics in Copenhagen in 1946, and in 1963 was appointed director of the Institute. Bohr was named professor of physics at the University of Copenhagen in 1956. In 1944–45 Bohr worked at the Los Alamos Scientific Laboratory, where the atomic bomb was developed. He was a member of the Institute for Advanced Study at Princeton,

N.J., in 1949, and he engaged in research at Columbia University in New York City in 1949–50. Bohr was awarded the Dannie Heineman Prize of the American Physical Society in 1960 and the Pius XI Medal in 1963.

Bohr wrote *Collective and Individual-Particle Aspects of Nuclear Structure*, with B. R. Mottelson (1953; 2d ed. paper 1957).

For background information *see* ATOMIC STRUCTURE AND SPECTRA; NUCLEAR STRUCTURE in the McGraw-Hill Encyclopedia of Science and Technology.   ☐

BOWEN, Norman Levi

American geologist
Born June 21, 1887, Kingston, Ontario, Canada
Died Sept. 11, 1956, Washington, D.C., U.S.A.

DURING HIS investigations of phase equilibria among silicate systems, Bowen discovered the significance of the reaction principle in petrogenesis. The experimental studies that led to his hypothesis, which has been called the most important contribution to petrology in the 20th century, established Bowen as one of the outstanding pioneers in experimental petrology.

Until recently the importance of experimental laboratory studies in geology was questioned by many workers, who believed that field observation alone—using the Earth as their laboratory—was sufficient. Furthermore, the findings of laboratory phase-equilibrium studies were considered suspect, because equilibrium is rarely attained in nature.

Bowen, however, strongly believed in the desirability of laboratory studies as an adjunct to geological field observations. He felt that the only practical method for studying the physical chemistry of geological processes was to determine what occurred under equilibrium conditions. Then, he thought, the investigator could evaluate the factors that led to the failure to attain equilibrium in nature and estimate the magnitude and direction of the effects of these deviations from equilibrium. Bowen conceived of this relationship as one in which the laboratory studies could provide a chemical basis for hypotheses on origins and the associated field studies could modify these as required by observation to provide an explanation of the mechanism of petrogenesis.

Bowen became interested in the physical chemical approach to geology as an undergraduate. His investigations of liquidus-solidus relations, both in his graduate work and in his early years as a researcher, laid the groundwork for his most important study: phase equilibria among silicates. These studies, from 1910 to 1917, led him to formulate his theory on reaction processes in magmas during the process of cooling.

In 1921, working at the Geophysical Laboratory of the Carnegie Institution of Washington, Bowen began to study the problem of diffusion against gravity of a heavy liquid into a lighter liquid using diopside (a silicate of calcium and magnesium commonly having a variable ferrous silicate content) and plagioclase (soda-lime silicates) melts; then he studied the extent of diffusion by measuring the refractive index of the glass across the contact plane of the solidified melts.

Bowen fused the results of his earlier work on phase equilibria among silicates with the results of his studies of diffusion to produce his paper "The reaction principle in petrology" (1922). In the paper he showed the relative unimportance of the eutectic relation when compared to the reaction relation between liquid and crystal phases. He demonstrated that the crystallization and differentiation of the rocks of an igneous sequence were controlled by a continuous and discontinuous reaction series, which he was able to define. Bowen then showed how this accounted for H. Rosenbusch's normal order of crystallization, an empirically derived rule for which no one had previously been able to find a theoretical basis.

Bowen also made a number of other contributions of fundamental importance to petrology. Among these were the succession of mineral assemblages that will be formed at successively higher temperatures in the metamorphism of impure carbonate rocks, the reactions in silicates of ferrous iron, and the importance of the residua system in petrogenesis. Equally significant is the legacy of his experimental philosophies and techniques, which have been of importance in developing ceramic technology.

The youngest son of a British immigrant, Bowen entered the Faculty of Arts at Queen's University in Kingston, receiving his A.M., with university medals in chemistry and mineralogy, in 1907. He then entered the Faculty of Applied Science at the university and received his B.Sc. in mineralogy and geology in 1909. The Massachusetts Institute of Technology awarded him his Ph.D. in 1912. Although he had been doing summer field work (for the Ontario Bureau of Mines from 1907 to 1909 and for the Geological Survey of Canada in 1910) prior to receiving his doctorate, Bowen decided to concentrate on experimental laboratory studies; he therefore joined the Carnegie Institution of Washington as an assistant petrologist in 1912. In 1919 he left the Institution to become professor of geology at Queen's University, but returned the following year. He left the Institution again in 1937 to accept the chair of Charles L. Hutchinson Distinguished Service Professor of Petrology at the University of Chicago. Bowen was named head of the geology department in 1945, but left the university in 1947 to return to the Carnegie Institution as a petrologist. He retired in 1952. Among the awards he received were the Bigsby Medal (1931) and the Wollaston Medal (1950) of the Geological Society of London, the Penrose Medal (1941) of the Geological Society of America, the Miller Medal (1943) of the Royal Society of Canada, and the Roebling Medal (1950) of the Mineralogical Society of America. Bowen was elected president of the Mineralogical Society of America in 1937 and of the Geological Society of America in 1946. He was elected to the National Academy of Sciences in 1935 and to foreign membership in the Royal Society of London in 1949.

Bowen wrote *The Evolution of the Igneous Rocks* (1928; 2d ed. 1956; paper 1956).

For background information *see* Fused-salt phase equilibria; Petrology; Silicate phase equilibria in the McGraw-Hill Encyclopedia of Science and Technology.   □

★ BRACHET, Jean Louis Auguste

Belgian biologist
Born Mar. 19, 1909, Etterbeek, Belgium

Brachet first became interested in the biochemical role of the cell nucleus when he was 18 years old. A lecture on cytology given by his teacher Pol Gérard aroused his attention; experiments carried out long before were described in detail to illustrate the fact that cells deprived of their nuclei could survive for hours, or even days, and maintain many of their former activities. This initial impetus guided Brachet's choice of study toward a then little explored subject: nucleic acids and their distribution in the nucelus and cytoplasm of living cells.

At that time the key words deoxyribonucleic acid (DNA) and ribonucleic acid (RNA) were still unknown; the terms then in use were "animal" and "plant" nucleic acids. Indeed, though evidence was scanty, it was thought that DNA occurred only in animal cells and RNA only in plant cells. Biochemical studies of nucleic acid synthesis in developing sea urchin eggs led Brachet in 1933 to the conclusion that the multiplication of nuclei and DNA synthesis were intimately linked. He was also able to show that the cytoplasm of these eggs contained large amounts of the "plant" nucleic acid. He thus provided for the first time clear evidence that RNA might well be a constituent of animal, as well as plant, cells. At that time there were few ready to accept such evidence. But Brachet's personal conviction led him to elaborate a simple cytochemical technique to determine the intracellular localization of RNA. The method was based on the acidic nature of nucleic acids, which causes them to combine readily with basic dyes; the "basophilia" of the cells, therefore, seemed likely to be due to the presence of nucleic acids. Simple staining, however, was not adequate to distinguish between the two types of nucleic acid. To achieve this, a method had to be found which could selectively eliminate one or the other of the acids from the cell. A specific test for RNA was found when Brachet succeeded in eliminating RNA by enzymatic degradation, by treating killed cells with ribonuclease. After a pretreatment of this kind, RNA-containing structures were no longer found to stain with basic dyes. It thus became possible to determine accurately the distribution of RNA in the cell by comparing normal and ribonuclease-treated,

stained cells. This method for the cytochemical detection of RNA has indeed become classical and has been used in hundreds of papers.

An extensive study of RNA distribution was carried out by Brachet in the late 1930s and led to the conclusion that RNA is present in the nucleus and the cytoplasm of all cells, both animal and plant. An attempt to correlate the RNA content of the cytoplasm and the biochemical properties of the cells brought out an important feature: Brachet—at the same time as T. O. Caspersson in Stockholm—was struck by the fact that the cells "rich" in RNA are always those which actively synthesize proteins. Such a correlation between RNA content and protein synthesis was not easily accepted by biochemists, although Brachet had already shown in 1941 that biochemical analyses of the RNA content of various tissues agree with the inferences drawn from the cytochemical tests.

Despite the difficulties of war conditions (Brachet's laboratory was closed and he spent several months in prison as a hostage), he managed to continue research. He and his colleagues R. Jeener and H. Chantrenne showed that the relationship between RNA content and protein synthesis still holds at the subcellular level; the theory that the microsomes (the particles which contain most of the cytoplasmic RNA) must be important agents in protein synthesis could be shown by indirect experiments. The direct demonstration of this now well-established fact could not be given by this Brussels group, because the necessary radioactive isotopes and equipment were not available in Belgium during the years after the war.

In view of technical and financial difficulties, Brachet went back to more biological problems: the biochemical mechanisms of cell differentiation during embryonic development, and the biochemical role of the cell nucleus. His experiments on frog eggs showed that substances which destroy RNA (the enzyme ribonuclease, for instance) or inhibit its synthesis (actinomycin) block the development of the embryos—demonstrating that ordered RNA and protein synthesis is an absolute requirement for morphogenesis. The biochemical functions of the cell nucleus were analyzed in unicellular organisms (amebas, the giant unicellular alga *Acetabularia*, sea urchin eggs); it is easy to separate these cells, mechanically, into two parts, nucleate and anucleate. It then becomes possible to compare the biochemical activities of the two kinds of fragments. The results obtained, in the case of animal organisms, were clear: Removal of the nucleus does not immediately abolish protein synthesis, but it ultimately results in the disappearance of cytoplasmic RNA. These early experiments, in 1955, agree perfectly with the now accepted view that cytoplasmic RNA is first synthesized in the nucleus and then transferred to the cytoplasm. A more complex situation was encountered in the case of the alga *Acetabularia*, where both RNA and protein synthesis continue for several weeks in the absence of the nucleus. The reasons for this paradox were made clear by later work of

Brachet and his colleagues: The chloroplasts (which bear chlorophyll, necessary for photosynthesis) contain DNA, and they can replicate and produce RNA in the absence of the nucleus. Therefore, net DNA, RNA, and protein syntheses are still possible in anucleate fragments of the alga. The composition and the possible functions of cytoplasmic DNA, both in eggs and in *Acetabularia*, continued to be one of the main subjects of research in Brachet's laboratory.

Son of a distinguished experimental embryologist, Brachet graduated from the medical school of the University of Brussels in 1934, and became a professor at the Faculty of Sciences of the university in 1938. In 1964 he was also appointed director of the Group on Molecular Embryology at the International Laboratory of Genetics and Biophysics, Naples. A recipient of the Francqui (Belgium), Mayer (France), and Heineken (Netherlands) prizes, Brachet was elected a foreign member of the American Academy of Sciences (1959), the U.S. National Academy of Sciences (1965), and the Royal Society of London (1966).

Brachet wrote *Embryologie chimique* (1944), *Chemical Embryology* (1950), *Biochemical Cytology* (1957), and *The Biochemistry of Development* (1960). With A. E. Mirsky he edited *The Cell* (6 vols., 1964).

For background information *see* CELL (BIOLOGICAL); CELL NUCLEUS; DEOXYRIBONUCLEIC ACID; NUCLEIC ACID; RIBONUCLEIC ACID in the McGraw-Hill Encyclopedia of Science and Technology. ☐

★ BRAUNSTEIN, Aleksandr Evseyevich

Soviet biochemist
Born May 26, 1902, Kharkov, Russia

Braunstein in 1937 discovered, in collaboration with Maria G. Kritzman, the enzymatic interconversion, in muscle and other types of cells, of amino and keto acids by way of intermolecular transfer of the amino group. This process is now called transamination. E. E. Snell in the United States in 1945, as well as other investigators, demonstrated the involvement of vitamin B_6, in the form of pyridoxal phosphate (PLP), in biological transamination and in the decarboxylation of amino acids. Braunstein then started extensive investigations on the functions of vitamin B_6 in intermediary nitrogen metabolism. He and his associates demonstrated several previously unknown coenzyme functions of PLP in the metabolism of tryptophan, of sulfur-containing and hydroxy amino acids. They detected some new enzymatic steps in amino acid catabolism, including the formation of alanine from tryptophan via kynurenine and of glycine

via aldol decondensation of threonine and its homologs. A general theory of the mechanism of PLP-dependent enzymatic reactions of amino acids, together with a classification of these reactions, was proposed by Braunstein and M. M. Shemyakin in 1952–53. Similar ideas were independently developed by Snell and co-workers. From 1960 onward Braunstein was engaged with a group of enzymologists, organic chemists, and physicists in systematic investigation of the molecular structure, catalytic mechanism, and selective inhibition of aminotransferases and other PLP-dependent enzymes.

Although the enzymatic transfer of hydrogen and of phosphate groups had been demonstrated earlier, it was the work of Braunstein on transamination that attracted general attention to the fundamental significance of various types of group transfer reactions in intermediary metabolism and in enzyme catalysis. In many cases, a specific group of the enzyme protein or of a coenzyme acts as the intermediate carrier of a substrate fragment; this is exemplified by the acceptor function of PLP in amino group transfer. The transamination reaction is frequently quoted in textbooks as a prototype of group transfer.

Braunstein's early work indicated the almost ubiquitous occurrence of transamination reactions in living cells, the participation of an extensive range of substrates, and the predominant role of glutamic acid among these. It was shown that the coupling of transamination with reversible deamination of glutamate and with other specific enzymatic transformations of glutamic and aspartic acids results in carrier-linked reaction sequences of major importance for the assimilation of ammonia nitrogen into amino acids, and for conversion of the amino acids to secondary and excretory metabolites of nitrogen (such as purine and pyrimidine nucleotides, ammonia, urea, and uric acid). In particular, it was demonstrated that one of the main pathways for the biosynthesis of many amino acids involves indirect reductive amination of keto acids by the joint action of aminotransferases and glutamate dehydrogenase (or alanine dehydrogenase in some species of microorganisms and higher plants). Reversal of this reaction sequence provides one of several alternative transamination-dependent paths for the indirect oxidative deamination of amino acids. These experimental findings and Braunstein's generalizations concerning the fundamental role of transamination as an essential link in the assimilation and dissimilation of nitrogen, in the integration and reciprocal control of intermediary nitrogen metabolism and cell respiration, were largely confirmed later with the advent of refined analytical methods. The work was extended by many other investigators.

Braunstein's second, and closely related, major field of research was the problem of enzymatic pyridoxal catalysis. Here the Braunstein-Snell theory was amply validated, and gained general acceptance. This theory was one of the first successful applications of modern physical organic chemistry to the interpretation of an extensive group of important biochemical reactions.

The investigations of Braunstein and his associates laid the basis for solution of various physiological and medical problems of practical importance. These relate to animal and human nutrition, to the mode of action of certain antibiotics and drugs, and to the pathogeny, diagnosis, and treatment of metabolic disorders and other diseases. Thus, for example, the assay of aminotransferase activity in the blood of patients proved of considerable value for the differential diagnosis of cardiac, hepatic, and other diseases. Braunstein's work on PLP enzymes contributed to elucidation of the nature of disturbances of tryptophan metabolism in B_6-deficient animals, and of the role of such disturbances (depression of nicotinic acid formation via kynurenine) in the pathogenesis of pellagra. It also provided a rationale for the detection and treatment of B_6 deficiency associated with normal and toxemic pregnancy. Later researches conducted in his laboratory were of importance in clarifying the biochemical mechanisms of action of several antibiotics and antimetabolites, including cycloserine, its derivatives, and different amino acid analogs. On this basis, rational principles were developed by R. M. Khomutov and others for the design of new selective inhibitors of PLP enzymes.

The chemical and biological aspects of transamination and other pyridoxal-catalyzed reactions and their key role in the metabolism of nitrogen and sulfur were surveyed by Braunstein in a number of review papers published in English or French, as well as in lectures delivered at international conferences and congresses.

Son of a professor of ophthalmology, Braunstein graduated from the State Medical Institute in Kharkov in 1925 and moved to Moscow. After 3 years of postgraduate studies in V. A. Engelhardt's group at the A. Bakh Institute of Biochemistry, he served until 1936 as senior investigator in several research institutes, working on problems of glycolytic and respiratory phosphorylation and on the metabolic detoxication of aromatic compounds. He received the degress of M.D. in 1928 and D.Biol.Sci. in 1938, and achieved the grade of professor in biochemistry in 1939. He successively became head of laboratories on intermediary nitrogen metabolism in the All-Union Institute of Experimental Medicine in 1936 and in the Institute of Biological and Medical Chemistry in 1944. In 1961 he moved to the Institute of Physico-Chemical Biology (now the Institute of Molecular Biology) of the Academy of Sciences of the U.S.S.R. as head of a laboratory working on the chemical basis of biological catalysis. He was elected to full membership of the Academy of Medical Sciences in 1945 and of the Academy of Sciences of the U.S.S.R. in 1964. He received an honorary doctorate of science from the Université Libre de Bruxelles, and was elected honorary member of several foreign scientific societies and academies, including the American Society of Biological Chemists and the American Academy of Arts and Sciences, both in 1961. In 1933 he was awarded a prize of the Mendeleyev Chemical Society, and shared with M. G. Kritzman a U.S.S.R. State Prize for achievements in the medical sciences in 1941.

Braunstein wrote *Biochemistry of Amino Acid Metabolism* (1949), in Russian, and the chapter "Pyridoxal Phosphate" in *The Enzymes*, Vol. II (2d ed. 1960). He was editor and coauthor of *Enzymes* (1964), Vol. II of the series *Fundamentals of Molecular Biology*, in Russian.

For background information *see* AMINO ACIDS; ENZYME; TRANSAMINATION; VITAMIN B$_6$ in the McGraw-Hill Encyclopedia of Science and Technology. □

★ BREMER, Frédéric

Belgian physiologist
Born June 28, 1892, Arlon, Belgium

A FTER AN initial period during which he studied spinal and cerebellar physiology, Bremer devoted himself mainly to the physiology of the cerebral cortex, together with the subcortical and commissural structures involved in its activities. His name is associated with an important development in the investigation of the neurophysiological mechanisms which condition the sleep and waking states of the mammalian brain. In 1935 he showed that the interruption, by a transsection of the rostral brainstem, of the flow of nervous impulses ascending toward the forebrain produces in the latter a functional condition which has many analogies with natural sleep and the sleeplike state produced by barbiturate drugs. The electrophysiological and pharmacological analyses of these two hypnoid states led him to the conclusion that the sleeplike condition which characterizes the residual activity of the forebrain when it is separated from the rest of the neuraxis by a mesencephalic transsection is due to the lack of a continuous energizing influence exerted normally on its nerve nets by the impact of indispensable afferent impulses. Sections of the spinal cord immediately below the medulla showed that this energizing influence is maintained in the intact, complete encephalon.

Bremer's experiments, which provided neurophysiologists with the now classical preparations of the *cerveau isolé* and the *encéphale isolé*, introduced the two concepts of a "cortical tonus" and of its critical reduction by the "deafferentation" of the forebrain. The fundamental significance of the two concepts was not affected when H. W. Magoun and G. Moruzzi demonstrated in 1949 that the ascending activating impulses which the mesencephalic section blocks are essentially those which are emitted by a portion of the brainstem neuronal network known as the reticular formation. The concepts survived, also, the discovery in 1959 by Moruzzi and his associates of an antagonistic hypnogenetic influence exerted on the arousal system by a nervous structure more caudally located in the brainstem core.

In the course of his study of the sleep processes, Bremer was led to analyze the various components of the elementary responses evoked in the cortical receiving areas by synchronous volleys of sensory impulses. He showed that the presence of the late oscillatory component of these evoked potentials is of critical importance for perceptual awareness, a fact which was later confirmed by the microphysiological recording of the discharges of neuronal units. In 1952 he made, with Terzuolo, a significant contribution to the knowledge of the reciprocal relation which exists between the cortical mantle and the ascending reticular formation. He described the process by which the cerebral cortex is able to promote its own arousal by a corticoreticular control mechanism. The analysis he and his associates made of the processes involved in arousal disclosed the powerful facilitatory effect exerted on the operations of the cortical receiving areas and of their thalamic relay nuclei by the direct or indirect stimulation of the reticular formation. Later such reticulocortical sensory dynamogenesis proved to be especially important for the visual area responses and to be associated there with the activity of oculomotor structures.

The theoretical interpretation of the electroencephalographic method discovered by H. Berger was promoted by Bremer's analysis of elementary responses. It also benefited from two other aspects of his research: first, his methodical analysis of the "spontaneous" oscillatory potentials of the brain cortex (the "brain waves"), which Bremer, on the basis of his spinal cord studies with V. Bonnet, attributed very early to synchronized synaptic potentials of the cortical nerve cells; and second, by his contribution to the elucidation of the various mechanisms of this bioelectrical synchronization.

The son of a teacher of Latin and Greek, Bremer received his M.D. from the University of Brussels in 1919. He studied neurology with Pierre Marie in Paris and physiology with W. B. Cannon in Boston, then did research in H. W. Cushing's laboratory in Boston and in C. S. Sherrington's laboratory in Oxford. After a period as instructor of physiology, he was, from 1932 until his retirement in 1962, professor and chairman of the department of physiopathology at the University of Brussels Medical School. The recipient of honorary degrees from the universities of Aix-Marseille, Montpellier, Strasbourg, and Utrecht, Bremer was elected a foreign member of the American Academy of Arts and Sciences in 1958.

Besides monographs on the cerebellum and muscle tone, Bremer wrote *L'Activité électrique du cortex cérébral* (1938) and *Some Problems in Neurophysiology* (1953), the texts of lectures delivered at the universities of Paris and London.

For background information *see* NERVOUS SYSTEM; SLEEP in the McGraw-Hill Encyclopedia of Science and Technology.   □

★ **BRINK, Royal Alexander**

American geneticist
Born Sept. 16, 1897, Woodstock, Ontario, Canada

BRINK'S MAJOR research dealt with a directed form of heritable change that he encountered in maize and named paramutation in 1958. He observed that the level of action of an *R* gene, which conditions anthocyanin formation in seed and plant, invariably was reduced following passage through a heterozygote with a stippled allele. The altered form of *R* was gametically transmissible, though it reverted partially toward the standard level when it was made homozygous. The stippled factor was not altered in the heterozygote with *R*. The *R* allele sensitive to this unusual kind of heritable change was said to be paramutable, and the stippled factor was described as paramutagenic. Counterparts of paramutation in maize had been reported earlier by Bateson and Pellew in the garden pea, by Lilienfeld in *Malva*, and by Renner in *Oenothera*, but these examples of the phenomenon were less favorable for study than the *R* case.

In cooperation with his graduate students and other associates, Brink showed that paramutation involves chromosome components that, unlike conventional genes, are extremely labile under certain conditions and can be heritably altered in particular ways at will. Biological interest in this phenomenon rests on the fact that the observed changes in level of gene action reflect the operation of elements in the chromosome. *R*-locus dependence of the *R* phenotype was proved in a test which showed that a paramutant *R* and a distinctively marked normal *R* persisted in their respective states in a common cytoplasm. The first *R* allele whose paramutability was studied conditioned pigment formation in both seed and plant. It was observed that sensitivity to paramutation was unaltered when this factor mutated to colorless plant, but was abolished by mutation to colorless seed. Evidently paramutability rests on an *R*-locus component intimately associated with seed pigmentation.

Three lines of evidence, all indirect, led Brink to conclude that paramutation occurs in vegetative cells. First, it was shown that conjugation at meiosis of a paramutable and a paramutagenic allele is not a condition of paramutation. Second, it was observed that following the application of pollen carrying a highly sensitive *R* allele to the silks of a plant heterozygous for a paramutagenic and a nonparamutagenic factor, the resulting seeds carrying the paramutagenic factor form significantly less pigment than the other class. Third, it was demonstrated by testing separately the pollen formed in different tassel branches that plants in which paramutation is occurring are mosaics for level of potential *R* action. Thus, paramutation may proceed at different rates in different cell lineages within the individual plant. The various states of *R* in pollen from a given tassel are assumed to reflect the sum of the paragenetic changes that have occurred between fertilization and plant maturity in the respective cell lineages entering the tassel.

Seed color phenotypes based on a paramutable *R* factor of given origin can be obtained in a range from self-color, in single dose, to near-colorless. These different levels of *R* pigmenting potential can be generated by passing *R* through heterozygotes carrying appropriately chosen paramutagenic alleles. The level of action of an *R* factor initially in an intermediate state can be raised by maintaining the factor heterozygous with a colorless allele, or it can be reduced by passing the factor through a heterozygote with the stippled, or other strongly paramutagenic, gene.

The continuous variation in level of *R* action that may be induced by these breeding procedures suggests that the chromosomal basis of paramutability is a repressor segment adjacent to the *R* gene consisting of repeating units whose numbers may be altered. The degree of repression of *R* action is assumed to be a function of the multiplicity of the units making up the repressor segment. If many units are present, *R* action is only weakly expressed, and vice versa. According to this hypothesis, paramutation consists in a change in the number of units within the repressor segment. Such changes may be visualized as occurring during somatic mitosis as a result of misreplication of the postulated repeating units.

Paramutation rests primarily on the metastability of paramutable *R* alleles, and it is not the result of a property conferred by a paramutagenic partner in a heterozygote. The level of action of a paramutable *R* of stock culture origin rises significantly in successive generations of hemizygotes, that is, in plants lacking an *R* partner. This fact shows that paramutagenic factors do not instigate paramutation; they act as adjuvants of the process, which can also occur in their absence. Recent studies have shown that the treatment of seed with alkylating agents, such as diethyl sulfate, regularly promotes heritable derepression of a paramutated *R* allele. This regular increase in level of *R* action is understandable on the assumption that the alkylating agent causes loss of material from the repressor segment either by direct deletion or through an effect on the chromosome replication process that leads indirectly to the loss of repressor units.

Born and reared on a dairy farm, Brink received his early education in a rural primary school and the Woodstock Collegiate Institute. He received a B.S.A. from the Ontario Agricultural College in 1919. Following a year as chemist with Western Canada Flour Mills, Winnipeg, he entered the University of Illinois and was awarded an M.S. in 1921. He continued graduate study in genetics with E. M. East at Harvard University, which granted him a D.Sc. in 1923. Brink was appointed to the staff of the department of genetics at the University of Wisconsin in 1922, and spent his entire professional career there. He was chairman of the department of genetics from 1939 to 1951. Brink was elected to the National Academy of Sciences in 1947 and to the American Academy of Arts and Sciences in 1960.

Managing editor of *Genetics* (1952–57), Brink also edited *Heritage from Mendel* (1965), the proceedings of the Mendel Centennial Symposium sponsored by the Genetics Society of America.

For background information *see* ALLELE; CHROMOSOME; GENE ACTION in the McGraw-Hill Encyclopedia of Science and Technology. □

★ BRODE, Robert Bigham

American physicist
Born June 12, 1900, Walla Walla, Wash., U.S.A.

BRODE SHOWED in his first research publication (1925) that molecules, such as nitrogen and carbon monoxide or methane and argon, with similar arrangements of their external electrons have very similar cross sections for the collision of slow electrons. His later observations on mercury, cadmium, and zinc were interesting in their marked similarity and in the magnitude of the cross sections. Cadmium was the largest and mercury the smallest. This is the inverse of the order of their ionization potentials. Similar results were obtained by Brode for the alkali

atoms. The very large cross sections that were found could have been expected from the low ionization potentials. For electrons with about 2-volts energy cesium, the atom with the lowest ionization potential, has a cross section that is 110 times the cross section of helium, the atom with the highest ionization potential. The alkali atoms have resonance peaks in their cross sections for energies near their excitation potentials. While the magnitude of the cross section is qualitatively explained by the binding forces on the external electrons, the quantitative theoretical handling of the problem requires, even for the alkali atoms, involved wave mechanical treatment that is only now possible with modern computers. The results of these computations are in satisfactory agreement with Brode's observations. The survival quality of Brode's work is indicated in a 1966 survey that describes his paper as one of the most used references in the field of collisions of charged particles.

In 1935 Brode spent a year in research with P. M. S. Blackett at Birkbeck College, London, working on counter-controlled cloud chambers. Returning to Berkeley, he developed cloud chamber techniques to give quantitative measurements of the specific ionization and momentum of high-energy cosmic-ray electrons. The application of this technique in 1938, with D. Corson, confirmed the theoretical prediction for the increasing specific ionization with the increasing energy for electrons having a relativistic mass above about four times the rest mass. This property of all high-energy charged masses has been important in distinguishing between protons and mesons with very high energy. After the war Brode resumed his measurements of momentum, specific ionization, and range of cosmic-ray mesons. From a large number of measurements he obtained a value for the rest mass of the mu meson of 210 ± 5 times the electron's rest mass. The excess of positive mu mesons and the related east-west asymmetry at sea level and

at mountain stations to 12,000 ft were studied. Observations of cosmic-radiation particles were made in a cloud chamber combined with the field of a permanent magnet and flown in a B-29 at 30,000 ft. As a part of the International Geophysical Year program, Brode established neutron monitor stations at Berkeley, Honolulu, and Elsworth (Antarctic).

Brode received his B.Sc. from Whitman College in 1921. In 1924 he received the first Ph.D. in physics awarded by the California Institute of Technology. The next 3 years were spent in postdoctoral research at Oxford as a Rhodes scholar, at Göttingen as an International Educational Board fellow, and at Princeton as a National Research Council fellow. In 1927 he was appointed assistant professor of physics at the University of California, Berkeley, becoming an associate professor in 1930 and a full professor in 1932. He retired in 1967.

During the war Brode was unit supervisor for research and development in the Johns Hopkins Applied Physics Laboratory, where the proximity fuse was developed. Later he was group leader for fusing in the Ordnance Division of the Los Alamos Atomic Laboratory. He was given the Presidential Certificate of Merit for these activities.

The development of the National Science Foundation into its position as a leader and supporter of American science has required the services of many scientists. Brode served as a member and as chairman of the Physics Advisory Panel, as a member of the University Science Development Panel, and as associate director for research in 1958–59. He was elected a member of the council or governing board of the American Physical Society, the American Association of Physics Teachers, and the American Institute of Physics. He served as vice-president for Section B and president of the Pacific Division of the American Association for the Advancement of Science.

With his background of 4 years of research and study abroad and his service on selection panels for Rhodes, National Research Council, Atomic Energy, National Science Foundation, and Fulbright awards, Brode was well prepared for his appointment to the Board of Foreign Scholarships by President Kennedy. In the organization of international conferences and commissions, he served as a United States delegate to two General Assembly meetings of the International Council of Scientific Unions and as vice-president during 1954–60 of the International Union of Pure and Applied Physics.

Brode was active in the University of California Academic Senate, where he served on many committees; he was chairman of the Berkeley Division, the state-wide Academic Council, the Budget Committee, and the Educational Policy Committee. He was a leader in the "oath controversy" between the faculty and the regents of the University of California, and worked for the restoration of academic freedom through the American Association of University Professors. He served in that organization on Committee A (Academic Freedom), on the Council, and as vice-president.

Brode was elected in 1949 to the National Academy of Sciences, of which his identical twin brother, the chemist Wallace Brode, also became a member.

For background information *see* CLOUD CHAMBER; COLLISION; MESON; SCATTERING EXPERIMENTS, ATOMIC AND MOLECULAR in the McGraw-Hill Encyclopedia of Science and Technology. □

★ BRODE, Wallace Reed

American chemist and spectroscopist
Born June 12, 1900, Walla Walla, Wash., U.S.A.

MUCH OF what is known of the influence of substituents on the absorption spectra of azo dyes is mainly due to Brode. Of some 150 technical papers published by him, about half are concerned with azo dyes. In his studies on color and constitution, Brode demonstrated substituent effects on resonance-dye structures in the induction of coplanarity, conjugation of resonant centers, and the partial or total inhibition of coplanarity of chromophoric-coupled resonant structures. Much of the monoazo study was broadened to include polyazo compounds and the effects induced by coplanar conjugation of disazo and polyazo compounds.

While much of Brode's earlier work in dyes involved the azo series, subsequent studies covered many classes of dyes, including phthalein and sulfonphthalein, anthraquinone, indigo, thioindigo, and natural dyestuffs. His extension of the observed phototropic effects in interconversion of *cis-* and *trans-*azo compounds to the *cis-* and *trans-*indigo and thioindigo series pro-

vided some of the best available examples of what he termed the "chameleon" effect, in which dyestuffs changed color to conform to the color of the light to which they were irradiated. The solutions of thioindigo and its derivatives change to red when exposed to red light and to blue when exposed to blue light: proof of the configuration being assigned through bridged rings which were specific to only one configuration.

As a by-product of his early work on the measurement of absorption spectra and optical rotation of the compounds he was studying, Brode had to design and build many of the essential instruments, including automatic recording spectrophotometers and spectropolarimeters. His development of the techniques and establishment of a laboratory for spectrophotometric and spectrographic studies led to his pioneering in the creation in the early 1930s of one of the first courses in chemical spectroscopy and to his writing the textbook *Chemical Spectroscopy* (1939; 2d ed. 1943). The combination of his training as a synthetic organic and dye chemist and as a designer and builder of optical instruments led to his chairmanship of the first committee on absorption spectra of the American Society for Testing Materials and to his honorary membership on the committee on emission spectra. From 1950 to 1960 he edited the *Journal of the Optical Society of America*. He was elected president of the Optical Society in 1961 and served on the board of governors of the American Institute of Physics in 1958 and from 1960 to 1963.

Although he was active in optics, Brode considered his principal career to have been that of a synthetic organic chemist. His major technical papers are mostly concerned with organic synthesis. He was one of five students of Roger Adams chosen to present papers at a symposium to honor that leader of American organic chemistry on his retirement in 1954. In this lecture Brode surveyed his own research studies, including the work initiated with Adams and continued in later years by Brode on the adsorption of asymmetric dyes on optically active fibers and the mechanism of dyeing of fibers. This work showed that asymmetric dyes are not preferentially adsorbed. Other researchers, however, had found to the contrary, and Brode had repeated some of these dissenting experiments but was unable to confirm them. The question was not fully settled until some 30 years later when Bradley, Brindley, and Easty in England repeated the Adams-Brode experiments and fully confirmed their validity.

The broad experience which Brode developed in the field of dyestuffs and color description led to some interesting related diversions in his contributions to science and education. He contributed extensively to the American Association for the Advancement of Science program in the elementary grades in experimental work involving color descriptions and dye reactions. With his wife, he collected American Indian artifacts and art work and developed a personal acquaintance with many Indian leaders. In particular, he studied the synthetic and natural dyes used by the Indians in the production of woven rugs and provided some helpful advice. Using samples from his extensive Indian rug collection, he gave popular lectures on the dyes used by the American Indians.

Widely known, but not always credited as to source, are the teaching models which Brode and his associates developed for organic chemistry. These "molecular models" sets, developed in the early 1930s, were designed as a low-price aide for individual students, and the laboratory manual prepared for use with these models was reprinted in several editions. These models have wooden pegs for single bonds, coil springs for double bonds, and brightly colored balls for atoms (yellow for hydrogen, black for carbon, and red for oxygen); they are designed on an inch-to-angstrom scale. Many research groups acquire the sets in quantity to study stereoisomerism, ring strain, and configuration problems.

Brode's father was a professor of zoology. An older brother became a professor of biology. Wallace Brode was one of a set of triplets; all three pursued scientific careers, Wallace and his identical twin, the physicist Robert Brode, achieving election to the National Academy of Sciences. Wallace Brode did his undergraduate work at Whitman College (B.S., 1921) and received his graduate degrees at the University of Illinois (M.S., 1922; Ph.D., 1925). He did postdoctoral work on a Guggenheim fellowship at Leipzig, Zurich, and Liverpool. From 1928 to 1948 he taught at Ohio State University, then served as associate director of the National Bureau of Standards from 1948 to 1958. During World War II he was head of the Paris Liaison Office of the Office of Scientific Research and Development, receiving for this service the Presidential Certificate of Merit. He headed the Science Department of the Navy Laboratory at Inyokern (China Lake) and served on the advisory boards of a number of defense and atomic energy activities. As science advisor to the Secretary of State from 1958 to 1960, he established the science office in the Department of State and the scientific attaché program in United States embassies in the major scientific nations. He wrote extensively on international science, national science policy, and scientific manpower in the United States and other nations and served as a member of the Scientific Manpower Commission. In addition to honorary degrees and honorary memberships in a number of scientific societies, Brode received the Priestley

Medal of the American Chemical Society, the Department of Commerce Exceptional Service Award, and the Distinguished Spectroscopist Award of the Society of Applied Spectroscopy. He was elected to the National Academy of Sciences in 1954.

Brode published more than 200 technical and survey articles in American and foreign scientific journals. In addition to his text, *Chemical Spectroscopy*, he coedited the manual *Laboratory Outlines and Notebook for Organic Chemistry* (1949), served as editor of *Science in Progress* (series 12–16, 1962–66), and contributed chapters to many standard reference texts.

For background information *see* DYE; DYEING; ORGANIC CHEMICAL SYNTHESIS; SPECTROSCOPY in the McGraw-Hill Encyclopedia of Science and Technology.   □

★ BROGLIE, Prince Louis de

French physicist
Born Aug. 15, 1892, Dieppe, Seine-Inférieure, France

IN 1905 Albert Einstein, in his theory of "light quanta," affirmed the coexistence in light of waves and of particles (today called photons) and drew from that the explanation of the photoelectric effect. During the following years he developed this idea in a series of works that are today too often forgotten. Having long meditated on Einstein's conceptions and on all the quantum phenomena then known, de Broglie, in some notes published in the proceedings of the Paris Academy of Sciences in 1923 and then in his doctoral thesis in 1924, extended the idea of the coexistence of waves and particles to all the particles of microphysics, particularly to electrons. The conception that guided him then was that these particles are very small regions of very high concentrations of energy in the interior of the wave transporting them.

The existence of the wave associated with the

particle in this new "wave mechanics" was soon confirmed by the success of the theoretical work of Erwin Schrödinger and by the experimental discovery by C. J. Davisson and Germer, then by G. P. Thomson, of the phenomenon of electron diffraction. Preserving his initial idea, de Broglie, in an article published in the *Journal de Physique* in May, 1927, developed his mode of envisaging the coexistence of waves and particles in the form of a "theory of double solution." At the Solvay Conference, which met at Brussels in October, 1927, the interpretation of the new mechanics upheld by Max Born, Niels Bohr, and their students and linked to Bohr's conception of "complementarity" was opposed to de Broglie's. Called upon at that time to uphold his teachings, de Broglie expounded at length the interpretation that, despite the important objections raised by Einstein and Schrödinger, was adopted by the majority of theoretical physicists.

For 15 years de Broglie reviewed his ideas on the theory of the double solution and considerably developed them. Only his three principal hypotheses will be stated here.

(1) The real wave (or wave v) is a physical process that evolves in space and time according to the equations of propagation well known in wave mechanics. As for the particle, it is a sort of small object, the seat of a very great concentration of energy, which is constantly located in its wave and which is displaced according to a law specified below. The wave ψ usually employed in quantum mechanics is a *fictitious* wave connected to the real wave v by the formula $\psi = Cv$, where C is a normalization constant so that the quantity $|\psi|^2$ can give in absolute value the probability of the particle's presence in the element of volume. The single fact of granting that the particle is constantly located in its own wave makes it possible to remove completely the very serious objections that can be made to the present interpretation.

(2) If the motion of the particle is not subject to the perturbations discussed in (3), that motion will be constantly defined by the "guiding law" stated as follows: "If the wave v is written in the form $v = a\,(x, y, z, t)\, \exp\,[\,(i\,\hbar)\,\varphi(x, y, z, t)\,]$ where a and φ are real, the quantity of motion of the particle is equal at every point of its trajectory to the gradient of the function φ at that point and at that instant." It is easily proved that this guiding law can also be stated this way: "The particle moves in its wave in such fashion that its internal vibration remains constantly in phase with the wave that carries it." When one accepts the guiding law, one can perceive the reason why the quantity $|\psi|^2$ gives at each point and at each instant the probability of the particle's presence. But a more rigorous demonstration of this deduction

requires the introduction of a supplementary hypothesis:

(3) The particle is constantly in energetic contact with a hidden medium that it is natural to identify with the "subquantum medium," the existence of which was suggested in 1954 by Bohm and Vigier in an article in the *Physical Review*. As a result of the continual perturbations that its permanent contact with the subquantum medium imposes upon it, the particle must be animated by a kind of brownian movement which constantly causes it to leap from one trajectory defined by the guidance formula to another, as in a hydrodynamic flow one molecule of a hot fluid passes constantly from one stream line to another. It is the incessant skipping of the particle in its wave that permits a better proof of the statistical significance of the quantity.

But then one is almost necessarily led to think that the subquantum medium constitutes a kind of hidden thermostat with which the particle is constantly in contact. On this basis, de Broglie was led to formulate a "hidden thermodynamics of particles," which, when better developed, seems to him bound to play a great role in the future progress of quantum physics.

De Broglie became convinced that the interpretation of wave mechanics based on the principles just stated will make possible an understanding of the true physical significance of the formalisms presently employed in quantum mechancis and an explanation of their success. The physical realities hidden behind the formalisms will finally be perceived and, undoubtedly, new explanations and predictions will be obtained. The present situation, then, seems analogous to that which existed at the time when classical thermodynamics constituted a rigorous formalism permitting exact predictions but resting on admittedly arbitrary, a priori principles. It is the statistical interpretation of thermodynamics, due principally to Boltzmann and Gibbs, which made it possible to understand the true nature of entropy and finally to predict or explain new phenomena.

At the University of Paris de Broglie received his Licencié ès lettres (1910), Licencié ès sciences (1913), and Docteur ès sciences (1924). He was professor of theoretical physics at the University of Paris from 1932 to 1962. Winner of the Nobel Prize for physics (1929), he was elected to the French Academy in 1944, to the Royal Society of London in 1953, to the U.S. National Academy of Sciences in 1948, and to the American Academy of Arts and Sciences in 1958.

De Broglie wrote *Matter and Light: The New Physics* (English transl. 1939), *New Perspectives in Physics* (English transl. 1962), *The Current Interpretation of Wave Mechanics: A*

Critical Study (English transl. 1964), *La thermodynamique de la particule isolée* (1964), and *Certitudes et incertitudes de la science* (1966). He edited *Wave Mechanics and Molecular Biology* (1966).

For background information *see* DE BROGLIE WAVELENGTH; QUANTUM MECHANICS; QUANTUM THEORY, NONRELATIVISTIC in the McGraw-Hill Encyclopedia of Science and Technology.   □

BRONK, Detlev Wulf

American biophysicist
Born Aug. 13, 1897, New York, N.Y., U.S.A.

AFTER ASSUMING the presidency of the Rockefeller Institute for Medical Research (now Rockefeller University) in 1953, Bronk guided its evolution into a unique center for graduate study in the United States and one of the finest graduate schools in the world. During his administration the Institute's university foundations were laid and its educational policies developed.

In 1901 John D. Rockefeller endowed the Institute in New York City as a pioneering grant-giving agency. By 1903 a decision was made to conduct research, and the Institute was modeled on the European laboratories presided over by such notables as Robert Koch, Louis Pasteur, and Ivan Pavlov. After World War II the trustees of the Institute decided that university and medical school laboratories had begun to undertake research that had once been in the exclusive domain of the Rockefeller. As a result, the Institute no longer securely held the position of innovator that had accounted to a large degree for its eminence. A committee was organized to chart the course of the Institute, and from this group emerged a plan to utilize the Institute's facilities for training talented young investigators and for working more intimately with universities.

Bronk was then asked to accept the post of president and chief executive officer of the Insti-

tute, combining two formerly separate positions, and to guide the reorganization. He decided to undertake the task, for he believed the new position provided an unusual opportunity to devote much of his time to research while developing a unique international institution for the furtherance of science. In 1954 the Institute's original charter was amended to make it a graduate university, and it became part of the University of the State of New York with the authority to grant the degrees of Ph.D. and Sc.D. At this time the name was shortened to the Rockefeller Institute to reflect its broadened purposes.

Among the many ways in which the Institute differed from conventional graduate schools were that it had no undergraduate college, it had a faculty-to-student ratio of 2:1, and there was no fixed program of study. Under Bronk's direction a graduate fellow was expected to choose his own curriculum by selecting a combination of courses, tutorials, and independent readings followed by self-directed study and research. Complete academic freedom was the keynote of Bronk's plan. At the Rockefeller a student could work for weeks, or even months, with a particular investigator and then withdraw without penalty to work with another if he so chose.

The success of Bronk's leadership is borne out by the statistics of the first decade of the new program. Of the more than 200 appointments to fellowships, 73 received their degrees and 118 were still studying at the Rockefeller. As a result of the achievements during this period, in the spring of 1965 the institution was renamed the Rockefeller University to reflect the changes and the new direction that had been taken under Bronk.

Bronk's administrative abilities benefited a number of academic institutions. While at Swarthmore College he helped to organize the honors program for undergraduates. Later he was the first director of the Johnson Research Foundation of Medical Physics at the University of Pennsylvania. Bronk also served as president of Johns Hopkins University, where he tried to bridge the gap between undergraduate and graduate study, emphasizing the progress of the individual student. During World War II he served as coordinator of research in the U.S. Army Air Corps Air Surgeon's office, where he was concerned with the physiological aspects of high-altitude flight.

As a researcher, Bronk worked in the areas of both biophysics and physiology. He studied the nature of sensation, body movement control, the chemical excitation of nerves and nerve impulses, and the electrochemical methods of measuring oxygen consumption in nerve fibers.

Bronk received his A.B. (1920) from Swarthmore College, and his M.S. (1922) and Ph.D. in physics and physiology (1926) from the University of Michigan. After serving as an instructor at the University of Pennsylvania and the University of Michigan, he joined the faculty at Swarthmore in 1924, becoming professor of zoology and dean of men in 1927. Two years later he accepted a position as professor of biophysics and director of the Johnson Research Foundation at the University of Pennsylvania. In 1949 he resigned these positions to become president of Johns Hopkins, where he remained until joining the Rockefeller Institute. Bronk was chairman of the National Research Council from 1946 to 1950 and president of the National Academy of Sciences–National Research Council from 1950 to 1962. Among the many honors he received were the Priestley Award (1956), the Franklin Medal of the Franklin Institute (1961), the Presidential Medal of Freedom (1964), and the Public Welfare Medal of the National Academy of Sciences (1964). ☐

★ BROWN, Harrison Scott

American geochemist
Born Sept. 26, 1917, Sheridan, Wyo., U.S.A.

BROWN BECAME interested in the problems of the origin and evolution of the solar system after World War II. At that time there was no direct measurement of the age of the Earth. The ages of numerous uranium- and thorium-bearing rocks had been determined, from which it was deduced that the Earth must be at least 2,000,-000,000 years old. Measurements of variations in the isotopic composition of lead ores indicated further that the Earth might be 3,300,000,000 years old, but direct measurement seemed impossible. The major difficulty was that, although the average isotopic composition of modern terrestrial lead could be determined readily enough, the isotopic composition of "primeval" lead, or lead as it was at the time of the Earth formation, was unknown.

Remelting and weathering of rocks had taken place on too vast a scale on Earth to make it likely that any primeval lead had been safely isolated from uranium and thorium since the time of Earth formation. Brown suggested, however, that perhaps nature had preserved a sample of primeval lead in certain of the extraterrestrial objects which collide with the Earth from time to time and which are called meteorites. He reasoned that lead, having a low oxygen affinity and a high affinity for sulfur, is probably concentrated primarily in the metallic, or "iron," meteorites and in the iron sulfide nodules which occur in such meteorites. By contrast, uranium and thorium have high oxygen affinities, and are probably concentrated primarily in the oxide phases of the silicate or "stony" meteorites. Thus the lead in iron meteorites would have been safely isolated from uranium and thorium since the time of their origin. It was not known, but it was suspected, that meteorites were formed at the time of the formation of the solar system. Were that assumption correct, the lead in iron meteorites should be "primeval."

Attempts were made to isolate lead from the Canyon Diablo meteorite, and it was soon found that the actual concentration of lead in the meteorite was far lower than had been supposed. Indeed, the concentrations turned out to be so low that the isolated lead was found to consist primarily of lead impurities introduced from chemicals and the air. This discovery led to the development by Brown and his students of chemical procedures for isolating lead from meteorites in microgram quantities free from contamination. Concomitantly, Mark Inghram at the University of Chicago developed powerful new tools of mass spectrometry, which made possible the precise determination of the isotopic composition of such minute quantities of lead. After many failures, Clair C. Patterson, one of Brown's students, succeeded in isolating contamination-free lead from the Canyon Diablo meteorite. Analysis of the lead by Inghram showed that it indeed possessed an isotopic composition unlike that of any terrestrial lead. Assuming the lead to be primeval, the age of the Earth was calculated to be 4,500,000,000 years. Subsequently, isolation of lead from stony meteorites by Patterson showed them also to be 4,500,000,000 years old, thus proving the original assumption concerning the equality of the age of the Earth and that of meteorites to be correct.

The techniques used in this early work were then applied to a variety of problems in solar system and terrestrial chronology by numerous workers. Brown and his students, Patterson and George Tilton, in collaboration with Inghram and Esper Larson, Jr., were the first to apply the techniques to the determination of the age of an ordinary granite and at the same time to determine the detailed distribution of uranium and lead between the constituent mineral phases. Subsequently, similar techniques were applied to the first precise dating of a sedimentary deposit by using potassium-40 and calcium-40. Brown suggested that it might be possible to extend these concepts and determine the age of the elements themselves by making use of possible extinct radioactive substances such as iodine-129. John Reynolds subsequently found isotopic anomalies in xenon extracted from meteorites, making it possible to establish a maximum interval between the formation of the elements and the formation of the solar system. Brown's interest in meteorites led him and his student Edward Goldberg to develop the neutron activation method of trace element analysis for the determination of gallium, gold, palladium, and rhenium. This work, together with later spectroscopic studies, demonstrated the existence of clear-cut chemical groups of iron meteorites which must have evolved under widely differing physicochemical conditions.

In collaboration with Leon T. Silver, Brown demonstrated that about one-third of the uranium and thorium in a typical granite exists in micromineral phases and interstitially is so loosely bound that it can be washed out of the pulverized rock with dilute acid. They demonstrated that the energy one can get out of granites in this manner is much greater than the energy required for processing, thus in principle placing all granitic rocks on Earth at man's disposal as a near-infinite source of energy. The energy releasable in this way from 1 ton of granite is equivalent to that contained in about 15 tons of coal. By studying the abundances of noble gases in the Earth's atmosphere, Brown was able to demonstrate that the atmosphere is almost entirely of secondary origin, and that during the early phases of Earth formation the chemical and physical processes involved must have taken place at fairly low temperatures (that is, at temperatures sufficiently low for hydrates of silicate minerals to be fairly stable).

Brown showed that planets can be classified into three groups: class I, those composed primarily of metals and silicates (Mercury, Venus, Earth, and Mars); class II, those composed primarily of methane, ammonia, and water (Uranus and Neptune); and class III, those composed primarily of hydrogen and helium (Jupiter and Saturn). Studies of the compositions of stars suggest that planets in systems associated with other stars can also be classified in this manner.

Son of a livestock broker, Brown began his schooling in Wyoming. Following the death of his father, his mother, who was a teacher of piano and a professional organist, moved to San Francisco, where Brown completed his primary

and secondary education. He received his B.S. in chemistry at the University of California at Berkeley in 1938 and his Ph.D. in chemistry at the Johns Hopkins University in 1941. Brown became interested in nuclear physics during his undergraduate days at Berkeley and undertook thesis work in mass spectrometry and the separation of isotopes by gaseous thermal diffusion. With the discovery of nuclear fission in 1939, he devoted his attention to the diffusion properties of uranium hexafluoride. By 1940 he and his professor at Johns Hopkins, Robert Fowler, found themselves with the largest gaseous fluorine-generating capacity in the United States. They soon were major suppliers of uranium tetrafluoride and hexafluoride to the embryo atomic project at Columbia University and elsewhere. In 1942 Brown was asked by G. T. Seaborg to join him at the Metallurgical Laboratories at the University of Chicago to work on the chemistry of plutonium. He started the project's program on transuranic anhydrous halides, then in 1943 moved to the newly created Clinton Laboratories at Oak Ridge, Tenn., as assistant director of chemistry. In 1946 he joined the staff of the Institute for Nuclear Studies at the University of Chicago and there started his work in geochemistry and cosmochemistry. In 1951 he became professor of geochemistry at the California Institute of Technology. With Trevor Gardner, he wrote the original proposal which gave rise to the creation of the Arms Control and Disarmament Agency within the federal government in 1961. He became foreign secretary of the National Academy of Sciences in 1962 and professor of science and government at the California Institute of Technology in 1967. He received the American Chemical Society's Award in Pure Chemistry in 1952, and was elected to the National Academy of Sciences in 1955.

Brown wrote *Must Destruction Be Our Destiny?* (1946), *The Challenge of Man's Future* (1954), and *The Next Hundred Years* (1957; paper 1963).

For background information *see* COSMOGONY; LEAD ISOTOPES, GEOCHEMISTRY OF; METEORITE; PLANET in the McGraw-Hill Encyclopedia of Science and Technology.   □

★ BRUN, Edmond Antoine

French physicist
Born Dec. 31, 1898, Saint Cannat, Bouches-du-Rhône, France

THROUGHOUT HIS career, which started in 1929 in the modest laboratory of the Lycée de Nice, Brun worked principally in the domain of aerodynamics combined with heat transfer called

aerothermodynamics. His thesis, prepared in Paris in the Laboratoire de Physique du Service des Recherches de l'Aéronautique and presented in 1935, dealt with the measurement of the equilibrium temperature which is reached by a perfectly insulating body in uniform translatory motion in a gas. He thus studied the kinetic heating of the flat plate and of the cylinder and presented recovery factor data for both laminar and turbulent flow.

In 1936 he pointed out that, in the case of constant physical properties, the heat transfer coefficient for high-speed flows is given by the same expression as for low-speed flows, if it is defined in terms of the difference between the actual wall temperature and the adiabatic wall temperature (given by the value of the recovery factor). This result must be established theoretically in the case of laminar flow, but Brun showed experimentally that it is also true in turbulent flow.

In 1937, at the request of the International Air Traffic Association, Brun started studying problems raised by the icing of airplanes. The thermodynamical aspect of the phenomenon led him to define the conditions of anti-icing more precisely. He gave the values of the heating rates necessary either for anti-icing or for deicing of leading edges of wings or of cockpits in terms of the icing conditions; he showed that the most economical conditions of thermal protection were met by a deicer with intermittent electrical heating.

Brun was led, in the study of icing of airplanes, to analyze the conditions of captation of supercooled water droplets by a solid body moving in a cloud at a temperature below 0°C. In 1943, he established, with Marcel Vasseur, the equations of the mechanics of suspensions, and he found a graphical method for drawing the trajectories of particles in suspension in a fluid when the flow field is not uniform. He also gave a method of calculation of anti-icers and applied the equations of the mechanics of suspensions to the study of the characteristics of some dust removers such as cyclones.

The calculation of the convective heat transfer at the nose of a body of revolution, carried out in connection with the problem of icing, served in 1947 as a starting point for the expression of the heat flux density at the nose of a missile during reentry into the atmosphere.

On his nomination as a professor at the Sorbonne in 1942, Brun became head of a laboratory supported by the Centre National de la Recherche Scientifique. He was mainly concerned with studies of heat and mass transfer, especially detailed explorations, both dynamical and thermal, of the boundary layer. This thin layer of fluid exists at the wall of a moving solid, and here are to be found, in the direction perpendicular to the wall, large variations of speed, temperature, and concentration. These rapid variations in the neighborhood of the wall account for both the friction of the fluid on the wall and the convection of heat and of mass from or toward the body. The analogies between these various phenomena led Brun and Gustave Ribaud to establish laws governing heat and mass transfer in good agreement with experiment.

When an insulating body is suddenly put in a gas flow at uniform speed, it heats up progressively until it reaches at each point an equilibrium temperature, which is the adiabatic wall temperature already mentioned. For the study of this unstationary regime, Brun gave a method of measurement of the coefficient of convection in his thesis (1935); this method essentially consists in placing at the surface of the insulating body a small conducting mass flush with the wall and in measuring the beginning of the heating up of this mass. The method, now widely used in accordance with the same unchanged process, is known as the calorimetric method. It was further refined in Brun's laboratory, particularly in the study of supersonic and hypersonic flows.

The study in this laboratory of mass transfer from cylinders and cones at an angle of attack showed the existence of new vortices with axis along the streamlines; it became possible to determine the streamlines by a detailed dynamical exploration of the boundary layer.

Brun's laboratory became an important experimental center for the aerodynamics and thermodynamics of rarefied gases. Flows at high Mach numbers (up to 20) and at low densities (down to 1 micron of mercury) can be obtained in wind tunnels. The Second Symposium on Rarefied Gas Dynamics was organized by Brun in Paris in 1961.

Studies of heat and mass transfer in porous media were also carried out and led to practical results on freezing and defreezing of soils, as well as studies of two-phase or n-phase flows in oil reservoirs.

A founder of the International Astronautical Academy, Brun was president of the Société Française d'Astronautique in 1940 and president of the International Astronautical Federation from 1962 to 1964. In 1963 he organized the International Astronautical Congress in Paris. Vice-president of the International Astronautical Academy, he also became president of the Société Française des Thermiciens in 1964. He was a fellow of the Royal Aeronautical Society, London (1958), honorary fellow of the American Institute of Aeronautics and Astronautics (1964), and fellow of the American Astronautical Society (1966). He was elected a foreign associate of the U.S. National Academy of Sciences in 1960. Among the honors he received were the Médaille d'Or de l'Institut Français des Combustibles et de l'Energie in 1961 and the Médaille de la Société des Ingenieurs Civils de France in 1963.

Brun wrote *Les chaleurs spécifiques* (1940), which received an award from the Académie des Sciences in 1942; *La Convection forcée de la chaleur en régime d'encoulement turbulent*, with Gustave Ribaud (1942); and *Transmission de la chaleur* (1948).

For background information *see* AEROTHERMO-DYNAMICS; BOUNDARY-LAYER FLOW; FLUID FLOW PROPERTIES in the McGraw-Hill Encyclopedia of Science and Technology.   ☐

★ **BUERGER, Martin Julian**

American crystallographer and mineralogist
Born Apr. 8, 1903, Detroit, Mich., U.S.A.

M ANY OF the classical fields of science involve crystalline matter in some way, so that some chemists, physicists, mineralogists, metallurgists, and ceramists interested in crystals have been drawn from time to time into the field of crystallography. The attraction of crystallography increased especially after W. H. and W. L. Bragg showed that the arrangements of atoms in crystals can be determined by x-ray diffraction data. As a graduate student in mineralogy at MIT, Buerger attended the lectures of W. L. Bragg, a visiting lecturer in 1928. He became convinced that an understanding of minerals and their interrelations must be based upon the arrangements of their atoms.

On receiving his doctorate in 1929, Buerger was appointed assistant professor of mineralogy and petrography at MIT, where he immediately established a small x-ray diffraction laboratory devoted to the study of the crystal structures of minerals. In the next few years he determined the arrangements of atoms in the minerals marcasite, löllingite, arsenopyrite, gudmundite, manganite, and valentinite, when World War II intervened. After the war he solved the structures of cubanite, berthierite, and pectolite. With the assistance of his graduate students, he unraveled the crystal structures of the minerals tourmaline, nepheline, livingstonite, jamesonite, coesite, cahnite, narsarsukite, high chalcocite, rhodizite bustamite, and rhodonite, as well as the structures of the nonmineral crystals Co_2S_3, diglycine hydrobromide, diglycine hydrochloride, potassium hexatitanate, and terramycin. For their doctoral dissertations his students solved many more structures under his supervision.

During his early contact with x-ray diffraction, Buerger revised some of the experimental apparatus commonly used, including the powder camera, whose present form he designed. He improved the Weissenberg method and instrumentation by introducing the equi-inclination technique and devised the back-reflection Weissenberg method for obtaining precise values of cell dimensions from single crystals. He invented the precession method now commonly used for determining the unit cell and space group of a crystal. These were developments of the 1930s. In 1952 the first counter diffractometer designed especially for measuring the intensities of the diffraction from single crystals was built in Buerger's laboratory, and in 1961 this was converted into the first automated diffractometer.

During the 1930s Fourier series began to be used in crystal structure analysis, the Patterson function was discovered, and their Harker sections pointed out. During World War II Buerger developed the "implication theory" of interpreting Harker sections, and his results, presented immediately after the war, had an important bearing on the main problem of x-ray crystallography, known as the "phase problem." The phase problem was the bottleneck in determining the arrangements of atoms in crystals. Any crystal structure can be revealed by a Fourier inversion of the amplitudes of the diffraction from the crystal. The difficulty is that the amplitudes are complex quantities, that is, each has both a magnitude and a phase. But since there exists no experimental way to measure the phase, the complex amplitudes required for the Fourier inversion are not fully available; thus the crystal structure analyst must solve his problem with only half the required data. But implication theory predicted that, for some symmetries at least, the crystal structures could be found without a knowledge of these phases, and therefore a general solution of crystal structures from experimental data could be devised in spite of the missing phases.

Another barrier found by crystallographers was Friedel's law, which states that the presence or absence of a center of symmetry cannot be determined by x-ray diffraction experiments. This situation has the same origin as the phase problem, and is a consequence of the impossibility of measuring phases. But that this was not wholly true should have been evident when Paul Niggli showed that space groups are characterized by systematic absences (called extinctions) of certain classes of reflections. Buerger contributed to space group classification by the invention of the *diffraction symbol*, which concentrated all diffraction information in a short list. By tabulating these symbols for all space groups, it was obvious that 58 of the 230 space groups could be unambiguously identified by simple qualitative means. Later, when he presented implication theory, he showed that if quantitative measurement of diffraction intensities were used, *all* space groups could be identified, except for separating the members of the 11 enantiomorphic pairs. This work, which was confirmed 4 years later in a statistical study by A. J. C. Wilson, succeeded in breaking the blocking effect of Friedel's law.

With the war over, Buerger, like many other crystallographers, turned his attention to the phase problem. Basing his approach on the notion of an "image," as suggested by Dorothy Wrinch, he developed the image theory of the Patterson function, discovered the basic image-locations theorem, invented image-seeking functions to search the Patterson function for the solution of the crystal structure, and established the basis for the present-day methods of solving crystal structures which make use of the Patterson function. The first structure to be solved by the new theory was that of the orthorhombic mineral berthierite, $FeSb_2S_4$, which in 1950 yielded to the new attack in a few hours.

Although Buerger made significant contributions to the theory of finding the arrangements of atoms in crystals and to the instrumentation used in gathering data for determining these arrangements, he regarded the field of crystal structure analysis chiefly as a necessary step in furnishing data for the explanation of crystal relations and behavior. He contributed to this larger objective in his discovery and explanation of lineage structure (an imperfection which arises during crystal growth) and in his development of general theories of polymorphism and twinning.

The great grandson of Ernst Moritz Buerger, one of the Lutheran clergymen who led the Saxon immigration to the United States in 1838, Buerger did his undergraduate work in mining engineering at MIT, receiving his B.S. in 1925. He received his M.S. (1927) and Ph.D. (1929) also at MIT, where he remained as a member of the faculty. His early work was in geology. He mapped parts of central Newfoundland in 1928–29 and was a member of the MacMillan Arctic Expedition of 1938. Buerger received the Day Medal of the Geological Society of America in 1951 and the Roebling Medal of the Mineralogical Society of America in 1958. He was elected to the National Academy of Sciences in 1953 and to many foreign societies and academies of science. In 1958 he received an honorary doctorate from the University of Bern. Buerger Bay in the Canadian Arctic, and the mineral buergerite were named in his honor.

Buerger was coeditor of the *Zeitschrift für Kristallographie* and the *International Tables for Crystallography*. He wrote *X-ray Crystallography* (1942); *Elementary Crystallography* (1956; rev. ed. 1963); *The Powder Method*, with Leonid V. Azaroff (1958); *Vector Space* (1959); *Crystal-Structure Analysis* (1960); and *The Precession Method in X-ray Crystallography* (1964). He also contributed nearly 200 articles to journals.

For background information *see* CRYSTAL STRUCTURE; CRYSTALLOGRAPHY; X-RAY CRYSTALLOGRAPHY; X-RAY DIFFRACTION in the McGraw-Hill Encyclopedia of Science and Technology. □

★ BURN, Joshua Harold

British pharmacologist
Born Mar. 6, 1892, Barnard Castle, Durham, England

ENTERING CAMBRIDGE University as a student of chemistry, Burn was to find his true life's interest after witnessing experimental demonstrations of physiological processes, as conducted by Joseph Barcroft. In 1914 Burn began working under H. H. Dale and further pursued his study of pharmacology.

Having learned from Dale how to perfuse organs removed from the body, he began to study the properties of tyramine, formed by decarboxylization of the amino acid tyrosine. At that time tyramine had been given vasoconstric-

tor properties. Burn soon discovered that tyramine's so-called property of constricting blood vessels vanished when it was injected into blood vessels perfused with blood by a pump instead of by the heart. But, in 1930, he found that tyramine's vasoconstrictor effect was restored when adrenaline (epinephrine) was added to the perfusing blood. This led him to prove that tyramine itself had little or no constrictor action but that its supposed vasoconstrictor action resulted from the fact that tyramine displaced adrenaline from blood vessel walls, and when the adrenaline entered the blood, it caused vasoconstriction. In 1958 with M. J. Rand he showed that this displacement mechanism also acted to release noradrenaline (norepinephrine). He had further demonstrated in 1932 that sympathetic nerve endings in blood vessels could take up adrenaline from the blood. This led in 1958 to his demonstration, again with Rand, that sympathetic nerve endings could take up noradrenaline, as well as liberate noradrenaline when they were stimulated. This finding was the origin of all the research on uptake which was done in the 1960s.

Using E. H. Starling's experimental heart-lung preparation of the dog, along with E. M. Vaughan Williams and J. M. Walker, Burn began to study the effect of infusing acetylcholine at a slow and steady rate into the atria of the heart. He found that when the atria were briefly stimulated at a frequency of 14 impulses per second during such an infusion, atrial fibrillation was produced which continued until the infusion was stopped. At that point normal atrial rhythm returned. They had found a method of producing atrial fibrillation at will and of maintaining it for as long as desired. It could be started or stopped as often as 10 times in a single experiment. With other colleagues Burn next studied ventricular fibrillation. They found that fibrillation in all cases arose when the refractory period was very short, and when the heart fibers were made to contract asynchronously by a rapid rate

of stimulation. They thus showed that fibrillation resulted from fibers stimulating each other. During the course of this work it was also demonstrated that the normal beating heart liberates both acetylcholine and catecholamines. Analyzing the physiologic function of the former, they found that when acetylcholine was not formed, or formed in too small an amount, the transmembrane potential fell to a point where impulses could no longer be propagated. The fall in the potential in the absence of acetylcholine was due to a fall in the permeability of the membrane to potassium ions, so that repolarization became impossible.

A third investigation by Burn concerned the mechanism of the release of noradrenaline from the sympathetic postganglionic fiber. For more than 50 years physiologists believed that the nerve impulses released noradrenaline directly. With Rand, Burn succeeded in establishing the view that the mechanism closely resembled that for the release of catecholamines from the adrenal medulla. The nerve impulse releases acetylcholine, which leaves the fiber. It then acts on the outside of the fiber, rendering it permeable to calcium ions. These ions then enter the fiber and release noradrenaline.

After World War I service in France, Burn did clinical work at Guy's Hospital, London, in 1918–20, then returned to research on biological standardization under H. H. Dale during 1920–25 and received his M.D. in 1925. From 1926 to 1937 he was director of the pharmacological laboratory of the Pharmaceutical Society in London. In 1937 he was appointed professor of pharmacology at Oxford University, a post he held until 1959, when he became emeritus professor of pharmacology. In 1959 he was named visiting professor to Washington University in St. Louis, Mo. Elected a fellow of the Royal Society of London in 1942, Burn in 1960 received a Gairdner Foundation Award.

Burn wrote *Biological Standardization* (1937), *Lecture Notes on Pharmacology* (1948; 8th ed. 1965), and *Autonomic Nervous System* (1963; 2d ed. 1965).

For background information *see* EPINEPHRINE; HEART (GANGLIONIC PACEMAKER); TYROSINE in the McGraw-Hill Encyclopedia of Science and Technology.   □

★ BURWELL, Charles Sidney

American physician
Born Apr. 10, 1893, Denver, Colo., U.S.A.
Died Sept. 3, 1967, Ipswich, Mass., U.S.A.

T HROUGHOUT HIS career Burwell was involved in the study of blood circulation. In his research he relied on data from tests on living patients, on anatomical peculiarities revealed

during surgery, on postmortems, and on tests performed postoperatively (up to 25 years later) on former patients. Beginning at Vanderbilt University and continuing in Boston, he investigated constrictive pericarditis, an uncommon but destructive disease, and the effects of operative treatment upon it. In 1941 he published a report, with Alfred Blalock, on 28 cases of the disease. Pericarditis, an inflammation of the membranous sac enclosing the heart, is constrictive when it interferes with the heart stroke and thus the circulation of the blood. The disorder is amenable to surgery, and both diagnosis and treatment depend upon an understanding of the physiologic abnormalities associated with the disease.

With his colleagues Burwell used the venous catheter to study chronic constrictive pericarditis in six men, with the result that the importance of constriction on *both* ventricles was emphasized. Blood flow and pressure were determined under conditions of rest and exercise, before and after operation. The pressure measurements, particularly those in the pulmonary circuit, were of great value to medical practice. Before operation each patient had a stroke output less than normal. This reduction in stroke volume is the primary dynamic abnormality of constrictive pericarditis. In 1931 F. A. Bainbridge and J. A. Menzies had found the stroke output to be dependent on three factors: myocardial contractility, the work load of the ventricles, and diastolic filling. Burwell and his colleagues found no definite evidence of myocardial contractility, though it is known from postmortems that in constrictive pericarditis myocardial fibers are often atrophic, and that the myocardium itself may be infiltrated by fibrous tissue, presumably a consequence of the original inflammatory process extending from the pericardium. The work load of the ventricles was not estimated because of difficulty in finding a zero point for pressure calculations.

Burwell made detailed studies of diastolic filling, generally held to be influenced by four factors: the diastolic filling pressure, adequacy of the blood available for venous return, the duration of diastole, and the ability of the ventricle to dilate. He found diastolic filling pressure to be high rather than low in the six patients. All six had complete adequacy of blood available for venous return. The duration of the diastole of the left ventricle was not shortened in the four patients in whom adequate preoperative measurements had been made. The ability of the ventricle to dilate sets a limit to the stroke output. Physiologic dilation is a necessary mechanism in the increase of stroke output. Such a dilation implies an increase in fiber length and a resultant increase in the force of contraction. These mechanisms would obviously be impaired by a constricting scar. Burwell emphasized the constancy and severity of this impairment in patients with constrictive pericarditis. Tests indicated that reduced stroke output was the major factor in the disability of this disease, and that the reduced stroke output was due to dilation of the ventricle being limited by the constricting scar. With the six patients he noted that in no case were the circulatory dynamics entirely normal, even when studied months or years after operation. He pointed out that most patients with the disease improved with surgery, but were rarely cured. This was borne out by his critical observations on series of patients over a period of years. In spite of the improved health of many patients after pericardiectomy, it was clear that the simple concept of stroke volume was not the whole story.

Myocardial fibrosis is a diffuse replacement, or invasion, of the myocardium by fibrous connective tissue to such an extent that there is interference with heart action. In 1957 Burwell and E. D. Robin studied the circulatory changes associated with diffuse myocardial fibrosis in 11 patients. They used standard methods of measurement and an innovation of their own—right-heart catheterization. Data were collected on the patients' volume of blood flow. Cardiac outputs varying from 2.0 to 5.3 liters per minute were recorded. The customary derivatives of cardiac output (cardiac index, stroke output, and stroke index) were found to be low, as was the cardiac output itself when related to actual oxygen consumption. Blood pressures in the systemic arteries were within normal limits in all patients. However, every patient showed a definite elevation of pressures in the pulmonary artery and "capillaries," the right atrium and ventricle, and the peripheral veins. Out of nine recorded right-ventricle pulse contours, eight showed a diastolic dip. Data indicated that cardiac failure of myocardial fibrosis was a form of low-output failure. As a working hypothesis, Burwell suggested that low-output failure resulted from two basic physiologic defects—limitation of diastolic filling and impairment of systolic emptying of the heart. The interference with diastolic filling was related to changes in the volume-elasticity characteristics of the fibrotic myocardium.

Burwell's post at the Boston Lying-in Hospital made it possible for him to combine his interests in heart disease and pregnancy. With the help of E. C. Eppinger, J. Metcalf, and D. Strayhorn, he contributed much on the physiology of pregnancy and the influence of heart disease on mother and baby. Again, his procedure was to study a series of patients with heart disease, but under the added load of pregnancy. He demonstrated clearly that most women with heart disease can go safely through pregnancy and pointed out the relation of this fact to the operative treatment of rheumatic, congenital, and various other forms of heart disease.

Raised mostly in Pennsylvania, Burwell graduated from Allegheny College in 1914 and from Harvard Medical School in 1919. He underwent postgraduate training in Boston, Baltimore, and Vienna. When he returned from Europe, he accepted a post at Vanderbilt University under G. Canby Robinson, who was then dean of the medical school. In 1928 he succeeded Robinson as professor of medicine at Vanderbilt and retained that post until 1935, when he became professor of medicine and dean of the faculty of medicine at Harvard. He was appointed director of the medical clinic at the Boston Lying-in Hospital in 1949. Elected to the American Academy of Arts and Sciences in 1939, Burwell received in 1959 the John Phillips Memorial Award of the American College of Physicians.

Burwell wrote *Heart Disease and Pregnancy: Physiology and Management*, with James Metcalfe (1958), covering his work in Boston.

For background information *see* CIRCULATION; HEART DISORDERS in the McGraw-Hill Encyclopedia of Science and Technology.   □

☆ BUSH, Vannevar

American electrical engineer
Born Mar. 11, 1890, Everett, Mass., U.S.A.

AS DIRECTOR of the Office of Scientific Research and Development (OSRD) during World War II, Bush was responsible for mobilizing and coordinating the United States scientific war effort, a task that included the development of radar and the atomic bomb. After the war he helped provide the impetus for the federal government's encouragement of science, especially basic research, and for the institution of agencies to facilitate such encouragement.

In 1940 Bush, then president of the Carnegie Institution in Washington, D.C., was appointed chairman of the National Defense Research Committee (NDRC) by President Roosevelt. This agency was set up to supplement Army and Navy research work on war devices. Bush brought to the committee his skills as teacher, original researcher, engineer, and administrator. In the same year the Uranium Committee, which had been studying the feasibility of nuclear explosives, was made a subcommittee of the NDRC.

When in 1941 the Office of Scientific Research and Development was established, Bush was appointed its director. This agency was to mobilize the total scientific war effort, to conduct broad research programs, and to advise the President on the status of scientific research and development in connection with defense. During the course of the war, under Bush's direction virtually the entire scientific manpower of the United States was at the disposal of the OSRD. The more than 2000 projects to which its scientists were assigned cost more than $300,000,000 directly, and the agency supervised the spending of many hundreds of millions more. The two most massive programs undertaken by the OSRD involved the development of tactical radar and the atomic bomb. The decision to make an all-out effort to produce the bomb was reached in 1941; thereafter, as a member of the Top Policy Group (headed by the U.S. President) and as chairman of its Military Policy Committee, Bush shared responsibility for the setting of policy throughout the program, and continued in this work after the task of administration and development had been taken over by the Army in 1943.

In 1944 the President asked Bush to make recommendations as to how the experience gained under the OSRD in mobilizing and di-

recting national scientific efforts might be applied under peacetime conditions. Bush's response was his report *Science, the Endless Frontier* (1945). Drawing on the studies of eminent scientists, engineers, and educators, he made proposals for the consolidation and utilization of scientific skills on a national level. He also urged government support for an unprecedented national effort in basic research. This recommendation was stimulated partly by the realization that, because of the needs of war, basic research had come almost to a standstill in the United States and partly by the fact that new methods of team research, which had been proved effective during the war, and the growing complexity of experimental equipment had made basic research much more costly than before. The proposals embodied in Bush's report led, among other consequences, to the establishment by an act of Congress of the National Science Foundation in 1951.

As an individual, Bush made numerous contributions, mostly in the fields of applied science and engineering. Beginning in 1930 at the Massachusetts Institute of Technology, he and a team from the Institute's electrical engineering staff developed the differential analyzer, a device for the machine solution of differential equations, ubiquitous in modern science. Applicable to such widely diverse fields as atomic physics and acoustics, the machine could handle as many as 18 independent variables simultaneously, and was a forerunner of later analog and digital computing devices. Bush was also responsible for the "Rapid Selector," which he developed in collaboration with Ralph Shaw. This machine was designed to cope with the problem of rapid information retrieval by utilizing microfilm. Using a photoelectric scanner, the machine could recognize a specific item on the film on the basis of a binary visual code, devised by Bush and Shaw, which was printed on the edge of the film. Although the "Rapid Selector" did not receive wide use, it did much to stimulate interest in the basic problems of information retrieval. Among Bush's other productions were the justifying typewriter, which automatically spaced copy so that both margins were even; the network analyzer, developed in the late 1920s, which could reproduce large electrical networks in miniature and simulate their performance under stress; gaseous conduction devices; and cathode arrangements and coatings for grid-controlled arcs.

Son of a clergyman, Bush received his B.S. and M.S. from Tufts College in 1913. He was granted his D.Eng. simultaneously by Harvard University and the Massachusetts Institute of Technology in 1916. After employment with the General Electric Company in 1913 and the U.S. Navy in 1914, Bush taught at Tufts College from 1914 to 1917. During World War I he did research in submarine detection for the Navy. In 1919 he returned to MIT as associate professor of electric power transmission and became pro-

fessor in 1923; he was appointed vice-president of the Institute and dean of the School of Engineering in 1932. Bush was elected president of the Carnegie Institution of Washington in 1938, a position he held until his retirement in 1955. He was chairman of the National Advisory Committee for Aeronautics in 1938–39. In 1940 he became chairman of the National Defense Research Committee, and from 1941 to 1947 directed the OSRD. He was chairman of the Joint Reseach and Development Board of the War and Navy departments in 1946, chairman of the Research and Development Board of the National Military Establishment in 1947–48, and later became honorary chairman of the Corporation, MIT. Granted many awards and some two dozen honorary degrees, he received the National Medal of Science in 1964.

Bush wrote *Operational Circuit Analysis* (1929), *Endless Horizon* (1946), a collection of papers and addresses, and *Modern Arms and Free Men* (1949).

For background information *see* DIFFERENTIAL ANALYZER; NUMBER SYSTEMS; RADAR in the McGraw-Hill Encyclopedia of Science and Technology.   □

★ BUSIGNIES, Henri Gaston

American engineer
Born Dec. 29, 1905, Sceaux, France

WHEN BUSIGNIES was 21, he invented the Hertzian compass, later known as the airborne radio compass. When tuned to a radio station, the radio compass needle indicates directly on a 360° scale the bearing of that radio station. This function was achieved first by the measurement of a ratio of signal amplitude between two fixed-cross receiving loops combined with antennas, and later by comparing the phase of the envelope output signal of a loop rotating at 5 or 10 turns per second with a fixed phase signal generated locally. This was the first continuously rotating directive antenna, later followed by rotating radar antennas. Shortly thereafter, in 1928, he joined the International Telephone and Telegraph Corporation (ITT) in Paris and developed some industrial models of the radio compass, as well as ship and land radio direction finders.

He then studied wave propagation (at first below 100 MHz) to the point where he developed a feel for what happens to an electromagnetic field and its magnetic and electric vectors in any situation, near long and short conductors, metal plates, good or poor conductors, ships, soil, and bodies of water of various conductivities. He calculated reflections and distortions and measured them experimentally, with the result that he developed his special feel for the subject. This familiarity helped him considerably in the design of accurate direction finders in the high-frequency range (3–30 MHz), which could be used for the detection of radio transmission from tanks, ships, and submarines. In the meantime the airborne radio compass design was perfected and was ready for application to airline or military aircraft. In 1937 he flew his radio compass on the United Airlines Flight Research Plane across the United States and observed the reflections of the beams of the radio beacons by mountains, and some errors introduced by the loop type of radio beacon transmitters (which were subsequently all replaced by vertical-antenna radio beacons). The mountain effects on the radio signals observed by radio compass were analyzed and described for the first time in a paper published in *Electrical Communication* in 1938. It was shown later that integration of the variations of bearings as a function of airplane displacement decreased error many times. An equivalent effect of error reduction by integration was proposed by the transmission of a wider spectrum, instead of a single frequency or a very limited spectrum. This research became the basis for the analysis of the behavior of various kinds of directive antenna systems to best discriminate between main and reflected waves and to avoid polarization errors. This resulted also in his first suggestions for Doppler-effect direction finders and navigation systems.

A serious problem in all receiving antennas used for high- and medium-frequency direction finders is the reradiation of energy by the conductors connecting the antenna or by the shield used to prevent these conductors from picking up energy directly. This reradiation causes "polarization errors," which happen when the wave, without changing its direction of propagation, changes from vertical to horizontal polarization, generally picked up by the feeder conductors or their shields. By placing the feeder cables of antennas at 90° from their orthodox position and then connecting these antennas

together or to the receiving equipment through a long rectangle of cables placed horizontally on the ground, the polarization errors were considerably reduced and the requirement for very large ground mats eliminated.

The first phase of World War II found Busignies with more than 10 years of experience in wave propagation and polarization effects, a strong knowledge of the ionosphere E and F layers, and experience in designing radio direction finders up to and including very high frequencies. He then thought that for the high-frequency (hf) range (that is, shortwave) the display of the bearing observed should be instantaneous (for instance, on a cathode-ray tube) for two very important reasons. First, the variations of polarization and fading could induce changes of signal intensity and bearing which, when observed continuously, would disclose more easily the most correct reading. Second, he realized that in military applications the enemy could decide to transmit extremely short messages to avoid detection. He then designed an instantaneous cathode-ray-tube bearing indicator, which is still in use over 25 years later. The bearing display shows as a sharp propeller-type pattern on a 360° scale; the eye can integrate and read this display very rapidly. This indicator was available in 1940 and he knew how to design a direction antenna system to use with it in the hf band.

When he joined ITT in the United States in late 1940, Busignies proposed to the U.S. Navy the development of hf direction finders to detect the position of enemy submarines; these finders were superior to any others because of the low polarization error and the instantaneous display. Early in 1941 the Navy responded with a development contract, which resulted in accurate and instantaneous hf/df (high-frequency direction finders, later called "Huff Duff"), which were installed throughout the world to detect enemy transmission. The Huff Duff system was credited, together with radar and sonar, with the winning of the battle of the Atlantic in 1942–43. For this work Busignies received the Presidential Certificate of Merit from President Truman in 1945. In the meantime the U.S. Army had asked for a transportable version of the Huff Duff, which became the SCR-291 and SCR-502, used to guide airplanes before loran was available. More than 1500 of these direction finders were used throughout the world. The Huff Duff was installed on aircraft carriers and destroyers, and the efficiency of the systems was described in several books and documents.

In France Busignies had also been working on radar problems. He directed the antenna and receiver development of the radar installed to protect the French base of Toulon in the Mediterranean; the system proved successful in 1941.

He decided that a considerable improvement of ordinary radar would be the elimination of all the fixed echoes caused by buildings, mountains, stacks, power and other lines, and other reflectors of radio energy, which prevented the observation of airplanes at all distances where these echoes were observed. Most of the time these fixed radar echoes were much stronger than the echoes from the airplanes, and covered large areas. He then invented MTI (moving target indicator) radar, using a coherent oscillator to produce the radar radio-frequency pulses. In this system, from one pulse to the next the airplane moves in space and the radio frequency changes phase (frequency-shift Doppler effect), while the phase of successive coherent pulses coming from fixed obstacles is quite the same because of the coherence of radio-frequency pulses. Every other pulse is received and delayed (in a delay line) for the time of a cycle of the recurrence frequency of the radar pulses, and then is opposed to the first pulse. The fixed echoes are eliminated because of the phase coherence, the moving aircraft echoes do not cancel because of the airplane movement, and the aircraft shows up on the radar screen with an improvement of 20–25 decibels with respect to ordinary radar. This system has been used in all surveillance, airport, and many military radars throughout the world and is still in use.

After the war Busignies proposed air navigation systems using radar principles and giving for the first time accurate indications of both distance and direction. A combination of efforts and inventions with the U.S. Navy resulted in the TACAN system, developed at ITT Laboratories under his direction, which became the standard for the United States and the world, and was adopted by all NATO countries. It became a civil aviation system under the name of VORTAC.

In 1959 Busignies proposed synchronous satellites for worldwide communications to the Congressional Committee on Space and Aeronautics. At the time many systems involving lower orbits had been proposed. The synchronous satellite is now the system used over the Atlantic and Pacific oceans.

Busignies received a degree in electrical engineering from the Institut Normal Electrotechnique in Paris in 1926. Joining the International Telephone and Telegraph Corporation in Paris in 1928, he moved to the United States in 1941 and became president of ITT's laboratories division in 1958 and vice-president and general technical director of ITT in 1960. In 1959 he received the Pioneer Award of the IRE professional group on Aeronautical and Navigational Electronics for the invention of the radio compass. In 1964 he received the Institute of Electrical and Electronic Engineers' David Sarnoff

Award. In 1966 he was elected to the National Academy of Engineering. Busignies was issued 140 patents.

For background information *see* Antenna (aerial); Communications satellite; Direction-finding equipment; Navigation systems, electronic; Radar in the McGraw-Hill Encyclopedia of Science and Technology.   □

★ BUTENANDT, Adolf

German biochemist
Born Mar. 24, 1903, Bremerhaven-Lehe, Germany

Butenandt began his independent scientific work in 1927 as an assistant at the Chemical Institute of the University of Göttingen, where he received his Ph.D. under the direction of Adolf Windaus with a dissertation on the constitution of rotenone, a botanical insecticide. Windaus, the famous researcher on sterols and vitamin D, proposed to his student Butenandt that he undertake the study of the female sex hormone formed in the ovarian follicle; this hormone later received the internationally recognized name of estrone. It had then become possible, through the test developed by Edgar Allen and E. A. Doisy, to detect estrone and to determine it quantitatively by its estrus-inducing effect on the vagina of rodents.

In 1929 Butenandt succeeded—independently of Doisy in St. Louis—in obtaining estrone in crystalline form from the urine of pregnant women. This success was made possible by cooperation with Walter Schoeller, the research director of Schering A.G., Berlin, who provided the concentrated extracts from pregnancy urine that Butenandt used as starting material for his work on estrone. Later Schoeller also had concentrates prepared from male urine and pig ovaries, which made it possible for Butenandt to extend his investigations to additional sex hormones as well: the male gonadic hormone testosterone and the pregnancy hormone progesterone.

In 1931 Butenandt—still in Göttingen—together with K. Tscherning, isolated the first male sex hormone, androsterone. In 1934 Butenandt, with U. Westphal, succeeded in obtaining the first preparation of progesterone in pure form. In the meantime he had assumed the directorship of the Organic Chemical Institute of the Institute of Technology (Technische Hochschule) in Danzig. His work on the constitution of the three sex hormones was carried out during this stay in Danzig. The close relationship of the hormones with each other and their membership in the steroid series were recognized. Progesterone and testosterone were synthesized, and in 1935 a degradation scheme for cholesterol to the then known steroid hormones was proposed, which is valid to this day. The scheme was finally proven only decades later in many laboratories throughout the world.

With these results Butenandt reached the first goal he had set at the beginning of his research. It was a fortunate accident that the gonadic hormones proved to be related to cholesterol; this had not been anticipated at the beginning of the work. In this way the considerable experience in the field of sterols that was at hand in Windaus's institute could be utilized. The determination of the constitution of estrone and of the subsequently discovered natural estrogens estriol (G. F. Marrian) and estradiol (E. Schwenck; Doisy) also coincided with the formulation of the valid structural formulas of the sterols and bile acids under the initiative of Rosenheim and King. Butenandt succeeded for the first time in preparing identical phenanthrene derivatives from the estrogens and the bile acids, so that the chemistry of the steroids and the sexual hormones mutually fertilized each other.

In 1936 Max Planck called the young professor from Danzig to the Kaiser Wilhelm Society. Butenandt succeeded Carl Neuberg as director of the Kaiser Wilhelm Institute of Biochemistry in Berlin-Dahlem. The events of World War II and the postwar period led to the removal of the Institute to Tübingen (1945–56). It was finally rededicated in 1957 as the Max Planck Institute of Biochemistry in Munich. In Berlin-Dahlem Butenandt brought his investigations of the sex hormones to a close, and with the zoologist Alfred Kühn took up new fields of research, for example, the mode of action of genes and the hormones of insects.

Taking as an example the biosynthesis of the eye pigments of insects as a function of specific genes, it was shown—independently of G. W. Beadle and E. L. Tatum—that individual genes are responsible for the biosynthesis of specific enzymes. It was possible to analyze a chain of genetic activity. The ommochromes, eye pigments of the insects, are formed from tryptophane according to the following scheme: tryptophane → kynurenine → hydroxykynurenine → ommochrome. Each step of the reaction is catalyzed by a specific enzyme, and each enzyme is synthesized as a function of a specific gene. In the ommochromes (xanthommatin, rhodommatin, ommatin D, ommin), representatives of a new class of natural pigments were recognized; they are phenoxazone pigments, which have proven to be widely distributed in the animal kingdom.

In 1953 Butenandt, together with Peter Karlson, succeeded in isolating the first crystalline insect hormone, the chrysalis-forming hormone ecdysone, which was recognized through the investigations of Karlson and W. Hoppe as a close relative of the sex hormones, being a derivative of cholesterol. This was again a great surprise! The chemical investigation of the insect hormones was begun in the expectation of discovering new types of substances, but the successful route led the wanderer back, after almost 35 years, to his first area of research and once more showed the great transformability and significance of the sterol skeleton in the realm of hormones. But in another area Butenandt succeeded in access to a new class of substances—in the area of pheromones, with the example of the sex attractive substance bombykol of the silkworm, *Bombyx mori*. In 1959 Butenandt and E. Hecker were able to report, as the result of 20 years' work, on the isolation of this material from the sacculi laterales, or glands of the hind portion, of the female silkworm. Bombykol was the first representative of this class of substances; it proved to be a hexadecadienol having the structure shown in the formula. It could also be obtained synthetically.

$$CH_3-(CH_2)_2-CH{\underset{cis}{=}}CH$$
$$-CH{\underset{trans}{=}}CH-(CH_2)_8-CH_2OH$$

Butenandt bestowed special love on virus research. The Max Planck Institute for Virus Research in Tübingen is the outgrowth of a center for virus research in Berlin-Dahlem. It has become a research center of international significance in the area of molecular biology.

Butenandt studied chemistry and biology at the universities of Marburg and Göttingen from 1921 to 1927, when he received his Ph.D. from the latter university. In 1931 he became privatdozent at the University of Göttingen and in 1933 associate professor at the Technical Institute of the Free State of Danzig. In 1935 he made an orientation trip to universities in the United States and Canada at the invitation of the Rockefeller Foundation, which was of great value for his later researches. In 1936 Butenandt became director of the Kaiser Wilhelm Institute of Biochemistry, which since 1949 has carried the name of Max Planck Institute of Biochemistry, after the Kaiser Wilhelm Society was renamed the Max Planck Society. In 1936–45 Butenandt was honorary professor at the University of Berlin, in 1945–46 he was professor of physiological chemistry at the University of Tübingen, and in 1956 he became professor of physiological chemistry at the University of Munich. For his work in the field of sex hormones Butenandt received the Nobel Prize in chemistry in 1939. In 1960 he was elected president of the Max Planck Society for the Advancement of Science, succeeding Otto Hahn.

For background information *see* ESTROGEN; HORMONE; PROGESTERONE; STEROID in the McGraw-Hill Encyclopedia of Science and Technology.   □

★ BYERLY, Perry

American geophysicist
Born May 28, 1897, Clarinda, Iowa, U.S.A.

IN 1923 Byerly, then a graduate student in physics at the University of California, entered the field of seismology at the suggestion of professors James B. Macelwane, S.J., and Andrew C. Lawson. He took charge of the university's two seismographic stations at Berkeley and Mount Hamilton in 1925. When he became director emeritus in 1963, there were 20 stations in the network. George D. Louderback was chairman of the department of geological sciences during the early years of Byerly's tenure and influenced him considerably. Since the state of California supported the stations, Byerly conceived his first duty to be the maintenance of a close watch on northern California earthquakes, both by seismometric instrumentation (epicenters) and by field observations (intensities). The same type of service for southern California was being developed by Harry O. Wood at the California Institute of Technology.

Byerly was concerned that epicenters located in Monterey and San Luis Obispo counties did not lie in the San Andreas Fault zone. In locating these, the east-west control came from the seismograms recorded at Tinemaha and Haiwee (Pasadena network) in the Owens Valley. The Sierran mass lies between. Byerly therefor suspected a delay of P waves under either the San Joaquin Valley or the Sierra Nevada. He established a station at Fresno and was able to show that the delay was under the Sierra Nevada and depended on the length of path under the range. This he interpreted as indicating a low-velocity "root" of the mountains penetrating into the mantle. Such a root had been postulated by Andrew C. Lawson from isostatic considerations. Studying three western United States earthquakes (Montana, Nevada, Texas), Byerly pointed out that the P travel-time curve had an abrupt bend at epicentral distances between 16° and 20°. This led to a continuing discussion as to what velocity distribution exists in the upper mantle, and to the sometimes acrimonious debate as to the possible existence of a low-velocity layer. Byerly also pointed out that the travel-time curves of individual earthquakes are best drawn as a series of straight lines with sharp bends or overlapping at certain critical distances (such as the one between 16° and 20°), and that these distances differ from earthquake to earthquake so that an averaged curve for many shocks loses the sharp discontinuity of slope. This suggests a discretely layered mantle. Such an idea proved unacceptable for many years but is now beginning to be considered.

Byerly became interested in the phase of the first motion of the P wave as a function of distance and direction from the source after reading an early paper by Sommeville. Byerly was the first to introduce a transform which allowed the use of seismograms of distant earthquakes as well as nearby records to compute the nature of the forces at the source of the earthquake from the direction of first motion. A number of his students further developed these methods in their doctoral theses. He also had a continued interest in the use of seismograms to interpret the surface structure of the Earth; and he was the first to study the crustal layering in North America from earthquake records. His treatment of the hinged pendulum seismograph, along with his discussion of the magnitudes of the various terms always neglected, was the first of its kind.

As the only geophysicist in a department of geologists, Byerly relied heavily on discussions with his students. These discussions were very lively, and not a matter of the professor speaking *ex cathedra*. Training students was his greatest pride. He was often called a "philosopher" because of his approach, and he did not feel that there was any finality in the conclusions drawn from scientific observations, such as the interpretations of crustal structures from seismograms.

Byerly moved from Iowa to California when 8 years old. His degrees (A.B., M.A., Ph.D., and LL.D.) were received from the University of California. He was secretary of the Seismological Society of America for 27 years, and later president and honorary member. He served as president of the International Association of Seismology and Physics of the Earth's Interior. He was elected to the National Academy of Sciences in 1946 and to the American Academy of Arts and Sciences in 1960.

For background information *see* EARTHQUAKE; SEISMOLOGY in the McGraw-Hill Encyclopedia of Science and Technology.   □

★ BYERS, Horace Robert

American meteorologist
Born Mar. 12, 1906, Seattle, Wash., U.S.A.

BYERS'S CAREER illustrates the effectiveness of team research, especially in the years since World War II when large government-sponsored programs have been mounted to solve some of the most pressing problems of the Earth's atmosphere. His best-known accomplishment was in exploring the inner workings of thunderstorms through a large project involving several government agencies from 1945 to 1949.

In a prewar study covering a network of reporting stations, Byers noted a sequence of events with the passage of thunderstorms that gave new clues to how the air circulated and how heat was exchanged within these storms. After the war, when personnel and equipment became available, a major attack on this problem was started jointly by the U.S. Weather Bureau, Air Force, Navy, NACA (predecessor of NASA), and the University of Chicago, all

under Byers's direction. By that time instrument flying had reached a stage where it was possible to fly through thunderstorms, and Byers organized flights with up to five airplanes penetrating the storms simultaneously at five different levels. Flown by Air Force pilots and equipped with instruments for a variety of measurements, these planes gave information that, when combined with observations from surface observing networks, radars, balloon soundings, and special equipment, revealed for the first time the true nature of thunderstorm circulations and thermodynamics. The data, collected and analyzed under Byers's direction by such presently well-known meteorologists as R. R. Braham, Jr., L. J. Battan, R. D. Coons, Harry Moses, Bernice Ackerman, and F. D. White, emphasized the importance of the downdraft. Previous models of thunderstorm circulation had either omitted the downdraft entirely or had granted it only a negligible role in the main convection motions of the storm. The most violent aspects—the heaviest rain, most frequent lightning, strongest and gustiest winds, sharpest temperature drops, and most striking pressure changes—were found by Byers and his team to be associated with the downdraft. The air was shown to be accelerated in its downward plunge by the negative buoyancy caused by cooling in evaporating rain. In a practical sense, the results showed how and under what circumstances flights in thunderstorms can be made. Thunderstorm flying was lifted from the folklore of the ready room to a scientifically based technique. The use of radar for this purpose was demonstrated, while new radar circuitry for this application was being developed by David Atlas in his association with the group. Present-day aircraft radar and the technique of its use evolved from these first steps.

Reassembling some of the leaders of his team and several new scientists and graduate students at the University of Chicago, Byers then turned his attention to the microphysics of convective clouds. He sought to discover how the cloud particles grow to precipitation sizes under a variety of conditions and how the circulation of air and the phase changes of water interact. This work was stimulated by the discoveries of Irving Langmuir, V. J. Schaefer, and Bernard Vonnegut that clouds could be artificially nucleated to increase or produce rainfall.

Another aspect studied further was the question of how lightning develops, a question which had not been clearly answered by the thunderstorm project, as had been hoped. With D. R. Fitzgerald, Byers scheduled flights in and around convective clouds with carefully calibrated instrument systems for measuring electrical effects. The data verified the theory that the electricity was generated by the formation of precipitation particles, often in the presence of ice in some form. However, other methods of charge generation continued to be advocated by others.

The team, which included Braham, Battan, Ackerman, and Fitzgerald, was augmented by E. W. Barrett, J. P. Lodge, Guy Goyer, and J. E. McDonald and later by T. R. Hoffer, L. R. Koenig, Motoi Kumai, Ottavio Vittori, Yoshiaki Toba, Ulrich Katz, and others. It devoted its attention to almost every aspect of the microphysics and chemistry of clouds, and the University of Chicago became one of the leading centers of cloud physics study. Again, planes were flown as the principal probing platforms, using unique instruments and sampling devices, while laboratory and theoretical investigations disclosed new properties and characteristics of cloud nucleants, rain, snow, and ice. Numerous discoveries emanated from the Chicago group to establish facts on which cloud science throughout the world has drawn heavily.

During this period Byers also became interested in meteorology in the mesoscale, that scale between roughly 10 and 100 mi, in which severe local storms act. He arranged to have Tetsuya Fujita come to Chicago from Japan to lead a subgroup in that study. This project grew into a large undertaking involving also interpretation and study of satellite information. When Byers left Chicago in 1965 to become dean of the college of geosciences at Texas A & M University, the direction of the Cloud Physics Laboratory was assumed by Braham.

Not all of Byers's research and scientific publications were performed in team efforts. As an individual, he achieved and published research results in several areas, ranging from local studies of fogs to thermodynamics of the large circulations of the atmosphere.

Byers received most of his schooling in Berkeley, where he graduated from the University of California (B.S., 1929). He then received a fellowship in meteorology at the Massachusetts Institute of Technology; he studied under C.-G. Rossby for 6 years, with interruptions, receiving an M.S. in 1932 and Sc.D. in 1935. His first permanent position was in the U.S. Weather Bureau in Washington, where he led a group, including Harry Wexler, in the introduction of the new Norwegian methods of weather analysis and forecasting. They also studied the upper air from airplane and radiosonde observations, which were then becoming available in quantity. In 1940 he accepted a position as associate professor at the University of Chicago, and with Rossby helped form a new department of meteorology. He became a full professor in 1944 and succeeded Rossby as chairman of the department in 1948, holding the post until 1960. He moved to Texas A & M University in 1965 to help that institution build toward excellence in the geosciences. Byers was elected to the National Academy of Sciences in 1952. He served as president of the American Meteorological Society in 1952–53; president of the Section of Meteorology, American Geophysical Union in 1947–49; and president of the International Association of Meteorology and Atmospheric Physics in 1960–63. Honors accorded him include the Robert M. Losey Award, American Institute of Aeronautics and Astronautics; Charles F. Brooks Award, American Meteorological Society; and Award of Merit, Chicago Technical Societies Council.

Byers wrote *General Meteorology* (1937; 3d ed. 1959) and *Elements of Cloud Physics* (1965).

For background information *see* CLOUD PHYSICS; LIGHTNING; METEOROLOGY; THUNDERSTORM; WEATHER (FORECASTING AND PREDICTION) in the McGraw-Hill Encyclopedia of Science and Technology.   □

★ CARMICHAEL, Leonard

*American psychologist and student of animal
 behavior*
Born Nov. 9, 1898, Philadelphia, Pa., U.S.A.

CARMICHAEL DEVELOPED techniques for the
study of the development of behavior in
fetal organisms and contributed to the understanding of behavior changes resulting from
maturation rather than individual learning. He
used electrophysiological techniques in the study
of the mechanisms underlying behavior. With an
associate he was the first American to record
human electroencephalograms and to study their
production and interpretation.

His early experiments demonstrated that the
embryos of the frog (*Rana sylvatica*) and the
salamander (*Amblystoma punctatum*) could be
reared in a solution of chloretone, in which
morphological growth continues but in which
bodily movement does not occur. When control
animals demonstrated coordinated swimming
movements, the experimental animals were
placed in water free of the anesthetic. In less
than 12 min, on the average, animals that had
not previously moved were swimming as well as
the control animals. This could be interpreted as
demonstrating that some complex adaptive behavior depends on the genetic code and a standard environment and not on individual habit
formation.

Later Carmichael was able to describe the
prenatal development of behavior in a number of
mammals. His monograph on the experimental
study of the fetal guinea pig traced the origin
and development of reflexes and complex patterns of behavior during the total prenatal
period. He devised techniques for maintaining
mammalian fetal organisms under relatively normal conditions while behavior is studied. He
showed that, prior to the onset of responses

related to receptor stimulation, muscles can be
made to respond to direct stimulation.

His study of fetal guinea pigs can be taken as
developing facts that are typical of many other
mammals as well. Active behavior in the prenatal guinea pig begins in the last hour of the
25th postinsemination day. Neck flexion and
forelimb movements are the first responses
noted. This fetus exists during its active prenatal
period of about 68 days in a condition much like
that of an astronaut in space. It is an essentially
weightless organism in its liquid environment.
This allows the animal to demonstrate coordinated responses that are not typical immediately
after birth, when the newborn organism exists in
a gravitational field and in an environment characterized by normal external physical energies.

During fetal life the patterns of behavior
released by the stimulation of specific receptor
areas remain surprisingly constant. What has
been called Carmichael's law states that anatomical behavior mechanisms may be elicited by
experimental means at a time prior to that when
the normal action of these patterns of behavior
is essential in the adaptive life of the organism.
He showed the relevance of these observations to
an understanding of various psychological processes—for example, perceptual phenomena. He
also published research on the postnatal maturation of specific behavior systems, such as the air-
writing reflex of falling animals.

Electrophysiological techniques were employed by Carmichael and his associates in the
study of the development of responses. For example, they studied the ontogeny of cerebral
electrical potentials in the fetal guinea pig. They
demonstrated that at 42 postinsemination days
the electrical cochlear effect could be recorded.
This is the same time in development that the
operatively removed guinea pig fetuses first respond to airborne auditory stimuli.

In other behavior studies Carmichael used
electrophysiological techniques. He and H. H.
Jasper were the first American investigators to
record human electroencephalograms. This
work, first done in 1934 and published in 1935,
confirmed the work of Hans Berger in Germany.
He and Jasper also described new electroencephalographic phenomena.

Carmichael adapted an electrical technique
for the recording of eye movements to the study
of reading and other visual tasks. This method
was later used in an elaborate experimental
study, conducted jointly with W. F. Dearborn,
that led to a book, *Reading and Visual Fatigue*
(1947). This study demonstrated that subjects
could read continuously for 6 hr from a book or
from microfilm without fatigue. Other investigations of Carmichael dealt with certain phenomena of learning in rats and other mammals;

motor processes related to handedness and the effect of language on perception; and special problems related to the training of Naval aviators.

Carmichael's father was a physician and his mother, before her marriage, was a teacher of psychology. He received his B.S. summa cum laude from Tufts College in 1921 and his Ph.D. from Harvard University in 1924. After teaching at Princeton University from 1924 to 1927 and at Brown University from 1927 to 1936, he was dean and professor of psychology at the University of Rochester from 1936 to 1938. From 1938 to 1952 he was president of Tufts University and director of its Laboratory of Sensory Physiology and Psychology. During World War II he was director of the National Roster of Scientific and Specialized Personnel in Washington; while continuing his duties as president of Tufts, he directed the Roster's 400 workers, who mobilized America's scientists and engineers for the war effort. From 1953 to 1964 he was secretary (administrative head) of the Smithsonian Institution. In 1964 he became vice-president for research exploration of the National Geographic Society. He was president of the American Psychological Association in 1940 and later became president of the International Primatological Society and of the section of Psychology and Animal Behavior of the International Union of Biological Sciences. Carmichael received a number of American and foreign awards. He was elected to the American Philosophical Society in 1942 and to the National Academy of Sciences in 1943.

Carmichael wrote many papers and was author of *The Making of the Modern Mind* (1956) and *Basic Psychology* (1957). He edited and contributed to *The Manual of Child Psychology* (1946; 2d ed. 1954).

For background information *see* BEHAVIOR, ONTOGENY OF; ELECTROENCEPHALOGRAPHY in the McGraw-Hill Encyclopedia of Science and Technology.   □

★ CHARGAFF, Erwin

American biochemist
Born Aug. 11, 1905, Austria

T RAINED AS a chemist, Chargaff was attracted early to the application of chemistry to the life sciences; the living cell remained at the center of his scientific interests. He liked to consider his profession as a branch of natural philosophy and himself as a remnant of an extinct species, the naturalist.

He ranged widely over many fields of biochemistry. In the beginning of his career he concerned himself particularly with the complex lipids of microorganisms and participated in the discovery of unusual fatty acids and waxes in the acid-fast mycobacteria (a group comprising the tubercle bacillus), the diphtheria bacteria, and so on. This led him to more diversified studies of the metabolism and the biological role of tissue lipids and, especially, of the lipid-containing conjugated proteins, the lipoproteins, about which he wrote one of the first reviews. He devoted much effort to investigation of the biochemistry of blood coagulation and to elucidation of the pivotal catalyst in this reaction, the thromboplastic protein. He was among the first to use the radioactive isotope of phosphorus in studies of phospholipid metabolism, and published the first paper on the synthesis of a radioactive organic compound, namely, a-glycerophosphoric acid. Other studies undertaken at about the same time concerned the biological oxidation of hydroxyamino acids and of cyclohexitols, such as the inositols.

The great caesura in Chargaff's scientific endeavors occurred in 1944, when O. T. Avery and collaborators showed that the principle active in microbial transformation was a deoxyribonucleic acid (DNA). This discovery made a deep impression on Chargaff, as it was evident to him that this meant that DNA was the principal, or perhaps the sole, operative constituent of the genes. At that time there did not yet exist a biochemistry of heredity. Brought up as he was, in common with his entire generation, with the notion that DNA was an unspecific aggregate of a few "tetranucleotides," a mere coat hanger for the all-important proteins, the demonstration that a DNA could confer new and inheritable properties to a cell meant to him that there must

exist many different DNA molecules, varying in chemical structure and composition. He set himself the task of testing this proposition.

By a happy coincidence, at about that time the

separation of minute amounts of amino acids by partition chromatography on filter paper had been described as a qualitative procedure, and photoelectric ultraviolet spectrophotometers had become available commercially. Since the nitrogenous constituents of the nucleic acids, the purines and pyrimidines, stand out by a very high and characteristic absorption of ultraviolet light, the combination of methods using paper chromatography and ultraviolet absorption made possible for the first time the precise estimation of nucleic acid composition. When DNA preparations of many different cellular species were isolated and studied with respect to their base composition, it became clear that DNA is a generic term covering a vast multitude of different macromolecules, widely differing in the proportions of the constituents. The tetranucleotide hypothesis was shown to be incorrect; it was demonstrated that DNA was in its composition characteristic of the species, though constant in different organs of the same organism. It became no exaggeration to state that there exist at least as many different DNA molecules as there are different species.

When Chargaff reviewed the results on the composition of DNA obtained in his laboratory, a remarkable generalization emerged, which became known as the base-pairing rules in DNA. These state that, despite far-reaching divergences in the proportions of their nitrogenous constituents, all DNA varieties exhibit the following regularities: (a) purines (adenine + guanine) equal pyrimidines (cytosine + thymine); (b) adenine equals thymine; (c) guanine equals cytosine; (d) 6-amino nucleotides (adenylic + cytidylic acids) equal 6-keto nucleotides (guanylic + thymidylic acids). These relationships, first pointed out in 1950, have not been without influence on modern biological thought.

As it is not improbable that the primary structure of DNA, that is, the specific sequence of its nucleotide constituents, carries the biological information often designated as the "genetic code," the importance of studies on the nucleotide sequence of the nucleic acids is evident. Much effort was devoted to this problem by Chargaff and his colleagues. The general interests of his laboratory were best described in the title of the Jesup Lectures that he gave in 1959 at Columbia University: "Chemical Aspects of Biological Specificity."

Chargaff was educated in Vienna at the Maximiliansgymnasium and the University of Vienna. He carried out his doctoral research under the direction of Fritz Feigl in Späth's Institute and received the Dr.Phil. in 1928. His second teacher was Rudolph J. Anderson at Yale University, with whom he worked from 1928 to 1930. He was assistant at the University of Berlin in 1930–33, followed by nearly 2 years in Calmette's laboratory at the Pasteur Institute in Paris. In 1935 he went to Columbia University, where he became professor of biochemistry in 1952. He received the Pasteur Medal in 1949, the Neuberg Medal in 1958, the Charles Léopold Mayer Prize of the French Academy of Sciences in 1963, the H. P. Heineken Prize of the Netherlands Academy of Sciences in 1964, and the Bertner Foundation Award in 1965. He was elected to the American Academy of Arts and Sciences in 1961, to the National Academy of Sciences in 1965, and as a foreign member of the Royal Physiographic Society in Lund in 1959.

Chargaff edited, with J. N. Davidson, *The Nucleic Acids* (3 vols., 1955, 1960) and wrote *Essays on Nucleic Acids* (1963).

For background information *see* DEOXYRIBONUCLEIC ACID; LIPID METABOLISM; NUCLEIC ACID in the McGraw-Hill Encyclopedia of Science and Technology.   □

★ CHEADLE, Vernon Irvin

American botanist
Born Feb. 6, 1910, Salem, S. Dak., U.S.A.

CHEADLE'S RESEARCH for the Ph.D. at Harvard University concerned anatomical differences between the monocotyledon families Liliaceae and Amaryllidaceae. These families were thought to differ principally in the position of the ovary in relation to other parts of the flower. The investigation was to determine whether the families could be separated on structural grounds. The research did not settle that problem but led to a wide variety of others. Cheadle chose the xylem (water-conducting tissue) and phloem (food-conducting tissue) for further study because of their importance in the welfare of land plants and their wide range of variability. The literature and thesis research confirmed how scanty was the knowledge of these tissues in the monocotyledons as a whole.

In 1936 Cheadle received a scholarship from Harvard's famous naturalist Thomas Barbour to collect plants in Cuba as a project of the Atkins Institute of the Arnold Arboretum of Harvard University. This provided him with the initial impetus to study phloem and xylem in a broad representation of monocotyledons. Later collecting trips took him over much of the United States and to Australia and South Africa. Research on these collections provided an exposition of evolutionary trends in the structure of conducting cells. Later work on other plants emphasized ultrastructure as revealed by electron microscopy.

Cheadle had given less attention to the phloem, but his early research did make clear, for example, that sieve-tube members (sieve elements) having end walls transversely placed with uniformly distributed pores are specialized, while those with oblique end walls and pores not uniformly distributed are primitive. These differences are correlated with differences in the appearance of phloem as seen in transections of vascular bundles in the shoot system. Phloem with primitive sieve-tube members has an irregular appearance because of variations in diameter of these members; phloem with specialized sieve-tube members is regular in appearance because of their uniformity of diameter. Evolutionary specialization of sieve-tube members began in the leaves and then occurred successively downward into the roots.

Cheadle's studies of xylem showed that the most evident features of primitive vessel members in the monocotyledons are great length and oblique end walls having many perforations. In contrast, highly evolved vessel members are short and have transversely placed end walls with a single perforation. All variations between these two extremes occur in the monocotyledons as a whole, and may be placed in an evolutionary sequence that seems clearly unidirectional. Study of vessels throughout the plants, in hundreds of species from most families of the monocotyledons, showed that vessels originated from tracheids in the roots and then successively developed upward in the plant. In every organ the vessels originated similarly in the latest-formed metaxylem, then in the earlier-formed metaxylem, and finally in protoxylem. Specialization of vessel members occurred in the same sequence throughout the plant and within the xylem of each organ. The specializations of xylem in the shoot system are generally correlated with the appearance of the xylem of vascular bundles, as seen in transections of the stems and leaves. For example, the highly specialized

bundles in corn have two large vessels, one at each side, separated by smaller cells. The bundles of a lily stem similarly seen have numerous tracheids of nearly uniform size. So clear is this series of developments that from study of a stem, one can predict with a high degree of accuracy the limits of specialization elsewhere in the plant. It is physiologically plausible that sieve-tube members specialize first in the leaves and thence downward, whereas the opposite is true of vessel members, for foods are elaborated principally in the leaves and migrate downward in the plant, while water and dissolved salts move into the roots and thence upward to the leaves.

The taxonomic implications of Cheadle's conclusions about tracheary elements are being utilized in discussions of possible relationships within the monocotyledons, and between them and the dicotyledons. Within certain limits, this projection can be done with a high degree of confidence because of the unidirectional evolution of such elements. Thus, present-day species with highly specialized tracheary elements could not have been progenitors of current species that have less specialized, or indeed primitive, tracheary elements. This negation of what otherwise might seem plausible relationships is especially useful. The level of tracheary specialization is much less valuable in determining positive relationships, and in this positive sense is useful only in combination with many other characters.

In 1950 Cheadle began a close association with Professor Katherine Esau at the University of California, Davis (and later at Santa Barbara). He spent a sabbatical year at Davis studying the bark of trees and found this new interest so attractive that he transferred from Rhode Island. A collaboration with Esau on studies of secondary phloem led to a series of papers on comparative structure in a large number of families in the dicotyledons, and on critically detailed analyses of this tissue in Calycanthaceae and *Liriodendron*. The papers clarified many debatable points and also isolated problems for solution. Electron microscopy is now greatly increasing information on the ultrastructure, ontogeny, and, by inference, functioning of sieve elements and their closely associated parenchyma cells. Development of xylem cells is similarly being studied. Confidence in the recognition of ultrastructural details and in the conclusions derived from study of them proved to be greatly enhanced by experience gained earlier in the study of variously prepared tissues and cells by light microscopy.

Cheadle spent a year at South Dakota State College and then went with his botany professor A. T. Evans to Miami University (Ohio), where he received his A.B. in 1932. He then went to Harvard University, where he earned an M.A. in 1934 and a Ph.D. in biology and botany in 1936. For 16 years he held a variety of positions at the University of Rhode Island (leaving for 2 years to serve in the Navy). In 1952 he became professor and chairman of the botany department and botanist in the Experiment Station at the University of California, Davis. In 1962 he became professor of botany and chancellor of the University of California, Santa Barbara. Elected to the American Academy of Arts and Sciences in 1956, Cheadle received a Merit Award of the Botanical Society of America in 1963.

For background information *see* PHLOEM; XYLEM in the McGraw-Hill Encyclopedia of Science and Technology.   □

★ CHEW, Geoffrey Foucar

American theoretical physicist
Born June 5, 1924, Washington, D.C., U.S.A.

DURING AN extended theoretical investigation of the strong short-range force between nuclear particles (hadrons), Chew and his co-workers were led in 1961 to make the "bootstrap" hypothesis. It proposes that no hadron is elementary, but each is a composite of other hadrons held together by forces arising from the exchange of still other hadrons. This hypothesis abandons the notion of fundamental "pointlike" constituents of matter and is correspondingly awkward to formulate within a subnuclear space-time continuum. As an alternative to the traditional space-time basis for nuclear dynamics, Chew and his collaborators employed the analytic matrix of hadron-scattering amplitudes, the so-called S matrix. It was argued that a particular boundary condition on the S matrix, usually described as "Regge asymptotic behavior," should be taken as the mathematical definition of the bootstrap. There subsequently developed

sufficient experimental verification of the bootstrap concept and the related Regge boundary condition to make this hypothesis a major subject of research in particle physics.

Chew's initial investigations, starting in 1952, were carried out within the traditional framework that assumed the nucleon and pi-meson to be elementary particles that are described by time-dependent wave functions satisfying a Schrödinger equation. Earlier, in 1937, Hideki Yukawa had developed a model which ascribed the force between two nucleons to the exchange of pi-mesons. Chew extended Yukawa's reasoning to achieve "force" between nucleon and pi-meson from "exchange" of nucleons, the strength and character of this new force being controlled by the same parameters that determined the nucleon-nucleon force. Using the theoretically predicted force, Chew was able qualitatively to explain the observed behavior of low-energy pions when scattered by nucleons, including the existence of the famous 1240-Mev, spin 3/2 resonance. In Chew's model this unstable particle is regarded as a pion-nucleon composite held together by nucleon exchange, just as in Yukawa's model the deuteron is a nucleon-nucleon composite held together by pion exchange.

In 1954 Francis Low discovered a new dynamical method, which he and Chew, working together at the University of Illinois, used to reformulate Chew's original model to avoid explicit reference to a Schrödinger equation. In the new framework the key role was played by the analytic properties of scattering amplitudes as a function of the energies of scattered particles. It turned out to be unnecessary to consider space-time at the subnuclear level.

The Chew-Low model was incomplete in that it treated the nucleon on a nonrelativistic basis, but in 1958 Stanley Mandelstam discovered that relativistic scattering amplitudes are analytic not only in energy but also in angle variables and that the combined analyticity properties have a dynamical content equivalent to that of the Chew-Low model. Chew and Mandelstam, working together at Berkeley, exploited Mandelstam's discovery to develop a detailed set of fully relativistic dynamical equations, the so-called N/D method, that showed how in principle any composite particle might be described in the same spirit as Chew's original model described the 1240-Mev resonance or Yukawa's model described the deuteron. The dynamical equations involved nothing but elements of the scattering matrix and made no reference to a Schrödinger equation or a Hamiltonian. The concept of "force" appeared as a natural and inevitable consequence of analyticity and Lorentz invariance.

Up to this point Chew had accepted the traditional idea that certain hadrons are elementary and others composite, but the N/D equations made it clear that forces are generated by exchange of any hadrons, whether elementary or composite, stable or unstable. Chew and Mandelstam introduced the term "bootstrap" in 1959 to characterize a model of the rho-meson in which this highly unstable particle is regarded as a composite of two pions *held together by rho exchange*. Such a model does not represent a complete bootstrap because the pions are treated as if elementary, but it was the first model to contain an ingredient of "self-generation."

The idea that all hadrons are equally composite and self-generating finally emerged in 1961 in connection with Regge asymptotic behavior. In 1958 Tullio Regge had deduced the asymptotic structure of nonrelativistic scattering amplitudes, and Mandelstam in 1959 pointed out that such asymptotic behavior, if generally valid, would circumvent an apparent mathematical difficulty in the N/D equations when forces arise from exchange of high-spin composite particles. Working in collaboration, Chew and Steven Frautschi further observed that nuclear reactions at very high energies but with small momentum transfers should be controlled by the so-called "Regge trajectories," which also would determine the masses and spins of composite particles—these latter corresponding to discrete points on trajectories. When Blankenbecler and Goldberger suggested that the nucleon might lie on a Regge trajectory, it suddenly became clear to Chew and Frautschi that within the framework of the analytic S matrix there were no known reasons why *all* hadrons should not lie on trajectories. Such a principle of "nuclear democracy," furthermore, could be formulated quite independently of special models, on which the distinction between elementary and composite particles previously had rested. It was nonetheless reassuring to Chew when he discovered soon afterward, in 1962, that a simple and plausible composite model of the nucleon could in fact be constructed along the same lines as that of the 1240-Mev resonance. Chew's bootstrap model of the nucleon subsequently was generalized by others and applied to a great variety of problems.

Chew gained a B.S. in 1944 at George Washington University, worked at Los Alamos during 1944–46 as an assistant to Edward Teller and Enrico Fermi, and then spent 2 years as a graduate student under Fermi at the University of Chicago, receiving his Ph.D. in 1948. After a year's research at Berkeley he was appointed to the University of California teaching staff, but moved to the University of Illinois in 1950, becoming a full professor there in 1955. In 1957 he returned to Berkeley, where he had joint responsibilities in the physics department and

Lawrence Radiation Laboratory. Chew was elected to the National Academy of Sciences in 1962, and in that same year was awarded the Hughes Prize of the American Physical Society for his work on the pion-nucleon interaction.

Chew wrote *The S-Matrix Theory of Strong Interactions* (1961) and *The Analytic S Matrix: A Basis for Nuclear Democracy* (1966).

For background information *see* ELEMENTARY PARTICLE; SCATTERING EXPERIMENTS, NUCLEAR in the McGraw-Hill Encyclopedia of Science and Technology. ☐

★ CHRISTOPHERS, Sir (Samuel) Rickard

British malariologist
Born Nov. 27, 1873, Liverpool, England

CHRISTOPHERS BECAME known for his work on malaria and for his studies on the systematics, bionomics, and structure of the mosquito. Among his contributions was his early work (1904) on *Leishmania*, the parasite that causes kala-azar, the distribution of which in the body tissues he was the first to describe; for this work he was awarded the Gaspar Medal by the Brazilian government in 1961. He was also the first to describe (1907) the life cycle of *Piroplasma* (*Babesia canis*) in the tick, on the structure of which arthropod he also made an early study. From 1898, however, to 1960, when he published, after some years' work in Cambridge, his monograph *Aedes aegypti: The Yellow Fever Mosquito*, Christophers worked mainly in connection with malaria in its many varied aspects and in related subjects.

Christophers's earliest work on malaria was with I. W. W. Stephens, when appointed to the Malaria Commission of the Royal Society and Colonial Office to carry out research on malaria and blackwater fever in tropical Africa. This research began shortly after Ross's discovery of the mosquito cycle and at a time when the prevalence of these diseases in Europeans in

Africa had become a matter requiring urgent attention. During some 2 years in central and western Africa, followed by a year in India, they established that in tropical Africa and to a varying extent in India malaria was not, as it seemed, mainly a disease of the visiting or resident European; rather, it was almost universally present in children of the indigenous population, leading to immunity in the adult and infection in the European. Stephens and Christophers had failed to trace the source of infection while investigating cases among European engineers and others living in railway construction camps near Lagos. Later in a small village near Accra they saw a native child suffering from an attack of fever and found that all the village children, seemingly quite well, but none of the adults, had parasites in their blood. It soon became clear that this was the usual condition to various degrees in tropical Africa and to some extent in India. The percentage of children showing parasites is now known as the endemic index of an area or child parasite rate of a community and is widely used in many ways, for example, as a guide in carrying out measures of protection.

Christophers carried out his researches on malaria mainly in India after entering the Indian Medical Service. Except for a time on first joining the service, when he worked on the kala-azar parasite and *Piroplasma* in the tick, Christophers until his retirement from India was almost entirely concerned with problems connected with malaria. Important in his many contributions to prevention of malaria in India were his investigations into malaria conditions in different regions, termed "malaria surveys." He studied the spleen and parasite rate and the systematics, structure, and breeding habits of the Indian species of *Anopheles*. On his retirement from India Christophers worked on a Leverhulme grant at the London School of Hygiene and Tropical Medicine; he concentrated first on dissociation constants of antimalarial drugs, determining those for the salts of atebrin (atabrine) and quinine, and later (with J. D. Fulton) on respiratory metabolism of *P. knowlesi*, a malarial parasite of monkeys. At Cambridge during and following World War II, he worked on mosquito repellents to protect troops.

Christophers graduated from University College, Liverpool (now Liverpool University), with an M.B. and a Ch.B. He served on the Malaria Commission of the Royal Society of London and the Colonial Office during 1898–1902 and then entered the Indian Medical Service. He was director of the King Institute of Preventive Medicine, Madras, in 1904–08 and was officer in charge of the Central Malaria Bureau in 1910–16. During 1916–19 he was on the Mesopotamian Expeditionary Force and was director of the Kala-azar Commission in 1924–25. Christophers was director of the Central Research Institute at Kasauli in 1925–32, after which he retired from the Indian Medical Service and returned to England, where he was professor of malaria studies at the University of London in 1932–38. Christophers was awarded the Order of the Indian Empire in 1915 and the Order of the British Empire in 1918. He was knighted in 1931.

For background information *see* HAEMOSPORIDIIDA; MALARIA; MOSQUITO; PARASITOLOGY, MEDICAL in the McGraw-Hill Encyclopedia of Science and Technology.   ☐

★ COCHRAN, William

British physicist
Born July 30, 1922, Newton Mearns, Scotland

IT IS impossible to draw a firm dividing line between crystallography and solid-state physics. Cochran worked in this border region, with incursions into topics as separated as biomolecular structures and the theory of ferroelectricity.

Pyrimidines, purines, nucleosides, and nucleotides are molecules occurring as components of nucleic acid. Cochran's work with others at the Cavendish Laboratory during the late 1940s and the early 1950s helped to determine the exact dimensions and stereochemistry of some of these comparatively simple molecules by using the techniques of x-ray crystallography; in particular, the work demonstrated the importance of hydrogen bonding for intermolecular associations. In collaboration with F. H. Crick, the first conclusive evidence was obtained for the occurrence of a helical molecular structure in nature, that of polymethylglutamate. The principal merit of this work, seen in retrospect, was that it played a part in leading Crick, in association with J. D. Watson, to the discovery of the helical structure of deoxyribonucleic acid (DNA).

The determination of a crystal structure is not

a straightforward matter of measurement of x-ray intensities followed by a routine calculation. While the x-ray measurements give the amplitudes of the terms in a Fourier series for the electron density of the crystal, the phase angle to be associated with each term is not directly measurable. This situation is known to crystallographers as the "phase problem," and Cochran made a number of contributions to the theory of its solution. Attempts, for the most part unsuccessful, were also made in collaboration with A. S. Douglas to solve the problem in particular instances by using one of the first automatic computers, the EDSAC.

Discouraged by lack of progress in this direction and feeling that x-ray crystallography was becoming increasingly the preserve of chemists and biologists, Cochran took a year's leave from his lectureship at Cambridge University to work with B. N. Brockhouse at the Chalk River Laboratories of Atomic Energy of Canada. Brockhouse was at that time pioneering the development of neutron spectroscopy as a means of studying the dynamics of atoms in crystals, and hence of interatomic forces. Cochran joined in this work and continued a long-distance collaboration with the Chalk River group over several years. This work led to an improved understanding of interatomic forces in ionic, covalent, and metallic crystals. Cochran developed the theory of the relation between the lattice dynamics of a crystal and its dielectric properties, and in particular applied the theory to treat the phenomenon of ferroelectricity in terms of crystal stability. The predictions made were later confirmed experimentally by R. A. Cowley for ferroelectric crystals having the barium titanate type of structure, and experiments using the technique of neutron spectroscopy led to the conclusion that materials having an even simpler type of crystal structure—for example, germanium telluride—can be ferroelectric.

Son of a Scottish farmer, Cochran graduated in physics from the University of Edinburgh in 1943. He spent 3 more years in Edinburgh as an assistant lecturer in physics, while working as a research student of C. A. Beevers in the department of chemistry. During 1946–64 he worked in the Cavendish Laboratory, apart from two periods of leave in the United States and Canada, and in 1964 returned to Edinburgh as professor of physics. He was elected a fellow of the Royal Society of London in 1962. He was awarded the Guthrie Medal of the Institute of Physics and the Physical Society in 1966 in recognition of his contributions to x-ray crystallography and to lattice dynamics.

Cochran wrote *The Determination of Crystal Structures*, with H. S. Lipson (1966).

For background information *see* CRYSTAL STRUCTURE; FERROELECTRICS; MOLECULAR BIOPHYSICS; X-RAY CRYSTALLOGRAPHY in the McGraw-Hill Encyclopedia of Science and Technology. □

COCKCROFT, Sir John (Douglas)

British nuclear physicist

Cockcroft died on Sept. 18, 1967, in Cambridge, England. See *McGraw-Hill Modern Men of Science*, Volume I.

★ COHEN, Seymour Stanley

American biochemist
Born Apr. 30, 1917, New York, N.Y., U.S.A.

COHEN STUDIED biochemical events in the multiplication of bacterial viruses or bacteriophages and of bacteria. Indeed, he was the first to begin a systematic biochemical study of bacteriophage multiplication specifically and of virus-cell interactions in general. In 1947 he demonstrated the extensive alteration in nucleic acid metabolism in cells infected by highly virulent viruses, resulting in the shift of synthesis away from polymeric products characteristic of the host to the types of nucleic acid and protein characteristic of the virus. He also introduced the use of radioactive isotopes into this type of study and by their use proved that viral nucleic acid is made after infection from low molecular weight precursors. These initiating studies in cellular pathology produced by viruses stamped certain virus-cell systems as highly favorable materials for the exaggeration of critical and interesting areas of metabolism, such as that of nucleic acid and protein synthesis. This led to the exploitation of these systems by numerous investigators in many directions, of which the discovery of messenger RNA is but one example. By the late 1940s Cohen had also studied the nutritional requirements for virus multiplication and showed how certain amino acid analogs can, in preventing protein synthesis, inhibit critical stages in virus synthesis. These early pioneering studies were recognized in awards of the American Society of Microbiology and the American Academy of Pediatrics in 1951 and 1952.

Cohen received his B.S. at the City College of New York in 1936 and then entered Columbia University. After working with Erwin Chargaff, he received his Ph.D. in biochemistry in 1941 for a dissertation on lipoproteins active in blood coagulation. He began work with viruses almost accidentally, having been appointed a fellow of the National Research Council under a newly established program of the National Foundation for Infantile Paralysis to train workers in virology. He was soon engaged in the isolation, characterization, and degradation of plant viruses in the department of Wendell Stanley at the Rockefeller Institute at Princeton. In this period he observed some curious crystallizations of plant viruses, and he demonstrated for the first time that a ribose nucleic acid, in this instance the nucleic acid of tobacco mosaic virus, is a very large polymer.

Shortly after the United States entered World War II, Cohen returned to Columbia University to undertake a purification of the typhus vaccine. The extension of these studies, which demonstrated interesting physical, chemical, and immunological properties of rickettsial components, brought him to the University of Pennsylvania in 1943. The Children's Hospital of Philadelphia, in which his laboratory was situated, placed him in contact with animal virology through Werner and Brigitte Henle and with bacteriophage through Thomas Anderson. At the end of the war he decided to investigate virus-cell interactions, and he explored the possibilities of study of animal viruses in tissue cultures. Believing that animal virology was not yet ready for this type of biochemistry, he began on the phage systems, in collaboration with Anderson. After learning some of the key biological techniques, he began the study of patterns of polymer biosynthesis in infected bacteria.

Despite the initial striking results of this study, it was clear that a knowledge of bacterial physiology would be important in dissecting the biochemical events in phage multiplication. To begin to develop this knowledge, he went to Paris in 1947 and 1948 to work with A. Lwoff and J. Monod at the Pasteur Institute. After returning to the Children's Hospital, Cohen focused on an analysis of possible branch points in sugar metabolism in the host bacterium, *Escherichia coli*, as a possible approach to the redirection of nucleic acid metabolism produced by virus infection. At that time only a single pathway of glucose metabolism, that of anaerobic glycolysis, was believed to be of functional significance. In these studies, Cohen detected, in collaboration with D. B. McNair Scott, the existence of an enzymatic oxidative

pathway for the conversion of glucose phosphate to ribose phosphate. He was also the first to use isotopic glucose to determine the relative utilization of sugar by an anaerobic route versus an oxidative pathway. These methods, with some modern improvements, are widely used today. By 1951 he had shown by this approach that virus infection actually affects the balance in these paths.

In 1952 he began the study of the composition of bacteriophage nucleic acids, in collaboration with G. R. Wyatt. This work led to the detection, isolation, and characterization of the first unique viral component, a previously unknown pyrimidine, 5-hydroxymethylcytosine. This unusual compound, absent from bacterial nucleic acids, pointed to the existence of new types of enzymes in virus-infected cells, that is, of enzymes synthesized in response to infection. In a series of studies of the metabolic origins of the new viral pyrimidine, Cohen and Barner demonstrated that a cell which is unable to synthesize the normal pyrimidine, thymine, acquires this ability after virus infection. In 1957, in collaboration with J. Flaks, he demonstrated the existence of several virus-induced enzymes which are capable of making both of these pyrimidines and whose synthesis is determined by the virus nucleic acid. These studies showed that a virus not only can shift the host's enzymes to synthesis of new polymers but compels the production of new enzymes, of new metabolic machinery to facilitate the production of viral components.

The study of the synthesis of virus-induced enzymes demonstrated numerous controls of such synthesis. The work of his laboratory showed that production of new types of ribose nucleic acid are essential to the appearance of "early" virus-induced enzymes; the enzymatic basis of the degradation of this nucleic acid was also clarified. Synthesis of early enzymes permitted production of viral DNA, and the synthesis of early enzymes was stopped shortly thereafter, to be followed by synthesis of virus structural proteins. These patterns have been shown to be characteristic of many types of virus infection; the dissection of the molecular mechanisms of these controls of polymer synthesis defines major problems and directions of work in contemporary virology. The discovery of the new viral pyrimidine and of its metabolic origins were recognized by a medal of the American Association for the Advancement of Science in 1955. In 1967 Cohen presented the Jesup Lectures on "Virus-Induced Enzymes" at Columbia University, and was elected to the National Academy of Sciences.

The study of virus-infected bacteria also led into many apparently peripheral fields. The work on pyrimidine origin led to discovery of some unusual phenomena of cell pathology, such as those of "thymineless death" and "unbalanced growth," which are now studied in many laboratories. An interest in the biosynthesis of thymine and pentose stimulated studies on the metabolism of the spongonucleoside, D-arabinosyl thymine, and his work on the origin and fate of D-arabinose culminated in work on the mode of action of the chemotherapeutically significant nucleosides, D-arabinosyl cytosine and D-arabinosyl adenine.

In very early work on the characterization of viral nucleic acids he had observed the reaction of the basic antibiotic streptomycin with these polymeric anions. After some 20 years of intermittent study on this problem, his laboratory helped to clarify the mechanism of the lethal action of the streptomycinoid drugs in terms of the production of a complex series of aberrations of nucleic acid metabolism and structure. In the last group of studies his work with A. Raina demonstrated the key role of the cationic polyamines in controlling synthesis of some classes of nucleic acid.

In 1954 Cohen became professor of biochemistry at the University of Pennsylvania, and in 1957 he was appointed Charles Hayden–American Cancer Society Professor at that university. His numerous experimental interests in virus and cell multiplication and pathology formed the basis for the development of a course in comparative biochemistry that he taught for many years. His teaching explored the problems of the nature and origin of biochemical diversity; he also wrote several essays on problems of biochemical evolution and innovation. In 1963 he became Hartzell Professor and chairman of the department of therapeutic research, a post that permitted him to stimulate research efforts in several biochemical areas that he considered to have been neglected. Despite numerous activities as chairman of an active department, teacher, consultant, and editor, he continued research activities among a relatively small group composed of a few students and postdoctoral fellows. These students and fellows included biochemists from both the United States and numerous foreign countries. In addition, Cohen spent many summers at the Marine Biological Laboratory at Woods Hole, Mass.

For background information *see* BACTERIOPHAGE; NUCLEIC ACID; VIRUS in the McGraw-Hill Encyclopedia of Science and Technology. □

★ COHN, Waldo E.

American biochemist
Born June 28, 1910, San Francisco, Calif., U.S.A.

Cohn's PRIMARY contribution was the development of a technique—elution chromatography on ion exchangers—that has proved invaluable in the study of nucleic acids, separating biochemical compounds, and other areas. Cohn embarked on this work in 1948, when he returned to biochemical research after World War II assignments as a radiochemist. He took up a problem that he and A. M. Brues had touched upon in prewar days at Harvard: the metabolic "turnover" of ribonucleic acid (RNA). Having demonstrated with the crude chemical techniques then available that RNA is continuously formed and degraded ("turned over") even in nongrowing animals whereas deoxyribonucleic acid (DNA), the stuff of chromosomes, is not, the question then posed was: Do all the four types of monomers (nucleotides) of RNA turn over at equal rates?

Cohn's approach was to ascertain the rate of radiophosphate incorporation into each mononucleotide component. A necessary element was the separation of each type of mononucleotide from the hydrolysis mixture of the total RNA. However, the only methods available were the imprecise and laborious preparative methods, involving precipitations and crystallizations, used by the previous generation of chemists to isolate and ascertain the chemical structures of the mononucleotides. A new technique that would permit quantitative separation and isolation of these compounds was essential.

Cohn's previous assignment at the Clinton Laboratories (since 1946 the Oak Ridge National Laboratory) during World War II had been to investigate the radiotoxicity of the fission products, the large number of pure radioactive elements created by the fission of U^{235} in nuclear reactors. This assignment was based on Cohn's pre- and postdoctoral experience with artificial radioisotopes in biological systems, which began in Berkeley in 1937 with cyclotron products (P^{32}, Na^{24}, and so on). However, most chemists in the Manhattan Project, as it was

known during the war, were engrossed with the problem of extracting the microquantities of plutonium product from the macroquantities of uranium parent and the highly radioactive fission products, and could not undertake the isolation and segregation of each of the many fission products. Hence Cohn and his associates (initially E. R. Tompkins and J. X. Khym, later G. W. Parker and P. C. Tompkins) undertook to isolate the individual fission product species.

Each fission product exists in minute quantities in the mass of uranium, and most emit highly energetic β- and γ-radiations. In addition, many of these are traditionally difficult to separate (such as the rare earths and Sr and Ba). A procedure was necessary that would be effective at low concentrations (no precipitations) and by remote control (behind protective shielding). No stable carrier could be added because of the projected subsequent biological investigative use. It was decided to explore the possibilities of elution chromatography on synthetic ion-exchange resins. This procedure, which was also being worked on by other Manhattan Project chemists (such as G. E. Boyd, J. A. Swartout, and J. Schubert), could be operated by fluid flow through a column, and therefore seemed a priori to have the mechanical simplicity required. This investigation, guided in part by the biochemist's familiarity with such complexes as calcium citrate, resulted in the important finding that even neighboring rare-earth cations can be separately removed from ion-exchange resin columns in the form of their complexes with polybasic acids (tartrates and citrates). This work led directly to the first isolation of element 61 (promethium) by Glendenin, Marinsky, and Coryell and to the large-scale production of pure rare-earth compounds by F. H. Spedding and co-workers, as well as to the production of individual fission product radioisotopes for distribution from Oak Ridge, starting in 1946.

The principle involved here—induction of different degrees of electrostatic charge on components of soluble mixtures, leading to different affinities for an ionized solid matrix—was applied by Cohn in 1948 to the mixtures of bases, nucleosides, and/or nucleotides derived from RNA hydrolysis. As these substances are amphoteric, different electrostatic net charges can be induced by pH control (a necessary component of the rare-earth separations) without the addition of complexing agents—although such agents were found useful in other situations (such as sugars, as in the later work of Khym and L. P. Zill).

The resulting excellent separations of nucleotides, while it settled the original question of a technique for separating the then known four nucleotides of RNA, permitted the discovery (with C. E. Carter) of an isomeric form of each of these four nucleotides, and later (with E. Volkin), led to the discovery of a third hitherto unknown isomeric form of each (the 5' phosphate esters of the nucleosides). The establishment of the structures of these compounds (with D. G. Doherty and Khym) raised serious questions as to the then accepted structure of ribonucleic acids (thought to be linked from 2' to 3' by phosphate residues) and led to the now accepted formulation of RNAs as 3':5' phosphodiesters (by D. M. Brown and A. R. Todd in 1951)—a structure almost identical to that already known for DNA. This formulation, in turn, makes plausible and feasible the present consideration of the formation of RNA on DNA "templates," a necessary part of the genetic "information transfer" chain of events.

Besides its value in exploring the chemistry and structure of nucleic acids, elution chromatography on ion exchangers proved of great usefulness in the separations of a large number of biochemically important compounds and led to the discovery of a host of them, especially as a result of the modifications and applications introduced by V. R. Potter and his colleagues. In addition, it finds use in analytical schemes (as in the amino acid analyzer of Stein and Moore), in organic reaction mechanisms, and as a tool for the separation of components of biochemcial reactions—the use for which it was originally invented by Cohn. The technique is now in use in the vast majority of biochemical and chemical laboratories and in chemical manufacture. Its widespread use and value underlies the American Chemical Society Award in Chromatography and Electrophoresis given to Cohn in 1962.

Subsequent work by Cohn was concerned more with the structure and chemistry of nucleic acids and their component nucleotides and less with chromatography. He ascertained the structure of pseudouridine, the first nucleoside to possess a unique base-ribose bond (C—C instead of C—N). His recent interests concerned the linear sequence of nucleotides in the transfer nucleic acids, which contain most of the minor or "odd" nucleosides uncovered by chromatography since 1950.

Another development stemming from the war work of Cohn and his associates at Oak Ridge was the production of radioisotopes other than fission products in reactors (C^{14}, P^{32}, and so on). He developed the production of P^{32} by exposure of sulfur to reactor neutrons and its subsequent extraction as phosphoric acid in carrier-free form. At one time in this period his product formed the total United States supply of P^{32}, and was released via Berkeley, whose cyclotron was completely engaged in uranium bombardment for the Oak Ridge plutonium chemists. P^{32}, C^{14}, and other such radioisotopes, with a great number of fission-produced radioisotopes, were included in the first catalog of radioisotopes available from Oak Ridge in 1946 (produced by Cohn with R. T. Overman and P. C. Aebersold). Cohn and his associates thus established the still-operating isotope production machinery at Oak Ridge.

Cohn received his B.S. in 1931, M.S. in chemistry in 1932, and Ph.D. in biochemistry in 1938 under D. M. Greenberg from the University of California, Berkeley. His graduate research involved the use of cyclotron-produced radioisotopes, and was thus among the first investigations in the United States to use these materials as tracers in the uncovering of metabolic and physiological processes. He continued this type of research during his postdoctoral years at Harvard Medical School (1939–42) before joining the Manhattan Project and moving to Oak Ridge, where he was a senior biochemist in the Biology Division of the Oak Ridge National Laboratory. He also was part-time director of the National Academy of Sciences Office of Biochemical Nomenclature, author or coauthor of over 70 research publications and reviews, and an editor of journals and book series in his field. Besides receiving the Chromatography Award of the American Chemical Society in 1962, Cohn was named a fellow of the American Academy of Arts and Sciences (1962) and of the American Association for the Advancement of Science (1964), received a Fulbright scholarship (1955) and two Guggenheim fellowships (1955 and 1962), was a visiting professor at the Institut de Biologie in Paris (1963) and the Rockefeller University in New York (1966), and was elected or appointed to various offices in the American Society of Biological Chemists and the American Society of Biological Chemists and the American Chemical Society. Cohn also had a long-standing interest in music, both as cellist and as the founder and conductor (1944–55) of the Oak Ridge Symphony Orchestra. He was elected to the Advisory Town Council of Oak Ridge in 1951 and again in 1953, and served as its chairman during the latter term.

For background information *see* NUCLEIC ACID; RADIOISOTOPE PRODUCTION in the McGraw-Hill Encyclopedia of Science and Technology. □

★ COLE, Kenneth Stewart

American biophysicist
Born July 10, 1900, Ithaca, N.Y., U.S.A.

As a classical physicist, Cole was primarily interested in understanding the structure and function of living cell membranes in general and of nerve membranes in particular. He and his co-workers largely concentrated on the electrical approach to these problems.

Following Hugo Fricke, he sharpened the analysis of, and did more than anyone else to establish, the now generally accepted principle that all living cell membranes have the electrical capacity of about 1 microfarad per square centimeter to be expected from a dielectric a few molecules thick. This principle has been found to hold for membranes ranging from those of plant cells about a centimeter in diameter, through marine and other egg cells, various nerve and muscle fibers, blood cells, yeast, and bacteria, and recently to mitochondria and pleuropneumonia-like organisms. It is now a highly plausible assumption that the double-layer structure, so widely found by electron microscopy, corresponds with this directly measured property of living cells. There is a dielectric-like loss often associated with this capacity, which Cole and his brother, Robert H. Cole, considered in some detail. This characteristic may help ultimately to formulate a membrane structure, but it is still a problem of solid-state physics in nonliving systems, often represented as a "Cole-Cole diagram."

Although Cole anticipated the two-factor theories of nerve excitation, he continued the more physical approach. With Howard J. Curtis, he showed that the capacity of a plant cell and a nerve membrane remains unchanged during the passage of an impulse, while the membrane conductance increases—thus providing a basic step for subsequent developments. Additional investigations by Cole with others, and many subsequent measurements by other workers, established another generalization—that physiological function and condition are correlated with the conductance of the membrane, while the capacity is comparatively unaffected. Cole and Alan L. Hodgkin found the resting membrane conductance of the squid giant axon to be .001 mho/cm^2 by means of conventional theory and new experiments. This first reliable value for an animal cell membrane also became an accepted generalization with other forms—

usually within an order of magnitude of it—and it showed that the axon conductance increases 40-fold during the passage of a nerve impulse.

Cole and Curtis, independently and simultaneously with Hodgkin and Andrew F. Huxley, made direct internal measurements of the change of membrane potential in the squid axon during activity and confirmed the observation that the action potential is larger than the resting potential. This "overshoot" had been anticipated, has since been generally found in many living forms, and was a key to the present understanding of activity. With Curtis and with Richard F. Baker, Cole further showed the membrane conductance to be a highly nonlinear relation between the electrical potential and current—often since called "rectification" or "anomalous rectification." With Hodgkin, Cole discovered the inductive reactance of a squid axon, and with Baker he localized it in the membrane and carefully measured its properties. This gave a quantitative basis to correlate many oscillatory and repetitive characteristics of nerve. Cole hinted that the rectification and inductive reactance might result from potassium ions, as was later confirmed. He showed an anomalous reactance to be a generally expected phenomenon of nonlinear systems—of which the more recently designated "delayed rectification" is a part.

Having long recognized the need to simplify the theoretical approach to nerve problems, Cole supported and collaborated with George H. Marmont in his investigation of the squid axon membrane by controlled current flow between large electrodes inside and outside the axon. With the axon no longer able to propagate an impulse, this "space-current clamp" situation—as it was later termed—substantiated much that had been found less directly and added a considerable amount of new, but mostly unpublished, information on the passive and active states of the membrane. Of most importance, however, this work emphasized to Cole the need to bring the explosive response of the membrane under control and recalled to him the simple mathematical and physical principle that a system which is unstable for a constant value of one variable is usually stable for a constant value of another variable. This led him in 1947 to apply sudden and controlled changes of the membrane potential to the squid axon. The resulting membrane currents not only were without any evidence of instability but were adequate to predict, better than qualitatively, the threshold for excitation, the rise of the action potential, its maximum value and subsequent decline during recovery, and the propagation of such an impulse for an axon in normal function.

These results were not published until 1949, but Cole communicated them to Hodgkin and later discussed them with him in detail in early 1948. With Huxley and Bernard Katz, Hodgkin then started a program based on this new concept of membrane potential control, which they christened the "voltage clamp." They improved the technique for its application and confirmed

Cole's work. Hodgkin and Huxley then went on to their revolutionary and now classic series of papers in 1952 on the ion conductances of the squid axon membrane, and a Nobel Prize in 1963 with J. C. Eccles.

Cole, Henry A. Antosiewicz, and P. Rabinowitz soon undertook the first automatic computer calculations with the Hodgkin and Huxley results to test them and to use them to explain further well-known and accepted experiments on nerve. An error in this work was detected by Cole, and the results were corrected and extended by Richard FitzHugh and Antosiewicz. With Cole's support, FitzHugh continued the analytical and computer investigations of the Hodgkin and Huxley formulations of the squid axon membrane properties. After further improving the technique, Cole and John W. Moore started again to test and to extend the Hodgkin and Huxley work. They soon began to find, as did others, significant variations from the earlier results. Thus the utility of the "voltage clamp" concept and the validity of all of the earlier work based on it were called into question. By extensive experimental and theoretical work, and in collaboration with Moore, Robert E. Taylor, FitzHugh, and others, Cole located the imperfections of the technique which were responsible for the anomalies. He then showed that the early experiments and the Hodgkin and Huxley conclusions based on them were essentially correct.

Cole and his colleagues steadily extended the range and depth of investigations based on the potential control, or "voltage clamp," concept. This concept was applied to numerous other excitable membranes by other investigators and by using other techniques—but with the similar and uniquely important results not yet to be obtained by any other approach. It seems certain that the concept for some time will continue to provide the most powerful means of investigating nerve membrane properties, and it may even lead to the ultimate explanation of the nerve impulse.

In another direction Cole, following E. Newton Harvey, devised a new method for measuring the surface force versus the surface area relation in sea urchin eggs. He confirmed Harvey's original observation that the tension is of the order of 0.1 dyne per centimeter, but further established that the tension is that to be expected of a solid elastic membrane and is not a capillary or interfacial tension. This discovery led James F. Danielli to do the experiments and formulate the theory suggesting that the living cell membrane is a lipid double layer with protein adsorbed on both sides. Although now more than 20 years old, this is still the most generally acceptable membrane structure theory, and it has also received considerable support from recent electron microscope observations.

Other published work of Cole's includes

assisting Charles G. Rogers in measuring the heat production of sea urchin eggs before and after fertilization, some electrolyte theory, an irradiation technique and parallax stereoscopy for x-rays, grasshopper egg membrane measurements with Theodore L. Jahn, an artificial membrane note with Robert B. Dean and Howard J. Curtis, mammalian circulation work with Barry G. King and Enid T. Oppenheimer, and a number of papers on instrumentation.

Son of a college classics professor and dean, Cole received his A.B. from Oberlin College in 1922 and his Ph.D. in experimental physics from Cornell in 1926. After 3 years of postdoctoral research at Harvard and Leipzig, he became assistant professor of physiology at the College of Physicians and Surgeons, Columbia University. In 1942 he was given the first biomedical appointment in the Metallurgical Laboratory in Chicago, continuing in charge of the Biology Section throughout World War II. During the war he and the members of the section and a cooperating section he organized in Clinton, Tenn., produced much of the foundation for what is now known of the biomedical effects of radiation. After the war Cole became professor of biophysics and physiology at Chicago (1946–49), technical director of the Naval Medical Research Institute (1949–54), organizer and chief of the Laboratory of Biophysics, National Institute of Neurological Diseases and Blindness (1954–66), and then senior research biophysicist at the National Institutes of Health and professor of biophysics at the University of California, Berkeley. Cole received an honorary Sc.D. from Oberlin in 1954, the Order of the Southern Cross from Brazil in 1966, an honorary Sc.D. from the University of Chicago in 1967, and an honorary M.D. from Uppsala University in 1967. He was elected to the National Academy of Sciences in 1956.

Cole wrote *Membranes, Ions, and Impulses* (1967).

For background information *see* BIOPHYSICS, MATHEMATICAL; BIOPOTENTIALS AND ELECTROPHYSIOLOGY; MECHANORECEPTORS; NERVOUS SYSTEM (INVERTEBRATE) in the McGraw-Hill Encyclopedia of Science and Technology.   □

★ CONDON, Edward Uhler

American physicist
Born Mar. 2, 1902, Alamogordo, N. Mex., U.S.A.

CONDON RECEIVED his Ph.D. at the University of California, Berkeley, in 1926. This was the year in which quantum mechanics was discovered and was beginning to produce revolutionary changes in the understanding of atomic, molecular, and nuclear structure. Condon made research contributions to each of these areas.

In chemical physics he is known for his contributions to the Franck-Condon principle. This represents an extension and quantum-mechanical treatment of some ideas first proposed by James Franck about the changes in nuclear motion in molecules that accompany electronic transitions in molecules. This work led to an interpretation of the intensity distribution in band systems and to the understanding of conditions under which light absorption or electron impact can lead to dissociation of molecules, usually producing fragments with considerable kinetic energy. Predictions of this kind were fully confirmed by mass spectroscopic experiments of Walker Bleakney and of John T. Tate and Wallace Lozier. In atomic physics Condon is known for the basic treatise *The Theory of Atomic Spectra* (1935), which has long been the standard work in the field. He also made numerous research contributions to this field and in the 1960s was working on a new treatise on the subject. In nuclear physics Condon is known for two major contributions. In the fall of 1928, with R. W. Gurney, he developed the barrier leakage or tunneling model for alpha-particle emission by natural radioactive elements, such as radium and uranium. This was the first application of quantum mechanics to a problem in nuclear structure. The same ideas were developed independently at the same time by George Gamow in Göttingen. In 1936–37, working with Gregory Breit and Richard Present, Condon made a detailed analysis of the theory underlying the proton-proton scattering experiments that had just been made by Merle Tuve, Lawrence Hafstad, and Norman Heydenburg at the Carnegie Institution of Washington. This work led to the recognition of the charge independence of the strong interaction forces between

nucleons, and therefore to the importance of a variable known as "isotopic spin" for the theory of nuclear structure. In the field of solid-state physics Condon developed ideas about the relation between the contact potential and the photoelectric threshold of semiconductors. These concepts stimulated further experimental research.

In 1948, while director of the National Bureau of Standards, Condon was the subject of a major public attack launched by J. Parnell Thomas, then chairman of the House Committee on Un-American Activities. Thomas accused him of being "perhaps one of the weakest links in our atomic security." Hearings were promised but never held because soon afterward Congressman Thomas had to serve a term in a federal penitentiary for taking salary kickbacks from the secretaries in his office. Nevertheless, harassments of this type continued intermittently over a period of 6 years. A brief hearing before a subcommittee of the House Committee on Un-American Activities was held in Chicago by several congressmen from that area just before the elections of 1952. As with all persons engaged in classified research, Condon had been investigated and cleared during World War II. Then he was the subject of unusually extensive investigation in 1948 as a result of Thomas's accusations. These resulted in full clearance by the Department of Commerce and by the Atomic Energy Commission. After Condon went to Corning, another hearing on old charges was held in April, 1954, before the Eastern Industrial Personnel Security Board. This resulted in another full clearance. But in October, 1954, a few weeks before the election, the clearance was suspended by action of the Secretary of the Navy. As a result, the government excluded Condon's services until the clearance was reinstated in 1966 after another detailed investigation.

Condon took an A.B. in 1924 and a Ph.D. in physics in 1926 at the University of California, Berkeley. His career was marked by a variety of activities outside the field of academic research. Besides teaching in university physics departments, he served during 1937–45 as associate director of research for the Westinghouse Electric Corporation. He was appointed by President Truman in October, 1945, as fourth director of the National Bureau of Standards. In October, 1951, he became director of research and development for Corning Glass Works, a post he held until the end of 1954. He continued as a research consultant to that company. During World War II he served on the committee to establish the Jet Propulsion Laboratory at the California Institute of Technology and on the S-1 Committee, which established the government atomic bomb project. He also had charge of the Westinghouse microwave radar research program and served as head of the theoretical division of the Lawrence Radiation Laboratory, Berkeley. After the war Condon served as scientific adviser to the Special Senate Committee on Atomic Energy, which drafted the legislation establishing the Atomic Energy Commission. He was a member of the faculty at Princeton University during 1928–37, chairman of the physics department at Washington University, St. Louis, during 1956–63, and professor of physics of the University of Colorado thereafter. He also served as president of the Colorado Scientific Development Commission by appointment of Governor John A. Love. In November, 1966, he undertook to serve as director of a study sponsored by the U.S. Air Force on the nature of reports of "unidentified flying objects."

Condon wrote the first book in English on quantum mechanics, *Quantum Mechanics*, with P. M. Morse (1929; paper 1963) and *The Theory of Atomic Spectra*, with G. H. Shortley (1935). With Hugh Odishaw, he edited, and wrote many of the chapters of, *Handbook of Physics* (1958). Beginning in 1956 he was editor of *Reviews of Modern Physics*, a quarterly journal published by the American Physical Society.

For background information *see* ATOMIC STRUCTURE AND SPECTRA; FRANCK-CONDON PRINCIPLE; ISOTOPIC SPIN; QUANTUM MECHANICS in the McGraw-Hill Encyclopedia of Science and Technology.   □

★ CONSTANCE, Lincoln

American botanist
Born Feb. 16, 1909, Eugene, Ore., U.S.A.

CONSTANCE WAS one of those who in the mid-20th century attempted to foster the development of a broadly based systematic botany. The goal was the effective utilization of the new comparative data emerging from anatomy-morphology, cytology, genetics, and biochemistry, and their synthesis into a general classification, phylogenetic in orientation, without splintering the field of taxonomy and within the framework of a system not precisely designed to accommodate such information. More or less by accident he also found himself a spokesman for a renascent plant taxonomy in his widely cited and influential essays: "The versatile taxonomist" (1951), "The role of plant ecology in biosystematics" (1953), "Plant taxonomy in an age of experiment" (1957), and "Systematic botany—an unending synthesis" (1964). In all of these he urged that taxonomists should welcome additional comparative information of whatever nature, but that diversity and novelty of data do not seriously alter the general goals of systematics. He also championed the relevance of continuing interest in, and support for, plant taxonomy in an era when the focus of attention was on the physicochemical and subcellular aspects of biology.

In the 1930s and 1940s the San Francisco Bay area was a center of ferment in genetical, ecological, and evolutionary biology, including research on plants. Ernest B. Babcock and G. Ledyard Stebbins were pursuing their critical investigations on the cytology, genetics, and evolution of *Crepis*. T. Harper Goodspeed and Roy Clausen were conducting independent studies of tobacco. Ralph W. Chaney and Herbert L. Mason were exploring the Tertiary history of Western floras. The team of Jens C. Clausen, David D. Keck, and William C. Hiesey was carrying out its classical transplant studies at Palo Alto and in the Sierra Nevada, attempting to determine the nature of species. An informal group known as the "biosystematists" developed among the biologists located around Berkeley, Stanford, and the California Academy of Sciences in San Francisco, providing a monthly forum for vigorous debate on such subjects as the proper definition of "species"; the significance of polyploidy; the causes, consequences, and evolutionary role of endemism and isolation; the various factors governing distribution through time and space. These discussions closely paralleled those topics included in Julian Huxley's *The New Systematics* (1940) and, although the biosystematists did not publish a rival volume, these seminars markedly influenced the thinking and subsequent writing and teaching of most of the participants.

There was considerable doubt that the old taxonomic framework could indeed respond with sufficient flexibility to accommodate all the new information and new concepts that were pouring in. The classical "species," cornerstone of all biological classification, was more than ever in danger of being regarded as a mere transitory evolutionary stepping stone or of being transformed into a purely genetically defined category that would no longer be available to the working taxonomist. Clausen, Keck, and Hiesey proposed to correlate the formal taxonomic categories with the Turessonian coenospecies, ecospecies, and ecotypes, which were based on ecological-genetical criteria. Wendell H. Camp

proposed that a new science of "biosystematy" be established to replace the now moribund traditional taxonomy. Many taxonomists preferred to close their eyes to the ferment, pretending that it did not concern them and ignoring the data now becoming available to them. More recently, the advocates of "phenetic" taxonomy have attempted to displace "phylogeny" as the philosophical core of any natural system of classification.

Together with many others, Constance took a liberal view toward the acceptance of new evidence, but a conservative attitude toward the fragmentation of systematic biology, the extravagant claims of successively fashionable subdisciplines, and the proposed abandonment of hard-won knowledge of relationships derived from other data at earlier periods. His own work was mostly monographic and dealt principally with two families of flowering plants, Umbelliferae and Hydrophyllaceae. In his investigations of Umbelliferae he collaborated with Mildred E. Mathias (Hassler), and together they authored most of the manual and flora treatments of American Umbelliferae, as well as a series of comprehensive monographs. With Minosuke Hiroe, he published a revision of *Umbelliferae of Japan* (1958) and, with C. Ritchie Bell, a series of papers embodying a survey of the chromosome numbers of the family. Marion S. Cave joined him in a 20-year survey of chromosome numbers in Hydrophyllaceae, one of the most thorough cytotaxonomic surveys of any family of flowering plants up to that time. His most widely read paper is probably "The systematics of the angiosperms" (1955).

Stimulated by a sabbatical trip to South America in 1954 (made possible by a Guggenheim fellowship), Constance became interested in the similarities and differences in the flora and vegetation between the temperate zones of the Northern and Southern hemispheres and the patterns of plant distribution within the Southern Hemisphere. Although he published little on phytogeography, it always fascinated him and profoundly influenced his taxonomic thinking, as shown by his selection of genera for monographic study and by his emphasis on the mapping of distributions. His friendly relations with Latin American botanists greatly assisted his taxonomic work. He was elected a corresponding member of both the Sociedad Argentina de Botánica and the Academia Chilena de Ciencias Naturales, as well as the Société de Biogéographie, Paris. He was exceptionally fortunate in his graduate students, and their cumulative contributions conspicuously outweigh his own.

Son of a lawyer-farmer, Constance graduated from the University of Oregon in biology (A.B., 1930). His early interest in natural history, largely stimulated by his mother as a compensation for the intellectual limitations of rural life, was encouraged by Louis F. Henderson, Albert R. Sweetser, Ethel I. Sanborn, and others. He received an M.A. in 1932 from the University of California, Berkeley, and a Ph.D. in 1934, working under the direction of Willis Linn Jepson, but strongly influenced also by William A. Setchell and his enthusiasm for plant geography. Constance's first teaching position was as instructor and later assistant professor at the State College of Washington in 1934–37. Then he returned to Berkeley to stay, although he served as visiting lecturer and acting director of the Gray Herbarium of Harvard University in 1948–49. During World War II he held various positions in the Office of Strategic Services in Washington, D.C., including that of geobotanist. For a decade he was heavily involved in university administration at Berkeley, serving as dean of the College of Letters and Science (1955–62) and vice-chancellor for academic affairs (1962–65). However, he always scrupulously maintained a tie with both undergraduate and graduate teaching and a thin but vital thread of research, and so he was able to return to the department of botany as professor and director of the University of California Herbarium.

For background information *see* PLANT CLASSIFICATION; PLANT GEOGRAPHY; PLANT KINGDOM in the McGraw-Hill Encyclopedia of Science and Technology.   ☐

★ COOPER, Gustav Arthur

American paleontologist and stratigrapher
Born Feb. 9, 1902, College Point, N.Y., U.S.A.

C OOPER STARTED his geological career at Colgate University with the intention of becoming a mineralogist, but the prevalence of fossils on the college campus soon turned him from the study of minerals. His work in paleon-

tology was aided by a scholarship from Colgate, permitting him to study for the Ph.D. at Yale University. His master's and doctor's theses were on the stratigraphy of the Hamilton Group of New York from the vicinity of Hamilton, the type area, to Lake Erie.

Although Cooper's studies at Yale led to a dissertation in stratigraphy, his main interest was in paleontology. While at Yale he was selected by Charles Schuchert to assist in a reclassification of the fossil brachiopods. This started Cooper on the main specialty of his career. His work was therefore divided between stratigraphy and paleontology, but the two are complementary.

Cooper's contributions in stratigraphy were the production of the Devonian correlation chart of the National Research Council and assistance in the Ordovician and Permian charts. His Devonian work, preliminary to the Devonian chart, consisted of completion of the Hamilton studies to include all of New York State and a survey of the Middle Devonian of the Midwest. His Hamilton work showed that the north end of the Catskill Mountain mass is of Hamilton age rather than younger, as had previously been thought. In the Devonian investigations in the Midwest, Cooper was joined by A. S. Warthin of Vassar College. This work led to a classification of the Traverse Group of Michigan and realignment of many formations. These studies gave him background for preparation of the Devonian correlation chart, a comprehensive diagram of the Devonian formations of North America. As chairman of the Devonian Committee, Cooper compiled most of the Devonian chart and proposed a new stage terminology and some innovations in age assignment.

Contribution to Ordovician stratigraphy was made not only on the National Research Council chart but on a diagram of Middle Ordovician formations that accompanied the monograph *Chazyan and Related Brachiopods* (1956). In the latter chart the great Ordovician developments in the Appalachians and the West were brought into focus for the first time. It recognized the facies development of the Ordovician, which had been overlooked by Appalachian geologists in prior studies, but which had been detailed by Cooper and his colleague B. N. Cooper of Virginia Polytechnic Institute in 1946 in Virginia and by John Rogers in Tennessee. On completing his Ordovician work Cooper devoted much attention to stratigraphic and paleontological studies in the Permian of the Glass Mountains of western Texas. These studies again emphasized facies relationships of the various strata, but rather than innovating they were a perfecting of details.

Cooper's brachiopod work started with

Schuchert at Yale and lasted for 2 years, in which two suborders, the Orthida and Penta-merida, were completed. This study emphasized the necessity of using a totality of characters in classification of the brachiopods and indicated the value of brachial valve structures in family classification. The latter theme was again emphasized in a study of the family Triplesiidae with E. O. Ulrich. Cooper published, with Ulrich, *Ozarkian and Canadian Brachiopoda* (1938), a hitherto poorly understood group of brachiopods which existed in Late Cambrian and Early Ordovician time. Although the Ozarkian and Canadian systems have been found unnecessary, the brachiopods of those times are distinctive and characteristic, representing some terminal stocks and some evolving groups. They furnish an evolutionary link between the Cambrian brachiopods and the great brachiopod expansion in the Ordovician. As a sequel to this work and in an effort to establish firmly lines of brachiopod evolution, the monograph mentioned earlier, *Chazyan and Related Brachiopods*, was produced. This treated 163 genera, many of them new, and afforded much new information on Middle Ordovician brachiopod stocks. These brachiopods were also used as the basis for the new stratigraphic scheme of the Middle Ordovician mentioned above.

Another important work on brachiopods was on the extensive superfamily Productidina, prepared with H. M. Muir-Wood of Great Britain. Cooper also published numerous shorter papers on brachiopods of all ages, including those of the modern seas, all having a bearing on classification.

After the Ordovician studies Cooper embarked in earnest on his monumental work dealing with the Permian brachiopods of western Texas. The Permian brachiopods represent the culmination of many Paleozoic stocks that became extinct at the end of that time. He had been collecting large limestone blocks in the mountain ranges of western Texas since 1939. These were dissolved with acid in the laboratory to obtain the silicified fossils entombed in them. Approximately 65 tons of limestone was processed and hundreds of thousands of specimens obtained, not only of brachiopods but of many other groups. The organization and sorting of this vast collection proved a gigantic task. With the help of a grant from the National Science Foundation, R. E. Grant was engaged as a collaborator. More than 200 genera were taken from these rocks. The specimens are so well preserved that new structures have been discovered in them that will help to clarify problems of some of the bizarre forms of brachiopods, such as the *Olhaminida* and the Richthofeniidae, as well as many of the other more usual types. The species number

nearly a thousand. This promises to be Cooper's biggest contribution to paleontology. The vast collection alone will offer study opportunities for years to come.

After graduating from Colgate University (B.S., 1924) Cooper spent another year at Colgate, in which he laid the groundwork for his future Devonian and brachiopod studies. He received an M.A. from Colgate in 1926 and a Ph.D. from Yale University in 1929, and remained at Yale for 2 years working with Schuchert. He left Yale for the Smithsonian Institution, Washington, where he was appointed in 1930 assistant curator in stratigraphic paleontology in the U.S. National Museum, a branch of the Smithsonian. In 1943 he became curator of invertebrate paleontology and paleobotany and in 1956 head curator of the department of geology. In 1963 that department was divided between paleontology and mineralogy, and Cooper became chairman of a new department of paleobiology. In 1967 he became a senior scientist to devote his full time to research. Cooper was honored by Colgate University in 1953 with a D.Sc. In 1958 he received the Mary Clarke Thompson Medal of the National Academy of Sciences for contributions to paleontology and stratigraphy, and in 1964 the Medal of the Paleontological Society. He served as the society's president in 1956–57.

For background information *see* Brachiopoda; Paleontology; Stratigraphy in the McGraw-Hill Encyclopedia of Science and Technology. ☐

★ COTTON, Frank Albert

American chemist
Born Apr. 9, 1930, Philadelphia, Pa., U.S.A.

COTTON'S MAIN contributions were in the area of molecular and electronic structures—that is, in the chemical bonding—in inorganic and organometallic molecules. His particular interest was the question of how these two features of the molecules mutually influence each other. Such investigations encompassed preparative chemistry, as well as the application of a broad range of physical measurements.

An early phase of his research, during the late 1950s, concerned the then unsolved problem of the importance of tetrahedral versus octahedral complexes among some of the lighter transition metal ions, such as Mn^{2+}, Fe^{2+}, Co^{2+}, and Ni^{2+}. With David M. L. Goodgame and Margaret Goodgame as his main collaborators, he conducted an extensive investigation in which many new, authentic tetrahedral complexes of these ions were prepared and characterized. Using

these and other compounds, with guidance from ligand field theory, they established the spectroscopic and magnetic criteria by which tetrahedral complexes can be reliably recognized and by which their interconversions with octahedral ones can be followed. One of the particularly interesting aspects of this work lay in the preparation of a great many tetrahedral nickel complexes at a time when it was generally felt that such complexes would be rare, or even nonexistent. Ligand field theory had predicted that Ni^{2+} tetrahedral complexes would be much less stable, relative to the octahedral ones, than those of any other common divalent ion. Conversely, it was also shown that *bis*-(β-ketoenolato) nickel (II) complexes were not tetrahedral, as had long been supposed, but generally were polymeric as a result of oxygen atoms being shared between metal ions, making each ion 6-coordinate. This work led to a study of the structures of *bis*-(β-ketoenolato) complexes of other ions, such as Co^{2+} and Zn^{2+}, in which it was shown that, as a general rule, these compounds polymerize by sharing oxygen atoms, thus providing coordination numbers higher than 4 for the metal atoms.

Cotton conducted a broad range of investigations pertaining to metal carbonyls and related molecules. His major purpose was to elucidate in detail the nature of bonding between metal atoms in a formal valence state of zero and molecules of carbon monoxide, isonitriles ($RN{\equiv}C$), and other neutral donor molecules of low basicity. The basic qualitative idea, proposed by L. C. Pauling many years ago, was that considerable multiple bonding must be present in the metal-ligand linkages. By investigating the bond lengths through x-ray crystallography, and the bond force constants through infrared spectra, this concept was verified and refined. Practical, simplified methods of using spectra to

investigate structures and bonding were developed.

In 1962 Cotton began theoretical, preparative, and x-ray crystallographic studies on compounds of the heavier transition metals in which there are groups of two, three, or six closely linked metal atoms. These are the metal atom cluster compounds. These clusters are persisting, polynuclear entities which can undergo various chemical transformations, including oxidation and reduction, while preserving their integrity. One of the most remarkable is the dinuclear Re_2 species, occurring in $Re_2Cl_8{}^{2-}$, $Re_2(O_2CC_nH_{2n+1})_4Cl_2$, and other species, which contains a quadruple bond. This is the strongest and most multiple linkage ever found between two atoms. It is made up of four compotents: a σ-bond, a pair of π-bonds, and a δ-bond. The first three are similar to bonds found in acetylenes ($-C{\equiv}N$, $C{\equiv}O$, and so on), but the δ-bond is peculiar to these and a few other species—$Mo_2(O_2CCH_3)_4$, $Tc_2Cl_8{}^{3-}$—and is found only in compounds where metal d-orbitals are available.

Cotton later studied organometallic molecules which can exist in two or more different but equivalent nuclear configurations and which undergo, at normal temperatures, rapid shifts from one configuration to another (at rates equal to, or greater than, 10^3 times per second). Such molecules are termed stereochemically nonrigid or fluxional. They continuously undergo intramolecular rearrangements, which are, however, degenerate in the sense that the product molecule is indistinguishable from the original. Cotton's studies, which consisted mainly in analyzing the temperature dependence of the nuclear magnetic resonance spectra, led to a very detailed picture of the processes or pathways by which some of these molecules rearrange.

Cotton received his primary education in the Philadelphia public schools. He attended Drexel Institute of Technology and received an A.B. from Temple University in 1951. His Ph.D. was obtained from Harvard University in 1955 for a thesis directed by Geoffrey Wilkinson, then an assistant professor there. Cotton was appointed an instructor at the Massachusetts Institute of Technology in 1955, and became a professor in 1961. In 1962 he was the first recipient of the American Chemical Society's Award in Inorganic Chemistry, and in 1963 he was awarded the Baekeland Medal of the North Jersey section of that society. He was elected a member of the National Academy of Sciences in 1967.

Cotton wrote *Advanced Inorganic Chemistry,* with G. Wilkinson (1962; 2d ed. 1966), *Chemical Applications of Group Theory* (1963), and a high school–junior college text, *Chemistry, an Investigative Approach*, with L. Lynch (1968). He edited eight volumes of the annual *Progress in Inorganic Chemistry*. His published articles, mostly research papers, numbered over 200.

For background information *see* COORDINATION CHEMISTRY; MOLECULAR STRUCTURE AND SPECTRA; ORGANOMETALLIC COMPOUND; TRANSITION ELEMENTS; X-RAY CRYSTALLOGRAPHY in the McGraw-Hill Encyclopedia of Science and Technology. □

★ COTTRELL, Alan Howard

British metallurgist and physicist
Born July 17, 1919, Birmingham, England

WHEN AN opportunity to do basic research came at the end of World War II, Cottrell chose to work on the subject of dislocations in crystals. At that time the idea that metals might owe their strength and ductility to dislocations was already over 10 years old, but it was still undeveloped and highly speculative, partly because no one then was able to see dislocations in crystals and partly because the mechanical properties of metals seemed too complex to unravel. At about that time N. F. Mott and F. R. N. Nabarro began to tackle the dislocation theory of mechanical properties, and they advanced some important ideas about the influence on the dislocations of foreign atoms situated in fixed positions in crystals. Cottrell then asked the question: What additional effects would appear when these atoms were allowed to move about by solid-state diffusion processes in dislocated crystals?

He quickly came to the conclusion that under certain circumstances these atoms would segregate to the dislocations and would there pin them down, thereby suppressing the ability of the material to deform plastically; and furthermore that this property of plasticity would be restored suddenly through an avalanche of plastic yielding, if the material were subjected to applied forces strong enough to jerk the dislocations away from their segregated atoms. Mild steel was known to behave just like this, its plasticity being suppressed by aging and restored by overstressing. The possibility that this behavior might be due to pinning of dislocations was greatly strengthened by experimental demonstrations that small numbers of carbon and nitrogen atoms in the metal are in fact responsible for the behavior and that their diffusion kinetics are consistent with the idea that the aging occurs by their migration to dislocations. Cottrell was in this way led to develop, in association with B. A. Bilby, a theory of the yielding and aging of steel. This theory was later elaborated and modified to take account of effects of grain boundaries in polycrystalline metal, of R. E. Peierls and Nabarro's ideas about the natural resistance to motion of dislocations at low temperatures, and of the fact that in fully strain-aged metals the dislocations are often too strongly pinned by foreign atoms to be directly releasable by externally applied forces.

Cottrell's interest in mobile atoms in crystals led him in 1954 to turn to problems of nuclear radiation damage in solids, which were then becoming important with the development of atomic power. Outstanding among these were the problems of the distortion of uranium fuel rods in nuclear reactors. With R. S. Barnes and A. T. Churchman, Cottrell showed that noble gases can expand into bubbles by capturing lattice vacancies from grain boundaries and that this swelling will be reduced if the bubbles are created in a finely dispersed form, by causing them to nucleate on large numbers of fine alloy precipitates. Cottrell also became interested in the effect of crystal distortion upon the mechanical properties of polycrystalline uranium and showed that this produces a special type of viscous flow, called irradiation creep, in the solid metal. This was confirmed experimentally, and metal fuel rods in the British power reactors were redesigned accordingly.

Other interests at that time were radiation damage in graphite and radiation embrittlement of steel. The second of these led Cottrell to consider the fracture of metals from the point of view of dislocation theory. C. Zener, Mott, and A. N. Stroh had already shown how avalanches of dislocations, released by the yield process, can nucleate cleavage cracks in steel at low temperatures. Cottrell and N. J. Petch then independently continued this theory to include the effect of grain size on the ductility of steel. The ductile fracture of metals was shown to be purely a process of plastic deformation. In association with Bilby and K. T. Swinden, Cottrell developed a theory which reconciled the brittleness of thick steel pieces with the ductility of thin pieces, based on the spreading of dislocations into the region ahead of a crack. Still more recently, working with A. Kelly, Cottrell used the analogy between dislocations and cracks to give a description of the atomic structures at the tips of cracks, thereby attempting to explain the basic differences in mechanical properties of various types of crystalline materials, such as diamond, rock salt, gold, and iron. He also considered how brittle nonmetallic solids might be made resistant to fracture by forming them into fiber bundles bonded by plastics or metals.

Cottrell received his B.Sc. in 1939 and his Ph.D. in 1942 from the University of Birmingham. During World War II he was concerned with metallurgical problems, mainly of armor plate. After the war he worked, first as a lecturer and later as professor of physical metallurgy, in the University of Birmingham. In 1955 he moved to the Atomic Energy Research Establishment, Harwell, and in 1958 was appointed Goldsmiths' Professor of Metallurgy at the University of Cambridge, a chair which he held until 1965. He then became chief adviser (studies) to the Secretary of State for Defense. He was elected a fellow of the Royal Society of London in 1955 and a foreign member of the American Academy of Arts and Sciences in 1960.

Cottrell wrote *Theoretical Structural Metallurgy* (1948; 2d ed. 1955), *Dislocations and Plastic Flow in Crystals* (1953), *Theory of Crystal Dislocations* (1963; paper 1964), *The Mechanical Properties of Matter* (1964), and *An Introduction to Metallurgy* (1967).

For background information *see* CRYSTAL DEFECTS; RADIATION DAMAGE (INANIMATE MATERIALS) in the McGraw-Hill Encyclopedia of Science and Technology.   □

★ COUCH, John Nathaniel

American botanist
Born Oct. 12, 1896, Prince Edward Co., Va., U.S.A.

COUCH'S WORK is characterized by diversity, which is often the case with a teacher as compared to a full-time research worker, but the main emphasis is on the fungi in their relationship to insects. His first notable contribution was the discovery of bisexual strains in the water mold *Dictyuchus*, which led to the discovery of similar strains in *Achlya* by Coker and A. B. Couch, the subsequent demonstration by J. R. Raper of the hormonal control of sex in *Achlya*,

and later the similar demonstration in *Dictyuchus* by Sherwood.

During the summer of 1926 spent in the rainforests of Jamaica, Couch became interested in *Septobasidium*, a fungal genus found on living trees and always associated with scale insects, with resultant damage or even death of the tree. When he started his work on the biology of this genus, two theories had been offered to explain the relationship between fungus and scale insects: that the fungus lives on the excretions of the scale insects, or that the fungus parasitizes and wipes out whole colonies of insects. Couch found that the fungus and scale insects live symbiotically at the expense of the host plant, a perennial relationship depending only upon the life of the tree. The fungus constructs minute "houses" in which the scale insects, protected from their enemies, suck the juices of the host plant, grow, and finally reproduce their young in vast numbers. These young may settle down beneath the same fungus under which they were born and repeat the cycle, or crawl to other fungus-insect colonies, or crawl out and settle down on the clean bark, thereby disseminating the fungus.

In return for a home and protection, a number of the scale insects are parasitized by the fungus. Such insects live longer than the healthy ones but never reproduce. It is from the parasitized insects that the fungus gets its nourishment. The spore-forming period of the fungus reaches its peak in mid-April and dwindles to nothing by the first of June; consequently, the greater number of parasitized insects will be found during late spring and summer, while the reverse is true in fall and winter when no spores are formed. The fungus spore enters the circulatory system of the crawling nymphs and de-

velops slowly in the hemocoele, establishing connection with the parent fungus only after the insect has molted for the last time. Such parasitized insects are finally killed and used up by the fungus. Through this partnership a compound type of organism is formed comparable with lichens but more complex in that a third organism, the living tree, is necessary. Several species of this genus cause damage to economic plants. Couch found that the disease may be controlled by spraying with a combination fungicide and insecticide in midspring, when the fungus is sporulating and the first nymphs are crawling.

During World War II mosquito larvae whose coeloms were filled with brown oval bodies were collected from around military camps in south Georgia and sent to Couch for identification of the "parasites." These turned out to be the resting sporangia of the genus *Coelomomyces*, which belongs in the Blastocladiales. From the material sent him Couch described 11 new species, several of which parasitized and killed some of the most important mosquito species of the Southeast—the first record of this fungus in the Western Hemisphere. He realized that this fungus might be important in the biological control of mosquitoes if it (1) proved to be fatal to mosquitoes, (2) were harmless to other organisms, (3) could be cultured in vitro or in larvae in large quantities, and (4) produced reproductive bodies which could be dried and mixed with an appropriate carrier for wide dissemination. The first two postulates were satisfied, but attempts so far to culture *Coelomomyces* in vitro have failed. The problem of culturing the parasite in larvae has been to get infection. Successful infection experiments have been carried out by others but only by using soil and detritus from a location where infected larvae had been found, and no correlation between egg hatching and sporangial germination was recognized.

Couch and his co-workers found perfect material for study in the local water reservoir at the University of North Carolina: *C. punctatus* in the malarial mosquito, *Anopheles quadrimaculatus*. The mosquito was colonized in the insectary by C. J. Umphlett, and thus a steady supply of eggs and large quantities of infected larvae collected from University Lake were available for use in germination and infection experiments. Couch found that the sporangia would germinate after 48 hr, the same length of time it took for the eggs to hatch; thus there was a remarkable time correlation between sporangial germination and egg hatching. The highest rate of infection occurred when germinating sporangia and hatching eggs were put together in small beakers (150 ml) and 24 hr later transferred to large containers in the greenhouse, where such experimentation was carried out. In view of the experience of other workers with soil, experiments were conducted to find out if soil is necessary for infection. Soil from locations where parasitized larvae had been found usually gave a high rate of infection, but was shown not to be essential.

Several sets of experiments were conducted to find out at what stage in the life of the mosquito infection occurs. Germinating sporangia were put with the first, second, third, and fourth instars, but only with the first did infection occur. To see if the sporangial inoculum could withstand prolonged drying, Couch mixed large numbers of sporangia with wet red clay, molded the clay into pieces the size of yeast cakes, and after drying for 3 months added a cake to a small pan of rainwater. Eggs were added at this time and at intervals of 48 hr for 2 weeks. Infected larvae were recovered from two such experiments.

While examining bits of boiled grass leaves used as bait for aquatic fungi in soil samples from the Philippine Islands, Couch observed sporangia formed on very delicate mycelia with spores arranged in coils. He first suspected a small chytrid, but studies showed that it was an undescribed type of actinomycete with sporangia in which there were motile spores, and hence it was given the name *Actinoplanes*, the actinomycete with planospores. Later studies on the structure and behavior of the spores, the structure and division of the chromatinic bodies, and the chemistry of the cell walls reinforced this conclusion. Isolations from soil samples from many parts of the world showed that these organisms are worldwide in distribution, occurring in practically all soils which contain humus. The greater number of these organisms prefer cellulose or other plant materials, but some were isolated on hair, bits of horn and hoof, and snake skin. The 2000 isolates, most of them incompletely studied, fall into five generic groups based on spore shape and structure and many other characters. Recently two genera were added by other workers. The precise role of these organisms in the soil is not known, but they probably assist in the formation of humus. All of the isolates are being tested by a pharmaceutical company for possible use as drugs, and a few show promise in the formation of cortisone and antibiotics.

The son of a Baptist minister, Couch attended Trinity College (now Duke University) and earned his A.B. (1919), M.A. (1922), and Ph.D. in botany (1924) from the University of North Carolina. After service in France during World War I he returned as instructor of botany at the university, where he subsequently became Kenan Professor in 1944 and head of the department during 1943–59. He acted as consultant for various phases of the National Science Foundation programs in Washington, D.C., India, and Japan. Elected to the National Academy of Sciences in 1943, he received a Merit Award of the Botanical Society of America in 1956.

Couch wrote *Gasteromycetes of the Eastern United States and Canada*, with W. C. Coker (1928), and *The Genus Septobasidium* (1938).

For background information *see* ACTINO-MYCETACEAE; FUNGI; FUNGISTAT AND FUNGICIDE; INSECTA; SOIL MICROORGANISMS in the McGraw-Hill Encyclopedia of Science and Technology. □

★ COULSON, Charles Alfred

British mathematician and theoretical chemist
Born Dec. 13, 1910, Dudley, Worcestershire, England

COULSON'S SCIENTIFIC work was a good illustration of the way in which during the 20th century many branches of science came so close together that they almost merged. He took degree examinations at Cambridge, first in mathematics and then in physics, ending with a Ph.D. in chemistry. The award of a prize fellowship at Trinity College, Cambridge, in 1934 gave him 4 years of complete freedom to do what he wanted; he worked as an experimental bacteriologist to get experience in a different kind of scientific inquiry from the physical sciences.

This overlapping of interests was shown in most of his scientific work. His best-known studies were in molecular structure, where he was the first person to make calculations of the energy levels of a polyatomic molecule. In 1926 E. Schrödinger's introduction of the wave equation had shown the lines on which this was to be done, as well as the likelihood that chemistry was to become more and more a part of physics. But in 1933, when Coulson set out to calculate the stability of the simplest of all polyatomic molecules, H_3^+, and one of the commonest, methane, CH_4, he found that he had to bring in considerable mathematical techniques even to evaluate some of the necessary integrals.

A similar overlap could be traced in his work on chemical bonds of fractional order. Ever since the 1860s chemists had talked about single, double, and triple bonds between a pair of atoms. They used the standard symbols, $-$, $=$, and $\equiv$ (for example, $H-H$, $O=O$, $N\equiv N$ for H_2, O_2, N_2). But in many of the most interesting molecules in organic chemistry it was becoming clear, from study of their lengths, that a large number of chemical bonds could not be described in this simple way. Linus Pauling had proposed a certain double-bond character for bonds that were stronger than single but less strong than double bonds. In 1937 Coulson generalized this within the approximation known as the method of molecular orbitals (to which indeed he made many contributions), and was able to define a fractional bond order for bonds intermediate between the integral values. This fractional bond order could be calculated, and properties of the bond and of the molecule as a whole would follow.

The idea of fractional bonds rationalized a lot of chemical structure and of chemical reactivity. Coulson himself was able to show that an old theory of partial valence due to J. Thiele could be put on a firm basis, and he introduced the idea of free valence.

Some of the most interesting general rules for the electrons in these organic molecules (the π-electrons, as they came to be called) could be found by using the theory of contour integration in a complex plane, thus uniting chemistry and mathematics. Together with his research student G. S. Rushbrooke, he showed that large planar organic molecules can be divided into two main groups with widely differing chemical properties. The first group (for example, benzene, naphthalene) were called alternants, since the atoms can be divided into two groups, so that no member of one group is adjacent to another member of the same group. The second group of molecules were called nonalternants (for example, azulene). In the ground states of alternant hydrocarbons the charges on all the atoms are equal.

In 1945–50 Coulson and another research student, H. C. Longuet-Higgins, wrote down very general rules showing the changes that will take place all over a molecule if a small change is made in one part of it. Thus the effect of replacing a CH group by a N atom, as in passing from benzene to pyridine, can be predicted easily by the aid of certain polarizability coefficients. The charges on the atoms and the orders of the bonds form a matrix whose behavior is crucial for the full description of a molecule.

It was natural that Coulson's interests should lead him into biochemistry. Together with A. and B. Pullman and R. Daudel, he started the molecular-orbital discussion of a family of organic molecules that cause tumors (carcinogenic molecules). He later became interested in the theory of drugs, and in the hydrogen-bond forces that hold together the two strands of a DNA nucleic acid chain or the α-helix of a polypeptide. In addition, he was one of the best-known writers and speakers on the relation between science and religion.

Coulson spent the years of World War II at Queens College, Dundee, lecturing in mathematics, physics, and chemistry. In 1945 he went to Oxford as the first Imperial Chemical Industries fellow in chemistry, and concurrently as lecturer in mathematics at University College. In 1947 he became Wheatstone Professor of Theoretical Physics at Kings College, London, and in 1952 Rouse Ball Professor of Mathematics at Oxford University and a fellow of Wadham College. He became a fellow of the Royal Society in 1951.

Coulson published over 300 scientific papers and the books *Waves* (6th ed. 1955), *Electricity* (3d rev. ed. 1956), *Valence* (1952; 2d ed. 1961), and a *Dictionary of π-Electron Calculations*, with A. Streitwiesser, Jr. (1965).

For background information *see* CHEMICAL BINDING; MOLECULAR STRUCTURE AND SPECTRA; ONCOLOGY; VALENCE in the McGraw-Hill Encyclopedia of Science and Technology. □

★ COURANT, Richard

American mathematician
Born Jan. 8, 1888, Lublinitz, Germany

FROM HIS student days in D. Hilbert's circle in Göttingen, Courant considered mathematics in the context of general scientific endeavor. His doctoral thesis was concerned with the calculus of variations, a subject that aims at determining functions for which given functional expressions attain maximal or minimal or, generally speaking, stationary values. Such variational problems are easily reduced to boundary-value problems for differential equations, but the solution of these equations can present serious difficulties. The foremost instances are the problem of minimal surfaces (to find a surface of least area spanning a prescribed curve in space) and the boundary-value problem of potential theory. K. F. Gauss and others in the early 19th century tried to dismiss these difficulties with the observation that the problems are equivalent to that of finding the minimum of positive "energy" expressions and that, therefore, the existence of a minimum and hence of the desired solution appears self-evident. This direct procedure, named Dirichlet's principle, served as the fundament on which Bernard Riemann built his geometric theory of functions of a complex variable, one of the central and exciting mathematical achievements of the 19th century. Riemann died before Weierstrass's devastating criticism of the reasoning in Dirichlet's principle became generally known; saving Riemann's theory became a major challenge and stimulus in mathematical analysis. Success was not achieved until 50 years later by Hilbert. His proof of the possibility of a "direct" solution of such variational problems initiated a long and, even now incomplete development of a deep theoretical character, affecting many applications, including numerical methods. Courant's doctoral dissertation (1910) under Hilbert's sponsorship simplified and modified Hilbert's approach and applied the principle to fundamental problems of geometric function theory; it established general theorems concerning conformal mapping of multiply connected Riemann surfaces of higher genus. Subsequent publications aimed at simplification and extension of Hilbert's theory of Dirichlet's principle; problems of conformal mapping were pursued with a view toward characterizing simple types of "normal" domains on which Riemann domains could be mapped conformally. Other publications emphasizing the viewpoints of variational calculus dealt with aspects of partial differential equations of physics.

Another series of Courant's publications originated from a famous problem of mathematical physics posed by H. A. Lorentz: Vibrating continua, such as a membrane, a plate, or a body of enclosed gas, possess an infinite sequence of eigenfrequencies corresponding to the fundamental tone and the succession of overtones of acoustical systems. For many key questions in physics it is important that approximately or asymptotically (that is, for large frequencies) the distribution of these frequencies depends, for homogeneous media, only on the volume of the vibrating continuous system and not on its shape in detail and that similar facts are true of nonhomogeneous media. The first proof was given by Herman Weyl; soon afterward Courant disposed of the problem and its ramification by a simple variational method based on the observation that the eigenfrequencies can be defined as successive maximinima of variational problems, the fundamental frequency being the first. Many other applications of this maximinimum principle were later given by Courant and others.

Yet another of Courant's publications treated the transition by limiting processes from finite difference equations to differential equations. The last of these, written in close collaboration with K. O. Friedrichs and Hans Lewy, though theoretical in its intention, subsequently had a considerable influence on the development of practical numerical methods for the solution of partial differential equations. It showed that in problems of wave propagation and the like the mesh width used for numerical calculations must be subjected to simple restrictions in order to secure convergence or stability. The connection between partial differential equations and "random walk" or stochastic processes also was discussed in this paper.

Other publications dealt with constructive, numerically applicable methods for solving differential equations of physics. Among publications of a later period were a series of papers on minimal surfaces which Courant solved on the basis of Dirichlet's principle; on Plateau's problem of minimal surfaces in given contours; and on the more general problems of J. Douglas, who had led the successful attack on these fascinating classical problems.

Courant was interested in furthering the publication of advanced mathematical textbooks in order to facilitate access to relevant developments in mathematical sciences. He founded a series of such books with the help of his friend Ferdinand Springer, the publisher. This series, continued after Courant's resignation as editor, contains almost 140 volumes.

Courant believed that scientific progress should be presented not merely in specialized papers but also in self-sufficient textbooks and monographs. In several of his works he combined the attitude of research with that of a wider expository scope. An elementary work on calculus, *Differential and Integral Calculus* (2 vols., 1936–37), emphasized the connection of calculus with applications. *What Is Mathematics?*, with H. Robbins (1941), aimed at a not necessarily professional public. With Friedrichs, Courant published *Supersonic Flow and Shock Waves* (1948), the result of research activities during World War II. *Dirichlet's Principle, Conformal Mapping and Minimal Surfaces* appeared in 1950. The most important of Courant's books is *Methods of Mathematical Physics* (2 vols.; English transl. 1953, 1962), partly rooted in Hilbert's tradition. It appeared in time to be helpful to the evolution of quantum

mechanics, mainly within the closely knit circle of young physicists who worked in Göttingen in the 1920s. The second volume, published a decade later in the United States, contained a last chapter written with the cooperation of Friedrichs and stimulated the field of partial differential equations. A third, supplementary volume bringing the subject up to date is in preparation. Most of Courant's books were translated into various languages.

Courant received his secondary education, largely in the classics, at a gymnasium in Breslau. He studied physics, mathematics, and philosophy briefly in Breslau and Zurich, then under Hilbert in Göttingen, where he received his doctor's degree in 1910. He then became assistant and privatdozent. His scientific development was impeded first by economic hardships, then by military service in the Prussian army, and soon afterward by service in World War I for more than 4 years. After a year in combat he was wounded, and subsequently worked on the development—technical, organizational, and educational—of wireless communications for use in the front lines. This activity brought him into contact with modern electronics in its early stages. After his discharge from the army in 1918 and a short interlude as a politician, he was called in 1919 to the University of Münster as a professor of mathematics, and he returned to Göttingen in 1920 as successor of Felix Klein to develop a center of mathematical sciences. The decisive support of his friends Niels and Harald Bohr and the Rockefeller Foundation and an enlightened Prussian minister of education led to the establishment of the Mathematics Institute and the strengthening of physics and other sciences in Göttingen. In 1933 the National Socialist government moved against Göttingen University, a center of independent liberal tradition. Courant left along with Max Born, James Franck, Emmy Noether, and others. In 1934, after an academic year as a visitor at Cambridge University, he joined the faculty of New York University on the suggestion of Abraham Flexner and helped develop graduate work. Together with K. O. Friedrichs and with J. J. Stoker, Courant made a systematic attempt at supplementing the more theoretical traditional pursuit of mathematics by drawing applied mathematicians into the program. After a few years of struggle the group at New York University became the nucleus of an increasingly intense effort organized by the Office of Scientific Research and Development (OSRD) under Warren Weaver, and it played a significant role in research arising in the technological war effort. Courant was involved as a member and consultant of the Applied Mathematics Panel of OSRD. After the war the NYU group developed into a more stable, largely government-supported Institute of Mathematical Sciences with Courant as director. Supported by the Atomic Energy Commission, one of the first big electronic computers was installed in the Institute. A grant by the Alfred P. Sloan Foundation and supplementary grants by the Ford Foundation and the National Science Foundation gave the Institute a home (1965), the magnificent Warren Weaver Hall, with excellent facilities for the large staff and more than 500 graduate students, as well as for numerous visitors from many parts of the world. The Institute was named after Courant. After his retirement as director and head of department, Courant served on the governing board of the Institute, as science advisor of the university, and as scientific consultant to government agencies and primarily to the International Business Machines Corp. Courant was elected to the National Academy of Sciences, the American Philosophical Society, the Accademia dei Lincei in Rome, the royal academies of the Netherlands and Denmark, the Academy in Göttingen, and the Academy of Sciences of the Soviet Union. Besides several honorary degrees, he received the Navy Distinguished Public Service Award (1958), the Knight-Commander's Cross and Star of the Order of Merit of the Federal Republic of Germany (1958), and the Award for Distinguished Service to Mathematics from the Mathematical Association of America (1965).

For background information *see* CALCULUS OF VARIATIONS; CONFORMAL MAPPING; GROUP THEORY; INTEGRAL TRANSFORM; VIBRATION in the McGraw-Hill Encyclopedia of Science and Technology.   □

★ COURRIER, Robert

French endocrinologist
Born Oct. 6, 1895, Saxon-Sion, Meurthe-et-Moselle, France

COURRIER WORKED chiefly on two subjects: the thyroid and the sex hormones. At the start of his research career (1922–24), he noted that animals that receive large doses of thyroid extract exhibit a thyroid gland that is at rest from the secretory viewpoint. It seemed to him that an equilibrium exists between the activity of the gland and the quantity of its hormone present in the blood, so that if the hormone is administered in excess, the corresponding gland no longer functions. Courrier verified this fact later, with Frédéric Joliot-Curie, by means of radioactivity: The injection of thyroxin opposes the penetration of radioactive iodine into the thyroid, and without iodine the activity of the thyroid stops.

Courrier, together with J. Roche, again found this phenomenon by the use of a new thyroid hormone, triiodothyronine.

It is now known that the pituitary gland plays an important role in these endocrine equilibria. Courrier observed, with Joliet-Curie and A. Horeau, that thyroxin, labeled with radioactive iodine, concentrates itself exactly in the pituitary in a selective manner. D. Bovet undertook the study of a new antithyroid, aminothiazole; with Bovet, Joliot-Curie, and Horeau, Courrier confirmed that this antithyroid does not oppose the penetration of iodine into the thyroid, but that it prevents the synthesis of the iodinated hormone.

The scientific activity of Courrier was devoted principally to the field of the sex hormones. He studied the testicle and the ovary. He adduced arguments in favor of the theory of his teacher P. Bouin, who, with his friend P. Ancel, defended the idea that the male hormone is produced, not by the seminiferous tubes, but by the interstitial gland situated between these tubes. Indeed, in certain hibernating mammals the seminiferous tubes can be completely at rest, while the interstitial gland is obviously active; in this case the male hormone is liberated in quantity, as demonstrated by the development of the secondary sexual characteristics. By long treatment of rats with gonadotropic hormones a collaborator of Courrier, M. Rivière, determined that a tumor of the interstitial gland develops. Courrier studied this tumor with Rivière and R. Colonge; it is easily transplanted from one rat to another and is composed uniquely of interstitial cells. It secretes androgens in abundance, as can be confirmed by grafting it to castrated males.

Courrier took an important part in the first researches on female hormones. He showed that in the guinea pig characteristic modifications appear in the genital apparatus when the first follicles ripen in the ovary. He found in women the follicular hormone that E. Allen and E. A. Doisy discovered in the sow. He showed the presence of this hormone in human amniotic fluid, and he observed that it can traverse the placenta and the mammary gland and strongly affect the fetus and the newborn (genital crisis). He adduced arguments in favor of the existence of two ovarian hormones at a time when unicism was defended by eminent specialists. He studied the functional relationships that link the two hormones of the ovary (antagonism and synergism).

Courrier carried out a detailed analysis of the endocrinology of gestation in an important book published in 1945. In this book is found his unexpected experience with experimental extra-uterine pregnancy, which normally evolves in the castrated female rabbit, while the removal of the ovaries always involves the interruption of normal uterine pregnancy in this species. When the fetus is in the uterus, the hormones are essential in order to permit this organ to develop and to follow the fetal expansion; but the extra-uterine fetus is free of uterine constraint. The uterus is nevertheless indispensable because the fetus can leave from it.

It was in Courrier's laboratory that his collaborators Horeau and J. Jacques carried out the synthesis of a new artificial estrogen derived from an acid named allenolic in honor of E. Allen. Courrier carried out a detailed physiological study on it. He also studied, with his student A. Jost, the first artificial progestive, pregneninolone, synthesized by German chemists. This substance is as progestive as the progesterone of the corpus luteum, but is more androgenic than the latter; this property resulted in grief when the product was utilized in pregnant women, since it traversed the placenta and partially masculinized female fetuses. One must never forget that the placenta can be permeable.

Courrier studied science at the University of Nancy and medicine at the universities of Nancy and Strasbourg (Agrégé des facultés de médecine, Docteur ès sciences). He was professor of medicine at the University of Algiers during 1926–38 and at the Collège de France during 1938–67. He was one of the members of the Centre National de la Recherche Scientifique (CNRS) from 1957 to 1962 and was awarded the Centre's Gold Medal in 1964. He was elected to the French Academy of Sciences in 1944 and, as a foreign member, to the Royal Society of London in 1953 and the American Academy of Arts and Sciences in 1956.

For background information see ANDROGEN; ENDOCRINE MECHANISMS; ESTROGEN; HORMONE; THYROID GLAND in the McGraw-Hill Encyclopedia of Science and Technology.   □

★ **CRAIG, Lyman Creighton**

American biochemist
Born June 12, 1906, Palmyra, Iowa, U.S.A.

WHILE CARRYING out structural studies on alkaloids of ergot, veratrine, and aconite during the 1930s at the Rockefeller Institute, Craig was impressed by the need for better techniques in separating, isolating, and characterizing pure, single substances. This led him to make the science and technology of separations a major goal in his career. The decision resulted in a long series of papers on micromethods for fractional crystallization, distillation, extraction, and dialysis. The first of these was important in the alkaloid studies, but the fractional extraction method became much more widely used in biochemistry. It included the design of a stepwise extraction train, which permitted up to 1000 simultaneous quantitative extractions to be made. This could be done in such a way that the result could be directly interpreted by the binomial theorem and the normal curve of error. The procedure was called "countercurrent distribution," or simply CCD.

A number of techniques were developed to make CCD less tedious. Among them was a method for recovering fragile solutes from dilute solution, the now well-known method of "rotary evaporation." The dialysis studies were begun also as a recovery method but soon developed into a major study, potentially as important as the extraction studies. These studies still remain under development. CCD gained acceptance during World War II when it became the tool for documenting the purity of many new synthetic potential antimalarials. It was subsequently used for a similar purpose in the rapidly developing field of the antibiotics, which included the penicillins, bacitracins, polymyxins, tyrocidines, actinomycins, and so forth. It often resolved preparations considered to be pure by other criteria into several components. Many new antibiotics were isolated in pure form for the first time with the technique. CCD proved to be especially useful for separating and characterizing larger solutes which associate strongly, such as the tyrocidines. A method was developed, called "the method of partial substitution," for determining the true molecular weight of this type of solute. The procedure, which was based on CCD, was applied to the hormone insulin, and clearly established its true molecular weight as being in the 6000 range, rather than 12,000. In other laboratories a number of hormones were isolated in pure form and characterized for the first time by CCD. These included ACTH, melatonin, oxytocin, vasopressin, parathyroid hormone, angiotensin, and others. CCD proved to be the best technique for separating the individual transfer ribonucleic acids from the complex mixture of the many different amino acid specific forms.

Craig's interest, with his series of papers on dialysis, began as a modest attempt to improve simple laboratory dialysis. However, he soon realized that, with the appropriate physical arrangement and adjustment of the effective pore size, dialysis through cellophane membranes could be used as a tool of high discrimination for separations, studies of purity, conformation, association, binding, and so on. The approach, which stressed the thinnest film of solution reproducibly realizable against the largest possible membrane surface, included a thin-film countercurrent dialyzer.

Craig began his structural studies when he went to the Rockefeller Institute as an assistant of W. A. Jacobs in 1933. He worked on the chemistry of the alkaloids of ergot, substances which had not previously yielded to chemical investigation. Soon Jacobs and Craig reported the isolation of an unknown amino acid, which they named lysergic acid. Considerably later the dimethyl amide of this acid, now well known as LSD, was prepared at the Sandoz Laboratories in Switzerland and found to have intense psychic properties. During the next few years the major structural features of lysergic acid, as well as those of the alkaloids, were elucidated at Rockefeller Institute. The alkaloids of ergot proved to be cyclic polypeptides of unusual structure, and to be the first members of a much larger group of modified polypeptides elaborated by lower organisms. These included the penicillins, gramicidins, tyrocidines, polymyxins, bacitracins, and others. Craig and his collaborators revealed most of the structural features of the tyrocidines, polymyxins, and bacitracins. CCD played an important role in this work.

In studies with proteins, in collaboration with R. Hill, he found that the CCD method would clearly separate for the first time the two protein chains in hemoglobin in preparative amounts. This made possible a major structural study of hemoglobin. The entire amino acid sequences of the α- and β-protein chains of human hemoglobin were established by a group of collaborators in Craig's laboratory. Subsequently, in collaboration with N. Hilschmann, he made the first breakthrough in sequence studies with Bence-Jones protein.

The son of a farmer who had served two terms in the Iowa state legislature, Craig, in taking up chemistry, was influenced by his older brother David, who became a well-known rubber chemist and editor of the *Journal of Rubber Chemistry*. Craig received his B.S. in 1928 and his Ph.D. in 1931 from Iowa State University. His original intention was to do research on organic insecticides and study their mechanism of action. He was awarded a postdoctoral National Research Council fellowship to pursue these studies, and he spent 2 years (1931–33) at the Johns Hopkins University synthesizing analogs of nicotine. Appointed an assistant in the department of chemical pharmacology at the Rockefeller Institute in 1933, he became an associate in 1937, an associate member in 1945, and a member in 1949. He was with the Office of Scientific Research and Development in 1944. Craig received the Albert Lasker Award in Basic Science in 1963 for his work on the CCD method and the Fisher Award in Analytical Chemistry of the American Chemical Society in 1965. He was elected to the National Academy of Sciences in 1950 and to the American Academy of Arts and Sciences in 1961.

For background information *see* DIALYSIS; EXTRACTION; POISON; PSYCHOTOMIMETIC DRUG in the McGraw-Hill Encyclopedia of Science and Technology. □

★ CRAM, Donald James

American organic chemist
Born Apr. 22, 1919, Chester, Vt., U.S.A.

THE SUBJECT common to Cram's broad research interests was the symmetry properties of organic compounds and their reaction intermediates. His earliest papers dealt with stereochemical evidence for the ethylene phenonium ion, the first of the many bridged carbonium ions discovered in the 1950s and 1960s as intermediates in a variety of carbonium ion molecular rearrangement reactions. In this research the relationships between the three-dimensional (stereochemical) structure of starting material and product were employed to infer

the structure of short-lived but discrete reaction intermediates.

Although it was known for almost 100 years that carbanions (compounds containing negatively charged carbon) are one of the most important reaction intermediates in organic reactions, their stereochemical capabilities were not examined until 1955. At that time Cram and his students reported that substitution reactions in which carbanions are intermediates can proceed with either retention, inversion, or complete loss of configuration. After that time they studied the relationships between the stereochemistry of such reactions and the symmetry properties of the anion, the character of the counterion, the properties of the medium, and the mechanism of stabilization of the anion by substituents. Carbanions were discovered which, although themselves symmetrical, were demonstrated to exist in environments that were asymmetric by virtue of asymmetric solvation or ion pairing. This work was complemented by the investigations of base-catalyzed proton or deuteron transfers in media which are potential deuteron or proton donors. The first intramolecular proton transfer in 1,3- and 1,5-allylic anion rearrangements was discovered, and the phenomenon was demonstrated to be general, performed by enzyme systems and simple basic catalysts alike. Intramolecular proton transfers from the front to the back face of planar carbanions were next observed, and the "conducted tour mechanism for proton conduction along negatively charged, conjugated pi-systems" was announced. This work anticipated 1,3- and 1,5-asymmetric induction during proton transfer reactions, and demonstrated the detailed mechanism by which an asymmetric center can be destroyed at one site and generated at a distant site without loss of optical properties.

The early work of A. McKenzie in Great Britain and M. Tiffeneau in France had demonstrated that in conversions of ketones containing an adjacent asymmetric center to secondary or tertiary alcohols the order in which substituents are introduced into a given molecule controls which disastereomer predominates in the product. In 1952 Cram and his students published their celebrated rule of "steric control of asymmetric induction." This rule correlated the configurations of the predominant isomer produced in these reactions with the size and arrangement of the substituents attached to the asymmetric center of the starting ketone. In subsequent studies models for 1,2- and 1,3-asymmetric induction were studied to gain insight into what structural and environmental features produce the high degrees of optical purity found in nature's elaborations of optically active compounds, and the high stereochemical order observed in certain commercial polymerization reactions.

These asymmetric induction studies were addressed to problems of dynamic stereochemistry and the symmetry properties of short-lived organic reaction intermediates. In his invention and study of the paracyclophanes which commenced in 1951, Cram and his co-workers became involved with problems in static stereochemistry. This highly symmetric class of compound was ideal for examination of transannular electronic and steric effects. Later the simplest member of the class, [2.2]paracyclophane, was found by others to be a monomer for a commercial polymerization by vapor deposition (Union Carbide Plastics Co.). Interring activation, deactivation, and directive influences of substituents in electrophilic substitution were examined and interpreted in these systems. Optically active compounds of a new type, which owed their activity to restricted rotation, were prepared, and their optical stability studied. The paracyclophanes were found to exhibit novel electronic spectra when the benzene rings were held within interference radius of one another. They also proved to be exceptionally strong π-bases due to transannular electron release.

A lawyer's son, Cram did his undergraduate work at Rollins College (B.S., 1941). After a year at the University of Nebraska (M.S., 1942), he worked as a research chemist at Merck and Co. on penicillin and streptomycin, the first of the natural antibiotics. In 1945 he entered Harvard University as a National Research Council fellow, and obtained his Ph.D. there in 1947. At the University of California at Los Angeles he was an American Chemical Society fellow for a year, was made assistant professor in 1948, and became full professor in 1956. In 1955 he was awarded a Guggenheim fellowship for study at the University of London and the Swiss Federal Institute of Technology (ETH) in Zurich. In 1956 he was visiting professor at the National University of Mexico and in 1958 guest professor at the University of Heidelberg. He was elected to the National Academy of Sciences in 1961, and won the American Chemical Society Award for Creative Work in Synthetic Organic Chemistry in 1965.

Organic Chemistry (1959; 2d ed. 1964), which Cram coauthored with G. S. Hammond, represented the first major departure in organization for a basic textbook on the subject since early in this century. It was translated into eight languages. Cram also wrote *Reaction Mechanism*, with G. S. Hammond and A. Lwowski (1962); *Fundamentals of Carbanion Chemistry* (1965); and *Elements of Organic Chemistry*, with J. Richards and G. S. Hammond (1967).

For background information *see* ORGANIC CHEMISTRY; ORGANIC REACTION MECHANISM in the McGraw-Hill Encyclopedia of Science and Technology. □

★ CRAMÉR, Harald

Swedish mathematician and statistician
Born Sept. 25, 1893, Stockholm, Sweden

THE EARLIEST investigations of Cramér concerned the analytic theory of numbers. The asymptotic behavior of various arithmetic functions presents unsolved problems of great interest. P. G. L. Dirichlet, G. F. B. Riemann, and their followers had discovered the intimate relations between this type of arithmetic functions and certain analytic functions represented by Dirichlet's series, such as the famous Riemann zeta function. Cramér's main achievement in this field was the proof (1922) of a new type of mean value relations for some of the arithmetic functions concerned. A typical case is the following. Let $r(n)$ denote the number of representations of the positive integer n as the sum of two squares, and consider the summatory function $R(x) = \Sigma r(n)$, the sum being extended to all integers $n \leq x$. It is almost obvious that for large x the function $R(x)$ is asymptoti-

cally of the same order of magnitude as πx. Starting from some earlier results by G. H. Hardy, Cramér proved that the mean value integral

$$x^{-\frac{3}{2}} \int_1^x \left[R(t) - \pi t \right]^2 \, dt$$

tends to a constant limit as x tends to infinity. Similar results were obtained in other cases, including functions directly associated with the distribution of prime numbers. The subject has since been extensively pursued by other authors.

About 1925 Cramér turned his research activities to the field of mathematical probability theory. The central limit theorem of this theory asserts that under general conditions the sum of a large number of independent random variables has a probability distribution approximately of the normal (Moivre-Laplace) type. In particular, if $x_1, x_2, \ldots$ are independent random variables, all having the same probability distribution with zero mean and unit variance, the difference

$$\Delta_n(x) = P \left\{ \frac{x_1 + \ldots + x_n}{n^{1/2}} \leq x \right\} - \Phi(x)$$

tends to zero for every fixed x as n tends to infinity. Here P denotes the probability of the relation between the brackets, while Φ is the standard normal function:

$$\Phi(x) = (2\pi)^{-1/2} \int_{-\infty}^x e^{-t^2/2} \, dt$$

It was proved by A. M. Liapounov that $\Delta_n(x)$ is for large n at most of the order of magnitude $n^{-1/2} \log n$. Cramér showed (1928) that under appropriate conditions there exists an asymptotic expansion in powers of $n^{-1/2}$:

$$\Delta_n(x) = A_1(x) n^{-1/2} + A_2(x) n^{-1} + \ldots$$

where the $A_i(x)$ are independent of n. It follows in particular that $\Delta_n(x)$ is of the order $n^{-1/2}$, which is a best possible result. Later it was shown by A. C. Berry and C. G. Esseen that the last statement is true even under more general conditions than those assumed by Cramér.

The "problem of large deviations" is concerned with the behavior of $\Delta_n(x)$ when x and n both tend to infinity. Cramér obtained (1937) a fundamental theorem giving an asymptotic expansion for this case. He also proved the following theorem conjectured by Paul Lévy. If $\Delta_n(x)$ is for some n identically zero for all x, then every x_i is normally distributed. Both these last-mentioned theorems of Cramér have served as starting points for important work by Y. V. Linnik and other Soviet mathematicians.

In his book *Mathematical Methods of Statistics* (1945), Cramér set forth a treatise of methods of statistical inference, based on rigorous mathematical probability theory. Among the new results contained in the book is a proof of the statement that, when an unknown parameter is estimated from a set of statistical data, the precision cannot be improved beyond a certain limit, given by the Cramér-Rao inequality.

Cramér's work on stochastic processes was at first concerned with processes with independent increments. For certain classes of these processes he obtained (1930, 1955) results which are generalizations of classical results associated with the problem of the "gambler's ruin." These results have applications to important practical problems of insurance risk.

For stationary processes he proved (1942) a fundamental theorem on spectral representation. Later he made, in collaboration with M. R. Leadbetter, an extensive study (1962–67) of the properties of the trajectories of these processes, particularly the distribution of the intersections between a trajectory and a given level or curve. As a particular case, an exact form of the extreme value distribution of the trajectories is obtained.

If the variable parameter of a stochastic process is interpreted as time, a process may be called "purely nondeterministic" if the infinitely remote past of the process does not contain any relevant information about its possible future behavior. In the simple particular case when the process is stationary, it is well known that the process admits a representation as the accumulated effect of past "impulses" or "innovations." Cramér showed (1961) that in the general case under mild regularity conditions there exists a similar although somewhat more complicated representation, closely related to the theory of spectral multiplicity of a self-adjoint transformation in Hilbert space.

Cramér came from an old Swedish family, members of which had been judges, teachers, and businessmen on the island of Gotland. He graduated from the University of Stockholm in 1917, worked for some years as insurance actuary, and from 1929 to 1958 was professor at Stockholm. From 1950 to 1961 he was engaged in university administration, first as president of the University of Stockholm and then as chancellor of the entire Swedish university system. He received honorary degrees from the universities of Princeton (1947), Copenhagen (1950), and Stockholm (1964). He was an honorary member of the International Institute of Statistics and a member of various academies, including the American Academy of Arts and Sciences.

Cramér wrote, in addition to the book already cited, *Random Variables and Probability Distributions* (1937; 2d ed. paper 1962), *The Elements of Probability Theory* (1955), and *Stationary and Related Stochastic Processes*, with M. R. Leadbetter (1967).

For background information *see* NUMBER THEORY; PROBABILITY; STATISTICS; STOCHASTIC PROCESS in the McGraw-Hill Encyclopedia of Science and Technology.   □

★ DALE, Sir Henry (Hallett)

British pharmacologist and physiologist
Born June 9, 1875, London, England

WORKING WITH the parasitic fungus ergot, Dale succeeded in 1914 in isolating the compound acetylcholine, and recognizing its effect, which is similar to that brought about by nerves of the parasympathetic system. The German pharmacologist Otto Loewi showed by experiment in 1921 that nerves do not act directly on the heart, but that the immediate result of nerve stimulation is the freeing of chemical substances that act directly in producing the functional changes in the heart characteristic of nerve action. For their discoveries relating to the chemical transmission of nerve impulses, Dale and Loewi shared the 1936 Nobel Prize for medicine or physiology.

About 1904 Dale's life-long friend T. R. Elliott had confirmed that adrenaline, which is produced in the medulla of the adrenal glands, produces effects similar to those produced by activity in the sympathetic system. Therefore, he proposed that the result of impulses in the sympathetic nerves is a release of adrenaline at the nerve endings, as the direct cause of the stimulation effect.

In 1914 Dale published his observations on what appeared to be the two distinct types of action of acetylcholine. Through what he termed its "muscarine" action, it reproduced at the periphery all the effects of parasympathetic nerves with a fidelity comparable to that with which adrenaline had been shown to reproduce those of the true sympathetic nerves. These parasympathomimetic effects of acetylcholine were readily abolished by atropine. When they were suppressed, another type of action was revealed. Dale termed this the "nicotine" action

because it closely resembled the action of that alkaloid in its intense stimulant effect on all autonomic ganglion cells and on some voluntary muscle fibers.

From these observations he concluded that there was some degree of biochemical similarity between (1) the ganglion cells of the involuntary nervous system and the terminations of the nerve fibers in striated muscle and (2) the mechanism connected with the peripheral terminations of parasympathetic nerves. He also speculated on the possible occurrence of acetylcholine in the animal body, and on its physiological significance if it should be found there.

Thus when, in the period 1921–26, Loewi established the characteristics of the peripheral transmission of effects from the autonomic nerves to effector units innervated by them, Dale was in a favorable position to accept Loewi's demonstration and to extend his experiments. In 1929, in collaboration with H. W. Dudley, Dale extracted and identified acetylcholine as a natural constituent of a mammalian organ.

In 1933, working in Dale's laboratory, H. C. Chang and J. H. Gaddum found that sympathetic ganglia are rich in acetylcholine. In the following year W. Feldberg, B. Minz, and H. Tsudzimura observed that the effects of splanchnic nerve stimulation are transmitted to the cells of the suprarenal medulla by the release of acetylcholine at the nerve endings. These medullary cells are morphological analogs of sympathetic ganglion cells. Feldberg, continuing his study in Dale's laboratory, found that this stimulating action of acetylcholine on the suprarenal medulla was one of its "nicotine" actions. Feldberg, Gaddum, M. Vogt, and G. L. Brown continued this line of experimentation with Dale, and under his direction, to establish the role of acetylcholine as the chemical transmitter of the effects of nerve impulses at ganglionic synapses and at nerve endings on voluntary muscle fibers.

Although Dale came to be recognized mainly as a pharmacologist, this happened by the accident of opportunity rather than by intention. At the time of his training, there were no academic chairs of pharmacology in England or any teaching of it beyond short courses of perfunctory lectures on materia medica. He graduated in 1898 from Trinity College, Cambridge, in physiology and zoology; and the tenure of its Coutts-Trotter studentship enabled him to spend 2 further years, till 1900, in an apprenticeship to research in physiology under the guidance of such eminent investigators as J. N. Langley, W. H. Gaskell, H. K. Anderson, and later, F. G. Hopkins. He then left Cambridge for St. Bartholomew's Hospital, where he spent another 2 years in obtaining the clinical experience required for medical qualification.

By 1902, therefore, he had still made no firm decision between medical practice and academic physiology for his main career. The choice, however, seemed then to be almost made for him by the fact that the George Henry Lewes studentship unexpectedly fell vacant. This had been founded by the English novelist George Eliot to provide support for 2 years of research in physiology. It was tenable only by Cambridge graduates and was one of the very few emoluments then available in England for the support of any research in the medical field. Having successfully applied for this studentship, Dale was able to spend most of the next 2 years in the department of physiology of University College, London. This department had a distinguished history, entitling it, indeed, to be regarded as a cradle, for England, of experimental physiology; for Michael Foster and John Burdon-Sanderson, who were to found the chairs of physiology in Cambridge and, some years later, in Oxford, had both been pupils there of William Sharpey. There, too, Sidney Ringer had discovered the first physiologically balanced saline solution, and Edward Schäfer (later Sir Edward Sharpey-Schäfer), then holding the professorship, had been concerned with the discovery of the potent endocrine principles of the adrenal medulla and the neurohypophysis. Before Dale's entry there, Schäfer had migrated to Edinburgh, and had been succeeded at University College by Ernest H. Starling, a vigorous and inspiring leader and a devoted champion of research in physiology. In a joint investigation with his brother-in-law, William M. Bayliss, Starling had recently discovered secretin, the chemical messenger for the secretion of the pancreatic juice, and had introduced the term "hormone" to describe its function. He invited Dale to study the histological changes in the pancreas caused by its action; but though this occupied Dale for most of his 2 years as the Lewes student, the results had no novel or lasting significance. Meanwhile, he had arranged to spend the final 4 months of his tenure in widening his research experience by a visit to the Institut für Experimentelle Therapie, in Frankfurt am Main, where Paul Ehrlich, its director, was then changing the focus of his activity from his "side-chain" theory of immunity to artificial chemotherapy. Returning then to University College, London, Dale found that the immediate prospect for an academic career in physiology, or in any allied experimental discipline, was exceedingly bleak. He had thoroughly enjoyed his experience in Starling's department, where he had made incidental contacts with many important investigators and a number of stimulating and lasting friendships—including

one with Loewi, then making an exploratory visit to physiological centers in London, Cambridge, and Oxford. Dale and Loewi were to maintain these friendly contacts until Loewi died in 1961.

Dale's immediate problem in 1904, however, when he was already 29 years old, was to find an opportunity to use such experience as he had accumulated, and one also to provide such material support as would enable him to marry and to feel settled in a useful career. And, unexpectedly, such an opportunity was soon to be offered, but of a kind and from a quarter which, at that time, were viewed with suspicion by many of conventional opinions in medical and academic circles. Henry Wellcome, who had become the sole proprietor of the pharmaceutical firm of Burroughs Wellcome and Co., wished to find somebody to undertake pharmacological researches in the physiological laboratories which he had established in connection with his business. With Starling's advice and encouragement and after discussion of details with Wellcome himself, Dale accepted this offer, and had no reason to regret that he had done so. At their first interview Wellcome had expressed a hope that Dale might find it possible "to do something about the pharmacology of ergot." Contrary to Dale's own expectation, his attempts to meet this request, with the help of hints derived from errors and from a remarkable succession of accidental observations, provided openings to researches on sympatholytic alkaloids, on sympathomimetic amines, on histamine and the relation of its activity to the anaphylactic and other "shock" reactions, and, as described above, on acetylcholine.

After 10 years at the Wellcome Laboratories, Dale accepted one of four departmental appointments in the new National Institute for Medical Research, only a month before the outbreak of World War I. His research activities were diverted for more than a decade by more urgent duties, including those concerned with the establishment of international standards and units for such new types of remedy as the endocrines, including the then recently discovered insulin, and the vitamins. Other interests and duties accumulated with his appointment as director of the National Institute and later as president of the Royal Society (1940–45). Association with a series of able colleagues, however, enabled him to take a part in extending the evidence for the chemical transmitter functions of acetylcholine, demonstrated meanwhile by Loewi for the effect of the vagus nerve on the frog's heart, to transmission at ganglionic synapses and at the end'.,gs of motor nerve fibers on the "end plates" of voluntary muscle. In addition to the Nobel Prize, Dale received the Royal (1924) and Copley (1937) medals of the

Royal Society. He was elected a foreign member of the American Academy of Arts and Sciences in 1927 and of the U.S. National Academy of Sciences in 1940.

For background information *see* ACETYLCHO-LINE; NERVOUS SYSTEM in the McGraw-Hill Encyclopedia of Science and Technology.   □

★ **DALITZ, Richard Henry**

British theoretical physicist
Born Feb. 28, 1925, Dimboola, Australia

AT BRISTOL University in 1948 C. F. Powell and his collaborators established the first example of τ^+-meson decay to three pions, $\tau^+ \to \pi^+ + \pi^+ + \pi^-$, in their studies of cosmic-ray interactions in nuclear emulsion, not much more than a year after this group reported the discovery of the positive pion. Later in 1948 Dalitz became a research assistant at Bristol. The discussion of these discoveries and of other elementary particle processes being investigated at Bristol aroused his interest in these new and rare phenomena and led him to follow closely the development of knowledge of elementary particles in later years.

Dalitz's first work, at Cambridge, was a discussion of the properties of internal conversion electron-positron pairs emitted in transitions between nuclear states of zero spin, a process then being investigated for O^{16} by S. Devons. In 1950 Dalitz's friend D. T. King at Bristol observed that close electron pairs occasionally originate very close to the high-energy cosmic-ray stars occurring in nuclear emulsion. In thinking about these pairs, Dalitz realized that internal pair conversion could occur for one of the two photons emitted in the normal decay process $\pi^0 \to \gamma + \gamma$ for the neutral pion, leading to the visible decay mode, $\pi^0 \to \gamma + e^+ + e^-$, and he calculated the branching ratio to be about 1.2%. Observations of the spatial distribution of such "Dalitz pairs," as they are generally termed, were used in the earliest determinations of the lifetime of the π^0-meson.

By 1953 about a dozen examples of τ^+-decay had been reported. Many other K-meson decay processes, including the $\theta^+ \to \pi^+ + \pi^0$ process, were also becoming established. The τ^+ and θ^+ masses were found to be equal, within appreciable experimental errors; the τ^+ and θ^+ lifetimes were found to have the same order of magnitude. Then Dalitz showed how to analyze the way the total energy is shared between the three pions from τ^+-decay, depending on their total spin J and parity P; it was convenient to represent each decay event by a point on a two-dimensional phase-space plot (often referred to as a "Dalitz plot," or "Dalitz-Fabri plot"). This analysis depended only on simple physical ideas, on the way the internal angular momenta sum to J and the way the orbital and intrinsic parities combine to give P, and on the role of the centrifugal barriers in controlling the energy dependence of the decay amplitude in certain regions of the phase-space plot. The analysis showed that certain qualitatively striking features would be expected in the Dalitz plot distribution if the spin-parity of the τ^+-meson were such $[P = (-1)^J]$ that angular momentum and parity conservation would permit this particle to decay also through the θ^+-mode. Even the early data on τ^+-decay indicated that these features were not the case, showing that the 3π-system from τ^+-decay did not have the same spin and parity as the 2π-system from θ^+-decay. But further experiments soon showed that the mass, lifetime, and scattering properties are the same for τ^+- and θ^+-mesons, to a high precision. This dilemma then emboldened T. D. Lee and C. N. Yang to ask whether there really existed any evidence for parity conservation in weak decay processes, a question which led them to their celebrated proposals for β-decay experiments to seek direct evidence for parity nonconservation in weak interactions.

By 1957 nuclear emulsion studies had given evidence for many examples of a new nuclear species, the Λ-hypernuclei, consisting of a Λ-hyperon bound to an ordinary nucleus. With B. W. Downs, a postdoctoral visitor at Birmingham University, Dalitz began an extensive study of the systematics of their binding energies and decay properties. Spin-parity values were established for a number of hypernuclear species from analysis of their decay modes. With this information, the observation by M. Block and his collaborators of the process $K^- + He^4 \to \pi^- + {}_\Lambda He^4$, for K^--mesons coming to rest in helium, directly determined the K-meson parity. These analyses also led to the first knowledge of the low-energy Λ-nucleon interaction, its scattering strength, and its dependence on the total spin.

At Cornell University L. Castillejo, F. J. Dyson, and Dalitz discussed the general solution of the Chew-Low dispersion theory equation for a special case of meson-nucleon scattering, with the conviction that many solutions must exist corresponding to the possible existence of resonant states (or unstable particles) whose occurrence is due to forces not included in these equations. Such solutions were found, and this "CDD ambiguity" (so called from the initials of the researchers) has appeared in one form or another in the solutions of all dispersion theoretic schemes.

At Chicago, with S. F. Tuan, Dalitz developed a reaction matrix formalism appropriate for the analysis of data on meson-baryon processes. They applied this to analyze the $\bar{K}N$ interaction when data on the K^--proton processes at low energies became available from hydrogen bubble chamber studies. The strong elastic scattering found in the $\bar{K}N$ state of zero isospin led directly to the prediction of a "Dalitz-Tuan resonance" below the K^--proton threshold, now identified as the π-Σ resonance $Y_0^*(1405)$.

After 1960 the list of elementary particles increased rapidly with the discovery of many highly unstable particles at higher mass values. This situation suggests that all these particles may be composite, representing the excited states of some substructure underlying them. The evidence that unitary symmetry holds well for these particles suggests that they may arise from the binding of massive particles by "superstrong forces" of very short range, these massive particles having some particular simplicity with respect to unitary symmetry. The triplet of quarks, first proposed by M. Gell-Mann and by G. Zweig, are the first candidates to consider. By taking this possibility seriously, Dalitz (with many others, independently) achieved some qualitative successes in accounting for the properties of the higher mass resonances in terms of supermultiplets and their rotational excitations. In the end, such a model will probably be too simple to account completely for the resonance states observed, but its qualitative successes do support the notion that some composite nature holds for the observed particle states.

Dalitz was educated at Scotch College, Melbourne, where his interest in mathematics was stimulated by a teacher, A. D. Ross. Dalitz graduated in mathematics (B.A., 1944) and physics (B.Sc., 1945) from Melbourne University. He became a research student at Trinity College, Cambridge, as the Aitchison traveling scholar of Melbourne University, and received the Ph.D. (theoretical physics) in 1951, after periods at Bristol and Birmingham universities. He was lecturer and later reader in R. E. Peierls's department of mathematical physics at Birmingham, where he was greatly influenced by

F. J. Dyson's lectures. Dalitz then spent 2 years' leave at Cornell University, working also at Stanford University, the Institute for Advanced Studies, and Brookhaven National Laboratory. In 1956 he joined the Enrico Fermi Institute of Nuclear Studies of the University of Chicago, where he was appointed full professor in 1959. In 1960 he was elected a fellow of the Royal Society, and he was appointed Royal Society Research Professor at Oxford in 1963. He was awarded the Maxwell Medal of the Institute of Physics and the Physical Society in 1966.

For background information *see* COSMIC RAYS; ELEMENTARY PARTICLE; MESON; NUCLEAR REACTION; RADIOACTIVITY in the McGraw-Hill Encyclopedia of Science and Technology.   ☐

★ DALLDORF, Gilbert

American experimental pathologist
Born Mar. 12, 1900, Davenport, Iowa, U.S.A.

FOLLOWING GRADUATE study with Ludwig Aschoff and James Ewing, Dalldorf collaborated for 10 years with Walter H. Eddy in the characterization of vitamin deficiency diseases. The goals were to determine the structural effects of vitamin deprivations and to measure the importance of newly recognized vitamins in terms of human disease. Many of their observations were summarized in a text, *The Avitaminoses* (1937; 3d ed. 1944). Clinical and community surveys were undertaken but failed to establish vitamin deficiencies as currently important causes of disease in the New York area. A good food supply and public education had evidently prevented deficiency diseases, other than those determined by organic defects.

A new and compelling challenge to the medical profession emerged during the 1930s, when epidemics of poliomyelitis grew in size and intensity. Dalldorf established a small experimental poliomyelitis station, initially to test methods of treatment and later to devise a prophylactic. It was discovered that monkeys infected with the choriomeningitis virus withstood experimental infections with virulent poliomyelitis viruses that otherwise were invariably fatal. This surprising phenomenon was named the "sparing effect." The same summer F. O. MacCallum and G. M. Findlay in Great Britain reported that Rift Valley fever similarly protected monkeys against yellow fever. They chose to call it the "interference phenomenon," and that term is now universally used.

Unfortunately the interference phenomenon has not been usefully adapted to current problems in infectious disease, with the possible exception of canine distemper. It was used to good purpose nearly 200 years ago by Thomas Archer, a colonial physician, who discovered that the course of whooping cough, then a serious, debilitating disease, could be aborted by smallpox vaccination. The influence of virus interference is widespread in nature, and its principal mechanism, the formation of an inhibitory protein called interferon, was discovered by A. Isaacs. Eventually this remarkable mechanism may be applied to serve a therapeutic purpose.

Dalldorf was given the Lasker Award in 1959 for his recognition of the interference phenomenon and the subsequent discovery of the Coxsackie viruses. The stimulus, in this case, was Charles Armstrong's adaptation of a particular strain of poliomyelitis virus to rodents. Dallorf undertook to repeat Armstrong's experience and to isolate viruses in mice. No recoveries were made but an occasional mouse showed minor responses, a little sluggishness, or a slight limp. In such animals close microscopic examination frequently revealed minute but distinctive lesions in the brainstem and spinal cord. Few of the specimens that induced these effects contained poliomyelitis virus as judged by monkey tests, and the experience suggested that viruses other than poliomyelitis were involved in the summer epidemics.

In association with Grace M. Sickles, the search for other viruses was expanded and intensified in the Division of Laboratories and Research of the New York State Department of Health. Efforts were made to increase the susceptibility of the mice or to find more suitable rodents. Jeppe Orskov had learned to infect newborn mice with a mouse disease by painting the virus on the dam's nipples, and this finding suggested the use of immature animals as possibly more susceptible hosts of the hypothetical intestinal viruses.

The technique proved to be incredibly successful, and specimens from poliomyelitis patients injected intracerebrally or intraperi-

toneally into newborn mice were frequently found to harbor viruses of a wholly new variety. They were named Coxsackie viruses because they were first found in patients from that New York town. They have been often called "polio's cousins" since they resemble poliomyelitis viruses in so many respects. The Russians prefer to call one of the many types of Coxsackie virus the poliomyelitis virus, type 4. Other types were later proven to be responsible for diseases for which etiological agents had not been established. Epidemic pleurodynia, or Bornholm disease, is an example of this group. The Coxsackie viruses are ecologically related to the poliomyelitis viruses, and the suppression of poliomyelitis by vaccination may alter their prevalence and severity in the future.

Immature and embryonic animals had previously served experimentalists in various ways but had not been used in the isolation of viruses. Ludwig Gross quickly applied the method in his studies of mouse leukemia and demonstrated the first leukemia virus. Many mosquito-borne viruses have been identified by means of immature mice, and the technique is widely used at present. The successful use of tissue culture in the propagation of poliomyelitis viruses was discovered by J. F. Enders, T. H. Weller, and F. C. Robbins in the same year, 1948, that the Coxsackie viruses were identified. These two techniques have been invaluable to virologists ever since.

Dalldorf received his B.S. from the University of Iowa in 1921 and his M.D. from New York University in 1924. He was pathologist at New York Hospital in 1926–29, and at Grasslands Hospital, New York, during 1929–45. He was on the staff of the New York State Department of Health during 1945–57, and from 1959 worked at the Memorial Walker Laboratory, Sloan-Kettering Institute. He was elected to the National Academy of Sciences in 1955.

For background information *see* COXSACKIE VIRUS; POLIOMYELITIS in the McGraw-Hill Encyclopedia of Science and Technology. □

★ DANCKWERTS, Peter Victor

British chemical engineer
Born Oct. 14, 1916, Southsea, Hampshire, England

DANCKWERTS BEGAN teaching and research in chemical engineering in 1948, at a time when scientific analysis of the problems of chemical engineering, although recognized to be desirable, had not yet attracted the enormous amount of attention bestowed on it today. In situations where the well-developed disciplines of fluid mechanics and chemical thermodynamics

and the laws of conservation could be applied, all was well in principle, although in application mistakes were often made. In many of the typical situations faced by chemical engineers, the models used and the analyses based on them were as crude as children's drawings. This did not matter too much, perhaps, when the engineering itself was fairly crude, and emphasis was more on making things work than on making them work well. Increasing competition in postwar markets and increasing sophistication in design created a need for more sophisticated concepts on which to base the scientific analysis of chemical engineering problems.

The relationship between a conceptual model and the engineering situation to which it relates is a subtle one. The model must incorporate some of the physical features of the actual situation—enough to predict the way in which the situation will respond to changes in operating conditions. On the other hand, a model which is slavish in detail will be too complicated to be useful. Utility is the criterion of a model for use in engineering analysis; it must lead to results which the designer can use with facility, and should itself be simple enough so that the practical man can return to it and extract new solutions to meet changed circumstances. Finally, the model should have a certain esthetic appeal.

Danckwerts first turned his attention to a classical chemical engineering process—the absorption of a gas by a liquid. Gas absorption is one of the commonest processes encountered in the chemical industry. The equipment used for the purpose consists typically of a tower packed with metal or ceramic cylindrical rings. The absorbent liquid trickles down over this extensive surface, and the gas usually passes upward in countercurrent flow. The design and performance of such equipment is a matter of considerable economic importance. The phenomena occurring in the gas and liquid streams are obviously very complicated, involving convection and diffusion, and in many cases chemical reaction as well. This is not a situation in which it would be constructive to try to make a completely faithful model of the process. Danckwerts proposed a "surface-renewal" model, in which the liquid at the surface of the descending film is supposed to be replaced piecewise in a random manner by liquid from the interior of the film. During its time of exposure each element of surface is supposed to absorb gas in the same way, as though it were stagnant. The model is reasonably realistic, contains the minimum number of parameters required to fit the facts, and provides an elegant basis for design calculations. It also forms the basis of methods whereby results of relatively simple, laboratory-scale experiments can be used to predict the effects of chemical reactions on rates of absorption in industrial equipment.

Another concept, which proved of considerable value to practicing chemical engineers, was that of the spread of residence times of material flowing in a continuous stream through a plant or process—the typical situation in the modern chemical industry. Usually, some of the material takes a longer time and some a shorter time than the average to pass through the process. This is likely to affect the efficiency of the plant or the acceptability of the product. For instance, if wet material passes through a drier, some may pass through too quickly and emerge undried, while some may remain too long and become charred. Danckwerts showed how the distribution of residence times about the average can be quantitatively defined, and how it can be measured by simple techniques. He pointed out how the information may be used by plant designers—either in calculating the behavior of a plant if the distribution of residence times were known, or in modifying the design so as to control the distribution and improve the performance. These ideas were widely taken up and developed, and they proved useful in many ways.

Danckwerts also contributed ideas to other topics, such as the quantitative study of mixtures and mixing processes and the behavior of granular materials. He considered that university workers can make valuable contributions to practical technology by devising new concepts and developing new lines of thought—a type of intellectual activity for which they may be better placed than their colleagues in industry, who are usually faced with urgent short-term problems.

Danckwerts received his B.A. from Balliol College, Oxford, in 1939. During World War II he was in the Royal Navy. In 1946 he went as a Commonwealth Fund fellow to the Massachusetts Institute of Technology, where he took his

S.M. in chemical engineering practice in 1948. He then joined the staff of the newly formed department of chemical engineering at Cambridge University. In 1954 he was appointed deputy director of research and development in the Industrial Group of the Atomic Energy Authority. He was appointed professor of chemical engineering science at Imperial College, London, in 1956. In 1959 he returned to Cambridge as Shell Professor of Chemical Engineering.

For background information *see* ABSORPTION; FLUID MECHANICS; MODEL THEORY in the McGraw-Hill Encyclopedia of Science and Technology. □

★ DANJON, André Louis

French astronomer
Born Apr. 6, 1890, Caen, Calvados, France
Died Apr. 21, 1967, Paris, France

WHILE PRIMARILY concerned with the development and improvement of instruments and methods in positional astronomy, Danjon devoted considerable efforts to directing the activities of the Strasbourg Observatory and later the Paris Observatory. At the latter he rebuilt the affiliated Meudon Observatory; created new services, such as the Radio Astronomy Department; and recruited a large number of scientists to work under his direction, increasing the staff from 60 to 350 in 18 years.

Positional astronomy had its beginnings with naked-eye observations in remotest antiquity. The introduction and evolution of early instruments, such as the armillary sphere and the triquetrum, led to increased precision; naked-eye techniques reached their apex with the work of Tycho Brahe. The introduction of the telescope and the subsequent employment of photographic methods raised the accuracy of the discipline to remarkable heights, as evidenced by the compilation of star catalogs of extreme precision.

In his study of the methods of positional astronomy, Danjon concluded that the transit instrument had attained its maximum precision. This led him to investigate new systems of reference, systems that were simpler and, above all, homogeneous. These studies culminated in the design of a fundamental new instrument, the prismatic 60° astrolabe, which became known as the Danjon astrolabe. The most essential aspects of the instrument are that it is impersonal and coaxial. The optical train includes a double symmetrical Wollaston prism, which is moved linearly by an electric motor with variable speed gearing, and an equilateral glass prism. Both the direct and the reflected star images are seen through the Wollaston prism, the movement of which is adjusted so that the ordinary image of the one and the extraordinary image of the other are seen as approximately stationary and side by side. By periodically making and breaking a circuit through the pen of a choronograph, a series of readings is obtained whose mean corresponds to the time at which the star was at an altitude of 60°. The prototype was built in 1951 at the Paris Observatory, and a final version was completed in 1956. The latter, which has a focal length of 100 cm and an aperture of 10 cm, can be used to observe stars down to a magnitude of 6.3 with a precision never before achieved in positional astronony: The mean quadratic error is $0.''17$, and this has been reduced to $0.''10$ at certain sites. The Danjon astrolabe was in operation at more than 30 observatories by the late 1960s and was used in several cooperative projects—for example, in the International Geophysical Year and in the compilation of a fundamental catalog.

Another transit instrument, designed by Danjon while he was at the Strasbourg Observatory, is a reflecting transit instrument whose essential part is a Wollaston reversing prism. The device has an aperture of 6 cm, giving a precision of $0.''01$ in star positions. Danjon later built two similar instruments of an improved design at the Paris Observatory.

Early in his career Danjon had been greatly interested in visual photometry. He improved various differential photometers, which could be used to compare stars—day and night—without intermediate artificial stars by superimposing star images rather than by placing them side by side. In 1921 he built a photometer for observations of the lunar eclipse, and then he constructed an Arago-Pickering photometer, with which he made tens of thousands of observations of double stars. Danjon followed this with a double-image photometer, which was used to compare directly the Sun with the Moon, and with a cat's-eye photometer for studying variable stars. The latter had the advantage of also being able to measure the brightness of extended images, for example, of the Moon or of the "Earth light." Through its use Danjon became the first to plot a curve for the brightness of the Earth and to compute the planet's albedo (0.39). Finally, he designed a photometer to be used for the observation of Mercury and Venus, using the Sun as a reference, during the daylight hours. Danjon made more than 30,000 observations between 1937 and 1947, enabling him to calculate an albedo of 0.055 for Mercury and of 0.64 for Venus.

Among the other instruments that he designed were two spectrographs and a half-wave interference micrometer, which is more luminous than the Michelson interferometer and useful for observations of double stars and of Jovian satellites.

In 1958 Danjon became interested in the rotation of the Earth, in which irregularities could be determined by using the fundamental catalog compiled with the aid of the impersonal prismatic 60° astrolabe. Three variations in the rate of rotation must be distinguished: a yearly variation, due probably to atmospheric effects; a latitude variation, determined by S. C. Chandler in 1885; and an empirical irregular variation, representing the difference between universal time and atomic time, which can be represented by a smooth curve whose general trend can vary abruptly. Danjon intuitively deduced that these abrupt transitions were related to solar activity. In December, 1958, he published his theory. The paper noted that a sudden increase in the rate of the Earth's rotation coincided with an exceptionally intense solar event which took place on Feb. 23, 1956. Later Danjon was able to relate a new, sudden change in the rotation of the Earth (the length of the day had increased by a little less than a millisecond on July 17, 1959) to an increase in solar activity on July 11, 14, and 16. He documented his calculations with indisputable evidence in *Notes et Informations de l'Observatoire de Paris.*

After studying at the Ecole Normale Supérieure in Paris from 1910 through 1914, Danjon served in the French army until 1919, when he became an astronomer at the Strasbourg Observatory. He obtained the degree of Docteur ès sciences in 1928 at Strasbourg. Two years later he was appointed director of the observatory and in 1931 professor at Strasbourg University. In 1935 Danjon was named dean of the Faculty of Sciences at the university, which was evacuated to Clermont-Ferrand during World War II. He surrendered these posts in 1945 to become director of the Paris Observatory. In 1946 he was

appointed a professor at the Sorbonne and in 1954 director of the Institut d'Astrophysique de Paris. He retired from all three posts in 1963. Danjon was elected to the Académie des Sciences in 1948, and he was president of the International Astronomical Union from 1955 to 1958.

Danjon wrote *Lunettes et Telescopes,* with A. Coudon (1935), and *Astronomie Generale* (1952).

For background information *see* ASTROLABE, PRISMATIC; ASTRONOMICAL INSTRUMENTS; EARTH (ORBITAL MOTION); PHOTOMETER in the McGraw-Hill Encyclopedia of Science and Technology. □

DARWIN, Charles Galton

British physicist
Born Dec. 19, 1887, Cambridge, England
Died Dec. 31, 1962, Cambridge, England

WHILE INVESTIGATING the diffraction of x-rays, Darwin developed a method of calculating the intensity of reflection and the shape of the reflection curve. Darwin's theory, discovered independently and about the same time by Ewald in Germany, is known as the dynamical theory of x-ray diffraction. The form of the angular distribution of intensity in the diffraction pattern from a perfect crystal, as originally calculated by Darwin, is known as a Darwin curve.

The discovery of x-rays by Wilhelm Roentgen in 1895 led to research into their fundamental nature. Arthur Sommerfield, through diffraction experiments with slits and gratings, soon established that these rays are part of the electromagnetic spectrum and that they have a wavelength of about 10^{-9} cm. When coupled with an earlier suggestion by William Barlow that interatomic distances are of the order of 10^{-8} cm, this led Max von Laue to theorize that if a crystal were an orderly array of atoms, diffraction phenomena would occur that would be characteristic of the crystalline arrangement. In 1912, in collaboration with Friedrich and Knipping, von Laue published a paper indicating that such phenomena do indeed occur. This paper led Darwin, working in collaboration with Henry G. J. Moseley at the University of Manchester, to search for a theory that would better account for the experimental measures of intensity than the simple assumption that each atom scatters radiation as though the others were absent. In July, 1913, Darwin and Moseley published a paper that was mostly experimental, measuring the intensities of beams reflected from a crystal by the ionization produced. However, the importance of temperature was realized, and a crude theory of reflection of white radiation was presented.

The following February, Darwin published a paper in which he calculated the intensity of reflection by a crystal, allowing for the effect of temperature and the refractive index of the rays. However, he showed that the calculated effect was much smaller than that observed if the crystals were perfect. In a paper published 2 months later, the discrepancy was shown not to be caused (as Darwin had at first supposed) by the influence of the waves due to one plane of atoms on the atoms of other planes, though this effect does indeed exist, but to the imperfection of the crystal. In a paper published in 1922, Darwin showed how the theory expressed in these earlier papers justified the method of calculation of atomic scattering from the intensity of crystal reflections used by Bragg, James, and Bosanquet.

In the 1914 papers Darwin had calculated the efficiency of x-ray reflection by a perfect crystal, showing that over a very short angular range the superficial layers give a complete reflection, and he found that the calculated integrated reflection is far smaller than that observed by him and Moseley. He rightly ascribed the discrepancy to the fact that a crystal is not ideally perfect but is composed of a mosaic of blocks in slightly different orientations. Paradoxically, he found that imperfection increases the intensity of reflection, because the mosaic elements at depths beneath the crystal surface are not robbed of their chance to reflect by more superficial elements, since these are set at slightly different angles. The formulas that Darwin established in these papers were the basis for interpreting subsequent quantitative measurements.

Another significant contribution to theoretical physics was Darwin's use of Dirac's electron theory to derive the explanation of the fine structure of the hydrogen spectrum. In 1927, using as his theme that the electron is to be taken as a wave of two components (like light)

and not of one (like sound), Darwin was able to derive two wave equations to fit the hydrogen spectrum. They were unsymmetrical, taking a different form according to the direction of space chosen as the prime axis. Darwin tried to interpret them in terms of a vector, but the vector was arbitrary to some degree. Although this was before Dirac's postulation of the electron with four wave functions, Darwin's solution later proved an approximation to Dirac's.

In February, 1928, Dirac's first paper on his new relativistic electron appeared. Darwin at once recognized its significance and translated Dirac's work from noncommutative algebra into the ordinary language of differential equations. He also showed that his own two equations were approximations to those derived from Dirac's theory. Then he applied the theory to the problem of the hydrogen atom and determined the energy levels, including their fine structure. In addition, Darwin's paper made the Dirac theory accessible to physicists not yet familiar with the new quantum mechanics, greatly accelerating its general acceptance. Darwin followed this with two papers, one on the magnetic moment of the new electron and the other on its diffraction. In the first paper he analyzed the magnetic field of a moving Dirac electron and showed the relation between the contributions of the current and the intrinsic magnetic moment of the electron. He also examined the relation between the polarization of an electron wave and that of a wave of light. In the second paper Darwin worked out the simplest case of diffraction, namely, that by a line grating exerting periodic electric or magnetic forces, including the polarizing effects if any.

Among the other areas in which Darwin made contributions were classical optics, magneto-optics, and the absorption and scattering of alpha particles. In his later years he was deeply concerned with eugenics.

The grandson of Charles Robert Darwin, the father of the theory of evolution by natural selection, and the eldest son of George Darwin, a prominent astronomer, Charles Galton Darwin studied at Trinity College, Cambridge, and at the University of Manchester, receiving the degrees of M.C., M.A., and Sc.D. After completing his studies at Trinity in 1909, he was appointed a reader in mathematical physics at Manchester, where he worked under the direction of Lord Rutherford. He left this post in 1914 to serve in the army and, following his return to civilian life, in 1919, became a fellow and lecturer at Christ's College, Cambridge. Four years later Darwin was appointed professor of natural philosophy at the University of Edinburgh, a position he retained until 1936, when he returned to Cambridge as master of Christ's College. In 1938 he accepted the directorship of the National Physical Laboratory, a position he held until his retirement in 1949. In 1941–42 Darwin was in charge of the British Central Scientific Office in Washington, D.C., set up to improve liaison between the scientific war efforts of Great Britain and the United States. Among the honors he received was the Royal Medal of the Royal Society of London (1935), of which he was elected a fellow in 1922.

Darwin wrote *The New Conceptions of Matter* (1931) and *The Next Million Years* (1952).

For background information *see* ATOMIC STRUCTURE AND SPECTRA; ELECTRON; QUANTUM THEORY, RELATIVISTIC; X-RAY DIFFRACTION in the McGraw-Hill Encyclopedia of Science and Technology.   □

★ DE BAKEY, Michael Ellis

American surgeon
Born Sept. 7, 1908, Lake Charles, La., U.S.A.

During the past few decades remarkable developments in cardiovascular surgery have resulted from vigorous research conducted by medical scientists throughout the world. Beginning with the revolutionary work of N. V. Eck, Rudolph Matas, Alexander Jassinowsky, Alexis Carrel, and Charles C. Guthrie more than a half century ago, and continuing with the subsequent outstanding contributions of René Leriche, Robert E. Gross, Alfred Blalock, Clarence Crafoord, Reynaldo Dos Santos, Jean Kunlin, John H. Gibbon, and others, cardiovascular surgery has enjoyed extremely rapid advances. Several developments were primarily responsible for these advances: (1) relatively safe, readily applicable methods of angiography, which permits precise identification of the site, nature, and extent of diseased arterial segments and their effect on the distal arterial circulation; (2) highly successful techniques of vascular surgery, including vascu-

lar replacements for occluded or diseased segments; and (3) increasingly vigorous research in medical and surgical treatment of previously hopeless diseases.

Early in his medical career De Bakey recognized the value of technologic development and commercial production of synthetic materials in correcting previously incurable cardiovascular disease. While a young medical student doing research in the experimental surgical laboratory at Tulane University, De Bakey devised a pump that would provide continuous flow through a perfusion circuit without causing damage to blood. Widely used for its original purpose, this invention was later to have far more extensive and significant application. Gibbon, working on development of a heart-lung machine in Philadelphia, learned of De Bakey's constant-injection roller pump and, aware of its superiority to other pumps, asked De Bakey to send him a pump for incorporation in the heart-lung machine with which he was experimenting. De Bakey's pump eliminated the need for valves to direct the flow of blood. Previous roller pumps used to move blood through the perfusion circuit had proved unsatisfactory because the rubber tubes compressed by the rollers gradually moved forward as the rollers passed over them. De Bakey eliminated this creeping effect by using a rubber tube with a projecting, flat, rubber flange, which was clamped between the semicircular metal bars. The tube was thus fixed in place, and the rollers did not move forward. De Bakey's pump provided one of the two essential components in the successful development of Gibbon's apparatus, which has become the basic mechanism for the heart-lung machine used throughout the world.

In other pioneering research De Bakey experimented with methods of replacing diseased, obstructed, or otherwise damaged tissues of the vascular system, first by grafting human blood vessels and later by using various synthetic materials for grafts. He found dacron to be unique among these in producing just the proper amount of tissue attachment without inflammatory reaction. The pseudoendothelium that developed in the lumen simulated the normal blood interface and functioned well indefinitely. Dacron maintained its integrity and did not produce progressive fibrous tissue reaction. With these techniques, De Bakey successfully replaced blood vessels in many parts of the body, including the aorta and smaller vessels that carry blood to the legs and the brain and various other vital organs.

With increasing experience with angiography in the course of his daily surgical work, De Bakey became aware of the patterns of vascular disease and of its segmental and localized nature. He shifted interest from the cause of arterial disease, which remains obscure and con-

troversial, to the anatomic-pathologic characteristics of the lesion itself and its hemodynamic
functional effects. This new approach permitted
leaping across the etiologic barrier to effective
treatment, which is the ultimate objective of all
medical research. On this basis he classified
arterial occlusive disease into four major types:
(1) lesions affecting the major branches of the
aortic arch, (2) lesions affecting the visceral
branches of the abdominal aorta, (3) lesions
affecting the coronary arteries, and (4) lesions
affecting the terminal abdominal aorta and its
major branches. The predominant underlying
pathologic lesion in all four types is atherosclerosis.

De Bakey began to apply more and more the
principles of vascular surgery, namely, excision
and graft replacement, endarterectomy, patch
graft angioplasty, and bypass operations, in the
treatment of all types of aneurysms and occlusive disease of the vascular system, in which
restoration of normal circulation was the primary aim. Accordingly, he performed successful
surgical treatment for the first time of a number
of life-threatening cardiovascular disorders, including the following: resection of an aneurysm
of the thoracic aorta (1951); resection with
homograft replacement of a fusiform aneurysm
of the descending thoracic aorta (1952);
thromboendarterectomy of the carotid artery for
stroke (1953); resection and homograft replacement of an aneurysm of the distal aortic arch
(1954); resection with homograft replacement
of a fusiform aneurysm of the thoracoabdominal
segment affecting the celiac, superior mesen-
teric, and renal arteries, with restoration of
continuity to all these major visceral branches
(1955); resection with homograft replacement
of a fusiform aneurysm of the entire ascending
aorta with use of cardiopulmonary bypass with
the artificial heart-lung apparatus (1956); and
resection with homograft replacement, including
the innominate and carotid arteries of a fusiform
aneurysm involving the entire aortic arch, with
use of the artificial heart-lung apparatus (1957).

Most recently, De Bakey, recognizing the advantages of collaborative efforts by biologic and
physical scientists in modern medical research,
directed an artificial heart program at Baylor
University College of Medicine, in conjunction
with Rice University. Because of the complex
problems involved in the development of total
artificial replacement for the malfunctioning
heart, De Bakey and his associates directed their
immediate attention to devising a booster pump
to be used temporarily in patients with cardiac
failure while the damaged heart is recuperating.
From his extensive experience with dacron for
artificial arteries, De Bakey conceived the idea
of lining his experimental paracorporeal ventricular bypass pump and all its connections

with dacron velour as a blood interface. The
velour, which minimizes trauma to the blood,
proved to be a key factor in the development of
a successful heart assistor. After conclusive evidence was obtained that the device performed
satisfactorily in an extensive series of animals,
De Bakey became the first, in August, 1966, to
apply the heart pump successfully in a patient.
The patient, previously incapacitated, recovered
completely and resumed normal living.

The son of a successful businessman, De
Bakey received his early education in southwest
Louisiana, his medical education at Tulane University, and his graduate medical education in
New Orleans under Alton Ochsner and in Strasbourg and Heidelburg, where he studied under
René Leriche and Martin Kirschner. He received
his B.S. in 1930, M.D. in 1932, and M.S. in
surgery in 1935 from Tulane. During World War
II he became director of the Surgical Consul-
tants Division in the Surgeon General's Office.
One of his important contributions while on
active duty in this office was his proposal of a
systematic follow-up of veterans with certain
medical histories, which subsequently led to the
establishment of the Committee on Veterans
Medical Problems of the National Research
Council and the extensive Medical Research
Program by the Veterans Administration. For
his war services he received the Legion of Merit.
After his discharge he returned to Tulane University School of Medicine, where he remained
until 1948, when he accepted the chairmanship
of surgery at Baylor University College of Medicine. For his contributions to medicine and
society, De Bakey received the Hektoen Gold
Medal (1954) and the Distinguished Service
Award (1959) of the American Medical Association, the Distinguished Service Award (1958)
and Leriche Award (1959) of the International
Society of Surgery, the Rudolph Matas Award
(1954), the Albert Lasker Award for Clinical
Research (1963), the first Gold Scalpel Award
of the International Cardiology Foundation, the
first Max Berg Award of the Berg Foundation,
the Drexel Institute Award, as well as numerous
honorary degrees.

De Bakey wrote *The Blood Bank and the
Technique and Therapeutics of Transfusions,*
with Robert A. Kilduffe (1942); *Minor Surgery,*
with Frederick Christopher (8th ed. 1959); and
*Battle Casualties: Incidence, Mortality, and
Logistic Considerations,* with Gilbert W. Beebe
(1952). He edited *The Year Book of Surgery.* In
addition, he wrote more than 700 articles and
chapters of books on surgical and scientific
subjects, and served on the editorial boards of
more than a dozen national and international
scientific publications.

For background information *see* CARDIO-
VASCULAR SYSTEM; CARDIOVASCULAR SYSTEM

DISORDERS; CIRCULATION DISORDERS; HEART DISORDERS; TRANSFUSION in the McGraw-Hill Encyclopedia of Science and Technology.   □

DEBYE, Peter Joseph William

American physical chemist

Debye died on Nov. 2, 1966, in Ithaca, N.Y., U.S.A. See *McGraw-Hill Modern Men of Science*, Volume I.

★ DENISSE, Jean-François

French astronomer
Born May 16, 1915, Saint-Quentin, Aisne, France

TRAINED AS a physicist, Denisse took an interest in radio-astronomical research when the pioneering discoveries of G. Reber and J. S. Hey became known in France shortly after World War II. The opening of this new spectral range for the study of cosmic bodies is still leading to major discoveries in all branches of astronomy. Denisse's main contribution in the field was the exploitation of this new tool for a better understanding of the Sun and of its various forms of activity and their relation with terrestrial effects in the upper atmosphere, together with basic theoretical studies aimed at a better knowledge of radio-wave generation and behavior in the extensive astrophysical plasmas.

Denisse's first research work was devoted to the study (1947) of solar waves radiated in the range of decimetric wavelengths. No high-resolution observations were available at that time, but from statistical studies it was possible to show that part of this radiation comes from the extended chromospheric plasma (the quiet component), and another component, slowly varying, is related to sunspots. Theoretical study of the quiet component led to the construction of a model for determination of variations with height of the electronic density and temperature in the chromospheric layers of the Sun. The varying component was shown being radiated by hot coronal condensations of gas located above the sunspots and embedded in their magnetic fields extending high into the solar atmosphere.

Denisse and M. R. Kundu noticed later a close correlation between these shortwave solar emissions and the degree of ionization of the terrestrial E layer, and they attributed this ionization to the x-ray bremsstrahlung emission of the hot solar condensations. That the solar condensations are also strong sources of x-rays was later directly demonstrated by space-borne x-ray detectors.

In 1953 Denisse was appointed to the Paris Observatory to lead a group of radio astronomers, including among others E. J. Blum, J. L. Steinberg, and A. Boischot. This group, with the development of the Radio Astronomy Center at Nançay, became a few years later one of the most active in the field. It was clear at that time that the most original contribution of radio astronomy to man's knowledge of the universe, and of the Sun in particular, was its ability to detect by their radio emission the invisible particles accelerated in cosmic plasmas to high energy from the thermal equilibrium of the ambient gases observed optically. Several powerful instruments (interferometers) were specially devised at Nançay to study the solar radio emissions on metric wavelengths where these solar particles were likely to be best observed. This work led in particular to the discovery of a new type of radio emission (the type IV burst), which was identified with synchrotron radiation of relativistic electrons in the coronal magnetic fields. This result was the first direct evidence of acceleration of particles during the process of solar flares, and brought about a direct access to the major problem of natural acceleration of particles in the cosmic plasmas.

Acceleration of high-energy particles by the Sun (as revealed by the type IV burst) proved to be extremely significant, notably in relation to most forms of perturbations induced by solar activity in the terrestrial upper atmosphere. Denisse and his collaborators (P. Simon and M. Pick) made notable contributions to the various aspects of solar terrestrial relationships. The arrival in the vicinity of the Earth of solar protons in the range of energy of tens of millions of electron volts produces strong ionization and absorption of radio waves in the upper atmosphere above the polar regions; these "polar cap absorptions" were shown to be strongly correlated with the type IV bursts, and this finding demonstrated that protons as well as electrons were readily accelerated during the process of a solar flare. It was shown along the same line that velocity and strength of the interplanetary shock waves that produce the geomagnetic storms are directly related to the energy developed in the type IV burst.

Interested in the various interpretations that can be given to the multiple aspects of the solar radio emissions, Denisse carried out theoretical investigations on the excitation and propagation of waves in plasma. In collaboration with J. L. Delcroix, he wrote a monograph on the subject, *Théorie des ondes dans les plasmas* (1958).

Son of a painter, Denisse graduated from the Ecole Normale Supérieure in Paris with a degree in physical science in 1942. He was in French West Africa up to the end of World War II. After several years as research assistant under Y. Rocard and at the National Bureau of Standards in Washington, D.C., and as associate professor at the University of Dakar, Denisse went to the Paris Observatory in 1953. He was appointed director of the Radio Astronomy Station at Nançay in 1955 and director of the Paris Observatory in 1963. He was a member of the advisory council to the French government for scientific and technical research from 1963 to 1967.

For background information *see* PLASMA PHYSICS; RADIO ASTRONOMY; SUN in the McGraw-Hill Encyclopedia of Science and Technology. □

★ DENT, Charles Enrique

British chemist and physician
Born Aug. 25, 1911, Burgos, Spain

THE DISCOVERY in 1944 by A. J. P. Martin and R. L. M. Synge of paper chromatography for the identification of amino acids in protein hydrolysates was applied by Dent to the analysis of more complex material, such as biological fluids. It was realized that this relatively simple semiquantitative method required only minor modifications to make it a new general method of chemistry, potentially applicable to any type of chemical substance and, when combined with specific detecting reagents, of remarkable specificity and sensitivity.

After toying with sugars, inorganic salts, purines, and other compounds, Dent concentrated his efforts on opening up the new world of chemistry revealed in the amino acid chromatograms of normal and pathological body fluids. When he had mapped the behavior of known amino acids, it became clear that many unknown amino acids were also present (shown by unidentifiable spots in the chromatograms). Improved chemical and chromatographic methods were devised for the isolation of pure substances from urine. β-Aminoisobutyric acid was an early substance isolated and identified from urine by his collaborators. Soon after, porphobilinogen was isolated in pure crystalline form for the first time by Roland G. Westall. Cystinuria and acute necrosis of the liver, then the only known amino acid disorders, were studied. Dent, with G. Alan Rose's help, suggested that cystinuria was a disorder of renal tubular function, a theory as yet unchallenged. Cystinuria and cystinosis were shown to be different diseases.

Dent early developed methods of random testing for metabolic disorders, various chemical and chromatographic methods being routinely applied to body fluids of patients with disorders of unknown origin. New amino acid diseases were identified with frequency by his research team—among them various forms of "Fanconi syndrome," Hartnup disease, argininosuccinic aciduria, and homocystinuria. Many similar diseases were later independently discovered by workers trained by his team. The fact that so many of these diseases are associated with mental deficiency led to his permanent interest in that subject. Treatment was attempted in all such cases, the most spectacularly successful being the care of a child with maple syrup urine disease.

The original patients with "Fanconi syndrome" and other disorders of renal tubular dysfunction frequently suffered from rickets (osteomalacia), a metabolic bone disease. Dent's studies of the various forms of metabolic bone diseases were further stimulated by a short visit to Fuller Albright's department at the Massachusetts General Hospital (during the tenure of a Rockefeller medical fellowship in G. H. Whipple's department at the University of Rochester), and by the appearance in 1948 of the now classic textbook of Albright and E. C. Reifenstein. In 1951 his own hospital (University College Hospital, London) provided him with beds and laboratories for patients with metabolic disorders; he also had facilities for outpatient clinics. This opportunity served to channel his interests, for patients with disorders of calcium, vitamin D, and bone metabolism were far commoner than those with amino acid disorders. One line of research involved a further study of renal tubular function in these patients. Another scrutinized the cause and treatment of osteomalacia, and of hyperparathyroidism secondary to other systemic diseases, such as renal glomerular failure and the group of malabsorption syndromes. Further study was directed toward improving the accuracy of diagnosis of primary hyperparathyroidism and with the associated problem of the differential diagnosis of hypercalcemia. The cortisone test was devised and was shown to distinguish hypercalcemia of primary hyperparathyroidism from that due to nearly all other causes. A chemical method for determining ionized calcium in plasma was devised by Rose and was found to be most useful in detecting marginally raised hypercalcemia. More recently accumulated evidence indicated that some cases of apparent primary hyperparathyroidism arise as a consequence of prolonged secondary hyperparathyroidism, and that this situation may be fairly common. The term "tertiary hyperparathyroidism" came into use to describe this condition.

The problem of renal stone formation was of continuing interest from the time of his early cystinuria studies. Cystine stones were shown to be capable of prevention, or of dissolution when already present, by strict adherence to a planned, high-fluid intake. A new cause of stone formation, xanthinuria, was discovered and defined. Calcium-containing stones were also studied, with special respect paid to those due to "idiopathic hypercalcuria." For the latter a treatment with low calcium intake was developed with promising results.

Most of the inborn errors of amino acid metabolism were shown to be hereditary, as well as many of the disorders of renal tubular dysfunction. Diseases such as fibrogenesis imperfecta ossium, osteopetrosis, metaphyseal dysostosis, primary hyperoxaluria, idiopathic osteoporosis, hypohyperparathyroidism, hypophosphatasia, sarcoidosis, and the various malabsorption syndromes were also investigated.

After a year as a clerk in the Midland Bank Ltd. and a year as a chemical technician, Dent took his B.Sc. (1931) in chemistry at Imperial College, London. He took his Ph.D. (1933) in organic chemistry, the subject being the structure and properties of copper phthalocyanine—later marketed as Monastral blue. After working in Imperial Chemical Industries (Dyestuffs Group), he began to study medicine at University College, London, in 1937. In September, 1939, he joined the British Expeditionary Force. He saw service in France, during which he was besieged for a week in Arras and was evacuated at Dunkirk. He returned in June, 1940, to his medical studies, but in November, 1940, he volunteered to join the British Censorship (Scientific Department), and for 2 years he sought enemy messages in secret writing in the mail passing through Bermuda. In 1942 he gave evidence in New York at the first trial of Nazi spies captured by this means. He qualified in medicine in 1944 and later joined the Medical Unit, University College Hospital, London, where he began to work on disorders of amino acid metabolism produced by dietary means. Soon afterward he was sent to the recently captured concentration camp at Belsen to study the treatment of starvation by amino acid mixtures. After the war he remained attached to University College Hospital, London. Elected a fellow of the Royal Society of London in 1962, Dent received a Gairdner Foundation Award in 1965. He was given an honorary M.D. by the University of Louvain in 1966.

For background information *see* AMINO ACIDS; CHROMATOGRAPHY; METABOLIC DISORDERS in the McGraw-Hill Encyclopedia of Science and Technology. ☐

★ DETHIER, Vincent Gaston

American biologist
Born Feb. 20, 1915, Boston, Mass., U.S.A.

INTERESTED IN the neural basis of behavior, Dethier employed insects as experimental animals. He became recognized primarily for his studies of the host plant relationship of plant-feeding caterpillars and his investigations of the chemical senses of insects. His other major contributions lie in the field of comparative psychology, where he studied the mechanisms of hunger and satiation in insects—in particular, the blowfly—and the application of the concept of motivation to these animals.

The ability of caterpillars to discriminate among species of plants and to restrict their feeding to certain species presented a unique opportunity to analyze behavior at a time when the study of animal behavior, especially that of invertebrates, was still more descriptive than analytical. Dethier was the first to prove that feeding preference by caterpillars is mediated by olfactory and gustatory stimuli produced by host plants. He proposed that the critical stimuli are token stimuli, principally components of essential oils, not absolutely associated with nutritional values.

Refined analytical techniques, such as gas chromatography, for detecting and characterizing relevant plant chemicals had not been developed at that time. Nonetheless, it was clear that further understanding of feeding behavior depended upon a knowledge of the physiology of the chemical senses. Accordingly, the locus of the chemical senses of caterpillars was sought by means of ablation experiments. When the organs were identified, their neuroanatomy was described. Attempts were made in 1937 to record action potentials from these receptors, but recording and amplifying instruments then available were unequal to the task.

Dethier turned his attention to a study of the evolutionary development of host plant relationships and feeding preferences. He investigated in detail the relation between swallowtail larvae and their host plants, the chemistry of these plants, and the role of the chemicals in regulating feeding preferences. This work led to a theory which, by relating known facts of animal geography and population genetics to facts of feeding behavior, attempted to explain origins and contemporary changes of restricted feeding habits.

After a 4-year interruption by the war, Dethier returned to the study of the chemical senses of insects. He chose as an experimental animal the black blowfly. This study led to a long series of investigations of the chemical senses of insects that constitute Dethier's most significant contribution to sensory physiology. At this time no insect chemoreceptor had been identified with absolute certainty. By exploiting D. E. Minnich's observation that flies extended their proboscis when sugar was applied to the feet or mouthparts, it was possible to identify the chemoreceptors behaviorally. Over the next 10 years the neuroanatomy of the receptors was elucidated and the stimulating efficiency of over 400 compounds assessed. From these and other studies emerged a hypothesis that the fly possesses single neuron receptors mediating acceptance and other single neuron receptors mediating rejection. Organic compounds that act on rejection (so-called salt receptors) were presumed to operate in a two-phase system—water and lipid. It has since been demonstrated that electrolytes are perceived by the salt receptor while nonpolar organic compounds act as narcotics on the acceptance receptors.

Parallel studies conducted on the olfactory receptors formed the basis for a hypothesis describing the nature of the receptor transducing mechanism. As a result of these coordinated behavioral and histological studies, a body of knowledge was built that made the fly chemoreceptive system one of the best known in the animal kingdom. The work presented physiologists with the unique opportunity of isolating a single chemoreceptive neuron, whose activities could be studied both at the behavioral and the molecular level. It paved the way for elaborate electrophysiological analyses that were subsequently developed by E. S. Hodgson, K. D. Roeder, and J. Y. Lettvin at Tufts University, H. Morita and his associates at Kyushu University, and by Dethier's students M. L. Wolbarsht and D. R. Evans at the Johns Hopkins University.

The background was also laid for studies of the regulation of food and water intake. In collaboration with Dietrich Bodenstein, techniques in microsurgery were developed that led to the discovery that ingestion is under direct oral sensory control and that satiation occurs as a result of inhibitory feedback from the foregut. Thus, for the blowfly a relatively complete understanding of feeding regulation was developed. The mechanism of thirst was also elucidated.

The fact that feeding could be satisfactorily explained without invoking central nervous system feeding centers of the sort known in vertebrate animals raised the question of whether or not the fly, and insects in general, behave in a manner that is qualitatively different from that of vertebrates. These considerations led Dethier to challenge the idea that higher animals exhibit forms of behavior (such as motivation) qualitatively different from the behavior of lower organisms. He held that a disciplined anthropomorphism is essential to inquiry if one is ever to find out whether there is truly a dichotomy in animal behavior. These ideas stimulated an intensive investigation into the whole question of motivation and learning in insects. Some of the results were the demonstration and analysis of central excitatory and inhibitory states in flies, confirmation of the dual role of sense organs as sources of specific information and generators of generalized excitation, and illustration of the importance of attention and arousal systems to insect behavior.

Son of a Belgian musician, Dethier was educated in the public schools of Boston. He went to Harvard, receiving his A.B. in 1936, A.M. in 1937, and Ph.D. in 1939. During World War II he served with the Army Air Corps in the African–Middle East theater, rising to the rank of major. After the war he held professorships at Ohio State University and the Johns Hopkins University. He spent a year at the London

School of Hygiene and Tropical Medicine as a Fulbright scholar, half a year in the Belgian Congo as a special fellow of the Belgian American Educational Foundation, and a year at the Landbouwhogeschool te Wageningen, Netherlands, as a Guggenheim fellow. From 1958 to 1967 he was a professor of zoology and psychology at the University of Pennsylvania and a member of the Institute of Neurological Sciences of the School of Medicine; later he became professor of biology at Princeton University. He was elected to the American Academy of Arts and Sciences in 1961 and to the National Academy of Sciences in 1965.

Dethier's ideas concerning the interrelations of insects and the numerous chemical stimuli in their lives were formulated in *Chemical Insect Attractants and Repellents* (1947), which became the basic reference for studies in this field. He also wrote *Animal Behavior*, with E. Stellar (1961; 2d ed. 1964), *To Know a Fly* (1963), and *The Physiology of Insect Senses* (1963).

For background information *see* INSECT PHYSIOLOGY; SENSE ORGANS in the McGraw-Hill Encyclopedia of Science and Technology.   □

★ DEUTSCH, Martin

American physicist
Born Jan. 29, 1917, Vienna, Austria

DEUTSCH AND his students observed in 1950 that the rate at which positrons are annihilated by electrons when passing through a gas depends strongly on the chemical nature of the gas and can be modified by a magnetic field. The same factors were observed to affect the energy distribution of the gamma rays resulting from the annihilation. The energy involved in the annihilation process is 10^5 times larger than chemical interactions and 10^9 times larger than magnetic interactions. Therefore Deutsch concluded that the annihilation must occur from a relatively stable electron-positron system and that it is the dynamics of this system that is affected by the weak perturbations.

Positronium is the bound system of electron and positron, closely analogous to the hydrogen atom. Some of its properties had been predicted theoretically. The interaction between the particles depends on the relative orientation of their spins, so that the dynamically most stable state (ground state) of positronium is split into two energetically slightly different states (fine structure). The state with opposed spins (para-positronium) transforms spontaneously into two gamma rays of equal energy with a mean life of about 10^{-10} sec. The state with parallel spins (ortho-positronium) has a 10^3 times longer lifetime and results in the emission of three gamma rays of variable energy. The presence of a magnetic field or collisions with certain types of molecules can cause reorientation of the particle spins, modifying the relative probability of the two annihilation modes. The quantitative experimental results showed that the proposed stable system is indeed positronium with the theoretically expected properties.

Deutsch and co-workers immediately performed a precision measurement of the energy difference between the ortho and para states. The importance of this measurement lay in the fact that positronium is the only available system involving only electromagnetic interactions. All ordinary atoms have properties depending to some degree on the structure of the nucleus. The quantum theory of electromagnetic interactions had been radically recast to interpret the precision measurement of the hydrogen fine structure by W. E. Lamb and R. C. Retherford in 1947. The fine structure of positronium provided a second powerful confirmation of the new theory.

Despite the "nonnuclear" character of positronium, Deutsch had been led to his investigation through a series of studies of nuclear processes. In the late 1930s, when he was a student of R. D. Evans at the Massachusetts Institute of Technology (MIT), many artificial radioactive nuclei were first becoming available. Together with A. Roberts and others, he planned a program to develop methods of nuclear spectroscopy that would illuminate the nature of nuclear energy states through the study of radioactive decay processes. World War II soon scattered the original group, but he maintained some continuity of the program in connection with his work on the fission process in Los Alamos and resumed his work at MIT at the end of the war. In a steady development, which lasted almost a quarter of a century, the program produced some of the earliest, reasonably complete studies of radioactive decay schemes by the systematic application of coincidence methods and of a high-luminosity magnetic spectrometer developed for this purpose. It yielded the first valid measurements of angular correlations of radioactive radiations and their polarization, the first application of scintillation counters to nuclear physics, and some of the earliest measurement of submicrosecond nuclear lifetimes. Many of these methods became standard procedures, developed further and refined by others. It was familiarity with the relevant techniques that led Deutsch to study the annihilation of positrons when the development of quantum electrodynamics in the late 1940s focused interest on this process. After the study of positronium he extended experiments to annihilation at high energies and applied this method to obtain the first determination of the spin orientation of positrons in beta decay, when this problem became of great importance in connection with the reformulation of beta-decay theory in 1957.

Deutsch received a B.S. (1937) and a Ph.D. in physics (1941) at MIT, where he remained as a member of the faculty, becoming professor of physics in 1953. He was elected to the American Academy of Arts and Sciences in 1953 and to the National Academy of Sciences in 1958.

For background information *see* POSITRONIUM; RADIOACTIVITY in the McGraw-Hill Encyclopedia of Science and Technology.   □

★ DICKE, Robert Henry

American physicist
Born May 6, 1916, St. Louis, Mo., U.S.A.

Dicke's scientific career can be divided into three periods.

(1) Most recently, beginning in 1956, he was concerned with cosmological, gravitational, and relativistic problems. Together with his colleagues R. Krotkov and P. G. Roll, he showed with an accuracy of one part in 10^{11} that the gravitational acceleration of heavy and light elements are equal. With C. Brans, a graduate student, Dicke investigated a new relativistic theory of gravitation called the scalar-tensor theory. He also showed the relation of this theory to general relativity, Einstein's theory of gravitation.

To provide a test for general relativity Dicke and his colleague H. M. Goldenberg measured the oblateness of the Sun during the summer of 1966. These measurements indicated that the Sun is oblate enough to account for 8% of the excess perihelion rotation of Mercury's orbit. If these measurements and the observations of Mercury's orbit are accurate and have been properly interpreted, they are in agreement with the scalar-tensor theory but not with Einstein's theory of gravitation. Dicke also investigated a number of possible astrophysical and geophysical implications of the scalar-tensor theory.

In 1964 with his colleagues P. J. E. Peebles, Roll, and D. T. Wilkinson, Dicke reactivated an old idea of G. Gamow and others, that the universe might have expanded out of a hot fireball. It was predicted that thermal radiation from this fireball should still remain in the universe as microwaves. The radiation was first observed by Arno A. Penzias and Robert W. Wilson of the Bell Telephone Laboratories, but its existence was confirmed by Roll and Wilkinson of the Princeton group.

(2) In 1941, after completing his graduate work, Dicke joined the Radiation Laboratory at the Massachusetts Institute of Technology to help with the development of microwave radar. Many of his 54 patents involve radar inventions. These include monopulse radar, coherent pulse radar, chirp radar, and a number of microwave components, including the "magic tee" and the balanced mixer. Among his nonradar inventions are the switched microwave radiometer (1944), the heart of most radio telescopes. The radiometer employed a "lock-in amplifier," a common ingredient in most of his subsequent experiments. He also holds the basic patent for the mirrored laser. Invented in 1956, a model of this coherent generator of infrared radiation was never constructed.

(3) In 1946 Dicke joined the faculty of Princeton University, and for 10 years his research was concerned with atomic physics, particularly various fundamental radiation processes. He developed the theory of collision reduction of Doppler broadened lines, including both the coated wall and the buffer gas techniques. The techniques, involving both a buffering gas and glass walls coated with silane, were first used in 1954 by his student J. P. Wittke to make what was at the time the highest-precision measurement of the hyperfine splitting of the ground state of atomic hydrogen. It was also used in 1955 by his student E. B. D. Lambe to make the first high-precision measurement of the electron *g* factor. In this connection Lambe

introduced the use of Teflon as a buffering wall material. In 1955 his student P. L. Bender introduced the use of the buffer gas technique in optical pumping. Earlier his student Bruce Hawkins had carried out one of the first two successful optical pumping experiments. This experiment overlapped, and was independent of, A. H. Kastler's experiment, the one first completed. Using optical pumping with the buffer gas technique and the buffer gas narrowing of magnetic dipole transitions, his colleague T. R. Carver first investigated the rubidium hyperfine transition with the expectation that this combination of techniques would make a good atomic clock. This technique, almost unmodified, has led to one of the principal commercially important atomic clocks.

The first quantum theory of the coherent emission of electromagnetic radiation was published by Dicke in 1953. He showed that for an assemblage of atoms there exists strongly radiating quantum mechanical states, which he called "superradiant," and that a compact system of atoms, initially excited, would spontaneously make transitions to these energy states. The operation of a laser can be described in terms of transitions between these states.

Dicke received an A.B. from Princeton University in 1939 and a Ph.D. from the University of Rochester in 1941. He was elected to the American Academy of Arts and Sciences in 1963 and was a recipient in 1967 of the Academy's Rumford Prize. He was elected to the National Academy of Sciences in 1967.

Dicke wrote *Principles of Microwave Circuits*, with C. G. Montgomery and E. M. Purcell (1948); *Introduction to Quantum Mechanics*, with J. P. Wittke (1960); and *The Theoretical Significance of Experimental Relativity* (1964).

For background information *see* ATOMIC CLOCK; RADAR; RELATIVITY in the McGraw-Hill Encyclopedia of Science and Technology.   □

★ DITCHBURN, Robert William

British physicist
Born Jan. 14, 1903, Lancashire, England

DITCHBURN MADE contributions to ultraviolet spectroscopy, vision, and solid-state physics. The absorption of radiation in ultraviolet light leading to the photoionization of atoms and molecules is important in relation to the balance of radiation and the formation of ionized layers in the terrestrial atmosphere; to the corresponding processes in the outer layers of the Sun and other stars; and to the interpretation of measurements on plasmas—more especially the high-temperature plasmas involved in experiments on controlled thermonuclear fusion. Ditchburn worked

in this field from 1925 onward and, with his colleagues, was responsible for development of techniques for vacuum ultraviolet absorption spectroscopy and for detailed experiments on photoionization in many elements (including the alkali and alkaline earth metals) and some molecules. Measurements were also made on the optical properties of solids in the visible and ultraviolet regions. A major series of experiments using intense sources of photons of energies greater than 20 volts for investigating gases and solids was under development in recent years.

As a result of observations during 1939-45 on performance of Naval personnel using optical instruments, Ditchburn was led to investigate the effect of small eye movements in visual perception. These movements remain even when a good subject believes he is fixating accurately on a well-defined target. They cause the retinal image to move to-and-fro in an irregular way across the mosaic of retinal receptors. An optical system was devised that allows the movements of the eye to control movements of a target, so that its image remains fixed on the retina despite rotation of the eye or translation of the head (stabilized retinal image). It was found that, when this apparatus is well adjusted, the target disappears in a few seconds. It is afterward seen intermittently and with a hazy appearance like an afterimage. In extreme conditions the whole field goes black. These observations showed that movements of the retinal image are essential for normal visual perception. In normal vision the movement of boundaries (between light and dark areas in the retinal image) across the receptor mosaic causes fluctuations of illumination and produces on-off signals in appropriate

fibers of the optic nerve. With the stabilized image these on-off signals are lost; each part of the retina suffers local adaptation, and only very weak signals remain. In this situation the visual perceptual system receives information that is both inadequate and outside normal visual experience. The "interpretation" of this information causes parts of targets to be seen clearly, while others are not seen at all; "false" interpretations occur, leading to the subject's "seeing" features that are not present in the target. From these fragmentations and errors some progress has been made in identifying units of pattern perception. The effects on color discrimination are most interesting.

Experiments on the stabilized image were carried out independently by L. A. Riggs and coworkers working in the United States and by L. Yarbus in the Soviet Union. The results obtained by the different groups are in general agreement. Much of the work on stabilized images may be understood in terms of concepts stated by W. H. Marshall and S. A. Talbot in 1942.

Son of a schoolmaster, Ditchburn graduated with a B.Sc. from Liverpool University in 1922, the year in which he entered Trinity College, Cambridge (senior scholar, 1923; Isaac Newton scholar, 1924–25). He received an M.A. and a Ph.D. at Cambridge in 1928, and became a fellow at Trinity College, Dublin, and professor of experimental philosophy (1929–46). He worked in the British Admiralty in 1942–45, and became professor of physics at Reading University in 1946. Recipient of the Physical Society of London's Thomas Young Award in 1959, he was elected a fellow of the Royal Society of London in 1962.

Ditchburn wrote *Light* (2d ed. 1963).

For background information *see* EYE; SPECTROSCOPY in the McGraw-Hill Encyclopedia of Science and Technology.   □

★ DJERASSI, Carl

American chemist
Born Oct. 29, 1923, Vienna, Austria

D JERASSI'S CHEMICAL work started with synthetic medicinals but shortly thereafter extended to steroids and eventually to other natural products, such as terpenoids, alkaloids, and antibiotics. Studies in the steroid field and subsequent work on structure elucidation of complex natural products were greatly dependent on the use of physical methods, and in this context Djerassi performed basic research on such physical tools. He developed optical rotatory dispersion and, at a later date, circular dichroism as standard tools of organic chemistry. His contributions to the use of mass spectrometry in structural and mechanistic organic chemistry were noteworthy. In the development of each of these techniques, steroids were used initially as model compounds and, if one common thread

can be discerned throughout the fabric of his scientific contributions, it was his use of steroids for biological, synthetic, physical, and mechanistic purposes.

Before entering graduate school, Djerassi was involved in research on antihistamines, and was a co-inventor of tripelennamine (Pyribenzamine, one of the first clinically efficacious antihistaminics, and still widely used in medicine). After completing his graduate studies, he continued his interest in the development of medicinal agents with his principal emphasis on steroids. Particularly productive were the years he spent at Syntex, S.A., in Mexico City. There, in association with his collaborators, he initiated a novel, industrially feasible synthesis of the female sex hormones estrone and estradiol; the first synthesis of cortisone from plant raw materials (diosgenin from yams and hecogenin from sisal); the development of the first oral contraceptive agent (norethisterone); and development of the powerful anti-inflammatory agents paramethasone acetate (Haldrone), flurandrenolone acetonide (Cordran), and fluocinolone acetonide (Synalar). The latter is now the most widely used topical corticosteroid in medicine, notably in the treatment of psoriasis.

Djerassi's first stay in Mexico (1949–52) was responsible for his interest in tropical plants. Upon his return to the United States he commenced a systematic chemical study of the constituents of such plants, especially of cacti. Giant cacti from Mexico and Central and South America proved to be a rich source of pentacyclic triterpenoids, and the structures of 20 new triterpenes were established over the course of a half dozen years. Other terpenoids whose constitution was elucidated during that time were

iresin (a novel sesquiterpene representing a "missing link" in terpene biogenesis) and cafestol (a pentacyclic diterpene from coffee). These chemical studies of giant cacti also resulted in the isolation of some new cactus

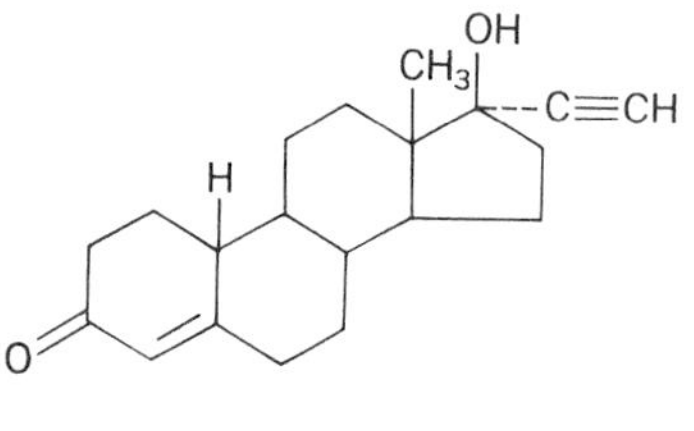

Norethisterone

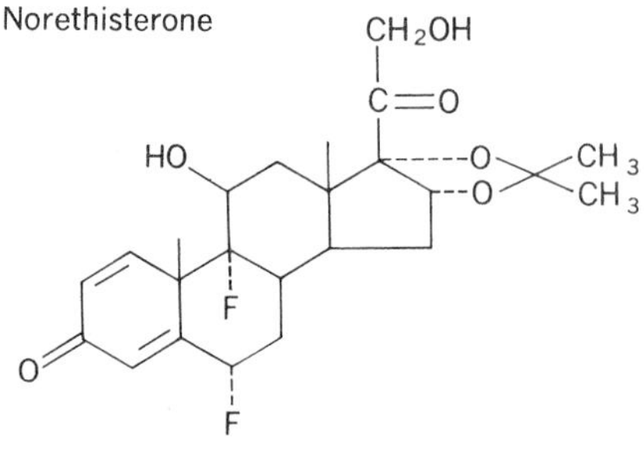

Fluocinolone acetonide

alkaloids, which turned his attention to the general field of alkaloid chemistry, notably of indole alkaloids from South American Apocynaceae species. During the past dozen years well over 50 new alkaloids were isolated and their structures established by his research group. Much of this work was aided by the use of physical methods, such as mass spectrometry, as discussed below.

Another area of natural products chemistry investigated by Djerassi and his students was the chemistry of macrolide antibiotics, which include a number of clinically important representatives (for example, erythromycin and nystatin). At the time that this work was undertaken, the structure of none of the macrolides was as yet known. In 1956 Djerassi and J. A. Zderic announced the first complete structure of a macrolide antibiotic, namely, methymycin. Subsequently, Djerassi and his colleagues were occupied with the chemistry of neomethymycin and erythromycin. He and his colleagues also investigated the important antifungal agents filipin and nystatin.

In 1953 Djerassi and his students started their systematic studies on optical rotatory dispersion, which ultimately led to the wide use that this method and the closely related method of circular dichroism now enjoy in organic chemistry. Optical rotatory dispersion (the variation of optical rotatory power with wavelength) is a phenomenon which was known since the last century but which, for all practical purposes, remained unused by organic chemists. For the 20-year period prior to 1953, less than a half dozen articles were concerned with organic

chemical applications of optical rotatory dispersion; but since the publication of Djerassi's book *Optical Rotatory Dispersion: Applications to Organic Chemistry* (1960), about a thousand papers have appeared dealing with organic and biochemical applications of optical rotatory dispersion and circular dichroism. His initial work concentrated on steroids and especially on steroid ketones, since the carbonyl chromophore exhibits maximal absorption in a convenient spectral range (about 290 mμ with relatively low extinction, which permits measurement of the optical rotation through the region of the absorption band. The resulting curve (see the figure), called a Cotton effect curve, was shown to be diagnostic—both in terms of shape and sign—with a particular optically active environment of the carbonyl group. Subsequent studies with many hundreds of model ketones showed that the Cotton effect curve could be employed for assignments of absolute configuration and for determination of the conformation of organic molecules. Thus, the absolute configurations of many natural products were established for the first time by this method. In fact, it was through the use of optical rotatory dispersion that Djerassi and his collaborators first demonstrated the existence of the "nonsteroidal" absolute configuration in terpenoids, such as cafestol and iresin. In 1963 K. Wellman, E. Bunnenberg, and Djerassi introduced the technique of measuring circular dichroism at low temperatures (down to the boiling point of liquid nitrogen), thus offering an additional approach for examining the subtle problems of conformational and rotational mobility.

Early in 1961, Djerassi and his associates at Stanford University started a series of investigations on the use of mass spectrometry in structural organic chemistry. The potential of this method in the natural products field had already been indicated a few years earlier by E. Stenhagen and R. Ryhage in Sweden, by R. I. Reed and J. Beynon in Britain, and by K. Biemann in the United States, but it soon became obvious that intelligent and extensive use of this tool would have to be based on a detailed knowledge of the fragmentation behavior of organic molecules after electron bombardment. A systematic

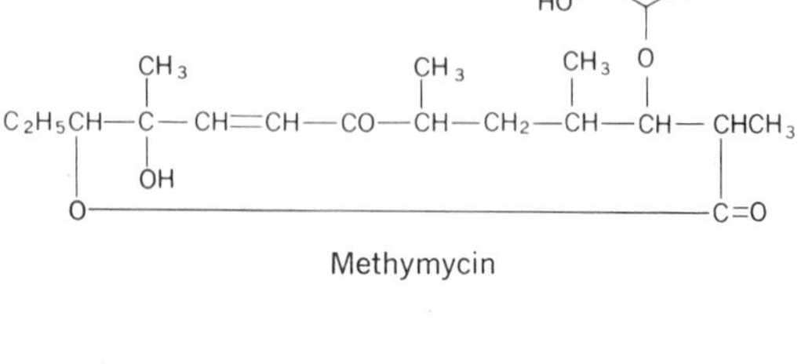

Methymycin

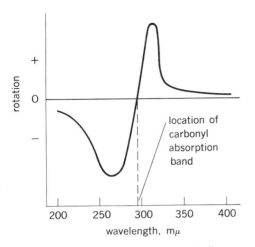

Positive Cotton effect curve of an optically active ketone.

study was undertaken at Stanford University of model compounds (frequently steroids) possessing a single functional group in order to determine how such a functionality affects the electron impact–induced fragmentation behavior of the molecule. The interplay of several such functionalities in one molecule was examined, with isotopic labeling and high-resolution mass spectrometry playing important roles. This work, performed in the 1960s and covered in about 150 articles and 4 books, showed that many standard organic chemical concepts from solution chemistry, especially as far as relative stability of carbonium ions and free radicals was concerned, could also be applied to interpretation and even prediction of fragmentation behavior of organic molecules after electron bombardment. It is safe to say that within another few years mass spectrometry will probably be the most widely used physical tool in organic chemistry, and this trend is already indicated by the ever-increasing number of articles being published on the subject. The combination of mass spectrometry with gas chromatography, as well as with various computer-aided data acquisition and data analysis methods, promises to have an enormous impact on the future conduct of organic chemical research.

Djerassi graduated summa cum laude from Kenyon College (A.B., 1942). After a year as research chemist at Ciba Pharmaceutical Co., Summit, N.J., he entered the University of Wisconsin, where he received his Ph.D. in organic chemistry in 1945. He returned to Ciba and remained there until 1949, when he became associate director of chemical research at Syntex, S.A., in Mexico City. During 1957–60, while on academic leave of absence, he was research vice-president of Syntex. From 1952 to 1959 he was associate professor and then professor of chemistry at Wayne State University; in 1959 he moved to Stanford University as professor of chemistry. He was a centenary lecturer of the British Chemical Society and a recipient of honorary doctorates from Kenyon College and the National University of Mexico. The American Chemical Society honored him with its Award in Pure Chemistry (1958), the Baekeland Medal (1959), and the Fritzsche Medal (1960). He was elected to the National Academy of Sciences in 1961.

Djerassi was the author or coauthor of nearly 600 scientific articles. In addition to four books on mass spectrometry, he wrote *Optical Rotatory Dispersion* (1960) and edited *Steroid Reactions* (1963).

For background information *see* ROTATORY DISPERSION; SPECTROSCOPY; SPECTRUM in the McGraw-Hill Encyclopedia of Science and Technology.   □

DOMAGK, Gerhard

German biochemist
Born Oct. 30, 1895, Lagow, Brandenburg, Germany
Died Apr. 24, 1964, Burberg, Württemburg-Baden, Germany

WHILE INVESTIGATING the potential therapeutic effect of various chemical compounds, a study that entailed the screening of many very different agents, Domagk discovered the first synthetic antimicrobial of broad clinical usefulness, sulfonamidocrysoidin. In recognition of the importance of this breakthrough to the medical community, Domagk was awarded the 1939 Nobel Prize for medicine or physiology.

Modern chemotherapy began about 1910, when Paul Ehrlich, a German biochemist, developed a specific chemical agent to combat a specific disease. Ehrlich had experimented for years with various chemical compounds to try to find a cure for the trypanosomes and, in 1907, formulated his 606th compound, dihydroxydiamino-arsenobenzene-dihydrobenzene (now also known as arsphenamine, 606, and Ehrlich 606). This proved of little value in treating the trypanosomes and was discarded, but 3 years later it was discovered to be effective in the treatment of syphilis. His announcement in 1910 of the successful therapeutic application of the chemical, which he called Salversan, triggered a search for other chemotherapeutic agents. However, except for the synthesis of the antimalarials plasmoquine and Atebrin, progress was negligible.

Domagk began his search for chemotherapeutic agents while on the staff of I. G. Farbenindustrie at Wuppertal-Elberfeld. His method was to first study the chemicals in vitro to find their effect upon the several microbic genera; then to find the doses that were tolerated by laboratory animals; and finally, if it seemed warranted, their effect upon the infections, natural or experimental, of man.

For several years this work yielded no clear leads, but at the end of 1932 a surprising result was obtained when a red azo dye combined with a sulfonamide radical—commercially marketed by I. G. Farbenindustrie under the trade name Prontosil Rubrum—was under investigation. Although preliminary tests with it had shown little bacterial activity while in the test tube, it seemed to have some protective power against streptococcal infections in the mouse. Furthermore, its toxicity was also low for mice.

In view of these findings it seemed worthwhile to repeat the mouse protection test with 26 animals and a test culture of hemolytic streptococci, which was always fatal when injected into the peritoneum. Fourteen mice were kept as controls and died within 4 days, most of them on the second day. The remaining 12 were treated with a single dose of the red dye 1.5 hr after the streptococcal injection. All remained in good condition during the 7 days they were under observation.

Three years elapsed before this striking result was reported in 1935. The reason why publication was delayed is unclear. However, during this period Domagk's daughter was infected by streptococci following the prick of a needle. The girl was near death until Domagk in desperation injected her with large quantities of Prontosil Rubrum, thus effecting a near miraculous recovery in his daughter.

Domagk's discovery opened an immense field for therapeutic advance. Not only was it immediately seized upon to treat the many previously fatal infections of hemolytic streptococci, but it also prompted an immediate inquiry in many laboratories as to whether Prontosil Rubrum or substances related to it could exert a similar effect upon human diseases caused by bacteria quite different from hemolytic streptococci. In England it was quickly found that cerebrospinal meningitis, pneumonia, and gonorrhea were but three of the diseases that could be brought under control through its use. Laboratory work also brought new understanding of the means by which the drug achieved its results, showing that the sulfonamide radical was dissociated in vivo and that this was responsible for the antibacterial effects. As a result, more powerful antibacterials, such as sulfanilamide, sulfapyridine, and sulfathiazole, were introduced.

During World War II, Domagk was chiefly concerned with the chemotherapeutic approach to tuberculosis. In 1944, when the antibiotics were becoming available, the most promising line of attack seemed to be by streptomycin, which had been discovered by Selman A. Waksman in the United States. Other approaches, such as the use of p-aminosalicylic acid, were also taken. Domagk, however, had tried using sulfonamide derivatives. Only sulfathiazole and sulfathiadiazole seemed to offer any sort of hope, and this effect appeared to come from the thiazole rather than from the SO group. He therefore synthesized aminothiazole and aminothiadiazole, and in 1946 Domagk reported success with the thiosemicarbazones. However, extended clinical trials later showed that these had a hepatic toxicity that precluded their general use. Furthermore, the almost simultaneous discovery of another antituberculosis drug, isonicotinic acid hydrazide, which did not have this failing, made use of the thiosemicarbazones unnecessary.

During the last few years of his active life, Domagk became increasingly interested in the problem of cancer. He hoped that a substance might be found that would be effectively cytostatic for tumor cells, that is, would destroy them without destroying the animal or human host. However, he achieved no striking success in this research.

Domagk began his studies at the University of Kiel shortly before World War I. Although his education was interrupted by military service, he returned to Kiel at the conclusion of the conflict, and was awarded his medical degree in 1921. After serving for short periods as an assistant at Kiel and then at the University of Greifswald, he joined the staff of I. G. Farbenindustrie. In 1927 he was appointed director of research in experimental pathology and bacteriology, and continued in this post for the remainder of his active career. For political reasons Domagk was forced to decline the Nobel Prize when it was awarded to him in 1939. However, in 1947, he was presented with the Nobel Medal, although the prize money had reverted to the foundation so he was unable to benefit from it. Domagk also received many other honors, among them the Paul Ehrlich Gold Medal and the Cameron Medal of the University of Edinburgh. In 1959 he was elected a fellow of the Royal Society of London.

For background information *see* ANTIMICROBIAL AGENTS; THIOSEMICARBAZONE in the McGraw-Hill Encyclopedia of Science and Technology.   ☐

★ DOUGLAS, Robert John Wilson

Canadian geologist
Born Aug. 3, 1920, Southampton, Ontario, Canada

THE STRUCTURES of the Rocky Mountains and Foothills of southern Alberta were thought for many years to be analogous to those of well-known mountain belts such as the Swiss Alps or Scottish Highlands. The nappes of the Swiss Alps developed from recumbent folds, with the great horizontal displacements achieved through attenuation and ultimate breaking of the inverted middle limb of the fold. The Scottish structures originated as a series of imbrications by high-angle reverse faults, with the deformed strata subsequently cut through by low-angle sole faults. Douglas contended that the mechanics of low-angle overthrusting as set forth by John L. Rich in 1934 were fundamental to the interpretation of Foothills structures. In the decade after 1945, when his investigations started, Douglas further developed the theory and its economic implications in exploration for oil and gas in the Foothills.

According to Rich, a low-angle thrust may originate in stratified rocks without prior folding as a fracture that follows, for considerable distance, close to the bedding in zones of easy gliding, such as shale, and cuts across intervening brittle strata at an angle. As a result of displacement, folds are produced in the overthrust mass, and the initial anticlinal and synclinal warps in the thrust plane may be accentuated. The shales serve to reduce frictional resistance and the force required to produce displacement.

In the southern Rocky Mountains and Foothills several scattered initial breaks were postulated by Douglas, the more westerly fractures originating first, low within the Palaeozoic and Proterozoic successions. These fractures were subsequently extended, preferentially following the bedding, upward through the Mesozoic and Tertiary strata to the surface and laterally in both directions along the strike. As the initial breaks grew, new ones formed, and eventually the extensions of the various thrusts interlocked and merged, or subsidiary connecting faults formed between them. Tear faults arose along the locus of the initial transverse cutoff of the strata by the thrust. Great lateral displacements were accomplished by the riding out of little deformed sheets of rock, the lower zones of gliding being brought into juxtaposition with higher zones. Concomitantly with displacement, the initial folds were induced, and subsequently drag folds developed with décollement at the thrust plane. Splays from the initial thrust plane, sigmoidal in cross section, asymptotically merged both downward with the thrust and upward with earlier-formed thrusts so that a succession of thin fault slices or imbrications were produced. These are considered to have been formed in succession from east to west within the overthrust mass, the easternmost slices being detached and overridden by the main overthrust mass along the newly formed splay.

Where associated with folds, most faults occur on the less steeply dipping or back limb of the anticline, dipping subparallel to the strata, and may have undergone steepening through collapse of the core of the fold, the concave character of fault plane imparting rotation to the strata even to the extent of overturning. Displacement on a new fault in footwall strata of a fault can bring about, as a result of the formation of an induced anticline, a superimposed anticline in both the hanging wall strata and the fault plane itself, the formation of another fault on the back limb of this anticline, and the cessation of displacement on the folded portion of the first-formed fault. The sequence of faulting and of the folding of strata and fault planes is considered by Douglas to be the result of a continuous, self-perpetuating process, but not all geologists agree; some think that superimposed folds and folded faults are the result of two stages of deformation, the formation of several fault slices and subsequent folding of them as a group.

Douglas's studies of the stratigraphy of the Mississippian established the present standard of succession and nomenclature, as well as the correlation between the outcrop and the subsurface extension of the system in southern Alberta. His studies on the petrography and classification of the carbonate rocks and their insoluble residues were some of the first undertaken, and formed the basis for conclusions regarding their mode of origin, environment of deposition, temporal equivalence of facies, and formation of cyclical alternations. He envisaged shallow, warm, clear seas with widespread shoals where the bulk of the rock-forming organisms, echinoderms, flourished and their calcareous remains accumulated to be subjected to the sorting processes of waves and currents. The shoals were interspersed with shallow-water banks where oolites formed and aragonite mud precipitated from waters saturated in calcium carbonate. Near shore, sandbars and beaches were formed of quartz, dolomite, and calcite derived from the erosion of older carbonate rocks and, together with the banks, produced conditions where influx of normal seawater was restricted and precipitation of gypsum and anhydrite took place. He also concluded that dolomitization was a secondary process but nearly contemporaneous with the deposition of the altered limestones, and was effected on a volume-for-volume basis so that the porosity present in the dolomites, which form some of the principal reservoirs for oil and gas, was inherited from the original limestone.

In 1963 Douglas, with three collaborators, prepared a synthesis of the geology of northern Canada pertinent to the assessment of the petroleum potential of the northernmost sedimentary basins. The study included restorations of the three-dimensional form of gross rock facies and their tectonic environment.

Douglas received his early education at Hawkesbury, Ontario, where his father was principal of the high school. He attended Queen's University, graduating in 1942 with a B.Sc. and the Manley B. Baker scholarship. From 1943 to 1945 he served in the Royal Canadian Air Force. He received his Ph.D. from Columbia University in 1950. Douglas joined the staff of the Geological Survey of Canada in 1947, becoming head of the Geology of Fuels Section in 1957, chief of the Regional Geology Division in 1964, and principal research scientist in 1966. He was elected a fellow of the Royal Society of Canada in 1959 and was awarded the Willet G. Miller Medal by the Society in 1965.

For background information *see* FAULT AND FAULT STRUCTURES; FOLD AND FOLD SYSTEMS; LIMESTONE; PETROLEUM GEOLOGY; STRATIGRAPHY in the McGraw-Hill Encyclopedia of Science and Technology.   □

★ DRAGSTEDT, Lester Reynold

American surgeon and physiologist
Born Oct. 2, 1893, Anaconda, Mont., U.S.A.

WHEN DRAGSTEDT began his work in 1916 as an assistant in the department of physiology at the University of Chicago under A. J. Carlson, he attempted to demonstrate the significance of acid gastric juice in producing ulcers in the stomach duodenum. This problem continued to engage his attention throughout his career.

He became an instructor in pharmacology at the State University of Iowa in 1917 and subsequently assistant professor of physiology. During this period, with his brother Carl, he found that dogs could survive the complete removal of the duodenum, thus indicating that the organ does not produce an internal secretion necessary for life as was previously believed. Allen Whipple cited this work as the stimulus for the development of his operation for the radical surgical treatment of carcinoma of the pancreas.

After a year of military service in World War I, Dragstedt returned to the University of Chicago to complete his work for a Ph.D. in physiology (1920) and then went to Rush Medical College for an M.D. (1921). In 1921 he became assistant professor of physiology at the University of Chicago and in 1923 professor of physiology and chairman of the department of physiology and pharmacology at Northwestern University Medical School. During this period he found that dogs from which the thyroid and parathyroid glands had been completely removed could be kept alive indefinitely and free from parathyroid tetany if placed on a diet of bread, milk, and lactose. Prior to this work it was commonly believed that removal of the parathyroid glands was inevitably fatal. De Noel Paton was chiefly responsible for the view that parathyroid tetany was due to intoxication with guanidine, a waste product of protein metabolism, and that it was the function of the parathyroid glands to detoxify or eliminate this substance. Dragstedt harmonized his findings with this view by suggesting that the toxic agents responsible for parathyroid tetany are produced in the intestinal tract by bacterial proteolysis and that his diet prevents their production by changing the intestinal flora and substituting bacterial fermentation for putrefaction. When Hanson and Collip later isolated the hormone of the parathyroids and demonstrated its relation to calcium metabolism, Dragstedt was chagrined at his attempt to explain his own experiments on the basis of Paton's ideas.

In 1925 D. B. Phemister was appointed chairman of the department of surgery at the University of Chicago. He persuaded Dragstedt to give up his post at Northwestern, secure additional clinical training in Vienna and Budapest, and join him in developing a university department, inspired by the threefold ideal of research, teaching, and surgical practice. It was at the University of Chicago that Dragstedt developed the concept that peptic ulcers are caused by an increase in the corrosive properties of the gastric content rather than a decrease in the resistance of a local area of the mucosa to the digestant action of gastric juice. He found by experiments on dogs that pure gastric juice such as may be secured from Pavlov pouches is an exceedingly corrosive fluid and can digest away the normal mucosa of the stomach or intestines and produce chronic, progressive peptic ulcers. In sharp contrast the normal gastric content, which is a mixture of gastric juice and food, is relatively innocuous. Organs such as the kidney and spleen were not digested if implanted into defects produced in the stomach wall and exposed to gastric digestion for prolonged periods. He theorized that normally the stomach does not digest itself because food, which is the usual stimulus for gastric secretion, buffers and reduces its corrosive properties. Should gastric secretion be stimulated by agencies other than food, however, or if a hypersecretion of gastric juice should occur, the gastric content might well approach the acid and pepsin concentration of pure gastric juice and so produce and maintain a chronic, progressive peptic ulcer.

Henning and Norpoth discovered that duodenal ulcer patients usually secrete abnormally large amounts of gastric juice in the fasting empty stomach at night. When Varco, Code, and Wangensteen found that a similar secretion of gastric juice induced in animals by histamine would regularly produce duodenal ulcers, it seemed probable that this was also the cause of these ulcers in man. The clinical impression that duodenal ulcers tend to occur in people subjected to long-continued anxiety, tension, and mental strain prompted Dragstedt to the view that the fasting hypersecretion in these patients might be of nervous origin and led to his introduction of vagotomy in the surgical treatment of duodenal ulcers in 1942. In succeeding years gastric vagotomy combined with gastroenterostomy or pyloroplasty was widely adopted and largely replaced the more hazardous operation of gastric resection in the treatment of this disease.

Although Dragstedt and his associates also treated gastric ulcers successfully by vagotomy and gastroenterostomy in 1943, this procedure suffered from the objection that failure to resect the stomach would be unfortunate should the diagnosis prove incorrect and the lesion prove to be a cancer. In the intervening years the sharp decline in the incidence of gastric cancer and the increasing reliability of diagnosis by biopsy of the lesion at the time of surgery have brought about a return to favor of vagotomy and gastroenterostomy in the treatment of gastric ulcers. Many surgeons believe that this operation leads to earlier recognition of gastric cancers masquerading as benign ulcers. Meanwhile, Dragstedt and E. R. Woodward continued their experimental studies on the physiology of the gastric antrum and secured conclusive evidence supporting Edkin's hypothesis that the stimulation of gastric secretion by food in the stomach is brought about by a hormome, gastrin, released into the bloodstream from the mucosa of the pyloric antrum. These experiments also led to the view that gastric ulcers are usually caused by a hypersecretion of gastric juice of hormonal or gastrin origin due to stasis of food in the stomach from pyloric stenosis or gastric atony.

When Phemister retired as chairman of the department of surgery at the University of Chicago in 1949, Dragstedt became chairman and Thomas D. Janes Distinguished Service Professor of Surgery. He left this position in 1959 to become research professor of surgery at the University of Florida, where Woodward, his former student and colleague, was professor of surgery and head of the department. There the two men continued their collaboration in surgical and physiological research and teaching. Dragstedt received the Distinguished Service Medal of the American Medical Association (1963), the Bigelow Gold Medal of the Boston Surgical Society (1964), the Samuel D. Gross Prize of the Philadelphia Academy of Surgery (1964), the Julius Friedenwald Medal of the American Gastroenterological Society (1964), the Silver (1945) and Gold (1953) medals of the American Medical Association for original investigation, and the Swedish Royal Order of the North Star (1967). An honorary fellow of the Royal College of Surgeons of England, the Royal College of Physicians and Surgeons of Canada, and the Swedish Surgical Society, he was elected to the National Academy of Sciences in 1950.

For background information *see* DIGESTIVE SYSTEM; PARATHYROID GLAND; PEPTIC ULCER in the McGraw-Hill Encyclopedia of Science and Technology.   □

★ DRICKAMER, Harry George

American chemist
Born Nov. 19, 1918, Cleveland, Ohio, U.S.A.

DRICKAMER'S PRINCIPAL area of research was concerned with the use of very high pressure to investigate the electronic structure of solids. In his laboratory techniques were developed to permit measurement of optical absorption to 170,000 atm, electrical resistance to 600,000 atm, x-ray diffraction to over 500,000 atm, and Mössbauer resonance to over 300,000 atm.

In the Schrödinger equation, which governs interaction among the electrons and nuclei that make up a solid, there appears a potential energy term that is a strong function of the distance between the atoms or ions. With pressure it is possible to vary the interatomic distances at constant temperature. It is this fact that makes pressure a prime variable for testing hypotheses concerning the properties of condensed systems. With the range of pressure involved in this work, it is possible to compress metals such as iron over 20%. The density of alkali halide crystals increases by a factor of 1.5–1.8, while some organic solids double in density. For many systems the atoms rearrange into a new crystal structure with different, and

often interesting, properties (for example, the transition from graphite to diamond).

One of the early results of the x-ray measurements was the demonstration that for typical ionic crystals (the alkali halides, MgO, some transition metal oxides) the relationship between pressure and volume could be described over the entire range in terms of electrostatic attraction, van der Waals attraction, and a repulsion term (the Born-Mayer equation), using only constants evaluated at 1 atm. Graphite crystallizes in planes of hexagonal rings, with each ring very similar to a benzene molecule without the hydrogens. X-ray studies showed that the rings tend to buckle with pressure and apparently tend ultimately to form a structure with the four nearest neighbors, which is the hexagonal analog of the four-coordinated diamond structure. Such "hexagonal diamonds" have been found in meteorites and in the products from graphite shocked to very high pressure. A wide variety of aromatic molecules and complexes of these molecules tend to react at high pressure in a crystalline solid in a manner quite analogous to graphite.

The electrons on a free atom can exist in a series of discrete energy levels. In a crystal, because of the Pauli principle, there are bands of allowed energy states separated by forbidden gaps. Many interesting properties of solids are determined by the location and condition of the highest energy band that contains any electrons (the valence band) and the next band higher in energy (the conduction band). Each state in an allowed band can contain two electrons. Thus, for a system with one valence electron per atom, such as copper or sodium, there are available states that permit electrons to be transported through the lattice under the influence of an electric field gradient. The resistance to transport comes from lattice vibrations that increase in amplitude with pressure. Such materials are good conductors and have a resistance that increases with temperature. These are typical metals. On the other hand, if atoms or ions consist of filled shells, as in NaCl or MgO, the valence band is filled and the electrons cannot reach the conduction band, so one has an insulator. If the gap is not too large, electrons can be excited across it thermally (or optically) and one has an intrinsic semiconductor, as in very pure silicon or germanium. The size of the gap can be measured either by optical absorption or from the temperature coefficient of thermal conductivity. The thermal excitation of electrons, and thus the conductivity, increases exponentially with temperature. When the gap disappears and the bands overlap, one has a metal such as calcium or strontium.

Drickamer's work showed that iodine, which is ordinarily a good insulator, exhibits metallic conductivity perpendicular to the plane of the molecules above 160,000 atm and in the molecular plane above 220,000 atm. Other insulators, such as SnI_4, and large aromatic molecules, such as pentacene, also become metallic at high pressure without a change of crystal structure. A number of semiconducting crystals with open structures undergo a first-order phase transition to a metallic state at high pressure. Silicon and germanium undergo such transitions to the white tin structure at high pressure. Other materials important commercially, such as GaAs, InSb, InAs, ZnS, ZnSe, and ZnTc, undergo similar transitions.

Optical studies provided information about a wide variety of electronic phenomena. Measurements of the location of absorption peaks as a function of pressure in crystals containing transition metal ions gave a critical test of some aspects of ligand field theory. Studies of color centers and other impurity centers in alkali halides tested various aspects of the theories originated to describe these phenomena.

Experiments on metals included observations of an unusual transition in cesium, rubidium, and probably potassium. In this transition an electron is transferred from one atomic state to another, which allows closer packing of the atoms without a change in their arrangement in space. Calcium and strontium, which, as already pointed out, are metals because of overlap of the filled valence band and empty conduction band, actually become semiconductors at high pressure, thus proving it is also possible to separate overlapping bands by decreasing interatomic distance. Mössbauer resonance studies on iron showed that the hexagonal close-packed phase that appears at 130,000 atm is not ferromagnetic.

Drickamer obtained his B.S., M.S., and Ph.D. at the University of Michigan in 1941, 1942, and 1946, respectively. During 1942–45 he worked as a chemical engineer at the Pan American Refining Corp. in Texas City. He went to the University of Illinois in 1946, becoming professor of physical chemistry and chemical engineering in 1953, and was also a member of the Center for Advanced Study. Drickamer received the Colburn Award of the American Institute of Chemical Engineers in 1947, the Ipatieff Award of the American Chemical Society in 1956, and the Oliver E. Buckley Solid State Physics Prize of the American Physical Society in 1967. He was elected to the National Academy of Sciences in 1965.

For background information *see* BAND THEORY OF SOLIDS; HIGH-PRESSURE PHENOMENA; HIGH-PRESSURE PROCESSES; NUCLEAR STRUCTURE in the McGraw-Hill Encyclopedia of Science and Technology.   □

DRYDEN, Hugh Latimer

American physicist and aeronautical engineer
Born July 2, 1898, Pocomoke City, Md., U.S.A.
Died Dec. 2, 1965, Washington, D.C., U.S.A.

A SPECIALIST in aerodynamics, Dryden gained international recognition for his fundamental work on air turbulence and boundary-layer control. Later, while directing the guided missile program of the National Bureau of Standards, he led the development of the first operational radar homing missile, the Bat.

During the late 1920s it was discovered that the findings on the same airship model tested in different wind tunnels varied by as much as 100%. Dryden, working at the National Bureau of Standards, undertook an investigation to determine the cause of the variation. He found that the airflow in the wind tunnels had turbulence and that the amount of turbulence varied in wind tunnels of different design. To measure the amount of turbulence, Dryden and his associates developed the hot-wire anemometer. In this device a change in resistance and a drop in voltage across a hot platinum wire result from variations in air speed. By using the anemometer to measure airflow in different wind tunnels, Dryden was able to show that a variation in turbulence of 1% was sufficient to cause a 100% variation in airship test results. He also found that he could increase the turbulence of a wind tunnel by introducing a wire screen of fine and coarse mesh, and—based on his findings—he and his associates were able to design wind tunnels of very low turbulence. Dryden then extended his research to include the effects of turbulence on airships and airplane wings. For any object in motion, the air at the surface is at rest with respect to the object, while the air a short distance away is moving at high speed relative to the object. The interface between these two airflows is called the boundary layer. He discovered that the turbulence most affected the flow that was very close to the surfaces of the models. His investigations of turbulence and the mechanics of the boundary layer led to improved design in airplanes and in predictions of their performance.

Late in 1940 the National Defense Research Committee began an investigation of a winged bomb that would automatically seek out a target and guide itself to it. Early in 1942 the National Bureau of Standards was asked to take over the aerodynamic and servomechanism (control) development of the weapon, and Dryden was appointed to take charge of the project.

Two basic types of radar homing missile were considered. One was a glider bomb with a radar receiver tuned to an enemy transmitter on which the bomb could home in. The other, also a glide bomb, contained both a transmitter and a receiver; the transmitter emitted short pulses of high intensity, and the missile was guided by the returning echoes from the target. Dryden's group investigated both types of missile. The receiver-containing missile, called the Pelican, was constructed first and tested in December, 1942. However, the results were unsatisfactory, and a decision was made to concentrate on the second type, called the Bat. Flight tests started in May, 1944, and the weapon proved effective. The Bat was put into production and used against Japanese shipping in the Okinawa campaign, thus becoming the first automatic guided missile to be used in combat.

Dryden's investigations covered many areas of aerodynamics in addition to wind-tunnel turbulence and boundary-layer flow. He pioneered studies of the effect of wind pressure on structures and on the streamlining of automobiles. He directed the National Bureau of Standards research on jet propulsion and on acoustic fuzes. A sports enthusiast, he even studied—in collaboration with Lyman J. Briggs—the coefficient of restitution and the spin of a baseball and the aerodynamic considerations in throwing a curve ball. Near the end of World War II, as deputy scientific director of the Army Air Force Scientific Advisory Group, which was headed by Theodor von Kármán, he toured Germany to investigate German scientific progress during the war years; in this capacity he was a contributor to *Toward New Horizons*, a report intended to channel military scientific research in the following decade.

Dryden studied at Johns Hopkins University (A.B., 1916; A.M., 1918; Ph.D., 1919). He joined the National Bureau of Standards in 1918 as a laboratory assistant. Two years later

he was appointed chief of the Aerodynamic Section, and in 1934 he was named chief of the Mechanics and Sound Division. Dryden served in the latter capacity until 1946, when he was appointed associate director of the Bureau. In 1947 he left to join the National Advisory Committee for Aeronautics as director of aeronautical research, and in 1950 he was named director of the Committee. In 1958 Dryden was a member of the President's advisory committee whose recommendations resulted in the establishment of the National Aeronautics and Space Administration, of which he became deputy administrator, a position he retained until his death. He received many awards in recognition of both his scientific efforts and his contributions to the United States, among them the Sylvanus Albert Reed Medal of the Institute of Aeronautical Sciences (for his work on boundary-layer phenomena), the Presidential Certificate of Merit (for his work on the Bat missile), the Medal of Freedom (for advising the U.S. Air Force on future research and development), the Langley Medal, and the von Kármán, Hill, and Goddard awards.

For background information *see* MISSILE; MISSILE GUIDANCE SYSTEMS; TURBULENT FLOW; WIND TUNNEL in the McGraw-Hill Encyclopedia of Science and Technology.   □

★ DUBININ, Mikhail Mikhailovich

Soviet physicochemist
Born Jan. 1, 1901, Moscow, Russia

DUBININ'S SCIENTIFIC interests were primarily in porous structures of solids and related adsorption and capillary phenomena.

Most adsorbents and catalysts are porous bodies. Their pore sizes may range from near-molecule to magnitudes observable visually with slight magnification. Active carbons—porous carbonaceous adsorbents—encompass all pore sizes from several angstroms to millions of angstroms. Detailed study of the porous structure of active carbons using combined methods (sorption, forcing mercury into pores, small-angle x-ray analysis, electron microscopy, and so on) revealed polymodal pore distribution according to effective radii, that is, the presence in active carbons of different pore varieties: macropores, transitional pores, and micropores. The established different mechanisms of adsorption and capillary phenomena in these pores served as a physical basis for their classification and its extension to adsorbents of different chemical nature.

The largest pores, macropores (effective radii $r > 2000$–3000 A, surface area S several square meters per gram), act as transport pores in most adsorption processes. In transitional pores (3000–$2000 > r > 15$–16 A; $S = 30$–500 square meters per gram) there occurs mono- and polymolecular adsorption of vapors, that is, formation of successive adsorption layers. At high relative pressures transitional pores undergo volume filling by the capillary condensation mechanism. The lower limit of effective pore radii corresponds to the limit of applicability of Kelvin's equation. Macropores and transitional pores are filled by mercury forced into them. The smallest pores, micropores ($r < 15$–16 A), are characterized by volume filling in adsorption of gases and vapors. Adsorption in micropores differs radically from layer-by-layer adsorption in larger pore varieties, and is described by the developed theory of volume filling of micropores, especially when the dispersion component of the adsorption interaction is the deciding factor. The macroscopic concept of surface area loses its physical meaning for micropores.

The principal theoretical investigations based on extensive experimental data involved the creation of the theory of gas and vapor adsorption in micropores. The main proposition of the theory is the temperature invariance of the characteristic curve expressing the dependence of the differential molar work of adsorption, that is, the variation in free energy, on the degree of filling of the adsorption space. In cooperation with L. V. Radushkevich, Dubinin substantiated the two-constant equation of the characteristic adsorption curve. Characteristic curves for different vapors are affine, the affinity coefficient being determined by the physical constants of the vapors adsorbed. With B. P. Bering and V. V. Serpinsky, Dubinin developed the thermodynamics of the volume filling of pores: transitional pores due to capillary condensation and micropores due to adsorption. This made it possible to show that the invariance of characteristic curves is a sufficiently good approximation in observing the thermodynamic criterion of the applicability of the theory. Thus, possessing a minimum of experimental information, such as a

one adsorption isotherm, it is easy to determine the two main constants of the adsorption equation: the limiting volume of the adsorption space (micropore volume) and the constant associated with the pore sizes. Using these constants, one can calculate to a good approximation adsorption equilibria and thermodynamic functions (heat and entropy of adsorption) for different vapors over a wide range of temperatures and equilibrium pressures. Recently Bering and Serpinsky of the laboratory headed by Dubinin suggested a new, more universal version of the theory of volume filling of micropores applicable to a wider range of adsorbents including zeolites and to a still wider region of fillings of the adsorption space.

On the basis of physically substantiated concepts of adsorbent pore varieties, the most rational classification of porous adsorbents and catalysts into macroporous, transitional-pore, and microporous ones was suggested. In addition to the indicated pure structural types of adsorbents, one frequently encounters adsorbents of mixed structural types containing two or all three pore varieties. For this general case methods for calculating the parameters of the structure of all pore varieties with the use of digital computers were developed (in cooperation with J. S. Lezin). On the basis of experimental data it was established, inter alia, that a number of adsorbents, for example, some active carbons and fine-pore silica gels, possess more complex porous structures reduceable to the presence in the adsorbent of two independent microporous structures with different micropore sizes within the general effective radii range from 6 to 14 A. These conclusions from adsorption measurements were directly confirmed by small-angle x-ray analysis.

Ways of controlling the development of different pore varieties in the course of synthesis of adsorbents and of modifying the chemical nature of their skeletons were elaborated. For nonspecific adsorption of gases and vapors by microporous adsorbents, a quantitative description of adsorption equilibria was given as a function of the parameters of the microporous structure of the adsorbents and the physical properties of the adsorbates. The features of filling of the adsorption space of micropores were studied on examples of microporous crystals: synthetic zeolites, whose micropore volumes were calculated from x-ray data. The secondary porous structures of molded zeolites were studied comprehensively by combined methods.

Dubinin graduated from the chemistry department of the Moscow Higher Technical School in 1921. He served on the staff of the school from 1922 to 1941, advancing from assistant to associate professor and in 1933 to professor. He was awarded a degree of doctor of chemical sciences in 1936 and in 1943 was elected a member of the U.S.S.R. Academy of Sciences. In 1946 he became head of the Department of Sorption on Processes at the Institute of Physical Chemistry of the U.S.S.R. Academy of Sciences. He was chairman of the Chemical Sciences Section in 1948–57 and a member of the presidium of the Academy in 1948–62. Dubinin won the U.S.S.R. State Prize in 1942 and 1950.

For background information *see* ACTIVATED CARBON; ADSORPTION; ORGANIC CHEMISTRY in the McGraw-Hill Encyclopedia of Science and Technology.   □

★ DUCKWORTH, Henry Edmison

Canadian physicist
Born Nov. 1, 1915, Brandon, Manitoba, Canada

B Y DETERMINING atomic masses with high precision, Duckworth provided evidence for sudden changes in nuclear stability that correspond to the completion of nuclear shells or to the onset of nuclear distortion. These determinations were made with specially constructed mass spectrometers of exceptionally high resolving power.

The fact that mass spectrometers could provide useful information concerning nuclear binding energies was demonstrated first by F. W. Aston at Cambridge in 1927. In the next decade this work was extended by Dempster at Chicago, Bainbridge at Harvard, and Mattauch in Vienna, who provided an overall, albeit approximate, view of the manner in which the nuclear binding energy varies with increasing atomic mass. Duckworth was a student of Dempster's during 1940–42, and realized that detailed information concerning nuclear structure, and of a unique sort, could be obtained with a mass spectrometer, provided the precision could be improved sufficiently. This led after World War II to the construction and utilization by Duckworth and his associates of a series of improved mass spectrometers, culminating in 1962 in an instrument whose resolving power exceeded a quarter million.

The first result of this work was the discovery in 1949 that the binding energy per nucleon displays a large and sudden decline at or near $A = 90$. This was immediately attributed to the closure of the $N = 50$ shell, in accordance with concurrent speculations concerning the existence of nuclear shell structure, and atomic mass evidence for other alleged shells or subshells was then sought. Definitive evidence was found for the $Z = 28$, $Z = 50$, and $N = 82$ shells, and useful information was given concerning the magnitudes of these effects. Also, a study was made in 1953 with B. G. Hogg of the mass region $140 \leqq A$ in the hope of discovering evidence for nuclear subshells among the rare-earth elements. Although no localized effects were observed, a broad region of extra stability was identified which did not appear to be explicable on the basis of nuclear shells or the underlying theory based on the independent particle model. It was to clarify this matter that the very large instrument, completed in 1962, was begun. In the meantime, in 1957 Nier and Johnson at Minnesota confirmed the existence of the region of extra stability above $A = 140$ and identified it with the $N = 90$ configuration.

The very high resolving power of the new mass spectrometer made it possible to determine directly the energy with which the last two neutrons in a nucleus are bound, rather than, as previously, the average binding energy per nucleon. As a result, local effects were greatly magnified, and the picture in the neighborhood of $N = 90$ emerged with unexpected clarity. Up to and including $N = 88$, the nucleus is described to a good approximation by the single-particle theory, and also to a fair approximation beyond $N = 92$. But the four neutrons $N = 89$, 90, 91, and 92 display an extra stability which can be reasonably associated with the nuclear distortion now known to exist in the rare-earth region. Thus, as far as nuclear distortion involving neutrons is concerned, it begins very suddenly at $N = 88$, it involves four neutrons principally (and perhaps only), and the magnitude of the effect can be estimated to good accuracy from the mass spectrometric data.

Duckworth and his associates utilized their data to predict the energies released in various nuclear transmutations. These predictions proved accurate to a few kilovolts of energy, and they corrected significant errors that had been made in the study of nuclear reactions and radioactive decays. A by-product of the work was the discovery in 1949 of the rare stable isotope of platinum at mass number 190.

Only child of a minister of the United Church of Canada, Duckworth graduated from the University of Manitoba with a B.A. in 1935 and a B.Sc. in 1936. Following 3 years of secondary and junior college teaching, he enrolled at the University of Chicago, where he obtained his Ph.D. in physics in 1942. Following 3 years of war research with the National Research Council of Canada, he was on the staff at the University of Manitoba (1945–46), Wesleyan University (1946–51), and McMaster University (1951–65). In 1965 he became vice-president of the University of Manitoba. Elected to the Royal Society of Canada in 1954, he was awarded the Medal of the Canadian Association of Physicists in 1964 and the Tory Medal of the Royal Society of Canada in 1965.

Duckworth wrote *Mass Spectroscopy* (1958), *Electricity and Magnetism* (1960; rev. ed. 1966), and *Little Men in the Unseen World* (1963) and edited the *Proceedings of the International Conference on Atomic Masses* (1960).

For background information *see* ATOMIC STRUCTURE AND SPECTRA; BINDING ENERGY, NUCLEAR; NUCLEAR STRUCTURE; SPECTROSCOPY in the McGraw-Hill Encyclopedia of Science and Technology.   □

★ **DUNN, Leslie Clarence**

American geneticist
Born Nov. 2, 1893, Buffalo, N.Y., U.S.A.

As a student, Dunn was impressed by the ease with which hereditary endowment (the genotype) can be analyzed into its transmission components (genes) by simple breeding experiments or by observations of gene frequencies in populations. He carried out many such analyses in chickens and in laboratory mice, and his interest was especially attracted by genes with drastic or abnormal effects. His analyses led to questions as to how different genes produce their different effects during the development of the individual. Several genes, some with lethal effects, were studied by examining early embryos, first in the chicken and later in the mouse. From this work the idea emerged that genes produce their effects by controlling the rates of specific processes in early development.

Discovery that the same kinds of abnormalities as those due to gene differences, such as absence of tail or disproportionate dwarfism, could occur in birds of normal genotype led to the recognition that environmental or accidental changes in early development can simulate the kinds of changes produced by gene differences. The use of simulation as a tool to explore causal relations in development was begun, but was chiefly exploited by W. Landauer in his studies of chemical teratology. In the laboratory mouse, Dunn's analyses of quantitative or intergrading differences in hair color and especially in localized absence of hair pigments (white spotting) showed that such differences can be resolved into components due to many genes, each with small effects interacting in complex ways.

A problem which occupied Dunn for many years was provided by the discovery in the mouse of a series of hereditary changes in one region of one linkage group (chromosome). The hereditary changes involved (1) early processes in the organization of the embryo, some of them providing examples of the origin of very early disturbances and abnormalities, such as absence of tail, limbs, and other parts, constituting the earliest effects of lethal genes in mammals; (2) the ratio in which some genes were transmitted to offspring through the sperm, certain lethal genes going from male carriers to over 90% of the progeny instead of the normal 50%; (3) effects on the probability of recombination of genes in this chromosome region through crossing-over exchange; and (4) effects on the fertility of males bearing certain combinations of such genes, varying from complete sterility to nearly normal. Interest in this chromosome region increased when it was discovered that its variant genes, generally lethals, are present in most natural populations of house mice in North America and elsewhere. It was shown that these genes are retained in the populations in spite of their lethal effects by an evolutionary force different from, and opposed to, natural selection; this force was called transmission ratio advantage. Studies of the population dynamics of this striking polymorphism indicated that it was probably fluctuating—the genes involved being propelled through the populations by high sperm transmission ratios and migrations and being subject to local extinction by random processes in small breeding groups. A rather novel type of flux equilibrium was suggested. An attempt was thus made in this case to bring into relation the structure of a region of the genetic material and its function in development and evolution.

At Dartmouth College (A.B., 1915) Dunn was attracted to the new field of genetics through the influence of John H. Gerould. He went in 1915 to the Bussey Institution of Harvard University, where he was a student and assistant of William E. Castle. His graduate work was interrupted in 1917–19 by war service as a lieutenant of infantry. On return from France he completed his doctoral research on linkage in mice and rats, took his Sc.D. at Harvard in 1920, and joined the staff of the Storrs Agricultural Experiment Station in Connecticut as a geneticist. In 1928 Dunn became professor of zoology at Columbia University, serving until 1962, when he became emeritus professor with a research laboratory at Nevis Biological Station, Irvington, N.Y. While at Columbia he was visiting professor or lecturer at Oslo, Berlin, London, and Harvard universities and the New School in New York City. He carried out research in human genetics in Rome. He was elected to the National Academy of Sciences and to the American Philosophical Society in 1943 and to the American Academy of Arts and Sciences in 1950.

Dunn wrote *Principles of Genetics*, with E. W. Sinnott (1925; 5th ed., with T. Dobzhansky, 1958); *Heredity and Variation* (1932); *Heredity, Race and Society*, with T. Dobzhansky (1946; rev. ed. 1952); *Race and Biology* (reprint 1965); *Heredity and Evolution in Human Populations* (1958; 2d ed. 1965); and *A Short History of Genetics* (1965). He also wrote some 250 articles in scientific periodicals and encyclopedias. He was editor of *Genetics, The American Naturalist*, and *Genetics in the 20th Century*.

For background information *see* CHROMOSOME; GENE ACTION; LETHAL GENE in the McGraw-Hill Encyclopedia of Science and Technology.   □

★ DYSON, Freeman John

American theoretical physicist
Born Dec. 15, 1923, Crowthorne, England

DYSON BELONGED to the class of physicists who solve problems rather than create new theories. He looked for problems in various branches of physics where a thorough mathematical analysis might lead to a useful clarification of ideas. He never worked at the same problem for more than 2 or 3 years. His main contributions were in the fields of quantum electrodynamics (1948), ferromagnetism (1955), field theory (1958), statistical mechanics (1961), and the stability of matter (1966). Only the first and last of these items will be discussed here.

Quantum electrodynamics is a theory invented about 1930 by Werner Heisenberg, Wolfgang Pauli, P. A. M. Dirac, and Enrico Fermi to describe the processes of atomic physics and electromagnetic radiation in a unified way. The theory was from the beginning enormously successful in accounting for the electric and magnetic properties of atoms, the emission and absorption of light, the creation and annihilation of electron-positron pairs, and a whole gamut of other phenomena observed in nature. The theory covers the central territory of physics, including all the familiar processes of heat, light, electricity, and chemistry; it excludes only the submicroscopic world of nuclear physics on the one hand and the astronomical world of gravitation on the other.

In the late 1930s it was found that quantum electrodynamics, in spite of its overwhelming successes, was mathematically inconsistent. To certain reasonable questions it gave unreasonable or absurd answers. In particular, it never was able to predict how much the energy levels of an atom would be affected by the existence of electromagnetic radiation. During the 1930s these difficulties were worrying only to theoreticians, because the experiments were then not accurate enough to detect any of the effects for which the theory gave ambiguous answers. However, in 1946 a far more exact measurement of the energy of the hydrogen atom, made by W. E. Lamb and R. C. Retherford at Columbia University, put the theory to a decisive test. Either the theory must explain the new observations, or it must be discarded.

Under the pressure of the Columbia experiments, first H. A. Bethe and then Julian Schwinger, Sin-Itiro Tomonaga, and R. P. Feynman succeeded in forcing the theory to speak

plainly. They were able, without changing the theory in any essential way, to extract from it definite values for the quantities that had been measured. In all cases the theoretical and experimental numbers agreed. It was at this happy moment in 1948 that Dyson arrived on the scene. His contribution was to tidy up and systematize the newly invented techniques of calculation. Bethe, Schwinger, Tomonaga, and Feynman had used different methods, each adapted to a special situation. Dyson was able to develop these methods into a general scheme, to show that they were all consistent with one another, and to formulate uniform rules of calculation applicable to all experimental situations. The main result of Dyson's work was to show that the mathematical ambiguities inherent in quantum electrodynamics would arise only when one tried to calculate unobservable quantities. He proved that for every measurable quantity the theory would give an unambiguous and finite value. In this way the theory was preserved as a working tool, although its basic mathematical inconsistency was not cured. It has survived triumphantly all the experimental tests made subsequently.

Dyson's work on the stability of matter was done in collaboration with Andrew Lenard. They gave the first mathematical proof that the electric forces between electrons and protons in ordinary matter cannot release an indefinite amount of energy; that is, the energy available in electric forces is strictly limited to a fixed amount in each atom. They also proved that matter would be unstable if the electrons did not satisfy the Pauli exclusion principle, which forbids two electrons to occupy the same quantum state. Thus the exclusion principle is both necessary and sufficient to ensure the stability of matter. This mathematical theorem perhaps explains why all particles in nature that are electrically charged and lack nuclear interactions are found to obey the exclusion principle.

Dyson was educated as a mathematician at the University of Cambridge. During World War II he was at the headquarters of the R.A.F. Bomber Command doing operations research. After the war he went to Cornell University to study physics with Bethe and Feynman, and in 1951 he became a professor there. In 1953 he moved to the Institute for Advanced Study, Princeton, N.J. Beside working on problems of pure physics, he helped to design the Triga reactor (1956) and the Orion spaceship (1959) at General Atomic in San Diego. He was elected to the Royal Society of London in 1952, to the American Academy of Arts and Sciences in 1958, and to the U.S. National Academy of Sciences in 1964.

For background information *see* EXCLUSION PRINCIPLE; NUCLEAR STRUCTURE; QUANTUM ELECTRODYNAMICS in the McGraw-Hill Encyclopedia of Science and Technology.   □

★ ECKART, Carl

American physicist and geophysicist
Born May 4, 1902, St. Louis, Mo., U.S.A.

ECKART HAD the good fortune to be a first-year graduate student in the laboratory of Arthur H. Compton at the time (1923) of the latter's discovery of the change of wavelength of x-rays on scattering by electrons. With G. E. M. Jauncey, Eckart showed that there would be no measurable change of wavelength on reflection from crystals, since the momentum of the photon would be transferred to an entire atom or possibly to the entire lattice. Ten years later, during the investigation of discrepancies in the values of the fundamental constants, he returned to a related problem, the reflection of x-rays from ruled gratings.

In 1924–25 he worked on apparent discrepancies between the theory of excitation and ionization and certain phenomena in low-voltage electric arcs. He explained some of these by demonstrating experimentally that the phenomenon was due to oscillations generated by the arc itself. With Karl T. Compton, he showed that other discrepancies were due to the electromotive force generated by differences in the concentration of free electrons in various parts of the arc plasma.

In 1925 Eckart proposed to investigate the L. de Broglie wave theory of quantum effects, and was awarded a National Research fellowship for this project. Temporarily diverted by W. Heisenberg's publication of matrix mechanics, he later showed the identity of this with Erwin Schrödinger's wave mechanics. During the 1930s he worked on various quantum theoretical problems, including the development of group theoretical methods for their solution. The numerical calculation of screening constants and the theoretical justification of approximations for molecular problems also occupied his attention. In 1940 he began developing a synthesis of classical continuum mechanics and thermodynamics, publishing a series of papers under the title of "Irreversible Thermodynamics."

During World War II Eckart led a project on underwater sound, which made him aware of the hydrodynamic and thermodynamic problems of the oceans, as well as of the stochastic problems of three-dimensional acoustics. A series of papers on the latter was published in 1953. His studies on the effects of thermal stratification in the atmosphere and oceans were summarized in book form in 1960. Thereafter he contributed to the transformation theory of the hydrodynamic equations.

Eckart received his B.S. (1922) and M.S. (1923) at Washington University and his Ph.D. in physics (1925) at Princeton University. A National Research Council and Guggenheim fellow from 1925 to 1928, in 1928 he joined the physics department of the University of Chicago. During World War II he was assistant director and later director of the division of war research of the University of California, and in 1946 he joined the faculty of that university as professor, serving as director of the marine physics laboratory, University of California, San Diego (1946–52), and of the Scripps Institution of Oceanography (1948–65). From 1965 to 1967 he was vice-chancellor for academic affairs at the University of California, San Diego. Elected to the National Academy of Sciences in 1953 and to the American Academy of Arts and Sciences in 1959, Eckart was awarded the National Academy's Agassiz Medal in 1966 for his contributions to oceanography.

Eckart wrote *Hydrodynamics of Oceans and Atmospheres* (1960).

For background information *see* QUANTUM MECHANICS; THERMODYNAMIC PROCESSES; UNDERWATER SOUND in the McGraw-Hill Encyclopedia of Science and Technology.   □

☆ ECKERT, John Presper

American engineer
Born Apr. 9, 1919, Philadelphia, Pa., U.S.A.

DURING WORLD WAR II it was realized in the U.S. War Department that the artillery firing tables for many American guns were useless in the terrain of North Africa. Firing tables were also required for the armament employed in aircraft. New tables had to be computed as rapidly as possible. To carry out this assignment, many hundreds of persons were employed by the Army

to operate mechanical calculating machines, but the job seemed endless despite the urgent need. In an attempt to speed up the task, the Army also used punched-card accounting machines and two differential analyzers.

At the Moore School of Engineering at the University of Pennsylvania, a much faster method of completing the project was considered by Eckert, then a 24-year-old graduate engineer, and John W. Mauchly, an associate professor of electrical engineering. Eckert worked on speeding up and increasing the accuracy of the differential analyzer at the university. This device was speeded up 10 times and its accuracy increased by a factor of 10. Because it was clear that further improvements with the differential analyzer would be a losing battle, Eckert and Mauchly considered a number of ways to overcome the limitations of this device and the desk calculator.

In the course of the work with the differential analyzer, several hundreds of vacuum tubes were incorporated in this machine. Both Eckert and Mauchly had independently built electronic counter circuits and this, in addition to the electronic experience with the differential analyzer, impressed them with the future potential of electronic experience with the differential analyzer, impressed them with the future potential of electronics for computing. They thought the next step might be to build an electronic integrator by simply adding or integrating long strings of pulses with vacuum tubes. It was realized, however, that long trains of pulses to represent numbers would be inefficient, and it was decided to make an arithmetic calculator with the information in coded form as it passed from one unit to another, and to add and perform other arithmetic operations in coded form as well. Finally, it was agreed to proceed with a general-purpose digital computer so that problems other than ballistic firing tables could be studied.

A proposal giving details of the plan was presented to the U.S. Army's Ordnance Department, and it eventually resulted in a contract to build a general-purpose digital machine. Later, in 1946, the world's first electronic computer, containing 19,000 vacuum tubes and 70,000 resistors, was completed. It was christened ENIAC (electronic numerical integrator and calculator). Eckert was chief engineer and Mauchly a consultant in the project, which, considering the final achievement, represented a small investment in time and resources. An average of 40 persons was employed in the undertaking. Of the 40, only a dozen were engineers or scientists. ENIAC had more than 500,000 hand-soldered connections and consumed over 100 kw of power—as much as a typical broadcasting station. The ENIAC equipment weighed 30 tons and filled a 30 × 50 ft room.

ENIAC was the prototype from which most other modern computers have evolved. It embodied almost all the concepts and components of today's high-speed digital computers. Its circuit design incorporated elements that have now become standard in computers, such as the gate (logical "and" element), the buffer (logical "or" element), and flip-flops. These were used as logic and as high-speed storage-and-control devices. It even had buffered and overlapped input and output, a feature not found in many later electronic computers. ENIAC could discriminate the sign of a number, compare quantities, add, subtract, multiply, divide, and extract square roots. Its accumulators combined the functions of an adding and storage unit. No central memory unit existed as such. Storage was localized within many of the functioning accumulator units of the computer. The accumulators could control the program path and provide for transfer of control and stored program control data. In addition to its cycling unit, 20 accumulators, and the master programmer, ENIAC included an initiating unit, a high-speed multiplier, a combined divider–square root unit, and three switch-controlled function tables. To make the electronics in the machine simple and reliable, vacuum tubes were employed very conservatively and in a relatively few basic circuit combinations. The success of the project was due in large part to the careful design and calculation of the circuits, which were used in such a way as to allow for the wide manufacturing variations and the considerable deterioration of the electronic parts available at that time. ENIAC was put to work at the U.S. Army's Aberdeen Proving Ground in Maryland in August, 1947, where it solved many of the trajectory problems of the atomic cannon, computed ballistics tables, and eventually was used in weather predictions, the hydrogen bomb calculations, cosmic-ray investigation, and wind tunnel design.

In 1948 Eckert became a partner in the newly formed Eckert-Mauchly Computer Corp. By 1949 a second electronic machine, BINAC (binary automatic computer), was produced that was faster and more economical to operate than ENIAC. Instead of punched cards, BINAC used magnetic tape to store information. Many electronic tubes were replaced with germanium diodes, enabling a great reduction in size and an increase in speed. Eckert's idea of using internal storage for all of the program control was used in this machine, although he had proposed it for the EDVAC (electronic discrete variable computer) while still at the University of Pennsylvania. Remington Rand, Inc. (now Sperry Rand Corp.) acquired the Eckert-Mauchly Computer Corp. in 1950.

The third computer, following BINAC, was UNIVAC I (universal automatic computer), the first computer designed to handle business data. Its ability to deal with numbers and descriptive material made it especially attractive for commercial use. It was the first commercial computer with a stored program and built-in automatic checking circuits, and contained many other innovations in the field. With the completion of UNIVAC I, electronic data processing moved into high gear. The computer had developed from a laboratory curiosity to a highly practical device with a multitude of applications destined to affect every individual's life.

Eckert attended the University of Pennsylvania, where he graduated from the Moore School in 1941 with a B.S. in electrical engineering and obtained his M.S. in 1943. In 1964 he received an honorary D.Sc. in engineering from the university. Prior to becoming a vice-president of UNIVAC in 1955, he served successively as director of research, director of commercial engineering, and executive assistant to the general manager. In recent years Eckert was technical adviser to the president of the UNIVAC Division. He was awarded the Horace N. Potts Medal by the Franklin Institute in 1949, and in that same year he was made a fellow of the Institute of Electrical and Electronic Engineers. In 1961 he and Mauchly received the John Scott Medal for "adding to the comfort, welfare, and happiness of mankind." This award was followed by receipt of the National Association of Manufacturers' Medal of Modern Pioneers in Creative Industry. In 1966 Eckert was the joint recipient with Mauchly of the Harry Goode Memorial Award for "contributions to and pioneering efforts in automatic computing." During 1948–66 Eckert was granted 85 patents from the U.S.

Patent Office. These patents were for numerous electronic inventions, ranging from a supersonic method of deflecting a light beam to a complete computing system.

For background information *see* COMPUTER; DIFFERENTIAL ANALYZER; DIGITAL COMPUTER in the McGraw-Hill Encyclopedia of Science and Technology.   □

★ EDSALL, John Tileston

American biochemist
Born Nov. 3, 1902, Philadelphia, Pa.

Edsall's scientific research was concerned with the structure and function of proteins. As a medical student at Harvard in 1924, he undertook research on the physiology of muscle with A. C. Redfield. Edsall continued work on the biochemistry of muscle as a student in Cambridge in 1924–26 in the department headed by Frederick Hopkins. On his return to Harvard Medical School, Edsall began the study of the muscle protein myosin from beef muscle in the laboratory of Edwin J. Cohn, a leader in the study of the physical chemistry of proteins. In 1928 Alexander von Muralt came from Switzerland to spend 2 years in the laboratory. He discovered that Edsall's myosin (actomyosin) preparations showed intense birefringence when subjected to mild shearing stress in flow. This led to a joint research by von Muralt and Edsall in which they demonstrated that actomyosin is a highly elongated structure, readily oriented in a velocity gradient, and that it is primarily responsible for the well-known birefringence of the muscle fiber. They were led to infer that actomyosin plays a fundamental role in the process of contraction in muscle—a hypothesis that was abundantly confirmed by later work.

During the 1930s Cohn, Edsall, Jeffries Wyman, J. P. Greenstein, T. L. McMeekin, and others undertook a comprehensive study of the physical chemistry of amino acids and peptides and the relation of their properties to those characteristic of the much larger protein molecules found in nature. Earlier E. Q. Adams in the United States and Niels Bjerrum in Denmark had demonstrated that amino acids, even when electrically neutral, are dipoles of very high electric moment; compared to most organic compounds, amino acids have very high melting points, which are best explained by interactions between electrically charged groups in the crystal lattice. The ionization constants of amino acids in solution also point to the type of structure known as a dipolar ion (zwitterion). For instance, the true formula for glycine, the simplest of the amino acids should be written $^+H_3N \cdot CH_2 \cdot COO^-$ rather than $H_2N \cdot CH_2 \cdot COOH$. The group at Harvard realized the implications of this structure for other properties of amino acids, peptides, and proteins. Wyman demonstrated that the dielectric constants of their solutions are extraordinarily high, surpassing those of all other compounds. J. L. Oncley, who joined the laboratory in 1936, made important dielectric constant studies on proteins. Moreover, these molecules, with two widely separated centers of charge, exert powerful electrostatic forces on neighboring molecules, including those of the surrounding solvent. The apparent molal volumes and heat capacities of amino acids and peptides in water are also smaller than those of most organic molecules because of electrostriction of the solvent.

Edsall studied the vibrational structure of these compounds by Raman spectroscopy in aqueous solution. He showed that amino, carboxyl, and other ionizable groups show characteristic vibrational frequencies which are markedly different for the ionized and un-ionized form of each of these groups. By means of such spectra, therefore, it was possible to identify the state of ionization of various groups in amino acid and peptide molecules and to show the simultaneous presence of positive and negative charges in different portions of the molecule.

The dipolar ion structure of amino acids and peptides also profoundly influences their solubility. Like most inorganic salts, the amino acids in general are far more soluble in water than in organic solvents; glycine, for example, is about 2500 times more soluble in water than in ethanol. Cohn, McMeekin, and Edsall showed that such relative solubility values can be systematically correlated with the structure of the molecule. The presence of electric charges favors solubility in water and other media of high dielectric constant, whereas nonpolar side chains favor solubility in media of low dielectric constants. Quantitative rules relating the structure of the solute to its relative solubility in water and in organic solvents were formulated on this basis. George Scatchard and John G.

Kirkwood, who were both in the chemistry department at MIT, collaborated closely with the workers at Harvard Medical School in this work. They developed an important extension of the Debye-Hückel theory of interionic attraction to describe quantitatively the interactions of these dipolar ions with ions and with other dipolar ions.

About 1940 Cohn, Edsall, Oncley, and their associates returned to intensive studies on proteins, which were greatly accelerated and expanded by the urgent practical need for blood plasma, and the proteins derived from it, in World War II. With strong support from the Office of Scientific Research and Development, Cohn instituted a very large program for fractionation of human blood plasma proteins to obtain purified serum albumin, γ-globulin, fibrinogen, thrombin, and other products needed for clinical use. Selective precipitation with ethanol at low temperature with suitable variation of pH and ionic strength permitted the large-scale separation in purified form of all these and other proteins. Cohn was the major director of this program, which came to include a large number of scientific workers, as well as many clinicians who were involved in the testing of the resulting products. Apart from their practical significance, these studies led to a great increase in the knowledge of blood plasma and to the separation of various proteins of great scientific interest which had not been characterized before, such as the α- and β-lipoproteins and the iron-binding protein, transferrin. Edsall's major concern during these years was the study of proteins involved in blood clotting, especially fibrinogen, prothrombin, and thrombin.

After 1945 Edsall concentrated on basic studies of the physical chemistry of proteins, especially blood proteins. He made extensive use of light-scattering measurements to determine the size and shape of protein molecules and the nature of their interactions with one another and with smaller ions and molecules. After the death of Cohn in 1953, Edsall moved to the Biological Laboratories of Harvard University in Cambridge, where he continued this work and also greatly extended his studies on the Raman spectroscopy of amino acids, peptides, and related molecules. He also studied the binding of metallic ions to amino acids and peptides.

From 1959 Edsall devoted his research primarily to the enzyme carbonic anhydrase, from red blood cells; this enzyme molecule, which contains an atom of zinc as an essential constituent, catalyzes the hydration of carbon dioxide and the dehydration of carbonic acid, and is of fundamental importance for the transport of carbon dioxide in the blood. E. E. Rickli in Edsall's laboratory soon demonstrated that human red blood cells contain at least two distinct enzymes, both having carbonic anhydrase activity; independent work in two other laboratories also demonstrated the same fact by different techniques, and a third minor enzyme was discovered as well. Recent researches in Edsall's laboratory were devoted to the further characterization of the conditions governing the activity of these enzymes and a study of their unusual physical properties, particularly their optical rotation and rotatory dispersion, which demonstrate strong interactions between the aromatic amino acid residues and the main framework of the molecule.

Edsall received his A.B. in 1923 and his M.D. in 1928 from Harvard University, where he was an instructor in biochemical sciences in 1928–32 and professor of biochemistry from 1932. He was a member of the U.S. National Commission for UNESCO during 1950–56. He was elected to the American Academy of Arts and Sciences in 1937 and to the National Academy of Sciences in 1951. He received the Passano Foundation Award in 1966.

In 1943 Edsall became coeditor of *Advances in Protein Chemistry*, a serial review publication, and in 1958 editor in chief of the *Journal of Biological Chemistry*. He wrote *Proteins, Amino Acids, and Peptides*, with Edwin J. Cohn (1943), and *Biophysical Chemistry*, with Jeffries Wyman (vol. 1, 1958; vol. 2, in preparation).

For background information *see* AMINO ACID; BLOOD; ENZYME; PROTEIN in the McGraw-Hill Encyclopedia of Science and Technology.   □

This approach, however, was found to be most fruitful in dealing with reactions of highly excited chemical states far from any equilibrium point. Eigen announced in 1954 the first of a series of methods for producing and measuring high-speed reactions in states relatively close to equilibrium, thus opening up many fields of chemistry to direct observation for the first time.

All the relaxation techniques devised by Eigen proceed by upsetting the balance of a chemical system near equilibrium; measurements are made as the system "relaxes" to a new equilibrium state. The reactants to be studied are commonly dissolved in an electrically conductive solution. The perturbation could be either single or periodic, according to the particular technique, and could take the form of a brief electrical pulse or an abrupt change in temperature, hydrostatic pressure, or electrical field intensity. Measurements were made either spectrophotometrically or conductometrically.

Eigen's own investigations employing relaxation techniques include the following: highly accurate measurements (1955, with DeMaeyer) of ionic dissociation and recombination in pure liquid water; studies of diffusion-controlled protolytic reactions in aqueous solutions (1955, with Schoen); a paper (1959, with Czerlinski) introducing the widely useful Joule heating–temperature jump technique; the elucidation of the discrete reaction steps causing sound absorption in 2-2 electrolyte solutions (with Tamm, 1962); investigations of the kinetics of keto-enol

EIGEN, Manfred

German chemist
Born May 9, 1927, Bochum, Germany

E IGEN AND his colleagues devised a battery of approaches to the study of high-speed chemical reactions, collectively known as relaxation techniques. These methods, together with the flash photolysis approach developed by the British chemists Ronald G. W. Norrish and George Porter, provided the basis for the rapid expansion of understanding of all sorts of fast reactions that began about 1950. Eigen, Norrish, and Porter shared the 1967 Nobel Prize in chemistry.

Prior to the 1950s, because of the limitations of methods available for the investigation of very fast reactions, such as those employing flame-front, shock tube, or fast mixing techniques, the lower limit of observable reaction time was in the tens of milliseconds. Flash photolysis, which came into use about 1949, proved to be a great advance and brought the limit of reaction measurements to below a millisecond.

tautomerism (with Ilgenfritz and Kruse, 1965).

Eigen turned his attention in the 1960s more and more to the application of relaxation techniques to the complex chemical events of molecular biology.

Relaxation techniques have yielded important results in fields as diverse as radiation chemistry, enzyme-catalyzed reactions, and transformation mechanisms of polypeptides.

Eigen received early training in physics and chemistry at the University of Göttingen, and after service in World War II obtained a doctorate in natural science there in 1951. After a year (1951–52) as an assistant at the university's Insitute for Physical Chemistry, he joined in 1953 the staff of the Max Planck Institute for Physical Chemistry, Göttingen. He became the Institute's director in 1964 and thereafter its chairman. He was elected a foreign honorary member of the American Academy of Arts and Sciences in 1964.

For background information *see* FAST CHEMICAL REACTIONS in the McGraw-Hill Encyclopedia of Science and Technology. □

★ ELKIND, Mortimer Murray

American biophysicist
Born Oct. 25, 1922, New York, N.Y., U.S.A.

WHY IS radiation (particulate and electromagnetic) lethal to living matter? Where in a cell are the lethal effects of radiation registered? Can cells tolerate some degree of radiation damage and, if so, can they repair such damage? These and other questions stimulated Elkind's imagination when he turned from pure physics to biology in 1953. For his discoveries and contributions in this area, he received an Ernest Orlando Lawrence Award from the U.S. Atomic Energy Commission in 1967.

Effects of solar radiation aside, interest in radiobiology in the sense that it is thought of today started in 1895 with Roentgen's discovery of x-rays. From the outset, biological and physical scientists inquired how matter is affected by radiation. It soon became apparent, even from these early observations, that radiation was an efficient producer of major biological effects. Cell viability and growth, for example, can be suppressed by the deposition of an amount of radiant energy sufficient to raise the average temperature of a cell by only a fraction of a degree. Indeed, animals exposed to quite moderate doses of 500 to 1000 rad can be killed with essentially no attendant increases in their body temperatures due to the exposure. Facts such as these, plus the discrete and random nature of radiation, led in the 1920s to the complementary concepts of "hits" and "targets." According to these ideas, small doses of radiation produce dramatic effects, in cells, for example, because relatively large amounts of energy are absorbed locally (the hits) in sites or structures (the targets) whose integrity is essential for coordinated function. As a physicist, Elkind was attracted to these ideas since they include the elegant feature of permitting the derivation of simple mathematical relationships between cause and effect.

Starting in 1953 with studies of the lethal effects of x-rays and alpha particles in yeast cells, Elkind soon became aware of the practical limitations of formal hit-target theory. While some inactivation schemes could be shown to fit a given set of data better than others, survival curve analysis alone lacked the elements of uniqueness needed for the unambiguous specification of target number and/or target organization. Moreover, this approach usually gave little insight into where and what are the targets.

To extract more biological information from survival measurements, Elkind turned first to experiments involving ultraviolet light and x-rays, and later to studies of radiation damage repair. Since the 2537-A line from a low pressure mercury discharge is absorbed preferentially in nucleic acids, sequential exposures involving x-rays and ultraviolet light yield insights into effects produced in these critical molecules. However, Elkind's most significant contributions came from his studies of damage repair. In addition to their bearing on the mechanism of damage registration, as well as repair, these studies were important because they were performed with mammalian cells and consequently had a greater relevance to effects in humans than might be expected from experiments with microbes.

By the late 1950s the pioneering work of T. T. Puck and his associates had brought the art of the in vitro cultivation of mammalian cells to the point where single-cell experiments could be performed with a quantitation equivalent to that available with bacteria and yeasts. This so impressed Elkind that he dropped microbes in favor of mammalian cells in spite of the greater costs involved and the considerably longer cycle times from the beginning to the end of each experiment. Not only did he change his experimental format, but at this juncture Elkind also altered his thinking about hit-target concepts by deciding to pursue their more general rather than specific implications.

In 1956 T. T. Puck and Philip Marcus published the first single-cell survival curve determined with mammalian cells. They used a line of cells derived originally from a human cervical carcinoma. In a general way this curve had features typical of survival curves measured with bacteria and yeasts. One feature of particular interest to Elkind, however, was the fact that the curve had a threshold. In the region of small doses the curve became progressively steeper. This characteristic meant that damage had to be accumulated for a lethal effect to be registered. From this it followed that, regardless of the particular target structure involved, a surviving cell is a *sublethally* damaged cell and, hence, a surviving cell may repair such damage. Elkind next devised a test for the repair of sublethal damage. The test was quite specific and yet simple since it consisted only of a second dose of radiation. If sublethal damage is repaired in time after a first dose, this can be demonstrated by irradiating surviving cells a second time to see if between the doses they have reassumed a capacity for sublethal damage. If sublethal damage is repaired, the net survival after dose fractionation should be higher than that for the same total dose given as one exposure. This indeed was what Elkind and his associates observed, as well as a number of other features later shown to be due to other important properties of mammalian cells.

The initial recovery experiments of Elkind and his associates were published in 1959. They have been confirmed in microbes, plant cells, many types of cultured mammalian cells, and normal and malignant mammalian cells grown and assayed in vivo. Elkind developed theoretical extensions of his results to the radiation responses of normal and malignant tissues; his predictions have been borne out in the observations of others.

Elkind did his undergraduate work in mechanical engineering at the Cooper Union School of Engineering, New York, where he received a B.M.E. in 1943. Following service as a Naval officer during World War II, he returned to engineering in 1946. In 1949 he was awarded a master's degree in mechanical engineering from the Brooklyn Polytechnic Institute, and then he continued his graduate study at the Massachusetts Institute of Technology, where he was awarded an M.S. in electrical engineering in 1951 and a Ph.D. in physics in 1953. He then spent 9 months at the Donner Laboratory, University of California, Berkeley, where he was first introduced to biological work. In 1954 he joined the National Cancer Institute, Bethesda, Md.

For background information *see* RADIATION BIOLOGY; RADIATION CYTOLOGY; RADIATION INJURY (BIOLOGY) in the McGraw-Hill Encyclopedia of Science and Technology.   □

★ EMMETT, Paul Hugh

American chemist
Born Sept. 22, 1900, Portland, Ore., U.S.A.

THE EARLY 1920s saw a turning point in the field of catalysis. During the 90 years since the coining of the word by J. J. Berzelius, attention had been directed mostly to developing and perfecting industrial catalytic processes, and relatively little attention had been given to the elucidation of the basic catalytic mechanisms. In the 1920s, however, the work of such leaders as Irving Langmuir, Hugh Taylor, and Eric Rideal directed attention toward the fundamental aspects of catalysis and surface chemistry in general. The book by Taylor and Rideal, combined with the book on organic catalysis by Paul Sabatier, afforded a rich and inspirational survey of the field and constituted a major influence on the work of Emmett as he entered the graduate school of the California Institute of Technology in 1922. The other influence that directed his career toward the study of surface chemistry was the contact with A. F. Benton, a former student of Taylor. Emmett worked under Benton for 2 of his 3 years of graduate work and from him received valuable laboratory training and a lasting interest in the fields of adsorption and catalysis.

After a year of teaching at Oregon State College in 1925–26, Emmett accepted a position at the Fixed Nitrogen Research Laboratory in Washington, D.C., because it promised an opportunity to pursue his new interest in catalysis. Circumstances served to plunge him into full responsibility and freedom in planning his career, for the inception of the synthetic ammonia industry in 1926 soon removed most of the skilled catalytic personnel to industrial jobs, and left Emmett in charge of his own program by 1927. Basically, the 11 years he spent at the Laboratory helped Emmett to focus his attention on the field of catalysis. His work there was centered upon trying to elucidate the mechanism of reactions important to the field of nitrogen fixation. It included a study of catalysts for ammonia synthesis and for the water-gas conversion reaction.

Perhaps foremost among the useful findings of his work on ammonia catalysts was the development of a method for measuring the surface areas of porous catalysts and of finely divided solids. The need for such a method arose from the desirability of finding some explanation for the differences in activity among the iron catalysts. The clue to the method was provided by a paper by Benton suggesting it might be possible to select on an adsorption isotherm for nitrogen at $-195°C$, a point corresponding to a monolayer of adsorbed gas. In the early 1930s Emmett organized a program to explore the possibility of measuring the surface areas of catalysts by the physical adsorption of gases near their boiling points. With the assistance of Stephen Brunauer, a large number of adsorption isotherms were measured on iron catalysts and interpreted by the "point B method" in terms of monolayers of adsorbed gas. This research led directly to the calculation of absolute surface areas. About this time Edward Teller and Brunauer worked out a mathematical approach to the interpretation of the shapes of the adsorption isotherms. This work, published as a collaborative paper by Brunauer, Emmett, and Teller and applied to the experimental work, promptly became known as the BET method for measuring surface areas. It is still an internationally used and approved method for obtaining the surface areas of finely divided or porous solids. The program of research leading to this method for measuring surface areas was probably the best known of all of Emmett's scientific activities.

The remaining work on iron catalysts involved chemisorption measurements for nitrogen and hydrogen on iron catalysts, phase studies of the solid iron-nitrogen compounds, and some measurements on the kinetics of ammonia synthesis. These studies combined to give a picture of the ammonia synthesis that is still fundamentally accepted. The "slow step" that is observed under usual synthesis conditions appears to reflect the rate of chemisorption of nitrogen by the promoted iron catalysts. However, the exact details of the synthesis are still undetermined and will probably be worked out in the years to come.

The other work Emmett and his group carried out at the Fixed Nitrogen Research Laboratory was directed toward the elucidation of the mechanism of the water-gas conversion reaction over iron oxide and cobalt catalysts. The group eventually centered its efforts on the measurement of a number of gas-solid equilibria in the interaction of hydrogen-water vapor mixtures with $Fe-Fe_3O_4$, $Fe-FeO$, $FeO-Fe_3O_4$, $Co-CoO$, and $SnO-SnO_2$. This work led to the first application of the thermal diffusion theory of David Enskog and of Sydney Chapman to actual gas-solid equilibria and succeeded in explaining the 40 per cent discrepancy that was encountered in the results of workers attempting to study the interaction of hydrogen–water vapor mixtures with the iron–iron oxide systems. It also led to a reliable value for the equilibrium constant of the water-gas conversion reaction. All of the experimental work on these metal oxide systems was done by Floyd Shultz.

In 1937 Emmett moved on to head the department of chemical engineering at the Johns Hopkins University, where a combination of teaching and research on the application and development of the surface area measuring procedures occupied his attention. In 1943 he joined the Manhattan Project and served under Harold Urey as chief of the chemical division concerned with the production and study of the chemical properties of the diffusion barrier, used later in the Oak Ridge diffusion plant for separating the isotopes of uranium. Emmett encouraged the continuation of the fluorocarbon research program of W. T. Miller that later proved so important in producing products contributing to the successful operation of the diffusion plant.

In early 1945 Emmett was appointed a senior fellow to direct a group on basic catalytic research at the Mellon Institute under the sponsorship of the Gulf Oil Company. They made use of newly available radioactive and nonradioactive isotopes to explore the nature of some of the catalysts and catalytic processes of potential value to the petroleum industry. In particular, Emmett studied the exchange of the hydrogen atoms of hydrocarbons with the deuterium content of deuterated silica-alumina catalysts, with R. Haldeman; the measurement of the adsorption of isobutane on silica-alumina catalysts by using radioactive isobutane, with Donald MacIver; and the mechanism of the Fischer-Tropsch synthesis of hydrocarbons over cobalt and iron catalysts by using tracers containing radioactive carbon, with J. T. Kummer, Thomas DeWitt, H. Podgurski, and W. Spencer. The Fischer-Tropsch work also led to a series of gas-solid equilibrium systems important to this hydrocarbon synthesis. These included a study of the equilibration of hydrogen-methane mixtures with $Fe\text{-}Fe_2C$, $Fe\text{-}Fe_3C$, $Ni\text{-}Ni_3C$, $Co\text{-}Co_2C$, carbon, $Mo\text{-}Mo_2C$, and $MoC\text{-}Mo_2C$. This work was done with the assistance of Luther Browning. Other studies involved adsorption measurements with L. Joyner and with R. Zabor and R. T. Davis. These were all directed toward the use of physical adsorption in measuring surface areas or the study of chemisorption on pertinent catalysts.

In 1955 Emmett was appointed W. R. Grace Professor of Chemistry at the Johns Hopkins University. The research efforts of his numerous students and postdoctorate assistants from that time were devoted to studying, with the help of radioactive hydrocarbons as tracers, the catalytic cracking of hydrocarbons over silica-alumina catalysts, and to the study of the catalytic properties of nickel-copper, nickel-iron, and iron catalysts in catalytic hydrogenation. In this latter endeavor he and his students were trying to obtain experimental data relative to the electronic factor in catalysis, as proposed by D. A. Dowden and others. The metal alloys were studied both as reduced from the oxides and prepared as thin films. Alloy films were prepared by M. K. Gharpurey and by John Campbell by successive deposition of nickel and copper and homogenization of the two elements into an alloy by heating. During the first years of this period, the assistance of R. J. Kokes should be especially acknowledged. Earlier he had been instrumental in suggesting and helping to develop a microcatalytic–chromatographic technique for studying rapidly the qualitative and quantitative behavior of various catalyst systems.

Emmett received his early training at Oregon State College, from which he obtained a B.S. in chemical engineering in 1922. He studied for 3 years for a Ph.D. at the California Institute of Technology. During this period he came under the inspiring influence of A. A. Noyes, R. C. Tolman, and R. A. Millikan. His honors included the Kendall Award of the American Chemical Society in Colloid Chemistry in 1958, the Pittsburgh Award of the American Chemical Society in 1953, the award of the degree of doctor honoris causa by the University of Lyon, France, in 1964, and the election to the Consejo Superior in Spain in 1964. He was elected to the National Academy of Sciences in 1955.

Emmett published about 150 technical papers and edited *Catalysis* (7 vols., 1954–60). He was a coauthor of *Catalysis Then and Now* (1965).

For background information *see* ADSORPTION; AMMONIA; CATALYSIS; FISCHER-TROPSCH PROCESS in the McGraw-Hill Encyclopedia of Science and Technology.   □

★ ENGELHARDT, Wladimir Aleksandrovitch

Soviet biochemist
Born Dec. 4, 1894, Moscow, Russia

ENGELHARDT'S RESEARCH was concerned principally with the study of biochemical processes associated with transformations of energy, such as cellular respiration, its mutual interrelations with fermentation, and the molecular basis of muscular contraction.

Transformations of energy are among the basic phenomena of life, and are involved in nearly all biological functions. The transformations are of two kinds: free energy of a chemical reaction into other types of chemical energy, and the further transformation of chemical energy into mechanical, osmotic, electrical, or other kinds of energy. Examples of these processes, which are important for the functioning of living matter, are the conversion of the energy of exergonic reactions of biological compounds into the potential energy of certain phosphorous compounds, and the utilization of this potential energy for the performance of work during the contraction of muscle. A key role belongs to adenosinetriphosphate (ATP), which serves as the store and universal source of driving force for innumerable metabolic processes.

When Engelhardt started his work in this field, it was known, from the work of O. Meyerhof and K. Lohmann and of J. Parnas, that ATP is formed during glycolytic (fermentative) breakdown of sugar and that its hydrolytic splitting is accompanied by liberation of a considerable amount of energy. In other words, the energy of glycolysis (fermentation) is transformed into the potential energy of labile phosphate bonds of ATP. Engelhardt demonstrated that ATP also can be formed during cellular respiration. Nucleated red blood cells possess an intense oxidative metabolism (respiration) and a high content of ATP. Engelhardt found that, if these cells are depleted of ATP by anaerobic incubation, an excess of oxygen respiration sets in and there is a rapid resynthesis of ATP from its split products, almost reaching the initial level. Thus the process of oxidative phosphorylation was discovered. An attempt was also made to determine the quantitative relationship between O_2 consumption above the normal level during the period of synthesis of ATP, and the amount of ATP synthesized. A value of P/O equal to about 1 was found. Later determinations by others using more efficient systems showed that the yield may often be higher by a factor of about 2, but the order of magnitude determined by Engelhardt was fairly accurate in terms of the rather crude methods then available. These findings led researchers to regard ATP as the common storing form for the energy of the two fundamental exergonic processes of cellular metabolism, fermentation and respiration.

From Pasteur's time scientists knew of the existence of an antagonistic interaction between aerobic and anaerobic metabolism, namely, the suppression of fermentation by respiration. Engelhardt proposed a plausible chemical interpretation of the basic mechanism of this "Pasteur effect." The hexose monophosphate stage appeared to be the crucial point at which the fate of the hexose molecule is determined. If it is phosphorylated to hexose diphosphate by transfer of a second phosphate from ATP, it enters the fermentative pathway. The enzyme catalyzing this transphosphorylation was found to be particularly sensitive to oxidative conditions. Presumably, under aerobic conditions in the cell it becomes inactivated, fermentation is suppressed, and the metabolism of the sugar molecule is shunted over to the respiratory pathway; that is, instead of being phosphorylated, the first carbon atom of the hexose monophosphate becomes oxidized, and the molecule is metabolized along the respiratory route.

In muscle the ATP, generated glycolytically or by oxidative phosphorylation, was regarded in the late 1930s as the immediate source of energy for muscular contraction. Nothing was known about the intimate mechanism that connects the source of energy with myosin, the contractile substance of muscle and its main protein. Engelhardt, in collaboration with his wife, M. N. Liubimova, discovered that the mechanism is the myosin itself, which possesses the enzymatic property to split ATP and thus to liberate the energy stored in its labile, energy-rich phosphate bond. The interrelation between energy source and contractile substance was shown to be that of enzyme and substrate. Myosin could duly be designated as a functional enzyme, which when exerting its catalytic activity carries out a definite physiological function.

The demonstration of the enzymatic (ATPase) properties of myosin was followed by the equally important observation that the relations between ATP and myosin are reciprocal. In experiments on artificially prepared myosin threads, it was shown that ATP alters their mechanical properties. These changes appear to be intimately connected with contraction and relaxation, the phases of muscular activity. In turn, the myosin, acting as an enzyme, liberates from ATP the energy necessary for the performance of work. These findings formed the basis of what has been designated as the mechanochemistry of muscular contraction. The subsequent discovery, by F. B. Straub in Hungary, of the second muscle protein, actin, which is closely associated with myosin, brought new details in this field. Later investigations by others on a large variety of subjects (such as spermatozoa, cilia of unicellular organisms, and protoplasma flow) have shown that similar fundamental principles apparently hold true for biological motility in general.

Engelhardt graduated from Moscow University in 1919. After 2 years in military service as head of a hospital during the civil war, he joined the Biochemical Institute in Moscow. From 1929 to 1956 he held professorships in biochemistry at the universities of Kazan, Leningrad, and Moscow. From 1935 he worked at the Institute of Biochemistry, Moscow, until his appointment in 1959 as director of the newly organized Institute of Molecular Biology of the U.S.S.R. Academy of Sciences in Moscow. Elected to the U.S.S.R. Academy of Sciences in 1946, he became a foreign member of the American Academy of Arts and Sciences in 1961.

For background information see ADENOSINETRIPHOSPHATE (ATP); ENERGY METABOLISM; FERMENTATION; MUSCLE (BIOPHYSICS) in the McGraw-Hill Encyclopedia of Science and Technology.   □

★ ESSEN, Louis

British physicist
Born Sept. 6, 1908, Nottingham, England

ESSEN JOINED the National Physical Laboratory (NPL) in 1929 and worked with D. W. Dye, who was engaged in his fundamental investigation on tuning forks and quartz oscillators. Together they designed a tuning fork clock good enough to reveal the variations in standard pendulum clocks. After Dye's death in 1932, Essen continued the work on quartz standards. He worked in the field of frequency

and time standards throughout his career and applied them to a number of interesting problems.

The Essen quartz ring clock was made in 1938, and has continued to serve widely as an observatory time standard. During 1940–45 he worked on urgent measurement problems at high radio and microwave frequencies such as the design and testing of radio frequency cables. He developed a number of measuring instruments, including cavity resonator wavemeters. The resonant frequencies of these wavemeters depend in a simple way on their dimensions and the electromagnetic constant c, or the velocity of light. It became obvious to him that the measurement of dimensions and resonant frequency would constitute a simple and accurate way of determining the value of c. Essen's first measurement of the velocity of light, carried out with A. C. Gordon-Smith in 1946, gave the value $299{,}792 \pm 3$ km/sec, and was thus 16 km/sec higher than the accepted value. With an improved cavity resonator he obtained in 1950 the value $299{,}792.5 \pm 1$ km/sec, which was confirmed in particular by K. D. Froome and E. Bergstrand, and remains the accepted value. Essen realized that the new techniques would enable the value of c to be used as a standard for distance measurement, which could be reduced to the measurement of the travel time of a pulse of light or radio waves. The measurements in air would require an accurate value of its refractive index. With Froome, he designed a cavity resonator method of measurement and obtained the values now universally accepted for modern geodetic surveying. Essen continued to be responsible for frequency standards at the NPL, and during visits to the United States in 1948 and 1953 he became very interested in the proposal first made by I. I. Rabi to use a hyperfine spectral line as a standard of time and frequency.

The atomic beam technique, which Essen discussed at Columbia University, the Massachusetts Institute of Technology, and the National Bureau of Standards, was quite new to him, but it was clear that his experiences with time measurement, quartz clocks, and microwave measurements would all be valuable in the development of an atomic standard. He started work at the NPL with J. V. L. Parry, and in 1955 their first atomic cesium standard was in operation. It was immediately obvious that, since the accuracy was so much greater than any astronomical unit, it was necessary to define an atomic unit for the purpose of furthering the investigation. Any new unit must, of course, be related to the old one in order to secure continuity of measurement; Essen and Parry therefore adopted a provisional unit equal to the mean solar second at that time. The mean solar second was known to vary, and an experiment was undertaken, together with the U.S. Naval Observatory, to relate the atomic unit with the second of ephemeris time. The measurements, which were extended over a period of 3 years to reduce the effect of the rather large errors in the astronomical measurements, gave a value of $9{,}192{,}631{,}770 \pm 20$ Hz for the frequency of cesium, and this has been used to define a unit of atomic time since 1958 with the full accuracy of atomic clocks. The initial work led to the construction of a second cesium standard at the NPL, which is accurate to 1 part in 10^{11} and has served as the British national standard since 1959. Many atomic clocks have now been constructed with a comparable accuracy, including a number of commercial models. A different type of standard, known as the hydrogen maser, was developed by N. F. Ramsey at Harvard University, and is of particular importance as a possible definitive standard.

The unit of time differs from those of length and mass in that it can be made available throughout the world by means of radio transmissions. In the United Kingdom standard frequency transmissions are made from the Rugby Post Office station on behalf of the NPL. Essen pointed out in 1954 the advantages of using very low frequency transmissions, and two Rugby transmissions on 60 and 16 kHz were widely used for the study of the propagation of radio waves. From 1955 onward the frequencies were expressed in terms of the atomic unit provisionally adopted, making it immediately available over a wide area. The transmissions were used for the first international comparison of atomic standards between the United Kingdom and the United States.

During the course of his work Essen carried out two very precise experiments concerned with the relativity theory. In the first, with G. A. Tomlinson in 1937, the frequencies of two quartz oscillators were compared as one was rotated.

The second experiment, carried out in 1955, was a fairly close analogy to the Michelson-Morley experiment, using radio waves instead of light waves. A simple experiment gave a null result with a much higher precision than that originally achieved. Essen was much intrigued by the controversy concerning certain aspects of relativity theory, and his experience in the precise measurements of time and velocity led him to examine closely the thought experiments in Einstein's papers. He reached the conclusion that these experiments could not give the results that Einstein obtained because they did not measure the quantity concerned. The results were obtained not from the experiments but from new assumptions made implicitly. He also suggested that, if the famous Michelson-Morley experiment is considered more carefully, it leads to the conclusion that, as far as the propagation of light is concerned, the Earth environment cannot be assumed to be the same as "free space," and that one obvious difference is the presence of an acceleration and a gravitational potential.

Essen gained a B.Sc. in physics (1928), Ph.D. (1941), and D.Sc. (1948) from London University. He was elected a fellow of the Royal Society of London in 1960, and received several awards and gold medals for his work on the velocity of light and time measurement, including the Charles Vernon Boys Prize from the Physical Society in 1957 and the A. S. Popov Gold Medal from the U.S.S.R. Academy of Sciences in 1959. He became a deputy chief scientific officer at the National Physical Laboratory in 1960. He was a member of the Institution of Electrical Engineers, serving on a number of its committees, and was active in the International Union for Scientific Radio, of which he was president of Commission 1.

For background information *see* ATOMIC CLOCK; FREQUENCY MEASUREMENT; LIGHT; QUARTZ CLOCK; RELATIVITY in the McGraw-Hill Encyclopedia of Science and Technology.   □

★ ESTES, William Kaye

American psychologist
Born June 17, 1919, Minneapolis, Minn., U.S.A.

FEARS AND anxieties develop through a learning process, and yet these emotional states involve such widespread and persisting disturbances of behavior that they cannot be explained on the basis of simple Pavlovian conditioning by stimulus substitution. Estes began studying this problem while still an undergraduate, working with B. F. Skinner, the innovator of methods for the analysis of behavior. They developed an experimental technique to elucidate the way in which a stimulus that precedes a painful or traumatic event, however brief that event, develops the capacity to suppress the organism's normal activity over relatively long periods of time.

The method for establishing a conditioned emotional response (CER), refined and extended by other investigators, has been widely applied for such purposes as analyzing effects of tranquilizing drugs, electroconvulsive shock, and various types of brain lesions. In Estes's own work, understanding of the CER set the stage for a major series of experiments analyzing the ways in which punishment affects behavior. In the classical psychological theories of reward and punishment, notably that of Edward L. Thorndike, it was assumed that a response which leads to reward is directly and automatically strengthened (that is, becomes more likely to recur under similar circumstances). However, the mode of operation of punishment long remained a controversial issue. Other learning theorists, and indeed Thorndike himself at different times, held on the one hand that punishment simply reduces the strength of the punished response, and on the other hand that punishment exerts its effects by instigating competing behaviors (such as withdrawal) which conflict with the punished response.

Estes's investigations adduced a number of new lines of evidence supporting a modified conflict theory, the primary mechanism being the establishment of a CER to cues which precede punishment. In one experiment, for example, he showed that effects of punishment on a simple instrumental response in the rat can be counteracted if conditions are arranged so that the CER undergoes experimental extinction (unlearning); in another he showed that effects of

punishment can be closely mimicked if the stimuli which normally lead to a given response are associated with a punishing stimulus (such as electric shock) even during a period when the response is physically prevented from occurring.

Theoretical problems which arose in analyzing the mechanism of punishment, and later in similar analyses of other learning processes, tended increasingly to require mathematical as well as experimental methods for their solution. Estes, influenced by the work of the behavior theorist Clark L. Hull, became increasingly interested in the possibility of progressing toward a general mathematical theory of learning. Drawing on a variety of mathematical models and techniques, some suggested by analogies between certain aspects of associative learning and multimolecular chemical reactions, and some by modern developments in probability theory and stochastic processes, Estes formulated a statistical theory of elementary learning processes. The theory, set forth in a series of papers between 1950 and 1955, took the form of a small set of basic concepts and axioms, together with methods of derivation which permitted generation of descriptive mathematical models for specific learning situations.

During the subsequent decade Estes and a growing number of students and colleagues tested consequences of the theory for numerous experimental phenomena, including verbal learning and memory, probability learning, competitive and cooperative interactions between individuals in minimal social situations, tachistoscopic perception, signal detection by human observers, and choice behavior. One of the most widely applied theoretical results was the "probability matching theorem," which states that under certain conditions an individual's probability of predicting an uncertain event (such as the fall of a die) will come with repeated experiences to approximate the true probability of the event.

These contributions to the methods and concepts of learning theory were recognized by the Distinguished Scientific Contribution Award of the American Psychological Association in 1962 and the Warren Medal of the Society of Experimental Psychologists in 1963.

Estes's inclinations turned toward science at an early age under the influence of his father, George D. Estes, a man of broad scholarly interests. He received his B.A. from the University of Minnesota in 1940, and his Ph.D. in psychology in 1943. He served in the armed forces from 1944 to 1946, first in an Air Force Gunnery Research Unit and then as a medical administrative officer in the Asiatic-Pacific theater. He joined the faculty of Indiana University in 1946 and reached the rank of professor in 1955 and research professor of psychology in 1960. He moved to Stanford University as a professor of psychology in 1962. He was elected to the National Academy of Sciences in 1963.

Estes wrote *An Experimental Study of Punishment* (1944) and *Modern Learning Theory*, with S. Koch and others (1954). He was co-editor of *Studies in Mathematical Learning Theory*, with R. R. Bush (1959), and coauthor of *Stimulus Sampling Theory*, with E. D. Neimark (1967). He became editor of the *Journal of Comparative and Physiological Psychology* in 1962.

For background information *see* LEARNING THEORIES; MEMORY; PROBLEM SOLVING (PSYCHOLOGY) in the McGraw-Hill Encyclopedia of Science and Technology.   □

★ FELL, Dame Honor (Bridget)

British cell biologist
Born May 22, 1900, Filey, Yorkshire, England

Fell concentrated her researches on the reactions of differentiated tissues isolated from the body and cultivated in vitro by the organ culture method. By this technique, largely developed at the Strangeways Laboratory, the normal structure and many of the physiological functions of tissues are maintained in culture, and early embryonic material continues to grow and develop in vitro.

For some years her work was related to developmental mechanics, with special reference to skeletogenesis. Though deprived of their normal association with muscles, nerves, blood vessels, and adjacent bones, skeletal rudiments from early chick embryos continued to develop in culture. Not only did the histological structure differentiate, but the isolated rudiments acquired much of their normal shape. The early stages of joint formation took place in vitro in the isolated limb blastema. It was possible to perform very delicate surgical operations on these explants and by this means to identify some of the factors concerned in early joint formation.

Tissues isolated in organ culture, when treated with certain vitamins and hormones, were found to undergo morphological changes similar to those produced by the same agents in the intact animal. For example, it is well known that, when animals are given too much vitamin A, severe changes appear in their skeleton: Their cartilage loses some of its intercellular material, and rarefaction of the bone leads to spontaneous fractures. In collaboration with Sir Edward Mellanby, Fell studied the effect of excess vitamin A, added to the culture medium, on explanted limb bones from fetal mice near term. They were astonished to observe that the intercellular material of both cartilage and bone disappeared in a few days under the influence of

the vitamin, though the cells appeared healthy and divided actively. Embryonic chick cartilage behaved in a similar way. In animals suffering from vitamin A deficiency, certain mucous epithelia, such as tracheal epithelium, become transformed into squamous, keratinizing tissue resembling the epidermis. Fell and Mellanby were able to produce the opposite effect in organ cultures of embryonic chicken skin exposed to excess of vitamin A. The epidermis of the controls formed a squamous, keratinizing epithelium in culture, but the epidermis of vitamin A–treated explants acquired a cubical or columnar structure, many of the cells becoming ciliated and mucus being profusely secreted. The effect was reversible in normal medium.

The fact that these and many other responses to biologically active agents could be produced in an in vitro system from which the complex systemic reactions of the body were excluded suggested that organ cultures would be ideal for biochemical study of vitamins and hormones. It was not until after World War II, however, that rapid development of microchemistry and simple fluid media made such a biochemical approach possible and thus enormously increased the value of organ culture as a research method. The technique has been applied to a very wide range of physiological problems.

Fell had long wished to identify the biochemical mechanism responsible for rapid dissolution of intercellular material in skeletal explants exposed to excess of vitamin A. She had noticed that tissue growing on a plasma-embryo extract clot in the presence of vitamin A always liquefied the clot much more than did controls on normal medium. This liquefying power indicated that vitamin A was increasing the proteolytic activity of the tissues, and she suspected that a cathepsin might be involved. Her biochemistry colleague, John Dingle, suggested that vitamin A affected the membranes of the lysosomes (cytoplasmic organelles that de Duve had shown to be associated with a wide range of acid hydrolases, including a protease). Dingle demonstrated that his hypothesis was correct by experiments on subcellular fractions, where vitamin A liberated the enzymes from the isolated lysosomes of rat liver; this effect had a high degree of molecular specificity. In cultures of embryonic cartilage, Fell, Dingle, and Lucy found that vitamin A greatly increased both synthesis and release into the culture medium of the lysosomal acid protease. This enzyme digested the protein moiety of the protein-mucopolysaccharide complex of the cartilage matrix and thus liberated chondroitin sulfate.

The enormous advantage of being able to examine not only the tissue but also its humoral environment was emphasized not only by these enzymic studies but also by observations on the synthesis and release of certain intercellular components. Fell and Dingle found that cartilaginous explants, exposed to hypervitaminosis A, may synthesize almost as much hexosamine and hydroxyproline as their untreated controls, but because of the abnormally large production of lysosomal hydrolases in the presence of the vitamin, a much greater proportion of these substances is released into the medium than is retained in the tissues by incorporation into intercellular material.

Fell's recent work with R. R. A. Coombs and Dingle demonstrated that complement-sufficient antiserum also causes breakdown of bone and cartilage matrix. This process, which is reversible, is accompanied by much-increased synthesis and release of lysosomal enzymes; a nonlysosomal enzyme, lactic acid dehydrogenase, was found to be unaffected.

Fell was a graduate (B.Sc., 1922) of Edinburgh University, where she took her Ph.D. in 1923 and D.Sc. in 1930. She became assistant to T. S. P. Strangeways at the Cambridge Research Hospital, later renamed the Strangeways Research Laboratory. In 1928, a year after Strangeways's death, she was put in temporary charge of the laboratory and in 1929 was appointed director. For many years she was also a member of the Royal Society's research staff. She was elected a fellow of the Royal Society in 1952 and was made a Dame Commander of the Order of the British Empire in 1963. She received the Prix Charles-Leopold Mayer of the Academie des Sciences de l'Institut de France in 1965.

For background information *see* BIOCHEMISTRY; CULTURE, TISSUE; ENZYME; SKELETAL SYSTEM; VITAMIN A in the McGraw-Hill Encyclopedia of Science and Technology.   □

★ FENN, Wallace Osgood

American physiologist
Born Aug. 27, 1893, Lanesboro, Mass., U.S.A.

As an undergraduate at Harvard, Fenn originally planned to become a forester, but accepted instead a graduate fellowship in plant physiology. His thesis work involved chiefly colloid chemistry and problems of salt antagonism. During World War I he was assigned from the infantry to work with L. J. Henderson at Harvard and was later commissioned and made camp nutrition officer at Camp Dodge, Iowa. In 1919 he received his Ph.D. and accepted a position as instructor in applied physiology at the Harvard Medical School. He worked with C. K. Drinker on the phagocytosis of solid particles and found that leukocytes ingest carbon particles more readily than quartz, a fact pertinent to problems of silicosis in the lung; the results were analyzed theoretically in terms of surface tension

relations. Then, in 1922, as a traveling fellow from the Rockefeller Institute for Medical Research, he began work with A. V. Hill, first in Manchester and later in London, on the heat production of muscles. He discovered that muscles automatically mobilize an extra amount of energy equal to the work they perform when they are permitted to contract and lift a load. This relation between work and heat has since become an important concept in muscle physiology.

After 2 years in England, Fenn returned to become professor of physiology and chairman of the department in the new School of Medicine and Dentistry at the University of Rochester. He continued his work on muscles, making some further measurements of heat production and observing the rate of oxygen consumption by muscle under different conditions. From high-speed motion pictures of sprint runners, Fenn measured the work done in the to-and-fro movements of the arms and legs, and the work of the body against gravity and wind resistance. He found that the total work of a runner was all that could be expected from the amount of oxygen he used. This meant that very little work could have been done against any viscous resistance in the muscles themselves. Fenn proposed, therefore, that speed of running is not limited by the viscosity of the muscles themselves, but rather by the time required to mobilize extra energy for the work required. In isolated muscles he further supported this idea by measuring the speed of shortening of muscles lifting different loads. The resulting force-velocity curve was thus shown not to be linear, as demanded by the viscosity theory. At this time Fenn also devised a differential volumeter of

sufficient sensitivity to demonstrate clearly that nerves consume more oxygen when they are stimulated to conduct nerve impulses than when they are merely resting.

Fenn next turned to his original interest, the

biological effects of electrolytes, and began some of the pioneer work on the movement of potassium between cells and their surroundings. He found that the cells usually are freely permeable to potassium, which tends to move toward the phase which shows the greater increase in acidity. A part of the buffering capacity of the body depends, therefore, on the free movements of potassium in and out of cells. When radioactive potassium first became available, he and his collaborators studied the distribution of injected potassium among the various tissues of the body. The research showed definitely that red blood corpuscles, like other cells of the body, are slowly permeable to potassium, although for most purposes they had always been regarded as permeable only to anions. Perhaps the most important of these studies was the demonstration that, when muscles are stimulated, they lose potassium in exchange for an equivalent amount of sodium. This interchange of electrolytes has since been shown by others to represent the fundamental mechanism involved in the conduction of a nerve impulse. By careful analysis of rat livers Fenn showed that the deposition of glycogen in the liver is always accompanied by the deposition of a fixed amount of water and potassium. Under the influence of epinephrine, either injected intravenously or liberated from the adrenal glands under the influence of inhaled carbon dioxide, he showed that both potassium and glucose escape from the liver into the bloodstream.

During World War II, Fenn offered his services for the study of pressure breathing, which had been suggested by the Air Force to enable aviators to obtain adequate oxygen at an altitude somewhat higher than was possible breathing 100% oxygen at ambient pressure. This work was carried on with H. Rahn and A. B. Otis and a crew of conscientious objectors assigned to the laboratory. Because of the advent of the pressurized cabin soon afterward, the practical value of this study for aviation was not as great as for clinical medicine in general, where it opened up many new avenues of investigation importantly affecting clinical physiology of the chest and lungs. In particular, Fenn and his collaborators were responsible for rediscovering forgotten data concerning the pressure-volume diagrams of the chest and lungs and for expanding these data in different directions. Another important aspect of this work was the development of the oxygen–carbon dioxide diagram of the respiratory gases, by means of which predictions could easily be made of the composition of the air in the lung alveoli under different ambient pressures with different mixtures of inhaled gases.

Fenn continued to work in the field of respiratory physiology, having become concerned chiefly with oxygen poisoning and inert gas narcosis. In experiments with fruit flies he found a striking synergism between high pressures of oxygen and inert gases. Recently, in extending this study to bacteria, he found that a culture of *Streptococcus faecalis* increases in total volume in proportion to the amount of lactic acid which is formed. Presumably because of this, the growth of these organisms is inhibited appropriately by an increase in hydrostatic pressure, as well as by oxygen and inert gases at sufficient partial pressures.

Fenn received his A.B. (1914), M.A. (1916), and Ph.D. in plant physiology (1919) from Harvard University. After working in England during 1922–24, he joined the faculty of the University of Rochester; he resigned as chairman of the physiology department in 1959, after 35 years. In 1961 he was appointed Distinguished University Professor of Physiology. Between 1962 and 1965 he served as the first director of the Space Science Center of the university. Besides several honorary degrees, he received the Modern Medicine Distinguished Achievement Award in 1965, the Antonio Feltrinelli International Prize of the Accademia Internazionale dei Linzei of Rome in 1964, and the Research Achievement Award of the American Heart Association in 1967. He was elected to the National Academy of Sciences in 1943, the American Philosophical Society in 1946, and the American Academy of Arts and Sciences in 1948.

Fenn wrote *History of the American Physiological Society: The Third Quarter Century* (1963), as well as some 200 scientific papers.

For background information *see* ION EXCHANGE; MUSCLE (BIOPHYSICS); RESPIRATION in the McGraw-Hill Encyclopedia of Science and Technology.   □

★ FESSARD, Alfred Eugène

French neurophysiologist and psychophysiologist
Born Apr. 28, 1900, Paris, France

FESSARD BEGAN his scientific career around 1925 and during the prewar period became known as one of the French pioneers in modern electrophysiology and elementary neurophysiology. At this time he was mainly occupied in showing that autorhythmic states of activity are a general occurrence in isolated excitable preparations such as nerve or muscle fibers, certain plant cells, stretch receptors, and ganglion cells when these are treated with different physical or chemical agents.

As a pupil of the great French psychologist Henri Piéron, Fessard became interested in problems of psychophysiology and did research in the fields of sensation—visual, auditory, and

tactile—and on voluntary movement in man. When the electroencephalographic technique was made available, he unified his interests by trying to correlate certain mental activities with EEG rhythms. It was he in fact who first introduced this technique to French medical circles, a merit later recognized when he was elected to the Académie Nationale de Médecine in 1961. He is mainly known for his discovery that the blocking reaction of the alpha rhythm may be conditioned, a property which has since been widely exploited by others.

The field of research in which Fessard worked most persistently is the physiology of the electrogenic organs known to exist in certain species of fish. He first worked with the torpedo fish and demonstrated the marked impedance drop in its electric organ at the time of discharge. Also, by nerve degeneration experiments he confirmed the old and puzzling observation that this organ has no electrical excitability of its own. With W. Feldberg he demonstrated the cholinergic nature of nerve-organ transmission of excitation, and with B. C. Abbott and X. Aubert he discovered in 1958 the initial cooling that accompanies the discharge and precedes the metabolic phase during which exothermic recovery reactions take place.

Fessard left to his collaborators, D. Albe-Fessard (his wife) and T. Szabo, the task of analyzing the electrogenic properties of electric organs of other fishes, such as rays, *Astroscopus*, mormyrids, *Gymnarchus*, and *Electrophorus*. His own interests were oriented around the then unsolved problem of the central control of discharges. First in the brain stem of torpedo he disclosed the locus of origin of the rhythmic command. Similar pacemaker sites were gradually discovered in the central nervous system of other fishes, such as *Electrophorus* (in Brazil, with A. Couceiro), rays, mormyrids, and *Gymnarchus* (with Szabo). A striking unity in the organization of the central nervous control, as

opposed to the great morphological diversity of the electric organs themselves, was thus revealed. When a sensory mechanism for object location was found by Lissmann and Machin (1958) in the electric fish, the problem of specific electroreceptors was posed. It was Szabo who discovered the autorhythmic activity of the cutaneous electroreceptors in the African electric fishes mormyrids and *Gymnarchus* (1961). Fessard and he studied the coding characteristics that give the informational content, representing the surrounding field intensity, to messages emitted by the electroreceptors. The manner in which the repetitive discharges of the electric organ are involved in the functioning of the electroreceptors was also demonstrated.

Together with his wife, a professor at the Paris Faculté des Sciences, Fessard sponsored the training of many young French workers and foreign fellows in the fields of electrophysiology and brain research. This group made many contributions concerning central nervous system activity at diverse levels, from single ganglion cells of *Aplysia* to the brains of pigeons, rats, cats, and monkeys. Implanted macro- or microelectrodes in chronic preparations were used to investigate nervous correlates of controlled manifestations in behavior. Fessard devoted most of his efforts to writing syntheses of the results of work from his laboratories. Here he expressed his own views on theoretical problems related to brain activity, such as those of transmission of information, integration, conditioning, and memory.

Fessard graduated from the Sorbonne in 1925 and received his D.Sc. there in 1936. He spent 1 year in England at the Cambridge Physiological Laboratory in 1936–37 as a Rockefeller fellow. After several years as associate director at Piéron's laboratory, he obtained means from the Centre National de la Recherche Scientifique to create an institute, now called Centre d'Études de Physiologie Nerveuse, of which he became director in 1947. He continued to hold this post after being appointed chairman in general neurophysiology at the Collège de France in 1949. In 1958 he played a major role in founding the International Brain Research Organization. A member of the French Académie des Sciences and of the Académie Nationale de Médecine, he was elected a foreign member of the Brazilian Academy of Sciences, foreign honorary member of the American Academy of Arts and Sciences, honorary life member of the New York Academy of Sciences, and honorary member of the Physiological Society of Great Britain. He was an officer of the Légion d'Honneur and commander of the Ordre National du Mérite.

Apart from a general article entitled "Les Organes électriques" (in *Traité de Zoologie* by

P. P. Grassé, 1958), titles of some of Fessard's main contributions to symposiums indicate the trend of his later scientific interests: "Mechanisms of Nervous Integration and Conscious Experience" (1954), "Corrélations neurophysiologiques de la formation des réflexes conditionnés," with H. Gastaut (1958), "Le conditionnement considéré à l'échelle du neurone" (1960), "The Role of Neuronal Networks in Sensory Communications within the Brain" (1961), "Thalamic Integrations and Their Consequences at the Telencephalic Level," with D. Albe-Fessard (1963).

For background information *see* BRAIN; ELECTRIC ORGAN (BIOLOGY); ELECTROENCEPHALOGRAPHY; NERVOUS SYSTEM in the McGraw-Hill Encyclopedia of Science and Technology.   □

★ FIESER, Louis Frederick

American chemist
Born Apr. 7, 1899, Columbus, Ohio, U.S.A.

A PLATINUM electrode introduced into a solution of quinone and hydroquinone at a fixed hydrogen ion concentration acquires an electric potential, which can be measured by making connection through a conducting liquid to a hydrogen electrode as reference half-cell.

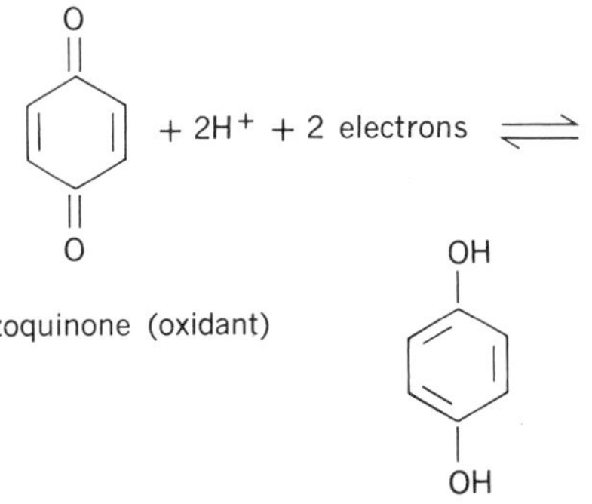

1,4-Benzoquinone (oxidant)

Hydroquinone (reductant)

The electrode potential E of the organic half-cell is dependent on the concentration of quinone, hydroquinone, and hydrogen ions in accordance with the equation

$$E^{25°} = E_0 + 0.05912 \log (H^+) +$$
$$0.02956 \log \frac{(quinone)}{(hydroquinone)}$$

The quantity E_0 is the normal potential characteristic of a particular quinone-hydroquinone system, and it is defined as the potential of the half-cell when the hydrogen-ion concentration is unity and the concentration of oxidant is equal to that of reductant. For 1,4-benzoquinone, $E_0^{25°} = 0.699$ volt. Extending his research for the doctorate at Harvard under James B. Conant, Fieser prepared many known and new quinones, measured the potentials, and correlated the results. *m*-Directing, electron-attracting groups such as NO_2, CN, $COAr$, CO_2H, and SO_3H, as well as halogens, raise the potential of the parent quinone, whereas a potential-lowering effect is exerted by electron-releasing groups NH_2, $N(CH_3)_2$, OH, OCH_3, CH_3, $NHCOCH_3$, and $OCOCH_3$.

A reinvestigation of the work by Russian and German groups on the reaction of the silver salt of hydroxynaphthoquinone with alkyl halides showed both groups to have been in error, and established that the hydroxy compound and its salt are α-naphthoquinones (1a, 2a) but that alkylation produces the α-ether (3) by displacement and the β-ether (4) by 1,4-addition. Several pairs of pure α- and β-ethers were prepared and characterized with the finding that the β-ethers such as (4) are higher in normal potential than the α-ethers (3) by 0.080 volt. Fieser inferred (1928) that a solution of the free hydroxyquinone contains no more than about 0.2% of the less stable tautomeric form (1β). The more elaborate tautomerism of 4-amino-1,2-naphthoquinone was studied in 1934 with his co-worker and wife, Mary.

Alkylation of the silver salt (2a) with an allylic halide gave, in addition to the two oxygen-ethers, an acidic product shown to be the result of carbon alkylation. With this novel reaction available, Fieser was able to achieve the first synthesis of the natural quinone pigment lapachol (1927), and so received the plaudits of Samuel C. Hooker, who in 1889 had discovered lapachol as a yellow pigment in the grain of bethabara wood. Lapachol has an isoprenoid side chain, and the alkylating agent for Fieser's synthesis was prepared by the 1,4-addition of hydrogen bromide to isoprene.

In 1929 Fieser and Emma M. Dietz at Bryn Mawr described a highly improved method for the synthesis of 1,2,5,6-dibenzanthracene. In 1930 Kennaway at the Royal Cancer Institute in

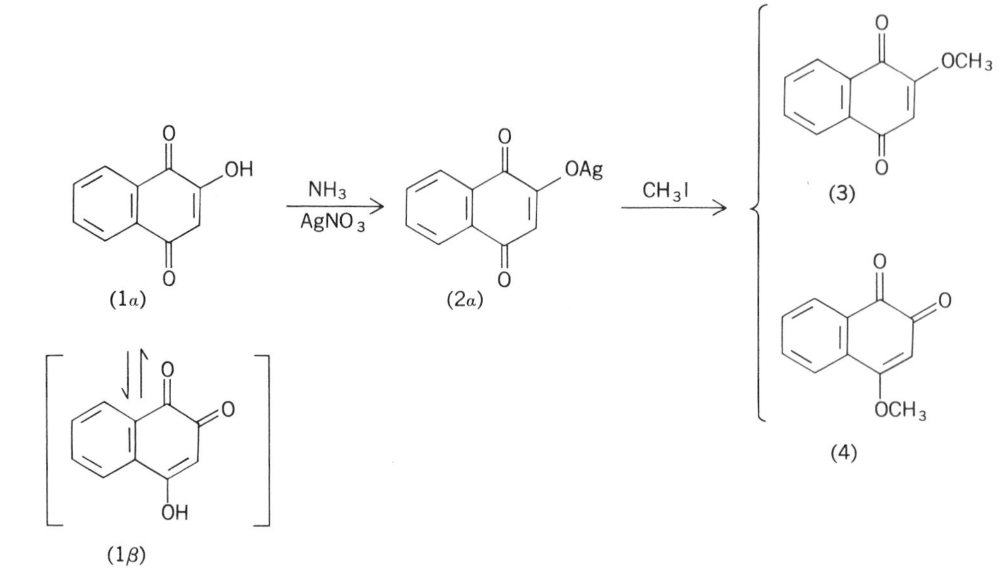

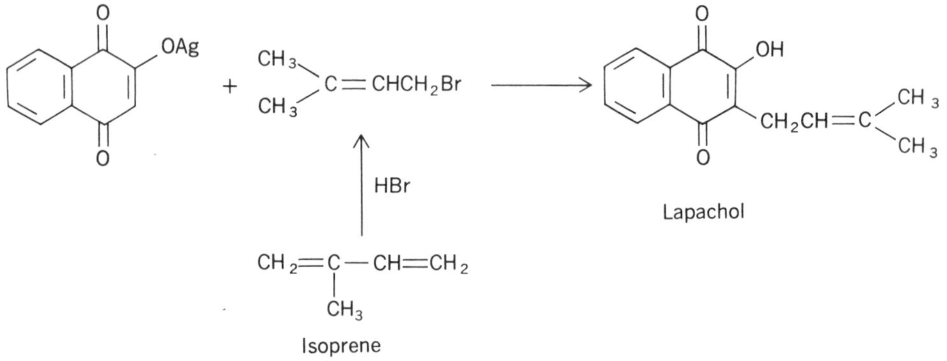

Lapachol

Isoprene

London reported that this hydrocarbon has the power to induce cancerous growth in mice; it was the first known pure carcinogen. When Wieland and Dane (1933) effected the chemical degradation of the bile acid derivative (1) to methylcholanthrene (2), the British group noted the structural similarity to 1,2,5,6-dibenzanthracene, prepared and tested the new hydrocarbon, and found it to be the most potent known carcinogen. Fieser and A. M. Seligman (1935) found the Fieser-Dietz synthesis to work well with the ketone (5) and so, by synthesis, made methylcholanthrene abundantly available for biological experimentation. With the collaboration of Seligman, E. B. Hershberg, M. S. Newman, and others, work on the synthesis of carcinogens was continued by Fieser until World War II; in recognition of this work Fieser received the Judd Prize for cancer research from Memorial Hospital (1941).

Work during 1929–39 by H. Dam, P. Karrer, E. A. Doisy, and others on the isolation from alfalfa of the antihemorrhagic principle, vitamin K_1, as a yellow oil suggested to Fieser that the substance may be a naphthoquinone, and possibly related to lapachol but with a larger isoprenoid side chain and no hydroxyl group. Bioassays of synthetic model compounds and study of their absorption spectra supported the idea, and in a communication in 1939 Fieser suggested that vitamin K_1 is either 2-methyl-3-phytyl-1,4-naphthoquinone (8) or the 2-ethyl

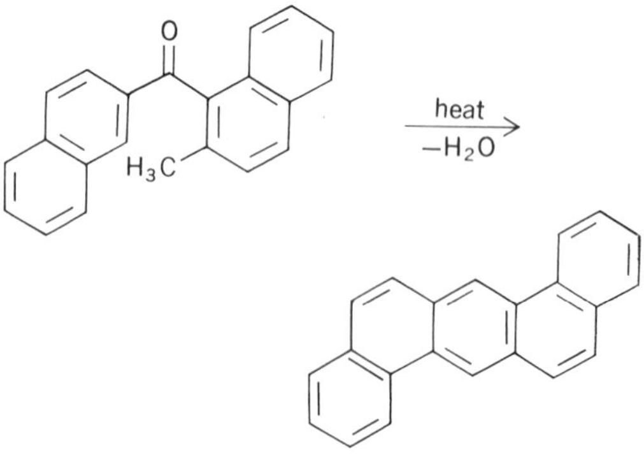

1,2,5,6,-Dibenzanthracene

compound. 2-Methyl-1,4-naphthohydroquinone (6) proved to be a better starting material for synthesis than the quinone, and condensation with phytol in dioxane in the presence of oxalic acid gave a mixture containing considerable substituted hydroquinone (7). The unchanged hydroquinone (6) was removed by extraction from ether with dilute alkaline hydrosulfite, and the more lipophilic phytyl-substituted hydroquinone was separated from the ether residue as a waxy, white solid by digestion with petroleum ether and centrifugation. Oxidation of the white sludge in ether with silver oxide and evaporation

gave pure 2-methyl-3-phytyl-1,4-naphthoquinone as a yellow oil. The synthetic material corresponded to natural vitamin K_1 in antihemorrhagic potency and absorption spectrum, and on reductive acetylation the substance gave a crystalline hydroquinone diacetate (melting point 59°C), as reported by Doisy for the K_1 derivative. Complete identification required only a mixed melting point determination and, when Doisy declined to cooperate until he had completed his own degradative study of structure, Fieser decided to apply what he had learned about the vitamin by its synthesis for the isola-

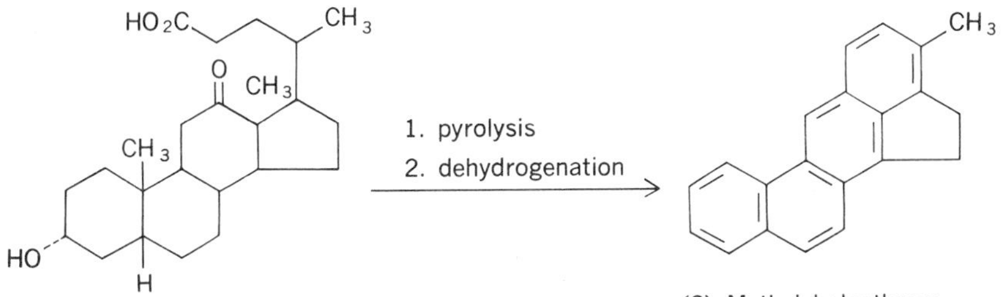

(1)

1. pyrolysis
2. dehydrogenation

(2) Methylcholanthrene

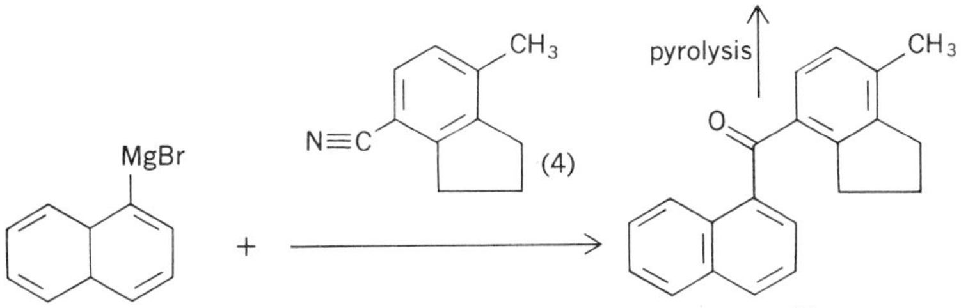

(3)

+ (4)

pyrolysis

(5)

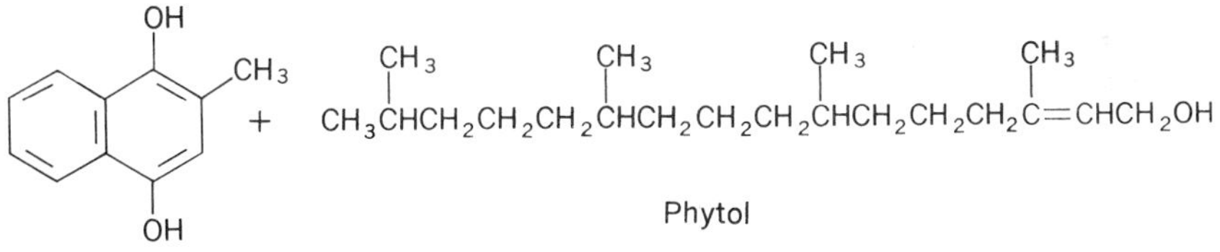

(6) Soluble aqueous KOH

Phytol

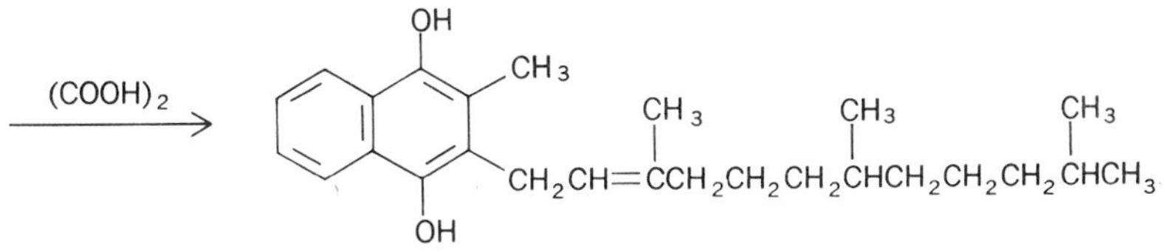

$(COOH)_2$

(7) Insoluble aqueous KOH

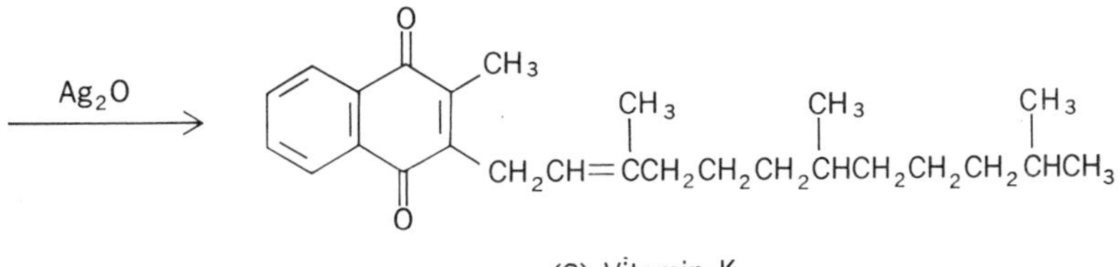

Ag_2O

(8) Vitamin K_1

tion of a comparison sample. A 5.3-g portion of a 3–5% alfalfa K_1 concentrate was reduced and put through the extraction and precipitation procedures worked out for the synthetic substance, and in a few hours 60 mg of pure vitamin K_1 was isolated. This quantity sufficed for analysis, color test, bioassay, determination of the spectrum, and for the preparation, analysis, and mixed melting point determination with the synthetic hydroquinone diacetate, which showed no depression. Finally, the 2-ethyl compound was synthesized and found devoid of vitamin K activity. Thus a program of synthetic research, independent of any work on the natural product itself, established that vitamin K_1 is 2-methyl-3-phytyl-1,4-naphthoquinone. Fieser's synthesis, protected by a patent assigned to Research Corp., provided a practical method for the manufacture of a vitamin factor which soon found significant uses in therapy. The amounts of vitamin K_1 present in green plants are much too small for use in therapy.

Fieser received his A.B. in 1920 from Williams College and his Ph.D. in chemistry in 1924 from Harvard University. In 1924–25 he did postdoctoral research in Frankfurt, Germany, and Oxford, England. He was a professor of chemistry at Bryn Mawr College in 1925–30, and then he joined the staff at Harvard, where he became Sheldon Emery Professor of Organic Chemistry in 1939. During World War II he developed napalm and other incendiaries and directed a large research group in exploiting the clue that lapachol derivatives possess antimalarial activity. This latter work was resumed at the time of the war in Vietnam, and new lapachol-like drugs of promise still await full evaluation. Lapachol itself is under investigation as an anticancer agent. Among the awards received by Fieser were the Manufacturing Chemists' Association Award for teaching (1959), the Norris Award for teaching (1959), and the American Chemical Society Award in Chemical Education (1967). He was elected to the National Academy of Sciences in 1940.

Fieser published about 340 research papers, 40 of which were based on his own experiments. He wrote *Organic Experiments* (4th ed. 1964) and *The Scientific Method: A Personal Account of Unusual Projects in War and in Peace* (1964). He and his wife were coauthors of *Organic Chemistry* (3d ed. 1956), *Steroids* (4th ed. 1959), *Introduction to Organic Chemistry* (1957), *Basic Organic Chemistry* (1959), *Style Guide for Chemists* (1960), *Advanced Organic Chemistry* (1961), *Topics in Organic Chemistry* (1963), and *Current Topics in Organic Chemistry* (1963).

For background information *see* ONCOLOGY; ORGANIC CHEMISTRY; POTENTIAL, ELECTRIC;

VITAMIN K in the McGraw-Hill Encyclopedia of Science and Technology.   □

★ FITCH, Val Logsdon

American physicist
Born Mar. 10, 1923, Merriman, Nebr., U.S.A.

BY THE late 1940s a clear distinction had been established between the strongly interacting π-meson, which is largely responsible for nuclear forces, and the weakly interacting μ-meson. So far as we know today the μ-meson is identical to the electron except that it is 207 times heavier, a heavy brother of the electron. In the early 1950s the weakness with which the μ-meson interacts with nuclear matter suggested a number of unique experiments. Among these was a proposal that the μ-meson could be an important probe of the electrical properties of the nucleus. The μ-meson, in coming to rest in matter, is eventually trapped in one of the outer Bohr orbits about a nucleus, and thereupon proceeds to cascade down through the various atomic orbits to the lowest state. The μ-mesonic atom differs in one importance respect from the conventional electronic atom. Because of the greater mass of the μ-meson, its Bohr orbit has a radius 207 times smaller than the corresponding electron orbit. Indeed, in the case of lead, the lowest level has an associated orbit so small that the μ-meson spends more than 50% of its time inside the nucleus. This nuclear penetration causes the energy levels to be substantially modified. For example, the transition energy between the two lowest atomic levels in lead is 18 mev if the lead nucleus is a point charge. With the nucleus extended to a radius of 8.4×10^{-13} cm, thought to be the proper value in 1952, the transition energy computes to be 4.5 mev. Fitch and L. J. Rainwater, working at the Nevis cyclotron at Columbia University, set about to study these radiations. They were the first to observe the spectral lines from these rather curious atoms. They discovered, in the case of lead nuclei, the K line is not at 4.5 mev, as had been predicted, but rather at 6 mev. Indeed, this result was so unexpected that they were unsuccessful in initial attempts to see the radiation because the spectrometer at first was not set to extend to 6 mev.

The immediate conclusion from these observations turned out to be correct, that is, the radius of the lead nucleus was very substantially smaller than had been determined previously by a variety of methods. All the other nuclei studied showed the smaller radii. Shortly afterward, the smaller nuclear radius was confirmed by the electron-scattering experiments of Robert Hofstadter and his co-workers at Stanford. The other older methods of determining nuclear radii have been refined and corrected to give consistent results. One of the spectacular features of the μ-mesonic atom is that the μ-meson, before it finally interacts with the nucleus, traverses about 1 meter of nuclear matter—and nuclear matter has a density 10^{13} times that of water!

After the studies of μ-mesonic atoms Fitch turned his attention to the newly discovered K-mesons (mesons with slightly more than half the mass of the proton) and contributed to the so-called $\tau\theta$ puzzle. This puzzle led T. D. Lee and C. N. Yang to suggest the violation of parity in the weak interactions.

The neutral K-mesons have always presented a fascinating picture. It was known in the early 1950s that the neutral K, the K^0, decays to π^+ and π^-. It was also known that the antiparticle, the $\bar{K}^0$, decays the same way. If one sees in a detector the π^+- and π^--mesons, one describes the decay, in the tradition of quantum mechanics, as having originated from a linear combination of the two particle states, either a $K^0 +$ $\bar{K}^0$ or $K^0 - \bar{K}^0$. Which is it? The $\pi^+\pi^-$ system is even under the combined operations of charge conjugation and parity, CP. If one defines $|\bar{K}^0 \cong CP \ |K^0 >$, then it is the first combination, $K^0 +$ $\bar{K}^0 = K_1{}^0$, that decays to $\pi^+\pi^-$. The second combination, $K_2{}^0 = K^0 - \bar{K}^0$, exists, but it cannot decay to π^+ and π^- if the interaction responsible for the decay of the particles is invariant under CP. Both the $K_1{}^0$ and the $K_2{}^0$ were found to exist as early as 1957. In 1964 Fitch and his collaborators, J. H. Christenson, J. W. Cronin, and R. Turlay, discovered that the $K_2{}^0$ also does decay to the $\pi^+\pi^-$-mesons. It happens very rarely, $1/250,000$ times as fast as the $K_1{}^0$ decays to $\pi^+\pi^-$. But it definitely does happen, and it means that CP is violated in the decay—that the universe is not completely symmetric under the combined operations of charge conjugation and parity.

This observation has important implications, particularly in view of a theorem which is at the core of all modern field theories, the TCP theorem. On the basis of special relativity it is possible to show that all interactions must be symmetrical under the combined operations of time reversal T, charge conjugation C, and parity P. With the violation of CP the TCP theorem requires a violation of time reversal invariance to correct the wronged—and to say that microscopic reactions are changed under time reversal has the most profound consequence, at least at the conceptual level. The present-day physics community is hotly pursuing this problem. It is interesting to observe that the studies of the K-meson have led to the overthrow of major symmetry principles—parity in 1957 and now charge conjugation parity.

Fitch had an early interest in chemistry. He was first exposed to physics when, in the U.S. Army, he was sent to Los Alamos, N.Mex., during World War II to work on the atomic bomb project. He participated in tests with the 509th Bombardment Group and in the initial bomb test at Alamogordo in July, 1945. He received his bachelor's degree in electrical engineering from McGill University in 1948 and a Ph.D. in physics from Columbia University in 1954. He became a professor of physics at Princeton University in 1960. In 1966 he was elected to the National Academy of Sciences and the American Academy of Arts and Sciences.

For background information *see* Meson; Relativity; Scattering experiments, nuclear in the McGraw-Hill Encyclopedia of Science and Technology. ☐

★ FITZ-JAMES, Philip Chester

Canadian microbiologist
Born Nov. 26, 1920, Vancouver, British Columbia, Canada

THE RESTING, heat- and chemical-resistant bacterial spore has fascinated microbiologists since the initial studies (published in 1877) of Ferdinand Cohn on *Bacillus subtilis* and his student Robert Koch on *B. anthrax*. This resting state in the life cycle of certain members of the genera *Bacillus* and *Clostridium* has been the object of much study as a physiological entity. Until about 1950, however, when Fitz-James began his studies on the bacterial spore, little was known of the exact structure and chemical nature of this completely resting cell. During the following 10 years, not only the general composition and structure of bacterial spores were described, but also their requirements for germination and their mode of formation. Moreover, the localization of chemical components in their

special layers of the spore was partly elucidated. By combining morphological (light and electron microscopy) and biochemical analyses, Fitz-James made a leading contribution to this work.

Fitz-James and his student Elizabeth Young found that spore formation is essentially a peculiar form of division, involving first a membrane folding at the cell end which encloses approximately half of the cell's deoxyribonucleic acid (DNA). In the resulting double-membrane forespore, the internal and external orientations of the cell membrane are preserved so that an outer zone now separates the original cell (sporangium) from the spore protoplast. In the space between the forespore membranes a layer (the cortex), originally described by Fitz-James's colleague C. F. Robinow, appears. The formation of the spore coat or coats commences and appears outside the outer membrane of the forming spore. By the use of mutants blocked at various stages of spore formation and by the use of antibiotics inhibiting cell wall and protein synthesis, the nature of much of this spore formation was worked out.

In 1953 Fitz-James was invited by C. L. Hannay to assist in a joint study of the characteristics of parasporal crystals, which form along with the spores in certain insect-pathogenic species of the B. cereus group. Later, Fitz-James and Young made initial biochemical and structural studies on the formation of these fascinating protein crystals in sporulating bacilli.

In 1955 Fitz-James became a morphological collaborator with Sol Spiegelman and Arthur Aronson and contributed to their studies on the isolation of nuclear bodies from bacterial protoplasts. Fitz-James continued to study the synthesis of cell components in growing protoplasts with both morphological and chemical methods. Later, by using protoplasting techniques, the dependence of sporulating cells on an intact cell wall was shown. Following Alexander Rich's demonstration of polysomes in red blood cells,

Fitz-James used protoplasts to isolate polyribosomes from B. megaterium. The growing protoplast system was shown by Fitz-James to be an ideal system for the study of the action of a number of membrane-active antibiotics and fatsoluble vitamins.

In 1962 a collaboration with Ronald Hancock demonstrated the failure of penicillin to inhibit the growing protoplast. At the same time, by comparing the effects of penicillin on cells growing in a variety of stabilizing media, they described the accumulation of what appeared to be open strands of cell wall at the growing sites of wall synthesis in dividing bacilli. From the work of J. L. Strominger and J. T. Park, it is now apparent that these are un-cross-linked monomer strands of mucopeptide. Thus, the initial lesion of penicillin action was sharply demonstrated using the electron microscope.

With the application of modern methods of fixation and embedding, Fitz-James, along with many other electron microscopists, encountered the fascinating membranous organelles in the growing and sporulating cells of the bacilli. His name for this organelle, the mesosome, is now commonly accepted. His later work was concentrated on a study of this organelle. During protoplasting, the organelle is expelled to the cell periphery as a protruding series of vesicles on the protoplast surface. A method of collecting these membrane organelles was developed. Combining both biochemical and morphological techniques, Fitz-James demonstrated that these organelles were active sites of phospholipid synthesis and had a precursor-product relationship with the plasma membrane of the cell. To elucidate these studies, he used cells recovering from a low-temperature shock treatment and growing protoplast systems. Both radioactive phosphorus and iron show prime labeling in the mesosome fractions. Thus, with their anchorage to the cellular DNA and their function as sites of membrane synthesis, the mesosomes are organelles ideally suited for the control of differentiation in the life cycle of Bacillus cells.

Son of a wood-products engineer of Anglo-Scot origin and an Irish mother of the Dublin Shaws, Fitz-James grew up in a land abounding in biology. As a teen-ager, he made hobbies of bird-banding and taxidermy. He also kept 10 beehives and tended a large garden. His early training at the University of British Columbia was in agricultural microbiology (B.S.A., 1943); on graduation he went to the Banting and Best Department of Medical Research at the University of Toronto to assist organic chemist Fergus MacDonald in the operation of a penicillin pilot plant. At Toronto he took an M.S.A. in physiology and biochemistry (1945) and then entered medicine in 1945 at the University of Western Ontario (M.D., 1949). After a year's internship in Vancouver, he enrolled for a Ph.D. (awarded in 1953) at Western, where under the combined guidance of R. J. Rossiter in biochemistry and R. G. E. Murray and C. F. Robinow in bacteriology he began his studies of the bacterial spore. He was awarded the Royal Society of Canada's Harrison Prize in 1963.

For background information *see* BACTERIAL ENDOSPORES; BACILLACEAE in the McGraw-Hill Encyclopedia of Science and Technology. □

★ FORBUSH, Scott Ellsworth

American geophysicist
Born Apr. 10, 1904, Hudson, Ohio, U.S.A.

THE CONTRIBUTIONS made by Forbush to geophysical knowledge resulted principally from his statistical investigations of time variations of cosmic-ray intensity and their relation to geomagnetic phenomena. For these researches the Institute of Physics and the Physical Society (London) awarded him the Sir Charles Chree Medal and Prize in 1961. In 1965 he received the John A. Fleming Award of the American Geophysical Union.

He started investigating cosmic-ray intensity variations in 1937, shortly after the first worldwide network of continuously recording cosmic-ray ionization chambers commenced operation. Maintenance and operation of these identical instruments at Godhaven (Greenland), Cheltenham (U.S.), Mexico City (Mexico), Huancayo (Peru), and Christchurch (New Zealand) were effected through the unselfish cooperation of the governments of these countries in a program sponsored by the Carnegie Institution of Washington.

In 1937 he discovered the worldwide decrease in cosmic-ray intensity associated with some magnetic storms—now called the Forbush effect. When this effect was observed, the variation of cosmic-ray intensity during the magnetic storm was sufficiently similar to that of the geomag-

netic field from the equatorial ring current (ERC) to suggest that it results from the influence of the magnetic field of the ERC on cosmic-ray trajectories. That this was not the cause was demonstrated in 1959 from results obtained by John Simpson and colleagues at the University of Chicago, using detectors in the *Explorer VI* satellite. Their results showed that the magnitude of the cosmic-ray intensity decrease is essentially the same out to distances of 7.5 earth radii, and thus was not due to the ERC but rather to the fact that inside the plasma cloud, coming from the Sun, the intensity is reduced by the effect of magnetic fields carried within the clouds.

In 1946 Forbush discovered the solar flare effect, or increase of cosmic-ray intensity due to protons ejected by the Sun in some large chromospheric eruptions. The solar flare event of Nov. 19, 1949, was recorded by Carnegie ionization chambers at Climax, Colo., Cheltenham, Md., and Huancayo, Peru. From this increase of about 200% at Climax (11,000 ft altitude), 45% at Cheltenham (near sea level), and undetectable at Huancayo (11,000 ft altitude at the geomagnetic equator), Forbush, M. Schein, and T. B. Stinchcomb showed that it is due principally to the nucleonic component generated in the atmosphere by relatively low-energy primaries. They consequently predicted that an increase at least 10 times greater would have been registered by a nucleonic detector. During this event N. Adams observed an increase of 550% in a neutron detector at Manchester, England, but thought it was due to instrumental troubles until he saw the predictions of Forbush, Schein, and Stinchcomb.

Forbush also established the solar cycle variation in cosmic-ray intensity from ionization chamber data over many years. This decrease of about 4% at sunspot maximum relative to that at sunspot minimum was later also found to be several times greater in neutron monitors.

Other investigations by Forbush included rigorous statistical analysis of the sidereal diurnal variation of cosmic-ray intensity, which was found too small to be statistically significant in contrast to the significant solar diurnal variation. He recently investigated the solar diurnal variation, using ionization chamber data from three stations covering the period 1937–66. Using the deviations of yearly means of the diurnal variation from the average for 25 years, he avoided the unpleasant uncertainties of atmospheric effects that have troubled many investigators. On the basis of rigorous statistical procedures he reliably demonstrated the remarkable agreement between the diurnal variation at Cheltenham, Christchurch, and Huancayo. In addition, he found that the amplitude of the diurnal variation varies with magnetic activity as measured by his values of the ERC field, and that in the complete absence of magnetic activity the diurnal variation tends to vanish.

Forbush also made the first comprehensive observations of magnetic field variations arising from the equatorial electrojet current system. These observations, made during the International Geophysical Year, included continuous registration at five locations and a survey along the west coast of South America from the Equator to about latitude 20° S. Forbush was the first to reliably determine the absolute field from the equatorial ring current, and showed that even on magnetically quiet days the annual mean ring current varies with the solar cycle, being more intense near the maxima of solar activity. He showed that the ERC vanishes only on a few quiet days near the minima of solar activity. While a visiting professor under Van Allen at the University of Iowa, he investigated, with D. Venkatesan and G. Pizzella, the temporal variations in the density of electrons trapped in the Van Allen radiation belt.

Forbush received his B.Sc. in physics from the Case School of Applied Science in 1925 and, after two quarters as a graduate student instructor in the physics department at Ohio State University, he joined the National Bureau of Standards. In 1927 he joined the staff of the Carnegie Institution of Washington, Department of Terrestrial Magnetism, and spent 2 years at its Huancayo Magnetic Observatory. He served on the staff of the Department's ill-fated, nonmagnetic research ship, the *Carnegie*. He said he owed his life to having been asleep in his cabin when an explosion occurred on Nov. 19, 1929, in the afterpart of the *Carnegie*, when it was anchored a mile from shore in Apia, Samoa. The ship burned and sank. Forbush later returned to Huancayo as observer in charge, and in 1931 was granted a year's leave of absence for graduate study in physics and mathematics at Johns Hopkins University. He did additional graduate study at George Washington University, the National Bureau of Standards, and the Department of Agriculture. During the war years Forbush was head of a mathematical analysis section at the Naval Ordnance Laboratory, and also worked in operations research in the Navy Department. In 1957 he became chairman of the section of analytical and statistical geophysics at the Department of Terrestrial Magnetism. He was elected to the National Academy of Sciences in 1962. In 1959 he was made an honorary professor of the University of San Marcos, Lima, Peru, the oldest university in the Western Hemisphere. In 1962 the Case Institute of Technology granted him an honorary D.Sc.

Forbush wrote *The Equatorial Electrojet in Peru*, with Mateo Casaverde (1961).

For background information *see* Cosmic rays; Geomagnetism; Sun in the McGraw-Hill Encyclopedia of Science and Technology.   □

FRANCK, James

American physicist
Born Aug. 26, 1882, Hamburg, Germany
Died May 21, 1964, Göttingen, Germany

WHILE ENGAGED in a quantitative study of elastic collisions between electrons and atoms, Franck and the German physicist Gustav Hertz formulated the concept of excitation potentials, gave experimental support to Niels Bohr's concept of the quantized atom, and provided a method for determining the value of Planck's constant. In recognition of their work, Franck and Hertz shared the 1925 Nobel Prize in physics (awarded in 1926).

The concept of the nuclear atom was developed by Ernest Rutherford during the first decade of the 20th century. In 1900 Max Planck had derived the basis for quantum theory, as well as an equation relating the energy of a quantum to its frequency multiplied by a proportionality constant, which is now known as Planck's constant, h. In 1913 Niels Bohr combined Rutherford's atom with Planck's quantum theory to propose an atom whose electrons occupy discrete energy levels surrounding the nucleus. His theory was greeted with skepticism, however, since for certain aspects classical laws still had to be applied simultaneously with quantum postulates with which they were in contradiction.

In 1912, working at the University of Berlin, Franck and Hertz began to study the effects of the impact between an electron and an atom. By 1913 they had devised a classic experiment: Atoms of mercury vapor were bombarded with electrons, whose energy was controlled by an accelerating voltage. As the voltage was increased slowly, a point was reached at which resonance occurred. Energy was then transferred to the atoms and the gas glowed. As a result of the experiment, in 1914 Franck and Hertz were able to announce three results: (1) Collisions of electrons with mercury atoms are perfectly elastic for electron energies up to 4.9 electron volts (ev). (2) Above this limit (4.9 ev) energy is transferred to the atom, but always in quanta of 4.9 ev, while any excess is retained as kinetic energy. (3) Inelastic collisions lead to the emission of light of the resonance line 2537 A of mercury, and this line only—the energy loss of the electron is equal to the quantum energy $h\nu$ of this line.

Franck and Hertz realized the importance of their discovery, which demonstrated the quantized energy transfer from kinetic to electromagnetic energy. Einstein's interpretation of the photoelectric effect had implied the quantized conversion of electromagnetic energy into kinetic and potential energy, but it was based on scanty experimental evidence. Far more clearly and directly than the photoelectric effect, the experiments of Franck and Hertz proved the reality of the energy quanta postulated by Planck and provided a new method to measure Planck's constant. Furthermore, the results gave experimental support to Bohr's theory of the quantized atom, which had been published some 6 months before, for they demonstrated that an atom can take up internal energy only in such discrete amounts as to transform it from one stationary state to another.

In 1925, while at the University of Göttingen, Franck published a paper dealing with the elementary processes of photochemical reactions. In this he drew upon the work of three previously unconnected sources: (1) Heinrich Lenz, in his theory of band spectra, had pointed out that the correspondence principle leads to a connection between the coupling strength of oscillatory and electronic motion, and the change of vibrational energy. (2) Franck and Max Born had separated clearly the electronic motion and that of the nuclei. (3) Mecke had observed a long series of vibrational transitions with markedly decreasing spacings in the spectrum of iodine. Utilizing these, Franck arrived at a clear, graphic statement of the connection between electron transition and the motion of nuclei. Later, E. U. Condon's quantum-mechanical treatment added rigor and quantitative information to what is now known as the Franck-Condon principle.

Having established many of the basic relationships determining the interaction between simple molecules and light quanta, in 1933 Franck became interested in the fundamental photochemical process in nature, photosynthesis.

He hoped at first that application of quantitative, physical experimentation to this process would clarify its most puzzling aspect, the mechanism by which a large portion of the energy of several quanta of visible light is converted into chemical energy. He carried out a large number of experimental investigations, particularly on the fluorescence of chlorophyll in the living cell. Franck found that a very high intensity of illumination brought the yield of fluorescence of chlorophyll in vivo to about twice the level observed in weak light.

These and similar findings led Franck to develop a biochemical and a biophysical model of photosynthesis. The biochemical model deals with the transformations involved in the conversion of carbon dioxide into carbohydrates. The biophysical model is concerned with the primary photochemical act in which light is converted into chemical energy.

During Franck's half-century of productive work, he investigated many phenomena, not all of which were related exclusively to physics. Among the many areas to which he made significant contributions were the formation and dissociation of molecules, the polarization of fluorescent light, and the development of the atomic bomb. While involved in the last-named project, Franck chaired a committee of scientists considering the social and political implications of employing the atomic bomb. Their conclusions, which were submitted to the Secretary of War in 1945, have become known as the Franck Report. The report urges the United States government to consider the use of the bomb as a fateful political decision and not merely as a matter of military tactics, to consider the danger of beginning a nuclear arms race, and to demonstrate the weapon in an appropriately selected uninhabited area so as not to take human life.

The son of a banker, Franck pursued his studies at the University of Heidelberg and the University of Berlin (Dr.Phil., 1906). He became an instructor at Berlin, and in 1916 was made an assistant professor and in 1918 an associate professor. He spent a year in the German army at the beginning of World War I. From 1917 to 1921 Franck was the head of a section at the Kaiser Wilhelm Institut für Physikalische Chemie, later called the Max Planck Institut. In 1921, however, he accepted the offer of a chair of experimental physics at the University of Göttingen. He remained at this post until 1933 when, in protest against Adolf Hitler's anti-Semitic policies, he resigned and left Germany. After spending more than a year in Denmark doing research at the University of Copenhagen, he moved to the United States and accepted a professorship at Johns Hopkins University in 1935. Three years later he was appointed professor of physical chemistry at the University of Chicago, where he later worked on the Metallurgical Project—which was part of the atomic bomb project—during World War II. Franck became professor emeritus in 1949. In addition to his Nobel Prize, Franck received many honors, among them the Rumford Medal of the American Academy of Arts and Sciences in 1955 and the Max Planck Medal of the German Physical Society in 1951. He was a foreign member of the Royal Society of London and a member of the U.S. National Academy of Sciences.

Franck wrote *Anregung von Quantensprüngen durch Stösse* (1926) and *Photosynthesis in Plants* (1949).

For background information *see* ATOMIC STRUCTURE AND SPECTRA; FRANCK-CONDON PRINCIPLE; MOLECULAR STRUCTURE AND SPECTRA; PHOTOSYNTHESIS in the McGraw-Hill Encyclopedia of Science and Technology.   □

★ FRENCH, Charles Stacy

American plant physiologist
Born Dec. 13, 1907, Lowell, Mass., U.S.A.

FRENCH HAD the good luck, as a college sophomore in 1928, to hear lectures on photosynthesis by Robert Emerson, who had just returned to Harvard after several years with Otto Warburg in Berlin. The fascination of deducing the nature of the photosynthetic process from simple but precise measurements of such phenomena as light absorption, gas exchange, and growth rate of photosynthetic cells under various controlled conditions greatly appealed to French. He learned from Emerson that in such experimental work an interest in development of techniques, mechanical contraptions, and application of the simpler principles of chemistry and physics to biological problems can lead to significant discoveries.

As a graduate student in general physiology at Harvard under W. J. Crozier, French participated in the Chlorella Club, a student discussion group led by William Arnold that included Pei-Sung Tang, Caryl Haskins, and Henry Kohn. With Tang and Kohn, he studied *Chlorella* respiration as influenced by temperature and oxygen pressure. He heard about photosynthetic bacteria from Albert Navez. After the *Chlorella* work he went in 1934 to the Hopkins Marine Station in California to learn from Cornelis B. van Niel how to grow photosynthetic bacteria and study their metabolism. A postdoctoral year with Emerson at the California Institute of Technology was followed by a year in Berlin with Warburg. The action spectrum and efficiency of bacterial photosynthesis were measured. This led to a comparative study of the absorption spectra of different photosynthetic bacteria, which French carried out at the Harvard Medical School's biochemistry department as a teaching fellow under Baird Hastings. Similar work on bacteria had been going on in the biophysical research group under Wassink at Utrecht. Thereafter the work of that group, later led by Jan B. Thomas, and French's interests in photosynthetic pigments remained closely associated.

As an assistant to James Franck at Chicago, French worked on the time course of chlorophyll fluorescence in leaves and on photooxidation in leaves free of carbon dioxide. He learned to make reliable physical measurements from Foster Rieke, Hans Gaffron, and Robert Livingston, other members of Franck's group.

The difference between two contrasting philosophies of experimental investigation became clear during this work on fluorescence. One approach to the understanding of a phenomenon is to devise a theoretical scheme to correlate the known facts, then to plan a few critical experiments to support the postulates of the theory. In simple enough systems with well-understood variables, the "theory first" philosophy may be useful. However, in complex and poorly understood systems, such as photosynthesis, French preferred the opposite philosophy, first developing a knowledge of the phenomenon by systematic measurements under very different conditions, then letting the theory develop on a broad basis of experimental experience.

A casual visit to Chicago by Mortimer Anson of the Rockefeller Institute led to collaborative experiments on oxygen evolution from chloroplasts, an effect that Anson had recently heard about when visiting Robert Hill in Cambridge. At Anson's suggestion this effect was named the "Hill reaction," a designation later used by all but Hill himself. Studies of the Hill reaction were continued at the botany department of the

University of Minnesota, where French taught plant physiology. There, in collaboration with A. Stanley Holt, he found that various dyes could be reduced by illuminated chloroplasts. He started a long-continued but only partially successful attempt to concentrate the photochemically active components of chloroplasts.

Later with Harold Milner and others at the Carnegie Institution, he continued the chloroplast fractionation experiments for several years, using his dye reduction method for the activity measurements of the fractions. To disintegrate chloroplasts for this work, he made a needle valve homogenizer, which has since been widely used for breaking bacteria. With Violet Koski Young, French measured the fluorescence spectra of photosynthetic pigments and confirmed the idea of energy transfer from "accessory pigments" to chlorophyll as a part of photosynthesis in live cells. To aid in the interpretation of fluorescence spectra and other data, a graphical computer called a "curve analyzer" was built. A recording fluorescence spectrophotometer, a derivative spectrophotometer, an automatic spectrophotometer for recording action spectra of photosynthesis, and several monochromators and platinum electrode assemblies for photosynthesis measurements were also constructed. With the derivative spectrophotometer the existence of several forms of chlorophyll in many different plants was confirmed, and a new form of chlorophyll absorbing at 695 $m\mu$ was discovered.

The chemical nature and method of participation of various plant pigments in photosynthesis were French's main concerns. These problems were approached in many different ways, ranging from studies of isolated pigments to kinetic studies of photosynthesis in whole plants. He worked on measurements of fluorescence, absorption, and action spectra of the individual forms of chlorophyll and of other pigments, so that their participation in photosynthesis could be understood in a quantitative sense.

Son of a New England doctor, French graduated from Harvard University with a B.S. in 1930 and Ph.D. in 1934. He worked a year with Robert Emerson in California and a year with Otto Warburg in Berlin. Two years as Austin teaching fellow at Harvard Medical School were followed by 3 years as assistant to James Franck at the University of Chicago. From 1941 to 1947 he taught plant physiology at the University of Minnesota. He became director of the department of plant biology at the Carnegie Institution of Washington at Stanford University in 1947. He was elected to the National Academy of Sciences in 1963.

For background information *see* CHLOROPHYLL; PHOTOSYNTHESIS; PLANT PHYSIOLOGY; SPECTROPHOTOMETRIC ANALYSIS in the McGraw-Hill Encyclopedia of Science and Technology. □

★ FREUDENBERG, Karl Johann

German chemist
Born Jan. 29, 1886, Weinheim, Baden, Germany

As a student of Emil Fischer, Freudenberg acquainted himself with the bifunctional linkage of hydrobenzoic acids. After taking his doctorate (1910), he worked another 3 years with Fischer and studied galloylgallic acid, as well as gallotannins. The acyl group migration and transesterification through methanol in the presence of diazomethane were observed.

After World War I the work on tannins was continued—for example, on hamamelitannin, from which a new branched hexose was isolated with the help of tannase. Chlorogenic acid was elucidated. Catechin was assigned to flavonoids; its constitution and the steric relationship with epicatechin was established. The tetramethyl catechin undergoes a pinacol rearrangement without racemization. This was explained through a phenonium ion mechanism (1927). The self-condensation of catechin to tannins was clarified. It was shown, at the same time as by Roux, that quebrachotannin is the condensation product of a trihydroxyflavandiol. The proanthocyanidins, as a broad group of natural tannins, were opened up; they are dimeric flavonoids.

In Freudenberg's stereochemistry research the configurational system of the α-hydroxy acids was extended through chemical transformations. The tertiary carbon atom of dihydroshikimic acid, as well as that of the methylethylpropylmethane obtained from it, was related to glucose through the implication of cis-transisomerism on the ring system of the acid. From this point on, in filling up some gaps, the absolute configuration of citronellal, camphor, and of the entire terpene-system was established through chemical transformations. Making use of the rule of shift (displacement rule), which was discovered during the hydrogenation of mandelic acid, the lactone-, amide-, and phenylhydrazide rules of Hudson were corrected, and the amino-, azido-, and halogeno-fatty acids were sterically related to α-hydroxy acids. It could then be predicted when the Walden inversion would take place and when not; also, the basis for the theoretical interpretation of the results later obtained by others was laid. As the validity of Tschugajeff's optical rule of distance was shown to be the same for steric changes as for chemical ones (1931), the van't Hoff law of superposition could be corrected. By using the displacement rule, the absolute configuration of the catechin and pinoresinol group as well as that of glucosamin was determined (1931). The presence of a clear relationship between cellulose and its oligosaccharides was shown. A result of the collaboration with Werner Kuhn was the explanation, by Kuhn, of the rule of shift through the measurement of the Cotton effect in the ultraviolet region.

In his work on cellulose and starch, Freudenberg found, by the acetolysis of cellulose, that two-thirds of all the glucose units pass through the biose stage (1921). This was explained through chains of uniformly linked units, as in cellobiose, and was shown to be in accordance with the x-ray diagrams. Staudinger and Haworth after a few years came to the same conclusion. The rotation and the rate of hydrolysis of cellulose and its oligosaccharides are also in accordance with this. The synthesis of methylated cellotriose confirms the uniformity of both glucoside bonds. 2,3,6-O-Methylglucose anhydride-1,4 was synthesized and found to be monomolecular (according to K. Hess, it should have been methyl cellulose). A crystalline "glucosan" of Hess is composed of 15–30 units. Cellulose, completely methylated in cold and obtained in good yields, has no end groups, and is degraded to 2,3,6-trimethylglucose in formic acid with 1% acetyl chloride at 20°C. In 1928 Freudenberg established the first valid formula of the molecular constitution of cellulose. In thoroughly methylated starch the branching was found at the sixth position. Schardinger's dextrins from starch are cyclooligosaccharides, and were supplemented through the discovery of cyclooctaamylose. The dark-colored addition product of cyclohexaamylose with iodine was identified as a clathrate compound. Its similarity with the iodine-starch complex, which is equally a clathrate, led to the conception of a helix with tubelike hollow spaces for a part of starch molecule (1938).

Working on mono- and oligosaccharides from 1921, Freudenberg clarified the structure of the acetone compounds of simple sugars, thus permitting the syntheses of disaccharides and trisaccharides, among them that of sophorose, laminaribiose, cellobiose, and 5-β-glucosidoglucose. Supernumerary acetohalogeno-sugars and acetylated glucosides led to the discovery of cyclic acetates. The 6-deoxyhexose system was extended. The hydrogenolysis of benzylidene and arylsulfonic acid compounds was achieved.

In his amino sugars and protein studies, Freudenberg hydrolyzed blood group A substance and found D-galactose, D-acetylglucosamine, and amino acids, among them L-threonine. Insulin, inactivated by various methods, was partly reactivated. From the behavior of insulin toward cysteine it was inferred in 1935 that the former is composed of at least two parallel protein chains which are joined together through SS-bridges in the form of ladder rungs. In 1941 sugars and amino sugars were separated by using exchangers; furthermore, sugars were separated from amino acids, as well as acidic, neutral, and basic amino acids from each other.

Freudenberg started work on lignin in 1922 to find if it, like cellulose, possesses a definite order. Lignin is a phenolic body rich in ethereal oxygen (1926), and even in wood has a refractive index of an aromatic substance (1929). It is not an artifact of carbohydrates. Along with Klason and others, Freudenberg assumed and then proved that spruce lignin is an oxidation product of coniferyl, p-coumaryl, and sinapinyl alcohols. Its oxidation to vanillin and vanillin derivatives was increased to more than 40% of the theoretically possible amount. The oxidation of methylated lignin yields about 30 substances, mostly methoxybenzoic acids. Enzymatic dehydrogenation of a suitable mixture of the p-hydroxycinnamyl alcohols gave artificial lignin that yielded the same acids on degradation (1950). Through dehydrogenation of coniferyl alcohol, about 30 oligolignols were isolated, which rendered information about the mechanism of formation and constitution of lignin. The intermediate products are quinone methides, to which water, phenols, or sugars are added. In this way phenols are formed again, which after dehydrogenation react further. The bonding to the polysaccharides is simultaneously explained. Schematic formula of spruce lignin explains all recorded information, and also a great amount of other information which was not considered at the time of its presentation. Of importance are the irregular sequence of units, which appear in various forms, and of isolated benzylaryl ether bonds, which are easily hydrolyzed to give oligolignols to a small extent.

In 1914 Freudenberg became privatdozent at the University of Kiel, with a 4-year leave for military service. He spent 1920–21 at the University of Munich and 1921–22 at the University of Freiburg as professor extraordinarius. During

1922–26 he was professor ordinarius of chemistry in Karlsruhe and during 1926–56 at Heidelberg. He then became director of a state research institute.

Freudenberg wrote *Die Chemie der natür-lichen Gerbstoffe* (1920), *Tannin, Cellulose, Lignin* (1933), and edited *Stereochemie* (1933). With Hans Plieninger, he wrote *Organische Chemie* (11th ed. 1963).

For background information *see* MONO-SACCHARIDE; OLIGOSACCHARIDE; STARCH; STEREO-CHEMISTRY; WOOD CHEMICALS in the McGraw-Hill Encyclopedia of Science and Technology. □

★ FREY-WYSSLING, Albert Friedrich

Swiss botanist
Born Nov. 8, 1900, Küsnacht-Zurich, Switzerland

AFTER WORLD WAR I research fellows in biology were still divided into two opposing camps: the "histomorphologists" and the "physiological chemists" (biochemists). The chemists called the histologists "stamp collectors," while the latter thought of their chemical colleagues as poor biologists because they analyzed awful mixtures of different cell constituents, whimsical breis, and structureless homogenates.

Frey-Wyssling recognized that this dispute arose from the fact that cytologists worked in the domain of microscopic dimensions but chemists in that of amicroscopic dimensions. He concluded that in the submicroscopic domain, which covers the dimensions of macromolecules with their characteristic shape and chemical behavior, morphology and chemistry would meet. He hoped to reestablish an undivided biology by research in this neglected field, so he undertook what he later called submicroscopic morphology (1938). He reactivated biological research with the polarizing microscope, which had been neglected in this century after a brilliant start at the Swiss Federal Institute of Technology (ETH) in Zurich by his early predecessors,

C. W. Nägeli, the first molecular biologist, and C. Cramer. In addition to the classical notion of intrinsic anisotropy, the concept of form aniso-tropy, developed after 1915 by H. Ambronn at the University of Jena, was introduced. This effect reveals fibrillar or lamellar systems whose periodicity lies below the resolution power of the light microscope (1926). The application of the relevant methods showed that plant cell walls consist of rodlike fibrils (then called micellar strands) embedded in an amorphous mass (now called matrix). The arrangement of the rodlets varies so that different textures of the same submicroscopic structure can be distinguished (fiber texture, helical texture, tubular texture, and so on). In starch granules a similar structure of spherically arranged rodlets was found, while the cuticular layer of epidermal cells and chloroplasts proved to have a submicroscopic lamellar structure.

These optical studies, based on effects of birefringence and dichroism, were supported by the x-ray analysis of the same or similar biological objects (W. T. Astbury, *Fundamentals of Fibre Structure*, 1933). The x-ray diffraction method permitted a more quantitative evaluation of the invisible structural elements. By staining plant fibers with colloidal gold and silver particles of about 100-A diameter, Frey-Wyssling could show that bast fibers must consist of microfibrils with about 250-A diameter which are subdivided into much smaller elementary fibrils with the order of 50-A diameter (1937).

In applying these indirect methods, an elaborate insight into submicroscopic morphology was gained (1938). When, in 1940, the electron microscope became a tool for biological research, the derived submicroscopic structures, now termed ultrastructures, could be imaged directly. The lamellar structure of chloroplasts, retinal rods, and the myelin sheath of nerves, as well as the fibrillar patterns of cell walls, connective tissue, muscles, and so forth, became evident. In this way the general concept of submicroscopic structures gained by indirect methods was corroborated.

Frey-Wyssling, together with K. Mühlethaler, utilized electron microscopy from the start. With the aid of the freeze-etching method developed at the ETH by H. Moor, researchers hope to help solve the multiple problems concerning the function of the numerous types of organelles revealed by the electron microscope in the cytoplasm (1965).

Whereas before 1940 only a few scientists were involved in submicroscopic research, the electron microscope mobilized a whole army of histologists, cytologists, bacteriologists, virologists, and so on, who considered submicroscopic morphology no longer an adequate term for their ambitions. This humble science thus became a highly diversified technical branch of biology with such proud titles as biophysics, ultrastructure research, and molecular biology.

Son of a college teacher, Frey-Wyssling was trained at the ETH. He majored in biology (Diploma of Natural Sciences, 1923) and obtained a Ph.D. in 1924. In 1925 he studied optics with H. Ambronn at the University of Jena and in the following year, plant physiology with M. Molliard at the Sorbonne in Paris. In 1927 at the ETH he qualified in general botany, and in 1928–32 he was plant physiologist to the Rubber Experiment Station AVROS in Medan (Sumatra, Indonesia). He then returned to the ETH as a lecturer, and was appointed full professor in the department of general botany and plant physiology in 1938. He became head of this department, and in 1948 established the electron microscopy laboratory as a third research laboratory, in addition to those on histochemistry and plant physiology. In 1957–61 he was rector of the ETH.

Frey-Wyssling wrote *Das Polarisationsmikroskop*, with H. Ambronn (1926); *Die Stoffausscheidung der höheren Pflanzen* (1935); *Submikroskopische Morphologie des Protoplasmas und seiner Derivate* (1938); *Submicroscopic Morphology of Protoplasm* (1948; 2d ed. 1953); *Submikroskopische Struktur des Cytoplasmas* (1955); *Macromolecules in Cell Structure* (1957); *Die pflanzliche Zellwand* (1959); and *Ultrastructural Plant Cytology*, with K. Mühlethaler (1965).

For background information *see* CELL WALLS IN PLANTS; DICHROISM (BIOLOGICAL TISSUE); MICROSCOPE, ELECTRON in the McGraw-Hill Encyclopedia of Science and Technology.   □

★ FRIEDLANDER, Gerhart

American nuclear chemist
Born July 28, 1916, Munich, Germany

WHEN THE Brookhaven National Laboratory's cosmotron, the first accelerator capable of producing particle beams in the billion-electron-volt (Bev or Gev) energy range, came into operation in 1952, it was widely and justifiably hailed as an important new tool for elementary particle physics. However, few scientists expected it to be of much interest for studies of nuclear reactions in complex nuclei because, with bombarding particles whose kinetic energies exceed the total binding energies of nuclei, one might expect nuclei to be broken up into their constituent neutrons and protons. Friedlander and his collaborators were able to show that, contrary to such predictions, protons in the Gev energy range produce a rich variety of nuclear reactions. For his extensive work on the systematic study

and interpretation of these reactions, Friedlander received the American Chemical Society's Award for Nuclear Applications in Chemistry in 1967.

In the years following World War II, reactions between various nuclei and protons of energies up to a few hundred million electron volts were extensively studied in a number of laboratories possessing synchrocyclotrons. Two principal types of reactions were recognized: spallation reactions, in which a number of nucleons (a term meaning neutrons and protons) or small nucleon aggregates, such as deuterons and alpha particles, are emitted (spalled off), leaving behind a single major residual nucleus; and fission reactions, in which the nucleus splits into two (or possibly more) fragments of comparable mass.

When Friedlander and his co-workers extended nuclear reaction studies into the Gev range, they found that spallation and fission reactions continued to be important, but they soon observed phenomena that led them to postulate a third class of reactions, which they termed fragmentation. The first evidence came from the observation that large quantities of light nuclei with mass numbers between 10 and 40 are formed when protons in the Gev range interact with heavy-element targets. The onset of these reactions was found to be in the neighborhood of 0.5 Gev, and as the bombarding energy is increased above that value, their probabilities increase steeply. The Brookhaven chemists postulated that the light fragments result from processes in which local energy deposition in a region of the target nucleus leads to breakup of the nucleus before the energy can be distributed throughout the nucleus. This would be a mecha-

nism distinctly different from that believed to be operative in spallation and fission. These are described as two-step processes in which a fast step consisting of a cascade of nucleon-nucleon collisions and lasting on the order of 10^{-22} sec leads to excited intermediate nuclei, and these in turn deexcite on a slower time scale ($\sim 10^{-15}$ to 10^{-20} sec) by particle emission or fission. Confirmatory evidence for the idea that fragmentation reactions cannot be described as two-step processes came from work of some of Friedlander's Brookhaven colleagues on the angular distribution of Na^{24} fragments produced from bismuth by 3-Gev protons.

The exact nature of fragmentation reactions is still being debated. Friedlander and his co-workers proposed that the partners of the light fragments may be found among the neutron-deficient isotopes of much heavier elements. This suggestion originally came from the observation that the excitation functions (formation probabilities as a function of bombarding energy) for the production of neutron-deficient species in the barium region from heavy-element bombardments have the same shape as those for light-fragment production. The hypothesis that these neutron-deficient products are formed in processes distinctly different from those leading to the (generally neutron-excess) fission products was further strengthened by a set of experiments carried out by Friedlander, L. Friedman, B. Gordon, and L. Yaffe. In this mass-spectrometric and radio-chemical study of cesium and barium isotopes formed from uranium by protons of various energies, it was shown that above about 0.5 Gev the isobaric yield distribution—that is, the distribution of primary yields of different products at a given mass number—is double-peaked with a valley near beta stability. The products on the neutron-deficient and neutron-excess side of beta stability were also shown to have quite different momentum properties.

Friedlander's experimental studies of fragmentation and other high-energy reactions were complemented by his interest in attempts to calculate the behavior of nuclei under high-energy bombardment on the basis of simple models. Only those reactions describable by the two-step mechanism lent themselves to this approach, but here, and particularly for spallation reactions, the calculations, carried out by Monte Carlo methods on high-speed computers, were quite successful in reproducing a large body of experimental data. Some of the special features of reactions at Gev energies not found at lower energies could be correlated with the production and subsequent interactions of pi mesons in nuclei. One of the major aims of the numerical calculations is to test, and hopefully to improve, the models and assumptions used through comparison of the computed results with experimental data.

Friedlander majored in chemistry at the University of California, Berkeley, earning his B.S. in 1939. He continued at the same university as a graduate student under Glenn T. Seaborg and received his Ph.D. in 1942. After a year's teaching at the University of Idaho, he joined the Los Alamos Laboratory in 1943, remaining there till 1946. For the next 2 years he worked at the General Electric Co.'s Research Laboratory in Schenectady, and in 1948 became a member of the staff of Brookhaven National Laboratory.

Associate editor of the *Annual Review of Nuclear Science*, Friedlander wrote *Introduction to Radiochemistry*, with J. W. Kennedy (1949), and *Nuclear and Radiochemistry*, with Kennedy and J. M. Miller (1955; 2d ed. 1964).

For background information *see* NUCLEAR CHEMISTRY; NUCLEAR REACTION in the McGraw-Hill Encyclopedia of Science and Technology. □

★ FRIEDMANN, Herbert

American zoologist and ornithologist
Born Apr. 22, 1900, New York, N.Y., U.S.A.

FROM THE beginning of his career Friedmann was interested in the evolutionary and ethological problems associated with reproductive parasitism, especially in birds. With extensive field experience with parasitic birds in the Americas and Africa, supplemented with wide reading and correspondence with collectors and observers the world over, he made this special aspect of avian biology almost a personal field. He also dealt with the taxonomy of birds of all parts of the world.

In 1950, while in South Africa studying a group of parasitic birds known as honey guides, he investigated their peculiar, symbiotic "guiding" behavior. One of their species was long known to guide humans to wild bees' nests. Previously it had been assumed that the birds fed on the honey and bee larvae and eggs, but Friedmann found that the primary interest of the birds was in the beeswax.

This discovery led to a prolonged study of the mechanism of wax digestion, as waxes were then considered indigestible and, hence, nonnutritious to animals. In the birds' intestinal tracts Friedmann found a wax-breaking bacterium, which he isolated and described as *Micrococcus cerolyticus*. This microbe was found on the wild bee comb, from which the birds acquired it when eating the comb. Its wax-breaking effect was found to be far greater in the presence of an avian cofactor than by itself, and it was found that this cofactor was added in the upper end of the small intestine. Beeswax passing through the alimentary tract of the honey guides lost more than half of its lipid content, which was absorbed as nutriment by the birds. The wax also underwent very marked changes in its saponification number, indicating that it was broken down into simpler fatty acids, which made it possible for the birds to utilize it.

From the start of the work on wax digestion, Friedmann realized that any organism, chemical, or process that could break down wax might conceivably be of interest in tuberculosis therapy. The tubercle bacillus has a waxy impregnation that protects it from the counter effects of the body and from medication. Anything that could break down this waxy protection might render the tubercle bacillus more readily susceptible to treatment. He found that the *Micrococcus* from the honey guides had a marked effect on the metabolism of the tubercle bacillus, suggesting that the results might be applicable to tuberculosis therapy.

Friedmann was also interested in the emergence of objective "natural history" out of the mysticism and allegorical attitude of the Middle Ages. For material he turned to works of art of medieval and Renaissance times. He published numerous studies of symbolic content and usage of various animal forms, in an effort to learn what they meant to the people at the time and to appraise the growth of knowledge of the animals themselves. Because the only interest in animals was an ecclesiastical one in the allegorical meanings, scholars of the time paid little attention to the animals as such. It required a profound mental reorientation to alter this approach, and until then the advance of observational biology was not possible. Friedmann's papers contributed to a historical survey of the transition from the logic of allegory to that of natural science.

After graduating with a B.S. from the College of the City of New York in 1920, Friedmann went to Cornell University, where he obtained a Ph.D. in ornithology in 1923. For the next 3 years he held a National Research Council postdoctoral fellowship at Harvard, but much of the time was spent in the field, in Argentina in 1923–24 and in Africa in 1924–25. Because of his interest in taxonomy, Friedmann gravitated from university teaching to museum research and curating as a professional career. Thus, after teaching at Cornell, Virginia, Brown, and Am-

herst, he left the campus for the museum in 1929, when he was appointed curator of birds in the U.S. National Museum, Smithsonian Institution, Washington, D.C. There he remained as head curator of zoology until 1961, when he retired to accept the directorship of the Los Angeles County Museum of Natural History. He also accepted nominal appointments as professor of zoology in residence at the University of California at Los Angeles and at the University of Southern California.

Friedmann's work on avian brood parasitism earned him the Leidy Medal of the Academy of Natural Sciences of Philadelphia in 1955, the Elliot Medal of the National Academy of Sciences in 1959, and the Brewster Medal of the American Ornithologists Union in 1964. He was elected to the National Academy of Sciences in 1962.

Friedmann published about 400 works, including the following books and monographs: *The Cowbirds* (1929); *Birds Collected by the Childs Frick Expedition to Ethiopia and Kenya* (2 vols., 1930, 1937); *Ornithology of Tropical East Africa*, with A. Loveridge (1937); *Birds of North and Middle America* (3 vols., 1941, 1950); *The Symbolic Goldfinch* (1946); *Parasitic Cuckoos of Africa* (1949); *Distributional Check List of Birds of Mexico*, with others (2 vols., paper 1950, 1957); *The Honey-Guides* (1955); *Check-list of North American Birds*, with others (5th ed. 1957); *The Parasitic Weaverbirds* (1960); and *Host Relations of the Parasitic Cowbirds* (1963).

For background information *see* ECOLOGIC INTERACTIONS; LIPID; WAX, ANIMAL AND VEGETABLE in the McGraw-Hill Encyclopedia of Science and Technology.   □

★ FRUTON, Joseph Stewart

American biochemist
Born May 14, 1912, Czestochowa, Poland

FRUTON'S PRINCIPAL research activities were on the chemistry of amino acids and peptides, the chemical mechanisms in the catalytic action of proteolytic enzymes, and the enzymic synthesis of peptide bonds. During World War II he worked on the chemistry of war gases, notably mustard gas and the nitrogen mustards.

On receiving his Ph.D. in 1934, Fruton joined the laboratory of Max Bergmann at the Rockefeller Institute and undertook the study of the specificity of enzymes that cleave proteins to small fragments. The best-known enzyme of this class is pepsin, which was obtained in crystalline form by J. H. Northrop in 1930; a few years later Northrop's colleague M. Kunitz crystallized

two other digestive proteinases, trypsin and chymotrypsin. At that time some biochemists believed that enzymes such as pepsin effect a physical deaggregation of small peptides thought to be associated by noncovalent bonds to form macromolecular proteins. In beginning the study of pepsin, trypsin, and chymotrypsin, Fruton assumed that this view was incorrect, and that these enzymes were peptidases, that is, they catalyze the hydrolysis of peptide bonds between the amino acid units of peptide chains. He further assumed that the action of a given proteinase on a peptide bond depends on the specific nature of the amino acid units joined by that bond. As there are about 20 different kinds of amino acid units in protein chains, the choice of the units preferred by an enzyme such as pepsin was uncertain. Fruton decided to be guided by the results of experiments in which each enzyme was allowed to act on a series of proteins of widely different amino acid composition. From the relative extent of fragmentation, he formulated the working hypothesis that pepsin and chymotrypsin preferentially cleave bonds involving aromatic amino acids (phenylalanine, tyrosine), and that trypsin prefers to act at bonds involving basic amino acids (arginine, lysine). The hypothesis was tested during 1937–39 by synthesizing appropriate small peptides of known structure and by subjecting them to the action of crystalline pepsin, trypsin, and chymotrypsin. In large part, the working hypothesis was fruitful, and synthetic substrates became available with chemical structures that could be varied systematically, thus permitting a start toward the definition of the specificity of these proteinases. This approach was actively continued after World War II by Fruton and in several other laboratories, notably those of H. Neurath and of C. Niemann. Furthermore, during the postwar period the knowledge of the specificity of the proteinases, in particular that

of trypsin, proved to be valuable for the controlled degradation of proteins in the determination of the sequence of the amino acid units in the peptide chains of proteins.

The success in finding synthetic substrates for the crystalline digestive proteinases led Fruton to initiate studies during 1938–41 on the specificity of other protein-cleaving enzymes, especially those found in animal tissues. The use of suitable peptide substrates permitted the differentiation, purification, and characterization of individual components of the multienzyme complex which includes the intracellular proteolytic enzymes of animal tissues. In addition, the application of this approach to the specificity and mode of action of several plant proteinases (papain, ficin) served as the starting point for later fruitful investigations, especially by E. L. Smith.

During 1949–52 Fruton showed that several proteolytic enzymes catalyze attack of a sensitive bond not only by water, to cause hydrolysis, but also by the amino group of a suitable amino acid derivative to form a new peptide bond. Such transfer reactions, termed "transpeptidation" or "transamidation" reactions, are effected by most members of this class of enzymes; exceptional efficiency in this regard is exhibited, however, by some enzymes (for example, dipeptidyl transferase) present in animal tissues characterized by active protein biosynthesis. Much of Fruton's recent work was concerned with the study of the polymerization by such enzymes of amino acid units to form well-defined peptides. Although the biological significance of this property remains to be elucidated, especially in relation to the enzymic mechanisms in the intracellular formation of proteins, it is already clear that in certain physiological processes, such as blood coagulation, transpeptidation plays an important role. The demonstration that proteinases, such as chymotrypsin or papain, catalyze transpeptidation reactions also focused attention on the chemical mechanism of catalysis by these and related enzymes, and led to the hypothesis that an acyl-enzyme intermediate is involved in the hydrolytic cleavage of suitable substrates. This hypothesis received extensive support, and was greatly extended through the recent studies of numerous workers, notably J. M. Sturtevant and M. L. Bender.

Recently, Fruton gave renewed attention to the chemical mechanism of pepsin catalysis through the development of new synthetic substrates for this enzyme, the study of the kinetics of pepsin action, and the selective chemical modification of pepsin by diazo compounds. From earlier work it seemed probable that the "active site" of pepsin contained an unusually reactive carboxyl group; the recent studies on the chemical modification of the enzyme give this hypothesis strong support. The role of carboxyl groups in the maintenance of the catalytic activity of other enzymes (for example, chymotrypsin) was also a recent interest in Fruton's laboratory.

From the beginning, Fruton's work depended heavily on the laboratory synthesis of peptides of known structure and the use of these compounds as models for the study of the behavior of the more complex proteins. For this reason the chemistry of amino acids and peptides received continuous attention, and considerable effort was devoted to the improvement of the art of peptide synthesis. In particular, research was conducted from time to time on the synthesis of peptides presenting special problems encountered with certain amino acids, such as serine, methionine, and tryptophan.

Fruton received his B.A. in 1931 and his Ph.D. in biochemistry under H. T. Clarke in 1934 at Columbia University. He was on the staff of the Rockefeller Institute for Medical Research from 1934 to 1945, when he moved to Yale University as associate professor of physiological chemistry. He was professor of biochemistry from 1950 to 1957, Eugene Higgins Professor of Biochemistry from 1957, chairman of the department of biochemistry from 1951 to 1967, and director of the Division of Science from 1959 to 1962. In 1944 he received the Lilly Award in Biological Chemistry of the American Chemical Society. He was elected to the National Academy of Sciences in 1952 and to the American Philosophical Society in 1967.

Fruton wrote *General Biochemistry*, with S. Simmonds (1953; 2d ed. 1958).

For background information *see* AMINO ACID; ENZYME; PROTEIN in the McGraw-Hill Encyclopedia of Science and Technology.   □

★ FUOSS, Raymond Matthew

American chemist
Born Sept. 28, 1905, Bellwood, Pa., U.S.A.

THE RESPONSE evoked by application of an electric field to a chemical system depends on the molecular structure of the system; therefore, the field serves as a research probe for exploring the system. Electrolytic solutions contain ions, which are atoms or molecules carrying electrostatic charges; an electric field superposes a component of motion in the field direction on the thermal motion of the ions; this component is measured as an electrical conductance. The magnitude of the conductance depends on the concentration of ions, on their charges, and on their mobilities. Polar dielectrics contain no free charges, but their molecules are electrically

asymmetric and experience a torque in an electric field; the resulting orientation superposed on the thermal motion is measured as a dielectric constant (and a dielectric loss in the dispersion range of frequency). Both the translatory motion of ions and the rotatory motion of dipoles depend on the structure of solute and solvent molecules and on their mutual interactions. Experimental determination of electrical properties and their theoretical interpretation in terms of molecular parameters form the general research field in which Fuoss was active from 1930 on. The systems studied include solutions of electrolytes in solvents ranging from nonpolar to highly polar, polymers (especially polar compounds), and polyelectrolytes.

When Fuoss began investigation of dilute solutions at Brown University with C. A. Kraus in 1930, the conductance of aqueous solutions had been studied since the time of Michael Faraday and Friedrich Kohlrausch; the pattern for strong electrolytes was familiar, and the limiting behavior for extremely dilute solutions was quantitatively predictable by the Debye-Hückel-Onsager theory. Weak electrolytes, on the other hand, conformed fairly well to the behavior predicted by the Arrhenius theory of incomplete dissociation. Some information was available for nonaqueous systems, especially work by Kraus on solutions in liquid ammonia and on a variety of organic solvents by Paul Walden. However, no general pattern for solvents in general was discernible. Salts that were typical strong electrolytes in water showed conductance curves in ammonia that closely resembled those for moderately weak electrolytes in water. In the organic solvents both minima and maxima in the conductance curves had been

observed, in contrast to the uniform curves characteristic of most aqueous solutions. The general impression was that the shape of the conductance curve was something quite specific for a given solute-solvent combination. By using a mixture of polar and nonpolar solvents, such as water with dioxane or benzene with ethylene chloride, Fuoss was able to trace the continuous transition from the water pattern to the benzene pattern. Theoretical analysis showed that the controlling parameter is the dielectric constant of the solvent. In solvents of high dielectric constant, the curves are concave-up and approach linearity in square root of concentration at low concentrations. As the dielectric constant is decreased, electrostatic attraction stabilizes pairs of oppositely charged ions, as N. Bjerrum suggested in 1926 for multivalent ions in water, and the Arrhenius-type curve becomes dominant. At still lower dielectric constants, clusters containing three, four, and more ions become stable; the triple ions account for the appearance of the minima in the conductance curves, and the shift in the location of the minimum with dielectric constant is given a satisfactory theoretical explanation. In 1935 Fuoss received the American Chemical Society Award "in recognition of his important research contributions which, for the first time, provide a comprehensive theory of electrolytic solutions applicable to all solvent media and to all electrolytes."

Also in 1935 an investigation of the electrical properties of polar polymers was started at the research laboratory of the General Electric Company in Schenectady. At that time a certain amount of engineering data was available: It was known that some plastics and elastomers had low dielectric constants and others had relatively high values; some showed negligible electrical losses while others were very lossy. The electrical properties were known to be sensitive to temperature and to change with frequency, but no comprehensive correlations between electrical properties and structure were known. Measured values varied from sample to sample. Therefore, it was necessary to develop research methods that would give reproducible results so that one could say that a given composition of matter would have a certain dielectric constant and loss factor at a given temperature and frequency. Elimination of surface effects and control of ionic content were the key problems. Once these problems were solved, it became possible to collect meaningful data on the electrical properties of various plasticizer-polymer compositions. Theoretical analysis of the results showed that the dielectric response of polar polymers was describable in terms of a distribution of relaxation times corresponding to the response of segments of different lengths in the polymer chain. Whether the dipole was attached directly to the chain, as in polyvinyl chloride, or coupled flexibly, as in polyvinyl chloroacetate, for example, had a predictable effect on dielectric relaxation. The shift of the dispersion region was correlated theoretically with temperature and plasticizer content. Location of the dispersion region was found to be controlled not only by plasticizer concentration, but also by the shape and size of the plasticizer molecule. About 65 research papers on polar polymers and on electrolytic solutions had been published when World War II interrupted fundamental research.

In 1945 Fuoss was invited to Yale as Sterling Professor of Chemistry and there continued research on the properties of electrochemical systems. Electrolytes and polymers were combined into a new type of synthetic molecule, the polyelectrolyte. A typical example is quaternized polyvinyl pyridine, a normal random-coil polymer, which in solution exhibits all the familiar properties of this class of compounds. On addition of alkyl halide, the pyridine nitrogens are converted to positively charged ions, while the halogen atom of the alkyl halide becomes a halide ion. The product differs in one fundamental way from a quaternary salt of low molecular weight, such as quaternized monomeric pyridine: The cationic sites are covalently bonded to the polymeric chain and never can diffuse apart on dilution as can the ions of ordinary salts. This restriction has a profound effect on the electrical properties of solutions of the polyelectrolyte; furthermore, the presence of the fixed charges on the polymer chain completely modifies the polymeric properties. The reduced viscosity increases on dilution, as does the ratio of osmotic pressure to concentration. For neutral polymers the effect is just the opposite. Light scattering is markedly reduced by quaternization. The solutions behave conductimetrically like weak electrolytes (although monomeric quaternary salts are typical strong electrolytes) and show a remarkably large Wien effect (increase of conductance, with field strength). All of the unusual properties can be masked by the addition of an excess of simple electrolyte. These effects can be explained in terms of a molecular model in which mobile counter ions are distributed both to the volume of solvent between polymer molecules and to the volume of the polymer coils. With increasing dilution more counter ions diffuse away from the polymer; the latter then expands because of increased electrostatic repulsion between uncompensated charges on the coil. The expansion in turn produces the higher viscosity. The increase in osmotic pressure ratio on dilution is due to dissociation of counter ions from the polyelectrolyte, which tends toward a cylindrical structure as the solution is diluted. Addition of simple electrolyte provides an excess of charges of both signs that screen the counter ions and the polymeric ions. Analogs of naturally occurring biochemical substances were synthesized by Fuoss; copolymers of acrylic acid and basic amine monomers gave polyampholytes that showed a characteristic isoelectric point.

The interaction of simple ions with each other and with solvent molecules was also a continuing field of interest for Fuoss. Conductance of a wide variety of electrolytes in mixtures of polar and nonpolar solvents showed that association to ion pairs conforms to a simple relationship, proportionality of logarithm of association constant to reciprocal of dielectric constant, which had been derived theoretically in 1958. In the region of high dielectric constants, conductance curves usually are concave-up and lie above the limiting tangent. This behavior was shown to be the consequence of the finite size of the ions by integration of the 1932 Onsager-Fuoss equations with appropriate boundary conditions. The theory gives a theoretical explanation of conductance data for the alkali halides in dioxane-water mixtures up to concentrations of the order of 0.01 normal in water. This theoretical work was done just before electronic computers were available. Consequently, mathematical approximations had to be made in order to simplify the equations to forms that could be handled by a human computer. In 1967 a number of these approximations were dropped, and the explicit functions resulting from the integration were programmed for machine calculation. The result is a theory for conductance of symmetrical salts that is valid up to about 0.1 normal in water. This is the upper limit of concentrations to which the model on which the theory is based (charged spheres in a continuum) might be expected to be valid. At higher concentrations the effects of nearest neighbor ions dominate, and the long-range averaging that describes the properties in the dilute range is no longer valid.

After graduating from Harvard (Sc.B., 1925), Fuoss spent an academic year at the University of Munich, where he worked with Heinrich Wieland, Kasimir Fajans, and Erich Lange. After several years as chemical consultant, he entered the Graduate School of Brown University in 1930 and received the Ph.D. in 1932. He was appointed research instructor at Brown in 1932 and later assistant professor for research. On leave of absence as International Research fellow in 1933–34, he worked with P. J. W. Debye in Leipzig and R. H. Fowler in Cambridge. In 1936 he joined the research staff of the General Electric Company, where most of his work on polar polymers was done. In 1945 he was appointed Sterling Professor of Chemistry at Yale. He was elected to the National Academy of Sciences in 1951 and to the American Academy of Arts and Sciences in 1958.

Fuoss published about 230 papers, most of them on electrical properties of chemical systems. He wrote *Electrolytic Conductance*, with F. Accascina (1959).

For background information *see* DIELECTRICS; ELECTROLYTIC CONDUCTANCE; POLYMER PROPERTIES in the McGraw-Hill Encyclopedia of Science and Technology.   □

★ FUSON, Reynold Clayton

American organic chemist
Born June 1, 1895, Wakefield, Ill., U.S.A.

REACTIONS OF the carbonyl group of aldehydes and ketones generally are hindered by the attached radicals, which may present a problem when the compounds are to be used in synthesis. Fuson had the idea of turning this drawback to advantage by introducing excessive hindrance

4,7-Dimethyl-α-indanone

5,8-Dimethyl-α-tetralone

Fig. 1. Structural formulas of 4,7-dimethyl-α-indanone and 5,8-dimethyl-α-tetralone.

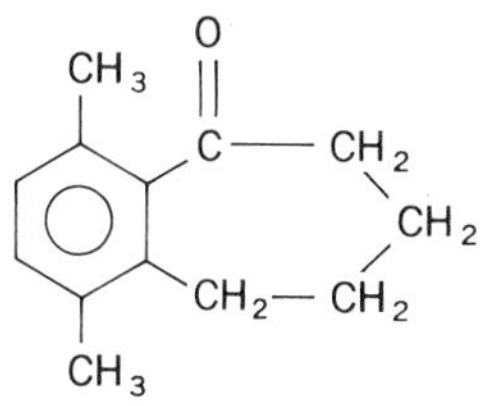

Fig. 2. 6, 9-Dimethylbenzosuberone.

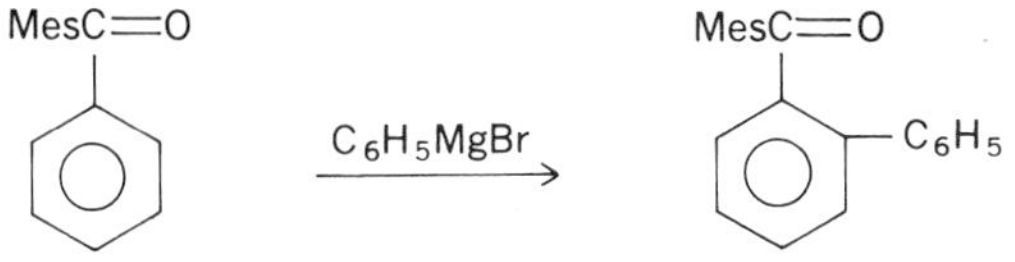

Fig. 3. Reaction of acetomesitylene.

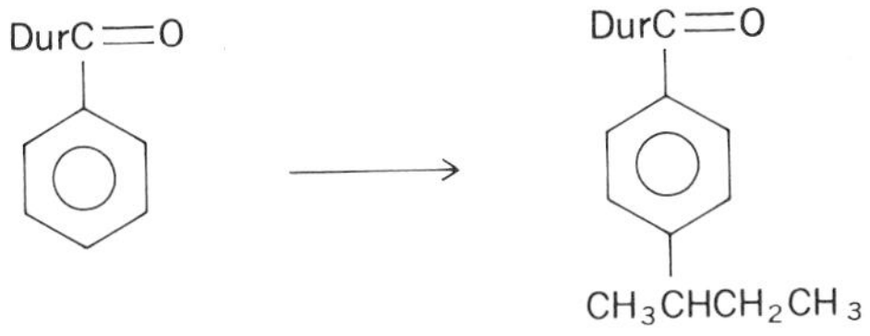

Fig. 4. Reaction of duryl phenyl ketone.

deliberately to find out what might happen when normal behavior of the carbonyl group is not possible.

Early experiments carried out by him and his students involved aromatic ketones in which the carbonyl group was hedged about by methyl groups in o-positions of the ring. Mesityl and duryl radicals were found to inhibit or greatly retard most of the reactions typical of carbonyl compounds. Failure of the reactions to proceed was linked with the inability of the carbonyl group to lie in the plane of the aromatic ring of the obstructing radicals. o-Disubstituted ketones were prepared by Kadesh, however, in which the carbonyl group must lie in the plane of the ring. The situation is achieved by making the carbonyl group a part of a 5- or 6-membered ring. Thus, in 4,7-dimethyl-a-indanone and 5,8-dimethyl-a-tetralone (Fig. 1), the ortho-methylene groups may be supposed to have an effect similar to that of a methyl group. The carbonyl group, constrained to lie in the plane of the bicyclic system, is not hindered. In 6,9-dimethyl-benzosuberone (Fig. 2), on the other hand, the 7-membered ring is sufficiently flexible to allow the carbonyl group to be twisted out of the plane of the aromatic ring. The behavior of the suberone, unlike that of the indanone and tetralone, is very similar to that of acetomesitylene (Fig. 3).

If the carbonyl group of an aryl ketone is sufficiently shackled by its neighbors to be unable to react in the 1,2-manner, the ketone may react as if the electron deficit of the carbonyl carbon atom has been transferred to the ring, that is, the benzene ring may behave as if it has

double bonds. This type of reaction was called by its discoverers Kohler and Nygaard "unlocking the benzene ring." Deliberate blocking of the carbonyl group with radicals of the mesityl type made it possible to study the unlocking reaction; o-alkylation or o-arylation of the benzene ring was accomplished. Phenylation of mesityl phenyl ketone, for example, occurred to the extent of 18% (M. D. Armstrong, S. B. Speck).

At this point new life was put into the study by the discovery that certain Grignard reagents, notably benzyl- and t-butylmagnesium chloride, are very much more effective in this type of attack than are reagents such as methyl, ethyl, and phenyl. This difference in reactivity was pointed out by Kharasch and Weinhouse, and later led to the discovery that Grignard reagents can be added to fulvenes (H. A. DeWald). The more powerful reagents differed from the others also in showing a preference for the p-position. sec-Butylmagnesium bromide, for instance, converted duryl phenyl ketone (Fig. 4) to p-sec-butylphenyl duryl ketone in a yield of 63% (R. Tull). The addition products are, of course, dihydrobenzenoid compounds, and can be aromatized by admitting air to the reaction vessel before the mixture is worked up.

An early example of the use of steric hindrance to interrupt a reaction sequence is the demonstration that the haloform reaction (Fig. 5) is stopped at the trihalomethyl ketone stage. Acetomesitylene and sodium hypobromite, for

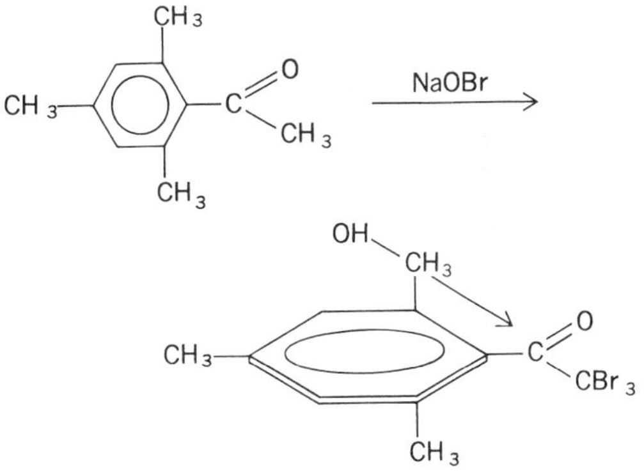

Fig. 5. Haloform reaction.

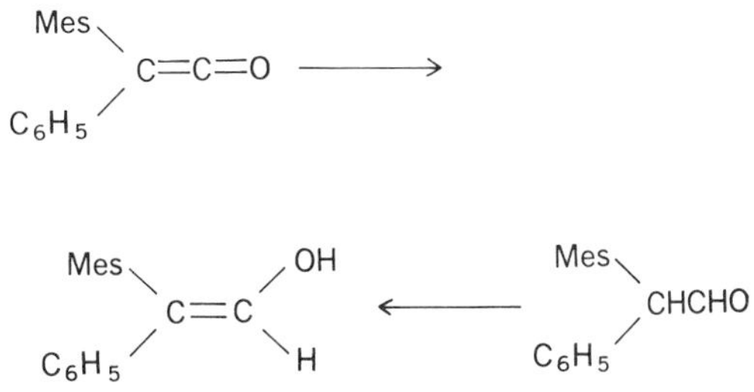

Fig. 6. Enol formation.

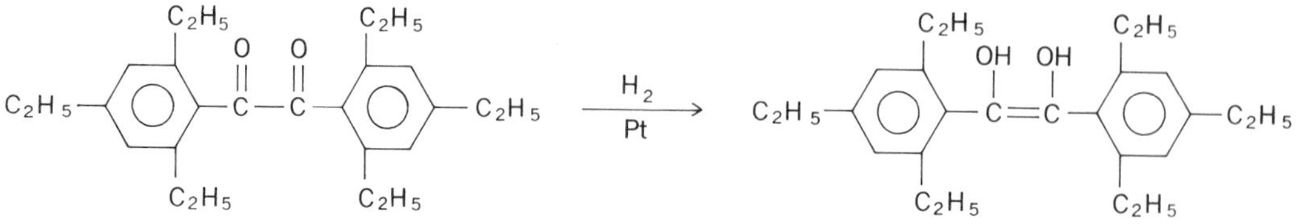

Fig. 7. Hydrogenation of benzils.

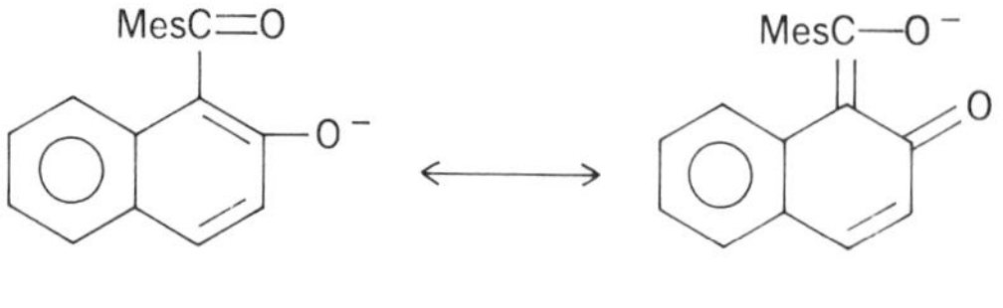

Fig. 8 Resonance structures I and II.

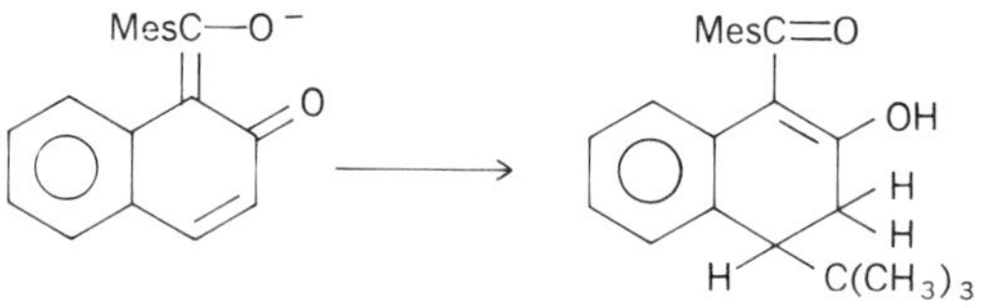

Fig. 9. 1,4-Addition reaction.

example, give mesityl tribromomethyl ketone in a yield of 89% (J. T. Walker). The base responsible for the cleavage is prevented by the *ortho*-methyl radicals from reaching the carbonyl group.

Another example of the interruption of a reaction sequence was encountered in the synthesis of aldehydes and ketones by way of the corresponding enols (Fig. 6). If the enol is sufficiently engulfed by the surrounding parts, it fails to ketonize. An example is the vinyl alcohol obtained by reduction of mesitylphenylketene. The reduction is accomplished with cyclohexylmagnesium chloride in 80% yield (R. E. Foster, W. J. Shenk, Jr., E. W. Maynert). The corre-

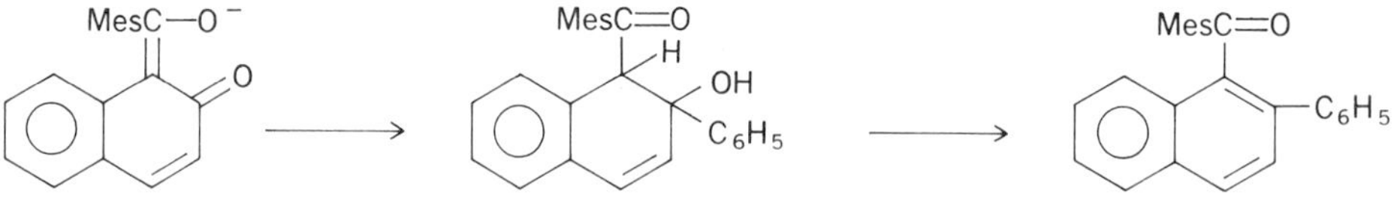

Grignard reagents on hindered *o*- and *p*-hydroxy ketones show still another way in which steric hindrance diverts a reaction from its normal course. The results obtained with them can be interpreted by assuming that they react as keto enolates. It is as if the imprisoned ketone group eludes its pickets and emerges at an unblocked position on the ring, now a cyclohexadienone. That is, the molecule behaves as if the $-O^-$ and $>C=O$ functions have been interchanged. If it is assumed that the anion is free, its behavior, in the case of 2-hydroxy-1-mesitoylnaphthalene, for example, would then be that corresponding to resonance structure II rather than resonance structure I (Fig. 8).

The reaction of *t*-butylmagnesium chloride may be formulated as a 1,4-addition (Fig. 9); the yield of dihydro compound amounts to 91% (F. T. Fang).

Reaction with the phenyl reagent would appear to be 1,2-addition (Fig. 10) followed in the work-up procedure by loss of the elements of water.

Fuson received his A.B. from the University of Montana in 1920, his M.A. from the University of California at Berkeley in 1921, and his Ph.D. from the University of Minnesota in 1924. He was a National Research fellow for 2 years, and an instructor for 1 year at Harvard University. He became a professor of chemistry at the University of Illinois in 1927. He was elected to the National Academy of Sciences in 1944, and received the Nichols Medal in 1953.

Fig. 10. 1,2-Addition reaction.

sponding aldehyde rearranged to the enol when heated at 150°C or when treated with alkali (T. L. Tan).

Hydrogenation of benzils (Fig. 7) to form the corresponding benzoins is halted at the enediol stage by hindrance. An example is the enedoil from hexaethylbenzil (J. W. Corse, C. H. McKeever).

The keto phenolates produced by the action of

Besides some 300 papers in chemical journals, Fuson wrote *Reactions of Organic Compounds* (1962) and *Systematic Identification of Organic Compounds*, with R. L. Shriner and D. Y. Curtin (5th ed. 1964).

For background information *see* CARBON; GRIGNARD REACTION; ORGANIC REACTION MECHANISM in the McGraw-Hill Encyclopedia of Science and Technology.   □

★ GALAMBOS, Robert

American psychologist
Born Apr. 20, 1914, Lorain, Ohio, U.S.A.

G ALAMBOS, A physiological psychologist, was concerned with brain research. His experiments with bats, performed in collaboration with D. R. Griffin, yielded his doctoral thesis (1941), which described the essential mechanisms these animals use to avoid obstacles as they fly about in total darkness. An Italian priest named Spallanzani knew in 1794 that normal bats with ears plugged fly awkwardly and smash into obstacles, and later experimenters suspected that sound emission and reception were the crucial factors in the skillful obstacle avoidance of bats. However, Galambos and Griffin were the first to record the ultrasonic cries that flying bats emit; they clearly demonstrated the correlation between successful avoidance and emission of these cries, described the special features of bat ears that enable them to hear sounds that humans cannot, and on the basis of these facts announced the theory that bats use the echoes of their high-pitched cries to locate and avoid the objects before them.

Galambos next studied the behavior of single nerve cells in the cat brain (1942). Using the then new microelectrodes which permit electrical recordings from one brain cell at a time and working with Hallowell Davis, he systematically explored the cochlear nucleus, the first auditory relay nucleus in the cat brain. There are about 80,000 nerve cells there, any one of which is likely to be found discharging itself a dozen or so times per second, even though no sound strikes the cat's ear. In response to sounds, such a cell reacts to some—not all—tones a cat can hear: One cell may respond to the low notes and another the high notes of the piano, and so which cells out of the available thousands respond seems to determine what

pitch will be experienced. The stimulated cell reacts, furthermore, by discharging either faster or slower than its base-line rate, so that each heard tone creates a unique pattern of excited and inhibited cells. These patterns, finally, are characteristically different for the same tone when soft as opposed to loud; thus the excitation-inhibition pattern is fundamental for the loudness experience as well. This same basic plan of nerve action was subsequently shown by other experimenters to hold for the cells involved in the sensations of touch and vision.

Besides pitch and loudness, human auditory experience includes the ability to locate where a sound comes from when heard with both ears (binaural localization). It is easy to show that a bat or a man with one ear plugged localizes sounds poorly; hence, the separate messages originating in the two ears must mix and interact in the brain to make normal localization possible. Using the microelectrode technique once more, Galambos and his collaborators uncovered the place where this mixing first occurs in the cat brain (the accessory nucleus of the superior olive) and showed that when sounds to the two ears are given first simultaneously, then separated by as little as 100 microseconds in time, nerve cells there detect the difference (1958).

Auditory attention and learning are two further problems Galambos studied in the laboratory. Sounds tend to be unheard unless one pays attention; this means the brain can admit sounds selectively, analyzing some and not others at a given moment or allowing a particular sound to enter at one time and not at another. Galambos studied a system of nerve fibers known to leave the brain and terminate in the ear and showed that activity in these feedback fibers makes the ear less sensitive to sounds (1956). However, he was not able to demonstrate convincingly that these fibers act during the listening process. As for learning, the simple fact that one recalls at will the notes of a favorite song illustrates the remarkable capacity of brains to store a series of auditory signals and retrieve them later as memories. Galambos investigated this biological equivalent of the tape recorder by examining the brain waves of cats and monkeys before and after they learned various tasks for which sounds were important cues. For instance, he and his collaborators placed wires deep in the brains by surgery, kept the animals in the laboratory as pets for months, and recorded their brain waves in response to click sounds day after day. Brain waves turned out to be large when an animal heard a sound for the first time, progressively smaller with its monotonous repetition hour after hour, and large once more when the experimenter fed the animal at the time of the clicks, in the way Pavlov rang a bell to signal the arrival of food for dogs. In these simple learning experiments sound-evoked activity appeared in regions of the brain previously thought to be uninvolved in the hearing process (1961).

Galambos pointed out in a theoretical paper (1962) the need for more information on the activities of glial cells in the brain. These cells, which outnumber by 10 to 1 the nerve cells in the human-type brain, may help make brains function as they do by collaborating and cooperating with the nerve cells in ways still unknown. Galambos's later research (1967) included attempts to prepare an antibody specific for glial cells with the ultimate aim of changing brain function by injecting such antibody into behaving animals.

Galambos attended Oberlin College (A.B., 1935; M.A., 1936); he took graduate degrees at Harvard (Ph.D., 1941) and the University of Rochester (M.D., 1947). After teaching anatomy briefly at the Emory University School of Medicine in 1946, he worked with S. S. Stevens at the Harvard Psychoacoustic Laboratory until joining the Walter Reed Army Institute of Research in Washington, D.C., in 1951. In 1962 he became Eugene Higgins Professor of Psychology and Physiology at Yale University. He was elected to the American Academy of Arts and Sciences in 1958 and to the National Academy of Sciences in 1961.

Galambos wrote *Nerves and Muscles* (paper, 1962) in the "Science Study Series" for high school students.

For background information *see* HEARING; NERVOUS SYSTEM DISORDERS; PHONORECEPTION in the McGraw-Hill Encyclopedia of Science and Technology.   □

★ GAUDIN, Antoine Marc

American mineral engineer
Born Aug. 8, 1900, Smyrna, Turkey

WHEN GAUDIN began his researches in the field of mineral engineering, it was not even called by any engineering name. He gave the field scientific cohesion by insisting on the relationship that must exist between the microscopic properties of minerals and their macroscopic properties (in which man is practically interested).

His work, which spanned almost a half century, elucidated the flotation process of mineral separation to the point that this once obscure method of mineral concentration is now clearly the major process in mineral engineering. Gaudin showed that flotation depends on the crystal structure of the surface of every mineral particle. This surficial crystal structure, in turn, depends upon the ability of the substratum to adsorb selectively upon itself in the proper orientation one or another of the ions in the surrounding bath.

When the mineral surface adsorbs hydrocarbon-bearing ions, with their hydrocarbon ends away from the mineral, it becomes indifferent to the fluid medium surrounding it, instead of being highly water-avid as usual. The result is that the surface sticks to the gas of an air bubble, with the consequent flotation of the particle attached to air. Conversely, if the mineral surface adsorbs instead a non-hydrocarbon-bearing ion or a hydrocarbon-bearing ion which also has several water-avid spots, it becomes "glued" to the water and sinks instead of floating. Combination of these effects on different minerals associated in an ore results in mineral A floating and mineral B sinking, which is the practical result sought by the technician. Improvements in the separation can result from changes in the proportions of reagents used, from the place and the sequence of their addition, from varying the fineness of grinding of the ore, from variations in the proportions of solids to water in the ore pulp, from the design of the flotation cell, and from the extent of the aeration used. All of these factors give wide scope to the technical skill of the operator.

Gaudin spent much effort in the detailed study of ores under the microscope. Many an ore contains 10 to 20 different mineral species, the nature of which must be known, as well as the structural and textural relationship between these minerals. Some ores are so coarsely associated that fracture to 5 mm permits very considerable liberation of the minerals from mutual attachment. In other cases even fracture to 5

microns (a size a thousand times smaller in diameter and a billion times smaller in volume) will not do. These facts may all be revealed by patient quantitative study under the microscope, petrographic or metallurgical, as the case requires. Gaudin's interest in these aspects of ores led to development of a technique called selective iridescent filming, which permits easy differentiation between solids that normally appear similar. It also led to a study of the dry synthesis of sulfide minerals, as a step to their understanding.

Among other problems to which Gaudin turned his attention was the size distribution of fragments produced by breaking, crushing, or grinding. Rather than accept a product as having a fragmentation resulting capriciously from the crushing tool used, he saw fragmentation as the result of a statistical process following laws worthy of being worked out. He and his former student Reinhardt Schuhmann, Jr., developed a widely used equation to describe the size distribution of a fragmented homogeneous rock. This work was further developed jointly with other students, particularly with Risto Hukki and with Thomas P. Meloy.

Gaudin also worked extensively with uranium ores, for which he and his associates developed the leading extraction process. This requires dissolving the uranium with a solvent (for example, aqueous sulfuric acid in oxidizing environment) from the residue and purifying the liquor by use of ion-exchange resins or by use of solvent extraction. This purification by ion-exchange resins uses the resins to remove selectively the uranium from solution until the liquor becomes barren, at which time it is discarded. The resin, when fully loaded with uranium, is contacted with an eluting liquor that reverses the process, taking the purified uranium in solution, from which it can be precipitated by changing the pH (for example, by adding ammonia). The process can be automated entirely. Where purification is by solvent extraction, the solvent is in the form of droplets, which otherwise behave exactly as an ion-exchanging resin.

For this development Gaudin received from his colleagues in the mining and metallurgical fields the Robert H. Richards Award in 1957. He was also the Sir Julius Wernher Memorial Lecturer of the Institution of Mining and Metallurgy of London, for which occasion he was given the honor of using Faraday's lecture room at the Royal Society.

Gaudin took a B.S. at the University of Paris in 1917 and an E.M. at Columbia University in 1921. In 1924–26 he was a lecturer in mining at Columbia, in 1926–29 an associate professor at the University of Utah, and in 1929–39 a research professor at the Montana School of Mines, which granted him the Sc.D. in 1941. He became Richards Professor at the Massachusetts Institute of Technology in 1939. A founding member of the National Academy of Engineering, he was elected to the American Academy of Arts and Sciences in 1956.

Gaudin wrote *Flotation* (2d ed. 1957) and *Principles of Mineral Dressing* (1939), as well as about 150 papers, some with coauthors.

For background information *see* FLOTATION; METAL AND MINERAL PROCESSING; MINERALOGY in the McGraw-Hill Encyclopedia of Science and Technology.   □

★ GEIJER, Per

Swedish geologist
Born May 7, 1886, Stockholm, Sweden

ORE DEPOSITS in two provinces of the Precambrian in Sweden and the general geology of these provinces were the chief subjects of Geijer's studies. His first published work (1910) was a monograph on the important magnetite deposits and the associated volcanics at Kiruna in northernmost Sweden. Two hypotheses, both implying a close genetic connection with the volcanics, had been proposed to explain the origin of these ores. One hypothesis proposed that they were formed magmatically, the other that they were the products of fumarolic action at the surface—what was later called an exhalative sedimentary process. The chief argument for the latter interpretation was the fact that the porphyry forming the footwall of the ore bodies contains, as vesicle fillings and the like, mineral aggregates closely related to the ores. Geijer's results confirmed the magmatic hypothesis, mainly through the study of details in the ores. The vesicle fillings of the porphyry were shown to be local concentrations in the solidifying rock and not the products of later fumarolic activity. However, the noted similarities led Geijer to the conclusion that volatiles had played an important role in the separation of the ores from the parent magma, and also in the determination of their further development.

Geijer continued to work on these problems with detailed studies on other deposits in the same province and with visits to genetically related deposits in Missouri (1913) and in Chile

(1928), compiling observations that brought out the significant features of the type. The magmatic interpretation is supported by the much later discovery of similar ores as lava flows in northern Chile (C. F. Park, Jr., and others) and the role of volatiles in the differentiation process by experimental work (R. Fischer).

A widespread but generally lean copper mineralization in the same part of Sweden was shown by Geijer to be associated with a regional scapolitization, which in turn was found to be connected with the intrusion of the Lina granite. From characteristic textural features of this granite, which forms a number of batholiths and stocks in northernmost Sweden and northern Finland, Geijer concluded that all these granite bodies stem from one vast reservoir of homogeneous magma, which in the depth underlay the region.

In the ore-bearing region of central Sweden, Geijer began (1914) the study of the renowned copper and pyrite mine at Falun and related deposits. He found that the metasomatic process by which these ores were formed had also greatly affected the siliceous volcanics around the ore bodies, and that this latter process implied the formation of such magnesian minerals as cordierite and anthophyllite. Independently and earlier, P. Eskola, from his studies on the genetically analogous Orijärvi deposit in Finland, had reached the same conclusion, which he presented in an excellent monograph; the mineralization was regarded as related to a granite intrusion. Geijer evolved this concept further and found that the sulfide mineralization in the whole region had occurred during the Svecofennian orogeny and the concomitant intrusion of the earliest group of Svecofennian granites. He pointed out (1916), from comparisons with younger mountain chains, that the emplacement of such granites was largely controlled by the fold structures of the invaded supracrustal rocks, and he also concluded that it took place while folding was still proceeding—what later was called synkinematic intrusion. He followed up these studies in a series of later works, up to 1965. The amount of magnesium introduced metasomatically was found to be enormous in some districts, as at Riddarhyttan, and comparable to what was recorded in other countries as accompanying the introduction of sulfides of lead and zinc in carbonate rocks. Fractionation of the ore-forming solutions was also studied, illustrated by certain characteristic combinations of sulfides of the various metals and the alteration products in the wall rock, and by local, pyrometasomatically formed concentrations of cerium minerals belonging to the same epoch of mineralization. The regional distribution of the latter, rare minerals was regarded by Geijer as an indication that the mineralizing

solutions might largely have risen in advance of the granite invasion.

Geijer also investigated many districts with iron ores in the same region, such as Norberg, Stråssa, Stripa, and others. Among pyrometasomatic deposits, formed during the same epoch as the sulfide ores, he found several occurrences with ludwigite and other borates, always accompanied by a pronouncedly magnesian skarn. His studies of quartz-banded ores contributed to the understanding of this much discussed type. Some arguments for an interpretation through an exhalative sedimentary process as far as local conditions were concerned were the regular association with rhyolitic volcanics, and the rare but significant occurrence of nonsulfidic lead in a manganiferous variety. Jointly with N. H. Magnusson, Geijer produced (1944) a survey of all iron ore deposits of the region and their geological setting.

Geijer entered Uppsala University in 1904 and received his doctorate there in 1910. He was dozent, Stockholm University, in 1910–25; geologist, Geological Survey of Sweden, during 1914–31; professor of mineralogy and geology, Royal Technological Institute, Stockholm, in 1931–41; and director, Geological Survey of Sweden, in 1942–51. After retirement he did research work in the Mineralogical Department, Swedish Museum of Natural History, in Stockholm. Geijer was elected to the Royal Swedish Academy of Science in 1939 and, as a foreign associate, to the U.S. National Academy of Sciences in 1958. The mineral perite, $PbBiO_2Cl$, was named after him.

For background information see MAGMA; MINERALOGY; OROGENY; PETROLOGY in the McGraw-Hill Encyclopedia of Science and Technology.   □

★ GELFAND, Izrail Moiseevich

Soviet mathematician
Born Aug. 20, 1913, Krasnye Okny, Russia

GELFAND'S MAIN work deals with functional analysis and has exerted a substantial influence in shaping many basic trends of scientific studies. He developed the theory of commutative normed rings. A normed ring is a set for whose elements the operations of addition, multiplication by a number, and multiplication have been determined, while for each element y a definite norm has been determined—the nonnegative number $||y||$. For example, the set $C(a,b)$ of all continuous functions $f(x)$ over the segment $[a,b]$ is a normed ring. The operations in this set are determined as usual operations on functions, while the norm is determined by the formula in Eq. (1).

The concept of the maximal ideal, which was introduced by Gelfand, is central in this theory. His approach cast new light on many sections of the classical analysis. Thus developed the well-

$$||f|| = \max_{a \leqslant x \leqslant b} |f(x)| \qquad (1)$$

known theorem by Norbert Wiener: "If a function $f(x)$ decomposes into an absolutely convergent Fourier series and nowhere vanished, then $1/f(x)$ has the same properties" is a simple consequence of the developed general theory. The ring operations and the norm exist also in the set of all continuous linear operators in the Hilbert space. Besides that, there is in this set an involution—transition from the operator A to the operator A^*, which is conjugate with it. In 1942 Gelfand and Naimark proved that any noncommutative normed ring with an involution can be realized as a ring of linear operators in the Hilbert space. This work was continued by Gelfand and Naimark in subsequent investigations, which dealt with the theory of infinite-dimensional representations of continuous groups.

The representation T of group G is a mapping of its elements $g \longrightarrow T(g)$ in a ring of linear operators, which satisfies the relationship in Eq. (2).

$$T(g_1 g_2) = T(g_1) \, T(g_2) \qquad (2)$$

This relationship is a far-ranging generalization of the functional equation shown as Eq. (3).

$$\varphi(x + y) = \varphi(x) \, \varphi(y) \qquad (3)$$

The equation is satisfied by the exponential function $\varphi(x) = \exp(ax)$. The problems of harmonic analysis on groups are closely related with the theory of representations. An analog of the decomposition of the functions into Fourier series and integrals is the decomposition of the functions on the group into series and integrals by functions which belong to irreducible representations.

The theory of representations for compact groups (an example of which can be served by the group of rotations of a three-dimensional space) was studied in detail by Shur, Frobenius, E. Cartan, H. Weyl, and others. In this case, all the irreducible representations of the group are finite-dimensional. For noncompact groups, for example, for a group of Lorentz transformations of the four-dimensional space-time, the situation seemed incomparably more complicated, and even the very statements of the basic problems were not clear.

In a series of works by Gelfand and co-workers, studies were made of infinite-dimensional representations of classical groups, and harmonic analysis on noncompact groups. The representations of the groups give a mathematical apparatus which makes it possible to utilize the symmetry of the object during its mathematical study (for example, to utilize in the study of the Schrödinger equation the symmetry of the Coulomb field of the atomic nucleus or the symmetry of the atom with respect to the rearrangements of the electrons and so on). These works by Gelfand and co-workers are used widely by physicists in attempts to develop a theory of the symmetry of elementary particles.

The theory of generalized functions occupies a large place in the studies by Gelfand. His interest was greatly stimulated by his previous works on the theory of infinite-dimensional representations, where these were essentially utilized in an implicit form. Following the appearance of the works by L. Schwarz, Gelfand and his students and colleagues performed the universal development of an apparatus of generalized functions after developing, in particular, a harmonic analysis of rapidly growing function; studied the applications to the theory of differential equations; and laid the geometric bases of integral transformations.

The work by Gelfand and his school has made a great contribution to the theory of the solution of the inverse Sturm-Liouville problem, which has diverse physical applications. A number of works by Gelfand deal with computational mathematics, in which he proposed a simple, stable algorithm for the numerical solution of the boundary-value problems for differential equations.

In recent years Gelfand became also interested in problems of biology and physiology, in particular in the principles of the organization of systems which have an appropriate behavior. Gelfand and his student Tsetlin proposed to utilize in neurophysiology a model of nonindividual control of complex systems which consist of a large number of elements. Such control can be set off against the method of "rigid" control, in which a higher-located center orders accurately what each element of the system has to do. As a basis for these neurophysiological models, Gelfand and Tsetlin used the work by the latter on games of automatic devices. In nonindividualized control a change in the work of the collective takes place not as a result of a new order from the center as to what each single element has to do, but only as a result of a change by the center of their interreaction. The representations developed on the basis of this language led to concrete and interesting results in the study of motions by man and animals.

Most of Gelfand's studies were performed jointly with students and colleagues, for whom such experience is an invaluable school of scientific activity. Gelfand's scientific school, the organizational center of which is his seminar at Moscow University, counts scores of well-known scientists, many of whom have come to the seminar as beginning students. In the stimulation of their studies, as well as of the work of many other scientists, Gelfand's notions have played a great role: his statements of the problems, his discussion of the results obtained, and so forth.

With an incomplete secondary education, Gelfand became a fellow of Moscow University in 1932. In 1940 he received the degree of doctor of physicomathematical sciences for his study of the theory of normed rings. Beginning in 1932, he taught in Moscow University (professor since 1943); from 1939 he worked in the V. A. Steklov Mathematical Institute of the Academy of Sciences of the U.S.S.R., and from 1966 in the Institute of Applied Mathematics of the Academy. He became an associate member of the Academy of Sciences of the U.S.S.R. in 1953, an honorary member of the American Academy of Arts and Sciences in 1964, and an honorary member of the London Mathematical Society.

For background information see RING THEORY; SET THEORY in the McGraw-Hill Encyclopedia of Science and Technology.   □

★ GERARD, Ralph Waldo

American physiologist
Born Oct. 7, 1900, Chicago, Ill., U.S.A.

A LONG career in analysis and research carried Gerard from chemistry, through electrophysiology and medicine, to the general examination of the brain and behavior, and ultimately to computer use in education.

Gerard's first contribution to neural science was the demonstration—partly with A. V. Hill and partly with O. Meyerhoff, who had made comparable studies on far more energetic muscle cells—of a minute increase in metabolism of nerve cells when carrying messages. Both the heat produced and oxygen used were so small

that new instruments were required to measure them, yet this work proved nerve activity to be a normal kind of body activity. Indeed, although the nerve impulse passes in a thousandth of a second, the chemical and physical changes that this tiny "explosion" sets up continue for minutes or hours and involve changes in ions and compounds, in electric circuits and flow, and in the ability of nerve to respond further.

To relate metabolism with activity, fine electrical measures were needed, and a capillary electrode was developed that could be inserted into single muscle, nerve, and other cells for more precise analysis. This technique was used by J. C. Eccles and A. L. Hodgkin in the studies for which they shared a Nobel Prize in 1963.

In further neural studies Gerard poked electrodes into the brain and thus revealed that incoming visual, auditory, tactile, and other sensory messages reach many regions of the cerebrum and cerebellum previously thought to have no such inputs. This neural activity also requires metabolic energy and is associated with an increased blood supply to the active regions. A small brain, like the frog's, can receive enough oxygen by diffusion and can continue vigorous activity—even show electrical convulsions under drug treatment—when removed from the body. The frog brain also carries waves of activity across a complete section by a newly recognized type of electrical mechanism.

The relation of nerve cell to nerve fiber also interested Gerard, since the fiber, though receiving its own nourishment, degenerates when separated from the cell. Gerard developed evidence that enzymes move from the cell down the fiber; this movement was later shown by P. A. Weiss to involve flow of the whole protoplasm. Such flow is related to the regeneration of a new

fiber in peripheral nerve. Regeneration was long believed impossible in the central nervous system, but Gerard and others proved this important capacity to be present under favorable conditions.

Such studies stimulated Gerard's interest in normal and disturbed brain functioning. He related learning and remembering to physiological and biochemical changes in appropriate brain regions and showed them to require considerable time to become "fixed"—a time that could be increased or shortened by various means, including drugs. On the abnormal side, he conducted an extensive study of the biological and psychosocial attributes of hospitalized schizophrenic and other patients; this work revealed a number of distinguishable subtypes of this psychosis.

Behavior and learning studies led Gerard to give more formal attention to education and to the application of modern computer and related technology in this field. This endeavor capped his lifelong interest in teaching science to laymen as well as to university students, and he early experimented with the laboratory research project method and with the animation of theoretical models in instructional films.

Given much attention by an intellectual father, Gerard entered the University of Chicago at 14, receiving there the B.S. in 1919, Ph.D. in 1921, and M.D. in 1924. He served as professor of physiology at two medical schools along the way. After an internship in Los Angeles and study in London and Berlin, Gerard was a professor of physiology at Chicago for about 25 years. He then was professor and director of laboratories in the Neuropsychiatric Institute, University of Illinois, and in the department of psychiatry and the Mental Health Research Institute, University of Michigan. He became dean of the graduate division and director of special studies at the University of California, Irvine, in 1966. Recipient of several honorary degrees, in 1955 Gerard was elected to both the American Academy of Arts and Sciences and the National Academy of Sciences.

Gerard wrote *Unresting Cells* (1940; 2d ed. 1949; paper 1961); *Body Functions* (1941); *Mirror to Physiology* (1958). He edited *Methods in Medical Research* (Vol. 3, 1950); *Food for Life* (1952; paper 1965); *Concepts of Biology*, with Russell B. Stevens (1958); *Psychopharmacology: Problems in Evaluation*, with J. O. Cole (1959); *Information Processing in the Nervous System*, with Jan W. Duyff (1963); and *Computers and Education*, with J. G. Miller (1967).

For background information *see* COMPUTER; MEMORY; NERVOUS SYSTEM in the McGraw-Hill Encyclopedia of Science and Technology.   ☐

GIBBS, William Francis

American naval architect and marine engineer

Gibbs died on Sept. 6, 1967, in New York, N.Y., U.S.A. See *McGraw-Hill Modern Men of Science*, Volume I.

★ GINZTON, Edward Leonard

American electronics engineer
Born Dec. 27, 1915, Ekaterinoslawsk, Russia

A MAJOR step in making the generation of microwaves practical was the invention at Stanford University in 1937 of the klystron tube. This invention, by Russell and Sigurd Varian, demonstrated that a stream of electrons could be made to generate radio-frequency currents by the principle of velocity modulation of the electron stream. It was soon evident that this invention was destined to play an important role in making practical utilization of a vast new portion of the radio-frequency spectrum. Before much could be done, however, the characteristics of the klystron had to be understood and measured. Yet in this new region of the electromagnetic spectrum, methods of measurement had not yet been developed and such commonplace and important quantities as wavelength, frequency, power, and impedance could only be guessed with the aid of the most rudimentary experiments.

While still a graduate student at Stanford, Ginzton was asked by the Varian brothers and Professor William W. Hansen to work in the physics department to help explore the characteristics of the klystron and the range of its usefulness, as well as to develop methods of microwave measurements. While a member of the now famous Stanford team of Russell and Sigurd Varian, David Webster, William Hansen, and John Woodyard, Ginzton demonstrated the usefulness of the klystron as an amplifier and superheterodyne receiver and in master oscillator power amplifier chains. He also helped develop methods of measuring power, wavelength, and other significant parameters.

World War II made the microwave field important overnight. The Stanford group transferred to the larger laboratories of the Sperry Gyroscope Company in New York, where their work was continued on an expanded and accelerated scale. Study of military applications for the klystron resulted in the development of such important applications as Doppler radar, pulsed radar, and microwave communications. Twice during the war Ginzton traveled to Great Britain to exchange information with members of British research establishments concerning the progress of the klystron research and related system development. While visiting the EMI Laboratories in 1944, he found that British research demonstrated the usefulness of the klystron for pulsed applications and that peak power of several kilowatts could be obtained. He realized immediately that still larger power could be obtained from the klystron and that only the effects of relativity would limit the voltage at which a klystron could work. This realization stimulated his ideas about the possible usefulness of the klystron at very high power and caused him to think about various new approaches to research in the microwave field.

After the war, Ginzton returned to Stanford as a member of the physics faculty and continued his work in the microwave field. He chose three closely related avenues of research: continuation of the development of methods of microwave measurements; development of the klystron with the intent of obtaining millions of watts of pulsed power; and application of such klystrons to the development of large electron accelerators for use in high-energy physics research.

In the first of these, Ginzton continued to work for many years, gradually attaining a satisfactory understanding of the various classes of physical phenomena basic to a satisfactory system of microwave measurements. In parallel with his research in this field, he taught graduate courses on microwave measurements, and the notes from his lectures eventually led to publication of a textbook on the subject.

The second avenue of research led to what is probably the outstanding accomplishment in Ginzton's career, the demonstration of the high-power klystron. Working closely with his colleague Marvin Chodorow, Ginzton decided that the idea of generating very high power could best be demonstrated by making one large extrapolation from the work of the British instead of the more conventional step-by-step increase of knowledge and experience. Ginzton and Chodorow decided to test the feasibility of building a klystron for the generation of pulse power at the level of about 25,000,000 watts at a wavelength of 10 cm. In this original investigation in the field of such unusually high power, many new and basic problems were encountered which had to be solved before a successful design could be established. Among the most important of these were: (1) the basic klystron theory had to be extended into the range of relativistic velocities; (2) the theory of mag-

netic focusing of the cylindrical electron beams had to be developed; (3) the practicality of obtaining emission from oxide cathodes at voltages approximating 500,000 volts had to be explored experimentally; (4) the voltage breakdown phenomena at microwave frequencies had to be understood; (5) methods of generating short pulses at about 100,000 volts and 1000 amp had to be developed, together with requisite gap switches; (6) pulse transformers, stepping up voltages to 500,000-volt range, had to be developed. As it turned out, none of these problems proved to be very difficult, and the first tube designed on paper operated successfully in 1949 after 2 years of work. For his work in this field, Ginzton was awarded the Morris Liebmann Memorial Prize in 1957.

In parallel with the klystron development, William Hansen developed the theory of the linear electron accelerator and demonstrated its validity on a small-scale machine. Hansen then proposed the construction of a billion-volt accelerator and sketched the design for a 220-ft machine to be powered by 22 of the high-power klystrons mentioned above. Unfortunately, Hansen died before this project was barely started and it became Ginzton's responsibility to complete this work. He supervised a small staff of co-workers and graduate students and the machine was completed in 1952. Perhaps the greatest demonstration of the usefulness of this accelerator was its use by Robert Hofstadter in measuring the size and charge distribution of a number of nuclei—the work for which Hofstadter was awarded the 1961 Nobel Prize in physics.

With the completion of the billion-volt machine, it was clear that smaller machines of the same variety could be used to generate x-rays and electrons for cancer therapy. With Henry Kaplan, Ginzton designed and supervised the construction of a 6,000,000-volt linear electron accelerator. This experimental machine was installed at the Stanford University department of radiology in 1955 and was used in pioneering research in the treatment of cancer. This work proved significant enough so that many such machines are now to be found in several parts of the world for routine treatment of cancer.

The success of the billion-volt linear accelerator showed that the usefulness of high-energy electrons for research on elementary particles would be greater at even higher energies, and that there were no fundamental reasons to limit the construction of a much larger machine. With Ginzton as the director of a new project, a group of Stanford physicists and engineers began to study the practicality, usefulness, and costs of a machine several miles in length. These studies resulted in a report entitled "Project M," which was submitted to the United States government in 1957. It described a 2-mile accelerator which would be capable of generating up to 50 billion volts and which could provide enormous intensities for research in high energy physics. Under Ginzton's supervision, the preliminary design of this machine was finished and the project received Congressional approval in 1961. The 2-mile accelerator was completed in 1966 and is being used for research as the highest energy electron accelerator in the world.

In 1948 Ginzton became deeply involved with the formation of Varian Associates. Just prior to the Congressional approval of the 2-mile accelerator, he was asked to become its board chairman. With approval of the project assured, Ginzton chose to continue with his work at Varian and left the Stanford project. This company is the principal manufacturer of high-power klystrons, linear electron accelerators, nuclear magnetic resonance spectrometers, electronic vacuum pumps, and other devices which not too long ago were subjects of theoretical and experimental research in the physics laboratories of Stanford and other universities.

Ginzton received his B.S. (1936) and M.S. (1937) at the University of California at Berkeley. He obtained his E.E. (1938) and Ph.D. (1940) under F. E. Terman at Stanford. He returned to Stanford after the war to join its faculty, remaining there as professor of applied physics and electrical engineering until 1961. He was also the director of the Microwave Laboratory from 1949 to 1961. One of the founders of Varian Associates, in 1959 he was appointed chairman of the board and in 1964 president. He was elected to the National Academy of Engineering in 1965 and to the National Academy of Sciences in 1966.

Ginzton wrote *Microwave Measurements* (1957) and numerous articles in technical journals. Approximately 40 patents were issued in his name for inventions in the fields of microwave measurements, microwave tubes, and other electronic devices.

For background information *see* KLYSTRON; MICROWAVE TUBE; PARTICLE ACCELERATOR in the McGraw-Hill Encyclopedia of Science and Technology. ☐

★ GODWIN, Harry

British botanist and Quaternary scientist
Born May 9, 1901, Rotherham, England

G ODWIN EXPLORED those scientific problems that call for knowledge of the natural environment and the disciplines both of botany and geology. In the 1920s he began investigations into the successional changes in fen vegetation and the controlling mechanisms of the hydro-

sere. From this study Godwin came to realize the anthropogenic character of many types of fen vegetation and proposed the concept of "deflected succession," which proved applicable to a wide range of ecological situations. Subsequently he extended his studies to raised mosses and the natural evolution of topogenous mire and fen to ombrogenous *Sphagnum* bog. By the time that he and his wife began to investigate British vegetational history by pollen analysis, they could draw upon a substantial knowledge of the ecological situations recorded in peat and lake deposits, particularly in the East Anglian Fenland basin, where they first concentrated their efforts and where their research was reinforced by the work of archeologists, geologists, geographers, and biologists of the Fenland Research Committee active in the 1930s. The coordination of the results of all these disciplines was assured by pollen analysis and the identification of macroscopic plant fossils. The stratigraphy and postglacial history of the Fenland basin were made clear as a result, especially as they reflected the intermittent progress and relaxation of marine invasion. At the classic site, Shippea Hill, no less than four archeological horizons were correlated with the stratigraphic sequence.

Meanwhile, the possibilities and limitations of pollen analysis came under review, and as analyses were extended over a wider area, a tentative zonation scheme was proposed for England and Wales, keyed to the Irish and Scandinavian systems. It proved a useful quasi-chronological basis for the division of postglacial time. From 1935 Godwin conducted investigations, parallel to those in the Fenland basin, in the derelict raised bogs of the Somerset Levels, where a profusion of archeological discoveries was co-

ordinated by means of frequent pollen diagrams and was related to a consistent stratigraphic sequence of peat types. In the course of this work many prehistoric wooden trackways were excavated and described, one series from the

Late Bronze Age and the other from the Neolithic, an attribution fully confirmed afterward by radiocarbon dating. At Star Carr in eastern Yorkshire extensive stratigraphic and pollen analytic studies of the former lake deposits provided detailed information on the hunter-fisher Mesolithic people. Star Carr proved to be the classic site for this culture in western Europe.

In the course of his studies Godwin accumulated a large index catalog to all identifications of higher plants referable to known stages of Quaternary history in Britain. This compilation also was found to provide a first factual basis for an objective history of the British flora. It became possible for the first time to dispense with the idea that the last glaciation swept the British Isles clear of flora and fauna. The history of the country from the treeless tundra of the Weichselian glaciation was traced from the tentative advances of woodland in the late-glacial period, to the blanketing by mixed oak forest that lasted through the postglacial thermal maximum, on to Neolithic and subsequent disforestation and replacement of continuous woodland by communities initiated and maintained by plant and animal husbandry.

By 1948 the University of Cambridge had established a subdepartment of Quaternary research, and many able research workers exploited diverse fields of Quaternary study under Godwin's direction. In particular, the interglacial periods proved exceedingly rewarding, and the sequence of East Anglian glaciations was substantially resolved by combined biological stratigraphic studies. Similar methods revealed at many places in the British Isles the triple stratigraphic sequence of the late-glacial Allerød oscillation, and pollen analyses, together with fruit and seed analyses, permitted a clear characterization of the vegetation and, indirectly, of the climate. Other and older Weichselian deposits were likewise described, thus providing a clear picture of vegetational conditions in southern England through the last glaciation. Meanwhile, a radiocarbon dating laboratory, established in the subdepartment in 1953, made it possible to confirm the identification of the late-glacial zones and to establish their synchroneity with the Allerød interstadial on the European mainland. The major postglacial pollen zones were also dated, as were the main horizons of the Fenland basin and Somerset Levels, the various manifestations of the Mesolithic and early Neolithic cultures in Britain, and many prehistoric structures and occupation levels of different ages. It was also possible to begin the resolution of the complex interaction of eustatic and isostatic effects upon relative changes in the level of the land and sea in the British Isles. The major restoration of water to the oceans, as the ice of the last glaciation melted, caused a world-wide rise in the sea level of 100 m or more; this was very rapid during the Boreal period (roughly 7600–5500 B.C.), effectively filling the North Sea basin and inhibiting further dry-land invasion of plants and animals from the continental mainland. It now appears that during its concluding stages, about 6000–3000 B.C., the so-called Neolithic raised beach of northern Britain was formed, as pollen anlyses had already suggested.

Godwin spent his entire academic career in the University of Cambridge, where in 1919 he entered as an open scholar of Clare College, of which he became a fellow in 1925. Successive teaching offices from 1923 onward led to the directorship of the subdepartment of Quaternary research in 1948 and the professorship of botany in 1960. He was elected to the Royal Society in 1945 and gave the Croonian Lecture in 1960. He received the Gold Medal of the Linnean Society of London in 1966.

Godwin wrote *History of the British Flora* (1956). He served as joint editor of the *New Phytologist* and of the *Journal of Ecology*.

For background information *see* GLACIAL EPOCH; PALEOBOTANY; PALYNOLOGY in the McGraw-Hill Encyclopedia of Science and Technology.   □

★ GOGUEL, Jean Marc

French geologist and geophysicist
Born Jan. 2, 1908, Paris, France

THE SON of Maurice Goguel, the historian of the origins of Christianity, Jean Goguel studied at the Ecole Polytechnique, where he received a solid mathematical and physical background, and at the School of Mines of Paris, where he was the student of Pierre Termier.

Entering the Geologic Map Service, which he never left and of which he later became director, he was assigned to map surveying in the sedimentary regions of the southern French Alps. This led him to take up all aspects of regional geology, including stratigraphy and even paleontology. These studies of regional geology subsequently extended to other parts of the French Alps and to other regions of France, enabling him to devote a small book to the geology of France. He also carried out numerous trips abroad.

In these regional studies he interested himself principally in tectonics, and he quickly realized that beyond the study of cartography and classical geometrics it was necessary to take up the mechanical study of tectonic deformations. He devoted an important memoir to this subject in 1942, and he never ceased thereafter to pursue this subject in depth. From the viewpoint of theoretical mechanics, he showed that the only schematics that can give satisfactory results are those of plasticity; the deformation does not begin to manifest itself until the stress exceeds a certain threshold level. His experiments on the deformation of rocks showed him the necessity of distinguishing different modes of evolution of rocks, all of which manifest themselves by a total deformation but obey completely different laws. Thus, the rapid deformations achieved in the laboratory are brought about by twinning, or mutual displacements of grains, while the slow deformations in nature are brought about essentially by recrystallization and diffusion.

These considerations, when applied to the genesis of mountains taken as a whole, permit a better understanding of the influence of the different natures of rocks and the role of different kinds of geologic folds. They lead, if not to a determination of the form of the folds, at least to an estimation of the total energy absorbed. When applied to the details of the deformations, they permit an interpretation of multiple particularities that provide information on the mode of deformation and the properties of different rocks. In particular, the relation between schistosity and stress was shown (with a maximum pressure perpendicular to the schistosity). Goguel recently proposed a new interpretation of the schistosity of crystallophylic rocks by means of a selection among the crystalline grains according to their orientation relative to the mechanical stress. Their solubility is in fact modified by their elastic strain and increases proportionally to the elastic energy stored per unit volume; the orientations for which this energy is minimum should be preferred. The detailed calculations based on the elastic coefficients for the principal minerals give results for their orientation that are, on the whole, in conformity with observation.

The systematic application of mechanical and physical considerations in the realm of geology led Goguel in two other directions. On the one hand, he was frequently called upon for studies of public works and construction of dams, tunnels, and so on. On the other hand, he undertook various aspects of geophysics, both prospecting (he was president of the European Association of Exploration Geophysicists) and fundamental. He devoted numerous publications—including an account of the entire subject—to gravimetry, from the scale of the prospector all the way to that of the Earth as a whole. In particular, he undertook to develop the idea of isostasy of the schematic models of geodesists and showed that it is compatible with all of the irregularities of the Earth's crust that geology suggests, including variations of elasticity or mechanical resistance.

He also devoted a great deal of attention to geothermy. In order to undertake analysis of the conditions for exploitation of geothermal energy, he analyzed the behavior of water in a heated porous terrane and specified the condition under which thermal convection can appear. He sought to interpret the temperature distributions that can result thereby and calculated the energy available in the sudden vaporization of a superheated moist terrane as a function of the porosity and temperature; the high value of this energy explains phreatic explosions.

Goguel was chief editor of the volume devoted to the Earth in the *Pleiad Encyclopedia;* this volume combined geophysics and geology. In his *Tectonics* (English transl. 1952) he sought to evolve a method of studying the deformation phenomenon of the solid Earth. He also wrote, in French, *Man in the Universe* (1947). Goguel was elected a foreign member of the American Academy of Arts and Sciences in 1958.

For background information *see* OROGENY; TECTONOPHYSICS; TERRESTRIAL GRAVITATION in the McGraw-Hill Encyclopedia of Science and Technology.   □

★ GOLDHABER, Maurice

American physicist
Born Apr. 18, 1911, Lemberg, Austria

GOLDHABER STARTED his research in nuclear physics at Cambridge University's Cavendish Laboratory, then under the direction of Ernest Rutherford. Goldhaber, collaborating with James Chadwick, discovered (1934) the nuclear photo-

electric effect, the first example being the disintegration of the deuteron by gamma rays from a radiothorium source. These gamma rays of well-known energy produce photoprotons and photoneutrons from deuterium. The energy of these particles can be measured, and thus the binding energy of the deuteron as well as the mass of the neutron can be obtained. Convincing evidence was obtained that the neutron is heavier than the proton, and it was concluded that a free neutron should be able to decay spontaneously by beta-ray activity into a proton. Decaying "elementary" particles are now known to be a very general phenomenon. With x-rays of higher energy, which became available later through the development of high-energy electron machines, all nuclei can be photodisintegrated so that copious sources of neutrons as well as of radioactive isotopes can be produced. The photodisintegration of deuterons also plays an important role in the neutron economy of those nuclear reactors where heavy water is used as a moderator.

After the discovery of slow neutrons by E. Fermi and his collaborators, Chadwick and Goldhaber established (1934–35) the disintegration of the light elements lithium, boron, and nitrogen by slow neutrons. These reactions have taken on particular importance: $Li^6 + n \rightarrow He^4 + H^3$ is the reaction by which tritium is produced, and in turn tritium is the best source of He^3, to which it decays. The reaction $B^{10} + n \rightarrow Li^7 + He^4$ is one of the standard methods of detecting slow neutrons. The reaction $N^{14} + n \rightarrow C^{14} + p$, first established (1936) in detail by W. E. Burcham and Goldhaber, is the most important source of C^{14}, both in nature and in artificial production. In 1935 H. J. Taylor and Goldhaber, using emulsions impregnated with lithium or boron, showed the usefulness of nuclear emulsions for the studies of nuclear

reactions taking place right inside the emulsion. The further development of these emulsions by C. F. Powell and G. Occhialini led to the detection of pi mesons. Goldhaber and G. H. Briggs made (1937) the first systematic study of slow neutron scattering in the majority of elements, and the cross sections they found were very useful later in the development of the first reactors.

In 1938 Goldhaber joined the faculty of the University of Illinois, where he and his wife, Gertrude Scharff-Goldhaber, showed that beta rays are identical with atomic electrons. If they were not identical, beta rays could fall into the K-shell, giving x-rays, but this cannot happen to identical particles because of the Pauli principle. Together with a number of students, they made further contributions to the understanding of slow neutrons. In 1940 J. W. Coltman and Goldhaber showed that beryllium has a sufficiently low cross section for slow neutrons to be a useful neutron moderator in reactors. They voluntarily kept this fact a secret during World War II and did not publish it until after the war. In 1946 A. A. Yalow and Goldhaber found the first example of a slow neutron resonance where scattering was more important than absorption.

In 1950 Goldhaber joined Brookhaven National Laboratory, where he specialized in the study of nuclear isomers and fundamental particles. Isomers are nuclei which do not differ in either their proton number or their neutron number, but possess a different internal structure and lifetime. Systematics of nuclear-level energies and spins and transition probabilities between nuclear levels were studied with E. der Mateosian, R. D. Hill, A. W. Sunyar, and Scharff-Goldhaber. K. T. Bainbridge, Goldhaber, and E. Wilson showed (1951) that the lifetime of an isomer is affected in a measurable way by its chemical state. In 1957 Goldhaber, L. Grodzins, and Sunyar established the fact that the elusive neutrino has a left-handed spin. They were able to show this by finding a K-electron–capturing nuclide (Eu^{152m}) in which neutrinos are emitted of approximately equal energy to that of a successive gamma ray. The gamma ray when emitted opposite to the neutrino has in this case the same helicity (handedness) as the neutrino and the correct energy to be resonant-scattered by the daughter product (Sm^{152}). By measuring the helicity of the gamma ray with the help of an analyzing magnet as absorber (see the figure), they were able to determine the neutrino helicity. This ended a long chapter of controversy in beta-ray research. The same authors also showed that beta rays produce circularly polarized x-rays. In 1966 der Mateosian and Goldhaber developed a new technique for searching for double beta decay by using a scintillating crystal of enriched $Ca^{40}F_2$. By this means they obtained improved lower limits for this process.

Among Goldhaber's theoretical contributions were an early suggestion of a "single-particle model" of nuclear transformations (1934); the Goldhaber-Teller "model" (1948), a model of photointeractions in nuclei (giant dipole resonance); the role of mixed configurations in nuclei, with A. de-Shalit (1953); a compound hypothesis of hyperons (1953, 1956); a review of the theory of electromagnetic transitions in nuclei, with J. Weneser (1955); decay modes of a $(k^0 + \bar{k}^0)$ system, with T. D. Lee and C. N. Yang (1958); and a discussion of tests of conservation laws for elementary particles, with G. Feinberg (1959).

Goldhaber was educated at the University of Berlin and Cambridge University, where he received his Ph.D. in 1936. He was Charles Kingsley Bye fellow of Magdalene College, Cambridge, for 2 years before going to the United States in 1938. He was assistant professor of physics at the University of Illinois in 1938–43, associate professor in 1943–45, and professor in 1945–50. In 1950 he became a senior scientist at Brookhaven National Laboratory, chairman of the Physics Department in 1960, and director in 1961. He was elected to the National Academy of Sciences in 1958.

For background information *see* ELEMENTARY PARTICLE; EXCLUSION PRINCIPLE; FISSION, NUCLEAR; NUCLEAR REACTION in the McGraw-Hill Encyclopedia of Science and Technology. □

★ GOLDMARK, Peter Carl

American scientist
Born Dec. 2, 1906, Budapest, Hungary

THE MANY aspects of handling information—aural and visual—occupied Goldmark's mind since 1929, when he built a simple television receiver with a postage stamp–sized screen while he was a student at the University of Vienna. His work had a profound influence in at least two major areas which blossomed into giant industries within the last decade or so: color television and the microgroove long-playing record. The first practical color television system was developed at CBS Laboratories under his direction, and the first color broadcast in history was transmitted from CBS's experimental transmitter in New York in August, 1940. Although his field-sequential system did not lead to the current standards of commercial color television broadcasting, it nevertheless found wide acceptance in closed-circuit medical, teaching, and industrial applications, because the modern field-sequential color camera is much smaller, lighter, and simpler to operate and maintain than the broadcast-standard models.

During World War II Goldmark was responsible for many military developments in the fields of electronic countermeasures and reconnaissance. In 1948 he and his associates at CBS Laboratories developed the long-playing record, which compressed the equivalent of six 78-rpm phonograph records into a single disk.

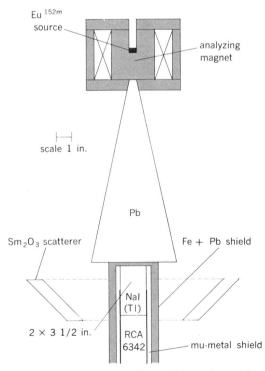

Experimental arrangement for analyzing the circular polarization of resonant-scattered gamma rays. The weight of the Sm_2O_3 scatterer is 1850 grams.

This compression and retrieval of information by phonographic, photographic, or any other graphic record was Goldmark's special field of endeavor, with the highest possible density at the highest possible resolution his aim. One of the results of his thinking was the Lunar Orbiter's dazzling photographs of the lunar surface, which were transmitted to the Earth with astonishing detail, even though they were taken from an average altitude of 29 mi above the Moon, some 238,000 mi from the Earth. An extremely bright, small, flying spot of light scanned the photographic film in three ways ("zone scanning") aboard the spacecraft line by line, so that the fluctuations in light, as it passed through the negative, were translated into electrical impulses for transmission to the ground recording system on Earth.

That small, intense spot of light, emitted by a special line-scan tube aboard the Orbiter, became feasible only after a number of major technical problems were overcome. Because of the high intensity of the beam, the phosphor on the anode burned away quickly. Goldmark and his associates solved the problem by building a rotating anode—a phosphor-coated metal drum which revolved rapidly in the path of the beam so that the coating could cool off before the same area on the anode was struck again. Another serious obstacle arose because the bearings on the revolving drum froze quickly when the then available lubricants boiled away in the high vacuum of the electron tube. Thus, a new type of lubricant had to be developed, one which would withstand not only the vacuum but also the extreme temperature changes encountered in space. Goldmark developed a metallic solid lubricant which extended the life of the bearings beyond that of the Lunar Orbiter missions.

Goldmark also played an active part in practically all of the work of CBS Laboratories. He contributed to such varied developments as special electron tubes, audio and acoustical systems, magnetic recording, and data storage and display.

One of the most complex systems developed under his supervision is a new computer-tape-driven, ultra-high-speed photocomposing system called the Linotron. It can produce electronically page-by-page composition at the rate of 1000 characters per second with high graphic arts quality.

One of Goldmark's great concerns was education, not only that of children but also that of adults and even of fellow scientists. Since he considered teaching in its broadest sense as one aspect of information handling, he felt that machines must also help teachers, instructors, and other communicators in amassing, storing, and reading out the increasingly vast amounts of information resulting from the rapid advances in many fields of science within the last decade. Educational technology was the subject of much of his effort in recent years, with a number of his systems approaching completion.

One such system, destined to play an important part in the establishment of a new educational art form, is Electronic Video Recording (EVR). Developed by Goldmark and his associates at CBS Laboratories, EVR represents a significant step in the application of television to education by making it possible for the first time to show on conventional television sets, in the home or classroom, prerecorded programming from motion picture film and video tape at low cost. The EVR system combines optics and electron physics to transfer any film or video taped programming to special unperforated thin film (or optical tape) stored in a small cartridge. The cartridge is inserted into a player attached to the antenna terminals of a television receiver and automatically played on a single television screen or several as the teacher desires. EVR provides the teacher with the advantage of adapting film from anywhere in the world to his lessons each day. He can show the same film as many times as he wishes or can reproduce it in either black and white or color.

To develop EVR, Goldmark and his associates had to overcome a series of difficult technological problems relating to film miniaturization. Before EVR the miniaturization of individual frames of film was technically unfeasible, because there was no method of projecting enough light through a miniaturized film to make it readable on a screen. Another major difficulty overcome by EVR technology involved showing for the first time both animated film and stills on the same optical tape. Thus, animation can be followed by an important document, which can be "frozen" on the television screen for class study.

Goldmark studied at the universities of Vienna and Berlin, receiving his B.Sc. (1930) and Ph.D. in physics (1931) from the former. He went to the United States in 1933 and joined CBS in New York in 1936 as chief engineer of its newly formed television research department. In 1950 he became vice-president in charge of engineering, and in 1954 was named president of CBS Laboratories, a division of the Columbia Broadcasting System. He served as visiting professor for medical electronics at the University of Pennsylvania Medical School. In 1954 Goldmark was awarded the Television Broadcasters Association Medal for his pioneering work in color television. From the Institute of Electrical and Electronics Engineers he received both the Morris Liebmann Memorial Prize for electronic research (1946) and the Vladimir K. Zworykin Television Prize (1961). He was elected to the National Academy of Engineering in 1966.

Goldmark received many patents in the fields of visual and audio communications, and wrote numerous papers in these fields.

For background information *see* COLOR TELEVISION; DISK RECORDING; TELEVISION CAMERA TUBE; TELEVISION SCANNING in the McGraw-Hill Encyclopedia of Science and Technology.   □

★ GOLDSMITH, Julian Royce

American geochemist
Born Feb. 26, 1918, Chicago, Ill., U.S.A.

THE CHEMISTRY of silicates and related substances, especially at high temperatures and high pressures, has for the most part been neglected by chemists. Chemistry as a science developed out of the study of mineralogy and geology, but in the area of inorganic chemistry it drifted away from the consideration of the materials of the Earth. In the early years of the 20th century, the Geophysical Laboratory of the Carnegie Institution of Washington began an intensive investigation of systems involving silicates, with particular emphasis on high-temperature crystal-liquid equilibria. The Geophysical Laboratory, staffed largely with scientists whose main interest was petrology and geology, operated almost alone in this field until shortly before World War II. In 1936 N. L. Bowen, who had been a pioneer in modern petrology at the Geophysical Laboratory and whose work greatly increased understanding of the evolution of igneous rocks, joined the faculty of the University of Chicago and set up a high-temperature laboratory. After the war a number of universities developed areas of what can be called modern experimental geochemistry, for the most part in the departments of geology or earth science.

Goldsmith was a student of Bowen, and his early work dealt with heterogeneous phase equilibria in silicate systems at elevated tempera-tures. The feldspar family of minerals is perhaps the most important mineral group in the Earth's crust, and in working with some of the feldspar-liquid (melt) equilibrium relations, it became apparent that many of the relationships observed in the natural minerals in rocks were not being adequately explained by the laboratory work on high-temperature equilibria, important as this work was in connection with some of the problems of differentiation and genesis of igneous rocks. At the time little or no active investigation of the role of order-disorder relations had been carried out in mineral structures, although in 1931 T. F. W. Barth and E. Posnjak had applied the "variate atom equipoint" concept to spinels. Also, in 1934 Barth had suggested that microcline, a triclinic potassium feldspar, might have an "ordered" array of Si and Al atoms, whereas the monoclinic modifications, such as sanidine or orthoclase, might be "disordered" with respect to Al and Si. All modifications have the same composition, $KAlSi_3O_8$. Goldsmith synthesized a series of feldspars ($KAlSi_3O_8$, $NaAlSi_3O_8$, and the $NaAlSi_3O_8$-$CaAl_2Si_2O_8$ solid solution series, or plagioclase feldspars) in which the aluminum was replaced by gallium, or the silicon was replaced by germanium, or both. This heavier element substitution was done to produce a larger difference in x-ray scattering power between the Al and Si sites in the crystals, for Al and Si are adjacent elements in the periodic table and, having similar x-ray scattering factors, cannot readily be differentiated in a crystal structure analysis. Although useful structural interpretations were obtained (largely in conjunction with F. Laves), the full exploitation of this line of investigation was seriously hampered by the fact that the low-temperature (and as is now known, the ordered) modifications of the feldspars cannot be synthesized, although there is no difficulty with the high-temperature (disordered) forms. This condition held true for the gallium and germanium feldspars as well as for the "normal" Al and Si counterparts.

It also became apparent that even in nature the high-temperature modifications (particularly $KAlSi_3O_8$) almost universally developed even at low temperatures and inverted to the low-temperature or stable modifications in the solid state only over some period of geologic time. In many cases, the high-temperature state has persisted, a clear indication of the failure of equilibrium. Failure to achieve equilibrium is also shown by the common presence of compositionally zoned plagioclase feldspars in igneous rocks, and Goldsmith pointed out the particular difficulty in the case of the plagioclase feldspars: The solid-state diffusion necessary to produce a homogeneous equilibrium composition requires breaking the very strong aluminum-oxygen and silicon-oxygen bonds concurrently with the migration of

Na and Ca in the structure, for the Na-Ca ratio is dependent upon the Al-Si ratio in the crystal. Equilibrium in this case becomes exceedingly difficult, even at temperatures close to the melting point.

These and similar observations led Goldsmith into consideration of the relationship between crystal structure and what might be called "ease of crystallization," or more generally between structural details and heterogeneous and homogeneous equilibria. In 1955 he received the Mineralogical Society of America Award for contributions to the understanding of the equilibrium relations and genesis of the feldspar group of minerals.

By this time Goldsmith was well into a series of laboratory investigations on the rhombohedral carbonates, using both natural and synthetic materials. These compounds are important in sedimentary and metamorphic petrology, and much of this work was done in collaboration with D. L. Graf. At elevated temperatures the carbonates are difficult to deal with because thermal decomposition becomes a factor, and much of the work must be done in high-pressure apparatus at elevated CO_2 pressures. The complex relations of both pressure and temperature in controlling the decomposition as well as the composition of solid solutions in systems such as $CaCO_3$-$MgCO_3$ and $CaCO_3$-$MnCO_3$ were elucidated, and the practicality of using the $MgCO_3$ content of calcite in geologic thermometry was demonstrated. The underlying factor is that increasing amounts of Mg become soluble in the calcite ($CaCO_3$) structure with the increasing temperature.

The compound dolomite, $CaMg(CO_3)_2$, looms important in this work, and equilibrium order-disorder relations between Ca and Mg were shown to exist at high temperatures. Dolomite is also a mineral that has not been synthesized at low temperatures (below approximately 200°C). Although it is an exceedingly common mineral, and many large rock units are almost pure dolomite, it is almost always observed to be a "secondary," or replacement, mineral. It is but rarely formed as a primary precipitate in carbonate sediments, even though it is now known to be the stable carbonate in equilibrium with seawater. This enigma, often referred to as the "dolomite problem," is largely explained by the fact that the ordered array of Ca and Mg atoms is attained only with great difficulty at low temperatures, where crystallization may be rapid but where diffusion is very slow. Furthermore, poorly ordered or nonstoichiometric dolomite-like phases (called protodolomite) may persist metastably over geologic time.

Goldsmith received his A.B. (1940) and Ph.D. (1947) from the University of Chicago. From 1942 to 1946 he was a research chemist at the Corning Glass Works. He joined the faculty of the University of Chicago in 1947 and became associate dean of the Division of the Physical Sciences in 1960 and chairman of the department of the geophysical sciences in 1963. Elected to the American Academy of Arts and Sciences in 1963, he was appointed by President Johnson to the National Science Board in 1964, and served as president of the Geochemical Society in 1966.

For background information *see* CARBONATE MINERALS; DOLOMITE; HIGH-PRESSURE PHENOMENA; SILICATE PHASE EQUILIBRIA in the McGraw-Hill Encyclopedia of Science and Technology.   □

★ GOLDSTEIN, Herbert

American physicist
Born June 26, 1922, New York, N.Y., U.S.A.

FOR HIS contributions to the development of reactor science, particularly in shielding against nuclear radiation, Goldstein received in 1962 the E. O. Lawrence Memorial Award of the U.S. Atomic Energy Commission.

One of the obstacles to the peaceful development of nuclear energy lies in the vast quantity of nuclear radiation released from an operating reactor. Much of this radiation is easily attenuated or is harmless (for example, the neutrinos), but the high-energy photon and neutron components require massive shielding. The first reactor shields in the days of the Manhattan Project in World War II had to be designed on the basis of scanty empirical data. After the war, however, it was realized that the development of economic nuclear power, as well as the success of applications where space and weight are at a premium (as in space propulsion), required a detailed and accurate knowledge of how photons and neutrons are attenuated through thick layers of shields. The fundamental equation describing the penetration of such neutral particles in matter is a linearized form of the same Boltzmann transport equation that forms the basis of the kinetic theory of gases. Initial attempts at solving the Boltzmann equation for shielding concentrated on the photon part of the problem, because the basic interactions of the photons with individual atoms and their constituents are simpler and better known than the interactions of the neutrons. Even so, the resulting photon transport equation seemed much too complicated for solution, and great effort was expended in devising simple approximations to the interaction processes leading to soluble equations. The extent and direction of the errors introduced by the approximations were largely unknown, and the results obtained were shrouded in uncertainty.

Entering the field in 1950 as a staff member of Nuclear Development Associates, Goldstein decided to apply the then emerging digital computer in large-scale numerical computations toward solving the Boltzmann equation without introducing physical approximations. Of the numerical techniques then known, he felt that the moments method developed by L. V. Spencer and U. Fano of the National Bureau of Standards gave the best promise of leading to the needed results. With the support of the Atomic Energy Commission he embarked on an extensive program, in collaboration with the National Bureau of Standards, to apply the moments method to the computation of photon attenuation in simple shields. The fruits of the program were published in 1954, in collaboration with J. Ernest Wilkins, Jr., in the report "Calculations of the Penetration of Gamma Rays." The penetration of photons from 0.25 to 10 Mev in energy were computed for a variety of materials ranging from water to uranium and for thicknesses up to 20 mean-free-path lengths. From the wide range of results obtained, a qualitative physical picture of attenuation mechanisms in thick shields was derived, enabling one to understand the errors introduced by earlier approximate treatments. The computations quickly found extensive applications in a variety of fields besides reactor shielding, including radiation medical therapy, irradiation sterilization of foods and other materials, and the design of fallout shelters.

Turning next to the neutron problem, Goldstein and his collaborators successfully applied the moments method to calculate the penetration of neutrons from fission in common moderators and shield materials such as light and heavy water, beryllium, graphite, lithium hydride, and so on. One by-product of the moments method is a very precise value for the mean square distance a neutron travels in slowing down to very low energies. This quantity plays an important role in one of the historic methods of reactor design. Goldstein's calculations of this mean square distance for water differed drastically from an apparently well-established experimental value. It was, moreover, possible to show

that uncertainties in the basic nuclear data or in the calculational method did not cause significant error in the theoretical value. Goldstein was able, on the other hand, to point to some possible sources of error in the experiments that had been overlooked. Measurements since 1959 have confirmed the theoretical prediction.

One of the greatest sources of uncertainties in the calculation of neutron penetration in shields lies in the basic cross-section data needed for the computations. To build up an adequate picture of how neutrons interact with a particular type of nucleus requires sifting and evaluating hundreds of diverse pieces of experimental and theoretical evidence. An often difficult and time-consuming part of this task is collecting these pieces of evidence out of a widespread and rapidly proliferating literature. Starting in 1956, Goldstein devised a computer-based system, called CINDA (Computer Index Neutron Data), for keeping track in a systematic and continuous fashion of the literature on neutron cross-sections. Operation of the system has since become an international cooperative venture with the assistance of governmental laboratories and of scientists in almost all countries involved in nuclear research. In 1966 CINDA contained some 40,000 entries relating to 8000 references on neutron data, with a doubling time of about 3 years.

Son of a teacher, Goldstein graduated from the College of the City of New York in 1940. He received a Ph.D. from MIT in 1943. During World War II he worked in the microwave radar field in the MIT Radiation Laboratory. In 1946 he was appointed instructor in the department of physics, Harvard University, and he joined Nuclear Development Associates in 1950. In 1961 he became professor of nuclear science and engineering at Columbia University.

Goldstein wrote *Classical Mechanics* (1950) and *Fundamental Aspects of Reactor Shielding* (1959).

For background information *see* BOLTZMANN STATISTICS; RADIOACTIVITY; REACTOR, NUCLEAR in the McGraw-Hill Encyclopedia of Science and Technology.   □

★ GORTER, Cornelis Jacobus

Dutch physicist
Born Aug. 14, 1907, Utrecht, Netherlands

GORTER WAS a pupil of the school of low-temperature physicists founded at the University of Leiden by H. Kamerlingh Onnes, who liquefied helium in 1908 and discovered superconductivity in 1911. Gorter's main fields of research were magnetism and superconductivity. Having started by studying paramagnetism in salts of the iron group and of the

rare earths, he soon met with the problem of the mechanisms which orient the ionic magnetic moments into the direction of an external magnetic field. One such mechanism is the interaction between the magnetic moments and the heat motion of the crystalline lattice in which they are placed. Another mechanism, pointed out by I. Waller, is the interaction between different magnetic moments. The first mechanism should lead to a relaxation time which increases rapidly upon decreasing the temperature, while the second should give a relaxation time which hardly depends on temperature. By introducing radiofrequency magnetic fields and studying the heat dissipation as well as the high-frequency susceptibility as a function of frequency, external magnetic field, and temperature, Gorter discovered and studied both relaxation processes. He then tried to observe the absorption frequency of radio power corresponding to transitions between the different possible orientations of the magnetic moments with respect to the constant external field. But his repeated attempts thus to observe nuclear magnetic resonance due to nuclear magnetic moments and, at higher frequencies, electron spin resonance remained unsuccessful, since the investigated substances were too pure and the microwave equipment was too simple, respectively. Later these resonances were discovered in the United States by I. I. Rabi, F. Bloch, and E. M. Purcell, and in the Soviet Union by E. Zavoisky. Magnetic resonances became important tools in physics and chemistry and have several practical applications.

A second group of magnetic researches was aimed at orienting atomic nuclei which possess a magnetic moment and then studying the anisotropy of their properties. Though the original suggestion, made in 1934, concerned orienting them in a large external field at extremely low temperatures, it was later pointed out that the interaction between the electrons in a paramagnetic ion and its nuclei must lead to considerable orienting at temperatures not quite so low.

The latter suggestion was independently made by M. E. Rose. Oriented nuclei, in fact, made possible the study of anisotropy of nuclear properties such as radioactive emissions, nuclear reactions, and scattering of other nuclei.

Gorter's third field of research in magnetism was antiferromagnetism, consisting in the formation of crystalline sublattices in a solid; these sublattices differ in the direction and sometimes in the magnitude of their magnetizations. In cooperation with N. J. Poulis and others, various properties were analyzed, including antiferromagnetic resonance of hydrated copper chloride, which is antiferromagnetic below a Néel temperature of 4.3°K.

Kamerlingh Onnes had found that superconductivity is disturbed upon application of a magnetic field which surpasses a critical field. This critical field is of the order of a few hundred oersteds near the absolute zero of temperature and gradually goes to zero when the transition temperature of the superconductor is approached. In 1933 Gorter gave a simple thermodynamical explanation of this. As a consequence of the surface currents induced just below the surface of the sample, its Gibbs free energy is raised proportionally to the square of the external magnetic field. As soon as this Gibbs free energy becomes equal to that of the nonsuperconductive normal metal, the sample passes into that normal state. In part of this work he cooperated with H. B. G. Casimir, with whom Gorter also introduced a so-called order parameter, describing a degree of superconductivity.

The discovery by W. J. de Haas and J. Voogd that in some alloys superconductivity persists up to much higher fields than should be expected from the thermodynamical argument was attributed by Gorter to the formation of a mixed structure of thin superconducting regions into which the magnetic field may partially penetrate so that the rise of the Gibbs free energy is much slower. In the 1950s these early suggestions, as well as those of F. London on the slight penetration of magnetic fields below the surface of a superconducting region, were transposed into an image on quantum mechanical basis by the Moscow school of L. D. Landau, V. L. Ginsburg, and A. A. Abrikosov. In that image the order parameter has the character of a wave function and thus is not a real but a complex quantity. This condition permits the introduction of a rigorous model of the "mixed" structure, which may occur under certain conditions. If, moreover, the metal contains local inhomogeneities of the right character, the "mixed" structure can stand up to magnetic fields of the order of 100,000 oersted and even then can carry considerable magnetic current. This finding is now used in superconducting magnets which can produce high magnetic fields without continuously converting precious electric energy into heat. American scientists, including J. E. Kunzler and B. T. Matthias, pioneered in finding the right metal compounds.

To magnetism and superconductivity, Gorter added research in other fields such as optics, metallophysics and, especially, liquid helium II. In the framework of the "two-fluid model," he introduced a nonlinear "mutual friction" between the normal fluid and the superfluid.

Son of a government official, Gorter studied in Leiden from 1924 to 1932 under W. J. de Haas and P. Ehrenfest. After occupying positions in Haarlem and the University of Groningen, he was appointed in 1940 as P. Zeeman's successor at the University of Amsterdam. In 1946 he returned to Leiden as director of the Kamerlingh Onnes Laboratory. In addition, he served in national scientific positions, such as chairman of the Foundation for Fundamental Research on Matter during 1955–60 and president of the Royal Netherlands Academy of Sciences and Letters during 1960–66. He was vice-president of the International Union of Pure and Applied Physics during 1946–51 and 1960–66, chairman of its commission on very low temperature, and chairman of the technical board of the International Institute of Refrigeration. He was awarded honorary degrees from three French universities and one Canadian university. In 1966 Gorter received the F. London Award for research in low-temperature physics. He was elected a foreign member of the American Academy of Arts and Sciences in 1952 and a foreign research associate of the National Academy of Sciences in 1967.

Besides his thesis, "Paramagnetische Eigenschaften von Salzen" (1932), Gorter wrote *Paramagnetic Relaxation* (1947) and edited five volumes of *Progress in Low-Temperature Physics* (1955–67).

For background information *see* ANTIFERROMAGNETISM; MAGNETIC RESONANCE; SUPERCONDUCTIVITY in the McGraw-Hill Encyclopedia of Science and Technology.   □

★ GRANIT, Ragnar Arthur

Swedish physiologist
Born Oct. 30, 1900, Helsinge, Finland

G RANIT IS best known for his work in vision and in the field of motor control by muscular afferents, for which he received the 1967 Nobel Prize in medicine or physiology. During his medical studies he became interested in the psychophysics of vision but soon concluded that a physiological approach was needed. E. D. Adrian had demonstrated the value of this approach in pioneer work with the eye of the conger eel. Granit's leading idea was that since the retina had been shown by S. Ramón y Cajal to

be a nervous center, it should be studied as such. He acquired the necessary background during 2 years in Sir Charles Sherrington's laboratory in Oxford. The idea was first tested psychophysically by the flicker method during 2 years at the Johnson Foundation, University of Pennsylvania. The so-called Granit-Harper law of summation was thus established.

Granit began electrophysiological work by developing his well-known analysis of the components of the electroretinogram in 1932. The question of whether light could inhibit, as well as elicit, impulses in the optic nerve seeemed fundamental at the time. In 1934 he produced evidence for inhibition, and this fact is today a cornerstone in visual physiology. Also unknown was the relation between amount of rhodopsin (visual purple) and retinal sensitivity. Granit, with T. Holmberg and M. Zewi, studied this quantitatively. It was further shown that intensities of spectral green which failed to bleach rhodopsin caused very large reductions of retinal sensitivity. The explanation may lie in the later discovery, by K. O. Donner and T. Reuter, of a strong feedback inhibition of sensitivity by small quantities of the photoproduct metarhodopsin II.

Thomas Young's conception of three types of fiber in the optic nerve for the three fundamental colors had been interpreted psychophysically by S. Hecht on the theory of three types of receptors (cones) with almost wholly overlapping spectral distributions of sensitivity. Granit's first tests with the electroretinogram in 1937 clearly indicated greater spectral differentiation. A microelectrode technique developed by Granit and G. Svaetichin in 1939 was the first ever used for sensory work. The technique soon showed that some optic nerve fibers (the dominators) responded to the whole spectrum, while others,

being narrow-banded "modulators," were color specific and occurred with slightly varying location within three main regions of the spectrum. This work was extended to a large number of species with variable cone populations. Finally, selective adaptation was used to isolate in a mammal (cat) the three basic spectral sensitivity curves for red, green, and blue. Other researchers have since demonstrated, in training experiments, color sensitivity in the cat. Granit concluded this phase of activity with a summary of his color work in his Thomas Young Oration in 1945, and he covered the whole of retinal electrophysiology in *Sensory Mechanisms of the Retina* in 1947.

Granit next turned to the length meters and tension meters in the muscles known as muscle spindles and tendon organs, respectively. The spindles are extremely complex organs with a motor innervation by special fibers, the gamma fibers, whose capacity for making spindles discharge had been demonstrated in his laboratory by L. Leksell. Granit found that sites in the brain and the cerebellum which excite or inhibit the muscles' motor or alpha neurones had parallel actions on the gamma motoneurones. The concept of the gamma loop through the length-measuring spindles, serving as a second motor system, was then developed experimentally, and it led to a differentiation of alpha and gamma rigidities in neuropathology. The concept of linked alpha and gamma action and its significance was elaborated. Breakdown of this linkage was observed after cerebellar ablation, and this was held to explain the clinical symptoms of dysmetria. Expanding this work to a circuit analysis of the components of the alpha and gamma reflex arcs, Granit differentiated tonic from phasic motoneurones; he studied, by extra- and intracellular recording, the effects of tendon organs and muscle spindles on motoneurones, the role of inhibition, including recurrent or feedback inhibition through fibers which return to the motoneurones from the outgoing axons, and so on. He maintained throughout this experimentation strong emphasis on the organizational aspects and the principles of motor control by the muscles' sense organs. In particular, the spindles were defined as sensory-motor end organs, at the same time measuring and controlling motor action. Finally, feeling the need for precise information on impulse frequency as an instrument of communication, Granit set out to establish by intra- and extracellular recording the rules by which excitation and inhibition balance out quantitatively at the membrane of single cells. He chose motoneurones as his prototype.

Granit graduated from the Swedish Normallyceum, Helsinki, in 1919, took Mag.Phil. and M.D. degrees at the University of Helsinki, and served there as professor of physiology during 1935–40. He was invited to a personal research chair in neurophysiology at the Royal Caroline Institute of Stockholm in 1940. In 1945 the Caroline Institute approved a building program for the Medical Nobel Institute, which was to be provided with three departments, one to be devoted to neurophysiology with Granit as director. A special chair of neurophysiology was erected for him by the Swedish government for this purpose. In 1945 Granit delivered the Thomas Young Oration of the Physical Society, London, and in 1960 he was elected a foreign member of the Royal Society of London. In 1967 he gave the Sherrington Lecture of the Royal Society of Medicine, London.

Granit wrote *Sensory Mechanisms of the Retina* (1947; 2d ed. 1963). He delivered the Silliman Lectures at Yale University in 1954, published as *Receptors and Sensory Perception: A Discussion of Aims, Means and Results of Electrophysiological Research into the Process of Reception* (1955). In 1965 Granit organized Nobel Symposium I for the Nobel Foundation. He edited the proceedings under the subtitle *Muscular Afferents and Motor Control* (1966). For the series "British Men of Science" he wrote *Charles Scott Sherrington: An Appraisal* (1966). In the Swedish language he published a collection of essays on the scientific life, *Ung Mans Väg till Minerva* (1941; 2d ed. 1958).

For background information *see* COLOR VISION; EYE; MOTOR SYSTEMS; PSYCHOPHYSICAL METHODS in the McGraw-Hill Encyclopedia of Science and Technology.   □

★ GREEN, David Ezra

American biochemist
Born Aug. 5, 1910, New York, N.Y., U.S.A.

THE UNDERGRADUATE and graduate training of Green at New York University (B.Sc., 1930, A.M., 1932) aroused in him an intense interest in the mechanisms of biological oxidations. This interest brought him in 1932 to the department of biochemistry of Cambridge University, where he received a Ph.D. in 1934 under Malcolm Dixon. Until 1940 he was part of the Cambridge group that laid the foundations of modern enzymology. Five oxidative enzymes were discovered and characterized during that period, notably α-glycerophosphate and β-hydroxybutyrate dehydrogenases. He was among the first to undertake the large-scale isolation of enzymes with functional groups, and he characterized a series of enzymes containing respectively flavin (for example, aldehyde and xanthine oxidases) and thiamine (yeast carboxylase) as prosthetic groups. His book *Mechanisms of Biological Oxidations* (1939) provides an account of the developments in oxidative enzymes in which he and other members of the Cambridge group took part. In addition to his isolation studies, Green was the first to demonstrate and analyze coenzyme-linked reactions between dehydrogenase systems, and he pioneered in the reconstitution of sequential reactions catalyzed by multiple enzymes linked via carriers.

At Harvard Medical School (1940–41) and at Columbia University Medical School (1941–48), Green extended his large-scale isolation studies to flavoprotein enzymes (L-amino acid oxidase, glycine oxidase), thiaminoprotein enzymes (pyruvate ketolase), and pyridoxal-containing enzymes (transaminases). A polyglutamyl derivative of p-aminobenzoate (later identified as a fragment of folic acid) was isolated and characterized.

In 1945 Green became engaged in the isolation of the pyruvate dehydrogenase system of animal tissues, and found it impossible to separate the dehydrogenase from a large group of accompanying enzymes catalyzing the citric cycle, terminal electron transfer, and oxidative phosphorylation. He concluded from this nonseparability that the pyruvate dehydrogenase is an integral part of an organized particulate system. This system, called the cyclophorase system, was conceived of as a single, complete operational unit. For some 5 years a lively controversy raged over the cyclophorase concept. With the discovery in 1950 (V. R. Potter, W. C. Schneider, A. L. Lehninger, and E. Kennedy) that the mitochondrion could be identified as the physical housing of the cyclophorase system, the notion of organized, structured enzyme systems became firmly established in biochemical thought.

In 1948 Green went to the University of Wisconsin to inaugurate the Institute for Enzyme Research, and he formed a research group, uniquely equipped for large-scale isolation and study of particulate systems. What follows is a chronicle of the group led by Green—a constantly changing group of postdoctoral fellows who stayed for periods of 1–5 years. In quick succession there came the isolation of the α-ketoglutarate and pyruvate dehydrogenating complexes; the isolation of the kinase systems for activation of acetate, succinate, and acetoacetate via acyl CoA formation; the large-scale isolation of purified coenzyme A; and finally the reconstruction of the entire fatty acid sequence from the isolated component enzymes and intermediates. Systems research was the specialty of the Institute group during 1948–55, culminating in the isolation and characterization of the fatty acid synthesizing system. The requirement for CO_2 by this system was rationalized in terms of a biotin-catalyzed carboxylation of acetyl CoA to malonyl CoA.

All of this set the stage for the systematic fragmentation and degradation of the mitochondrion, which started in 1955. The mitochondrion was comminuted into submitochondrial particles, the particles into complexes, and the complexes into the component catalytic proteins. This breakdown led to the concept of the electron transfer chain as a composite of four separable complexes. As a by-product, these fragmentation studies initiated the discovery and chemical characterization of coenzyme Q, and the recognition of nonheme iron and copper as integral oxidation-reduction components of the electron transfer chain. Coenzyme Q and cytochrome *c* were shown to be mobile components linking the various complexes. In addition to the catalytic components of the chain and of the other mitochondrial systems, Green and his colleagues discovered a set of organizing proteins, such as structural protein, which were intrinsic parts of all mitochondrial systems. The 1:1 relation of catalytic and organizing proteins had profoundly influenced thought about the genetic aspects of mitochondrial biosyntheses.

The role of lipid in mitochondrial function was then systematically probed. Mitochondrial lipid was shown to be predominantly phospholipid ($> 90\%$) and to be bonded hydrophobically to protein. The essentiality of phospholipid for the electron transfer process was conclusively demonstrated. The predominantly hydrophobic character of lipid-protein binding in the mitochondrion was the critical observation that eventually led to a reexamination and rejection of the Danielli-Davson model of membrane structure and to a definition of membrane systems in terms of nesting lipoprotein repeating units. The ultrastructural study of the mitochondrion, initiated in 1960–61 by H. Fernandez-Moran and Green, revealed the presence of tripartite repeating units in the inner membrane, and it soon became evident that repeating units are the hallmarks of all membranes.

High-resolution electron micrographic as well as biochemical studies revealed the individual repeating unit to be built up of a base piece (membrane-forming sector) and a detachable sector (headpiece plus stalk). These sectors were identified with the various operational systems of the mitochondrion (for example, inner membrane base pieces with complexes of the chain and outer membrane base pieces with the dehydrogenating complexes of the citric acid cycle). The successful separation of inner and outer membranes was a necessary preliminary to localization of mitochondrial enzymes in sectors of repeating units of the respective membranes. The *de novo* formation of membranes from repeating units and of repeating units from sectors showed that self-assembly of the mitochondrion from the disaggregated sectors of repeating units was feasible.

The delineation of the ultrastructural picture and the definition of membrane systems led rapidly to a spate of related developments: the demonstration of lipid as the determinant of membrane formation by restriction of binding modalities; the demonstration of reconstitution of the chain as a membrane phenomenon (all the complexes in the same membrane) and not as a molecular interaction; the role of carnitine in promoting transfer of CoA across the outer membrane; the inhibition by atractyloside of transmembrane phosphoryl transfer reactions catalyzed by the outer membrane; and the demonstration of transitions in the geometric form of repeating units (during swelling and during controlled respiration). These developments opened the door to a much more realistic interpretation of the electron transfer process and of high-energy bond formation.

In the late 1960s Green and his group were engaged in an attempt to relate high-energy bond formation to conformational changes during electron transfer, and to elucidate the nature of the molecules which are partners in the first high-energy compound formed by electron transfer.

Recipient of the American Chemical Society Award in Enzyme Chemistry in 1946, Green was elected to the American Academy of Arts and Sciences in 1960 and the National Academy of Sciences in 1962.

Besides the book mentioned above, Green wrote *Molecular Insights into the Living Process*, with Goldberger (1967).

For background information *see* BIOLOGICAL OXIDATION; ENZYME; LIPID; MITOCHONDRIA in the McGraw-Hill Encyclopedia of Science and Technology.   □

★ GUILFORD, Joy Paul

American psychologist
Born Mar. 7, 1897, Marquette, Nebr., U.S.A.

A MAN of many interests in his general field, Guilford was most productive in the area of psychological measurement. His output was in the form of invention or improvement of methods (psychophysical, scaling, and testing), and of application of those methods to psychological problems. His book *Psychometric Methods*

(1936; 2d ed. 1954) brought together and systematized such procedures, including factor analysis, all of which were given basic, quantitative theory.

In psychophysics he proposed a power law to the effect that stimulus changes $\triangle S$, which give equal increments on a psychological variable, are proportional to the nth power of the absolute quantity ϕ on the stimulus variable at which the increment occurs. This relationship was designed to replace the Weber law, which is the special case in which $n = 1.0$. To replace the Fechner logarithmic psychophysical law, relating psychological quantity to physical quantity, he proposed another power law, which states that a measured psychological quantity ψ is proportional to a corresponding physical-stimulus quantity ϕ to some power β. Later, S. S. Stevens demonstrated that this law applies to a number of perceptual variables, the exponent varying to suit the circumstances. The power law of psychophysics thus became known as "Stevens' law."

Guilford made a number of novel applications of scaling methods to the measurement of subjective experiences, such as preferences or values, particularly affective values of colors, sounds, odors, and of some of their combinations. He demonstrated the possibility of deriving quantitative relationships between degrees of preference and variables describing appearances of colors (hue, value, and chroma of the Munsell scale) or properties of sounds (pitch, loudness). He proposed a field of "psychodynamics" for this kind of investigation, which was later pursued imaginatively by Gösta Ekman and others in Sweden.

Guilford's greatest contributions, however, were in the field of testing, particularly in con-

nection with intelligence. From his student days he seriously doubted the validity of the doctrine that intelligence is one global ability, a single variable along which individuals differ in a linear fashion. He was also keenly aware of the lack of basic psychological theory needed to support testing operations.

Utilizing the multiple-factor methods developed in the United States by L. L. Thurstone and applied by him in some preliminary investigations, Guilford and others demonstrated additional distinct intellectual abilities. When the number of abilities approached 40, Guilford developed a comprehensive and systematic theory of the intellectual abilities, known as the "structure of intellect" (SI), which took on a stable form in 1958.

The theory is represented by a three-dimensional, rectangular model with 120 rectangular cells, each representing a different ability. One dimension of the model represents five discrete kinds of *operation:* cognition (knowing, recognizing, understanding), memory (learning or committing information to storage), divergent production (generating logical alternatives), convergent production (generating logically necessary conclusions), and evaluation (deciding truth values or relative values of alternatives). A second dimension of the SI model represents four large *content* categories of information: figural (perceived, concrete), symbolic (signs, for example, letters or numbers), semantic ("thoughts"), and behavioral (psychological events, mental states). The third dimension of the model has six kinds of *products:* units, classes, relations, systems, transformations, and implications. The six kinds of products constitute a psychologic or an empirically derived logic, with clear parallels in modern formal logic. Multiplying the four content categories by the six product categories yields 24 basic categories of information, a psychoepistemology, also empirically derived. Any one ability in the SI model is clearly defined by its unique combination of operation, content, and product categories (for example, cognition of semantic systems, which would mean the ability to grasp in thought complex organizations or structures).

By analogy to the chemists' periodic table, which led to the discovery of new elements, the SI model successfully predicted abilities to be demonstrated, and now the number yet to be isolated is in a small minority. Even more significant is the general psychological theory that was deduced from the SI theory and its basic concepts. The type of psychology generated is well described as "informational-operational." It conceives of an organism psychologically as a processor of information, by analogy to a modern computer rather than to the behaviorists' oversimplified "touch-and-go," stimulus-response mechanism. Complex psychological activities, such as problem solving and creative production, can now be accounted for in terms of operational models by utilizing SI concepts.

The SI model revealed many aspects of intellectual functioning that are not touched by traditional intelligence scales, large portions of which are devoted to cognition abilities, which essentially tell how well the long-term memory storage is stocked with information. Very seriously neglected had been the productive-thinking and evaluative categories, with little to indicate potential for problem solving and creative performance. SI conceptions are having some impact upon education and its goals, curricula, and teaching and examining procedures.

Guilford received his A.B. (1922) and A.M. (1924) at the University of Nebraska and his Ph.D. (1927) at Cornell University. He taught at several universities—Illinois, Kansas, Nebraska, Northwestern, and Southern California. During World War II he served as aviation psychologist in the Army Air Force, directing various research units, with the terminal rank of colonel; he received the Legion of Merit Award for this work. Other recognitions included the American Psychological Association's Walter V. Bingham Lectureship (1959), Distinguished Scientific Contribution Award (1964), and the first Richardson Creativity Award (1966) besides several honorary degrees. He was elected to the National Academy of Sciences in 1954.

In addition to the book mentioned, Guilford wrote *Fundamental Statistics in Psychology and Education* (1942; 4th ed. 1965), *General Psychology* (1939; 2d ed. 1952), *Personality* (1959), and *The Nature of Human Intelligence* (1967).

For background information *see* INTELLIGENCE; PSYCHOLOGY, PHYSIOLOGICAL AND EXPERIMENTAL; PSYCHOPHYSICAL METHODS in the McGraw-Hill Encyclopedia of Science and Technology. ☐

★ GUILLEMIN, Ernst Adolph

American electrical engineer
Born May 8, 1898, Milwaukee, Wis., U.S.A.

THE TEACHING of electrical engineering subjects, in particular electrical network theory, was of primary interest to Guillemin, and led to his research, both theoretical and practical. Early in his teaching career he had a deep interest in the importance of providing students with information of a lasting basic character rather than the currently popular applicational topics, which provided momentary interest but did not enhance the ability to solve new problems by unconventional means. Thus, much of his time and energy was spent in curriculum revision activities, which proved to be an uphill struggle against deeply entrenched conservatism during the decade preceding World War II.

The relatively small group of electrical engineering faculty at the Massachusetts Institute of

Technology (MIT) who were interested in bringing about these curriculum revisions were all specializing in communications subjects, including electronic circuit theory. This circumstance was rather natural, since in this area the majority of problems were far from having reached a status of conventionality, and hence they required much basic thinking to provide any acceptable solutions at all. The faculty working in these areas were compelled to use much more flexible methods of attack, so the basic scientific approach was part of their way of life. The advent of the war and the establishment of the Radiation Laboratory at MIT marked the turning point in these efforts. Because of the predominance of conventionality in the training of electrical engineers up to this point, the Radiation Laboratory had to look for the majority of its staff to physicists, both theoretical and experimental, notwithstanding that the task was eminently of an engineering nature.

In the postwar years emphasis on basic science in the engineering curriculum suddenly became popular, and the pendulum swung too far in the opposite direction. Several attempts have been made to settle down at some compromise point but have been unsuccessful because of a feeling that stagnation must be avoided at all costs. Everything must be changed, whether for better or for worse.

Fortunately in the field of circuit theory the postwar attitude created an opportunity to make some sweeping changes reaching down to the sophomore or "first-course" level. Here it was felt that the treatment of circuit theory should limit its considerations to lumped, linear, passive, and bilateral elements, since these form an essential and indispensable background for the more difficult circuit problems dealing with active, nonbilateral, and nonlinear elements.

Linear circuit theory is linear system theory, regardless of whether that system is electrical, mechanical, acoustical, or a combination of these. Even problems in economics and business procedures, or any others in which the controlling relations are linear, may be included in this broad class. All of the theory of classical dynamics is applicable here, as is the theory of linear algebra and of functions of a complex variable, with its collateral overlap in potential theory and conformal mapping. Last but not least is the pertinence of combinatorial topology, through which the properties of circuits dealing with invariance to changes in geometrical form or topological structure, as well as questions relating to the introduction and transformation of variables, can be studied effectively. Linear system theory, together with the collateral branches of physics and mathematics upon which it rests, is indeed the essential foundation. Without it no engineer can get beyond the conventional things he has learned to do by rote; with it his horizon is practically unlimited, for he can adapt and devise and thus create methods of solution where none existed before.

The mention of Fourier or Laplace theory in the above summary of linear system theory content is studiously avoided. Fourier representation is a mathematical trick, dealing with the subject of how one constructs arbitrary functions out of sinusoids. The given function emerges as the result of an interference of sinusoidal components, and hence is also referred to as an interference pattern. One can build the same interference pattern out of sinusoids with steady amplitudes, or out of sinusoids with exponentially growing or decaying amplitudes, or out of endless mixtures of these; and there are all sorts of rules as to what can and what cannot be built in this way and what restrictions must be placed upon the mixtures, and so forth. This is Fourier theory. It has nothing whatever to do with circuit theory; but when Fourier theory is applied to the problem of computing network response, some additional restrictions and rules enter the picture. It is important to be able to distinguish between conditions imposed by Fourier theory and those imposed by circuit theory. In the usual presentation of this topic, especially in the watered-down variety that is injected into an introductory circuits subject, these restrictions become gloriously mixed up. The student who does not have a classical background in circuit theory cannot possibly salvage anything useful from such a presentation. Fourier and Laplace theory are tremendously useful aids in the practical application of circuit theory, but their introduction into the curriculum should not come until an adequate understanding of classical network theory has been achieved.

Guillemin's research activities were concerned with a wide variety of network analysis and synthesis problems. Among these was the synthesis of a network for the generation of essentially rectangular pulses for radar applications during World War II. This work was later extended to consider pulses of arbitrary shape. A related problem was the design of a network to produce loran pulses. Here the conventional procedure involved an oscillator to generate the carrier, means for its amplitude modulation, a filter to eliminate interference from the resulting spectrum, and a matching network to adapt the filter output to a given antenna. These four operations were combined into a single pulse-generating network excited by the discharge of a condenser, resulting in greatly increased overall efficiency and reduced size and weight of the total apparatus. These and numerous other problems were solved through formulating an approach aimed as directly as possible at the desired functional result, avoiding existing conventional approaches, wherever this seemed wise.

Guillemin received his B.S. in electrical engineering from the University of Wisconsin in 1922, his S.M. from MIT in 1924, and his Ph.D. in physics and mathematics from the University of Munich in 1926. He returned to MIT as an instructor in electrical engineering and there

spent his entire career, as an assistant professor from 1928 to 1936, associate professor from 1936 to 1944, and full professor thereafter. He was appointed to the Edwin Sibly Webster Chair in 1960 and was retired in 1963. In 1948 he was awarded the President's Certificate of Merit for his contributions to the war effort as consultant to the Radiation Laboratory. In 1961 he was awarded the Medal of Honor of the Institute of Radio Engineers and in 1962 he received the Medal in Electrical Engineering Education from the American Institute of Electrical Engineers. He was a fellow of the Institute of Electrical and Electronic Engineers, the American Academy of Arts and Sciences, and the Royal Society of Arts.

Guillemin wrote *Communication Networks* (2 vols., 1931, 1935), *The Mathematics of Circuit Analysis* (1949), *Introductory Circuit Theory* (1953), *Synthesis of Passive Networks* (1957), and *Theory of Linear Physical Systems* (1963).

For background information *see* CIRCUIT, ELECTRIC; COMMUNICATIONS, ELECTRICAL; ELECTRICAL ENGINEERING; NETWORK THEORY, ELECTRICAL in the McGraw-Hill Encyclopedia of Science and Technology.   □

★ HADDOW, Sir Alexander

British physician
Born Jan. 18, 1907, Broxburn, West Lothian, Scotland

WHILE DOING bacteriological research at the University of Edinburgh medical school in the early 1930s, Haddow discovered the so-called Haddow phenomenon. Sir Ernest Kennaway, J. W. Cook, and others had already opened up the new field of the carcinogenic hydrocarbons; then Haddow discovered a correlation between carcinogenic and growth-inhibiting properties, similar to that which exists in the case of ionizing radiations. This suggested that the first stage of carcinogenesis lies in interference—of a kind unspecified at the time, but the nature of which is now becoming clearer—with the mechanisms normally responsible for cell division and growth. The work, both at Edinburgh and subsequently at the Research Institute of the Royal Cancer Hospital, where he moved in 1936, involved the systemic treatment of tumor-bearing animals with a long series of carcinogenic and noncarcinogenic hydrocarbons.

Haddow's research continued throughout World War II. He investigated the influence of synthetic estrogens on advanced malignant disease, with special reference to cancer of the breast. He also made the discovery by accident that the injection of the flavin 9-phenyl-5:6-benzo-iso-alloxazine into albino rats produces an artificial coloring of the rat's hair—an observation of considerable potential interest in the study of pigmentation, evolution, and growth. Also by accident came the discovery of the capacity of xanthopterin and other related pterins, pyrimidines, and purines to evoke massive cell division in the kidney epithelium in many species—with its implications for the physiological regulation of organ size. Both were

subjects in which Haddow remained intensely interested.

More important, however, during this period was an investigation that he carried out with W. A. Sexton into the biological properties of urethane, a substance that had long been used in medicine as a mild hypnotic. These experiments, using animal tumors, eventually led to the discovery (by others) of the capacity of this simple substance to effect temporary remission in the chronic leukemias in man.

In the late 1940s Haddow and his colleagues G. A. R. Kon, R. J. C. Harris, and E. M. F. Roe became especially interested in the growth-inhibitory and carcinogenic properties of 4-aminostilbene. This opened up a whole new field of investigation, including a substantial program of synthesis in the field of nitrogen mustard derivatives. This, in turn, with the assistance of F. Bergel, G. M. Timmis, W. C. J. Ross, and others, led to the introduction of the drugs myleran, chlorambucil, and melphalan into clinical medicine for the treatment of the chronic leukemias, malignant melanoma, myelomatosis, and ovarian cancer.

This and other work with the so-called alkylating carcinogens constituted Haddow's main field of research over the last decade. Inevitably it led ever deeper into the fundamentals of biology. In the 1950s his colleagues R. J. Goldacre, A. Loveless, and Ross drew attention to the possible importance of chemical cross linkage (between then unspecified receptors) in the action of the alkylating carcinogens. In the 1960s his colleagues P. Lawley and P. Brookes obtained products of the alkylation of nucleic acid by both sulfur and nitrogen mustards, almost certainly produced by cross linking of the twin helices of the molecule of DNA—a discovery with profound implications in base removal, base substitution, and alterations of pairing in the cytogenetic code.

Haddow's later papers dealt with the role of metals in carcinogenesis and the phenomenon of mirror imaging or complete transposition of the viscera in the rat.

Haddow attended the University of Edinburgh, where he received an M.B. and a Ch.B. in 1929, a Ph.D. and an M.D. in 1937, and a D.Sc. in 1938. While Haddow was a medical student, Lorrain Smith's philosophical discourses on growth aroused his interest in cancer. After qualifying in medicine, he spent a year as a houseman in the Royal Infirmary of Edinburgh, and was then appointed assistant lecturer in bacteriology under T. J. Mackie at the University of Edinburgh. He took up the study of tumor immunology and bacterial variation, finding new examples of the phenomenon of secondary colony development in bacteria and working out an analogy with tumor induction that later proved of use as a model system of carcinogenesis—in advance of the great modern developments in bacterial cytology and genetics. In 1936 he left Edinburgh to go to the Chester Beatty Research Institute of the Royal Cancer Hospital in London, of which he later became director. He also became professor of experimental pathology at the University of London in 1946. He was elected to the Royal Society of London in 1958 and to the American Academy of Arts and Sciences in 1961.

For background information *see* BACTERIAL GENETICS; NUCLEIC ACID; ONCOLOGY; TUMOR in the McGraw-Hill Encyclopedia of Science and Technology.   □

★ HAMBURGER, Viktor

American embryologist
Born July 9, 1900, Landeshut, Silesia, Germany

HAMBURGER'S MAJOR contributions were in the field of experimental neurogenesis (analysis of the developmental mechanisms by which the complex structure of the nervous system and the patterns of peripheral nerve pathways are created). R. G. Harrison and his student S. R. Detwiler had introduced the methods and concepts of experimental embryology to this area. Among Hamburger's early investigations were inquiries into the factors which determine the configuration of peripheral nerve patterns. By transplanting organ primordia, such as limb buds, to atypical positions and allowing them to be invaded by foreign nerves, it was possible to assess the respective roles of intrinsic properties of the nerve fibers and of their substrate in the orientation (directional outgrowth) of the fibers. The peripheral fields of nerve distribution prepare track systems; but specific affinities, probably of a biochemical nature, between different types of nerve fibers and the matrix on which they grow are responsible for the detailed specification of the nerve patterns. While previous investigations in this area had been confined to amphibian embryos, Hamburger applied the methods and techniques of microneurosurgery to the chick embryo. This technical advance opened up new possibilities of experimentation on an amniote embryo and of analysis of a wide range of embryological problems begond the scope of neurogenesis. The step from the amphibian to the chick embryo was dictated by the more complex organization of the avian nervous system (approaching that of the mammal, whose fetuses are not readily available for experimentation).

Hamburger then explored the "trophic" relationships between the outgrowing nerve fiber and its environment. The neuroblast, in spinning out its fiber, acquires a second milieu, in addition to the one surrounding the cell body. One can modify the conditions to which the outgrowing axons are exposed; a radical change is the elimination of their peripheral field of distribution by extirpation of organ primordia, such as limb buds, in stages preceding the nerve ingrowth. Hamburger found in such experiments severe repercussions on the nerve cell body, which is the metabolic center of the neuron, to the point of cellular atrophy or complete cellular breakdown. The further analysis of this phenomenon of trophic dependency on peripheral conditions led to the discovery, by R. Levi-Montalcini, of a proteinic nerve growth factor specific for sympathetic and sensory ganglion cells.

In later years Hamburger turned his attention to an exploration of the embryology of behavior. Progress in this area had been impeded by the lack of adequate tools for rigorous analysis. A significant advance was made by introducing the previously mentioned methods of microneurosurgery to this field. The investigation of motility in normal chick embryos and in embryos with diverse neurological lesions brought to light new phenomena that necessitated a reappraisal of the ideas on which previous work had been based. The motility of the chick embryo was found to be characterized by three features that had not been recognized before: It is *spontaneous* (that is, the discharges are generated in the central nervous system, and not by sensory stimulation), the activity is *periodic*, and the movements are uncoordinated *random* movements. Sensory stimulation was shown to be ineffective in eliciting the basic motility patterns. The latter point challenges the notion held by prominent behaviorists that the sensory input during the prenatal phase plays a significant role in the molding of postnatal behavior patterns.

Hamburger was mindful of the promulgation of concepts and methodology of the general field of experimental embryology. His *Manual of Experimental Embryology* (1942; 2d ed. 1960) gives equal weight to theoretical and practical aspects and stresses the opportunities for experimentation on living embryos. The manual has encouraged the establishment of laboratory courses in this area. Workers in the field of chick embryology had been handicapped by the lack of precision in the identification of developmental stages on the basis of chronological age. Hamburger, together with Hamilton, overcame this difficulty by creating a standard stage series based on reliable morphological criteria. This stage series has been adopted by practically all laboratories using the chick embryo.

The son of an industrialist, Hamburger received his advanced education at the universities of Heidelberg (1919–20), Munich (1920–21), and finally Freiburg (Ph.D., 1924), where he became the student of the leading German experimental embryologist, Hans Spemann. He spent several years in the Division for Experimental Embryology at the Kaiser Wilhelm Institute for Biology (now the Max Planck Institute) in Berlin-Dahlem. In 1927 he returned to Freiburg as a privatdozent. In 1932 he received a Rockefeller fellowship to continue research at the University of Chicago under F. R. Lillie, in whose laboratory pioneer work had been done on avian experimental embryology. In 1935 he joined the faculty at Washington University in St. Louis. He became chairman of the department of zoology there in 1941, and retired from this position in 1966. He was elected to the National Academy of Sciences in 1953 and to the American Academy of Arts and Sciences in 1959.

For background information *see* EMBRYOLOGY, EXPERIMENTAL; NERVOUS SYSTEM in the McGraw-Hill Encyclopedia of Science and Technology. □

★ HAMMOND, George Simms

American chemist
Born May 22, 1921, Auburn, Maine, U.S.A.

THE PERIOD of development of the science of chemical dynamics is not clearly marked. At the turn of the century a number of men, notably S. Arrhenius and T. M. Lowry, were working very hard to understand the underlying principles of chemical dynamics. A. G. Donnan belonged to the same school, although his contribution is not generally recognized, largely because of an awkwardness in his discussions. In any event, these men established the existence of a close relationship between the rates of chemical reaction and the chemical potentials in react-

ing systems. In the 1920s enormous progress was made in the area of organic chemistry by a kind of pseudothermodynamic methodology. Leaders were Sir Robert Robinson and Sir Christopher Ingold. They realized that variation in the nature of the substituents remote from the reaction center in complex molecules could have a profound influence on the quantitative characteristics of reactivity, and that these subtle influences could be a valuable probe in the study of reaction mechanisms. During the next two decades, 1930–50, this kind of thinking was expanded remarkably by many people, the foremost probably being Paul Bartlett and Saul Winstein. Principal emphasis was on organic chemistry, and the active field became largely associated with organic reaction mechanisms, although Henry Taube and others pioneered similar study of inorganic reactions. Complementary work by Henry Eyring and Louis Hammett led to development of a general theory of reaction rates in which chemical potentials were posited to play a role in determining reaction rates analogous to their role in determining the position of equilibrium in chemical reactions.

Hammond entered the field of reaction mechanisms during the late 1940s. The bent of his interests was strongly influenced by the fact that he took his doctoral degree with Bartlett and then did postdoctoral work with Winstein. During the first 10 years of his independent career, Hammond pursued the goals traditional to physical organic chemistry at the time. His first work dealt with the mechanism of a curious transformation which is known as the benzidine rearrangement; he showed that a highly imaginative theory of the mechanism of the reaction could not be right in detail because it

predicted a rate law for the reaction that was not in accord with experimental observations. He studied the effects of remote substituents in solvolytic displacement reactions and was one of the first to point out the existence of systematic deviations from the Hammett equation, a valuable correlation of the reactivities of various derivatives of benzene. He also undertook studies of the reactions of transient species, known as free radicals, and suggested an interesting but short-lived theory as to the mode of action of antioxidants.

During 1948–58 Hammond felt increasing dissatisfaction with current theories of chemical reactivity. They depended too strongly on a posteriori rationalization of experimental results in terms of highly artificial models, in which electrons were chased around structural formulas written on pieces of paper. Another unattractive feature of established practice was the unnatural separation of organic and inorganic chemistry. In 1955 Hammond published an intuitive theoretical paper in which he suggested a rational basis for the seemingly whimsical relationships between variation in reaction rates and the overall energy changes in elementary reactions. After that time he became increasingly interested in theories of rate processes.

In 1952 Hammond began the study of the mechanisms of photochemical reactions, although he did not publish in the field until 1959. He went on to produce more than 50 papers on the subject. The underlying theme in his study was preoccupation with the chemical behavior of energy-rich molecules, which cannot possibly follow the principles of pseudoequilibrium states in their dynamic behavior. Among his strongest interests was study of the transfer of electronic excitation energy from one molecule to another, a critical step in "sensitized" photoreactions, in which light is absorbed by one species and chemistry is done by another. The work was extended into the field of high-energy radiation chemistry with promising results. While photochemical studies were under way in Hammond's laboratory, he also initiated a program for study of the kinetics and mechanisms of reactions of metallic compounds with molecular oxygen. Included were reactions in which oxidizable metallic compounds serve as catalysts for the oxidation of cosubstrates. The work may ultimately supplement studies of the role of metal-containing oxidases in biological systems.

Hammond received his B.S. (1943) at Bates College and his M.S. and Ph.D. in chemistry (1947) at Harvard University. He taught at Iowa State University from 1948 to 1958, then moved to the California Institute of Technology, where he was professor of organic chemistry from 1958 to 1964 and Arthur Amos Noyes Professor of Chemistry from 1964. He received the American Chemical Society's Award in Petroleum Chemistry in 1961. He was elected to the National Academy of Sciences in 1963 and to the American Academy of Arts and Sciences in 1965.

Hammond wrote *Quantitative Organic Analysis*, with J. S. Fritz (1957), and *Organic Chemistry*, with D. J. Cram (1959).

For background information *see* Free radical; Kinetics (chemical); Photochemistry in the McGraw-Hill Encyclopedia of Science and Technology. □

★ HANBURY BROWN, Robert

British astronomer
Born Aug. 31, 1916, Aruvankadu, India

Hanbury brown in 1936 joined the original team, under R. A. Watson-Watt, which developed radar in Great Britain. He was also one of a small group, led by E. G. Bowen, who pioneered airborne radar. In the course of this work he carried out several thousand hours of experimental work in aircraft on the use of radar for night fighting and the detection of ships and submarines. After the war he joined A. C. B. Lovell at Jodrell Bank and applied his experience in the techniques of radar to astronomy. At that time a large, fixed paraboloid antenna (218 ft in diameter) had been built by the staff at Jodrell Bank for an experiment on radar, which was unsuccessful. Hanbury Brown applied this large antenna to the reception of cosmic radio waves and used it to make detailed radio maps of the limited region of sky within its field of view. The most striking feature of these maps was the radio emission from our own galaxy, and this suggested a search for a similar phenomenon in other, more distant galaxies. In 1949 Hanbury Brown, working with C. Hazard, succeeded in detecting the radio emission from the nearest large galaxy, the Great Spiral Nebula in Andromeda Messier 31. In the next few years they used the large, fixed paraboloid to survey other, more distant galaxies, the so-called radio stars, and our own Milky Way. One valuable byproduct of this work was to demonstrate the application and potentialities of a large pencil-beam instrument, which was an important step in the evolution of the steerable 250-ft paraboloid at Jodrell Bank.

The point sources of radio emission, or radio stars, were at that time a complete mystery, and in 1949 Hanbury Brown decided that a valuable clue to their nature would be to measure their apparent angular size. However, if, as some people thought, these sources are bodies like stars, then a measurement of their angular size would require an instrument with a resolving power at radio wavelengths very much less than one second of arc. Such high resolving power could, in principle, be achieved by making a radio interferometer with an extremely long base line; but this raised the difficult technical problem of combining the radiation received at two widely separated receivers with the necessary stability of phase. While thinking of ways around this problem, Hanbury Brown realized that there are similarities between the radiation received at two separated points which can be exploited to make an interferometer without necessarily preserving relative phase. He put forward the idea of correlating the low-frequency fluctuations in the intensities of the radiation received by two spaced detectors. This proposal was tested in a radio interferometer, which in 1952 was used to measure the angular size of the two principal radio sources in Cygnus and Cassiopeia. A mathematical analysis of this idea, carried out with R. Q. Twiss, confirmed that it has two advantages: Not only does it make possible the construction of interferometers with extremely high resolving power, but it obviates the errors introduced by atmospheric scintillation. Hanbury Brown and Twiss also realized that it could be applied to optical astronomy to solve the classical problem of measuring the angular size of the bright visible stars and, in particular, of the hot stars that had not previously been measured. When considered from an optical, rather than a radio, point of view, they saw that the technique implied that there is a correlation in the arrival time of photons at two spaced detectors. To confirm this conclusion, Hanbury Brown set up an optical system and electronic correlator; with Twiss, he showed that this correlation between photons does exist and that it is in quantitative agreement with theory. As a next step, they modified two former Army searchlights to act as light collectors and measured the angular size of the hot star Sirius in 1956. This new technique was called "intensity interferometry."

The next stage in the program was to develop a full-scale stellar-intensity interferometer to measure the angular size of several stars and, in particular, to measure for the first time hot stars in the spectral range O to F. The principal objective of this program was to establish the temperature scale for hot stars. A stellar interferometer, using two mosaic mirrors (22 ft in diameter) moving on a circular railway track (618 ft in diameter) and an associated electronic correlator, was developed in Great Britain and installed in 1962 at the Narrabri Observatory of Sydney University in Australia. Using this instrument, Hanbury Brown and his colleagues measured the angular size of Vega in 1964 and later measured many more hot stars. The observational results from this work are expected to contribute substantially to our knowledge of the temperatures and the actual sizes of the hot stars.

Hanbury Brown studied engineering at Brighton Technical College and took an external degree at London University. He was a postgraduate student at the City and Guilds College. He joined the Air Ministry's radar research team at Bawdsey Manor in 1936 and worked on radar until 1947. From 1942 to 1945 he worked at the Naval Research Laboratory in Washington, D.C., as a member of the British Air Commission. In 1947 he joined Watson-Watt as a private consultant on radar, and in 1949 he joined Lovell at Jodrell Bank. He was appointed professor of radio astronomy at the University of Manchester in 1960, and left Great Britain in 1962 to become professor of physics (astronomy) in the University of Sydney. He was elected a fellow of the Royal Society in 1960.

Hanbury Brown wrote *The Exploration of Space by Radio*, with A. C. B. Lovell (1957).

For background information *see* INTERFEROMETRY; RADAR; RADIO ASTRONOMY in the McGraw-Hill Encyclopedia of Science and Technology. ☐

★ HARRAR, Jacob George

American biologist, plant pathologist, and foundation executive
Born Dec. 2, 1906, Painesville, Ohio, U.S.A.

A BIOLOGIST and plant pathologist by training, with wide experience in research, teaching, and administration in his field and numerous scientific publications to his credit, Harrar was chosen in 1942 to create and administer in Mexico the Rockefeller Foundation's first cooperative assistance program in agricultural science. Under his leadership, the foundation's program proved itself one of the most successful efforts toward scientifically increasing the quantity and quality of food crops, particularly cereals; the program now extends throughout Latin America, Africa, and Asia. Harrar's role evolved from scientific experimenter and administrator of the foundation's agricultural program in Mexico to director of its entire agricultural program, to vice-president, and, in 1961, to president.

As president, Harrar worked with his board of trustees and officers in revising and reorienting the program of the foundation to cope more fully with the problems of the contemporary world. By decision of the board of trustees in 1963, the foundation is concentrating its efforts in five areas: the conquest of hunger by improving the quantity and quality of food supplies; the solution of population problems; the strengthening of emerging centers of learning in the developing nations; the provision of better educational opportunities for the disadvantaged groups in the United States; and the enhancement of the cultural lives of Americans.

In 1942, several years before the U.S. government embarked on the Point Four Program initiated by President Truman, the foundation had come to the realization that, for humanitarian, social, economic, and political reasons, the great gap between the standards of living in the underdeveloped nations and those of the more advanced, industrialized nations would have to be closed, and that the most effective way to do this was to provide skillful technical assistance. To carry out such an assistance program required a whole new cadre of exceptionally qualified professional men—well-trained scientists with the ability to teach and demonstrate the methods of modern science and the use of its tools to the future scientists and leaders of the developing nations. In the beginning, these were Americans, but as capable, young nationals were selected and prepared, they replaced the American scientists.

The initial thrust of the Rockefeller Foundation's program in Mexico was to work closely with the Mexican government in an attempt to increase those basic foods essential to the diet of the Mexican people. The foundation's efforts were primarily directed toward raising the yields of both corn and wheat by improving plant varieties, increasing the fertility of the soil, and controlling the pests and pathogens that took so heavy a toll of Mexico's agricultural products. Harrar organized a team of American specialists, experienced in the several disciplines of plant science, who immediately went to work to solve the country's serious food production problems. Low-yielding, inefficient varieties of food crops were replaced by improved varieties adapted for disease resistance and local climatic, soil, and topographical conditions. While the plant breeders, plant pathologists, and plant physiologists were thus engaged, the entomologists were developing methods for the control of insect pests, and the soil scientists were improving the systems of soil management and water utilization and encouraging the increased use of chemical fertilizers. Each of the American specialists became the leader of small groups of Mexican agronomists who had been assigned to the foundation's program by the Mexican Ministry of Agriculture. These young Mexicans, some 700 in all, received training and gained experience in research methods on the problems which were limiting their country's production of food crops. As each project showed it was on the way to becoming a success, other food crops were added; besides corn and wheat, eventually there were sections on potatoes, vegetables, sorghum, barley, and forage and pasture legumes and grasses. The last step was to extend the work into the animal sciences, with research on poultry, dairy and beef cattle, swine, and sheep.

Under Harrar's guidance, the foundation's program followed the same pattern in each crop improvement project. First, the indigenous varieties were collected and tested; the best were then selected for immediate release to the Mexican farmers. Promising tested materials from other countries were brought in and tested for their suitability to the Mexican environment. From the germ plasm banks thus created, the plant scientists were able to create higher-yielding, disease-resistant varieties adapted to particular Mexican regions. Mexico became self-sufficient in wheat production in 1956 and in corn production in 1958. In 1960 the cooperative program was converted into the National Institute of Agricultural Research, directed and managed by Mexican scientists. Even though the population of Mexico has almost doubled since 1943, today the country can produce all the corn it needs on less land by using adapted hybrid varieties. Mexico now has a wheat surplus and is beginning to devote some of its wheat lands to other food crops. This was made possible by the development of rust-resistant, dwarf varieties of wheat that make highly efficient use of fertilizers.

Within a few years the success of the Mexican cooperative program led to invitations to the foundation from Colombia, Chile, and India to establish similar types of research and training projects in those countries in intimate association with national leadership and institutions. Still later, in cooperation with the Ford Foundation, the International Rice Research Institute was established in Asia, with the Philippines as the host country. Currently, an international center for the improvement of maize and wheat is being established in Mexico, and in prospect are tropical research centers in Colombia and Nigeria. The Ford and Rockefeller foundations are associated in various ways in the planning and development of these autonomous international centers, which will be operated under the authority of an international board of trustees with a thoroughly international staff of qualified investigators. The object of this international program is the mobilization of science at centers where its application can be most effective in bringing about substantial increases in world food production during the years ahead.

As a result of his long and varied experience in the area of assistance to the developing nations, Harrar came to believe there are certain basic principles that could serve as a guide to most cooperative assistance programs abroad. All of these principles are predicated on the optimistic assumption that society everywhere will make rapid and substantial progress toward population stabilization. The greatest obstacle to providing sufficient food for the world's hungry is uncontrolled population growth. Unless the rate of human increase can be significantly reduced and ultimately stabilized, all efforts to provide adequate food, feed, and other material requirements for human life and comfort will surely come to naught. The principles are:

1. The highest form of assistance the advanced nations can provide is to help the developing nations help themselves achieve realistic and important national goals. Each nation's objective should be to develop to the maximum its own human and natural resources, free from dependence upon aid from abroad. And, when foreign assistance is supplied by the more advanced countries, except in dire emergencies it should be directed toward the goal of local self-sufficiency and the avoidance of a permanent dependence on charity from abroad.

2. The solution of the food problems of the underdeveloped countries and the world in general in the near future will not be based on breakthroughs in nonconventional agriculture, but will have to be based on improvements in present conventional practices. This means increasing the fertility of the soil, applying both chemical and organic fertilizers, controlling pests and diseases, making use of the best cultural practices, and planting new varieties which will produce greater yields, have higher nutritive value, and be resistant to disease. Experiments in nonconventional agriculture—such as hydro-

ponics; farming the sea for protein sources; developing edible protein compounds from leaves, certain petroleum compounds, and natural gas; and utilizing microorganisms as potential major sources of protein—are all potential sources of food, but cannot be counted on to add substantially to the world's food supplies in the early future.

3. Another important requisite for successful technical cooperation is a keen desire and demonstrated interest on the part of the developing nation to improve its economic viability and to correct its deficit position as regards food production. Without this willingness on the part of the nation itself and without vigorous local initiative and enterprise, the most up-to-date scientific knowledge and the most modern tools and equipment will be of no avail.

4. To be successful, agriculture must be approached as a business—as a way of earning a living—and conducted along the same principles as any other economically productive enterprise. In many of the underdeveloped areas, agriculture is looked upon as a way of life. Since this way of life is firmly entrenched in the traditional social structure, agriculture cannot become a productive sector of the economy and the level of food production cannot be effectively raised, unless there is a "rationalization" of agriculture—the application of scientific methods to the production of food. Moreover, like a successful business, productive agriculture requires the assistance of capital, credit, equipment, markets, transportation facilities, skilled personnel, high levels of education, and continuing research to discover and apply new technologies. Agriculture cannot function successfully if it is treated as an isolated segment of the country's economy, but must be integrated with the rest of the society—industry, banking and commerce, the educational system, public health and nutrition, transportation and communication. Agriculture should be able to draw upon all these components for support and reinforcement, and it in turn will be in a position to complement and benefit them.

5. Modern science and technology have now provided the knowledge to transform the food production of the world. The Earth could today produce at least two or three times more on existing arable land by the known methods of conventional agriculture. As far as scientific knowledge is concerned, there is no reason why all men should not be adequately fed, and there is no longer any excuse for human starvation. The tools, methods, and materials are all available and their uses are well enough understood so that, with suitably planned programs, areas of underproduction could begin to achieve their full agricultural potential. However, it is no simple or easy task to modernize traditional

agricultural practice, and ultimate success depends on intelligent understanding, progressive attitudes, knowledgeable and capable leadership, and a sense of dedicated determination on the part of everyone concerned.

The son of an engineer, Harrar graduated from Oberlin College in 1928 and received the M.S. from Iowa State University in 1929. He then joined the faculty of the University of Puerto Rico, where he was professor and head of the department of biology. Four years later he returned to the United States to resume his graduate studies, and in 1935 received a Ph.D. in plant pathology from the University of Minnesota. He was then appointed to the staff of Virginia Polytechnic Institute, where he became a professor in the department of biology. In 1941 he went to Washington State College as professor, head of the department of plant pathology, and head of the plant pathology division of the university's agricultural experiment station. In 1942 he was appointed to the Rockefeller Foundation. The recipient of numerous honors, degrees, and citations from foreign governments and from both American and foreign universities, he was awarded the Public Welfare Medal of the National Academy of Sciences in 1963. He was elected to the American Academy of Arts and Sciences in 1952 and to the National Academy of Sciences in 1966.

Harrar wrote *Guide to Southern Trees*, with E. S. Harrar (1946), *Principles of Plant Pathology*, with E. C. Stakman (1957), various scientific research papers in the fields of phytopathology and mycology, and many articles of general interest on world food problems, population, private philanthropy, economic development overseas, and environmental quality.

For background information *see* AGRICULTURAL CHEMISTRY; AGRICULTURAL ENGINEERING; AGRICULTURAL SCIENCE (ANIMAL); AGRICULTURAL SCIENCE (PLANT); AGRICULTURE in the McGraw-Hill Encyclopedia of Science and Technology.   □

★ HARRIS, Geoffrey Wingfield

English anatomist
Born June 4, 1913, London, England

IN THE early 1930s much was known concerning the function of the ductless (endocrine) glands of the body and the action of the chemicals (hormones) that they secrete into the blood stream. Little information was available, however, about the factors responsible for regulating the activity of these glands. A few important observations had been made which indicated that they were under some form of central nervous control. For example, it was known that

in the rabbit and a few other mammals ovulation was normally triggered by the act of coitus. It seemed likely that mating in these animals excited a nervous reflex which, in turn, led to increased secretion of gonadotropic (luteinizing) hormone from the anterior pituitary gland, which then resulted in ovulation.

In his first research Harris tested this idea. He applied electrical stimuli to the hypothalamus, the part of the brain closest to, and connected by a stalk with, the pituitary gland, and found that it was possible to excite the suggested reflex pathways artificially and thus produce gonadotropin secretion and ovulation. With this direct evidence that the hypothalamus could influence the secretion of gonadotropic hormone, Harris argued in 1937: "It might be theorized that the hypothalamus controls the secretion of hormones, other than the gonadotropic hormone, from the anterior lobe. . . . There is no reason to doubt that the thyrotropic, adrenotropic, lactogenic, parathyrotropic and growth hormones are not similarly controlled." This hypothesis remained a focal point in his work.

To study the secretion of other anterior pituitary hormones following hypothalamic stimulation, it became necessary to devise a method of electrical stimulation which could be applied in unanesthetized and unrestrained animals over long periods of time. For this purpose the remote-control method was developed. Pickup units were implanted in rabbits so that the necessary voltages for brain stimulation could be induced in the freely moving animal from a field coil surrounding the animal's cage. This technique was tested by applying stimuli to the nerve supply of the posterior pituitary gland, the secretory responses of which can be measured in

a matter of seconds. It was found that secretion of posterior-lobe hormones could be easily obtained and quantitated against the duration and intensity of stimulation. Using this technique, Harris found (with de Groot) that hypothalamic stimulation can excite secretion of the adreno-corticotropic hormone, and (with Woods) secretion of thyrotropic hormone. These experiments and others dealing with hypothalamic lesions gradually made it possible to plot different regions in the hypothalamus of importance for the control of the spectrum of pituitary hormones.

In studying the effects of hypothalamic stimulation on anterior pituitary activity, Harris was struck by the fact that, although stimulation of the hypothalamus easily evoked increased secretion of anterior pituitary hormones, electrical stimulation of the pituitary gland itself was ineffective. Simultaneous with these observations were the publications of many histologists that very few, if any, nerve fibers pass from the hypothalamus into the anterior pituitary. It seemed, then, that the anterior pituitary is a gland under nervous control, but lacking a nerve supply—in other words, that a final link in the control mechanism is humoral in nature. In 1930 and 1933 Popa and Fielding had described in the human a local vascular system in the pituitary stalk, called the hypophyseal portal vessels, that connects the median eminence at the base of the hypothalamus with the anterior pituitary gland. In 1944 Harris suggested that this portal vascular system might form the final link in the anatomical pathway by which the brain controls the anterior pituitary gland, and thus the other major endocrine glands in the body. With J. D. Green, he investigated and described the anatomy of these vessels in a number of laboratory mammals. To see if these vessels had any specific importance for anterior pituitary function, he studied rats in which the pituitary stalk had been cut. In some of these animals vascular regeneration was allowed to occur, and these showed a return of anterior pituitary function; in other animals regeneration was blocked, and obvious signs of pituitary deficiency were observed. Further work, in collaboration with Dora Jacobsohn, showed clearly for the first time that pituitary transplants, in which the transplanted tissue becomes revascularized by these vessels, can function in an apparently normal manner although vascularization by other vessels results in an inactive gland. Harris suggested that different nerve tracts in the hypothalamus might liberate humoral agents (now termed "releasing factors") into the portal vessels and that these releasing factors might affect the secretory activity of the cells in the anterior pituitary gland. Workers in many laboratories in different countries later succeeded in extracting various releasing factors from hypothalamic tissue and in purifying them to a greater or lesser extent (possibly they are polypeptides). Harris and his group studied the physiology and chemistry of the releasing factor which regulates the secretion of luteinizing hormone, and they also developed a technique for measuring the amounts of this factor present in portal vessel blood from the pituitary stalk of rats.

Harris then turned his attention to the feedback action which the hormones in the blood exert on the brain. By developing a technique for implanting minute solid fragments of hormones in different areas of the brain, he, with Michael, showed that it was possible to define areas in cats' brains which regulate sexual behavior. He and others also showed the importance of hormones in the fetus for differentiating the brain into a male or female type.

Harris was educated at Dulwich College boys' school, at Cambridge University (B.A., 1935), and at St. Mary's Hospital, London (M.B., B.Chir., 1939). He was successively lecturer in anatomy, Cambridge University, 1940–47; lecturer in physiology, Cambridge University, 1948–52; and Fitzmary Professor of Physiology, London University, 1953–62. In 1962 he became Dr. Lee's Professor of Anatomy, Oxford University. In 1953 he was elected a fellow of the Royal Society of London, and was made a fellow of Hertford College, Oxford, in 1962 on being appointed to the chair of anatomy. In 1965 he became an honorary member of the American Academy of Arts and Sciences.

Harris wrote *Neural Control of the Pituitary Gland* (1955) and coedited with B. T. Donovan, and contributed to, *The Pituitary Gland* (1966).

For background information *see* ENDOCRINE GLAND; ENDOCRINE MECHANISMS; HORMONE; HORMONE, ADENOHYPOPHYSEAL; PITUITARY GLAND in the McGraw-Hill Encyclopedia of Science and Technology.   ☐

☆ HARRISON, James Merritt

Canadian geologist
Born Sept. 20, 1915, Regina, Saskatchewan, Canada

IF ONE were compelled to set forth Dr. Harrison's chief distinction in a word or two the definition that would come most readily to mind is 'diplomat scientist.' He possesses that peculiar and valuable skill of harmonizing many divergent views and disciplines so that they become dedicated to common endeavors—endeavors whose scope far transcends organizational and even national boundaries." These words, from his nomination for the Gold Medal of the Professional Institute of the Civil Service of Canada (1966), epitomize those special qualities which made possible Harrison's major contributions to science.

Harrison's first major scientific study of the anorthosites of southeastern Ontario (1944) was undertaken at a time when there was a wide

disparity of opinion on the origin of these rocks. Anorthosites are composed almost entirely of plagioclase feldspar. Experimental work indicated that temperatures required to keep such monomineralic rocks molten are much higher than are likely to occur in nature. It was widely believed that the anorthosites formed by the settling of feldspar crystals from crystallizing gabbroic magmas and that anorthosites do not exist as magmas. Harrison's detailed studies indicated that anorthosite magmas may exist and that anorthosite bodies may be emplaced as magmas. He pointed out that volatiles and titanium oxides and alkalies in an anorthosite magma may lower the melting point several hundred degrees, so that the temperature of crystallization is not unreasonably high.

From his studies of the Precambrian volcanic, sedimentary, and granitic rocks of central Manitoba (1949) and the alterations they have undergone since their formation hundreds of millions of years ago, Harrison showed that increasing intensity of regional metamorphism is marked by changes in mineral composition. Based on these changes, he divided the rocks into grades or zones. In the basic volcanic flows he recognized the concentration of certain minerals in particular layers by metamorphic differentiation that produced a pronounced banding or foliation in originally structureless rocks. He also demonstrated that ultrametamorphic processes had produced granitic rocks and that a considerable proportion of the granites in the region had been formed in this way.

In studies in the Flin Flon–Sherridon–Herb Lake mineral belt in west-central Manitoba, Harrison recognized (1951) a major structural lineament or composite of lineaments along the contact between the gneisses and schists of the Kisseynew complex to the north and the Amisk volcanic rocks to the south. He showed that this lineament was probably due to a deformed thrust fault, along which the Kisseynew gneisses had

been moved southeast over the Amisk-Missi strata. He suggested that the important mineral deposits of the district are related to faults extending north and south from the major fault and that the major fault marks the boundary between pyrrhotite-rich sulfide deposits to the north and pyrite-rich sulfide deposits to the south.

In 1950 Harrison undertook detailed study of a cross section of the Labrador Trough—a great belt of Proterozoic rocks in Quebec and Labrador containing large bodies of iron ore. In cooperation with geologists of the Iron Ore Co. of Canada, he worked out the stratigraphy, structure, and age relations of the rocks and iron ores of the belt. This early work (1952) formed the basis for the many studies that followed by other workers.

In 1956 Harrison was appointed director of the Geological Survey of Canada. This appointment curtailed his individual research but gave full play to his administrative and organizational talents and his gift of inspiring cooperation among his associates. During Harrison's regime as director of the Survey, the initial reconnaissance geological mapping of Canada approached completion. He became architect of the transition of the Survey from an organization concerned primarily with regional mapping to a research institution engaged mainly in the solution of the many fundamental problems brought to light by the regional mapping. That the Geological Survey became a vigorous, vibrant research institute of world repute is a tribute to Harrison's leadership in this transition. This was recognized by his appointment in 1964 as assistant deputy minister (research) of the Department of Mines and Technical Surveys, of which the Geological Survey was one of six branches, all concerned with the earth sciences. The Department of Mines and Technical Surveys was reorganized in 1966 and renamed the Department of Energy, Mines, and Resources. Harrison became assistant deputy minister (mines and geosciences) in the new department.

As the director of the Geological Survey of Canada, Harrison became chairman of the Canadian National Committee for Geology, and was thus involved in the international aspects of science. At the International Geological Congress in Copenhagen in 1960, Harrison played an important role in the formation of the International Union of Geological Sciences, and in 1961 he was elected its first president. The successful development of the International Union owes much to the ability of its first president to inspire collaboration. In 1963, following his presidency of the International Union, Harrison was elected to the Executive of the International Council of Scientific Unions as first vice-president, and in 1966 he became president.

Harrison received his B.Sc. from the University of Manitoba in 1935. After several years' employment as a chemist, he enrolled at Queen's University for graduate studies in geology, receiving his M.A. in 1941 and his Ph.D. in 1943. He then joined the Geological Survey of Canada and thereafter remained in government service. Harrison's contributions, especially in the field of international science, have been widely recognized. In 1963 he was the recipient of the Kemp Memorial Gold Medal from Columbia University for his "outstanding contributions to geological science in the field of public service"; in 1965 he was elected foreign associate of the U.S. National Academy of Sciences and received an honorary D.Sc. from the University of Manitoba; in 1966 he was awarded the Blaylock Medal of the Canadian Institute of Mining and Metallurgy for distinguished service to Canada in the field of geology and the International Cooperation Year Medal by the Canadian government. In 1967 he was elected president of the Royal Society of Canada.

For background information see FELDSPAR; IGNEOUS ROCKS; METAMORPHIC ROCKS; VOLCANOLOGY in the McGraw-Hill Encyclopedia of Science and Technology.   □

☆ HARTLINE, Haldan Keffer

American biophysicist
Born Dec. 22, 1903, Bloomsburg, Pa., U.S.A.

HARTLINE'S RESEARCHES over 40 years were concerned with basic aspects of the process of vision. In particular, he elucidated the electrical activity occurring in the eye and optic nerve at the cellular level, thereby enhancing the study not only of vision but of sense perception in general. For his work he received a share of the Nobel Prize for medicine or physiology in 1967.

Hartline's early studies of vision concerned the electrical responses of the retina, recorded as electroretinograms. He showed that these could be obtained from intact animals, without operation. He used invertebrates, especially insects, and various vertebrates, including human subjects. He was the first to record the form of the human electroretinogram.

By 1927 the British physiologist E. D. Adrian had measured the massed electrical discharge of the fibers in the optic nerve of the eel. Hartline sought to record the activity of single nerve fibers by using the methods of fiber isolation developed by Adrian and D. W. Bronk. He decided to experiment with the horseshoe crab (*Limulus*), since the compound eye of this antique and primitive creature, with its very large individual photoreceptors (ommatidia) and long optic nerve, seemed to afford a good chance of recording the electrical behavior of single nerve fibers. In 1932 Hartline and C. H. Graham at the Eldridge Reeves Johnson Foundation for Medical Physics succeeded in obtaining such recordings. They found that a single fiber of the optic nerve conveys information by means of trains of uniform nerve impulses, just as all other nerve fibers, sensory and motor, were known to do. Nerve impulses, as manifested by the electrical pulses that accompany them, are of fixed size and shape in any given nerve fiber; only the frequency of the impulse discharge varies. In the eye the brighter the light shining on a receptor, the higher is the frequency of discharge of impulses in its optic nerve fiber.

Experiments during the 1930s included the study of single receptor responses to short flashes of light. The neural discharge was shown to depend only on the energy of the flash (product of intensity by duration), as in the exposure of a photographic film. This was interpreted as an instance of the Bunsen-Roscoe law of photochemistry, applied to the photosensory mechanism of the receptor. Later Hartline, with P. R. MacDonald, studied the processes of light and dark adaptation of single *Limulus* photoreceptor cells, showing that the visual processes, familiar to everyone, are based in large measure on mechanisms residing in the receptors.

In 1935 Hartline and Graham measured the response of *Limulus* receptors to flashes of light at different wavelengths. Some years later, when the American biochemists Ruth Hubbard and George Wald made direct measurements of the absorption spectrum of *Limulus* rhodopsin, these earlier measurements of the spectral sensitivity of single receptors were found to be in good agreement.

Hartline moved into another field of vision when, in 1938, he took up the study of the vertebrate eye, using microdissection techniques to record the activity of individual fibers in the optic nerve. He found that the fibers making up the nerve did not all behave in the same way.

some discharging impulses only under steady light, others only as the light waxed or waned. Here was a demonstration that visual information begins to be differentiated from the very moment it is received, in the receptors themselves and in the retina, before the data have passed into the nervous system as a whole.

Following these experiments, Hartline returned to the horseshoe crab, investigating the phenomenon of the "generator potential." This takes place as the visual receptors depolarize the associated nerve fibers. As early as 1935 he had recorded such activity, but not until the early 1950s was detailed information forthcoming. Employing intracellular microelectrodes, Hartline (then at Johns Hopkins University), with H. G. Wagner and E. F. MacNichol, Jr., was able to record the slow depolarization of receptor cells that is an intermediate step between the primary photochemical events in the receptor and the local electric currents that generate the trains of nerve impulses in the receptor's nerve fiber.

About this time Hartline took up the study of interaction in the retina of *Limulus*, which consists of a plexus of nerve fibers, rich in synaptic regions, just back of the mosaic of ommatidia and interconnecting them. A few years earlier he had discovered that neighboring ommatidia inhibit one another mutually. With Wagner and F. Ratliff, he began a detailed quantitative analysis of this process, which he and Ratliff continued in their laboratory at the Rockefeller University.

Inhibitory interaction is a contrast-enhancing mechanism: Receptors in brightly lighted regions of the receptor mosaic inhibit those in dimly lighted neighboring regions more than the latter inhibit the former. Since the inhibitory interaction is stronger for near neighbors than for widely separated ones, edges and contours in the retinal image are accented. Thus a simple retinal mechanism effects a step in the integration of visual information. Hartline and Ratliff's experimental studies led to a mathematical formulation of the inhibitory interaction useful in the study of spatial aspects of visual pattern resolution and recognition. In recent years they and their colleagues extended these studies to the dynamics of the receptors and their interactions, with a view to understanding visual phenomena such as motion detection. Their studies also aimed at the elucidation of the mechanisms responsible for the generation of complex patterns of neural activity in the visual pathway, patterns that are highly specific to particular features of the patterns of the light and shade in the retinal image. Their contributions opened up new aspects of the study of the organs of perception and their influence on, and integration with, the nervous system as a whole.

After undergraduate work at Lafayette College (B.S., 1923) in Pennsylvania, Hartline went to Johns Hopkins University, where he received his M.D. in 1927; he stayed for another 2 years as a National Research Council fellow. From 1929 to 1931 he was a Johnson Traveling Research Scholar at the universities of Leipzig and Munich, returning to the United States to join the Johnson Research Foundation for Medical Physics at the University of Pennsylvania. There he remained, except for a year at the Cornell University Medical College in New York, until 1949, when he moved to Johns Hopkins as professor of biophysics. In 1953 Hartline joined the Rockefeller University in New York as professor. In addition to the Nobel Prize, he received the Howell Award in Physiology, the Warren Medal of the Society of Experimental Psychologists, and the A. A. Michelson Award of Case Institute. In 1959 he was awarded a honorary degree (D.Sc.) by Lafayette College. A member of the American Philosophical Society, he was elected to the National Academy of Sciences in 1948 and to the American Academy of Arts and Sciences in 1957. In 1966 he was elected a foreign member of the Royal Society in London.

For background information *see* EYE; VISION in the McGraw-Hill Encyclopedia of Science and Technology. □

★ HAUROWITZ, Felix Michael

American biochemist
Born Mar. 1, 1896, Prague, Czechoslovakia

THE EARLY scientific work of Haurowitz dealt principally with the chemistry of hemoglobin (Hb), the red pigment of the blood; Hb combines reversibly with oxygen, O_2, and carries O_2 from the lung to the tissues. Hemoglobin consists of a colorless protein, called globin, and a red material, called heme; the weight ratio of heme to globin is approximately

1:25. Heme is the ferrous complex of proto-porphyrin, a deep red organic compound which binds the iron atom very firmly. The Hb molecule, which has a molecular weight of approximately 68,000, consists of four subunits, each containing one heme. Haurowitz worked first with horse Hb, which can easily be obtained in the crystalline state. He demonstrated (1929) with H. Waelsch that heme is linked to the globin moiety of Hb by means of its iron atom. Oxidation of Hb by various oxidizing agents yields the ferric compound methemoglobin. Haurowitz succeeded (1935) in crystallizing complexes of methemoglobin with cyanide, fluoride, and hydrogen peroxide and demonstrated (1937) that the reduction of hemin to heme requires only one equivalent of hydrazine. Microscopy revealed (1938) that the combination of crystalline horse Hb with O_2 is accompanied by the conversion of the hexagonal hemoglobin plates into elongated oxyhemoglobin prisms. Evidently the binding of O_2 to Hb affects the combination of the four subunits of the Hb molecule. This is a typical allosteric reaction and is unique in that the allosteric change can be observed under the microscope. The rearrangement of the peptide structure of Hb which accompanies the combination with O_2 was clarified (1962) by x-ray diffraction analysis in the laboratory of M. F. Perutz.

Comparison of hemin with porphyrin complexes of other metals revealed (1933, 1938) correlations between the optical absorption of these complexes, their fluorescence, and their magnetic susceptibility. In contrast to other metal-porphyrins, hemin acts as a catalyst in the decomposition of H_2O_2. A short-lived hemin-H_2O_2 complex was observed (1937) when H_2O_2 was added to a solution of hemin in aqueous pyridine. It corresponds to the enzyme-substrate complexes postulated by M. Michaelis and M. L. Menten. Analogous complexes of catalase and peroxidase with H_2O_2 were later observed by Britton Chance.

In 1930 Haurowitz succeeded in preparing crystals of human hemoglobin by slow-freezing its aqueous solution and removing the ice crystals. F. von Krueger and his coworkers had found in 1910 that the umbilical blood of newborn children remains red after alkalinization, whereas the maternal blood under the same conditions is rapidly decomposed to a dark brown product. Kinetic analysis of the decomposition rate of the hemoglobin of newborn children revealed (1930) that the blood of the newborn contains a mixture consisting of 70–85% of fetal and 15–30% of adult hemoglobin. Haurowitz succeeded in isolating and crystallizing the human fetal Hb, whose crystals were quite different from those of the adult Hb. The affinity of the fetal Hb to O_2 was found (1935) to be higher than that of the adult Hb as long as both were in the red cells; after hemolysis of the red cells, O_2 was bound more firmly by the adult Hb. In both fetal and adult Hb the same heme was found; they differed from each other in their globin moieties. Other authors later discovered fetal Hb in patients suffering from Mediterranean anemia (thalassemia).

In 1929 Haurowitz became interested in immunochemical problems and started a series of investigations with the virologist F. Breinl in Prague. Although it was known then that the antibody properties are linked to the globulin fraction of the immune serum, it was not yet clear whether the antibodies are indeed globulins, or whether they are substances of an unknown nature, contaminated by globulins. To answer this question, Haurowitz isolated antigen-antibody precipitates and determined their amount gravimetrically; the antigens used were hemoglobin, azoproteins, or iodoproteins, which, owing to their color or their content of a specific constituent, could be determined quantitatively. The antibody content of the precipitates was obtained as the difference between the total weight and the weight of the antigen. The analyses showed that the substance which combined with the antigen had the properties of the serum globulins, and that the amount of globulin bound per milligram of antigen increased when the number of determinant groups per antigen molecule was increased. Haurowitz concluded (1930) that antibodies are indeed serum globulins, and that the specific combining site of an antibody molecule is complementarily adjusted to the determinant group of the homologous antigen. The mutual attraction of antigen and antibody was attributed to the mutual close fit which enables the combining sites to approach each other to such an extent that the short-range intermolecular forces become efficient. Although this view has been quite generally accepted, it is not yet clear how this complementariness is accomplished.

Haurowitz introduced the idea that the antigen may act as a template (or mold) in the formation of the antibody; he compared the action of the antigen to that of an electrode of complicated shape in galvanoplastics. Although it is not yet clear whether the antigen molecules act as templates, the idea of template action is now widely accepted and has been applied successfully to the biosynthesis of nucleic acids and proteins.

Using antigens whose determinant groups were labeled by radioactive isotopes, Haurowitz demonstrated (1952, 1961) the persistence of the radioactive label in phagocytic cells (macrophages) of the spleen, lung, lymph nodes, and liver over periods of many months, in agreement with the template theory which postulates that antibody can be formed only in the presence of antigen. It was also found that injection of an antigen containing two or more different determinant groups leads to the formation of multiple antibodies, each directed against only one of the antigenic determinants. Accordingly, injection of natural protein antigens generally yields a multiplicity of antibodies directed against various determinant groups in the surface of the antigenic protein molecules.

In view of the heterogeneity of antibodies against most antigens, Haurowitz attempted to isolate antibodies against single, small determinants of well-known chemical structure, such as the azophenylarsonate group of azoproteins, which are prepared by coupling of diazotized *p*-aminophenylarsonic acid to a protein carrier, for example, to bovine serum albumin (BSA). The antibodies directed against the *p*-azophenylarsonate group can be separated from the antibodies directed against BSA by precipitation of the former with an azoprotein in which the azophenylarsonate group is bound to another protein, for instance, ovalbumin. Haurowitz found that the antigen-antibody precipitate dissociates on acidification, and thus he succeeded in 1948 in preparing purified antibodies directed against simple haptens.

The ultimate goal of the immunochemical work of Haurowitz was the clarification of the mechanism of antibody formation, and the answer to the question whether the injected antigen acts as a template for the peptide chains of the nascent antibody molecules, or whether the antigen selects between an enormous number of globulin types which either are preformed or are formed by random mutations of the globulin-forming cells. A critical review of these problems was published by Haurowitz in *Nature* (1956) and in *Physiological Reviews* (1965).

In other experimental work Haurowitz was concerned with problems of protein biochemistry. He found that the optical rotation of proteins depends to a great extent on the number of their cystine residues (1961), and that peptides in vitro undergo transpeptidations in the presence of pepsin or chymotrypsin (1959). Similar transpeptidations may occur in vivo.

Haurowitz received his M.D. in 1922 and his D.Sc. in 1923 at the German University in Prague, where he was appointed in 1930 associate professor of physiological chemistry. In 1939 he became chairman of the department of biological chemistry at the University of Istanbul. In 1948 he moved to the United States, where he was appointed professor and later Distinguished Service Professor in the chemistry department of Indiana University. In 1956 he was elected to the Leopoldina Academy of Scientists (Germany). In 1960 he received the Paul Ehrlich Prize and Gold Medal for his work in immunochemistry.

Haurowitz wrote *Progress in Biochemistry* (1924; 5th ed. 1959), *Biochemistry: An Intro-* *ductory Textbook* (1955), and *Chemistry and Function of Proteins* (2d ed. 1963).

For background information *see* ANTIBODY; ANTIGEN; HEMOGLOBIN in the McGraw-Hill Encyclopedia of Science and Technology. □

★ HAWTHORNE, William Rede

British mechanical engineer
Born May 22, 1913, Benton, Newcastle on Tyne, England

HAWTHORNE WAS responsible for the design and development of the combustion chambers in the Whittle turbojet engine, which first flew in May, 1941. In July, 1940, when the Royal Aircraft Establishment (RAE) seconded Hawthorne to work with Frank Whittle's group, the problem of producing combustion chambers which would operate satisfactorily for more than 45 minutes had begun to limit the development of the engine for flight. The object of the combustion chamber in the turbojet engine was to raise the temperature of the air leaving the compressor at about 400°F to about 1450°F, at which temperature the gases entered the turbine. The temperature was increased by burning kerosine with the air as completely as possible in the smallest space and with a minimum drop in pressure. Realizing that the heat release rates required were much larger than had previously been obtained, efforts had been made to vaporize the fuel before it entered the combustion zone. Because of cracking and carbonization in the fuel vaporizers, these efforts had been unsuccessful.

During his graduate work at the Massachusetts Institute of Technology from 1935 to 1937, Hawthorne had studied the burning of a jet of combustible gas entering into, and burning in, surrounding air. At this time the combustion of fuels in furnaces had been treated in terms of chemical reaction rate theory. The work of Burke and Schumann on laminar diffusion flames had introduced the notion that, when a slow-moving jet of combustible gas is burning in air, the burning rate is determined by the rate at which fuel gas and oxygen diffuse toward the flame front, in which the reaction rate is relatively very rapid. Hawthorne showed that, when the velocity of the jet of gas is so high that the jet is turbulent, the turbulent mixing rate dominates the rate of combustion of the fuel. In the course of this work he showed that a sample of gas withdrawn from the turbulent flame may contain both free oxygen and unburned fuel gas. Thus, although at the sampling point the time mean concentration showed that there was enough oxygen to burn the fuel, the flame still consisted of eddies of unburned fuel alternating rapidly with eddies of unburned oxygen. He devised an "unmixedness" factor to measure this departure from uniform mixing. Hawthorne brought to the development of the combustion chamber for the Whittle engine the belief that in industrial combustion aerodynamic rather than chemical processes are dominant. By meticulous attention to the aerodynamic and mixing problems, a system based on atomized liquid spray injection of the fuel was developed to a satisfactory state.

In 1941 Hawthorne returned to the RAE as head of the Gas Turbine Division. The work of the Division included the extension of the work on axial compressors and internal aerodynamics (which had been started at the RAE by A. A. Griffith, H. Constant, and others before the war), performance prediction, turbojet engine testing both stationary and in flight, combustion and mixing problems, turbine blade vibration, as well as numerous other aspects of jet and rocket engines. Hawthorne was able to spare some time from his administrative duties to investigate the one-dimensional flow of compressible gases. He showed that, when a gas moves at high speed down a long tube, the effect of friction causes the Mach number to approach unity. He also showed that a similar choking effect occurs when heat is added to a moving stream of gas. Later, with A. H. Shapiro, he published a paper on the mechanics and thermodynamics of steady one-dimensional gas flow, which summarized the effects of area change, friction, and heat addition, removal, and mixing, and described methods of calculation, for which tables were subsequently compiled.

After World War II during 5 years at MIT, Hawthorne began to investigate the details of the flow in compressors and turbines. He continued this work at Cambridge, where he went in 1951. In an attempt to make a better prediction of the flow in turbomachinery, he assumed that each blade row in an axial compressor or turbine constitutes an actuator disk across which the flow velocity, angle, and pressure were changed by the action of the blades. The disturbance introduced by the actuator disk produces radial velocities which decays as distance from the disk increases. Approximate methods were evolved for computing the flow through successive actuator disks representing each blade row in a multistage compressor. The theoretical predictions were verified by experiments done by his students J. H. Horlock and J. Ringrose on annular cascades and compressors.

Along the inner and outer walls of the casing which contains the blades, the flow is complicated by the existence of wall boundary layers. It was found during World War II that the effect of the flow in these boundary layers is to reduce the work done in a compressor stage, an important matter in equipment which has to be as light and compact as possible. It had long been recognized that, when a river flows around a bend, the centrifugal pressure gradient acting on the slow-moving fluid in the boundary layer at the bottom of the river sets up transverse velocities—a secondary flow—normal to the main direction of the flow, so that a spiral motion persists far downstream of the bend. In 1949 Squire showed that these effects are due to the stretching of the vortex filaments present in the nonuniform flow approaching the bend and could, therefore, be predicted by appealing to the classical hydrodynamic theory of the flow of an inviscid fluid. In 1950 Hawthorne produced a general formula for the growth of the streamwise component of vorticity in a three-dimensional flow; in a classical experiment with his student H. Eichenberger he showed that, when a nonuniform flow enters a bent pipe, the flow first spirals in one direction and then, if the bend goes on long enough, the direction of the spiraling changes repeatedly. The theory was extended to the flow around struts, such as the bridge pier in a river, and a cusped profile was developed theoretically which reduced the secondary flow. This shape was shown experimentally to reduce the scouring of river beds at the nose of bridge piers. The theory was also successfully applied to nonuniform flow through the blades of turbomachines. Recently Hawthorne developed a systematic approach to the solution of problems in steady nonuniform flow of an inviscid fluid.

The advent of the computer has opened up new possibilities both in the application of secondary flow theory and its interaction with viscous boundary layers, and in the computation of three-dimensional effects in compressors and turbines. Many organizations are actively developing techniques for the latter purpose, and it is likely that the design of turbomachinery will be greatly advanced thereby.

In 1956 Hawthorne invented the Dracone flexible barge—a long, cylindrical plastic tube with faired ends which, when filled with oil, fresh water, or other fluids, floats in seawater and can be towed. Over 80 such vessels have been built ranging in size from 100 ft long with 5-ft diameter (50 tons capacity) to 300 ft long with 14-ft diameter (1100 tons capacity), and many are in use in various parts of the world. Unusual problems had to be solved, many of them hydrodynamic. The barge yaws and flexes under tow unless stabilized; it tends to porpoise beneath the waves at high speeds, and in rough seas internal pressure waves produce large dynamic stresses in the skin and cause the tail to flick with large accelerations. The construction of the skin also posed new problems in the engineering of high-strength rubberized fabrics.

In 1934 Hawthorne graduated with a B.A. in engineering from Cambridge University at the top of his class. After a year's practical work with Babcock and Wilcox Ltd. in Scotland, he went to MIT as a Commonwealth Fund fellow and received his Sc.D. in fuel technology. In 1937–39 he was a development engineer with Babcock and Wilcox Ltd., working on heat transfer and forced circulation boilers. In 1940 he joined the RAE, and in 1944–45 he was sent to the British Air Commission, Washington, D.C., for technical liaison duties with United States agencies and firms. After a year as deputy director (engine research), Ministry of Supply, London, he joined in 1946 the staff of the mechanical engineering department, MIT, as an associate professor; in 1948 he became George Westinghouse Professor. In 1951 he went to Cambridge as professor of applied thermodynamics. In 1955–56 he was the Hunsaker Professor of Aeronautical Engineering at MIT, and returned there in 1962–63 with frequent subsequent visits as a visiting institute professor. He was elected to the Royal Society in 1955, and became a foreign associate of the U.S. National Academy of Sciences in 1965.

For background information *see* AEROTHERMO-DYNAMICS; COMBUSTION CHAMBER; FLOW OF FLUIDS; THERMODYNAMIC PRINCIPLES in the McGraw-Hill Encyclopedia of Science and Technology.   □

★ HEBB, Donald Olding

Canadian psychologist
Born July 22, 1904, Chester, Nova Scotia, Canada

T HE PROBLEM with which Hebb's principal work began was met in the Montreal Neurological Institute during his 2-year appointment as research fellow in 1937–39. There Wilder Penfield had developed methods for the removal of scar tissue from the brain (for the treatment of epilepsy) that left the remaining brain substance in very nearly normal condition. The result was that the patient's intelligence—his

IQ—might show no effect of even large bilateral lesions in the frontal lobe. About this time S. N. Rowe also reported a case of removal of the entire right half of the cortex, despite which the patient could solve test problems at a level of superior intelligence. However, there was evidence to indicate that similarly large injuries to the infant brain produced serious retardation.

From these facts it seemed clear that the relation of intelligence to brain was quite different from what had been supposed. Some of the tissue of the brain, apparently, may be needed for the development of intelligence but may not be necessary for its maintenance. So the questions arose: What kind of development can this be? What are the changes in brain function during growth that, once established, tend to be irreversible? Psychologically, it seemed that the changes were the development of concepts; if so, what is a conceptual activity, or an idea, in terms of brain function? Without much progress Hebb worked on this problem from 1939 to 1944, when he became aware of the work of Rafael Lorente de Nó and saw some of the new possibilities it opened up.

At this time there were two classes of theory concerning the neural basis of behavior. One kind of theory assumed that all behavior is under the control of connections running from sensory surface to motor organ and treated all learning as the acquisition of new connections of this kind. The other deemphasized connections, utilizing instead one form or another of the field conception of physics; the sensory control of behavior was ascribed to distributions or ratios of excitation in the statistically homogeneous

mass of cortical neurons. In neither theory was there any provision for an activity in the brain other than what is directly initiated and controlled by sensory input: no autonomy, no holding of an excitation or delay in transmission. It seemed to Hebb, however, that the essence of a conceptual process or idea lies in its independence of the present sensory activity. Lorente de Nó's closed loops showed how this process might be possible. A reverberation could occur in which cell A excites cell B, B in turn reexcites A, which reexcites B, and so on; in this way an excitation fed into the cortex could continue after the removal of the stimulus, or some other activity in the cortex might start the reverberation in the total absence of the adequate stimulus event. Thus Hebb began looking at the possibility that an idea is a reverberation in a closed system in the cortex.

This line of speculation meant that thought consists of an interplay between closed systems in the brain, and between them and sense input and motor output (the latter always initiating some sensory feedback). However, the closed systems would hardly consist of the simple loops demonstrated anatomically by Lorente de Nó, but instead would have to be more complex. Hebb assumed that a learning process would be necessary to organize a number of simple loops into a more complex system. Also, it seemed that though there might be some degree of autonomy in their activity they could hardly function normally in the continued absence of sensory stimulation. It was these two assumptions that led to Hebb's experiments on the relation of the mammal to his sensory environment: first, the role of sensory events during the early growth period in the development of intelligence and personality; and second, their role at maturity in the maintenance of normal mental function.

The first kind of experiment was done with rats and dogs, depriving them of normal surroundings during growth (the same sort of procedure that was later used by H. F. Harlow for his studies of the infant monkey). The second was done with college students, who were paid to act as subjects in a procedure that allowed them to be physically comfortable but deprived them of vision and minimized auditory experience and tactual and somesthetic experience. In both kinds of experiment the results were dramatic. The rats and dogs were retarded in intelligence, and the dogs were persistently and extremely abnormal in motivation and social behavior as well. The college students showed loss of problem-solving ability, complained that they could not maintain a connected stream of thought, and in some cases developed elaborate visual and somesthetic hallucinations (in the latter, a student might report that his mind had left his body, that his head felt detached from his neck, or that he seemed to have two bodies lying side by side). These results are clearly related to certain hallucinatory experiences of long-distance truck drivers and pilots of aircraft at high altitudes. In general, the studies of the role of the normally varied sensory input showed

that the mammal has a much closer psychological dependence on his environment than had been supposed.

Both of Hebb's parents were doctors. He attended Dalhousie University (B.A., 1925). Abandoning the idea of novel writing as a career, he entered McGill University and began the study of psychology (M.A., 1932). He then went to Chicago to work with K. S. Lashley. When Lashley went to Harvard, Hebb followed and obtained the Ph.D. under his direction in 1936. Then came the appointment with Penfield (1937–39), 3 years of teaching at Queen's University during 1939–42, and a 5-year appointment as research fellow at the Yerkes Laboratories of Primate Biology, Orange Park, Fla. (a chimpanzee research station). In 1947 he was appointed professor of psychology at McGill. Awarded the Warren Medal of the Society of Experimental Psychologists in 1958, Hebb became a fellow of the Royal Society of Canada in 1959, a foreign member of the American Academy of Arts and Sciences in 1961, and a fellow of the Royal Society of London in 1966.

Hebb wrote *Organization of Behavior* (1949) and *Textbook of Psychology* (1958; 2d ed. 1966).

For background information *see* BRAIN; ENVIRONMENT; INTELLIGENCE; MOTOR SYSTEMS in the McGraw-Hill Encyclopedia of Science and Technology.   □

★ HEIDELBERGER, Michael

American immunochemist
Born Apr. 29, 1888, New York, N.Y., U.S.A.

KNOWING HIS preference at an early age, Heidelberger was trained in organic and analytical chemistry and worked for a year with Richard Willstätter in Zurich after receiving his Ph.D. at Columbia University in 1911, under the direction of M. T. Bogert. He was associated with W. A. Jacobs at the Rockefeller Institute in chemotherapeutic studies, culminating in the synthesis of Tryparsamide, a remedy for African sleeping sickness. At the hospital of the Institute, in D. D. Van Slyke's laboratory, he devised a method for the preparation of large quantities of crystalline equine oxyhemoglobin with its oxygen-carrying capacity unimpaired. During the course of this research, Heidelberger invented the refrigerated centrifuge, since then an indispensable and ubiquitous aid in biochemistry. He developed an interest in immunochemistry during a joint investigation on hemoglobin with Karl Landsteiner. He then joined forces with O. T. Avery, who with A. R. Dochez had discovered the "soluble specific substance" or capsular, type-specific, antigenic material of *Pneumococcus*. Their joint research, later assisted by W. F. Goebel, gave the first intimation of the importance of polysaccharides in immune phenomena, since each of the pneumococcal types investigated possessed a chemically different capsule composed of sugars. After a year spent in reorganizing the clinical chemical laboratories of Mt. Sinai Hospital in New York, and at the invitation of W. W. Palmer, in 1928 Heidelberger joined the department of medicine at the College of Physicians and Surgeons of Columbia University as the first full-time research chemist in a department of medicine; he received also the appointment of chemist to the Presbyterian Hospital.

After perusal of Arrhenius's *Immunochemistry*, Bordet's *Traité d'Immunologie*, and some of the polemics between the schools of Bordet and Ehrlich, it became evident to Heidelberger that many of the most fundamental problems of immunology were incapable of solution with the purely relative methods of titration then available, and that it should be possible to apply microanalytical methods conforming to the rigid criteria of analytical chemistry. The time (1928) seemed propitious, for L. D. Felton had shown that partially purified antibodies could be obtained by pouring hyperimmune antipneumococcal horse serum into 10 to 20 volumes of slightly acidulated water. Most of the antibodies were precipitated with the water-insoluble globulins of the serum, and a high proportion of the nonspecific proteins remained in solution. The precipitate, dissolved in buffered saline, furnished the antibody solution. The initial antigens used were the capsular polysaccharides of the pneumococcal types II and III, which Heidelberger and Avery had shown to be free of nitrogen. In these immune systems, then, to equal volumes of an antibody solution of known nitrogen content one could add increasing amounts of polysaccharide, allow the resulting precipitation to go to completion, and measure nitrogen microanalytically by difference in the supernatant solution.

Analyses of this nature were carried out with F. E. Kendall, then modified and extended to whole serums and to protein-antiprotein systems, and a quantitative theory of immune precipitation was proposed. With E. A. Kabat, this quantitative, absolute method for the estimation of precipitating antibodies was extended to the measurement in weight units of bacterial agglutinins. From the new quantitative theory Heidelberger could predict a method for the isolation of analytically pure antibodies, and when this was realized (also independently by K. Goodner and F. L. Horsfall, Jr.), the last link was forged in the chain of evidence that antibodies were actually modified serum globulins. From this point on, it became possible to devise rational theories as to how and where in the animal body antibodies are formed, and to isolate highly purified antibodies and study their physical and chemical properties.

Heidelberger extended the new quantitative methods to a study of complement and showed that complement added weight to immune precipitates, thus putting an end to the long dispute as to whether complement had actual substance or was merely an unstable colloidal state of serum proteins. With M. Mayer, A. J. Weil, H. P. Treffers, O. G. Bier, A. G. Osler, and others, he studied the mechanism of the fixation of complement in immune reactions, rediscovering the importance of magnesium ions and proposing a theory of complement fixation.

All of these methods and their extension and development in the hands of the original group and many others provided a solid basis for the development of immunology into a flourishing, modern science of extraordinary power.

During World War II Heidelberger and Catherine MacPherson adapted the quantitative method to estimate the small amounts of antibody formed in man (medical student volunteers) following the injection of pneumococcal polysaccharides. On the basis of their data, a field trial was made in a large training center for aviators which had been plagued by epidemics of pneumonia. This resulted in the cessation within 2 weeks in the 10,000 injected subjects of cases of pneumonia due to the pneumococcal types whose polysaccharides had been injected.

Subsequent studies of Heidelberger and his coworkers dealt mainly with relations between chemical constitution and immunological specificity, principally with respect to carbohydrates but later also in protein-antiprotein systems. He showed how many immunological cross-reactions could be predicted from the original quantitative theory of immune precipitation, and how much could be learned of the chemistry of polysaccharides from such cross-reactions.

Heidelberger was raised in New York City. He

received his B.S. (1908), A.M. (1909), and Ph.D. (1911) at Columbia University. After 27 years at the College of Physicians and Surgeons of Columbia University, he was visiting professor of immunochemistry at the Institute of Microbiology of Rutgers University in 1955–64. In 1964 he went to the department of pathology in the Medical School of New York University as adjunct professor of pathology. Besides a number of honorary degrees, Heidelberger received the Lasker Award of the American Public Health Association in 1953, the von Behring Award in 1954, the Pasteur Medal of the Swedish Medical Society in 1960, and the T. Duckett Jones Memorial Award of the Helen Hay Whitney Foundation in 1964. He was a foreign member of the Royal Danish Academy of Sciences and the Accademia Nazionale dei Lincei, and an officer of the Légion d'Honneur. He was elected to the National Academy of Sciences in 1942.

Heidelberger was coeditor, with O. J. Plescia, of *Immunochemical Approaches to Problems in Microbiology* (1961). He wrote *Lectures in Immunochemistry* (1956).

For background information *see* ANTIBODY; ANTIGEN; COMPLEMENT (SERUM); IMMUNITY; PNEUMOCOCCUS in the McGraw-Hill Encyclopedia of Science and Technology.   □

★ HEIM, Roger Jean

French naturalist and writer
Born Feb. 12, 1900, Paris, France

HEIM SUCCESSIVELY studied various spheres of mycology, especially the systematics, anatomy, and biology of higher mushrooms and their chemical, toxicologic, and phylogenetic aspects. Study trips in tropical countries enabled him to collect a considerable number of specimens; this, in turn, led him to cultivate many species. He explored Madagascar, West Africa, New Caledonia, New Guinea, New Zealand, Australia, Cambodia, Thailand, the Philippines, Japan, India, and particularly Mexico and Equatorial Africa.

He notably enriched the inventory of tropical, as well as European, species, in particular the *Inocybes,* which was the subject of his doctoral dissertation (1931), the *Lactarius, Russula, Agaricus* in general, the *Polyporus,* and the *Boletus.* He defined in detail the Agaricales with hymenia in tubes.

Heim was responsible for the term *Termitomyces* as well as for the discovery of most of the species making up this genus. He described their development and the connections that closely relate the macrotermites to the mushrooms growing in the interior of these insects' nests, on piles built by them. He was responsible for most knowledge about this strange group of "Cryptogamia" and he clarified the complex circumstances of the association from which these Agaricales stem.

His work continued that of his teacher Patouillard on the general classification of higher mushrooms; Heim established that the configuration of the hymenium does not allow one to predict kinships and that the filiation shows a grouping together of very different forms whose study and cultivation seem to reveal phyletic kinship. Thus the hymenium with pores is not the monopoly of the *Polyporus* and the *Boletus,* where the Fries tradition has localized them. In the same way the Boletaceae do not necessarily have tubes, and the Agaricales can be tubular and not foliated. In addition to this concept, he formulated the following: The exotic species make evident the retrograde and degraded forms, adapted to conditions of hypogeous or xerophilous life. For this reason he felt that several groups of the basidial gasteromycete forms have a tendency toward a state of degradation, which finally tends toward an angiocarpous state, then toward a subterranean state, and to a closed and globose form, but that these mushrooms are not primitive.

For some 10 years part of Heim's investigations centered on the hallucinogenic mushrooms of Mexico and on the fungal madness of the Kuma in New Guinea, both of which he studied with the American ethnologist R. Gordon Wasson; these researches are universally recognized today. The recent discovery of the existence in diverse regions of Mexico of a religious cult believed to have disappeared after the coming of the Spaniards was largely due to Wasson and his wife. The cult's rites derived from the psychotropic action of certain mushrooms. Absorption of these mushrooms was associated with nocturnal ceremonies in which the ecstatic state of the shamans played an essential role—divinatory and hallucinatory—before a crowd of faithful who asked questions of their "curandera." In the course of his investigations with Wasson, Heim described some 15 species belonging to the Agaricales *Psilocybe* and *Stropharia*, some of which were used by the Indians. With his assistant R. Cailleux, he cultivated the species semi-industrially in his laboratory in the Museum of Paris. He then entrusted the chemical study of these mushrooms to Albert Hofmann of Basel, after having verified that identical physiological actions were produced by the cultivated and by the natural species. These two indoline substances responsible for the hallucinogenic actions were isolated in collaboration with Hofmann, who with his students made the double synthesis called by the Franco-Swiss team psilocybin and psilocin; the first is the ester phosphoric acid of the second, which is identified with 4-hydroxy-dimethyltryptamine.

The study of these mushrooms' properties and two isolated substances were the subject of many publications in the medical and physiological world, and therapeutic psychiatry gained some useful information, the first results of which were published by Jean Delay and his students. This work made known the power of these drugs to restore lost memories, permitting mental patients to reconstitute the genesis and evolution of their affection by approaching their physician with confidence.

Whereas Wasson was interested in the sources of the cult and its archeological evidences, Heim was drawn more to the purely mycologic, anatomic, biologic, and cultural phases. Their research, done in collaboration with Delay and his students, led to the fundamental work *Les Champignons Hallucinogènes du Mexique* (1958). In 1963 Heim summarized his work in this field in *Champignons Toxiques et Hallucinogènes*.

Heim was also one of the first to penetrate the structure of the spores' membranes of the Hymenomycetes. He discovered and named the ectospore, the fine membrane that envelops the basidiospores and which he represented, by examining them under an electron microscope, as belonging to the *Ganoderma* genus—the first contribution of this nature. As a consequence, the staff he assembled at the Museum of Paris published some original studies on the structure of the teguments of spores as seen in photon and electron microscopes.

Son of an engineer, Heim graduated as an engineer-chemist from the Ecole Centrale des Arts et Manufactures in Paris (1923), but immediately abandoned his industrial career to devote himself to botany. A licentiate in science, he received his doctorate from the Sorbonne, and studied under Gabriel Bertrand at the Institut Pasteur and under N. T. Patouillard at the Museum of Natural History. Heim pursued his entire career in the latter institution in the department of cryptogamy. He was préparateur in 1926, assistant to Louis Mangin from 1929 to 1932, and vice-director of the laboratory from 1932 to 1945, becoming director of the laboratory in the Ecole des Hautes Etudes in 1943. He was made titular professor of the chair of cryptogamy in 1945 and was director of the Museum of Natural History from 1951 to 1966, when he resigned from his administrative duties to devote more time to his work, his laboratory, and his students. As director of the museum, Heim built the new Bibliothèque Centrale, filled with 600,000 volumes; had the amphitheater restored; had greenhouses and laboratories of paleontology, entomology, and ecology built; modernized the arboretum of Chèvreloup; acquired property at Menton; more than doubled the scientific personnel of the museum and created five chairs; founded the laboratories of the museum in tropical Africa; and established the basis in Paris for the Museum of Evolution. In 1962 in La Maboké, Central African Republic, Heim founded and became director of an important experimental station that undertook studies of both a botanical and a polyvalent character. It was there that in 1965 he and Roger Cailleux achieved the industrial cultivation of the tropical psalliota, *Psalliota* (or *Agaricus*) *subedulis*. In 1958 Heim became president of the Singer-Polignac Foundation. Through the organization he brought about an important French expedition to study the coral reefs of New Caledonia (1961–65) and the construction of the Gauguin Museum in Tahiti (1965). Heim became a member of the Académie des Sciences in 1946 and was its president in 1963; he was made a member of the Académie d'Agriculture in 1945, and an honorary or corresponding member of many foreign academies and societies. In 1958 he received a Darwin-Wallace Medal of the Linnean Society of London.

Heim wrote, in addition to the works cited above, *Champignons d'Europe* (1957), *Tableaux d'un Monde Etrange* (1948), *Fungi Iberici, Lactaires d'Afrique Centrale*, and *Lactario-Russulés de Madagascar*, as well as numerous papers and articles. He founded and directed the publications *Revue de Mycologie, Cahiers du Pacifique*, and *Cahiers de La Maboké*. He also directed the *Annales des Sciences Naturelles*. He was also a well-known writer on the French language, on the protection of nature, and on the consequences of overpopulation. He was a founder of the International Union for the Conservation of Nature, and its president from 1955 to 1959. Among his many publications in these fields were *Destruction et protection de la nature* (1952), *La langue française et la science* (1955), and *Un naturaliste autour du monde* (1955).

For background information *see* BASIDIO-

MYCETES; ISOPTERA; MUSHROOM; MYCOLOGY in the McGraw-Hill Encyclopedia of Science and Technology.   □

★ HERGET, Paul

American astronomer
Born Jan. 30, 1908, Cincinnati, Ohio, U.S.A.

HERGET'S SCIENTIFIC career was largely directed by his passionate fondness for computation, starting long before the invention of electronic computers. During his first course in calculus, he used Machin's formula to compute the value of π to 32 decimal places, aided only by a lead pencil. In 1931 he was appointed assistant observer at the Cincinnati Observatory to compute the reductions of meridian circle observations. His independent interests turned toward the computation of orbits of newly discovered comets and minor planets. His first published paper was an eight-decimal-place table of sines and cosines, occupying only one page. With the discovery of two new moons of Jupiter at the Mount Wilson Observatory in 1938, he provided the computations and predictions of their orbits.

During World War II he served as a civilian scientist on the staff of the U.S. Naval Observatory and acquired extensive experience in the use of standard IBM accounting machines for scientific computations. On one occasion the solution of 250,000 spherical triangles was required in tabular form to support the task of detecting the location of enemy submarines on the high seas. In the early days of the Oak Ridge atomic bomb project, he assisted in setting up the computational procedures for production control and process improvement of uranium-235.

After the war Herget returned to the Cincinnati Observatory as director, and accepted the responsibility of operating the Minor Planet Center of the International Astronomical Union. The Center's project has a threefold require-

ment: (*a*) the collection of tens of thousands of observations of minor planets made at observatories all over the world; (*b*) the computation of the perturbations exerted by the major planets upon the orbit of each of the minor planets; and (*c*) the adjustment of the initial elements of each orbit to bring it into agreement with the observations. With the development of electronic computers, this project led to a succession of improved methods and new programs for each new generation of machines.

During this period Herget also undertook to aid colleagues in other areas of science. He collaborated in a neurological experiment in which the added pressures induced by the injection of spinal fluids could be used to diagnose the extent of a brain tumor. The data of each subject could be represented by a characteristic hyperbola. In the area of photogrammetry, he introduced the use of electronic computers for analytical extension, and the analysis of reconnaissance photos. In the area of machine tool design, he devised computational methods of testing the tolerance limits of cam grinders. He also served as a consultant to the Atlas missile project in establishing real-time guidance control and target accuracy.

In 1955 the prospects of an American space program presented many new scientific and technical problems. Launching of missiles was already an accomplished fact, but now the test was whether or not they had reached full orbital velocity. Once in orbit the satellite is continually subjected to oblique forces produced by the spheroidal shape of the Earth. The calculation of these effects is an involved and complicated process. Predictions are required continuously, partly to alert observers, partly to satisfy the public interest, and partly to ascertain the expected lifetime of the satellite. Finally there is the problem of how to adjust the orbit computed for the satellite so that it will be brought into agreement with the observations. In the early Vanguard project there was usually not more than one observation per revolution around the Earth, whereas the existence of many observations would have eased the problem. Herget was head of the Vanguard Computing Center and was responsible for the organization and design of all the necessary electronic computer programs and operations at the time when the first Sputnik was launched by the Soviet Union.

Later Project Mercury involved many similar problems, but also the life of the astronaut was at stake. Both launching and observing capabilities had improved considerably, but the requirements of the mission also increased. It was necessary to respond at any moment to any emergency. The computer programs were more sophisticated and more powerful. Information concerning the exact second to fire the retrorockets was continually in the computer memory and was checked against the preset timers in the spacecraft. At every moment full information concerning the next emergency landing area was available. A special program computed the "splash-down" point on the Earth after the retrorockets were fired. Again Herget designed the details of these computer programs.

He later computed an accurate comparison of the orbit of Mars, and the orbits of all of the outer satellites of Jupiter. He devised a computer program for preliminary orbits, which is able to utilize as many observations as may be available at the time.

Herget received his A.B. (1931), M.A. (1933), and Ph.D. in mathematics and astronomy (1935) at the University of Cincinnati. At the Cincinnati Observatory he was assistant observer from 1931 to 1943, when he became director. At the University of Cincinnati he was an instructor of astronomy in 1931–40, assistant professor in 1940–43, and professor in 1943–65; he was named Distinguished Service Professor of Astronomy in 1965. He was president of Commission 20 (Minor Planets, Comets, and Satellites) of the International Astronomical Union from 1961 to 1967. He was elected to the National Academy of Sciences in 1962. Herget was awarded the William Howard Taft Medal of the University of Cincinnati Alumni Association for "notable achievement" and the James Craig Watson Gold Medal of the National Academy of Sciences for "noteworthy astronomical research," both in 1965.

Herget wrote *The Computation of Orbits* (1948).

For background information *see* CELESTIAL MECHANICS; ORBITAL MOTION; SATELLITE, ARTIFICIAL; SPACE PROBE in the McGraw-Hill Encyclopedia of Science and Technology.   □

★ HERZBERG, Gerhard

Canadian physicist
Born Dec. 25, 1904, Hamburg, Germany

B Y HIS research in atomic and molecular spectroscopy, Herzberg contributed to many areas of physics, chemistry, and astronomy; by his three comprehensive volumes, *Molecular Spectra and Molecular Structure* (1939–66), he provided for many other research workers the basis for further work. In the field of atomic spectra his main contributions are his determinations of the Lamb shifts in the ground state of deuterium and the ground and first excited states of He and Li$^+$. These determinations represented an important confirmation of the predictions of quantum electrodynamics. In the field of molecular spectroscopy his contributions are divided between diatomic and polyatomic molecules. Apart from many studies of individual diatomic molecules, including a number of new molecules not known until then (such as CP, PN, B$_2$, BN, and CH$^+$), he devoted a good deal of effort to the investigation of dissociation and predissociation phenomena and to the elucidation of forbidden transitions.

One of the most important quantities characterizing a diatomic molecule is its dissociation energy. Following the early work of James Franck and of R. T. Birge and H. Sponer, Herzberg realized in 1929 that the correlation rules of E. P. Wigner and E. E. Witmer must be applied to the dissociation process and therefore that the value of the dissociation energy of O$_2$ must be modified. Later, on the basis of new spectra obtained by him, Herzberg derived a very precise and reliable value for this quantity. In 1960 he and A. Monfils accomplished a very considerable improvement in the accuracy of the experimental values for the dissociation energies of H$_2$, HD, and D$_2$. At about the same time C. C. J. Roothahn and his associates carried the theoretical prediction of these quantities to higher approximations. There is now a small but definite discrepancy between the experimental and the theoretical value. The resolution of this discrepancy is bound to lead to important refinements in the theory.

Noteworthy among Herzberg's many studies of forbidden transitions was his discovery in 1931 of what are now known as the Herzberg bands of O$_2$. Because of its importance for the absorption spectrum of air and for the understanding of the upper atmosphere (light of the night sky, ozone production, and so on), this electronic transition has been studied by many scien-

tists. In 1952 Herzberg carried through a definitive fine-structure analysis. The spectrograms on which this work was based were obtained with a large absorption tube in which, by means of multiple traversals, an absorbing path of up to

5000 m could be obtained. In addition to the Herzberg bands of O_2, he observed and analyzed three other forbidden transitions in O_2, including the infrared atmospheric oxygen bands which are prominent in the infrared solar spectrum. With his long absorption tube he also observed for the first time the quadrupole infrared spectrum of H_2 predicted by him 10 years earlier, and later, in a smaller tube, the dipole infrared spectrum of HD.

One important contribution to nuclear physics, based on Rasetti's Raman spectrum of N_2, was the recognition, together with W. Heitler, that the N nuclei follow Bose statistics and not Fermi statistics. The latter result would have been expected on the assumption generally made at the time (1929, before the discovery of neutrons) that the nuclei consist of protons and electrons.

The spectra of polyatomic molecules present naturally many additional complications compared to diatomic molecules. Herzberg studied many individual molecules including many polyatomic free radicals. Indeed, most present knowledge of the structure of simple free radicals (in the gaseous state) is based on the work of Herzberg and his colleagues at Ottawa. The most important of these radicals are CH_3 and CH_2, whose spectra were obtained by him in 1956 and 1959, respectively. CH_3 was shown to have a planar (or nearly planar) structure, while CH_2 was shown to be linear (or nearly linear) in its ground state. This ground state is a triplet state ($^3\Sigma_g{}^-$), but not very high above this state is a singlet state in which the molecule is bent. This situation was not foreseen by theory, but has led in recent years to many interesting chemical applications.

Both for the infrared and Raman spectra and the electronic spectra of polyatomic molecules, symmetry properties of the molecule are of decisive importance. The effect of these symmetry properties on the selection rules for electronic spectra was first recognized in a basic paper by Edward Teller and Herzberg in 1934. Their conclusions are still widely applied to the interpretation of spectra of polyatomic molecules.

In 1942 Herzberg recognized an interesting effect called l-type doubling in the infrared spectra of linear molecules. It consists in the splitting of all energy levels in which a bending vibration is singly (or multiply) excited, and it plays an important role in the spectra of linear molecules and, in a somewhat different form, also in the spectra of symmetric top molecules.

In the first approach to the geometrical structure of polyatomic molecules, it was generally assumed that similar bonds have equal lengths in different molecules. In 1937 Herzberg and his associates were the first to show that the length of the C-C single bond depends on what other bonds are in the neighborhood. The C-C bond is shortened when it is adjacent to a triple bond and is shortened still further when there is an adjacent triple bond on each side. Many instances of this kind are now known.

There are many applications of molecular spectra in astrophysical problems. Herzberg made significant contributions to this borderline field. In 1938 he became interested in the problem of detecting molecular hydrogen in the atmospheres of the outer planets; he suggested that since very large amounts were expected the quadrupole rotation-vibration spectrum might be used for detecting it (since an ordinary infrared spectrum does not exist). Ten years later he produced this spectrum in the laboratory by means of the long absorption tube already mentioned. Another 10 years later the quadrupole lines were observed by C. C. Kiess and collaborators in the spectrum of Jupiter. Earlier Herzberg had produced the 3-0 band of the pressure-induced H_2 spectrum in the laboratory at low temperature and had shown that it agreed with a feature observed by G. P. Kuiper in the spectrum of Uranus. In this way the presence of large amounts of hydrogen in these atmospheres was established.

The 4050 group of comets remained a puzzle until in 1942 Herzberg produced it in the laboratory. Later his colleague A. E. Douglas showed it to be due to the C_3 radical, a radical not known until then but now recognized as an important constituent of carbon vapor. Another contribution to astrophysics was Herzberg's identification, together with Douglas, of four interstellar lines as being due to the CH^+ ion.

After his early education in Hamburg, Herzberg studied at the Technical University at Darmstadt, where he obtained a Dr.Ing. under H. Rau (a pupil of W. Wien). He spent one postdoctorate year in Göttingen with Max Born and James Franck and another in Bristol with A. M. Tyndall. He returned to Darmstadt as privatdozent and taught there until 1935, when the laws promulgated by the Nazis forced him to emigrate. He found a haven at the University of Saskatchewan, where he soon was appointed research professor of physics, and remained there until 1945. After his 3-year stay at the Yerkes Observatory of the University of Chicago, he returned to Canada to become a principal research officer at the National Research Council. But soon after his arrival he was appointed director of the Pure Physics Division, and he continued in this position. Herzberg received the Henry Marshall Tory Medal of the Royal Society of Canada in 1953, gave the 1960 Bakerian Lecture of the Royal Society of London, and was awarded the Ives Medal of the Optical Society of

America in 1963. President of the Royal Society of Canada in 1966–67, he was elected to the Royal Society of London in 1951, the Pontifical Academy of Sciences in 1964, and the American Academy of Arts and Sciences in 1965.

Herzberg wrote *Atomic Spectra and Atomic Structure* (1937; 2d ed. 1944) and *Molecular Spectra and Molecular Structure: Vol. I, Spectra of Diatomic Molecules* (1939; 2d ed. 1950); Vol. II, *Infrared and Raman Spectra of Polyatomic Molecules* (1945); Vol. III, *Electronic Spectra and Electronic Structure of Polyatomic Molecules* (1966).

For background information *see* ATOMIC STRUCTURE AND SPECTRA; MOLECULAR STRUCTURE AND SPECTRA; SPECTROSCOPY in the McGraw-Hill Encyclopedia of Science and Technology. □

★ HERZFELD, Karl Ferdinand

American physicist
Born Feb. 24, 1892, Vienna, Austria

HERZFELD'S MAIN scientific work can be divided into five groups.

(1) *Theory of liquids.* Herzfeld early attempted to calculate the entropy of aqueous salt solution and to explain it by complex formation with the water molecules surrounding the ions. In 1925, with W. Heitler, he proposed an approximate theory for binary solutions. A kinetic theory for osmotic pressure and decrease of vapor pressure in dilute solutions was attempted, based on the idea that the kinetic energy of the solute produces a tension in the solvent (1921, 1937, 1938). In 1958 he developed a general theory of viscosity and bulk viscosity.

(2) *Crystal dynamics.* In 1918 Max Born and A. Landé had tried to build a theory of simple ionic crystals as being held together by the electric attraction of the ions, while being prevented from collapsing by interaction of the electrons (then thought of as arranged in rings, following earlier suggestions by Niels Bohr). But then Irving Langmuir's and G. N. Lewis's ideas of a cubic arrangement became known, and K. Fajans, partly with Herzfeld's collaboration, started systematic investigations in that field. In 1923 Herzfeld, partly with H. G. Grimm, worked out thermodynamically the mutual solubility limits of alkali halide crystals. In a paper which would sound trivial today but was a new idea then, they proposed that energy relations decide which compounds exist in the crystalline state, and illustrated this by numerical calculation (for example, $NaCl_2$ has a much higher energy than $NaCl + \frac{1}{2}Cl_2$ and therefore does not exist). Herzfeld pointed out in 1927 that the refractive index could be used to decide whether a crystal would be metallically conducting; in 1966 H. G. Drickamer and others confirmed his equation through their measurement of TlI under high pressures. In 1938 Herzfeld and R. H. Lyddane investigated the distribution of Debye waves in simple ionic crystals in more detail than had been done before. He and Maria Goeppert Mayer investigated theoretically the electrical behavior of hydrogen dissolved in palladium. An attempt was also made by these two to understand melting; in 1934 they calculated the temperature at which a crystal would become unstable under the combined influence of anharmonicity and thermal vibrations.

(3) *Optics.* In 1924 Herzfeld tried to understand the quantum theory of dispersion by transferring from classical theory the concept of phase shift. With K. L. Wolf, he tested the classical formula on experimental data, attempting to calculate far-ultraviolet absorptions. In the later 1930s he suggested to Goeppert Mayer and A. Sklar the quantum theoretical calculation of excited states in aromatic molecules, and applied their methods to substituted benzenes and, with Sklar, to polymethine dyes. With Goeppert Mayer he calculated in 1936 the influence of forced emission and of "magnetic" transitions on dispersion. In 1964 he pointed out the difficulty of explaining the transparency to visible light of dipole liquids, like water or alcohol.

(4) *Theory of chemical reactions.* M. Trautz in 1909–19 had developed the general scheme. M. Bodenstein had recognized that theoretically the situation was simplest in gas reactions; he had developed the difficult experimental technique and, with his collaborators, made many careful measurements. The formation of the three analogous compounds HCl, HBr, and HI from the elements might be expected to proceed in the same manner, but this is not the case. Only the formation of the iodide behaves as expected; the rate is proportional to the product of the amounts of hydrogen and iodine, since one mole-

cule of hydrogen and one of iodine have to collide to form two molecules of HI. The formation of HCl goes very quickly (explosions can arise) and W. Nernst explained this in 1918 as due to chains, with the atoms as chain carriers. HBr is complicated, the rate being proportional to the H_2 concentration and the square root of the bromine concentration, with the product acting as inhibitor. In 1919 Herzfeld explained this by the processes $Br_2 \rightleftharpoons 2Br$, $Br + H_2 \rightarrow HBr + H$, $H + Br_2 \rightarrow HBr + Br$; and the inhibition by $H + HBr \rightarrow H_2 + Br$. The same problem was also attacked by H. Christiansen, who thought, however, that "hot" molecules (instead of free atoms) were the carriers, and by M. Polanyi, who in 1920 pointed out difficulties with the assumption that two free atoms coming together could form a molecule. This would still possess dissociation energy and so would fly apart again. Herzfeld drew the consequence in 1921 that two atoms could combine only in the presence of a third body to take away some energy (three-body collision) and, therefore, that dissociation of a diatomic molecule was a bimolecular reaction. Bodenstein soon proved the three-body collision assumption by investigating the formation of HBr under the action of light.

F. Paneth was producing free methyl radicals, CH_3, in a gas stream by heating lead tetramethyl; he used as detectors thin metal layers ("mirrors"), which the radicals removed by compound formation, but he could not put his conclusions into mathematical form; this was, however, remedied in a joint paper with Herzfeld in 1931. F. O. Rice had developed the idea that many organic reactions went, in the gas phase at elevated temperatures, over radicals. Joining forces with Herzfeld, Rice supplied the chemical intuition and ideas and Herzfeld put these into mathematical form, rejecting those which did not give, in the working out, the deceptively simple experimental results. At that time many of the significant data for the individual binding energies were unknown, and Rice's intuition and the fitting into the scheme narrowed them down into a range which later experiments confirmed. The free-radical theory first met considerable resistance but is now (with some modifications) widely accepted. Herzfeld played a similar cooperative role later, when James Franck tried to unravel the complicated reactions involved in photosynthesis.

(5) *Ultrasonics.* In 1927 R. W. Wood was making some spectacular experiments with ultrasonic waves. When Herzfeld mentioned these to Rice, the latter suggested that ultrasonic absorption measurements might give a clue to the rate of energy transfer in molecules, a problem then being widely discussed among scientists interested in reaction kinetics. The result was a 1928 paper in which Rice and Herzfeld gave equations relating sound absorption to the "relaxation time" of energy transfer, thus repeating earlier but ignored work by H. A. Lorentz, Sir James Jeans, and Albert Einstein. This paper was the starting point of much new work; in particular, J. C. Hubbard made many precise measurements in gases. In connection with this work, Herzfeld in 1938 showed that the reflection coefficient of high-frequency sound waves may be considerably decreased by heat conduction to the reflector.

The measured relaxation times in gases extend over a very wide range, but there was no understanding why energy exchange is so difficult in one case, so easy in another. In 1936 L. D. Landau and Edward Teller wrote a fundamental paper in which they showed the dependence of the relaxation time on the molecular constants, in particular the force of interaction, and on the temperature, but still no numerical calculation was possible. Z. I. Slawsky applied quantum theory (theory of inelastic scattering) to the problem in 1951. J. O. Hirschfelder and his collaborators at the University of Wisconsin had determined the force of interaction between many molecules from transport properties and their temperature dependence, and it occurred to Herzfeld that these data could be used to supply the missing constants. This was done in collaboration with Slawsky and R. N. Schwartz, with astonishing agreement with experiment in many cases (1952, 1954). Thereafter Herzfeld spent much time enlarging, modifying, and refining these calculations.

Herzfeld studied at Vienna (1910–12), Zurich (1912–13), and Göttingen (1913), receiving his Ph.D. from Vienna in 1914. After service in the Austro-Hungarian army during World War I, he became in 1920 privatdozent for theoretical physics and chemistry at Munich. From 1926 to 1936 he was guest professor and then professor of physics at the Johns Hopkins University. He then went to the Catholic University of America as professor of physics and chairman of the department, holding the latter position until 1961. Elected to the American Academy of Arts and Sciences in 1958 and the National Academy of Sciences in 1960, Herzfeld received several honorary degrees and in 1965 the papal medal "Benemerenti."

Herzfeld wrote *Kinetische Theorie der Wärme* (1925) and *Absorption and Dispersion of Ultrasonic Waves*, with T. A. Litovitz (1959), besides contributing articles to the *Handbuch der Physik, Handbuch der Experimental Physik,* and other volumes.

For background information *see* IONIC CRYSTALS; STATISTICAL MECHANICS; THERMODYNAMIC PRINCIPLES; ULTRASONICS; VISCOSITY OF LIQUIDS in the McGraw-Hill Encyclopedia of Science and Technology.   □

HEVESY, George de

Hungarian-Swedish chemist

Hevesy died on July 5, 1966, in Freiburg, West Germany. See *McGraw-Hill Modern Men of Science*, Volume I.

HEYROVSKÝ, Jaroslav

Czechoslovakian physical chemist

Heyrovský died on Mar. 27, 1967, in Prague, Czechoslovakia. See *McGraw-Hill Modern Men of Science*, Volume I.

★ HILLIER, James

American physicist
Born Aug. 22, 1915, Brantford, Ontario, Canada

HILLIER'S PRINCIPAL contribution to science was the development of the electron microscope from primitive beginnings into an effective and universally accepted research tool. By a sequence of step-by-step improvements—chief among them being the compensation of field asymmetries of electron lenses—he was able to narrow the gap between actual performance and theoretical expectation (which places the limit of resolution of the electron microscope nearly three orders of magnitude beyond that of the light microscope). In 1960 Hillier received an Albert Lasker Award from the American Public Health Association for his pioneering contributions to the development of the electron microscope as a vital tool of medical research.

The theoretical basis for electron optics was laid as early as 1830 by W. R. Hamilton, who demonstrated that the same mathematical equations governed the paths of particles in mechanical force fields and of light rays in optical media. In 1926 Hans Busch showed that axially symmetric magnetic and electric fields acted upon charged particles, such as electrons, in essentially the same manner as conventional glass lenses act upon light rays. The analogy extended even beyond geometrical optics. Louis de Broglie in 1924 showed that particles in motion had associated with them a wavelength inversely proportional to the particle momentum; for 50-kilovolt electrons this wavelength was smaller than that of light by a factor of the order of 10^5. Early workers in the field were quick to reason that this wavelength would establish an ultimate limit to the resolution in particle images in the same manner as the wavelength of light establishes an ultimate limit to the resolution in light images. Taking account of observed limitations of electron lenses, Max Knoll and Ernst Ruska, in describing work associated with the construction of their first magnetic electron microscope at the Technische Hochschule in Berlin in 1932, could estimate correctly that a gain in resolution by a factor of about 1000 should be realizable with an electron microscope.

However, this promising prospect seemed remote indeed in 1937, when Hillier and Albert Prebus, both graduate students at the University of Toronto, undertook to build a magnetic electron microscope. It was only in 1934 that E. Driest and H. O. Mueller had been able to demonstrate resolution exceeding that of the light microscope with an improved version of Ruska's electron microscope. The whole problem of the interaction of the object and the electron beam was as yet unexplored; electron imaging of organic specimens, such as bacteria, came considerably later. The vacuum system, the method of introducing the specimen and the photographic plates, the electron source, and the electrical and mechanical stability of the system all presented formidable problems. It is noteworthy that in Germany the pioneers Knoll and Ruska were pressed to apply their talents in other, more profitable fields and that it was not until 1937 that Ruska was able to find, at Siemens and Halske in Berlin, the support needed to develop the electron microscope into a practical instrument.

In this perspective the completion in Toronto in 1939 of a well-functioning electron microscope with a demonstrated resolution of 100 angstrom units was a remarkable accomplishment, particularly since Hillier and Prebus had to rely entirely on their own resources. The following year Hillier was persuaded by V. K. Zworykin of the Radio Corporation of America to join his research staff in Camden, N.J. There he was able to draw on a wider range of talent in engineering design. Within less than a year Hillier realized the completion of the model B electron microscope—the instrument on which most of the older electron microscopists served their apprenticeship.

From this point on, Hillier's approach was three-pronged. In one direction he worked continuously at improving the performance of the instrument. In the second he pursued the development of its applications by many close collaborators with research specialists in medicine, biology, chemistry, and metallurgy. By achieving considerable understanding in depth in each field, it was possible for him to give expert guidance in the use of the electron microscope and to assist research men in the proper interpretation of the new information revealed by the electron micrograph. As part of this effort, he became a visiting lecturer in the department of biology at Princeton University and a staff member of the Sloan Kettering Institute for Cancer Research and of the Marine Biological Laboratory in Woods Hole. In the third direction he searched for a way of adding information concerning chemical and crystal structure of specimens to the essentially geometrical information provided by the electron microscope. Noteworthy was his conception of electron-probe microanalysis and the development in 1944 of the first instrument of this type.

Hillier's contributions to the improvement in the performance of the electron microscope covered a wide range. Among his contributions were the automatically biased electron source; the two-component, distortion-free projection lens; a convenient mode of microscope operation without a limiting objective aperture, with contrast resulting from spherical aberration; and, most important, the compensation of field asymmetries (1945–46), which had constituted the major barrier to a close approach to the theoretical limit of resolution of the instrument. The basic principle he developed was realized in more convenient form in the "stigmators" incorporated in all modern electron microscopes. With their aid both the ultimate resolution and, in particular, the average resolution of electron micrographs were greatly improved.

Hillier received his college education at the University of Toronto, which granted him a B.A. in mathematics and physics in 1937, an M.A. in physics in 1938, and a Ph.D. in physics in 1941. From 1940 to 1953 he was research engineer at RCA Laboratories in Camden and Princeton, N.J. In 1953 he became director of the research department of Melpar, Inc., returning the following year to RCA to assume a sequence of administrative positions in research and engineering. In 1957 he became general manager of RCA Laboratories in Princeton, and in 1958 was elected vice-president.

Hillier published widely on subjects related to electronic instrumentation, electron microscopy, and research management. He was a coauthor of *Electron Optics and the Electron Microscope* (1945).

For background information *see* ELECTRON LENS; MICROSCOPE, ELECTRON in the McGraw-Hill Encyclopedia of Science and Technology. □

HINSHELWOOD, Sir Cyril (Norman)

British chemist

Hinshelwood died on Oct. 9, 1967, in London, England. See *McGraw-Hill Modern Men of Science*, Volume I.

★ HIRSCHFELDER, Joseph Oakland

American chemist and physicist
Born May 27, 1911, Baltimore, Md., U.S.A.

A T THE Bikini bomb tests in 1946, Hirschfelder had the title of "chief phenomenologist" and the responsibility of predicting a wide assortment of weapons effects. His training in theoretical chemistry provided a broad base for delving into all sorts of scientific and engineering problems and making semiquantitative predictions as to their behavior. Theoretical chemistry seeks to determine the physical and chemical properties of materials, to relate these macroscopic properties to the individual molecules, and to determine the structure and properties of the individual molecules. Thus, theoretical chemistry serves as the "middleman" between the theoretical physicists on the one hand and the practical engineers and experimental scientists on the other. "For his contributions to quantum chemistry and in particular to the understanding of the nature of intermolecular forces; to the development of the theory of transport phenomena; and to the theory of flames; and in recognition of his influence on the development of research in many fields of theoretical chemistry," Hirschfelder received the

Debye Award of the American Chemical Society in 1966.

As a chemist, he was primarily concerned with the rates of reactions. From the molecular point of view, this means violent collisions in which the reacting molecules are torn apart and reorganized. It has been extremely difficult to make accurate theoretical predictions of the cross sections for such reactions. Hirschfelder therefore tackled a much easier problem that involved the same sort of mathematical treatment. Instead of considering violent collisions, he examined the gentler thermal collisions in which at most only the rotational and vibrational quantum numbers are changed. Thermal collisions are responsible for the equation of state and transport properties of gases and liquids. With the availability of improved mathematical methods and high-speed computing machines, it has become feasible to calculate chemical reaction rates on a rigorous molecular basis. This is the current goal of many theoretical chemists.

Hirschfelder is best known for the treatise *Molecular Theory of Gases and Liquids* (1954), in which the generalized equations of aerodynamics (the equation of state of gases, the equation of motion, the equation for conservation of energy, and the equations of diffusion) are derived by statistical mechanics in terms of the properties of the individual molecules. The coefficients of heat conductivity, viscosity, and diffusion are expressed in terms of molecular collision cross sections. By means of quantum or classical mechanics, the molecular collision cross sections are expressed in terms of the energy of interaction between the colliding molecules. Similarly, the virial coefficients which occur in the equation of state are also expressed in terms of the energy of interaction of pairs of molecules. Finally, the molecular interaction energy is determined either by semiempirical considerations or by solving a set of quantum mechanical equations in which the electrons are bound to the nuclei by electrostatic coulombic forces (in much the same manner as the planets are attracted to the Sun). The whole hierarchy of equations is exceedingly complicated. Nevertheless, the equations are very useful for predicting or extrapolating the behavior of gases to extreme conditions where no experimental data exist. For example, they were used to estimate the heat transfer to the nose cone of a satellite on reentry into the Earth's atmosphere. For this work he was made a lifetime honorary member of the American Society of Mechanical Engineers.

Another use of the generalized equations of aerodynamics was to predict the behavior of flames and detonations. Here it was necessary to solve these equations in conjunction with idealized boundary conditions. To the far left, the reacting gases at ambient temperature are flow-ing with the flame (or detonation) velocity toward the right; by the time the gases have reached the far right, they have achieved complete thermal and chemical equilibrium. To make the problem mathematically clean, Hirschfelder and Charles F. Curtiss assumed the existence of a flame holder which had two functions: to extract heat from the hot gases and to prevent the product gases from diffusing backward into the mixing chamber. With these boundary conditions the equations of aerodynamics have at most two solutions: one corresponding to a subsonic flame velocity and the other to a supersonic detonation velocity. "For distinguished, continuing, and encouraging contributions to the field of combustion," Hirschfelder was given the Sir Alfred Egerton Gold Medal of the International Combustion Society.

Hirschfelder's research was largely inspired by Henry Eyring, who served as his major professor during his graduate work at Princeton University. To Eyring every problem in nature could be studied theoretically. No matter how complicated the system, there was usually only *one* slow step or bottleneck that determined its behavior. With Eyring as his mentor, Hirschfelder helped to develop the theory of absolute reaction rates, the structure of liquids, and the quantum mechanical structure of molecules. During this same period he worked with Eugene Wigner on a group theoretic problem, the separation of the rotational coordinates from an *N*-body system, and with Edward Condon on the polarizability of molecular hydrogen.

During the first part of World War II, Hirschfelder worked for the National Defense Research Council on the performance of guns and rockets. His first job was to systematize the thermochemistry of powder gases. However, it soon became evident that the current theories of interior ballistics were incomplete and could not make use of precise thermochemical data. Therefore, with Curtiss and Richard Kershner, he developed the system of interior ballistics for guns and rockets currently used by the American armed services. This was the first system of ballistics that took into account the heat transfer from the powder gas to the surface of the bore (this is not important in a large cannon, but in an elephant rifle 30 times as much energy goes into heating the bore as into pushing the bullet). Their greatest success was in using this treatment to explain quantitatively the performance of recoilless guns within a few days after the first German recoilless gun was discovered by the Allies.

In 1943–46 Hirschfelder was group leader in both the Ordnance and Theoretical divisions at Los Alamos. He and John Magee were the first to predict fallout from atomic bombs, before any atomic bombs had been exploded. Their predictions were quantitatively accurate as a result of careful studies of the kinetics of formation of industrial carbon black, the micromeritic behavior of different types of smokes, and the physics of the blown sands over the Sahara!

In the 1960s Hirschfelder worked on new mathematical techniques for solving the equations of molecular quantum mechanics. By making use of improved methods and high-speed computing machines, he was hopeful that theoretical chemistry could cope successfully with many of the difficult problems of nature.

Hirschfelder's paternal grandfather was the first child to be born in Oakland, Calif., and became the first professor of clinical medicine at Leland Stanford University. His father, Arthur Douglass Hirschfelder, wrote the treatise *Diseases of the Heart and Aorta*, and was the first doctor in the United States to use the electrocardiogram; later he became professor of pharmacology at the University of Minnesota. Hirschfelder himself was raised in Minneapolis. He attended the University of Minnesota for 2 years and spent the next 2 years at Yale University, where he received a B.S. in chemistry in 1931. In 1936 he received a Ph.D. in physics and chemistry at Princeton University. In 1937 he studied as a fellow of the Institute for Advanced Studies under John von Neumann. In that year he went to the University of Wisconsin, where he later became Homer Adkins Professor of Chemistry and director of the Theoretical Chemistry Institute. He was elected to the National Academy of Sciences in 1953, to the American Academy of Arts and Sciences in 1959, and to the Norwegian Royal Society in 1965.

Hirschfelder wrote *Molecular Theory of Gases and Liquids*, with C. F. Curtiss and R. B. Bird (1954). For the AEC he was senior editor of *The Effects of Atomic Weapons* (1950).

For background information *see* AERODYNAMICS; BALLISTICS, INTERIOR; QUANTUM CHEMISTRY; STATISTICAL MECHANICS; THERMOCHEMISTRY in the McGraw-Hill Encyclopedia of Science and Technology.   □

★ HISAW, Frederick Lee

American zoologist
Born Aug. 23, 1891, Jolly, Mo., U.S.A.

Hisaw's EARLY scientific interests were in natural history and ecology. At the close of World War I, he became assistant professor and mammalogist in the experiment station of Kansas State Agricultural College. This marked a sharp change of emphasis in his research. His duties as mammalogist were concerned primarily with the control of mammals injurious to agriculture, the most destructive being the pocket gopher (*Geomys bursarius*), a native rodent which became a serious pest to the growing of alfalfa. Hisaw noticed that the bony structure of the pelvis in these animals was so reduced that birth of young could not be accomplished unless some adaptive provision was made for enlarging the birth canal. Such adaptation was provided, indeed, by the disappearance of the pubic bones for a considerable distance right and left of the midline on each side of the pubic symphysis and replacement of those lost parts by a ligament. This adaptive process occurred only in females as they approached sexual maturity, and was found to be controlled by the ovaries as a secondary sexual characteristic. It was thus possible for the female pocket gopher to have an unusually narrow pelvis adapted for living in a burrow and at the same time to be able to give birth to her young.

These observations raised questions about other mammals, such as certain rodents and moles, that live in narrow subterranean tunnels and are known to have greatly reduced pelvic girdles. Also, the possibility was considered that animals such as the guinea pig, which give birth to large, fully developed young, might encounter morphological problems at the time of parturition. A study of several mammalian species established that embryology of the pelvis in all is similar and that adaptive modifications which appear later are derived in different ways. The pelvis in moles, for instance, shows extreme reduction in both males and females, so much so that the viscera are not enclosed in the pelvic birth canal. This pelvic reduction is determined

entirely by genetic rather than endocrine factors. The pelvic bones in guinea pigs become freely disarticulated during late pregnancy, both at the symphysis pubis and the sacroiliac unions, thus allowing birth of the large-sized young. The disarticulation is accomplished by the cooperative actions of two hormones: estrogen, a steroidal hormone secreted by the ovaries which feminizes the pelvis, as mentioned for the pocket gopher; and relaxin, a peptide hormone secreted by the ovaries and uterus which produces the remarkable relaxation of the pelvic ligaments. Relaxin, found in a wide range of mammalian species, is a hormone of pregnancy secreted by the genital tract under the influence of estrogen and progesterone. Relaxin is known also to take part in certain reactions other than pelvic relaxation. In monkeys (*Macaca mulatta*) relaxin, in addition to producing modifications of the pelvis similar to those seen in the guinea pig, also enhances the effects of estrogen and progesterone on uterine growth and produces vascular changes in the endometrium at the site of implantation of an ovum and during placental development.

Hisaw and his students became interested in other aspects of the physiology of reproduction, particularly in the comparative endocrinology of the hormones concerned. These studies were started in the early 1920s, when little or nothing was known regarding the chemical nature of most hormones. Experimentation was conducted by surgical techniques and by administering organ and tissue extracts prepared by fractionation methods. Much of the work done during this period by investigators using simple techniques and crude preparations was confirmed later when many hormones became available in chemically pure or more nearly pure form. For instance, Hisaw and H. L. Fevold fractionated the pituitary gonadotropic hormones and demonstrated the presence of a follicle stimulating hormone (FSH) and a follicle luteinizing hormone (LH) and, with able students, studied the relations of these gonadotropins to follicular growth, ovulation, and luteal development and their action on the testis in males. They also described the synergistic or augmentation reaction between FSH and LH in follicular growth and estrogen secretion. Hisaw and C. K. Weichert were the first to produce deciduomata in ovariectomized laboratory rodents by using extracts of the corpus luteum. Working with H. L. Fevold, R. K. Meyer, and S. L. Leonard, and using similar preparations, Hisaw produced development of a progestation reaction in the uterine endometrium of ovariectomized monkeys characteristic of the reaction seen during the luteal phase of a normal menstrual cycle. He also obtained decidual plaques in the endometrium similar to those seen at normal implantation sites of fertilized ova.

Hisaw's interest in the physiology of reproduction was intensified by the current advances in endocrine techniques and by observations on endocrine adaptations in the evolution of viviparity among the vertebrates, particularly in primates. This led to studies of the endocrines responsible for the cyclic changes in the female reproductive tract of monkeys, the physiology of menstruation, and endometrial modifications during placental development. The morphologi-

cal variations of a normal menstrual cycle, as well as endometrial changes at placentation, were reproduced in ovariectomized animals with remarkable fidelity by administering proper dosages of estrogens, progesterone, and relaxin. This research was recognized by an award from the American Gynecological Society.

Hisaw was reared on a farm and attended one-room, rural schools. He was a student at the University of Missouri Preparatory School for a year, and on graduation in 1910 enrolled in the university, where he received his A.B. in 1914 and B.S. in 1915. The summers of 1914 and 1915 were spent doing field work on aquatic insects with G. S. Dodds in the Rocky Mountains of Colorado; this work led to the A.M. in 1916. Hisaw accepted an associate professorship in the University of Mississippi but resigned in 1917 to enlist in the infantry of World War I. In 1919 he accepted an appointment as assistant professor of zoology and experiment station mammalogist at the Kansas State Agricultural College, earned a Ph.D. while on leave at the University of Wisconsin in 1924, and accepted an assistant professorship in that university. He was invited to Harvard University as professor of zoology in 1935, was appointed Fisher Professor of Natural History there in 1953, and became emeritus in 1962. He was elected to the American Academy of Arts and Sciences in 1936 and to the National Academy of Sciences in 1947.

For background information *see* Endocrine mechanisms; Menstruation; Pelvis; Pregnancy; Uterus in the McGraw-Hill Encyclopedia of Science and Technology. ☐

★ HOLLAENDER, Alexander

American biophysicist
Born Dec. 19, 1898, Samter, Germany

THE MAJOR theme in Hollaender's work was the basic interaction of various forms of physical energy with biological systems and functions. Two related subthemes arose from this major interest: the basic mechanisms in dividing cells and the transmission of genetic characteristics from generation to generation. One of the simplest types of physical energy to measure easily and reproducibly is radiation. Therefore, Hollaender concentrated on learning all he could about the interaction of various forms of radiation (ultraviolet, near-ultraviolet, and ionizing) on biological systems. He investigated by several different techniques the nature of the biological components that are sensitive to radiation, particularly their chemical composition, the effects of radiation on them, and recovery and repair of radiation-damaged cells.

Because of his interest in the physical nature of biological interactions, he thought that train-

ing in chemistry, especially physical chemistry, would be an excellent background for such an approach to biology. He started his work in the early 1930s, a time that was very exciting in the natural sciences because of the rapid and extensive developments in the study of atoms and nuclei. Everyone was interested in the effects of radiation, the characteristics of new types of radiations, and new particles. A number of phenomena were reported that were on the border line of biology, as well as on the border line of detectability. Many people were excited about the problem of the so-called mitogenetic radiation, which allegedly was emitted by dividing cells and could be absorbed by nondividing cells, the latter then being induced to divide or undergo mitosis. The existence of such a type of radiation would not have been impossible, but the experiments concerning it were difficult. Many hundreds of articles and more than a dozen books on the subject had appeared. It is, of course, not possible to demonstrate that a phenomenon does not exist in an absolute sense; however, Hollaender showed that there was no scientific proof for the existence of the phenomenon of mitogenetic radiation in any repeatable condition. This work was published in a monograph in 1936 by the National Research Council; and then very little work was done on the subject.

The experimental work involved in arriving at this negative conclusion led him to an intensive study of the effects of low levels of radiation, and he attempted to develop exacting methods of observation of cell division and effects of radiation on cells. As a result, he was able to recognize the ability of simple bacteria to recover from the effects of ultraviolet radiation, and the subtle delays in division that accompany radiation damage. These effects formed the basis for some of the more important developments concerning repair and recovery concepts in radiation biology.

Hollaender made a careful study of the effects

of monochromatic ultraviolet light on various biological systems, such as the inactivation of viruses (for example, tobacco mosaic virus), and the production of mutations in various organisms, such as *Trichophyton mentagrophytes, Aspergillus terreus,* and *Penicillium notatum.* Different macromolecular constituents of biological systems have different absorption spectra. Some wavelengths are absorbed more strongly than others. Any crucial component of a biological system will be affected most by the ultraviolet wavelength it absorbs most strongly. Therefore, by observing the effectiveness of different wavelengths, one can get a clue as to what the important macromolecular constituents are in mutation production and survival.

In 1937–38 he observed that mutations were produced most effectively by wavelengths around 2650 angstroms (A). Such wavelengths are strongly absorbed by nucleic acids, and the effectiveness of mutation production as a function of wavelength is very similar to the absorption spectrum of nucleic acids. The inference from these experiments was that the absorbing molecule must be a nucleic acid and that the most effective radiation in mutation production is on the nucleic acids rather than on proteins. This was the first clear indication that genes are composed largely of nucleic acid or at least are closely associated in their activity with nucleic acid molecules. This discovery, by action spectroscopy, was actually made before it was known, for example, that the "transforming principle" is nucleic acid. The effect of light in inactivating tobacco mosaic virus indicated that the inactivation spectrum was similar to a nucleoprotein. This result was obtained before it was clearly recognized that crystalline tobacco mosaic virus contains nucleic acids.

Hollaender's studies on the effects of different wavelengths on mutation induction broadened into the area concerning the actual processes of mutation production, and into investigations of the decreased ability of certain mutants to produce particular chemical deficiencies that result in the accumulation of pigments in the organisms. These observations served as a basis for studying the effects of mutations on *P. notatum* and provided an excellent way of producing a number of mutations in this mold in which there was increased penicillin production.

The wavelength that was most effective in producing mutations was also highly effective in killing microorganisms—a finding that had been observed by other investigators. At that time excellent ultraviolet resonance lamps were manufactured inexpensively. These lamps gave a very high percentage of their radiation close to the wavelength that is highly effective for mutation production and microorganism destruction. Hollaender applied this knowledge to investigations concerning the control of airborne infections, a problem that was very serious in the many training camps during the early years of World War II; control by ultraviolet radiation was fairly successful.

Hollaender observed that long-wavelength ultraviolet (wavelengths about 3600 A), which had little effect on cell killing if handled properly, could affect physiological properties of bacterial cultures drastically. They could, for example, extend the lag phase of growth. This delay in growth and division is now used as a tool by many investigators in studying secondary effects of radiation, and seems to be a way of prolonging the time during which cells may be able to repair radiation damage. He noted that organisms kept in the dark after ultraviolet irradiation, under conditions in which they were not permitted to divide, would ultimately survive to a much larger extent. These findings of the early 1940s subsequently were investigated extensively and elaborated in the very complex systems of radiation repair that are now known in microorganisms.

The early indications of investigations of action spectra for mutation production were that nucleic acids are some of the most important components of living systems. This led Hollaender to investigate further, and in particular to encourage others to investigate, the purification of nucleic acids and to study nucleic acid chemistry at the Oak Ridge National Laboratory Biology Division. Hollaender visualized that one of the more serious problems facing the atomic energy field was the effects of radiation on mammals and in particular man, especially at low levels of radiation. He helped initiate a large-scale study to find out the effects of radiation on mice at both the genetic and somatic levels, and he encouraged the cooperation of workers in these mammalian studies with those doing basic work on the effects of radiation on nucleic acids, viruses, microorganisms, and insects. These studies have been a model for large-scale biological investigations of some of the fundamental aspects of deleterious agents in the environment. Hollaender continued developing his ideas on recovery from radiation damage and on the effects of x-rays on the structure of nucleic acids and bacteria. With his collaborators he showed that radiation depolymerizes nucleic acids and that bacteria exhibit recovery phenomena following x-irradiation, just as they do following ultraviolet irradiation. He felt that the physical nature of the radiation damage and the biological response to this damage are of equal importance. He attempted to emphasize these aspects, as well as the applied aspects of this knowledge, at Oak Ridge.

During his time at Oak Ridge Hollaender became deeply involved in international relations in the biological sciences with regard to international cooperation in radiation research

and photobiology. He took a deep interest in biological sciences in the Latin American countries and helped organize symposiums there in cooperation with American colleagues. He took on the responsibility of reorganizing the Comité International de Photobiologie after World War II, and he helped organize the International Association for Radiation Research, which sponsors international congresses in this field. He also helped develop broad educational cooperative programs among the southeastern universities and at Oak Ridge, and developed programs for bringing visiting lecturers, faculty members, and students from small colleges into the Oak Ridge Biology Division, where they were able to reap the benefits of modern science to take back to their own institutions.

Hollaender took his A.B. (1929), M.A. (1930), and Ph.D. in physical chemistry (1931) at the University of Wisconsin. There he was a National Research Council fellow in 1931–33 and a Rockefeller fellow in 1934; he worked on a National Research Council project in 1934–37. From 1937 to 1950 he was associated with the Washington Biophysics Institute of the National Institutes of Health. He was appointed director of the Biology Division at the Oak Ridge National Laboratory in 1946 and from 1957 served also as professor of radiation biology at the University of Tennessee. The recipient of honorary degrees from the University of Vermont, Leeds University, and Marquette University, Hollaender was elected to the National Academy of Sciences in 1957 and to the American Academy of Arts and Sciences in 1960.

Hollaender edited *Radiation Biology* (3 vols., 1954–56).

For background information *see* MUTATION; NUCLEIC ACID; RADIATION BIOLOGY; ULTRAVIOLET RADIATION (BIOLOGY) in the McGraw-Hill Encyclopedia of Science and Technology.   □

★ HOLLEY, Robert William

American biochemist
Born Jan. 28, 1922, Urbana, Ill., U.S.A.

IN MARCH, 1965, Holley and his co-workers published the first nucleotide sequence of a nucleic acid. The sequence was that of an alanine transfer ribonucleic acid (RNA) isolated from bakers' yeast. The publication was the culmination of nearly 7 years of work in which procedures were first developed for the isolation of pure transfer RNAs; then the first chemical structure of a nucleic acid was elucidated. For this work Holley received the Albert Lasker Award for Basic Medical Research in 1965, and his group received the Distinguished Service Award of the U.S. Department of Agriculture.

Holley's studies with transfer RNAs actually began in 1956 in James Bonner's laboratories at the California Institute of Technology, where Holley obtained early evidence for the existence of these RNAs and for their role as acceptors of activated amino acids. During the next few years work in the laboratories of M. B. Hoagland, F. A. Lipmann, Paul Berg, and others established that a different transfer RNA serves as acceptor for each of the 20 different amino acids, and that the transfer RNAs carry specific amino acids to the site of protein synthesis, where they help to determine the amino acid sequence of the protein.

The relatively low molecular weights (25,000–30,000) of transfer RNAs make them particularly suitable for chemical studies. As isolated from living cells, however, transfer RNAs are obtained as a mixture that contains at least 20 different species. For detailed chemical studies a single RNA species is needed. Therefore, Holley set out in 1958 to attempt to isolate individual transfer RNAs. In pioneering work, which lasted nearly 4 years, Holley, with B. P. Doctor, J. Apgar, and S. H. Merrill, showed that the Craig countercurrent distribution technique could be exploited for the fractionation of transfer RNAs. Three purified transfer RNAs were isolated: the alanine-, tyrosine-, and valine-specific RNAs of bakers' yeast. A procedure was developed for the large-scale preparation of the mixture of transfer RNAs from yeast; the combination of methods then made it possible to isolate 10–20 milligrams of a purified RNA per week. A total of approximately 1 gram of the highly purified alanine transfer RNA was prepared and used in structural studies during the subsequent 2½ years.

The approach that was used in the elucidation of the structure of the alanine transfer RNA was to break the molecule into pieces, identify the pieces, and then reconstruct the original structure by determining the way in which the pieces were attached to one another originally. The purified alanine transfer RNA was broken into pieces with two specific hydrolytic enzymes, and the pieces that were formed were separated and identified. This work, done in collaboration with J. T. Madison, A. Zamir, and G. Everett, took approximately 2 years. Major technical problems included the fractionation of the complex mixture of pieces, the identification of previously unknown nucleotides, and the development of methods for the determination of the nucleotide sequences of the larger pieces. Once the structures of the pieces were known, the research entered the completely unknown area of determination of long nucleotide sequences. The problem was to determine the way in which the pieces that had already been identified were arranged in the original structure. This was done, in collaboration with J. Penswick and Apgar, by cleaving the RNA molecule into halves, and into other large fragments, by very brief digestion with one of the hydrolytic enzymes (ribonuclease T1). The entire nucleotide sequence of the RNA was then reconstructed from the structures of these large pieces.

Holley studied chemistry at the University of Illinois, where he obtained his A.B. in 1942. He received his Ph.D. in organic chemistry under A. T. Blomquist from Cornell University in 1947. During World War II he worked on penicillin research in Vincent du Vigneaud's laboratories at Cornell University Medical College. As an American Chemical Society postdoctoral fellow with C. M. Stevens at Washington State College in 1947–48 he worked on beta-lactams. During 1948–57 he was an assistant professor and associate professor of organic chemistry at the New York State Agricultural Experiment Station, Cornell University, where he worked on plant hormones, volatile constituents of fruits, nitrogen metabolism of plants, and peptide synthesis. He was a Guggenheim fellow at the California Institute of Technology in 1955–56. During 1957–64 he was a research chemist at the Plant, Soil and Nutrition Laboratory, Agricultural Research Service, U.S. Department of Agriculture, at Cornell University; it was in this laboratory, with invaluable support from the National Science Foundation, that the work on nucleic acid structure was carried out. He became a professor of biochemistry at Cornell University in 1962, and was associated full-time with the university from 1964. He was chairman of biochemistry and molecular biology at Cornell University in 1965–66. On leave 1966–67 as a National Science Foundation senior postdoctoral fellow at the Salk Institute for Biological Studies and the Scripps Clinic and Research Foundation, he studied factors that influence growth of mammalian cells in culture.

For background information *see* NUCLEIC ACID in the McGraw-Hill Encyclopedia of Science and Technology.   □

★ HOLTEDAHL, Olaf

Norwegian geologist
Born June 24, 1885, Oslo, Norway

THE SCIENTIFIC activity of Holtedahl was devoted first and foremost to the geologic history of Norway and to a considerable extent to the geology of the Polar Regions. Publishing his first paper in 1907, he began in Norway with stratigraphical and paleontological investigations on the Cambro-Silurian deposits of the Oslo Region. Later he made studies of the "Eocambrian" formations of Finnmark in the extreme north of the country and of the "Sparagmite Group" in the southeast. The demonstration of the similarity between unsorted conglomerates in the Sparagmite Group and the previously known tillites (of undoubted glacial origin) of Finnmark was important for correlation purposes and for knowledge of the distribution of glacial phenomena from the "dawn" of Cambrian time. In 1936 Holtedahl and T. F. W. Barth took up the problem of the age of the large gneiss district in the northwestern part of lower Norway, which until then had been marked on official geologic maps as a Precambrian complex comparable to that of southeastern Norway. Holtedahl wrote some synoptic papers on the Scandinavian Caledonides advocating the view, now generally held, that the structure of the gneiss area is of Caledonian (Lower Paleozoic) age, and that Eocambrian and Cambro-Silurian metamorphic rocks make up parts of the complex.

On a 1931 excursion Holtedahl and his students discovered fossils of Lower Permian age in sediments at the base of the Oslo Region lavas belonging to the alkaline complex of igneous rocks made famous by the brilliant publications of W. C. Brøgger. The age of this complex had been regarded as probably Devonian. A detail mapping of the district around Oslo was made in 1952, and a color map, accompanied by a guidebook edited by Holtedahl and J. A. Dons, was published. In the first number of a new series of publications, Holtedahl gave a general survey of some principal tectonic structures, mainly concerning ring-fracture phenomena and the emplacement of plutonic bodies; these problems he later explored further. He also contributed to the Quaternary geology of Norway with articles on the history of the waning of the last inland ice and on the corresponding advance of the sea and uplift of the land in lowland districts in southeastern Norway.

Holtedahl made studies of the topography of the sea bottom off the long coast of Norway based on official charts and more recent echosounding work. These studies resulted in the publication in 1940 of a series of colored bathymetrical maps covering the whole distance from the Skagerrak to eastern Finnmark. To the south the marginal, no doubt primarily tectonic, depression of the Norwegian Channel is a dominant feature. An important feature further to the north is a commonly well-marked and regular boundary between the rocky land and the banks, with their loose deposits; and furthermore, in many districts, there is a marked trench at the boundary. It was concluded that these are fault lines and that the landmass had been uplifted probably in Tertiary time. The existence of a similar submarine topography outside other coasts, such as of western Greenland and northern Labrador, was noted.

As a member of the Norwegian Spitsbergen expeditions in 1909–11, Holtedahl carried out geologic work in the northwestern part of West Spitsbergen. His principal report dealt with the (pre-Devonian) Hecla Hoek formations and with Carboniferous formations, but he also studied the Old Red sandstones on the northern coast. With A. Hoel, he showed, furthermore, that the gneiss and granite masses of the extreme northwest do not, as previously believed, represent Precambrian rocks but Caledonian ones intruded into the Hecla Hoek. In 1918 he studied the lower Paleozoic formations in Bear Island and in 1921 organized and led a Norwegian expedition to the Soviet twin islands of Novaya Zemlya north of the Ural Mountains. The resultant three-volume scientific report consisted of 45 papers on geology, botany, and zoology. Holtedahl's contribution on the rock formations included a brief survey of Paleozoic sedimentary series in other Arctic regions. Through publications on lower Paleozoic fossils collected by Norwegian expeditions ("Fram" and "Gjøa") in Arctic America, he had acquired some knowledge of the stratigraphy of this part of the North Polar Regions. At the request of the Aeroarctic

Society, whose president was Fridtjof Nansen, he worked out a colored geologic map (no doubt the first one) of Arctic regions, "Geologische Karte der Arktis" (with text), printed in Germany in 1930.

In 1927–28 Holtedahl carried out geologic and geomorphological investigations in some western Antarctic and some subantarctic islands (Southern Shetlands, South Georgia, and others) as part of the Norwegian research work (1927–37) instituted and financed by Consul Lars Christensen. Holtedahl was the editor of the report on the scientific results.

Holtedahl was educated at the University of Oslo, where he received his Ph.D. in 1913. He became a research fellow there in 1910, lecturer in 1914, and professor of geology in 1920; he retired in 1955. He was president of the Norwegian Geological Society, the Norwegian Geographical Society, and the Norwegian Academy of Science and Arts. A member of the Royal Society of London, as well as of a number of other learned societies in various other countries, he received the Wollaston Medal of the Geological Society of London, the von Buch Medal of Deutsche Geologische Gesellschaft, and other awards.

In addition to the works mentioned, Holtedahl wrote *Norges geologi* (2 vols., 1953), in Norwegian. He edited *Geology of Norway* (paper, 1960) for the International Geologic Congress.

For background information *see* ANTARCTICA; ARCTIC AND SUBARCTIC ISLANDS; GEOLOGICAL TIME SCALE; GEOLOGY in the McGraw-Hill Encyclopedia of Science and Technology.   □

★ HOLTFRETER, Johannes Friedrich Karl

American zoologist
Born Jan. 9, 1901, Richtenberg, Germany

EMBRYOLOGICAL RESEARCH had entered a period of great expectations when Holtfreter began his studies in the 1920s. This outlook was due mainly to the discovery of the "organizer" by H. Spemann and the revelations which the organizer concept promised to bring to the problems of morphogenetic regulation, tissue organization, and the differential fate of the embryonic cells. The designation "organizer" was given to a vaguely delineated dorsal area in the amphibian gastrula which later moves to the interior and forms the primordia of the mesodermal axial system. These primordia were shown to act as "primary inductors"; they evoke in the overlying ectoderm the differentiation of specific structures, such as brain or spinal cord.

Through his experiments with amphibian embryos, Holtfreter greatly contributed to the clarification of the organizer. Its alleged all-powerful role in embryological development was reduced to certain intrinsic properties and activating functions which can be defined morphogenetically, although not yet in biochemical terms. There emerged the concept of synergistically operating systems of inductive tissues, which are arranged in certain anatomical patterns and operate in predictable sequences. An embryonic tissue whose course of differentiation has been determined by primary inductors becomes itself inductive and initiates the emergence of new structures which, in turn, may operate as tertiary inductors. Synchronized with this ordered display of inductors, the responsiveness of the reacting tissues to inducing stimuli ("competence") changes with age and tissue type. It became clear that these controlled tissue interrelations represent one of the most crucial mechanisms by which the typical pattern of cell differentiations of the amphibian body is elaborated. This situation seems to apply to the vertebrates in general.

In the early 1930s Holtfreter was one of the pioneers who divested the induction phenomenon of its vitalistic connotations and made it accessible to biochemical analysis. He showed that inductors retain inducing power after they have been boiled, frozen, or treated with fat solvents and other chemicals. These and other experiments indicated that induction is mediated

by the transmission of some chemical message from the inducing to the reacting cells.

Rather perplexing was the discovery that the capacity to elicit inductions is not confined to embryonic tissues. Holtfreter tested a diversity of tissues from a wide range of adult animals—from invertebrates to mammals, including man. When implanted into the amphibian gastrula, practically all of the foreign tissues tested—whether fresh or denatured—proved to be powerful inductors. Some tissues could induce structures such as a head or a tail, which were neither less organized nor less complex than those obtained with implanted live organizer material. Thus, it was necessary to distinguish strictly between two properties of the organizer, that of emitting inductive agents, and that of being capable of a remarkable self-regulated organization when this material, or parts of it, are transplanted or explanted. However, the inducing agents do not control the typical tissue configuration of the induced mass of cells. Once induced, the cells differentiate independently of further external directives, and their tissue-specific organization proceeds autonomously.

In the subsequent endeavors of many investigators to isolate and to characterize chemically the inducing agent(s), Holtfreter remained a critical observer. The extensive efforts toward this goal have not been very rewarding as yet. The elusiveness of the problem is illustrated by the fact that not only a great diversity of defined substances (such as nucleic acids, proteins, and steroids) can elicit inductions but also that, as shown by Holtfreter in 1945, even a shock treatment of the ectoderm with distilled water, alkali, or alcohol mimics the natural inductors.

Emphasis shifted from the inducing to the reacting tissues. If it is inconceivable that any chemical substance can organize the cells into their normal pattern of discrete and yet interwoven tissues, what then are the organizing mechanisms involved? Holtfreter realized that important clues for an answer are to be sought in what W. Vogt had described as "morphogenetic cell movements." It turned out that these movements harbored many problems which could be tackled experimentally. For instance: What are the inherent and the environmental factors which determine the collective and directed movements of the embryonic cell layers? What controls the locomotion and the progressive changes in shape of the individual cells? Why do certain cell types tend to establish surface epithelia, and others inner tubular structures; whereas still others disperse, or infiltrate other tissues, or reaggregate to form new tissue configurations?

It soon became apparent that in addition to localized, oriented, and stage-dependent cell movements there is another phenomenon which is, morphogenetically, of equal significance. This phenomenon had been referred to as differential "cell affinities" by Holtfreter in 1939 or as selective cell adhesions. Experimental studies demonstrated the existence of stage-specific and tissue-specific differences in regard to the presence, absence, or degree of adhesion between homologous and heterologous cells. It was concluded that this scheme of preferential cell adhesions imposes decisive regulatory limitations upon the display of cellular movements. Holtfreter suggested in 1948 and 1955 that the key to a better understanding of both these somewhat antagonistic phenomena—morphogenetic movements and selective cell adhesions—is contained in the structural and kinetic properties of the cell membrane. He proposed, furthermore, that the organization of the embryonic cells into tissue patterns is accomplished chiefly through the combined operation of these two morphogenetic mechanisms. The issue, however, continued to be the subject of research by Holtfreter and other investigators.

Holtfreter studied at the universities of Rostock, Leipzig, and Freiburg, receiving his Ph.D. in zoology at Freiburg in 1924. He was an assistant in the department of embryology at the Kaiser Wilhelm Institute of Biology (1928–33), lecturer and associate professor at the Zoological Institute, University of Munich (1933–38), guest lecturer at Cambridge University, England (1939–40), and a Rockefeller and Guggenheim fellow in the zoology department at McGill University (1942–46). In 1946 he joined the faculty of the University of Rochester, becoming professor of zoology there in 1948. He was elected to the National Academy of Sciences in 1955 and to the American Academy of Arts and Sciences in 1957.

For background information *see* ANIMAL MORPHOGENESIS; EMBRYOLOGY; EMBRYONIC DIFFERENTIATION; EMBRYONIC INDUCTION in the McGraw-Hill Encyclopedia of Science and Technology.   □

★ HORECKER, Bernard Leonard

American biochemist and molecular biologist
Born Oct. 31, 1914, Chicago, Ill., U.S.A.

HORECKER'S NAME is associated with the pathway of carbohydrate metabolism variously known as the "pentose phosphate pathway," the "hexose monophosphate shunt," or the "oxidative pathway." In the early 1930s the work of G. Embden, Otto Meyerhof, J. K. Parnas, and others had established the major outlines of the glycolytic pathway, which was shown to be the major route of carbohydrate metabolism in animal cells and in yeast. However, Otto Warburg, Fritz Lipmann, and Frank Dickens had already suggested the existence of another pathway in which glucose-6-phosphate was oxidized directly to phosphogluconic acid, pentose phosphate, and CO_2. It was not until nearly 20 years later that the nature of this pathway and its physiological significance were clarified. Horecker purified the enzyme phosphogluconic dehydrogenase and showed that it catalyzed the oxidative decarboxylation of phosphogluconic acid to produce a new pentose ester, ribulose-5-phosphate, which was the immediate precursor of the ribose-5-phosphate of nucleic acid and nucleotides.

In 1938 Zacharias Dische had obtained evidence which indicated that red cell extracts were able to convert pentose phosphate to hexose phosphate, suggesting that the hexose monophosphate pathway might function as a cyclic mechanism for the oxidation of carbohydrates. This was the problem next taken up by Horecker and his collaborators. In the course of their studies on the formation of hexose monophosphate from pentose monophosphate, two new enzymes, transketolase and transaldolase, were isolated and characterized. Together with E. Racker and his collaborators, they established that transketolase contained thiamine pyrophosphate as the prosthetic group. This enzyme utilized ribose phosphate and xylulose phosphate (formed from ribulose phosphate) for the formation of the seven-carbon compound sedoheptulose phosphate. The second enzyme, transaldolase, catalyzed a transfer of three carbon atoms from sedoheptulose phosphate to triose phosphate, producing fructose phosphate and a new four-carbon sugar, erythrose phosphate. As a result of these studies from the laboratories of Horecker and Racker, the role of the pentose phosphate pathway as a reversible mechanism for the formation of pentose phosphate from hexose phosphate was established. Later studies suggested that a second major function of the pathway was the production of reduced triphosphopyridine nucleotide, which is now known to be essential in biosynthetic reactions.

At about the time that Horecker and Racker were working out the details of the pentose phosphate pathway, Melvin Calvin and his co-workers were using radioactive carbon dioxide to elucidate the path of carbon in photosynthesis. They had obtained evidence that ribulose diphosphate and sedoheptulose phosphate played key roles in this process. On the basis of Calvin's isotope evidence, it was predicted that a pentose ester, probably ribulose diphosphate, would be the primary acceptor for carbon dioxide in photosynthesis. This was confirmed when Horecker and his co-workers demonstrated that spinach extracts were able to produce phosphoglyceric acid from carbon dioxide and ribose phosphate. They also isolated the enzyme phosphoribulokinase and ribulose diphosphate

carboxylase (carboxydismutase), which together with phosphoribose isomerase were responsible for the overall reaction in this system. Finally, since the labeling patterns obtained by Calvin with radioactive carbon dioxide indicated that ribulose diphosphate arose from fructose phosphate by the pentose phosphate pathway, the essential role of this pathway in photosynthesis, as well as for the production of nucleic acids and nucleotides, was established.

Horecker later extended his studies on pentose metabolism to acetic acid fermentations in microorganisms. He demonstrated that the key step in these fermentations was the cleavage of xylulose phosphate to acetyl phosphate and triose phosphate, a reaction catalyzed by the thiamine pyrophosphate enzyme, phosphoketolase. This type of cleavage reaction has since been shown to be common to a number of bacterial fermentations.

Horecker then turned his attention to the specific mechanisms involved in carbon-carbon bond cleavage and synthesis in carbohydrate metabolism. Aldol condensations and cleavages had been established as important events in carbohydrate metabolism, particularly in the pentose phosphate pathway, but little information was available regarding the reaction mechanisms. Studies with the enzyme transaldolase, begun in 1961 by Horecker and his collaborators, led to the discovery of a Schiff base intermediate formed between the substrate and lysyl residues in the enzyme. The Schiff base mechanism was soon found to be generally applicable to a wide variety of aldolases, and it was extended by F. H. Westheimer to the decarboxylation of oxaloacetate. Horecker and his collaborators reduced the Schiff base intermediates with sodium borohydride, thus labeling the active site peptide, and then showed that the peptides isolated from rabbit muscle aldolase and rabbit liver aldolase were of similar, but not identical, amino acid sequence and composition. It was thus established that the aldolases of rabbit liver and rabbit muscle are distinct proteins, but genetically closely related, probably having evolved from a common precursor protein.

Horecker's earlier work, in collaboration with E. Haas and T. R. Hogness, resulted in the isolation from yeast of the first cytochrome c reductase, which was identified as a flavoprotein containing riboflavin phosphate. Later he isolated a similar enzyme from rat liver and showed it to be a flavoprotein containing flavin adenine dinucleotide. On the basis of Warburg's early studies, it had been anticipated that these enzymes would catalyze key steps in the oxidation of substrates by molecular oxygen. However, the isolated cytochrome reductases were shown not to participate in the main electron transport scheme, and later work provided evidence that they play an important function in the triphosphopyridine nucleotide-linked hydroxylation reactions.

Horecker received his B.S. (1936) and Ph.D. in chemistry (1939) at the University of Chicago, where his teachers were T. R. Hogness and E. Haas. At the National Institutes of Health during World War II, while studying methods for the detection of incipient carbon monoxide poisoning in aviators, he discovered the near-infrared absorption bands of hemoglobin. After the war he again took up his studies on enzymes and carbohydrate metabolism, and in 1957–58 studied on a Rockefeller Public Service Award at the Pasteur Institut in Paris. In 1959 he became head of the department of microbiology at New York University School of Medicine and in 1963 head of the department of molecular biology at the Albert Einstein College of Medicine. Recipient of the American Chemical Society Award in Enzyme Chemistry in 1952, Horecker was elected to the National Academy of Sciences in 1961 and to the American Academy of Arts and Sciences in 1962.

Horecker wrote *Pentose Metabolism in Bacteria* (1963).

For background information *see* BACTERIAL METABOLISM (CATABOLISM); CARBOHYDRATE METABOLISM; PHOTOSYNTHESIS; SCHIFF BASE in the McGraw-Hill Encyclopedia of Science and Technology. ☐

★ HORNIG, Donald Frederick

American chemist
Born Mar. 17, 1920, Milwaukee, Wis., U.S.A.

HORNIG'S SCIENTIFIC work had its roots in his education during the flowering of chemical physics in the 1930s and his experiences in a variety of areas during World War II. The first influence led him to studies of molecular structure and vibrational spectra and to the extended studies of the dynamics, structure, and spectra of molecular crystals. The second led to the parallel investigations of the structure of shock waves, rotational relaxation in shock waves, very fast chemical reactions at high temperatures, and combustion phenomena.

He first gained notice through his development and optimization of fast, sensitive radiation thermocouples for infrared spectrometers. Many wartime spectrometers employed detectors of his design and construction. His main work began with a theoretical paper inspired by the activities of E. Bright Wilson, Jr., and his associates, in which the theoretical foundations for the classification of molecular motions and spectra in crystals were examined. Hornig showed that the zero-wave-number modes of vibration which could be active as fundamentals in infrared or Raman spectra could be classified under the crystallographic point group. Further, he examined the effect of weak coupling between molecular units and the correlation between free molecule symmetry, the local symmetry of the molecule in the crystal, and the crystal symmetry.

In a long series of papers Hornig and his students related these principles to the low-temperature spectra of ordered phases of simple molecules such as the ammonium halides, hydrogen halides, hydrogen sulfide, and methane. He utilized the changed selection rules in the crystal to correct and complete the assignment of the vibrational spectrum of benzene, which had been brilliantly worked out by C. K. Ingold and his co-workers. At that time many phase transitions in ammonium salts and other simple, high-symmetry crystals were thought to originate in the onset of free molecular rotation. By identifying the librational frequencies and showing that libration persisted above the transition, Hornig first demonstrated unambiguously that rotation was not involved, and that the transitions entailed the disordering of the equilibrium orientations as had been anticipated theoretically by Frankel.

Later he showed, however, that in the NaCl phase of NH_4I hindered rotation could account for the spectrum. This was even more clearly evident in dilute solutions of CH_4 in A, an isomorphous crystal of nearly identical dimensions to CH_4. Hornig and H. F. King developed the theory of the rotational states of a tetrahedron in an octahedral field, in which they used the symmetry group of 576 elements to classify the states and carry out the calculations. With the aid of the theory, the spectra were interpreted in a reasonably quantitative way.

In the course of this work Hornig and his co-workers developed the very powerful method of isomorphous substitution, in which a molecule is studied as a very dilute solution in an isomorphous lattice, either of a related substance or an isotopically different lattice of the same substance. Examples are CH_4 in either A or CD_4. In this way the effects of the equilibrium field of the crystal could be separated from the coupling to the motions of other molecules. The power of the isomorphous substitution method prompted a series of studies of the hydrogen bond, particularly in water and ice. These studies led to the conclusion that the barrier to proton transfer was very high and that even in moderately strong H-bonds the spectral lines are intrinsically sharp. The normally observed broad bands arise from coupling to other motions.

A striking observation made by Hornig and Busing, later studied by several co-workers in detail, was that negative ions could affect the intensities of Raman spectra of water by factors up to 10, whereas in passing from Li^+ to Cs^+ or even polyvalent positive ions the effect was negligible. This effect was explained in a semiquantitative theory by Hornig and T. Wall, but the details of the interaction have yet to be cleared up.

Perhaps the most novel idea introduced by Hornig was that of studying the structure of shock waves by their optical reflection characteristics. Although extremely difficult experimentally, the reflectivity being of the order of 10^{-6} and the available time of the order of 10^{-5} sec, he and his co-workers developed it into a powerful tool which measured for the first time the shock compression process which takes place in about 10^{-11} sec. Subsequently, he related rotational relaxations of diatomic molecules to the bulk viscosity, and showed that for monatomic gases the macroscopic Navier-Stokes equations, while inadequate by perhaps 25%, did just about as well in describing these processes which occur in a few mean free paths as did higher-order kinetic theories.

As a by-product of his work on shock waves and his acquaintance with the work of G. B. Kistiakowsky on reaction kinetics, Hornig studied the kinetics of dissociation of diatomic and simple polyatomic molecules in shock waves at higher temperatures. Finally, together with Burns, he combined the shock wave and flash photolysis methods of R. G. W. Norrish to measure atom recombination rates at very high temperatures.

Hornig's last experimental work before entering public service was the observation of optical reflection from detonation waves in H_2-O_2. This led to the observation that the shock compression in the detonation was essentially normal for the unreacted gas mixture but that reaction distorted the compression wave even in the first 10^{-11} sec. These first measurements of the gaseous detonation process, done with M. L. N. Shastri, had not been completed when he abandoned experimental work for service with President Johnson.

Hornig was educated in the public schools of Milwaukee and at Milwaukee County Day School. He went on a National Scholarship to Harvard, where he received his B.S. in 1940 and his Ph.D. in 1943. During the war he worked at Woods Hole on conventional explosives and at Los Alamos on the nuclear bomb. In 1946 he went to Brown University, where he became director of the Metcalf Research Laboratory in 1949, professor in 1951, and acting dean of the Graduate School in 1953. Later he moved to Princeton, where he became chairman of the chemistry department and Donner Professor of Science in 1958. In 1959 President Eisenhower named him a member of his Science Advisory Committee, and he was reappointed in 1961 by President Kennedy. In 1964 President Johnson appointed him Special Assistant to the President for Science and Technology, director of the Office of Science and Technology in the Executive Office of the President, chairman of the President's Science Advisory Committee, and chairman of the Federal Council for Science and Technology. Hornig was elected to the American Academy of Arts and Sciences in 1952 and to the National Academy of Sciences in 1957.

For background information *see* CRYSTALLOGRAPHY; MOLECULAR STRUCTURE AND SPECTRA; SHOCK WAVE in the McGraw-Hill Encyclopedia of Science and Technology.   □

★ HORSFALL, James Gordon

American plant pathologist
Born Jan. 9, 1905, Mountain Grove, Mo., U.S.A.

HORSFALL INVESTIGATED diseases of the seed, the seedling, the root, the stem, the water system, the leaf, and the fruit of plants. He described and named "inoculum potential," which is the quantitative relationship between the number of propagules of the pathogen and the amount of resultant disease as related to the plant environment. He and his colleague A. E. Dimond described and named "high sugar disease" and "low sugar disease," whereby sugar, that ubiquitous carbohydrate, increases some classes of diseases (especially those caused by obligate parasites) and reduces other classes of diseases (especially those caused by weak parasites). These sugar disease concepts gathered into one theory numerous isolated bits of data on the effects of light, darkness, weed killers, hormones, insecticides, and other diseases on plant diseases. This theory came much later and moved more rapidly than the concept of inoculum potential.

Despite all this work on the nature of plant

disease, Horsfall's real interest was in chemicals that can control plant disease: what they are, what they do, how they do it, and how to find better ones. On his first job Horsfall investigated the control of decay in tomato seedlings by soaking the seeds in copper sulfate. He then discovered better chemicals than copper sulfate for more diseases. Copper sulfate and calcium hydroxide were ingredients in the famed Bordeaux mixture, an empirical but classical fungicide to control many plant diseases. His early work, coinciding with the immense drought that caused the great dust bowl of the 1930s, led to his discovery of some of the insidious routes by which Bordeaux mixture damages the host while controlling disease.

It was in the 1930s also that there was excitement in the medical field over the discovery of the sulfanilamides. Since sulfanilamides are organic compounds, the question arose: Why not use organic fungicides for farm crops? In 1938 Horsfall discovered the fungicidal effectiveness of chloranil, which promptly began to replace the old copper seed treatments. This research led in 1940 to the discovery of the effectiveness, and later worldwide usefulness, of the ethylene-bisdithiocarbamates and to extensive researches on their mode of action. In 1948 Horsfall wrote of 2,4-dinitro-6-(1-methylheptyl)phenyl crotonate, which is now widely used to control the powdery mildew class of plant diseases. While investigating the mode of action of these compounds, Horsfall published numerous papers with his colleagues on the relation of structure to fungicidal activity, the effect of fat-solubilizing substituents on permeability of the molecules, the role of electronegative groups in the molecule, and stereochemistry.

At the same time Horsfall and his colleague G. A. Zentmyer and later Dimond plunged into a new field of endotherapy or chemotherapy of plant disease—the procedure of injecting fungicides into diseased plants to cure them. How-

ever, little practical success materialized. The Dutch elm disease, a prime target, still resists treatment. Effective compounds were discovered, but detailed researches into the mechanisms of action show that the invading fungus can be starved or killed down to a low level of the plant. But the plant, unlike an animal, has no phagocytosis system to kill off the last stragglers and thus permit recovery. The elm tree finally succumbs.

The son of a college president, Horsfall majored in soil science as an undergraduate at the University of Arkansas, where he received his B.S. with highest honors in 1925. Cornell University granted him a Ph.D. in plant pathology in 1929. He immediately joined the staff of the New York State Agricultural Experiment Station of Cornell University and reached the rank of professor in 1936. He moved to the Connecticut Agricultural Experiment Station in 1939 as chief of the Plant Pathology Department, and became vice-director in 1947 and director in 1948. The recipient of honorary degrees from the universities of Vermont and Turin, Italy, Horsfall was elected to the American Academy of Arts and Sciences in 1951 and to the National Academy of Sciences in 1953.

Horsfall wrote *Fungicides and Their Action* (1945) and *Principles of Fungicidal Action* (1956). He coedited, with Dimond, *Plant Pathology: An Advanced Treatise* (3 vols., 1959–60).

For background information *see* AGRICULTURAL SCIENCE (PLANT); FUNGISTAT AND FUNGICIDE; PLANT DISEASE in the McGraw-Hill Encyclopedia of Science and Technology. ☐

★ HÖRSTADIUS, Sven Otto

Swedish zoologist
Born Feb. 18, 1898, Stockholm, Sweden

ZOOLOGY IN Sweden had mainly been dealing with anatomy and taxonomy when John Runnström in the 1910s took up experimental embryology. This branch of the science had been inaugurated in the 1890s by Wilhelm Roux with amphibians and by Theodor Boveri, Hans Driesch, Curt Herbst, and Thomas H. Morgan with sea urchins as material. Runnström turned the interest of his first pupil, Hörstadius, to the same field.

Hans Spemann had invented (1906) a new method for embryonic transplantations in amphibians, using fine glass needles instead of knives. Hörstadius worked out a method for transplanting fragments of cleavage stages in the small sea urchin eggs (less than 100 μ in diameter). By vital staining of some of the fragments, the fate of the different layers of the

egg could be established. In the 16-cell stage the egg axis (the animal-vegetal axis) is already clearly recognizable, the egg consisting of eight animal mesomeres, four big macromeres, and at the vegetal pole four small micromeres. After the two following cleavages the egg is segmented into five layers, called an_1, an_2, veg_1, veg_2, and the micromeres. The first step of the analysis was to ascertain what these layers give rise to in normal development. The skeleton-forming cells in the larva are derived from the micromeres. Contrary to previous statements, it was found that the limit between the skin (ectoderm) and the archenteron (entoderm and mesoderm) lies between veg_1 and veg_2, and not between an_2 and veg_1. The basis was then laid for an analysis of the potentialities of the different layers.

Isolated fragments of sea urchin eggs often differentiate in another way than they should have done in the larva. Isolated animal halves never gastrulate, and as a rule they do not form a ciliated band (the swimming organ of the larva) or a mouth, as this material normally should have done. Instead, the tuft of long, immovable cilia at the animal pole is more or less extended over the surface of the half. But if four micromeres are implanted into an animal half, this extension of the tuft is inhibited, and not only the mouth and ciliated band but also an archenteron are induced, the half developing into a small pluteus larva. It was proved in a variety of ways that the atypical differentiation of the isolated half is due to lack of vegetal influences. A great number of experiments with fragments and transplants in different combinations confirm the hypothesis of Runnström that there exist along the egg axis two gradients, one animal and one vegetal, which both reach to the opposite pole, thus overlapping through the whole egg, and which interact mutually and are partially hostile to each other. Another experiment may illustrate this. If micromeres are im-

planted in the animal pole of an animal half, a small archenteron and skeleton are formed there as expected, but such organs appear also on the opposite, most vegetal side, where in isolated animal halves an invagination never occurs. The explanation is that the animal gradient has been so weakened by the implanted micromeres that the vegetal forces present now in relation to the animal ones are strong enough to assert themselves.

Since Driesch, it was known that meridional halves give twin larvae. Meridional fragments show bilateral organization. Even fragments less than 1/8 can give small plutei. How is the dorsoventral axis oriented in relation to that of the whole egg? Left and right as well as ventral halves do not change the position of the axis, but in dorsal halves it is reversed. Evidently each part of the egg can form a ventral side, the original ventral side inhibiting other parts. Therefore the dorsal side is least inhibited and takes the lead in dorsal halves.

Driesch abandoned biology and became a philosopher. He maintained that fragments from all parts of an egg could give a whole organism, because of a mysterious force, the "entelechi." Hörstadius showed that Driesch's conception of "vitalism" in development was based on a misinterpretation of experiments.

After the analysis by operative methods, Hörstadius turned toward problems of a more physiological type. It is well known that some substances can vegetalize (lithium ions) or animalize (for example, iodosobenzoic acid) whole eggs. Hörstadius found that dinitrophenol acts in the former and trypsin in the latter direction, and he studied the action of many other substances, such as amino acids and homologs, on the metabolism of the larva. Together with Lars Josefsson and Runnström, he tested the morphogenetic effects of fractions extracted from lyophilized sea urchin eggs.

Hörstadius was the first to show that, in an individual derived from an egg with cytoplasm from one species and nucleus from another, a species character developed according to the nucleus. Eggs of two sea urchin species were each deprived of their nucleus and fertilized with sperm of the other species. A skeleton character of the sperm species appeared, but a weak influence of the mother in the opposite combination was not quite excluded. This work was further extended by Leopold von Ubisch.

The neural crest, the material in the ridge surrounding the neural plate in vertebrates, contributes to the nervous system and the head skeleton and produces the pigment cells of the body. Hörstadius undertook, together with S. Sellman, a thorough analysis of the skeleton-forming capacity by local vital staining, extirpations, transplantations to other parts of the body or exchange of pieces, and so forth. The position of material for the different arches was mapped out. It was found that part of the forebrain material is situated in the transverse ridge. Parts with different properties were identified. Material could migrate in wrong paths and in the wrong place behave in its own way. The whole problem of the crest in its different aspects was reviewed in "The neural crest: Its properties and derivatives in the light of experimental research" (1950).

Hörstadius also published papers on the descriptive embryology of echinoderms and, together with Greta Hörstadius, on protein digestion in gastropods. He was one of the earlier bird photographers in Sweden.

Hörstadius graduated from the University of Stockholm in 1930 and was lecturer and associate professor in zoology during 1929–42. In 1938–42 he was also head of the department for developmental physiology and genetics at the Wenner-Gren Institute of Experimental Biology. In 1942 he became professor of zoology at the University of Uppsala, from which he retired in 1964. He was president of the International Union of Biological Sciences (IUBS) in 1953–58 and of the International Council of Scientific Unions (ICSU) in 1962–63. He was a founder member of the Council of the World Wildlife Fund and became chairman of the European Section of the International Council for Bird Preservation. President of the Swedish Ornithological Society, he organized as secretary general the 10th International Ornithological Congress in Uppsala in 1950. He was also active in nature protection in Sweden. A member of the Royal Society of London and the Academia Pontificia, Vatican, as well as many other academies and learned societies, he received the Prix Albert Brachet from the Belgian Academy of Science in 1936. He was made doctor honoris causa by the universities of Paris (1954) and Cambridge (1960).

For background information *see* ANIMAL MORPHOGENESIS; CELL LINEAGE; EMBRYOLOGY, EXPERIMENTAL; NEURAL CREST in the McGraw-Hill Encyclopedia of Science and Technology. □

★ HOTCHKISS, Rollin Douglas

American molecular biologist
Born Sept. 8, 1911, South Britain, Conn., U.S.A.

Beginning in 1946, Hotchkiss was generally involved in making the genetic transformation of bacterial cells by DNA a quantitative process, orderly in its response to time of contact and concentration of DNA. This involved the first use of specific selective markers and required further definition of such features of transformation as dependence on the molecular integrity of DNA, the cultural environment of the recipient cells, and specific marker arrangements, such as linkage in both DNA and the cells. He also earlier developed a histochemical stain specific for polysaccharides and participated with R. J. Dubos in the isolation and purification of the first polypeptide antibiotics, gramicidin and tyrocidine.

As a principle linking these and a considerable number of other interests, Hotchkiss was always less interested in structure than in mechanism, which he considered "structure in motion." It was there that some of the principal challenges were opening up in chemistry and biochemistry at the time of his graduate degree in organic chemistry in 1935. Although the era of isolation and identification of natural products had begun to accelerate and was to continue to do so, the accumulating structural information formed even at that time a growing basis for those interested in inquiring into the mechanisms of natural processes.

At the Rockefeller Institute Hospital, Hotchkiss realized that biochemistry offered even more of process and mechanism than organic chemistry. Assigned to an immunochemical program, he took greatest interest in the serological cross-reactions between antipneumococcal antisera and various substances bearing or resembling units of the polyuronide-containing, pectinlike bacterial polysaccharides. With W. F. Goebel, he studied by synthesis and degradation the disaccharide units these contained. Striking

farther afield toward mechanisms, he made artificial antigens containing various polyanionic substances imitating the natural polysaccharides of pneumococci. At this time (1936) he probably made one of the first "biological" experiments with a synthetic polymer, showing a considerable cross-reaction between one of the specific antibodies and gumlike copolymers of acrylic acid and vinyl alcohol.

The discovery of an antibacterial antagonism between a soil bacillus, *Bacillus brevis*, and a wide variety of gram-positive pathogenic bacteria by Dubos in 1939 offered a new challenge. In collaborative work Hotchkiss was able to crystallize highly growth-inhibitory crystalline polypeptides, gramicidin and tyrocidine, from the cultures. Hotchkiss carried the structural work on the composition of these early antibiotics far enough to be able to list the component amino acids, but he set aside the structural study in favor of studies of the mode of action of antibiotics on bacteria.

Two principles of antibacterial action appeared. It was found that gramicidin blocks phosphate accumulation and esterification in respiring bacteria, although it does not interfere with the underlying respiration or glycolysis. Hotchkiss showed in 1944 for the first time that phosphorylation also is blocked by dinitrophenol and sodium azide, acting upon bacteria, yeast, and cellfree extracts of kidney. This discovery of "uncoupling agents" depended upon the growing recognition of the significance of oxidative phosphorylation, as well as the early suggestion by C. E. Clifton that dinitrophenol and azide prevented polysaccharide synthesis. Another, more direct cytotoxicity was demonstrated for tyrocidine—a gross destruction of selective permeability, permitting the leaching out from bacteria of various phosphates, inorganic and esterified, as well as amino acids and ultraviolet-absorbing coenzymes. This is brought about by tyrocidine and a series of some 20 or more cationic and anionic surface-active agents quite generally for a variety of bacteria and yeast strains, at whatever concentrations are sufficient to kill the cells. The action is physical and immediate and also characteristic of the phenolic antiseptics, but not of various dyes, oxidants, and halogen- or metal-bearing antiseptics. The first direct injury is succeeded in some bacteria by later autolysis.

Somewhat earlier, Hotchkiss had spent a year at the Carlsberg Laboratory, Copenhagen, where he intended to measure intracellular localization and production of sulfhydryl groups, for he believed that oxidative control of these groups activated or controlled various enzymes at cell division and growth. His work evolved rather into a study of sulfhydryl groups and total peptide bonds in purified proteins.

The interest of Hotchkiss in cell organization led to measurements of enzyme distribution in cell particulates with A. Claude, which initiated studies continued actively by G. H. Hogeboom on mitochondria and microsomes. It was Hotchkiss's hope in this early work to show that phosphorylative energy accumulated by the mitochondria was used elsewhere by way of soluble enzymes to synthesize other cell particles and products. Little success was encountered at that time (1946) in finding enzymatic activities or the syntheses now known to be associated with the microsome (crude ribosome) fractions. In trying to measure the accumulation of biosynthetic products, a method was devised for staining with fuchsin-sulfite polysaccharides oxidized with periodate (now the standard PAS, or periodic acid–Schiff histochemical stain). Other attempts were made to find protein and nucleic acid syntheses. Washed bacteria were shown to make protein from amino acids if energy was available, but the proteins were not characterized, and purine or pyrimidine bases did not clearly go into nucleic acids. These systems were disrupted by various antibiotics, but those early findings, so quickly superseded after isotopes were available, threw only a little light on metabolic pathways or specific blocks of syntheses at that time.

The bacterial transformation to capsule production seemed to offer a specific synthesis which could be "turned on" at will, and in this way Hotchkiss came to study genetic controls. As already mentioned, these were extended to the quantitative selective traits, and formal evidence was obtained of the equivalence of mutational and transformable traits, of their additivity, and of their linkage, essentially fulfilling the expectations of gene material. The DNA implicated by O. T. Avery and co-workers was shown to have the expected purine and pyrimidine bases and essentially no amino acid. Quantitative paper chromatography of the bases was initiated showing characteristic base distributions but was not further developed. Emphasis was placed especially on the rate of cell-DNA interaction and the time and rate of production of genetically altered cells, cell enzymes, and the replication of the newly introduced DNA.

Son of a factory mechanic, Hotchkiss graduated from Yale University with a B.S. in 1932 and a Ph.D. in organic chemistry in 1935. He joined the Rockefeller Institute in 1935. He was a Rockefeller Foundation fellow in the Carlsberg Laboratory (with K. Linderstrøm-Lang) in 1937–38. He was appointed visiting professor in the biology department of the Massachusetts Institute of Technology in 1958. He was elected to the National Academy of Sciences in 1961.

Hotchkiss was associate editor of *Methods of Biochemical Analysis*, edited by David Glick (14 vols., 1954–66), and of the *Journal of Cell Biology, Journal of Biochemistry*, and *Journal of*

Analytical Chemistry. He contributed over 90 articles in scientific journals representing biochemistry, microbiology, and genetics.

For background information *see* ANTIBIOTIC; BACTERIAL GENETICS; DEOXYRIBONUCLEIC ACID; ENZYME; NUCLEOPROTEIN in the McGraw-Hill Encyclopedia of Science and Technology. □

★ HOUSTON, William Vermillion

American physicist
Born Jan. 19, 1900, Mount Gilead, Ohio, U.S.A.

IN THE 1920s a large part of the attention of physicists was directed toward the study of spectroscopy as a means of understanding the structure of atoms and molecules. N. Bohr's 1913 theory of the hydrogen atom was rapidly accepted because of its remarkable success in giving a quantitative description of the gross features of the hydrogen spectrum. A. J. W. Sommerfeld in 1916 extended Bohr's analysis to include the relativistic dependence of the electron mass on its velocity and predicted a fine structure of the Balmer lines and the prominent lines in the spectrum of ionized helium. Earlier observations by A. A. Michelson, based on the visibility of the fringes in his interferometer, had indicated at least a doublet structure for H_α, and the new theories suggested a promising field for detailed spectroscopic study of the Balmer lines as well as a general study of spectral regularities.

Houston was attracted to this field during his association with Michelson and R. A. Millikan at the University of Chicago; he saw in it the possibility of further experimental tests of the newly developing quantum theories. His first published results on the Balmer lines (1926) showed that the treatment by Sommerfeld, while predicting a complexity that was certainly present, did not in all respects describe the observa-

tions. Rather, the hypothesis of a magnetic electron, newly proposed by G. E. Uhlenbeck and S. A. Goudsmit, appeared to come closer. Houston continued this work with a series of graduate students and other associates and reached the definitive conclusion that still further corrections to the theory would be necessary for a satisfactory detailed description of the observations. His student S. Pasternack then showed that agreement could be attained if a suitable correction was made to the *s*-level, and he estimated the necessary magnitude. After the war this explanation became well established through the work of W. E. Lamb and R. C. Retherford.

Houston's general program of precise spectroscopic measurements led along the way to several other results. Among these was the design of a double Fabry-Perot interferometer, in which an interferometer of small plate separation gives a rather wide dispersion between successive orders of interference, while a second interferometer of wide plate separation provides a higher resolving power. Houston and his students made measurements with various combinations of interferometers and prism spectrometers that gave precision values of the Rydberg constants and so a useful relationship between the values of *e*, *m*, and *h*. His measurements on the Zeeman effect in various elements led to a correction of the generally accepted value of e/m and to a suggestion that the Landé *g* value for a magnetic electron might differ from the integer 2.

During a year's study in Germany with Sommerfeld and W. K. Heisenberg, Houston became interested in applying the newly developed wave mechanics to other fields of physics. In Heisenberg's institute he made a detailed study of the spectrum of a two-electron atom and showed the nature of the transition between Russell-Saunders and *j-j* coupling in terms of the ratio between the spin-orbit interaction of the individual electrons and the electrostatic interaction between the two electrons. While in Sommerfeld's institute he proposed to treat the resistance of a metal as due to the scattering of electrons as waves, rather than as point particles. This provided an understanding of electrical resistance as due to the nuclear temperature motion rather than merely to a nuclear cross section. Using a well-known Debye formula for x-ray scattering, he showed resistance to be proportional to the temperature at high temperatures and to approach zero as the square of the temperature if the zero point motion of the lattice were neglected. However, the zero point motion cannot be neglected, and Houston showed in the following year that the Fermi-Dirac statistics, combined with the conservation of energy in the electron scattering, leads to an electrical resistance proportional to T^5 at very low temperatures, in spite of the zero point vibrations. This analysis also led to an understanding of the residual resistance at low temperatures as caused by impurities or imperfections in the crystal lattice, and the sudden change in resistance at the melting point as caused by the disappearance of the crystal structure.

Houston's theoretical work on electrical conductivity led to an enduring interest in the behavior of electrons in solids and to various theoretical and experimental studies on the participation of the crystal surface in the photoelectric effect, the temperature dependence of cold electron emission, the distribution of normal vibrations in crystals, and the behavior of superconductors in magnetic fields.

Houston graduated in 1920 with a B.A. and a B.S. from Ohio State University. After receiving his Ph.D. in physics in 1925 from Ohio State, he went to the California Institute of Technology as a National Research fellow, was appointed to the faculty, and remained until the end of World War II. During the war he was on leave to the Columbia University Division of War Research, where he led a group in developing a homing antisubmarine device, which was effective in the Battle of the Atlantic. At the end of the war he went to the Rice Institute in Houston as president and professor of physics; he continued teaching and research along with his administrative duties. He was elected to the National Academy of Sciences in 1943, and was president of the American Physical Society in 1962.

Houston wrote *Principles of Mathematical Physics* (1934; 2d ed. 1948) and *Principles of Quantum Mechanics* (1951; paper 1959).

For background information *see* ATOMIC STRUCTURE AND SPECTRA; INTERFEROMETRY; RESISTIVITY, ELECTRICAL in the McGraw-Hill Encyclopedia of Science and Technology.   □

☆ HOYLE, Fred

British mathematician and astronomer
Born June 24, 1915, Bingley, Yorkshire, England

IN THE decades following the postulation of the theory of a steady-state universe, Hoyle was its outstanding spokesman and staunchest defender. He modified Albert Einstein's equations of general relativity in such a way as to lead to a mathematical form of the steady-state theory, which provides for a homogeneous, isotropic model of the universe with the continuous creation of matter.

In 1948 the British astronomers Hermann Bondi and Thomas Gold presented a theory of the steady-state, or continuous-creation, universe.

They began with the assumption that, if the universe is homogeneous in space, it must also be homogeneous in time; that is, the universe must have always looked in the past, and will always look in the future, essentially the same as it looks now. Since the universe is steadily expanding, they maintained that elementary matter is continuously created to fill the void of space. From these randomly produced particles agglomerations of matter the size of galaxies and of clusters of galaxies eventually are formed. When the continuing expansion of the universe removes some galaxies from the range of vision, other newly formed systems take their place to keep the universe in a steady state. However, the Bondi-Gold model of the universe was not based on a generalized field theory, but on an intuitive physical principle.

About 6 months previously at Cambridge University, Hoyle had set out to develop a mathematical basis within the logical framework of the theory of relativity for steady-state theory. Einstein had generalized the ordinary laws of motion in three-dimensional space to describe the properties and the noneuclidean geometry of the four-dimensional space-time field. These generalizations took the form of four equations, one for the law of conservation of energy and three for the conservation of momentum. Hoyle first defined energy and momentum, which are not defined by the general theory of relativity, in such a way as to account for a generalized analog of fluid stresses, and then framed a law of origin of matter so as to be able to introduce it into the four conservation equations. The equations then implied a relation between the expansion of the universe and the origin of matter within it: The rate of expansion and the rate of origin of matter

would tend to regulate each other. This interaction between the expansion and the creation of matter maintains a steady state in which the mean density of matter in the universe remains constant.

The model universe employed in the theory is a modified version of the original de Sitter universe, removing Willem de Sitter's restriction that the universe must be empty of matter. Hoyle explained the concept of continuous creation of new matter in space, which appears to be a violation of the law of conservation of energy, as being possible because the universe—in de Sitter's model—is an open system. According to Einstein's general theory, in an open, infinitely expanding universe, local concentrations of energy are related to the energy of expansion of the whole universe. It is this expansion energy that can lead to the continuous creation of local matter.

In the light of empirical observations during the 1950s and 1960s that appeared to favor an evolutionary, or "big-bang," rather than a steady-state universe, Hoyle was forced to modify his conclusions several times. Although it is theoretically possible to subject the steady-state theory to empirical testing, the limitations of the precision of the instruments that must be used have negated attempts.

Hoyle also made a number of significant contributions to astrophysics. In collaboration with E. M. Burbidge, G. R. Burbidge, and W. A. Fowler, he proposed a comprehensive theory of all of the elements in stars, starting from pure hydrogen. Hoyle described a scheme of nuclear reactions within stellar interiors that goes beyond the hydrogen-helium mechanism elaborated by Hans Bethe. He also did considerable work on stellar origins and, together with Fowler, predicted the existence of very massive objects 6 months or more before the discovery of quasi-stellars.

Hoyle attended Emmanuel College, Cambridge, receiving his M.A. in 1939. In that year he was elected a fellow of St. Johns College, Cambridge. During World War II Hoyle worked on radar development for the British Admiralty. He returned to Cambridge in 1945 as lecturer in mathematics. He became Plumian Professor of Astronomy and Experimental Philosophy in 1958 and director of the Institute of Theoretical Astronomy in 1966. He joined the staff of the Mount Wilson and Palomar observatories in 1956, dividing his time between California and Cambridge afterward. He was elected to the Royal Society of London in 1957.

A prolific author, Hoyle wrote several successful science fiction novels, a radio play, and a number of books to explain science to the layman. Among his nonfiction works are *Some Recent Researches in Solar Physics* (1949), *The Nature of the Universe* (1950), *Frontiers of Astronomy* (1955), *Galaxies, Nuclei, and Quasars* (1965), *Of Men and Galaxies* (1966), and *Man in the Universe* (1966).

For background information *see* COSMOGONY; COSMOLOGY; ELEMENTS AND NUCLIDES (ORIGIN) in the McGraw-Hill Encyclopedia of Science and Technology. □

★ HUBBERT, Marion King

American geologist and geophysicist
Born Oct. 5, 1903, San Saba, Tex., U.S.A.

HUBBERT'S WORK, for which the Arthur L. Day Medal of the Geological Society of America was awarded in 1954, was concerned principally with the physics of terrestrial phenomena. His investigations were general in nature, dealing with such problems as strength of the Earth and flow of underground fluids.

During the first quarter of this century one of the paradoxical problems concerning the study of the Earth arose from the evidence that the Earth is simultaneously an elastic rigid body and a weak and highly deformable body. During most of the 19th century the Earth was thought to be a molten body with a thin, solid crust. By about 1880 the study of earth tides by George Darwin and others and the pioneer work in instrumental seismology were providing evidence that the Earth is solid to a depth about halfway to its center and that as a whole it responds to short-term stresses as an elastic body of great rigidity. Yet the repeated deformation of rocks into mountain ranges during geological history indicated a high degree of deformability. In addition, in the great shield areas of crystalline, granitic-type rocks of northeastern Canada and Scandinavia, from which continental glaciers had disappeared only about 10,000 years ago, there was evidence that a slow uplift was occurring in response to the removal of the ice load. Several hundred meters of uplift had occurred already, and in both areas the uplift was still proceeding.

A resolution of the paradox of a simultaneously strong and weak Earth was accomplished by Hubbert. He proposed: Suppose that one were to construct on a laboratory scale of about 1 m a model of a block of the Earth 1000 km or more in diameter. What would the mechanical properties of the reduced block have to be in order that it would respond to stresses in a manner dynamically similar to the original? He found that the ratio of the strength of the model materials to that of the Earth materials would have to be as in Eq. (1). Here δ is the ratio of

$$\frac{\text{Strength of model}}{\text{Strength of rock}} = \delta\lambda \qquad (1)$$

densities and λ that of lengths of the model and the Earth. With δ set conveniently equal to 1 and a size reduction from 1000 km to 1 m, the strength of the model materials would have to be 10^{-6} of the strength of the Earth. For an Earth having the strength of granite, the model would have to be constructed of material one-millionth as strong—something of the order of very soft mud. Conversely, an Earth composed of the strongest rocks would behave on a size scale of 1000 km like very soft mud on a laboratory scale.

Hubbert's interest in flow of underground fluids began during the early 1930s, while he was engaged in geophysical earth-resistivity studies involving electrical conduction through inhomogeneous ground. He became interested in the question of what must be the field equations for the flow of water and other fluids in porous and permeable underground space, analogous to those equations for the conduction of electricity. He devised a two-field theory similar to that for electrical conduction. This consisted of a field of force per unit of mass, with a characteristic vector $\mathbf{E}$, and a field of flow whose vector may be either $\mathbf{q}$, the volume of fluid crossing a unit area in a unit time, or $\rho\mathbf{q}$, the corresponding mass rate of flow, where ρ is the fluid density. The force intensity $\mathbf{E}$ was shown to be the vector sum of the force per unit mass exerted upon an element of fluid at a given point by gravity and that produced by the gradient of the pressure, as in Eq. (2). Here $\mathbf{g}$ is the acceleration of gravity

$$\mathbf{E} = \mathbf{g} - (1/\rho) \text{ grad } p \qquad (2)$$

and p the pressure at a given point. The coupling between the force field and the flow field is given by the linear equation shown as Eq. (3), which

$$\mathbf{q} = \sigma\mathbf{E} = -Nd^2 (\rho/\mu) [\mathbf{g} - (1/\rho) \text{ grad } p] \quad (3)$$

is a physical statement of Darcy's law and is the fluid analog of Ohm's law in electricity. Here N is a dimensionless shape factor, d a characteristic length of the pore system of the solid, and μ the viscosity of the fluid. The lumped parameter σ is fluid conductivity. Provided the density of the fluid is a function of the pressure only, the field of force is irrotational and has a potential Φ given by Eq. (4). Here

$$\Phi = -\int_{P_0}^{P} E_s\, ds = gz + \int_{p_0}^{p} \frac{dp}{\rho} \qquad (4)$$

P_0 is a point at which Φ is assigned the value of 0, P a general field point, z the elevation of P, and p_0 and p the fluid pressures at P_0 and P. For these conditions Darcy's law is expressible by Eq. (5).

$$\mathbf{q} = -\sigma \text{ grad } \Phi \qquad (5)$$

The flow of fluids through porous solids, while similar to electrical conduction, differs in several fundamental respects. Unlike electric current, gaseous fluids are compressible. Also, whereas there is only a single electrical entity to be conducted, there are multiple fluids, both liquids and gases, which differ in density, viscosity, and compressibility. Hence, at a given point in space characterized by a pressure p and an elevation z, there will be as many different potentials Φ and vectors $\mathbf{E}$, each with a different direction and magnitude, as there are different fluids to be considered. This is the mechanism involved in the migration and entrapment of petroleum and natural gas in underground space. Here, the ambient fluid is water and, initially, particles of oil and gas occur in a highly dispersed state from which they are driven to positions of concentration and entrapment. The theory developed by Hubbert led to an almost revolutionary reassessment of the techniques of exploration for oil and gas because it showed that the stable entrapment of these fluids is possible at underground positions, where it would have been impossible under previously held hydrostatic premises.

Prior to Hubbert's work most attempts at analytical treatment of the flow of fluids through porous solids was based upon a one-field approach, involving the generally untenable assumption that the flow field has a velocity potential. Such approaches led to an almost complete suppression of the dynamical aspects of fluid flow and to the erroneous conclusion that different fluid components in the same space would flow in the same direction. Consequently, a valid understanding of the flow behavior of multifluid systems was seriously inhibited for several decades.

Hubbert attended small one- and two-teacher country schools, then spent 1 year in a private high school and 2 years in a small junior college in Texas before going to the University of Chicago, where he received the degrees of B.S. (1926), M.S. (1928), and Ph.D. (1937) in geology, physics, and mathematics. During the 1930s he taught geology and geophysics for 10 years at Columbia University and did summer field work with the Illinois and U.S. geological surveys. He then spent 20 years with the Shell Oil Company and Shell Development Company in Houston, Tex., as research geophysicist, associate director of research, and the chief consultant in general geology. From 1963, he served as research geophysicist with the U.S. Geological Survey in Washington, D.C., and professor of geology and geophysics at Stanford University. He was elected to the National Academy of Sciences in 1955 and to the American Academy of Arts and Sciences in 1956. He was president of the Geological Society of America during 1962.

Hubbert wrote *Theory of Ground-Water Motion* (1940); *Role of Fluid Pressure in Mechanics of Overthrust Faulting*, with William W. Rubey (1959); and *Energy Resources* (1962).

For background information *see* FLUID-FLOW PRINCIPLES; OROGENY; PETROLEUM GEOLOGY; TECTONOPHYSICS in the McGraw-Hill Encyclopedia of Science and Technology.   □

★ HUBBS, Carl Leavitt

American biologist
Born Oct. 18, 1894, Williams, Ariz., U.S.A.

HUBBS STUDIED fishes and other aquatic vertebrates and their environments. He contributed to the systematics of fishes of all continents —freshwater and marine, littoral and bathybial, benthic and pelagic. He dealt also with their distribution, ecology, life history, genetics, and evolution and with the complex interrelations between fishes and man. Increasingly, he became concerned with the deciphering of past environments, especially as these are related to faunal changes, paleoclimatology, and the life and populations of primitive man.

While at the University of Michigan from 1920 to 1944, Hubbs amassed one of the world's major fish collections, particularly outstanding for the rich freshwater faunas of North and Middle America. He activated a new era of research on the systematics, distribution, and biology of these faunas, which ichthyologists for about a quarter century had fallaciously thought to have been almost completely known. As secretary, editor, and president, he played a major role in the organization and growth of the American Society of Ichthyologists and Herpetologists and its journal, *Copeia*.

In collaboration with his wife, Laura, Hubbs pioneered at Michigan in the application of experimental breeding to systematics of fishes, particularly the Poeciliidae. Most notable was their discovery and initial analysis of the purely matroclinous, gynogenetic reproduction of an all-female fish species, the "Amazon molly" (*Mollienisia*, now *Poecilia*, *formosa*). They experimentally verified and analyzed hybridization in nature between species of sunfish (Centrarchidae). Analysis of natural hybrids, still being continued, led to a fuller understanding of the environmental conditioning of such hybridization, of the genetic parameters, and of its speciational bearings. Interspecific hybridization in nature was found to be very frequent under certain conditions, especially in freshwater regions that were greatly disturbed by climatic changes during the Ice Age.

Studies of the fish faunas of now isolated waters of the American West led Hubbs into investigations of the pluvial lakes and streams that abounded during the Pleistocene in now parched areas. He was introduced to these problems in 1915, while serving as student assistant to John Otterbein Snyder in a summer survey of the fish faunas of the basin of the vast ancient Lake Bonneville (now represented by Great Salt Lake). On subsequent trips, largely in association with Robert Rush Miller, he explored nearly all of the many, now isolated basins of the western United States, discovering a multitude of new fishes, determining the extent of the present fish faunas, and deciphering evidence of ancient lakes and streams. The closely correlated history of the fishes and waters was monographed by Hubbs and Miller in 1948. The studies, still continuing, pertained to zoogeography, rate of speciation and role of isolation, paleoclimatology, and the influence of past ample waters on human populations. Recently, Hubbs applied radiocarbon dating to these studies. In 1964 the U.S. Geological Survey, recognizing his part in interpreting the paleohydrography of the West, named one of the extinct waters Lake Hubbs.

Correlated analyses of other present and past environments also attracted Hubbs's interest. Anomalous distributions of fishes and other organisms along the Pacific coast invited him to undertake a long-term analysis of ocean temperatures along shore. This involved extensive temperature surveys, determination of the role of upwelling due to wind direction, and discovery of a short-period, wide-amplitude bouncing of the thermocline. Through use of isotopes in dating and in paleotemperature measurements, he extended the present temperature survey and the correlated faunal changes back through Holocene and in places into Pleistocene time. The occurrence in the mid-1800s of subtropical elements in the Californian shore-fish fauna led Hubbs to make a study of meteorologic data that indicates a warm period then. Closely related faunal elements on the two sides of the tropics led Hubbs to formulate the concept of antitropicality and to hypothesize that Pleistocene cooling of the world ocean allowed the transgression of the tropics by certain temperate-zone organisms. Use of Indian midden shells in correlated dating and paleotemperature determinations led Hubbs into archeological studies and human paleoecology.

Throughout his career Hubbs applied himself to problems of human concern. He organized and for its first 5 years (1930–35) directed the state-supported Institute for Fisheries Research at the University of Michigan, pioneering in applications of research to fish management, especially through improvement of the habitat. In 1939 he served as field representative of the Department of Interior to improve the federal administration of wildlife resources in Alaska. He contributed to research on stream pollution, to combating the destructive effects of excessive use of poison in fish management, and, with associates, to determining the effects on fishes of explosions used in seismic exploration for oil. He was a leader in applying principles of conservation to aquatic as well as terrestrial life, especially in national parks. He was active in movements to establish land and water reserves for research, teaching, and public welfare.

Hubbs's many students have played a large role in teaching and research in ichthyology and other biological disciplines, in fisheries research, and in fisheries and wildlife management.

Hubbs's interest in natural history was early aroused by his maternal grandmother, one of the first woman physicians, and by his father, a Civil War veteran who, self-trained, engaged in mineral explorations, assaying, and mining in the pioneer West. This early interest in natural history led Hubbs, through boyhood shell collecting and bird watching, into intense specialization in ichthyology as a student at Stanford, where he was rigorously trained by Charles Henry Gilbert and was the last student of the master ichthyologist David Starr Jordan. He received his A.B. (1916) and A.M. (1917) from Stanford and his Ph.D. (1927) from Michigan. After serving for 3 years as assistant curator in charge of fishes, amphibians, and reptiles at the

Field Museum of Natural History, he spent 24 years (1920–44) on the curatorial and teaching staffs at the University of Michigan, before joining the Scripps Institution of Oceanography of the University of California, San Diego. He was elected to the National Academy of Sciences in 1952 and to foreign membership in the Linnean Society of London in 1965. He was granted the Henry Russel Award at Michigan for 1929–30; he was faculty lecturer at the University of California, Los Angeles, in 1954, received the Joseph Leidy Award and Medal from the Academy of Natural Sciences of Philadelphia in 1964, and the Fellows Medal of the California Academy of Sciences in 1966. Many genera and species were named in his honor.

Hubbs was coauthor of *Methods for the Improvement of Michigan Trout Streams*, with J. R. Greeley and C. M. Tarzwell (1932); *Minnows of Michigan*, with G. P. Cooper (1936); *The Small-mouthed Bass*, with R. M. Bailey (1938); *Improvement of Lakes for Fishing*, with R. W. Eschmeyer (1938); and *Fishes of the Great Lakes Region*, with K. F. Lagler (1947, 1964). He edited *Zoogeography* (1958) and authored more than 500 articles and notes.

For background information *see* PALEOECOLOGY; PISCES (ZOOLOGY); ZOOGEOGRAPHY in the McGraw-Hill Encyclopedia of Science and Technology. □

★ HUISGEN, Rolf

German chemist
Born June 13, 1920, Gerolstein, Eifel, Germany

AFTER THESIS work on a structural problem in the natural product field, a traditional area of German chemistry, Huisgen was fascinated by the new concepts of reaction mechanisms developed mainly in England and the United States. He started systematic investigations along similar lines after World War II and helped to overcome the prejudice—widespread at that time in Germany—that mechanistic chemistry is hardly more than a harmless intellectual diversion. In 1961 Huisgen obtained the Liebig Medal of the German Chemical Society for his research studies.

Work on the radical phenylation of aromatic compounds led Huisgen into the field of diazo chemistry. The generation of radicals or ions from nitrosoacylamines is preceded by an intramolecular acyl shift to diazoesters. He investigated the structure and reactivity of this class of short-lived compounds. Four topics dominated Huisgen's work of the last 15 years: medium-sized ring effects, the chemistry of arynes, cyclo-additions, and valence tautomerism phenomena.

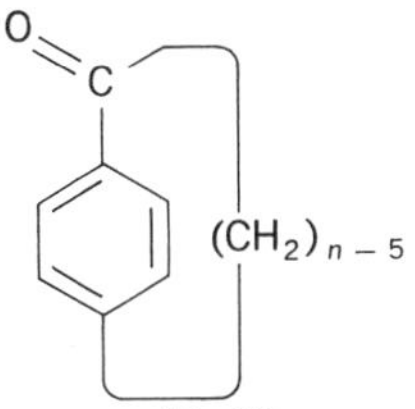

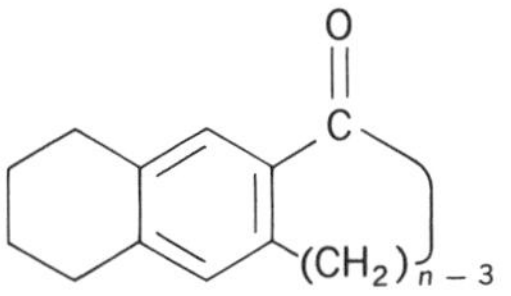

Intramolecular Friedel-Crafts acylation at high dilution made ring ketones of types I and II over a wide range of ring sizes accessible. These compounds and their derivatives offered models for the study of the steric inhibition of resonance —dependent on the ring size—in regard to spectral and chemical properties. The long-known special properties of five- and six-membered lactones found a simple explanation in their *cis*-ester group (III). Dipole moments and reaction kinetics revealed that the inversion from *cis*-(III) to *trans*-lactones (IV) takes place with an increase in the ring size. An analogous phenomenon was found in cyclic amides. The phenonium ion (V), formed by transannular cyclization, offers perhaps the best-proven case of benzene-ring participation in ionization.

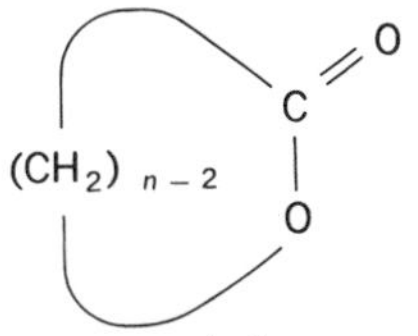

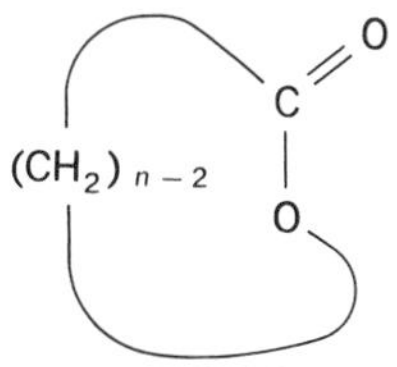

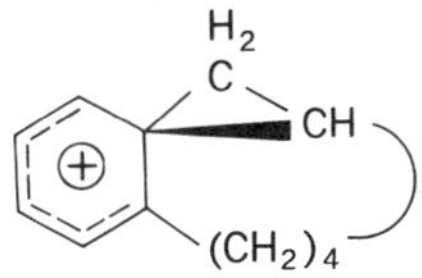

In 1955 Huisgen showed that isomeric aryl halides react with organolithium compounds to form identical mixtures of substitution products. Systematic studies elucidated the chemical properties of the aryne intermediates, which are involved in nucleophilic substitutions by an elimination-addition mechanism. Competition experiments proved that one and the same intermediate C_6H_4 (benzyne, VI) occurs in processes as different as, for example, the treatment of *o*-fluorobromobenzene with magnesium and the decomposition of benzenediazonium *o*-carboxylate.

The generalization of the principle involved in the azide and diazoalkane additions led in 1960 to the fruitful concept of the 1,3-dipolar cyclo-addition (VII), whose scope and mechanism were studied systematically in the Munich Labo-

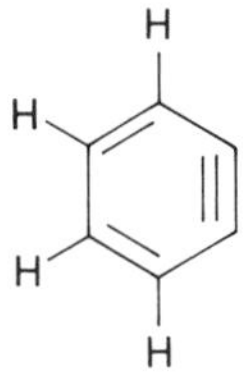

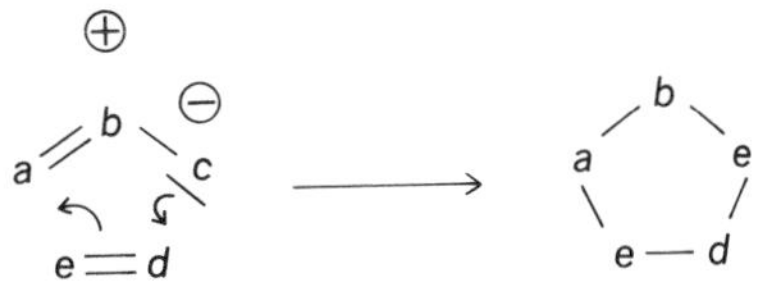

ratories. Among the many new classes of 1,3-dipoles which were predicted and experimentally proven were the nitrile ylides, nitrile imines, azomethine ylides, mesoionic oxazolones, keto-carbenes, and ketoazenes. A large number of five-membered heterocycles—many of them new—became available by the concerted ring closure of a 1,3-dipole *a-b-c* and a dipolarophile *d-e*. In the new synthetic principle of 1,4-dipolar cyclo-addition, six-membered rings are built up by stepwise bond formation. Though more limited in application than the 1,3-dipolar counterpart, the synthetic potential is far from being exhausted. Huisgen's studies stimulated work on cycloaddition reactions in many countries.

Kinetic investigations proved the existence of a valence tautomerism in cyclooctatetraene (VIII) with a 0.01% equilibrium concentration of bicyclooctatriene (IX), which is responsible for the Diels-Alder additions of VIII. By the same dilatometric technique, valence tautomerism phenomena in benzocyclobutenes and cyclooctatrienes were quantitatively established. The halogenation of VIII, yielding the bicyclic halide X, turned out to be a multistep reaction sequence that includes a unique cis addition.

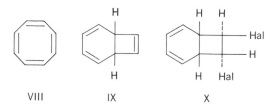

VIII   IX   X

Huisgen investigated a number of other research topics, which will not be described here in detail, including radical and polar additions to N-N double bonds, the kinetics of the Beckmann rearrangement, the steric course of amine additions to acetylenic systems, new rearrangements of amine N-oxides caused by electrophilic reagents, and the successful preparation of phenylpentazole (X), an aromatic ring system built up from nitrogen atoms only (with I. Ugi, 1956). XI has a half-life of 13 min at 0°C.

$$C_6H_5 - N \begin{array}{c} N = N \\ | \\ N = N \end{array}$$

XI

Huisgen studied chemistry at the universities of Bonn and Munich (Dr. rer. nat., 1942). In 1947 he finished the German "Habilitation" and became dozent at the University of Munich. During 1949–52 Huisgen served as professor extraordinarius in Tübingen. He returned in 1952 to Munich as professor of organic chemistry. He was made a member of the Bavarian Academy of Science and the Deutsche Akademie der Naturforscher Leopoldina and a foreign member of the American Academy of Arts and Sciences. In 1965 he was awarded the Médaille Lavoisier de la Société Chimique de France. Huisgen lectured often in the United States and published some 260 papers in chemical journals and handbooks.

For background information *see* CALORIMETRY; DIAZOTIZATION; DIPOLE MOMENT; KINETICS (CHEMICAL) in the McGraw-Hill Encyclopedia of Science and Technology.   ☐

★ HUIZENGA, John Robert

American nuclear chemist
Born Apr. 21, 1921, Fulton, Ill., U.S.A.

Huizenga made major contributions to the understanding of nuclear properties of heavy elements. A unique characteristic of the heavy elements is the ease by which they divide into smaller fragments, a mechanism now well known as nuclear fission. In fact, isotopes of uranium and of heavier elements disintegrate spontaneously by the fission process, although with extremely different probabilities. For his research on nuclear reactions, and nuclear fission in particular, Huizenga received in 1966 the U.S. Atomic Energy Commission's E. O. Lawrence Memorial Award.

From 1939, when Otto Hahn and Fritz Strassmann discovered nuclear fission, continuing attempts have been made to elucidate this most complicated of all nuclear reactions. Although several exciting advances have been made, important puzzles remain, among which is the asymmetric mass division of heavy nuclei in fission.

In 1951 Huizenga and R. B. Duffield proposed a relationship between thermal neutron fission cross sections and thermal neutron capture cross sections. The competition between these two processes is related directly to the relative lifetimes for a heavy nucleus to decay by fission and γ-ray emission. Since the γ-ray emission lifetime is expected on both theoretical and experimental grounds to be a slowly varying function of excitation energy, it was viewed by the two scientists as a barometer against which the lifetime for decay by fission could be measured. The cross-section ratio measures the fissionability of a particular nuclide. (Nuclide is a general term meaning a nuclear species of any atomic charge and weight, whereas the term isotope is limited to a nuclear species belonging to a certain element of fixed atomic charge and varying only in atomic weight.) The rapid change in fissionability as a function of excitation energy was interpreted to be associated with a strong dependence of the fission lifetime on excitation energy. In the reactions under discussion, the important parameter is the energy excess over the fission barrier, which is introduced by the thermal neutron capture in terms of binding energy.

When intense neutron fluxes became available in the materials testing reactor (MTR) in Idaho, a program was initiated with several other scientists to produce unknown transuranic nuclei by multiple neutron capture. Isotopes were successively formed which increase by one unit in atomic weight until a beta unstable isotope is reached, and at this point the capture is transferred into the next element. This process is often referred to as neutron capture on a slow time scale. These studies were partially motivated and aided by the type of theoretical framework mentioned earlier, and led to the discovery, identification, and elucidation of the nuclear properties of a large number of new transuranic nuclei.

From measurements of the spontaneous fission lifetimes of a number of new nuclides discovered in the MTR irradiations, Huizenga found that the spontaneous fission half-lives for isotopes of a given element go through a maximum with increasing mass number, contrary to the then existing theory. This discovery was applied almost immediately in sorting out the radioactivities produced in the world's first thermonuclear explosion ("Mike," November, 1952). From samples of this debris, scientists from Argonne, Berkeley, and Los Alamos made the joint discovery of elements 99 and 100, named einsteinium and fermium by the discoverers after the world-renowed scientists Einstein and Fermi. Neutron capture in a thermonuclear device occurs in only a small fraction of a second, and hence is referred to as neutron capture on a fast time scale in contrast to the type of neutron capture which occurs in a reactor. One of the nuclides discovered by Huizenga and his collaborators in "Mike," Cm^{250}, has a spontaneous fission half-life of the order of 10,000 years. Because of the postulated similarity between these man-made explosions and those of a certain type of stars called supernovae, Huizenga postulated that the present energy and x-ray source of the supernova called Crab Nebula may be due, at least partially, to the spontaneous decay of Cm^{250}.

Later Huizenga and his associates extended their studies of the lifetime of a compound nucleus for decay by fission to higher energies by experimentally determining the competition between neutron emission and fission for many nuclides. They interpreted these studies theoretically in terms of the neutron binding energy and fission threshold, as well as the nuclear level densities of the residual nucleus formed by neutron emission and of the transition state nucleus in fission. The transition nucleus in fission is analogous to the "activated complex" in chemical reactions. By studying the angular correlation of fission fragments with different projectile beams inducing fission and by making use of statistical theory, Huizenga determined the actual deformation or "shape" of the transition nuclei from gold to fermium. This was a major development in support of the liquid drop theory of fission. More recently, investigational studies centered on the determination of spins and parities of the low-lying excited states of the very short-lived transition state nucleus. In this way one can obtain data about the same nucleus in two completely different deformations. Such information on nuclear pairing and structure is valuable in advancing knowledge of nuclear matter.

Huizenga majored in chemistry and mathematics at Calvin College, receiving his A.B. in 1944. After 2 months in the graduate school of the University of Illinois, he joined the Manhattan Project in Oak Ridge, where he was first introduced to nuclear fission in experiments designed to measure the isotopic ratio of uranium samples by a fission fragment–counting technique with thermal neutrons. He received his Ph.D. at the University of Illinois in 1949; he then joined the Argonne National Laboratory, where he remained until August, 1967, except for a year as a Fulbright fellow in 1954–55 in the Netherlands and a year as a Guggenheim fellow and visiting professor at the University of Paris in 1964–65. Huizenga was appointed professor of chemistry and physics at the University of Rochester in 1967.

For background information *see* FISSION, NUCLEAR; RADIOACTIVITY; THERMAL NEUTRONS in the McGraw-Hill Encyclopedia of Science and Technology. ☐

☆ HUNT, Frederick Vinton

American acoustical physicist and engineer
Born Feb. 5, 1905, Barnesville, Ohio, U.S.A.

AT THE Harvard Underwater Sound Laboratory during World War II, Hunt directed a research group that developed a number of important techniques and weapons—including scanning sonar and the acoustic torpedo—with both immediate and long-range applications in the field of underwater acoustics.

In 1941 Hunt, who was then associate professor of physics and communication engineering at

Harvard University, proposed jointly with the physicist Philip M. Morse that Cambridge, Mass. (the site of Harvard), should be the location for one of the submarine detection laboratories which the National Defense Research Committee was planning for the east coast. The proposal was accepted, and Hunt was made the head of the new establishment, called the Harvard Underwater Sound Laboratory (HUSL). This laboratory had two objectives. The first was the improvement of existing devices for underwater detection; the second was the conception and design of new equipment. Hunt was involved in every aspect of the project. Apart from his scientific and administrative contributions, his efforts to recruit a large scientific staff played a great part in assuring the project's success. Among the improvements effected by the laboratory group was the concept of simultaneous lobe comparison, later designated as the bearing deviation indicator (BDI).

More significant, however, were the group's innovations. One of these was scanning sonar, a new technique of underwater acoustic detection. (Hunt coined the term "sonar" in 1942.) In this device a sound pulse was emitted continually in all directions. At the same time a directional receiving beam swept in a rapid circle in the horizontal plane. When the emitted sound pulse encountered an object, the resulting echo was reflected through the plane of the scanning beam. The angle and time of arrival of this pulse as it encountered the receiving beam gave the direction and range of the object in question. For "display" this system used an oscilloscope tube, on which the object was shown as a dot of light. The great advantage of scanning sonar over the range recorder then in use was that the former was alert continuously in all directions, while the latter had to be aimed, like a flashlight.

Another product of the HUSL was the acoustic, or homing, torpedo; its development from initial outline to service use took a remarkably

short 18 months. The weapon was similar to an ordinary torpedo except for its method of target seeking. After being aimed in the approximate direction of the target, the torpedo approached until it was close enough for its miniature sonar system to go into action. Thereafter, the sonar (either active or passive) guided the weapon to the target by means of sounds emitted or reflected by the target itself. Because of this feature the acoustic torpedo needed no torpedo tubes, and could simply be cast overboard from the deck of a ship.

A by-product of this work was the acoustic beeper, which, attached to torpedos in the final stages of testing, aided the Navy in the recovery of some 700 lost missiles. Another achievement of the laboratory team was the National Defense Research Committee's *Summary Technical Report on Magnetostriction Transducers*, which became an important source book in its field. ("Transducer" is the general term for any device that generates or receives sound underwater.)

After the war Hunt came increasingly to believe in the importance of long-range underwater detection on a global scale. A speech on this topic, delivered by him in 1950, helped stimulate a number of efforts in this direction, including the Artemis project undertaken by the United States government.

In addition to his work in underwater acoustics, Hunt was active in a number of other fields. During the 1930s, together with the physicist J. A. Pierce, he was concerned with fundamental research in phonograph reproduction and the development of lightweight pickup arms. Hunt received 13 patents on various inventions.

Hunt pursued a distinguished teaching career, particularly after World War II, when as head of the Harvard Acoustics Research Laboratory he stimulated research in a wide variety of topics, ranging from basic work on the cavitation process in liquids to the adaptation of radio-astronomy signal processing techniques to acoustic receiving systems.

The son of a bank official, Hunt received a B.A. in 1924 and B.E.E. in 1925 at Ohio State University; at Harvard University he took an A.M. in 1928 and a Ph.D. in physics in 1934. Meanwhile, he became a laboratory assistant at Harvard in 1928, rising to instructor in 1929, assistant professor in 1937, and associate professor of physics and communication engineering in 1940. In 1941 he joined a group at the Massachusetts Institute of Technology studying acoustic weapons, and the next year he became director of the newly established Harvard Underwater Sound Laboratory, a post he retained until the dissolution of the laboratory in 1946. After the war Hunt became in 1946 Gordon-McKay Professor of Applied Physics and in 1953 Rumford

Professor of Physics at Harvard. In 1947 Hunt received the Medal for Merit for his work at the HUSL. In 1965 he was awarded the Pioneers of Underwater Acoustics Medal of the Acoustical Society of America and the John H. Potts Memorial Award of the Audio Engineering Society. He was elected to the American Academy of Arts and Sciences in 1940.

Hunt wrote *Electroacoustics* (1954).

For background information *see* ACOUSTIC TORPEDO; SONAR; UNDERWATER SOUND in the McGraw-Hill Encyclopedia of Science and Technology. ☐

★ HUTCHINSON, George Evelyn

American zoologist
Born Jan. 30, 1903, Cambridge, England

HUTCHINSON'S EARLY work was primarily on the systematics and distribution of aquatic Hemiptera. In 1926–28 he took part in an investigation of the pan lakes of the Western Transvaal, South Africa, which subsequently were hardly studied. He worked on the limnology of the lakes of the western end of the Tibetan plateau in 1932. With G. A. Riley, he began a study of Linsley Pond in 1935, which demonstrated the importance of horizontal water movements in transport of material from the hypolimnion into the free water, even at levels of strong stratification. As early as 1941, with E. Pollard and W. T. Edmondson, Hutchinson made an attempt to use radiophosphorus to trace the metabolism of this element in the lake, but the quantities available from the Yale cyclotron were inadequate. With V. T. Bowen, he renewed this work after the war and obtained clear evidence of phosphorus circulation in conditions of stratification.

The general problem of the relation of the annual cycle of phytoplankton to chemical change was investigated; the general scheme elaborated by Pearsall was subjected to critical evaluation, and the significance of some, but not all, of his conclusions emphasized. Analytical work, with A. C. Wollack, on a core from Linsley Pond, which had been studied by pollen analysis by E. S. Deevey, initiated a series of studies on the chemistry of lake sediments. In recent years, with U. M. Cowgill, Hutchinson presented such studies on a greatly extended scale. Current work on the Lago di Monterosi is providing a great deal of new data on lacustrine geochemistry, including the behavior of a number of elements not previously considered in this type of work.

The studies made on phytoplankton succession led in 1941 to a preliminary consideration of competitive phenomena and niche specificity in lakes. In the past decade this was developed mainly from a theoretical point of view, leading to the elaboration of the concept of the niche as an *n*-dimensional space, an idea which some other ecologists have found useful. In recent years Hutchinson turned his attention to evolutionary problems, particularly in relation to man.

Hutchinson's interest in all forms of natural history was strongly encouraged by the atmosphere of an academic home. He received his B.A. in 1924 and his M.A. in 1928 from Cambridge University. He was senior lecturer in zoology at the University of Witwatersrand, South Africa, in 1926–28, and then moved to Yale University, where he became a professor in 1945. He was elected to the American Academy of Arts and Sciences in 1949 and to the National Academy of Sciences in 1950.

Hutchinson wrote *Treatise on Limnology* (2 vols., 1957, 1967) and *The Ecological Theater and the Evolutionary Play* (1965).

For background information *see* FRESH-WATER ECOSYSTEM; HEMIPTERA; LIMNOLOGY; MARINE MICROBIOLOGY in the McGraw-Hill Encyclopedia of Science and Technology. ☐

★ HUTCHINSON, John

British botanical taxonomist
Born Apr. 7, 1884, Wark on Tyne, England

HUTCHINSON BECAME best known for his work on the phylogeny and classification of angiosperms. His famous *Families of Flowering Plants* (2 vols., 1926, 1934) earned him an honorary degree of doctor of laws in 1934 from Scotland's oldest university, St. Andrew's.

Hutchinson's knowledge of angiosperms was largely gained while writing *Flora of West Tropical Africa*, which took up most of his time during 11 years as a botanist in the Kew Herbarium. In his studies he constantly considered the existing classifications of flowering plants, especially those of George Bentham and J. D.

Hooker in Britain and of Adolf Engler and Prantl in Germany; the Engler-Prantl system at that time was criticized by various botanists, such as C. E. Bessey in the United States, Hans Hallier in Germany, and N. Arber and J. Parkin in Britain.

Consequently, Hutchinson studied intensively those families which were supposed to be the most primitive: on the one hand, those with free petals, free stamens, and free carpels, known as Ranales (sensu lato), which occupied first place in the Bentham and Hooker system, and on the other hand, the group popularly known as Amentiferae, with flowers mostly in catkins and without petals, placed first in the Engler-Prantl system. He soon came to the conclusion that families with bisexual flowers, free petals, free carpels, and so forth, such as Magnoliaceae and Ranunculaceae, represent the most primitive groups of living plants, and that apetalous, amentiferous families, such as Fagaceae (oaks), Moraceae (mulberries), and Utricaceae (nettles) are the most advanced, because of the reduction of the petals and other parts of their flowers, leading to largely unisexual character. At the same time he became convinced that Magnoliaceae and Ranunculaceae, through parallel evolution, largely share the same type of floral structure but are not otherwise closely related, and that each family should be regarded as the starting point of two separate lines of evolution, the one (Magnoliaceae) fundamentally woody, which he called the Lignosae, and the other (Ranunculaceae) fundamentally herbaceous, which he termed the Herbaceae. The classification resulting from this hypothesis was more fully shown in the second edition of his *Families of Flowering Plants* (1959), illustrated mostly by his own black and white drawings and accompanied by an artificial key to the families, which has proved useful throughout the world.

Although his knowledge of plants was mainly gained from herbarium specimens, Hutchinson also traveled extensively to study plants in the field. In 1928–29 he explored South Africa and made a large collection of herbarium specimens and living succulent plants for Kew. He was privileged to meet and make a friend of Field Marshal J. C. Smuts, also a keen field botanist, with whom he visited parts of the northern Transvaal; and in 1930 he accompanied Smuts on a special expedition from Pretoria via the Victoria Falls as far north as Lake Tanganyika. Even if nothing else had been collected on that trip, Hutchinson considered that it was well worth while because of the discovery of a new species of *Pteronia* (Asteraceae) over 1300 mi from the remainder of the genus, otherwise confined to South and South-West Africa. He named the species *Pteronia smutsii*. The results of these expeditions were published by Hutchinson in his *Botanist in Southern Africa* (1946), with a foreword by Smuts.

Hutchinson rose to eminence in the botanical world largely by his own effort and enterprise. Educated at a village school, he was barely 16 years old when he started work under his father, a gardener, and earned 6 shillings a week. He joined Kew Gardens in 1904, and was soon transferred to the herbarium, where he met the famous botanist Sir Joseph Dalton Hooker, whose work he was one day destined to carry on. Hutchinson worked at the herbarium until his retirement, as keeper of museums, in 1948. Hutchinson received the 1958 Darwin-Wallace Medal of the Linnean Society of London, which was awarded to 20 world botanists and zoologists in recognition of their work on evolution and classification, and the same society's Gold Medal in 1964. He was elected a fellow of the Royal Society of London in 1947.

Hutchinson also wrote *The Story of Plants and Their Uses to Man*, with R. Melville (1948); *British Wild Flowers*, the volumes of which are published in the Penguin series; and *The Genera of Flowering Plants (Angiospermae)* (1964).

For background information *see* ANGIOSPERMAE; PLANT CLASSIFICATION; PLANT KINGDOM in the McGraw-Hill Encyclopedia of Science and Technology. □

★ HUXLEY, Hugh Esmor

British molecular biologist
Born Feb. 25, 1924, Birkenhead, England

HUXLEY DEMONSTRATED in a series of experiments, several of them carried out in collaboration with Jean Hanson, that striated muscles are built up from overlapping arrays of protein filaments which slide past each other when the muscle contracts.

By the late 1940s biochemical studies on

muscle had established that the contractile material consisted very largely of two principle proteins, actin and myosin, which serve both as structural proteins and as working parts of the machinery which converts chemically stored energy into mechanical work. It was known that these proteins form a complex and are represented in muscle by filaments, and it was generally believed that these filaments shorten when the muscle contracts.

Early electron microscope studies on muscle had shown the presence within the contractile elements, the myofibrils, of longitudinally arranged filaments and had confirmed the existence of the various details of the cross striations described by classical light microscopists. However, the rather primitive techniques then available did not give more detailed structural data. Low-angle x-ray diffraction photographs, (those revealing periodicities from 10 to 1000 A), which could reveal structural regularities in the muscle at the level of organization of the protein filaments, had not been taken, largely because of technical limitations of the existing diffraction cameras. Consequently, only very vague and unsatisfactory theories had been put forward to explain the nature of muscular contraction in molecular terms.

Huxley began working on crystalline proteins as a research student with J. C. Kendrew and M. F. Perutz in 1958. In the course of experiments on the changes in the x-ray diffraction diagram from hemoglobin crystals produced by changes in the degree of hydration, he was impressed by the very considerable deterioration in pattern which occurred when the specimen was allowed to dry completely. He began to wonder whether muscle, whose low-angle x-ray diffraction diagram had hitherto only been recorded from dry samples, might give a much better pattern if it were examined in the fully hydrated fresh, living condition. Such specimens, however, would contain 80% water and they would therefore be expected to give a rather weak pattern, even

though it might be a sharp one, so that an x-ray camera capable of recording the reflections in much shorter times than had previously been considered possible was an essential requirement for the experiment. Fortunately a very-fine-focus x-ray tube with high specific loading (high x-ray output per unit area) had just been designed by W. Ehrenberg. Huxley realized that this could serve as the x-ray source for a miniature low-angle camera working at very small specimen film distances, resulting in a very large gain in speed over conventional designs and reducing exposure times from weeks to hours.

When this camera was put into operation, Huxley was able to record a number of entirely new sets of low-angle x-ray reflections from living muscle. These showed that the filaments were spaced out in a double hexagonal lattice with the primary set of filaments about 400–450 A apart, and with secondary filaments parallel to the first set and lying between them. The results indicated that the protein myosin was contained in one type of filament, and the protein actin in the other. Other features of the x-ray diagrams indicated that these filaments are built of large structural units assembled with great precision and that the internal structure of at least one type of filament is not changed when the muscle is stretched.

Huxley then began to use the electron microscope and the newly developed thin-sectioning technique and confirmed the existence of the double array of filaments, which could now be seen clearly in cross sections of muscle. In collaboration with J. Hanson, he studied the appearance of isolated myofibrils from striated muscle in the phase-contrast light microscope. Hanson and Huxley found that myosin is located in the A-bands of muscle, and they concluded that it is present in the form of thick filaments which extend continuously from end to end of that band. Thinner filaments containing actin were found to overlap partially the thick filaments (forming the double array detected by x-ray diffraction), to extend beyond the ends of the A-bands and across the I-bands, and to attach to structures (Z lines) at either end of the sarcomeres. Subsequently, Hanson and Huxley found, by observing the band pattern changes during contractions produced by giving the fibrils small amounts of adenosinetriphosphate, that the filaments do not change in length, but slide past each other, the thin filaments being drawn in toward the center of the A-band as the muscle shortens.

Huxley then developed techniques for cutting extremely thin sections of muscle (less than one-millionth of an inch in thickness) and for staining them so that they could be examined at high resolution in the electron microscope. These techniques showed unambiguously the thick and thin filaments lying alongside each other in longitudinal sections, thus providing very strong support for the sliding filament model, which was at first very controversial. Later, electron microscope studies of muscle and muscle protein made by the negative staining techniques (which Huxley was one of the first to use) showed further structural detail of the way the protein molecules are arranged within the filaments of muscle to give a contractile system. More recently, the application of further developments in x-ray tube and camera design enabled him to begin studying the low-angle x-ray diagrams from striated muscle while the tissue is carrying out an active contraction under electrical stimulation.

Huxley began studying for his degree in physics at Christ College, Cambridge, in the early years of World War II. During 1943–47 he was engaged on research and development of radar equipment for the Royal Air Force, for which he was made a member of the Order of the British Empire. After the war he returned to Cambridge, completed his degree (M.A.) in physics, and in 1950 began work as a research student in the Medical Research Council's unit for molecular biology, then located in the Cavendish Laboratory. After receiving his Ph.D. in 1952 at Cambridge, Huxley worked in the biology department, MIT, in F. O. Schmitt's group, where he learned electron microscopy. He went back to Cambridge in 1954, worked in the biophysics department, University College, London for 6 years, and then returned to Cambridge to the Medical Research Council's Laboratory of Molecular Biology. Huxley became a fellow of the Royal Society of London in 1960.

For background information *see* MICROSCOPE, ELECTRON; MUSCLE (BIOPHYSICS); X-RAY TUBE in the McGraw-Hill Encyclopedia of Science and Technology.   □

☆ HUXLEY, Sir Julian (Sorell)

British biologist
Born June 22, 1887, Bloomsbury, London, England

HUXLEY PLAYED a leading part in the introduction of experimental methods and concepts into biological research and teaching in Britain. The fields to which he made valuable contributions, many carried out with his students and colleagues, are so numerous that only the most important can be considered here.

Huxley was one of the first to recognize the importance of C. M. Child's theory of axial gradients as a general principle capable of providing working hypotheses for research, which was very successful. By application of temperature gradients to frog eggs, Huxley (with

M. Tazelaar and G. de Beer) obtained marked modifications of development. His studies (with F. Gross) on regeneration and reorganization in the worm *Sabella* introduced a principle of alternative differentiation. Huxley was one of the first to recognize that early embryonic differentiation is chemical in nature, and to use the technique of grafting portions of chick embryos onto the chorioallantoic membrane to test their powers of differentiation. He showed (with P. D. F. Murray) that the capacity for regulation first shown by an organ field as a whole becomes devolved onto smaller subunits, each capable of regulation within itself, until the organ becomes a mosaic of self-differentiating tissues. Huxley's *Elements of Experimental Embryology*, with de Beer (1934; reprinted in facsimile in 1963), is a classic in the field.

By administration of thyroid extract Huxley obtained metamorphosis in axolotls, and he showed (with L. T. Hogben) that iodine induces metamorphosis in newts. Narcosis does impede metamorphosis. Time factors, growth rates, and tissue specificity were shown to play important parts in the process.

The reverse of development, or dedifferentiation, was the aim of many studies by Huxley (some with de Beer). He showed that there could be a balance in organisms such that under some circumstances one part thrives while another is reduced. By inhibiting the larval body of the sea urchin, he induced the metamorphosis of the larva and production of the adult sea urchin body. This concept of differential inhibition bears on cancer biology, which was subjected by Huxley to analysis.

Intimately connected with embryonic development and cancer is growth, and Huxley showed

in subjects as diverse as insects, crabs, and mammals that the rate at which certain parts grow is a function of the rate of growth of the whole organism, in accordance with a simple formula involving a growth coefficient that can be negative as well as positive; this explains the disappearance of certain structures, as well as the disparate growth of others.

Growth fields, gradient fields, and morphogenetic fields were generalized by Huxley into a fundamental field concept in biology. A field is a region of an organism throughout which an agency is at work in a coordinated manner, resulting in the establishment of an equilibrium within the area of the field. It is a unitary system which can be altered or deformed as a whole. The field concept applies to developmental and regenerative processes and is basic to their explanation in causal terms.

Huxley's contributions to genetics were not only in problems of linkage of genes and sex ratios in species crosses but also, and most important, in the control by genes of the rates at which developmental processes occur. These researches (with E. B. Ford) connect genetics with embryology, and they have opened a whole branch of biology, developmental genetics.

What is now universally known as the "new systematics" owes its inception to Huxley, who showed that the study of the differences between species must not be restricted to comparisons of museum materials, but must involve an integration of such comparisons with studies in ecology, genetics, physiology, population analysis, statistics, selection theory, geographical distribution and isolation, and ethology. Huxley saw the need for a concept of graded character differences within the geographical range of species, and he introduced the term "cline," which has been accepted as indispensable.

At a time when most biologists were huddled in laboratories, poring down microscopes and over dissecting dishes, Huxley was one of the first to go out into the field and stimulate an interest in ecology. He showed that accurate observation of bird behavior was not only scientific in itself but led to basic principles of ethology. His classic studies on grebes, divers, herons, and so forth led to a new understanding of instincts, territory occupation, and the elements and significance of ritualization, and also to a reassessment of sexual selection theory. Huxley showed that, as originally conceived by Darwin, the theory applies to a few species, but is a special case of a wider category of phenomena that make up epigamic selection, important not to only one sex but to the whole species, while certain characters which Darwin thought to be of sexual selection significance really serve warning, threat, or recognition functions.

In the early years of this century evolutionary studies were bedeviled by the antagonism between Darwinian selectionist and the Mendelian geneticist schools, until R. A. Fisher showed how they not only could but must be integrated into a synthetic theory. Huxley's book *Evolution: The Modern Synthesis* (1942; reprint 1963) covers the whole field of evolution as a cosmic, dynamic process, including natural selection, adaptation, genetic systems, the species problem, and evolutionary trends. He showed that selection acts upon the phenotype and drew attention to the fact, long ignored, that the terms used in taxonomic classification are a mixture of some that denote divergence during evolution ("clades") and others which represent stages of evolution ("grades") in which different lineages are included. A classic example is the group Reptilia, which includes a number of completely separate lines, such as those leading to mammals (and there are probably half a dozen of these), to birds, and to other fossil and living forms. The entire classification of the plant and animal kingdoms remains to be redrafted so that this fact is taken into account.

Huxley's grandfather T. H. Huxley, in his Romanes Lecture in 1893, thought that there was an absolute antithesis between organic evolution and ethics. In his own Romanes Lecture in 1943 Huxley showed how this antithesis can be resolved, because ethics is not a fixed principle but develops in individuals and evolves in societies. The basic social nature of man, inherited from his prehuman ancestors, has, at the human level, brought about a new mechanism, psychosocial evolution, characterized by the overlapping of the parental with the infantile generation (which is helpless by itself) over a prolonged period when, by care, speech, exchange of experience, and memory, social processes were built up. Huxley showed that psychosocial evolution and selection (his terms) are colored by ethical principles that are no less important for the continued evolution and survival of human populations than are their genes, anatomical structures, or physiological norms, but, unlike these, are not conveyed to the next generation through the genetic mechanism but must be imparted to each generation afresh. This form of education is the basis of civilization, and involves the overcoming by each individual of the ethical conflict with the parent as the object of love and of hate. Its result is cultural evolution.

Huxley's father, Leonard Huxley, was a biographer and historian, his grandfather T. H. Huxley a noted scientist, his brother Aldous Huxley a famous author, and his half-brother Andrew Fielding Huxley a Nobel Laureate for physiology. Julian Huxley was educated at Eton and Balliol College, Oxford. He was lecturer at Balliol in 1910–12, assistant professor at the Rice Institute in Houston, Tex., in 1912–16, lieutenant in the British army in 1916–18, fellow of New College and lecturer in zoology at Oxford in 1919–25, professor of zoology at King's College in London in 1925–27, Fullerian Professor of Physiology at the Royal Institution in 1926–

29, general supervisor of biological films for G. B. Instructional Films in 1933–36, secretary of the Zoological Society of London in 1935–42, and first director general of UNESCO in 1946–48. He was elected a fellow of the Royal Society in 1938 and was awarded its Darwin Medal in 1958. He was a corresponding member of the French Academy of Sciences and foreign member of the Hungarian Academy of Sciences and American Academy of Arts and Sciences. He was knighted in 1958.

Huxley wrote numerous articles in scientific journals and, in addition to the books mentioned above, *Essays of a Biologist* (1923), *Problems of Relative Growth* (1932), *Evolution in Action* (1953), and *Religion Without Revelation* (rev. ed. 1957; paper 1959).

For background information *see* ANIMAL EVOLUTION; ANIMAL SYSTEMATICS; BEHAVIOR, ONTOGENY OF; ENDOCRINE MECHANISMS in the McGraw-Hill Encyclopedia of Science and Technology. □

★ IMSCHENETSKY, Alexandr Alexandrovich

Soviet microbiologist
Born Jan. 8, 1905, Kiev, Russia

IMSCHENETSKY'S MAIN research work concerned ecological physiology of microorganisms, their adaption to environment, and their role in decomposition of various substances. He gave special attention to physiological activity of thermophilic bacteria. Acceleration of growth and enzymatic processes at higher temperatures is the most specific feature of thermophilic bacteria. The growth of some thermophilic cultures in ferments is completed within 3–4 hr, the most rapid rate known among all living forms. Enzymes of some thermophilic microorganisms retain their activity at 90°C, thus suggesting certain peculiarities of enzyme proteins. The "parallel" bacterial forms were found; they perform a certain process under mesophilic conditions while thermophilic forms carry on the same process at higher temperatures. Physiological properties of thermophilic forms were shown to be of more than purely theoretical interest.

Imschenetsky investigated chemosynthesis by studying the biology of nitrifying *Nitrosomonas* bacteria. Ammonia oxidation to nitrites is performed by bacteria of such narrow specialization that it is impossible to find any definite indication of their at least temporary heterotrophic existence. *Nitrosomonas* strains isolated from soils rich in organic substances were found by Imschenetsky and co-workers to bear much higher concentrations of these substances than cultures isolated from soils with poor content of organic substances. *Nitrosomonas* cells can store nitrogen-containing compounds, further oxidizing them to nitrous acid. Such residual nitrification is similar to residual respiration of heterotrophs. However, nitrifying forms do not consume oxygen for oxidation of carbon-containing substances and do not form carbon dioxide. Hydroxylamine is the main intermediate product in ammonia oxidation. Imschenetsky and co-workers were the first to show (1954) a possibility of ammonia oxidation by cellfree preparations of *Nitrosomonas.*

Cellulose decomposition by microorganisms is very important in carbon turnover in nature. Carbon of the atmospheric carbon dioxide fixed in plants by photosynthesis is again released by microorganisms into the atmosphere as carbon dioxide. Imschenetsky was the first to isolate a considerable number of pure bacterial cultures carrying out aerobic and anaerobic cellulose decomposition and to study their morphology and physiology. The decomposition of cellulose under aerobic conditions by Myxobacteria was demonstrated. Imschenetsky rejected the proposal by S. N. Vinogradsky that cellulose is oxidized to hydroxycellulose and proved that hydroxycellulose is not formed: The slime is not the product of cellulose decomposition, but is synthesized by cellulolytic bacteria and has the same composition as the slime produced by Myxobacteria, which cannot decompose cellulose. Aerobic cellulolytic bacteria hydrolyzed cellulose by the enzymes cellulase and cellobiase to glucose, which was then oxidized to carbon dioxide. Cellulose hydrolysis by pure cultures of thermophilic, anaerobic, cellulolytic, spore-forming bacteria is so effective that large amounts of glucose are accumulated in nutrient medium. Glucose is partly fermented with the formation of formic, acetic, butyric, and lactic acids, and hydrogen and carbon dioxide.

In his studies of bacterial anatomy Imschenetsky found that all bacteria contain considerable amounts of DNA. Using comparative morphology, he showed that, unlike Eubacteriales, cells of Myxobacteria contain nuclei which can be seen distinctly with the optical microscope both in living and in fixed, stained cells. In the presence of salts bacteria can produce giant cells of yeastlike or other form. Some scientists are inclined to regard these cells as a stage in the bacterial life cycle. But these are degenerative reactive forms, enlarging and then dying upon prolonged action of the factor inducing their formation.

The problem of microbial variability is of great interest not only for genetics but for general microbiology as well. Imschenetsky and co-workers studied the action of various mutagens on molds and bacteria and the effect of different mutagenic doses on frequency of formation of morphological and physiological mutants. He also investigated physiology of growth, nutrition, and formation of physiologically active substances in the mutants. As a result of experimental selection, active *Penicillium* cultures producing penicillin and active *Aspergillus* mutants producing citric acid and enzymes (such as amylase and proteinase) were obtained.

New methods of direct selection of useful mutants were tested. Under the action of various mitotic poisons, stable polyploid cultures of *Candida* yeast developed with cell volume 40-fold larger than the initial culture. DNA content per cell was always higher in polyploid than in haploid forms. Some polyploid cultures accumulated more biomass per unit of glucose utilized —perhaps because respiration of polyploid forms is less intensive than that of cells of the initial form.

Space investigation opened new fields of science, including exobiology. In 1960 Imschenetsky and co-workers began to study the extreme effects of space on microorganisms. Several bacteria and fungi were shown to survive a very high vacuum (10^{-10}mm Hg). Microorganisms can be protected against very high ultraviolet doses (7.8×10^7 ergs/cm^2) by a thin (600-A) film. Investigations were carried out with an apparatus called "Artificial Mars," which reproduced daily temperature deviations, atmospheric gas composition, and other conditions on Mars. Lack of water was shown to be the main factor limiting growth of microorganisms. However, xerophilic bacteria isolated from desert soils can grow under Martian conditions. These results proved the necessity of sterilization of spacecraft sent to other planets. One of the most interesting branches of exobiology is an elucidation of principles and methods for the detection of extraterrestrial life. Organic substances found on a planet do not necessarily prove the existence of life there; for instance, various organic substances in meteorites (carbonaceous chondrites) are of abiotic origin.

Abiotic formation of organic substances in space can be easily explained by purely chemical syntheses of amino acids, carbohydrates, purines, and so forth from gases and simple inorganic compounds by physical factors in space. The only reliable methods for the detection of extraterrestrial life are based on the presence of multiplying cells. Imschenetsky and co-workers compared different methods for automatic detection of microbial growth by nephelometry, manometry, and potentiometry and by determination of ATP, porphyrin-containing enzymes, and radioactive carbon dioxide released upon microbial decomposition of organic substances of nutrient medium containing labeled carbon. These methods can be used for the construction of automatic biological stations sent to other planets.

Microbiological analysis of meteorites found on Earth showed that they are quickly contaminated with soil microflora. However, meteorites found in ice or snow (in the Arctic) or sand (in deserts) were proved suitable for analysis.

Recently Imschenetsky investigated applicability of fungal and bacterial enzymes as medicines. Fungal proteinases with fibrinolytic action were obtained which quickly dissolved thrombi experimentally induced in dogs. Bacterial enzyme systems capable of decomposing cholesterol were also studied, as well as the enzyme uricase, which decomposes uric acid.

Imschenetsky was educated at the Voronezh State University and graduated in 1926. In 1930 he became a postgraduate student in the Microbiological Laboratory (later Institute of Microbiology) of the Academy of Sciences of the U.S.S.R., in 1932 a senior research worker, and in 1941 a department head of the Institute. In 1945 he became a vice-director and in 1949 the director of the Institute of the Academy of Sciences of the U.S.S.R. In 1939 he was granted a doctorate in biology and in 1944 the rank of professor of microbiology. In 1946 Imschenetsky was elected a corresponding member and in 1962 a fellow of the Academy of Sciences.

Imschenetsky wrote (in Russian) *Bacterial Structure* (1940), *Microbiological Processes at High Temperatures* (1944), *Microbiology of Cellulose* (1953), and *Experimental Variation in Microorganisms* (1956).

For background information *see* BACTERIAL METABOLISM; MICROORGANISMS; SPACE BIOLOGY in the McGraw-Hill Encyclopedia of Science and Technology.   □

★ INGLE, Dwight Joyce

American physiologist
Born Sept. 4, 1907, Kendrick, Idaho, U.S.A.

As a graduate student in psychology at the University of Minnesota in 1931, Ingle became interested in the physiological differences between rats selectively bred for high and low voluntary activity. He tested the possibility that inactivity was due to incapacity for muscle work. Although the hypothesis was incorrect, he developed a series of studies of factors which influenced the work output of the rat gastrocnemius muscle under a variety of conditions, including the demonstration that under controlled conditions the muscle of an anesthetized, normal rat could work for nearly 3 weeks in response to faradic stimulation.

When a reliable method for the measurement of the working capacity of individual muscles became available, Ingle's interest turned to situ-

which demonstrated new methods of inducing glycosuria in intact rats and new methods of suppressing glycosuria in depancreatized rats and in rats having steroid diabetes. He developed a technique for the continuous injection of various solutions into animals over long periods of time. With this technique he studied the factors necessary for the survival of the eviscerate rat, and was able to keep liverless animals alive for several days. From studies of the variety of metabolic effects influenced by the adrenocortical secretion, he developed the concept of the "permissive" action of hormones. In the past few years Ingle expanded his views on the "permissibility" of hormone action. These ideas were applied to studies on the role of the adrenal cortex in homeostasis, and to the theory of Hans Selye that stress may, through the pituitary-adrenal system, be responsible for the appearance of certain disease states both in animals and man.

Ingle found evidence contradicting those researchers, notably Selye, who argued that the damaging effects of stress in certain situations are primarily due to hypersecretion by the adrenal cortex. By reproducing the situations in adrenalectomized animals, Ingle observed the same damaging effects from stress when adrenal steroids were supplied at a constant but not excessive rate. The role of the adrenal cortex thus appears to be a subtle "permissive" or supporting one, rather than a primarily causal one in these situations.

Ingle received his B.S. in 1929 and his M.S. in 1931 from the University of Idaho and his Ph.D. in psychology in 1941 from the University of Minnesota. He was a research physiologist and later a research scientist at the Upjohn Co. during 1941–53. In 1953 he went to the University of Chicago as professor of physiology in the Ben May Laboratory for Cancer Research, and from 1959 was chairman of the department of physiology at the university. Among the many honors received by Ingle were the W. E. Upjohn Prize, the Roche-Organ Award of the Laurentian Hormone Conference, and the Koch Award of the Endocrine Society. He was elected to the American Academy of Arts and Sciences in 1956 and to the National Academy of Sciences in 1963.

Ingle wrote *Physiological and Therapeutic Effects of Corticotropin (ACTH) and Cortisone*, with B. L. Baker (1953); *Principles of Research in Biology and Medicine* (1958); and *I Went to See the Elephant* (1963). He edited *A Dozen Doctors* (1963) and *Life and Disease* (1963). In 1957 Ingles founded, and subsequently edited, *Perspectives in Biology and Medicine*, a journal of ideas, especially new hypotheses. Encouraging

ations where muscular weakness was a constant and clearly evident occurrence. Such was the case in adrenalectomized animals. The possible use of the characteristic fatigue of the muscles of adrenalectomized animals as an assay method for adrenal cortical hormones was an obvious extension of Ingle's work. In 1934 he joined E. C. Kendall and Harold Mason in determining by the muscle work test the biological activity of the various fractions and finally of the crystalline compounds that were isolated from adrenal extracts. In 1935 he was able to report for the first time the marked biological activity of what was then known as compound E, now known as cortisone.

In 1936, in collaboration with George Higgins, Ingle demonstrated the reciprocal relationship between the adrenal cortex and the anterior lobe of the pituitary in the control of their respective secretory activity. He showed that the administration of excess amounts of adrenal steroids results in atrophy of the adrenal cortex, an effect that he also demonstrated was due to the suppression of corticotropin secretion. In 1938, having joined the staff of the George S. Cox Medical Research Institute in Philadelphia, he began studies that culminated in the demonstration in 1940 that the administration of cortisone to rats produces the condition now known as steroid diabetes. During this period there was also a clear demonstration of qualitative as well as quantitative differences in the biological effects of the adrenocorticosteroids.

In 1941 he joined the research staff of the Upjohn Co. in Kalamazoo, where he remained until 1953. During this time he worked extensively, but not exclusively, on the adrenal cortex, reporting on the biological activities of many new adrenal steroids and analogs. He published a series of studies on experimental diabetes a humanistic approach to science, the journal was selected by the American Medical Writers' Association to receive an "Honor Awaid for Distinguished Service in Medical Journalism" in 1964.

For background information *see* ADRENAL CORTEX STEROID; ADRENAL GLAND; HORMONE, ADRENAL CORTEX in the McGraw-Hill Encyclopedia of Science and Technology. ☐

★ ISELIN, Columbus O'Donnell

American oceanographer
Born Sept. 25, 1904, New Rochelle, N.Y., U.S.A.

MODERN OCEANOGRAPHY in the United States started in about 1925. Thus, Iselin's career in marine science coincided with, and was much influenced by, the almost explosive development of the subject during the last 30 years. Although his own field work and published papers dealt almost exclusively with the western half of the North Atlantic and more particularly with the Gulf Stream system, for a number of years he gave general introductory courses in physical oceanography at both Harvard and MIT, and he played a part in the evolution of both a national and an international program in marine science. The Woods Hole Oceanographic Institution, where he was primarily employed from 1930, was the first private marine laboratory in the United States to operate a seagoing research vessel and he was its first captain. He closely followed the improved design of subsequent research ships, and recently he engaged in the testing of more specialized observational platforms, such as deep-diving small submarines, buoy systems, and especially instrumented aircraft.

There are two main reasons for the rapid recent development of oceanography in the United States: During World War II it was found that the subject could contribute significantly to undersea warfare operations, and at the same time there was much opportunity for original research. There is little doubt that both factors will continue to exert an influence during the next generation of oceanographers and, thanks to the development of big electronic computers, the huge mass of rapidly accumulating data can be handled with a minimum of drudgery. It is also true that the future of theoretical studies of ocean systems can more effectively be dealt with by computers. Thus, the prospects in marine science seem bright. Prompt publication of results is no longer a serious problem.

Iselin was one of the first to realize that along a well-developed continental shelf that receives sufficient land drainage it is the rivers that supply the energy for the prevailing shallow-water currents. This is in contrast with the oceans beyond the 200-meter depth contour, where the prevailing winds are the main source of energy. He was an early proponent of the now generally agreed fact that together the oceans and the atmosphere constitute a huge and complex heat engine powered by the Sun. It is the details of the transfer of heat, water vapor, and salts between the two fluids that researchers are now trying to understand fully.

To the huge potential of marine resources, both biological and chemical, Iselin also gave considerable thought. The present lack of ownership of most of these resources presents both a curious economic problem and one for which international law is hopelessly unprepared.

In short, oceanography presents a very broad spectrum of problems in biology, physics, chemistry, and the so-called social sciences. It is furthermore only a part, but a most neglected part, of the environmental sciences.

The son of a banker, Iselin studied at Harvard University, receiving the A.B. in 1926 and A.M. in 1928. In 1929 he was appointed assistant curator of oceanography at the university's Museum of Comparative Zoology, a position he held for 19 years. In 1930, when the Woods Hole Oceanographic Institution was founded, Iselin was named general assistant to the director and captain of the Institution's research vessel. Two years later he became physical oceanographer at Woods Hole, and during 1940–50 and 1956–58 served as director of the institution. Between his two terms as director Iselin served as senior physical oceanographer and after the second term as Henry Bryant Bigelow Oceanographer. Concurrently with his service at Woods Hole, Iselin filled a number of other posts. In 1936 he served as lecturer at the Massachusetts Institute of Technology, and in 1959 was appointed professor of physical oceanography there. Harvard named him an assistant professor in 1936, an associate professor in 1939, and professor of physical oceanography in 1960. Iselin was actively engaged in undersea warfare research during World War II, for which he received the Medal of Merit in 1948. Among the other honors conferred upon Iselin were the Agassiz Medal of the National Academy of Sciences (1943) and the Henry Bryant Bigelow Medal of the Woods Hole Oceanographic Institution (1966). In 1951 Iselin was elected to the National Academy of Sciences.

For background information *see* OCEANOGRAPHY; SEA WATER in the McGraw-Hill Encyclopedia of Science and Technology.   □

★ JACOBSON, Leon Orris

American hematologist
Born Dec. 16, 1911, Sims, N.Dak., U.S.A.

I N THE course of more than 25 years of research on blood formation, Jacobson made significant contributions to nuclear medicine and to the treatment of diseases of the blood. He was a pioneer in the clinical use of radioactive isotopes, and he discovered the main site of formation of the hormone erythropoietin, which controls the formation of red blood cells. His discovery of the role of the spleen in replacing blood-forming tissue destroyed by radiation has had far-reaching consequences in the fields of immunology, genetics, and transplantation.

In 1939, while still an intern in the University of Chicago Hospitals and Clinics, Jacobson conducted experiments on the use of radioactive phosphorus in the treatment of blood disorders. Although these experiments did not lead directly to a successful therapeutic technique, they were an important forerunner of the later extensive medical use of radioisotopes.

During World War II Jacobson served as health director of the Plutonium Project at the University of Chicago and successfully introduced the use of a nitrogen mustard as a treatment for Hodgkin's disease, a leukemia-like disorder of the white blood cells. Nitrogen mustard is still being used, in the same dosage schedule which Jacobson worked out, as an effective treatment for this disorder.

Following the war, Jacobson began to explore methods by which experimental animals, and man, might be spared the toxic effects of radiation. This work culminated in 1949 in the finding that shielding of the spleen would protect mice from otherwise lethal doses of radiation. Jacobson and his associates soon established that this protection resulted from regrowth of blood-forming tissue destroyed by radiation and suggested that migration of the cells from the shielded spleen was responsible for the repopulation. Jacobson also found that survival of irradiated mice could be ensured by injections of spleen cells or embryonic blood-forming tissue from nonirradiated mice.

Based on these experiments, the technique of using bone marrow infusion to treat animals who had received doses of radiation was developed. This technique was used by the French to treat the workers injured in a Yugoslavian atomic plant disaster and by others to treat the destruction of blood-forming tissue occurring after whole-body irradiation in the treatment of leukemia. Recent developments in the field of organ transplantation came about in part because of Jacobson's finding that irradiated mice would accept foreign tissue without rejecting it. This discovery also made it possible to produce "chimeric" mice of mixed "parentage" by injecting irradiated mice of one strain with marrow cells from mice of another strain. Such animals are a unique research tool for fundamental studies in genetics and immunity.

More recently, Jacobson turned his attention to the study of factors which regulate the production of mature blood cells from their undifferentiated precursors. He and his group introduced new bioassay methods which established the existence of a hormone—named erythropoietin—which stimulates the production of red blood cells. In addition, the Jacobson group established that erythropoietin is a glycoprotein, that the kidney is a major site of production of the hormone, and that cobaltous chloride is an effective agent for triggering the hormone's action. Jacobson's studies on erythropoietin gave the biochemist a model for the study of cell differentiation, the radiologist a system for the measurement of radiation damage to undifferentiated blood cells, and the clinician a method for measuring blood levels of erythropoietin in anemic patients.

Jacobson was born in a frontier trading town which has since disappeared from the map. The depression interrupted his education at North Dakota State University, and for a short period he taught in a one-room school house before finishing his undergraduate studies in 1935. He went on to earn his M.D. at the University of Chicago School of Medicine in 1939. He remained at the university in the department of medicine, and was made a professor in 1951 and chairman of the department in 1961. From 1951 to 1967 he was director of the Argonne Cancer Research Hospital, which the university operates for the U.S. Atomic Energy Commission. In 1965 Jacobson was named the Joseph Regenstein Professor of Biological and Medical Sciences and in

1966 dean of the university's Division of the Biological Sciences. He was elected to the National Academy of Sciences in 1965, and received a number of awards, including the Robert Roesler de Villiers Prize of the Leukemia Society of New York, the Borden Award for research in the medical sciences, and the American Nuclear Society Award for distinguished service in the advancement of nuclear science.

For background information *see* BLOOD; CLINICAL PATHOLOGY; RADIATION INJURY (BIOLOGY); RADIOISOTOPE (BIOLOGY) in the McGraw-Hill Encyclopedia of Science and Technology. □

★ **JACOBSON, Nathan**

American mathematician
Born Apr. 8, 1910, Warsaw, Poland

IN MATHEMATICS, particularly in algebra, one often separates out of a given concrete situation an abstract internal structure. For example, in studying the symmetries of a geometric object, one is led to the notion of a transformation group and then to the notion of an abstract group, which is a collection of elements of unspecified nature with an internal composition satisfying some simple axioms. The study of these abstract systems with a view to eventual classification into isomorphism classes comprises the structure theory of groups. This theory, which is concerned with the internal composition, gives a deep insight into transformation groups; however, it neglects the aspect of transformation groups that is concerned with the action of the group on the objects that are transformed. Thus, one has to supplement the structure theory with a theory of realization of the abstract groups as transformation groups. The most important part of this so-called representation theory deals with the realization of groups as groups of linear transformations in vector spaces. In a similar manner the study of

other important algebraic systems can be split into a structure theory, a representation theory, and the interplay between these two.

Jacobson's principal contributions to algebra were concerned with these aspects of three types of algebraic systems: associative rings, Lie algebras, and Jordan algebras. In the theory of associative rings, his main contribution was to the development of a structure theory of arbitrary (associative) rings. The theory of finite-dimensional associative algebras over the fields of complex numbers or of real numbers was created in the last half of the 19th century, and a deep structure theory for such algebras was developed by T. Molien, G. Frobenius, E. Cartan, and others. In 1907 J. H. M. Wedderburn developed a theory of finite-dimensional associative algebras over arbitrary fields. This was based on new methods and constituted a theory of great elegance, which had a profound influence on the development of algebra in the United States and Germany in the 1920s and 1930s. In 1926 E. Artin extended the Wedderburn theory from finite-dimensional algebras to rings satisfying the minimum condition for one-sided ideals. The class of rings to which this theory is applicable is considerably broader than that covered by the Wedderburn theory. However, the Artin structure theory is not applicable to infinite-dimensional algebras such as one encounters in analysis, notably in the theory of normed rings or Banach algebras that was initiated by the Soviet mathematician I. Gelfand in 1941. In a series of three papers published in 1945, Jacobson developed a general structure theory of rings and gave some important applications of this theory. The main elements of Jacobson's theory were (1) a general definition of the radical of a ring and a corresponding notion of semisimplicity, (2) a partial analysis of semisimple rings in terms of primitive rings, (3) a structure theory for primitive rings (due independently to C. Chevalley), and (4) specialization of the theory to the particular case of algebraic algebras. One of the main achievements of the theory was the reduction of a problem of Kurosch on algebraic algebras of bounded degree, an analog of Burnside's problem on groups, to the case of nil algebras. This special case was quickly settled by J. Levitzki, and the resulting theorem was generalized to algebras satisfying polynomial identities by I. Kaplansky.

Jacobson's main contribution to Lie algebras was to structure theory, notably to the classification of simple Lie algebras over an arbitrary field of characteristic 0 and to the initiation of the structure theory of Lie algebras of prime characteristic. The classification of finite-dimensional simple Lie algebras over the fields of complex numbers or real numbers was achieved by Cartan at the end of the 19th century and the beginning of the 20th. In 1935 W. Landherr considered the problem of classifying such algebras over arbitrary fields of characteristic 0 and gave a solution for one type of these algebras. This was taken up by Jacobson for the other "classical types" in several papers appearing in 1937–38. Jacobson showed that the Lie algebra problems were equivalent to problems of classifying finite-dimensional simple associative algebras with involution. The work of Landherr and Jacobson was significant also because it was the first important example of the use of what is now called Galois cohomology and "descent" in classification problems. Jacobson's main contribution to the theory of Lie algebras of prime characteristic was the introduction of the notion of a restricted Lie algebra of characteristic p (or p-Lie algebra) and the development of a Galois theory of purely inseparable field extensions in which the restricted Lie algebra of derivations plays the role of the group of automorphisms of the classical Galois theory.

After about 1950 Jacobson's main research efforts were in the theory of Jordan algebras. In this connection his main contributions were to representation theory and to the development of a structure theory that is a perfect analog of Artin's structure theory of associative rings. This was developed further by a number of mathematicians, in particular by Jacobson's student Kevin McCrimmon, who succeeded in extending the theory beyond the case of algebras of characteristic not 2. The idea of this extension is the replacement of the bilinear product in a Jordan algebra by a linear-quadratic composition that was introduced by Jacobson in the original theory.

Taken to the United States in 1917, Jacobson grew up in Alabama, Mississippi, and Georgia, where his father owned small clothing stores. He earned his A.B. from the University of Alabama in 1930 and received his Ph.D. at Princeton in 1934. He taught at Bryn Mawr, the University of Chicago, the University of California, the University of North Carolina, Johns Hopkins, and from 1947 onward at Yale. He was elected a member of the National Academy of Sciences in 1954.

Jacobson wrote *Theory of Rings* (1943), *Lectures in Abstract Algebra* (3 vols., 1951–64; reprinted 1964), *Structure of Rings* (1956; rev. ed. 1964), *Lie Algebras* (1962), and *Structure and Representations of Jordan Algebras* (1968).

For background information *see* COMPLEX NUMBERS AND COMPLEX VARIABLES; GROUP THEORY; RING THEORY; SET THEORY in the McGraw-Hill Encyclopedia of Science and Technology.   □

★ **JACQUINOT, Pierre**

French physicist
Born Jan. 18, 1910, Frouard, France

JACQUINOT'S RESEARCHES were concerned with atomic spectroscopy, that is, the study of atoms by means of their spectra, and the instrumental methods of optical spectroscopy. His first work, from 1933 to 1938, related to the Zeeman effect, or alteration of the spectral lines by a magnetic field, which provides valuable information regarding interactions among atomic electrons. Jacquinot was then able to analyze in detail a number of cases which up to that time had been poorly understood, and in particular to explore a series of examples of intermediary coupling between the extreme modes of coupling of two electrons. Later he studied in detail several examples of the Zeeman effect with "forbidden" lines, as well as the complex phenomena which are produced with certain lines of helium under the combined action of an external magnetic field and the electric fields which the ions exercise on each other in a luminous discharge. These studies of complex effects are important because too hasty an interpretation of the observed spectra can lead to erroneous interpretations of the "multipolar" character of certain atomic rays.

Jacquinot discovered in 1939, thanks to refined techniques, a completely new spectrum of helium which results from the intercombination between the singlet levels (termed parahelium) and the triplet levels (termed orthohelium) and which had been considered impossible up to that time. These lines had escaped observation previously because they are much weaker (as much as 10,000 times) than the normal lines of helium to which they very closely adjoin (of the order of 0.1 A). Having studied various optical methods in which the images of the lines (or, more generally, optical objects of small dimension) remain concentrated as much as possible about their center despite the inevitable diffraction, Jacquinot was able to discover these intercombination lines of helium, which have very great theoretical importance. He then extended his optical research to establish the optimum concentration of energy at the center of the images; he named this procedure apodization. In general, apodization is obtained by placing over the pupil (opening) of the optical instrument a screen whose variable absorption from one point to another can be calculated and adjusted to obtain the desired result. Apodization now constitutes a chapter in texts on advanced optics.

These studies led Jacquinot to a series of theoretical and experimental studies of the very principles of the optical methods of spectroscopy. He was thus able to show that the resolvance (resolution power) and the luminosity (or, more precisely, the optical acceptance) of any spectrographic apparatus are related in magnitude and have a constant product for each type of method employed, when either the resolvance or the luminosity is varied. This product is proportional to the transverse area of the system and to a coefficient Q which characterizes the method itself. Contrary to the general belief, this coefficient Q is much greater for gratings than for prisms, and greater for certain interference devices than for gratings. This means that for specified resolvance and dimensions a grating device will always be more luminous than a prism device, and that still better performance can be obtained by using, for example, a Fabry-Perot or Michelson interferometer. These findings, published in 1954, were not generally accepted at first, and some disputatious publications resulted. They are now accepted methods by all specialists in this field, and interference spectroscopy has made great progress throughout the world. In particular, several new methods were developed by Jacquinot and his collaborators Pierre Connes and Robert Chabbal.

Methods utilizing the Fabry-Perot interference apparatus have been highly developed with the use of a photoelectric receptor either to obtain much greater resolvances or to operate in the infrared. One of the interference methods, Fourier spectroscopy, invented simultaneously and independently—starting from very different viewpoints—by the British astronomer Peter Fellgett and by Jacquinot, is highly regarded. Unlike all other methods, Fourier spectroscopy does not make use of any selection or dispersion apparatus, but records an interferogram, that is, the signal supplied by a double-beam Michelson interferometer wherein the path difference is varied progressively. To obtain the spectrum itself, it is necessary to calculate the Fourier transform of the interferogram; even in the most elaborate cases this can now be done by means of electronic calculators. This method adds to the widely accepted optical properties common to interference methods the advantage that no information is rejected and all of the variations found in the spectrum are received simultaneously by the receptor. This fact confers a considerable superiority on this method in the infrared region, compared with conventional methods wherein the spectrum is explored sequentially. Very spectacular results in the spectroscopy of planetary atmospheres in the infrared were obtained by Connes, who learned how to master the technical difficulties which arise from the extraordinary mechanical precision required. All of these new methods were utilized in the laboratory which Jacquinot directed by a large research group working on the classification and the theory of atomic spectra, as well as on the effects associated with the properties of atomic nuclei (hyperfine structure and isotopic displacements).

In 1932 Jacquinot obtained the Agrégation de physique after his university studies at Nancy and in 1937 the degree of Docteur ès sciences at the University of Paris. He became professor at the University of Clermont-Ferrand in 1942 and at the University of Paris in 1946. From 1951 he was director of the Aimé Cotton Laboratory of the National Center for Scientific Research (CNRS) at Bellevue. From 1962 he was director general of CNRS. Recipient of the 1950 Holweck Medal of the Société française de Physique and Physical Society, London, Jacquinot was elected to the French Academy of Sciences in 1966.

For background information *see* ATOMIC STRUCTURE AND SPECTRA; DIFFRACTION; DIFFRACTION GRATING; NUCLEAR MOMENTS; SPECTROSCOPY in the McGraw-Hill Encyclopedia of Science and Technology.   □

★ JOHN, Fritz

American mathematician
Born June 14, 1910, Berlin, Germany

FOR MANY years John explored mathematical problems that are not "well-posed." This concept goes back to an illuminating classification of mathematical questions by the French mathematician Jacques Hadamard; he defined a "well-posed" problem in essence as one that is analogous to that of predicting the effects of known physical causes. Mathematically speaking, in a problem of this type one is asked to solve "equations" (like those needed to describe a physical system) for cases in which there are various additional pieces of information, called

"data" (describing, for example, the initial state of the physical system and the outside influences it is exposed to). To be "well-posed," the equations should have only one solution for all possible data. Moreover, that solution should be affected little by small changes in the data, so that even imperfect knowledge of the data might lead to a useful approximate answer. Well-posed problems also are the ones that mathematical analysis is best able to handle, at least in principle, though the actual solution may be quite difficult.

A classic example of a well-posed problem is that of determining the motion of a planet in the gravitational field of a spherical central body of known mass. In this case, the two additional data needed are the position and velocity of the planet at a single moment. The mathematical problem here is a standard initial value problem for ordinary differential equations. However, such clean-cut problems, involving predictions of effects of causes that are perfectly known and independent of each other, are not the only concern of the scientist. Frequently the physical conditions are not known precisely and have to be inferred from limited observations. Thus, a whole series of observations of an artificial satellite may be needed to determine simultaneously the gravitational and aerodynamic forces acting on the satellite and to predict its motion. In other problems the question is not so much to find out the effects of known conditions as to find the conditions that will produce a desired effect or an observed effect.

From the point of view of Hadamard's criterion, all such problems are "improperly posed." They usually contain a superabundance of data that are consistent only when derived from actual observations; a slight change can make the data inconsistent and the problem unsolvable. While such problems have always arisen in practice, they have been solved by

ad hoc methods that do not fit into the orderly pattern characteristic of most of mathematics. John was led to consider in his Ph.D. thesis instances of improperly posed problems in determining a function from its integrals over various manifolds, a problem that arises when an attempt is made to find a field of force from its effects on a solid in different positions. Later he encountered other improperly posed problems in studying the propagation of solutions of partial differential equations.

Problems of this type in many instances turned out to be related to the classical process of "continuation of analytic functions," which itself represents an extreme example of an improperly posed problem. Most exact relations between quantities encountered in practical applications are expressed by means of "analytic functions." A relation $w = f(z)$ between two quantities w and z is called an analytic function if near any point z_0, where it holds, the relation can be represented by an infinite series of the type $w = f(z) = c_0 + c_1(z - z_0) + c_2(z - z_0)^2 + c_3(z - z_0)^3 + \ldots$ with suitable numerical coefficients c_0, c_1, c_2, $\ldots$. Analytic functions have the peculiar property of "unique continuation"; that is, precise knowledge of the relation $w = f(z)$ for all z near any particular value z_0 fixes the relation everywhere. The process of recovering f for all z (for which it makes sense) from known values of f for z near z_0 is called "analytic continuation." It resembles the task of reconstructing a whole tree from a tiny piece of a leaf. The difficulty with the process of analytic continuation is that it requires absolutely perfect knowledge of the data, that is, of the values of f near z_0, and hence that it cannot be carried out numerically or applied where the data have the slightest uncertainty. This situation is typical for a large class of improperly posed problems. However, John showed that in many cases such seemingly untractable problems completely change their character and become accessible to numerical solution if to the data there is added a single piece of information, namely, an estimate of the maximum size of the solution to be expected. With a restriction on the size of the solution, perfect knowledge of the data is not necessary for an approximate determination of the solution. Here a finer distinction between improper problems came to light, bearing on the relation of the accuracy of the data to that of the solution. The "well-behaved" problems are those in which the number of significant figures in the answer exceeds a fixed percentage of those in the data; no numerical solution seems feasible for problems that are not well-behaved.

John was active in mathematical analysis, geometry, and applied mathematics, in particular in the general theory of partial differential equations, hydrodynamics, mathematical theory of elasticity, inequalities, and numerical analysis. He studied at Göttingen University, coming under the influence of R. Courant, Herglotz, and Weyl, and received his Ph.D. there in 1933. He left his native Germany in 1934 and, after a stay at Cambridge University, went to the United States in 1935. He taught until 1942 at the University of Kentucky, worked from 1942 to 1945 at the Ballistic Research Laboratory at Aberdeen, Md., and was thereafter associated with New York University, except for the year 1950–51, when he was director of research of the Institute for Numerical Analysis in Los Angeles.

John wrote *Plane Waves and Spherical Means Applied to Partial Differential Equations* (1955); *Partial Differential Equations*, with L. Bers and M. Schechter (1964); *Introduction to Calculus and Analysis I*, with R. Courant (1965); and *Advanced Numerical Analysis* (1967).

For background information *see* COMPLEX NUMBERS AND COMPLEX VARIABLES; NUMERICAL ANALYSIS; PARTIAL DIFFERENTIATION in the McGraw-Hill Encyclopedia of Science and Technology. ☐

★ KAC, Mark

American mathematician
Born Aug. 3, 1914, Krzemieniec, Poland

KAC'S SCIENTIFIC contributions were concerned
mainly with probability theory and its applications. His early work, an outgrowth of a
collaboration with his teacher H. Steinhaus, was
directed toward exhibiting the normal distribution in mathematical contexts far removed from
those associated with chance or randomness.
This culminated in a theorem, proved jointly
with P. Erdös, that if $\nu(n)$ denotes the number
of prime divisions of n, then for every real ω the
density of the set of integers n for which

$$\nu(n) < \log \log n + \omega \sqrt{\log \log n}$$

is given by the error integral

$$\frac{1}{\sqrt{2\pi}} \int_{-\infty}^{\omega} e^{-u^2/2} \, du$$

After World War II Kac began a study of
distributions of functionals over the space of
continuous functions with respect to the Wiener
measure. The original motivation for this work
was to provide a machinery for proving certain
limit theorems and for calculating limiting distributions. For example, let $X_1, X_2, \ldots$ be
identically distributed independent random variables, each with mean zero and variance 1. Let
$s_n = X_1 + \ldots + X_n$ and let N_n denote the
number of $s'_k s$, $k = 1, 2, 3, \ldots, n$, which are
positive. One may wish to know whether the probability that $N_n/n < \omega$ approaches a limit as
$n \to \infty$ and, if so, what this limit actually is. In a
series of papers, some written jointly with Erdös,
Kac developed a pattern for dealing with such
problems. The underlying idea became known as
the "invariance principle." For the case in question, one proves that

$$\lim_{n \to \infty} \left\{ \text{Prob} \, \frac{Nn}{n} < \omega \right\}$$

is equal to the Wiener measure of the set of continuous functions

$$x(\tau), \, (x(0) = 0), 0 \leqq \tau \leqq 1$$

for which

$$\int_0^t V(x(\tau)) d\tau < \omega t$$

where $V(x)$ is 1 for $x > 0$ and 0 for $x \leqq 0$.

The calculation of this Wiener measure can in
turn be reduced to solving a certain parabolic
differential equation closely related to the
Schrödinger equation of quantum mechanics. The
final answer, which was known before in some
special cases, is

$$\lim_{n \to \infty} \text{Prob} \left\{ \frac{Nn}{n} < \omega \right\} = \frac{2}{\pi} \arcsin \sqrt{\omega}$$

where $0 \leqq \omega \leqq 1$.

The fact that distributions of functionals of
the form

$$\int_0^t V(x(\tau)) d\tau$$

can be reduced to solving equations related to
the Schrödinger equation suggested that one
might reverse the usual trend and use the theory
of Wiener measure to study the Schrödinger
equation and other related equations. Kac originated several developments in this direction by
showing how the Wiener theory of measure and
integration in the space of continuous functions
can be used to study asymptotic properties of
eigenvalues of a wide class of operators and to
obtain new (though classical in appearance)
formulas in potential theory.

From his student days Kac was interested in
applications of probability theory to physics.
During World War II, while working on problems of random noise in radar, he and A. J. F.
Siegert gave a complete statistical description of
the output of a receiver with a square-law detector. (This work led in a natural way to his
interest in distributions of functionals over the
space of continuous functions.)

Earlier Kac proved (extending a result of
J. E. Littlewood and A. C. Offord) that a polynomial of degree n whose coefficients are independent random variables with the same normal
distribution with mean zero has on the average
$(2/\pi) \log n$ real roots. To derive this result, he
introduced a general formula for the average
number of real roots of a random function. The
formula turned out to be essentially the same as

that introduced by S. O. Rice several years before. Sometimes referred to as the Rice-Kac formula, it has since been used in many different connections.

In 1946 Kac gave a complete solution of the Ehrenfest ("dog flea") model, which was proposed in 1907 to illustrate how reversible models can exhibit seemingly irreversible behavior. His interest in, and liking for, simplified mathematical models of complex physical phenomena led Kac to introduce a one-dimensional "caricature" of a Maxwell gas on which one could examine in detail the derivation of the Boltzmann equation and, in particular, prove rigorously the theorem on "propagation of chaos."

He also first considered a model of a one-dimensional gas of hard rods with an exponential attraction. He succeeded in deriving the equation of state of this gas in terms of the largest eigenvalue of a certain integral operator. Later, in collaboration with G. E. Uhlenbeck and P. C. Hemmer, he showed that in a certain limiting case this equation of state goes over into the classical van der Waals equation.

Kac received the degree of magister of philosophy in 1935 and the Ph.D. in mathematics in 1937 from the John Casimir University of Lwów, Poland. In 1938 he went to the Johns Hopkins University on a fellowship provided by the Parnas Foundation, and in 1939 he joined the faculty of Cornell University. He became a professor at the Rockefeller University in 1961, and in the spring of 1963 he served as the H. A. Lorentz Visiting Professor of Theoretical Physics at the University of Leiden. Kac held a Guggenheim fellowship in 1946 and received the Chauvenet Prize of the Mathematical Association of America in 1949. In 1965 he was elected to the National Academy of Sciences.

For background information see CALCULUS, DIFFERENTIAL AND INTEGRAL; DISTRIBUTION (PROBABILITY); INFINITY; PROBABILITY in the McGraw-Hill Encyclopedia of Science and Technology.   □

★ KALMAN, Rudolf Emil

American mathematician and electrical engineer
Born May 19, 1930, Budapest, Hungary

KALMAN'S WORK was directed toward the scientific understanding of the creative processes in modern engineering, as manifested in the organization of control, computer, and information systems. His approach consistently emphasized mathematical ideas. Engineering, like mathematics but unlike the natural sciences, excels in creating something new rather than in explaining natural phenomena. That such an abstract approach to engineering can have very practical benefits was demonstrated in 1963

when a United States Moon probe, which was guided by a "Kalman filter," achieved a successful landing on the Moon. Today all countries use Kalman filters for the guidance of space vehicles.

Statistical filtering was the creation (simultaneously and independently in 1941) of the Soviet mathematician Andrei Kolmogorov and the American mathematician Norbert Wiener. They built upon earlier work of the Swedish mathematician-econometrician Hermann Wold. All three were interested in the questions: Can statistical information about the past be used to produce valid predictions about the future? Can the chance events of the past, patiently observed and then subjected to heavy mathematical analysis, reveal something valuable about the future? If so, how reliably? The first answer was given in terms of harmonic analysis and probability theory, in whose mathematical development during the 1930s Wiener and Kolmogorov were leaders. They showed how to compute from the covariance of a random process the input-output function of a linear filter. This filter, now known as a "Wiener filter," performs prediction by smoothing and storing statistical data. Wiener used the Wiener-Hopf integral equation, whereas Kolmogorov worked with a more abstract setup via Hilbert space. The implementation of the Kolmogorov-Wiener theory presented stubborn difficulties. Many engineers (including Bode, Shannon, Ragazzini, Pugachev, and Battin) contributed to explaining the theory but were unable to make major practical applications because of the great difficulties in computation.

In 1959 Kalman undertook a complete reformulation of the problem. He introduced two new principles: (1) Prediction is possible only to the extent that the future depends on past

causes stored within a dynamical system. (2) The predictor must mimic the process on which it operates, and so the predictor must itself be a dynamical system. Drawing on revitalized knowledge in the field of differential equations, he assumed that the dynamics of the process to be predicted are known but obscured by noise, and he computed from this an explicit description of the optimal filter; that is, the Kalman filter was given not merely in the input-output sense (prescription) but in terms of the equations of motion (blueprint or computer program). These computations were similar in spirit to those of Kolmogorov. Slightly later, Bucy obtained a solution of the Wiener-Hopf equation using starting assumptions similar to Kalman's. After Bucy joined the Research Institute for Advanced Study (RIAS), his results were quickly shown to be equivalent to Kalman's.

Collaterally, Kalman's work in mathematical system theory led to the development of the concept of "controllability"—man's ability to affect his environment with the means (control variables) at his disposal. In an ordinary linear differential equation with constant coefficients, $dx/dt = Fx + Gu(t)$ (where $x =$ state vector and $u(t) =$ control vector), there is complete controllability if, and only if, rank $(G, FG, \ldots)$ $= \dim X$. This very simple criterion, discovered in 1957, explains the success of all intuitive engineering methods for constructing control systems. Explicit recognition of the importance of controllability has greatly simplified the study and implementation of control systems. It plays a major role in optimal control theory (Bellman, Pontryagin), stability theory (Popov, Kalman), and even network theory (Youla).

By dualizing the notion of controllability into "observability," Kalman was able to show that his filtering theory is the *dual* of optimal control theory in a strict mathematical sense. For this contribution he was chosen Outstanding Young Scientist of the Year in 1962 by the Maryland Academy of Sciences. The controllability condition played a key role in fully explicating the connections between the Kolmogorov-Wiener theory and the Kalman-Bucy theory, and it provided important motivation for introducing modern algebra into the theory of dynamical systems.

Kalman believed that much of mathematical research can be viewed as abstract experimentation with systems which may become reality in the future. Because of the enormous progress in computer technology, the actual building of complex systems is no longer a critical problem, but such systems may be futile or even harmful if their creation is not preceded by incisive mathematical study. There is here a very important interaction between the abstract world of mathematics and the needs of a complex society; it is an area of scientific study where only the first steps have been taken.

Son of an electrical engineer, Kalman gained an S.B. in 1953 and an S.M. in 1954 at MIT. After independent research in control at the Du

Pont Experimental Station, he joined the staff of Columbia University, from which he received his D.Sci. in 1957, under J. R. Ragazzini. He went to IBM Laboratories to work on the then new applied-mathematical problems of computer control of large systems, but he changed a year later to do basic research in mathematics and control, joining Solomon Lefschetz's group at RIAS in Baltimore. He remained there during the entire lifespan of the group. In 1964 he went to Stanford University as a professor.

Kalman coauthored *Topics in Mathematical System Theory* (1968).

For background information *see* COMMUNICATIONS, ELECTRICAL; COMPUTER; FILTER, ELECTRIC; STATISTICS in the McGraw-Hill Encyclopedia of Science and Technology.   □

★ KANTROWITZ, Arthur Robert

American physicist
Born Oct. 20, 1913, New York, N.Y., U.S.A.

FLUID MECHANICS separated from physics in the middle of the 19th century, when physics concentrated on the microscopic structure of matter. The fluid mechanics of the day required virtually no understanding of these phenomena for complete macroscopic descriptions, and research into the structure of matter involved little fluid mechanics. Fluid mechanics was pursued by engineers who sought to provide a basis for the design of ships, airplanes, turbo machinery, and so on. By the 1930s these disciplines were entirely separate, with the result that virtually no one was educated in both areas. However, in recent years some scientists have become concerned with many examples of high-speed gas motion which is strongly influenced by the molecular and atomic structure of the gas. For this reason Kantrowitz became concerned with reuniting these disciplines.

Kantrowitz developed an interest in science at about the age of 12 and always concentrated on applied physics. For a time he considered an engineering education. However, it became apparent to him that the engineering education of the 1930s was deficient in that it gave no attention to modern science. He therefore chose the alternative of studying pure physics, but without altering his intention to pursue applied physics. Physics at Columbia, at the time Kantrowitz attended, was largely a preparation for research in nuclear physics, which provided him with a background in atomic physics and quantum mechanics, among other related subjects. It also provided a survey of nuclear physics and revealed for Kantrowitz the tantalizing possibility of nuclear energy. This possibility was deeply discounted by most of the leading nuclear physicists at the time, but this did not discourage him.

The depression of the 1930s clouded Kantrowitz's future while he was in the middle of his graduate studies, and it seemed at one stage it might be impossible for him even to work as a physicist. He therefore jumped at the opportunity offered in a neighboring field, aeronautics, by the National Advisory Committee for Aeronautics, the predecessor of NASA. This agency maintained a laboratory at Langley Field, Va., which was mostly concerned with work in fluid mechanics, but physicists were sometimes employed as laboratory technicians because they were available at less cost than people with engineering degrees. Economic pressure thus created a situation where the best opportunity to distinguish himself lay in combining the physics he had learned with the fluid mechanics interests of the laboratory. After a short period at Langley he obtained a leave of absence and completed the course work of the graduate physics program at Columbia.

Upon returning to Langley Field in 1938, Kantrowitz conceived, with Eastman Jacobs, an early version of what is now sought as the controlled fusion reaction. The two built a large toroidal magnetic field in which they hoped to contain a high-temperature plasma. They knew that their apparatus was too small to achieve a nuclear reaction and hoped only to exhibit that high-temperature gases could be so contained. Nevertheless, after working very hard for 18 months on a budget of $5000, they ran into containment problems and the project was cancelled. The project was formative for Kantrowitz in that he did all the theoretical calculations for the controlled fusion device and learned a great deal of high-temperature gas physics. However, the shock of the project's cancellation at the first technical difficulty was hard to overcome.

After a fallow period Kantrowitz began to work on the fluid mechanical problems which were important to the laboratory generally and mainly on the problems of supersonic aerodynamics. He did early research on supersonic diffusers and supersonic compressors which are now of great use. During this period he discovered a relationship between the microscopic physics he had learned at school and the fluid mechanics he had learned at the laboratory, namely, that the rapid changes in temperature occurring in a flowing gas cause departures from equilibrium molecular vibration. He was able to show that this departure from thermal equilibrium can be measured simply with the traditional instruments of fluid mechanics, an impact tube and manometers. This simple experiment was accepted at Columbia as his Ph.D. thesis.

Following World War II Kantrowitz accepted a position at Cornell University in aeronautical engineering, later broadened to include engineering physics, that gave him an excellent opportunity to develop this interdisciplinary area. He noticed in the late 1940s that shock waves such as can be produced in shock tubes can easily produce temperatures so high that many molecular and atomic phenomena are exhibited and very well studied. The high-temperature shock tube thus provides the ideal vehicle for the study of the interdisciplinary boundary between fluid mechanics and gas physics. In the early 1950s at Cornell, together with a group of students including Edwin L. Resler, S. C. Lin, and Harry E. Petschek, he developed an understanding of high-temperature argon shock waves, including their electrical and optical phenomena. This work was of some interest to astrophysicists because some vaguely similar phenomena occur in astronomical shock waves, but its real importance lay in its serving as a predecessor to the work on atmospheric reentry.

Reentering the atmosphere at velocities approaching those attained by satellites produces all sorts of phenomena requiring an intimate admixture of the disciplines of atomic and molecular physics with those of fluid mechanics. The work that Kantrowitz and his students carried out at Cornell prepared them to play a significant role in providing a scientific basis for the technology of reentry vehicles. He worked on this technology in the late 1950s and early 1960s at the Avco Everett Research Laboratory, created by Avco with Air Force funds in 1955. Subsequently, a number of other applications of these interdisciplinary areas between fluid mechanics and gas physics have appeared. One is the interaction between electromagnetic fields and moving gas, which is important for the kind of magnetic containment that Kantrowitz attempted in the late 1930s and which is now a full-blown international research effort. Another application is the generation of electricity directly from moving high-temperature gases embodied in the magnetohydrodynamic generator, currently approaching practical utility for various purposes. Still another area profiting from this work is the application of fluid mechanics to lasers.

Another interdisciplinary area also attracted Kantrowitz's attention, that between fluid mechanics and medicine. Physicians must deal with blood and other body fluids in motion, and many other fluid mechanical phenomena are important in medicine. Yet fluid mechanics is not part of the education of physicians. The area became especially important in the development of artificial circulatory devices. Kantrowitz collaborated with his brother Adrian, a cardiovascular surgeon, and with other surgeons in the attempt to make such devices and to apply more than intuitive fluid mechanics to their design.

Kantrowitz received his B.S. (1934), M.A. (1936), and Ph.D. (1947) at Columbia University. After working for the National Advisory Committee on Aeronautics from 1935 to 1946, he became associate professor, then professor, of aeronautical engineering and engineering physics at Cornell University. In 1955 he joined the Avco Corp. as director of the Avco-Everett Research Laboratory, becoming a vice-president and director of the corporation the following year. He was a visiting lecturer at Harvard in 1952, a fellow in the School for Advanced Study, Massachusetts Institute of Technology, in 1957, and a visiting institute professor at MIT in 1957–58 and 1961–67. He was elected to the American Academy of Arts and Sciences in 1957 and to the National Academy of Sciences in 1966.

For background information *see* AERONAUTICAL ENGINEERING; FLUID MECHANICS; QUANTUM MECHANICS; SUPERAERODYNAMICS in the McGraw-Hill Encyclopedia of Science and Technology. □

★ KAPLANSKY, Irving

American mathematician
Born Mar. 22, 1917, Toronto, Ontario, Canada

A RECURRING theme in Kaplansky's work might be described as "algebra with an infinite flavor." A relatively unsophisticated instance is provided by the theory of infinite-dimensional quadratic forms. Let Q be a nonsingular quadratic form over a field F. Q has a discriminant d, determined up to a square. If F is finite, it is a standard theorem that d is the only invariant needed to characterize Q. But now suppose that the underlying vector space is infinite-dimensional (and countable). There is no visible way to define a discriminant. One is led to suspect that none is needed, and this is indeed so: All these quadratic forms are equivalent. Such an

evaporation of invariants on passing from the finite to the infinite occurs frequently in many other contexts.

There are cases in which an algebraic hypothesis forces an object to be finite even though a priori it might be infinite. In 1947 Kaplansky heard N. Jacobson lecture on a pretty theorem of Marshall Hall: If a division ring D satisfies the identity $(xy-yx)^2z = z(xy-yx)^2$, then D is a field or is four-dimensional over its center. Jacobson asked whether this was an isolated phenomenon or part of a coherent pattern. After a while the question was posed: If a division ring D satisfies any identity whatsoever, is it necessarily finite-dimensional over its center? This was answered in the affirmative by Kaplansky, and the somewhat involved proof was promptly simplified by Harish-Chandra. Rings satisfying a polynomial identity later became a basic part of the arsenal of ring theorists. They were, for instance, useful in studying A. Kurosh's problem, which asks whether every finitely generated algebraic algebra is finite-dimensional. Kaplansky found the answer to be affirmative in the presence of a polynomial identity, and he used this to effect a reduction of the problem to primitive and nil algebras. These partial results acquired greater importance after the general question was answered negatively by E. S. Golod in 1964.

There is a unique instance in which a given algebraic object is infinite and a reduction can be made to the countable case: Every projective module over an arbitrary ring is a direct sum of countably generated modules. This theorem was discovered as a by-product of an investigation of the homological dimension of valuation rings.

The preceding algebraic results were inspired by the needs of algebra itself. Another circle of ideas had its origin in the theory of bounded operators on a Hilbert space, which was founded around the beginning of the 20th century to systematize and advance work on differential and integral equations. Later it turned out to be just the right vehicle for the mathematical formulation of quantum mechanics. Starting about 1935, there began a systematic study of algebras of such operators. The direction taken by the Soviet school, headed by I. M. Gelfand, was to study uniformly closed self-adjoint algebras (christened "C*-algebras" by I. E. Segal). Motivated by discoveries being made concerning representations of Lie groups, Kaplansky studied a special class of C*-algebras, giving them the name "CCR-algebras." The basic theorem was that the structure space of a CCR-algebra is of the second category. Actually, he first found a parallel, purely algebraic theorem applying to a class of rings called π-regular rings. The algebraic theorem is much easier to prove, but nevertheless the key ideas are already there. This is a convincing demonstration of the usefulness of looking for related phenomena in different branches of mathematics.

In the United States research on algebras of operators took a different direction under the lead of F. J. Murray and J. von Neumann. From the start their work had a highly algebraic flavor. Von Neumann invented the concept of "continuous geometries" as a purely algebraic setting for this kind of work. Besides reasonable postulates of a geometric type, he invoked a final axiom of continuity which was cumbersome to state and to apply. Kaplansky reviewed von Neumann's monumental work on continuous geometry at various times in the first half of the 1950s. This thought eventually became dominant: All the examples he could construct violating the continuity axiom were far from the type that occurred in connection with Hilbert space, in that there was nothing resembling the operation of orthogonal complementation. The idea that the presence of an orthogonal complementation might make it possible to prove the continuity axiom became virtually an obsession. The proof was eventually found; Kaplansky's theorem is stated in the title of his paper, "Any orthocomplemented complete modular lattice is a continuous geometry."

Kaplansky's parents emigrated from Poland to Canada just before World War I. His undergraduate studies were at the University of Toronto (B.A., 1938) and his graduate work at Harvard (Ph.D., 1941). He stayed at Harvard as an instructor until 1944, when he joined the Applied Mathematics Group of the National Defense Research Council at Columbia University. At the end of World War II he joined the University of Chicago as an instructor, becoming chairman of the department of mathematics in 1962. He held a Guggenheim fellowship in 1948–49. He was elected to the American Academy of Arts and Sciences in 1964 and to the National Academy of Sciences in 1966.

Kaplansky wrote *Infinite Abelian Groups* (1954) and *An Introduction to Differential Algebra* (1957).

For background information *see* BOOLEAN ALGEBRA; LATTICE (MATHEMATICS); RING THEORY in the McGraw-Hill Encyclopedia of Science and Technology. □

★ KARGIN, Valentin Alekseevich

Soviet chemist
Born Jan. 23, 1907, Dnepropetrovsk, Russia

KARGIN STARTED his research with a study of colloid solutions, in which dispersed substances are not separate molecules but relatively large particles that are charged and thus repelling each other, rather than coagulating into the larger aggregates. The addition of salts decreases the charge of such particles and thus causes degradation of colloid solutions because of sorbtion of the ions by the particles. While studying these systems, Kargin discovered that along with the physical phenomena the salt action on colloid solutions was accompanied by pure chemical phenomena, such as reaction of the salt with the compounds present in the colloid. This reaction resulted in the formation of insoluble compounds and in degradation of the colloid solution. He had also elucidated the role of chemical processes of sorbtion of salts by colloids and by soils and the mechanism of chemical reactions between the substances in the colloid state. The chemical reactions were found to occur, not as a result of a particle collision, but only when at least one of the reacting substances is somewhat soluble; therefore the reaction is realized through real solution. The role of chemical phenomena in colloid systems turned out to be unexpectedly large.

In the 1920s it had been discovered that particles of many substances treated earlier as colloid particles are in fact large molecules of linear structure. Later it was shown that these molecules are able to change their shape, and large, elastic deformations of rubberlike substances were attributed to the molecular flexibility of polymers. The concept of high polymer behavior arose, and Kargin showed that polymer solutions of all concentrations obey the phase rule and are true uniphase solutions and not colloid systems.

But the main trend in Kargin's research was the study of the structure of the polymers and the relation between their structure and behavior. In 1950, with Slonimsky, he investigated deformation of amorphous polymers in a wide range of temperatures in terms of deformation of flexible molecules and their models in a viscous medium developed in time. As a result, he formulated the idea of three physical states of amorphous polymers (vitreous, high elastic, and fluid), with transition points depending on size and flexibility of chain molecules and on intermolecular interaction. This research was the basis for the thermomechanical method of polymer characterization, a method widely used in the preliminary estimation of polymers.

The first structural model of polymers was very simple because it seemed obvious that somewhat regular structures could not be made up from very long, threadlike molecules of different size and shape. Polymers were long considered systems of randomly tangled chain molecules with local order, and clarification of the real structure of these important compounds became possible only through modern electron microscopy.

Kargin had started his study of the structure of amorphous polymers in 1956–57 in the University of Moscow with the simplest phenomena. The polymer molecules were found either to coil into globules (similar to liquid drops) or to form linear bundles made up usually of some tens of molecules if the molecules are flexible enough and straightened. Globules and bundles are the simplest structural elements for creation of the more complex structures in amorphous polymers. These structures could be very large and highly perfected even in amorphous polymers arising without crystallization, but only as the result of the addition of the primary structural elements of the regular geometrical forms. In the case of strong polyacids and their esters, the polymers can even approach visible dimensions. Crystallization of polymers, which occurs only when their molecules are straightened and combined into bundles, results in even more perfect forms of the secondary structures.

Formation of supermolecular structures was found to take place in all classes of polymers. Development of the experimental technique enabled Kargin to observe structures not only in crystallizing polymers but in rubber and glass. The structures turned out to play equally impor-

tant roles in metals and silicates as in polymer behavior. The question was put forward of regulation of properties not only by variation of the chemical composition, but also by the structure of polymers from the moment of their preparation. Supermolecular structures arise not only in solid polymers, but as well in melt state, in relatively diluted solutions, and sometimes directly in the formation of the macromolecules at polymerization.

As these ideas were developed, the role of structural phenomena in synthesis of polymer molecules was elucidated. It was found that, when transferring monomer molecules into solid state or into complexes, or when creating conditions of association of monomer molecules in liquid state and in the solution, one could efficiently influence not only the polymerization rates but also the direction of the polymerization process. It thus became possible to polymerize compounds which previously could not be polymerized under normal conditions for thermodynamic or kinetic reasons. One consequence of this approach was matrix polymerization, in which the polymerizing compound forms a complex with the polymer matrix and the new polymer molecule is a copy of the one on which the polymerization has been achieved. This process to some extent models the formation of proteins on nucleic acid molecules. As the result of all these works, the general picture of formation, structure, and properties of polymers is being developed.

Kargin graduated from the University of Moscow in 1930, and became head of the laboratory of colloid chemistry in the Karpov Institute in 1937. He founded the chair of high polymers at the University of Moscow in 1955. In 1946 Kargin was elected a corresponding member and in 1953 a member of the Academy of Sciences of the U.S.S.R.

For background information *see* ADSORPTION; POLYMYER, INORGANIC; POLYMERIZATION; POLYMER PROPERTIES in the McGraw-Hill Encyclopedia of Science and Technology.   □

★ KASTLER, Alfred

French physicist
Born May 3, 1902, Guebwiller, Alsace, Germany

WHEN KASTLER was still a student at the Ecole Normale Supérieure in Paris, his teacher Eugène Bloch introduced him to quantum physics and drew his attention to A. J. W. Sommerfeld's book *Atombau und Spektrallinien*. In this book the young student was especially interested by the "Auswahlprinzip" of Rubinowicz, which develops the consequences of conservation of angular momentum in the inter-

action between light and atoms. This principle guided Kastler in his work in spectroscopy. In his thesis at the University of Bordeaux, he studied stepwise excitation of the mercury atom and showed how selective excitation of Zeeman sublevels of excited states could be obtained by suitable polarization of the exciting monochromatic radiations. After the discovery in 1935 by R. Bernard of the strong emission of the sodium D line in the twilight luminescence of the sky, Kastler and his collaborators proved that this emission is an optical resonance phenomenon produced by sunlight on sodium atoms located in the high atmosphere. This proof was established by showing that the twilight D line is easily absorbed by a layer of sodium vapor and that it has the same small polarization as sodium resonance light produced in the laboratory.

After the development of radio-frequency spectroscopy following World War II, Francis Bitter suggested in 1949 that a search be made for methods to extend this branch of spectroscopy to excited states of atoms. At this time a former student of Kastler, Jean Brossel, worked with Bitter at MIT. Brossel and Kastler proposed use of the method now known as the "double-resonance method," which combines optical resonance with radio-frequency resonance. The principle of this method is: By optical excitation of atoms with polarized light, or even with a space-directed beam of natural light, a selective excitation of given Zeeman levels of the excited state is obtained. This selective excitation gives rise to polarization of the emitted resonance light. If a radio-frequency field is applied to the atoms during their short life in the excited state and if the resonance condition is fulfilled, transitions between Zeeman levels occur. This "magnetic resonance" can be monitored by the change of polarization of the resonance light emitted.

The pioneer work in this field was done by Brossel at MIT. He studied the excited state 6^3P_1

of the mercury atom, which is reached from the ground state by excitation with the ultraviolet mercury line 2537 A. Brossel showed how this method leads to measurements of Zeeman intervals (g-factors), lifetimes of excited states, and—in the case of the odd isotopes possessing nuclear spin—hyperfine intervals. Brossel's method was extended to alkali atoms. This extension resulted in the measurements of the electric quadrupole moments of the nuclei of these atoms. Much work in this field was done by G. W. Series and his co-workers in Oxford, England, and by Hans Koppermann's research group in Heidelberg, Germany.

In their first paper Brossel and Kastler had noticed that excitation of atoms by electron impact also leads to selective excitation of magnetic sublevels of excited states, and that magnetic resonance of these states can be monitored by measuring the depolarization of the spectral lines emitted. This method, developed in Paris by Jean-Claude Pebay-Peyroula, made it possible to measure the structure of many excited states of atoms.

In 1950 Kastler completed the double-resonance by proposing the "method of optical pumping," which leads to a selective population of Zeeman levels of atomic ground states or of metastable states. This method is based on the principle of conservation of angular momentum in the interaction of light and matter. It uses circularly polarized light for optically exciting atoms. Circularly polarized light carries angular momentum, and in the absorption process this angular momentum is transferred to the atoms. As the spontaneous emission process which follows absorption is a random process, part of the angular momentum is kept by the atoms returning to the ground state. In this way an anisotropic or dissymmetric situation is produced in a vapor, which is called "atomic orientation" (if a dissymmetry of population exists between positive and negative m-states) or "atomic alignment" (if different $|m|$-states have different populations). The success of optical pumping depends on the speed of relaxation processes which tend to restore thermal equilibrium. In diluted vapors relaxation occurs during wall collisions. Experiments showed that relaxation is a slow process or that it can be slowed down artificially by using wall coatings, by heating the walls, or by adding buffer gases.

The process of optical pumping can be monitored by optical signals. During this process the vapor becomes more transparent, and the intensity and the polarization of the resonance light undergo changes. Magnetic and hyperfine resonance in the ground state can also be detected optically by such changes. The double-resonance method and the optical pumping method form the optical methods of radio-frequency resonance and of atomic orientation. In 1951 Brossel and Kastler started a research team at the Laboratoire de Physique of the Ecole Normale Supérieure to develop these methods systematically.

During 1951–66 substantial results were obtained under their direction by a dozen research fellows working on their theses in physics. Among these results are the study of multiple quantum transitions in the radio-frequency range; the achievement of nuclear orientation in mercury vapor and in cadmium vapor and the precise measurements of the nuclear magnetic moments of these species; the study of relaxation processes and collision processes, including exchange collisions; the discovery and systematic investigation of coherence effects (such effects appear in multiple scattering of resonance light and in virtual transitions produced by radio-frequency power); the discovery of displacements of atomic energy levels by electromagnetic radiation; and the measurement of fine structures and hyperfine structures of many excited levels of He^4 and He^3.

Kastler went to elementary school in Guebwiller and to the Oberrealschule and lycée Bartholdi in Colmar. He attended the Ecole Normale Supérieure from 1921 to 1926, then spent 5 years as a high school teacher in Alsace and Bordeaux. In 1931 Pierre Daure, a professor at the University of Bordeaux, offered him an assistantship in his laboratory, where Kastler achieved his thesis in physics in 1936. After teaching as assistant professor at Clermont-Ferrand for 2 years, Kastler returned to the University of Bordeaux in 1938 as a full professor of physics. He went to Paris in 1941 and thereafter taught physics at the Ecole Normale Supérieure and at the Faculty of Science of Paris. He occupied the Francqui chair at the University of Louvain in 1953–54. He was doctor honoris causa of the universities of Louvain (1955), Pisa (1960), and Oxford (1966) and of the university Laval of Quebec (1967) and an honorary member of the French and Polish physical societies and of the Optical Society of America, which awarded him the first Mees Medal in 1962. The Physical Society of London awarded him the Holweck Prize in 1954. He was elected to the Royal Academy of Science of Belgium in 1954, to the Academie des Sciences de Paris in 1964, and to the Academy of Science of Poland in 1967. The city of Paris honored him by its scientific prize in 1963, and the Centre National de la Recherche Scientifique by its Gold Medal in 1965. In 1966 he was awarded the Nobel Prize in physics for "the discovery and development of optical methods for studying Hertzian resonances in atoms."

For background information *see* ATOMIC STRUCTURE AND SPECTRA; RADIO-FREQUENCY SPEC-TROSCOPY; SPECTROSCOPY in the McGraw-Hill Encyclopedia of Science and Technology.   □

★ KATCHALSKI, Ephraim

Israeli molecular biologist
Born May 16, 1916, Kiev, Russia

KATCHALSKI PIONEERED in the preparation of synthetic high-molecular-weight model compounds of proteins. These are most useful in the elucidation of the chemical structure and biological function of proteins. His synthesis of polylysine in 1947 was a milestone in this approach.

Physical, chemical, and enzymatic techniques have been used to establish the macromolecular conformation of the protein molecule and to explore the nature of the sites on the molecule responsible for its biological activity. In this task one encounters great difficulties because of the enormous complexity of the protein molecule and the large variety of intra- and intermolecular forces determining its structure and activity. Katchalski believed that a synthetic approach might lead to a better understanding of the nature of some characteristic features of proteins, and that by the preparation of high-molecular-weight model compounds resembling natural polypeptides or proteins it would be possible to clarify somewhat not only the factors determining the stability, conformation, and physicochemical properties of proteins, but also some of the characteristics determining their biological properties.

The high-molecular-weight model compounds chosen by Katchalski were the poly-α-amino acids, synthetic polymers composed of α-amino acid residues linked by peptide bonds. During the 1950s he and his associates developed methods which permit the synthesis of a large variety of amino acid polymers in a wide range of average molecular weight. Because of their relative simplicity, polyamino acids indeed provided useful models for studying the physicochemical properties of high-molecular-weight peptide chains in the solid state and in solution, and such studies shed new light on the nature of the secondary and tertiary structures prevailing in proteins. The determination of the characteristic helical structure of polyproline, for example, permitted the elucidation of the triple-stranded helical structure of collagen. Studies of the helix-coil transition in synthetic polypeptides, resulting from changes in solvent composition, temperature, and pH, proved useful in estimating the role of various intramolecular forces, such as hydrogen bonding and hydrophobic and electrostatic interactions, in determining the stability and conformation of native proteins, as well as in understanding the phenomenon of denaturation.

Already in 1948 Katchalski has shown that the synthetic polylysine may be digested by trypsin. Detailed studies of the enzymic digestion of many different amino acid polymers and oligopeptides led to a better understanding of the specificity and mode of action of proteolytic enzymes. Proline iminopeptidase, a new proteolytic enzyme, was discovered with the aid of the polyamino acid polyproline. In continuation of Katchalski's work, Michael Sela prepared in 1960 completely synthetic polypeptide antigens, which enabled a systematic study of the chemical basis of antigenicity.

Katchalski and his associates investigated in detail the inactivation of bacteria by basic polyamino acids, and they showed in 1955 that a random copolymer composed of the same amino acids as gramicidin S possessed, under the experimental conditions used, an antibacterial activity similar to that of the natural antibiotic. A copolymer of ornithine and leucine even surpassed the natural antibiotic in its activity toward *Escherichia coli*. Basic polyamino acids also inactivate bacteriophages, and Katchalski distinguished between a reversible and an irreversible stage in the inactivation of coliphage with polylysine.

Polyamino acids have recently acquired an important role in investigating problems of protein biosynthesis related to the nature of the genetic code. Nirenberg and Matthaei were the first to show in 1961 that polyphenylalanine can be synthesized by a cell-free system from *E. coli*, containing ribosomes, transfer RNA, labeled amino acids, and an amino acid activating system, when the natural messenger RNAs are replaced by synthetic polyuridylic acid. Similarly, polyadenylic acid led to the formation of polylysine and polycytidylic acid coded for polyproline. Katchalski and his colleagues developed a method for the fractionation of amino acid–specific transfer RNAs by preparing transfer RNA–polyamino acid derivatives.

Another major interest of Katchalski was the chemical reactivity of functional groups in polymers and the possibility of their use as chemical reagents. This led, on the one hand, to the development of methods for the synthesis of cyclic and linear peptides with the aid of insoluble active esters of amino acid and peptides. On the other hand, it led to his detailed characterization of a series of water-insoluble enzymes, which may exist not only in a powder form but also as membranes.

Largely as the result of Katchalski's investigations, a large and increasing number of laboratories over the world have chosen in the last decade to study the chemical, physical, and biological properties of synthetic polypeptides as a promising tool for the elucidation of the structure and the biological function of proteins.

Katchalski graduated from the Hebrew University, Jerusalem, in 1941, and was an assistant there until 1945. In 1949 he became head of the Department of Biophysics of the newly created Weizmann Institute of Science in Rehovoth, Israel. He spent extended periods as guest scientist: in 1949 at the Brooklyn Polytechnical Institute and Columbia University, in 1951 and 1957 at Harvard University, and in 1964 at the University of California, Los Angeles. Katchalski was a founding member of the Israel Academy of Sciences and Humanities. In 1966 he became a member of the U.S. National Academy of Sciences, as well as a foreign honorary member of the American Academy of Arts and Sciences.

For background information *see* AMINO ACIDS; PROTEIN in the McGraw-Hill Encyclopedia of Science and Technology. □

★ KAVANAGH, Thomas Christian

American engineer
Born Aug. 17, 1912, New York, N.Y., U.S.A.

KAVANAGH'S PROFESSIONAL practice was characterized by the creative cross-fertilization of engineering disciplines, an approach which can best be summed up as systems engineering. This powerful unification of thought considers the numerous interactions and feedbacks concomitant with the increasingly large number of alternates in overall design to arrive at a system providing optimum satisfaction of objectives. The "system" is understood to be an integrated and often complex assembly of many interacting elements or disciplines, including man himself, designed to carry out collectively a predetermined function.

Kavanagh's interests centered on research, development, planning, design, and construction of large systems projects—building complexes, bridge and highway systems, waterfront and

ocean facilities, radio telescopes, hardened underground facilities, stadiums and sport centers, foundations, tunnels, subways, and general transport systems.

A typical systems project for which Kavanagh acted as chief engineer was the design and construction of the radar and radio telescope at the Arecibo Ionospheric Observatory, reported to be the largest antenna of its kind. The Arecibo observatory, located near the north coast of Puerto Rico, is unique in that it is equipped with a vast, fixed spherical reflector, coupled with an independently suspended but movable feed. This departure from the conventional, steerable parabolic reflector was dictated by the high costs and technical difficulties associated with building the steerable type of structure in the large-scale proportions necessary for ionospheric research. Research is conducted with this facility in three principal areas: (1) ionospheric studies; (2) solar, planetary, and lunar studies; and (3) outer space studies.

Location of the observatory in the tropics was dictated by astronomical requirements for the maximum number of opportunities to observe various elements of the solar system. Geological considerations, site topography, and the physical features of the reflector suggested the advantages of limestone "sinkhole" terrain, volcanic cones, or extinct craters, while operational needs required a site reasonably remote from densely populated areas, major electrical installations, and air traffic lanes. The site selected was a large, natural, roughly spherical depression, or sinkhole.

The reflector is a segment of a sphere with an 870-ft radius, a horizontal aperture of 1000 ft, and a depth of 158 ft. It is constructed of mesh supported on a grid of cables pretensioned and stabilized with tie-down cables. The movable feed, capable of scanning the sky to 20° from the zenith, moves in azimuth and altitude along a spherical surface 435 ft above the reflector. The 96-ft line feed projects below a carriage house that rides along the curved lower chords of an inverted bowstring framework. These feedarm trusses, in turn, rotate around a ring girder on the underside of an equilateral-triangular, steel-truss platform with 216-ft sides. The entire platform assemblage is suspended by main steel cables from three tall reinforced-concrete towers, with backstays leading to massive anchorages. The symmetry of the structural system was selected by Kavanagh because it distributes the vertical loads uniformly to the supporting cables despite the change of positions of the movable components. Kavanagh further incorporated a stiffening of the platform by prestressed tie-downs at the corners to minimize thermal and wind displacements and to satisfy rigid requirements for performance tolerances. The principle of the spherical reflector is that the waves reflected from the dish converge at points along the line feed. The cross section of the line feed varies along the length, and is designed to control the phase of energy at each point. Slots, with lengths determined by the electrical requirement of amplitude variation, are provided on each face of the line feed. The waves thus reach a point at the top of the line feed in proper phase, as though this were the focus of a paraboloid reflector.

The antenna was designed to be operated at 430 millicycles (mc) or a wavelength of 27 in., with a beam width of 1/6 degree. This dictated a tolerance of ±3-in.-maximum permissible feed deviation, and not more than ±1-in. deviation of the reflector from a true sphere, during operating conditions for which 30-mph wind and ±15°F temperature variations were specified. The entire structure, when locked, was designed to withstand hurricane winds of 140 mph. The electrohydraulic systems selected for both elevation and azimuth drives consist of an electric motor, a servopump, a torque motor, a synchroresolver, and a hydraulic motor. The 430-mc transmission line, extending from the operations building to the line feed, is an aluminum WR-2100 wave guide with special rotary and expansion joints permitting motion and a special slotted linear joint at the feed takeoff point. The radar transmitter was designed to generate a variety of pulse-wave shapes with durations ranging from 2 microseconds to 10 milliseconds. It can be operated either as a pulse radar with 2.5-Mw peak power or as a continuous-wave radar with 150-kw average power output. The instrument can receive or transmit or do both simultaneously.

The system began operating in 1963, and checks showed the structure to be three to five times more accurate than the specified tolerances. It performed so well that modifications were begun to adapt the instrument to shorter wavelengths permitted by its greater accuracy.

Educated in New York City schools and col-

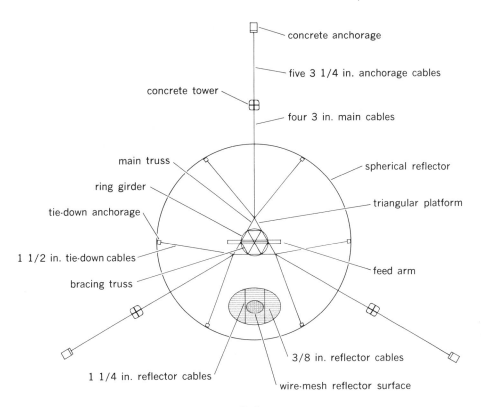

concrete anchorage

five 3 1/4 in. anchorage cables

concrete tower

four 3 in. main cables

main truss

spherical reflector

ring girder

triangular platform

tie-down anchorage

feed arm

1 1/2 in. tie-down cables

bracing truss

3/8 in. reflector cables

1 1/4 in. reflector cables

wire-mesh reflector surface

PLAN

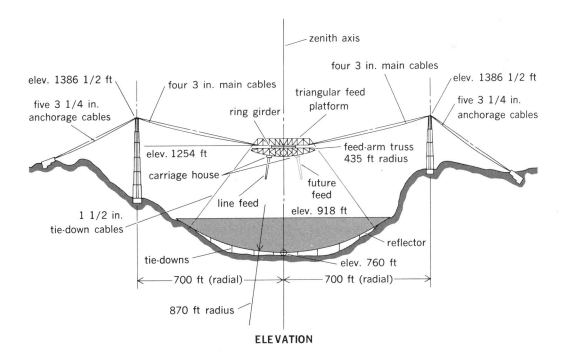

zenith axis

four 3 in. main cables

elev. 1386 1/2 ft

four 3 in. main cables

triangular feed platform

elev. 1386 1/2 ft

five 3 1/4 in. anchorage cables

ring girder

five 3 1/4 in. anchorage cables

elev. 1254 ft

feed-arm truss 435 ft radius

carriage house

future feed

line feed

elev. 918 ft

1 1/2 in. tie-down cables

reflector

tie-downs

elev. 760 ft

700 ft (radial)

700 ft (radial)

870 ft radius

ELEVATION

Plan and elevation of Arecibo Ionospheric Observatory, Puerto Rico.

leges, Kavanagh received the B.S. (1932) and M.C.E. (1933) from City College and M.B.A. (1942) and Eng.Sc.D. (1948) from New York University. He was employed in industry and the office of the chief engineer, New York City, before becoming professor of civil engineering at Pennsylvania State University (1948–52) and professor and chairman of the department of civil engineering at New York University (1952–54). In 1953 he became a partner of the New York consulting firm of Praeger-Kavanagh-Waterbury, serving also from 1956 as adjunct professor in the graduate school at Columbia University. He was a founding member of the National Academy of Engineering.

For background information *see* ANTENNA (AERIAL); RADIO TELESCOPE; SYSTEMS ENGINEERING in the McGraw-Hill Encyclopedia of Science and Technology.   □

KEILIN, David

British biochemist
Born Mar. 21, 1887, Moscow, Russia
Died Feb. 27, 1963, Cambridge, England

WHILE INVESTIGATING cellular respiration and biological oxidoreductions, Keilin discovered cytochrome, comprising a group of hemochromogens that are very widely distributed in living cells and act as intermediate hydrogen carriers in cell oxidations. This discovery, in turn, led to his formulation of a new concept of cellular respiration.

In the late 1920s studies of cellular respiration were clouded by two conflicting theories. One, the dehydrase (dehydrogenase) theory proposed by the German biochemist Heinrich Wieland, maintained that intracellular oxidations depend upon catalytic hydrogen transfer from cellular metabolites to hydrogen acceptors. The other, the Atmungsferment (respiratory enzyme) theory proposed by the German biochemist Otto Heinrich Warburg, held that the addition of oxygen is pivotal and that this addition is catalyzed by enzymes containing iron atoms.

About 1920 Keilin began to study the life cycle of the horse botfly, *Gasterophilus intestinalis*. When the *Gasterophilus* larvae develop in the horse's stomach, they turn red because of the formation in their bodies of oxyhemoglobin. However, that oxyhemoglobin, which is located mainly in the tracheal cells of the larvae, differs from the blood pigment of the host. Painstaking observations on the behavior of the larval respiratory apparatus enabled Keilin to show that the hemoglobin-laden tracheal cells help the larvae to make efficient use of the intermittent contact with the air bubbles derived from the air spaces of the ingested food. These cells take up a much larger amount of oxygen than is required for immediate needs and store it in the form of oxyhemoglobin to be utilized during the intervals when there is no contact with air bubbles. Pursuing the fate of the larval hemoglobin further, Keilin encountered another peculiar phenomenon: Unlike the larva itself, the adult botfly showed on spectroscopic examination no sign of the absorption bands of either oxyhemoglobin or hemoglobin, but instead the thoracic muscles of the insect exhibited a spectrum composed of four entirely different bands.

At this point it became essential to obtain evidence that the new absorption spectrum, though different from hemoglobin, is not due to a transformation product formed from the larval hemoglobin during metamorphosis. Bearing that in mind, Keilin proceeded to examine spectroscopically the thoracic muscles of other insects, and in particular those of the blowfly, *Calliphora erythrocephala*, the wax moth, *Galleria mellonella*, and the honeybee, *Apis mellifera*, none of which possesses hemoglobin during the larval stage. He then discovered that in their wing muscles all these insects exhibited the peculiar four-banded spectrum. Moreover, the same spectrum could be demonstrated in various tissues of other animals and even in some plants and microorganisms. Baker's yeast in particular not only proved to be an excellent material but made possible the demonstration of yet another surprising phenomenon: Whereas shaking a yeast suspension in air caused the absorption bands to disappear, these bands reappeared when the suspension was left standing undisturbed for a brief period of time. Analogous phenomena could be observed when a similar experiment was performed with a live insect: The four absorption bands were much stronger in active specimens of *Galleria* vibrating their wings than when the insect was at rest. Keilin recognized these spectral changes as being the outcome of reversible oxidation of an intercellular component to which he gave the name cytochrome, meaning "cellular pigment."

In 1925, following up the discovery of cytochrome by further intensive study, Keilin soon arrived at the conclusion that this respiratory pigment, which he showed to be common to animal cells, yeast, and higher plants, has a key position in the process of cellular respiration. He proceeded by carefully designed and critically assessed experiments to unravel the mystery of the mechanisms underlying the so-called activation of hydrogen and oxygen in respiring cells. He was able to produce unequivocal evidence that, far from being unreconcilable, the two then prevailing concepts of hydrogen and oxygen activation complemented each other. He introduced into his experiments several metabolic inhibitors with which he could selectively suppress different parts of the catalytic mechanisms. In this way he succeeded in showing that cytochromes *a*, *b*, and *c* perform the role of respiratory carriers or oxidation-reduction catalysts and in this capacity function as an essential link between the hydrogen-accepting enzymes (dehydrogenases) and an enzyme which interacts directly with oxygen, to which he gave the name cytochrome oxidase.

Keilin also performed extensive studies on the hemoglobin of lower forms of life. His extraordinarily fine spectroscopic observations, combined with a profound knowledge of the biology of animals, plants, and microorganisms, led him to the discovery of trace amounts of hemoglobin in yeasts, in several protozoa, and in certain fungi. He also devoted much time to the study of hemoglobin in the root nodules of leguminous plants. In 1945, in collaboration with Y. L. Wang, he discovered that it is only after the invasion of root cells by the symbiotic microorganism *Rhizobium* that root cells acquire the ability to form hemoglobin. *Rhizobium* not only induces growth and multiplication of the root cells, but in addition it supplies the factor essential for hemoglobin synthesis.

Keilin also made significant contributions to biochemistry through his studies on enzymes which contain hematin in the prosthetic group, and in particular catalase. Through these studies Keilin established a new principle in biological catalysis, the so-called coupled oxidations dependent on the peroxidatic properties of catalase. This coupling occurs between two reactions, namely, an enzymic aerobic oxidation process, such as the oxidation of uric acid by urate oxidase or of glucose by glucose oxidase, both of which are accompanied by formation of hydrogen peroxide, and a peroxidatic type of reaction in which hydrogen is utilized by catalase for the oxidation of another substrate, for example, ethanol or iodide. Keilin investigated other aspects of catalase activity, such as the mechanism of the interaction between this enzyme and hydrogen peroxide, organic perox-

ides, and certain enzymic inhibitors; the supposed role of catalase in the oxidation of thiol compounds; and the chemical relationship between catalase and peroxidase. Keilin also studied several other enzymes in detail, including succinic dehydrogenase, D-amino acid oxidase, uricase, and glucose oxidase.

The fourth child in a family of seven, Keilin was the youngest of three sons of a Polish businessman. His early education was in Warsaw, but in 1904 he went to the University of Liège. After receiving the Diplôme de la Candidature de Sciences Naturelles in 1905, he began his graduate work at the Collège de France. Ten years later he received a D.Sc. from the Sorbonne. He then accepted a position as a research assistant at the University of Cambridge, transferring to its Molteno Institute of Biology and Parasitology when that was opened in 1921. Keilin had been elected to the Beit Memorial Research fellowship in 1920, but in 1925 he surrendered this post to accept a position as lecturer in parasitology at the university. He was appointed Quick Professor of Biology and director of the Molteno Institute in 1931, retaining these posts until his death. Among the awards and honors he received were the Royal Medal and the Copley Medal of the Royal Society of London in 1939 and 1951, respectively. Keilin was elected to the Royal Society in 1928 and, as a foreign member, to the American Academy of Arts and Sciences in 1959.

For background information *see* BIOLOGICAL OXIDATION; CYTOCHROME in the McGraw-Hill Encyclopedia of Science and Technology.   □

★ KELLOGG, Arthur Remington

American zoologist and paleontologist
Born Oct. 5, 1892, Davenport, Iowa, U.S.A.

WILDLIFE IN a large tract of uncut woods near the family home in the suburbs of Kansas City, Mo., aroused the interest of Kellogg as a 10-year-old boy. Following graduation from Westport High School, he majored in biology at the University of Kansas. While he was a junior the curator of the university's Museum of Birds and Mammals obtained for him an appointment as taxonomic assistant. He was also employed during the summer by the Bureau of Biological Survey, U.S. Department of Agriculture, to conduct field surveys of animal and plant life in North Dakota and Montana. Identification of white whale, porpoise, walrus, and seal skeletons in the university museum's collections stimulated a desire to study the history of these specialized marine mammals. This resolve led Kellogg to continue graduate studies at the University of California, Berkeley, where J. C. Merriam was

the professor of vertebrate paleontology. Kellogg was invited to review the fossil record of the seals, sea lions, and walruses whose remains had been found in Pacific Coast Tertiary geologic formations. Before this report was completed, World War I intervened and he enlisted in the Army. He was sent overseas to the Central Medical Laboratory at Dijon, France, where he was assigned to a unit directed by Major Edward A. Goldman, one of the last of the general field naturalists. After the war Kellogg returned to the Bureau of Biological Survey on a full-time basis and worked on general natural history studies for 8 years prior to his transfer to the Smithsonian Institution in 1928. By this time Kellogg had decided to concentrate his research efforts on living and fossil cetaceans. Merriam, who had recently been appointed president of the Carnegie Institution of Washington, facilitated these studies with an annual research grant from the Institution. The grant was earmarked for an investigation of the earliest-known predecessors of the typical cetaceans, the Archaeoceti, found in the older Tertiary rocks that correspond in age to the early part of the Age of Mammals. Even these archaic mammals were well specialized in many respects for continuous life in the water.

In the earlier stages the marine mammal studies were largely descriptive, but as they progressed the importance of fossil cetaceans for geologic correlation became apparent. As a collateral investigation, the recorded occurrences of migrating whales in the several oceans were collated. These observations confirmed the belief, later supported by whale marking, that whalebone whales make seasonal migrations from tropical calving grounds to the food banks located on or near the colder waters of the Arctic and Antarctic regions. The location of fossil remains tends to confirm the conclusion that the precursors of present-day whalebone

whales followed similar migration routes, and that similar types of fossilized skeletal remains occur in geologic formations of corresponding age on the old shores that bordered these oceans.

Examination of fossilized cetacean skeletons excavated in sedimentary strata deposited on ancient beaches, estuaries, and river deltas revealed that, although these air-breathing mammals had been adapted for habitual aquatic existence, no fundamentally new structures had been added in the course of geologic time, and that the functioning of the entire body is conditioned by adjustments of old organs to an exclusive life in the water.

Under the auspices of the Economic Committee of the League of Nations, eight experts, including Kellogg, met at Berlin on Apr. 3, 1930, to consider the desirability of an international convention for preserving whales from threatened extinction by the unrestrained exploitation practiced by the pelagic floating factories. This Geneva treaty for the regulation of whaling (1931) proved to be less effective than anticipated. In 1937 Kellogg was appointed by the State Department as the United States delegate to an international conference on whaling at London, which resulted in the adoption of a protocol establishing a sanctuary in a sector of the Antarctic Ocean and for protection of whales in the Arctic Ocean. Similar international conferences followed in Oslo in 1938; in London in 1938, 1944, and 1945; and in Washington in 1946, when Kellogg served as chairman of both the American delegation and the conference, which was attended by representatives of 19 nations. The Washington conference concluded with a convention providing for the establishment of an international commission for the regulation of whaling. On this commission Kellogg served as vice-chairman and as chairman.

Kellogg took his A.B. in 1915 and M.A. in 1916 at the University of Kansas and his Ph.D. in 1928 at the University of California. He was taxonomic assistant in 1913–16 at the Museum of Birds and Mammals of the University of Kansas and a teaching fellow in 1916–19 at the department of zoology of the University of California. With the Bureau of Biological Survey, U.S. Department of Agriculture, he was assistant biologist in 1920–24 and associate biologist in 1924–28. He was assistant curator (1928–40) and curator (1941–48) of the Division of Mammals at the U.S. National Museum, Smithsonian Institution, and was director of the museum from 1948 to 1962. He also served as assistant secretary to the Smithsonian Institution from 1958 to 1962, when he became a research associate. He was elected to the National Academy of Sciences in 1951, to the American Philosophical

Society in 1955, and to the American Academy of Arts and Sciences in 1960.

For background information *see* CETACEA FOSSILS; PALEONTOLOGY; WHALE in the McGraw-Hill Encyclopedia of Science and Technology. □

★ KEMBLE, Edwin Crawford

American physicist
Born Jan. 28, 1889, Delaware, Ohio, U.S.A.

K EMBLE'S SCIENTIFIC career reflects a gradual shift of interest from problems of the theory of band spectra to more general aspects of quantum theory and to general education in science on the undergraduate level.

He began work on the quantum theory as a graduate student in 1916, when American interest in that subject was rudimentary and largely negative. His first two papers were fumbling attempts to adapt Max Planck's pre-Bohr theory to the interpretation of the infrared absorption spectra of diatomic molecules. Niels Bohr's epoch-making initial theory of the spectrum of hydrogen was 3 years old, but Kemble's two papers contained no reference to it and clung to the classical identification of the motional frequencies of radiating and absorbing molecules with corresponding spectroscopic frequencies.

Kemble's starting point was Niels Bjerrum's 1912 interpretation of the absorption bands in the near-infrared spectra of CO and HCl as vibration-rotation bands, that is, bands due to molecules vibrating with a common frequency ν_v and simultaneously rotating with a frequency ν_r that varies from molecule to molecule. The bands are double, and classical theory identifies the frequencies of the two maxima as $\nu_v + \nu_r^*$ and $\nu_v - \nu_r^*$, where ν_r^* is the most probable value of ν_r. From the spacing of the maxima, Bjerrum could work out a corresponding value of the moment of inertia J on the assumption that ν_r^* could be identified with the frequency of rotation

of a molecule with average rotational energy kT. The subsequent discovery (1913) that the HCl band in the neighborhood of 3.48 μ can be resolved into a double series of nearly equidistant lines created a quantum theory problem. Clearly the individual lines must belong to quantized rotational states. Using a rule for the quantization of angular momentum, one could deduce a new value of J from the line spacing to compare with the one previously deprived from the measurements of ν_r^*. Two different rotational quantum conditions had been proposed, one making the angular momentum any integral multiple of h/π, the other making it an integral multiple of $h/2\pi$. Comparing the two corresponding values of J with the one calculated from ν_r^*, Bjerrum was led to give preference to the h/π proposal.

Kemble's initial contribution was to work out, on the basis of Willard Gibbs's statistical mechanics, the classical law governing the distribution of angular velocities in an assemblage of diatomic molecules with two rotational degrees of freedom. It turned out that the most probable angular velocity for given values of J and T is 0.7 of the angular velocity for average rotational energy. The required correction to Bjerrum's original evaluation of J from ν_r^* led to a reversal of the previous conclusion: The quantum unit for angular momentum must be $h/2\pi$, not h/π. Meanwhile the new rule was confirmed by Bohr's theory of the hydrogen atom. Kemble's formulation of the distribution law for angular velocities also made it possible to work out a theory of the relative intensities of the lines in a vibration-rotation band, and to make a substantial improvement on previous attempts to account for the anomalous rotational specific heat of hydrogen at low temperatures.

Kemble's second 1916 paper drew attention to the weak CO absorption band at approximately half the wavelength of the strong vibration-rotation band of CO at 4.66 μ. Classically, a molecule executing large-amplitude vibrations with the frequency of the 4.66-μ band should also emit and absorb a first harmonic overtone at 2.33 μ. Could the faint band at 2.34 μ be a true harmonic of its much stronger companion? On a purely classical basis, the vibrational amplitudes at laboratory temperatures would be much too small to produce the effect. On the other hand, how else could one explain the existence of the short-wavelength band? Molecules with a whole quantum of vibrational energy would have an amplitude of vibration equal to about 10% of the normal internuclear distance—large enough to generate overtones. Just how the motion of such one-quantum molecules could influence the absorption spectrum of the cold gas was by no means apparent, but it seemed clear that quantization of vibrational motion must be responsible for the phenomenon. On this basis, Kemble predicted that similar faint harmonic bands in the infrared spectra of other diatomic molecules would be found. A search was instituted in collaboration with J. B. Brinsmade, a fellow graduate student who had just built a suitable spectrometer. The anticipated new bands were found in the spectra of HCl and HBr, but careful measurements showed that in all three cases, CO, HCl, and HBr, the frequency of the high-frequency band is a little *less* than twice that of the fundamental.

There the matter rested from June, 1917, until Kemble's return to Harvard University after World War I in the fall of 1919. At that time the reformulation of the theory of the vibration-rotation bands in terms of Bohr's assumptions became the first order of business. On the new basis the approximate "harmonics" had an obvious explanation as two-quantum transitions in vibrational quantum number. Bohr's correspondence principle correlated these bands with classical harmonics without requiring an exact harmonic frequency relation. The decided asymmetry of the HCl bands could be explained by the interaction of rotational and vibrational motions.

For the next 8 years Kemble's research activities were devoted to the quantum theory of molecular motions and band spectra. Appointment to the chairmanship of a National Research Council Committee to study molecular spectra in gases led to fruitful collaboration with an outstanding and enthusiastic group of colleagues. It was an exciting period of voluminous scientific correspondence.

In 1928 he was asked to write a synopsis of the new quantum mechanics of Werner Heisenberg and Erwin Schrödinger for the first volume of the series *Reviews of Modern Physics*. In carrying out this assignment in collaboration with E. L. Hill, Kemble's central interest was diverted from the special problems of molecular spectra to the more general questions surrounding the revolutionary new theory. Soon he was at work on the preparation of a comprehensive volume dealing at length with the principles, mathematical methods, and general philosophy of the revised theory of quanta. The problem of digesting and organizing the available material on a level suitable for American graduate students proved formidable. The volume which eventually appeared, *Fundamental Principles of Quantum Mechanics* (1937), was written in the simple language of wave mechanics. By strict adherence to P. W. Bridgman's operational point of view, it avoided much of the metaphysical confusion surrounding the Heisenberg uncertainty principle. Emphasis was placed on the subjective nature of the wave functions used to describe what is known of the state of a physical system. The book achieved no major breakthrough, but it proved useful to many students of physics, and is to be reckoned as Kemble's major contribution to theoretical physics. Byproducts included articles on the Wentzel-Kramers-Brillouin method of approximation, the theory of quantum mechanical measurements, subjective probability, and quantum statistical mechanics. In papers published in 1939, Kemble proposed the elimination of the conflict between the second law of thermodynamics and such fluctuation phenomena as Brownian movement by replacing all statements made in thermodynamics about individual physical systems by parallel statements about Gibbsian ensembles of such systems.

At the close of World War II, Kemble virtually abandoned his career as a mathematical physicist to devote his energies to the problems of general education in the sciences.

Kemble graduated from the Case School of Applied Science with a B.S. in 1911 and took his A.M. in 1914 and Ph.D. in 1917 at Harvard University. In 1911–13 he was an assistant instructor in physics at the Carnegie Institution of Technology, and in 1917–18 an engineering physicist for the Curtiss Motor Corp. He joined the Harvard faculty in 1919, becoming professor of physics in 1930 and serving as chairman of the department in 1940–45. He became professor emeritus in 1957. Kemble was elected to the American Academy of Arts and Sciences in 1922 and to the National Academy of Sciences in 1931.

In addition to his book on quantum mechanics, Kemble was coauthor of *Report on Molecular Spectra in Gases* (1926) and author of *From Geometric Astronomy to the Mechanical Theory of Heat* (1966), Vol. 1 of a projected text, *Physical Science, Its Structure and Development*.

For background information *see* ABSORPTION (ELECTROMAGNETIC RADIATION); MOLECULAR STRUCTURE AND SPECTRA; QUANTUM MECHANICS; VALENCE; VELOCITY in the McGraw-Hill Encyclopedia of Science and Technology.   □

★ KENNEDY, Eugene Patrick

American biochemist
Born Sept. 4, 1919, Chicago, Ill., U.S.A.

KENNEDY WORKED out the pathways for the formation of triglycerides and phospholipids in living cells. With his collaborator S. B. Weiss, he discovered the first cytidine-containing coenzymes and elucidated their function as essential cofactors in the enzyme-catalyzed reactions leading to the formation of phospholipids.

The problem of the biological synthesis of phospholipids had been a subject of interest and speculation for decades before Kennedy began his investigations of lipid biosynthesis in 1952. Studying cellfree enzyme systems from liver with the aid of the isotope-tracer technique, Kennedy found that glycerol, a building block for both triglyceride and phospholipid, must be phosphorylated with the formation of L-glycerol 3-phosphate as the first step in its conversion to a lipid. His experiments, together with the independent work of A. Kornberg, indicated that the next stage involves the acylation of glycerophosphate to form phosphatidic acid, an intermediate central in lipid biosynthesis. It was found that phosphatidic acids may be dephosphorylated by a specific phosphatase, with the formation of α,β-diglycerides. The acylation of such diglycerides by long-chain fatty acyl derivatives of coenzyme A was discovered to lead to the biosynthesis of triglyceride (neutral fat).

An investigation of the pathways for the conversion of choline into the phospholipid lecithin led to the observation that certain commercial preparations of adenosinetriphosphate (ATP) appeared to stimulate this process in particulate fractions from liver, while other preparations did not. Careful analysis revealed that the true cofactor is cytidine 5'-triphosphate (CTP), a trace contaminant in commercial preparations of ATP. Kennedy then synthesized cytidine diphosphate choline and cytidine diphosphate ethanolamine and showed that these nucleotides are the naturally occurring cofactors that are the immediate precursors of phosphatidylcholine and phosphatidylethanolamine. Further work led also to the synthesis of cytidine diphosphate diglyceride and the discovery of its role in the biogenesis of several phospholipids.

Kennedy later turned to studies of the biochemical basis of membrane function. He and his collaborators discovered that a membrane-localized protein is an essential component of the lactose transport system in *Escherichia coli* and devised means for the specific labeling and identification of this protein. It was established that this membrane protein is the long-sought product of the *y* gene of the lac operon (lactose permease).

Kennedy received a B.Sc. in chemistry at De Paul University in 1941 and a Ph.D. in biochemistry at the University of Chicago in 1949. As a Ph.D. candidate, working under the direction of A. L. Lehninger, he was the first to show that the mitochondria are the intracellular site of the reactions of the Krebs cycle, fatty acid oxidation, and oxidative phosphorylation. After postdoctoral work in 1949–50 in the laboratories of H. A. Barker and F. Lipmann, he returned to the department of biochemistry and the Ben May Laboratory of the University of Chicago, remaining until 1956. During 1959–60 he was a senior postdoctoral fellow of the National Science Foundation at Oxford University, England. In 1960 he was named Hamilton Kuhn Professor in the department of biological chemistry in the Harvard Medical School and served as head of that department during 1960–65. He received the American Chemical Society Paul-Lewis Award in 1958, and was elected to the National Academy of Sciences in 1964.

For background information *see* COENZYME; ENZYME; KREBS CYCLE; LIPID in the McGraw-Hill Encyclopedia of Science and Technology. □

★ KENNEDY, George Clayton

American geochemist
Born Sept. 22, 1919, Dillon, Mont., U.S.A.

KENNEDY PIONEERED in the field of high-temperature and high-pressure chemistry in an attempt to understand the physical and chemical environments in which various mineral assemblages originated.

At Harvard Kennedy studied under Louis Caryl Graton, whose primary concern was the genesis of ore deposits rather than their description. Graton approached this problem from a physicochemical point of view and constantly emphasized the lack of real experimental data required to verify those postulated chemical reactions at high temperatures and high pressures that had important bearing on the origin of ore deposits.

In 1941 Kennedy began work on hydrothermal chemistry at moderate to high temperatures and pressures with the hope of recreating in the laboratory the natural environment encountered in the crust and upper mantle of the Earth. His first effort was to determine the solubility of quartz in water at high temperatures and high pressures. Quartz veins—believed to have been emplaced by ascending, high-temperature, predominantly aqueous solutions—are the hosts of gold throughout the world. Kennedy's investigation showed that solids are soluble in gases and that their solubility at a given temperature is linear with the density of the gas and not with the pressure of the gas. He worked out the general relations governing the solubility of solids in supercritical gases. At this time it became evident that no adequate pressure-volume-temperature (PVT) data for water and other gases of geological consequence were available. Consequently, Kennedy next systematically examined the equations of state of such geologically important gases as water and carbon dioxide and made new measurements of volume at temperatures up to 1000°C and pressures up to 2000 atmospheres. Kennedy's continuing study of the transport of solids in gases included examinations of the binary system H_2O-NaCl and H_2O-CO_2, as well as a general investigation of phase equilibria where one or more of the fluids involved was gaseous.

Ore deposits are generally believed to come from escaping high-temperature aqueous solutions derived from the freezing of rock melts in the crust of the Earth. The chemistry of these rock melts varies widely for reasons that are the subject of considerable speculation. Kennedy undertook to examine some of the chemical factors that control the sequence of crystallization and differentiation of freezing rock melts. An unexpected and early discovery was that the state of oxidation of iron in a melt sharply controlled the chemistry of the freezing process and the chemistry of rock differentiates. This early discovery was explored at length by a number of later workers. Kennedy repeated his experiments on the freezing of rock melts at very high pressures—pressures equivalent to depths of 150 km in the Earth's crust—and explored the effect of pressure on sequence of crystallization. This work generated a number of postulates as

to the structure of the Earth's mantle and the variations of seismic velocities with depth in the Earth's crust.

Some specific results of Kennedy's investigations are the following: His studies of cesium revealed a pressure-temperature phase diagram of a totally new type, one exhibiting four liquid-solid or solid-liquid transitions at constant temperature as the pressure is increased. His steam tables are now accepted as the standard by the National Bureau of Standards for the range above 360°, 300 bars. He also produced the only complete phase diagrams on the system NaCl-H_2O at high pressures and temperatures. These data are basic in the problem of producing fresh water from seawater. His studies at high temperatures and high pressures of the systems SiO_2-H_2O, H_2O-CO_2, Al_2O_3-H_2O, the brucite-periclase equilibrium, the stability relations of grossularite-hydrogrossularite, and the hydrothermal synthesis of silicates and other rock-forming minerals contributed basically to knowledge of the geochemistry of the Earth's crust. With Heard and Wasserburg, Kennedy discovered the upper critical end point in the silica-water system. Above this point silica and water are miscible in all proportions. This discovery cleared the way for understanding quartz veins and pegmatites.

Kennedy's researches pointed up the inadequacy of high-pressure and high-temperature apparatus and of calibration techniques for both temperature and pressure under extreme conditions. Simultaneously with his geological investigations, therefore, Kennedy worked on calibration of the high-pressure scale and the design of apparatus. The so-called simple squeeze, which he devolped with D. T. Griggs in 1955, is now a key tool in almost all modern high-pressure laboratories. He greatly improved the precision of the thermoluminescence method for dating young lava flows and clay archeological artifacts.

Kennedy was raised on a cattle and sheep ranch in southwestern Montana. From Harvard University, where he majored in geology, he received his B.S. (1940), A.M. (1941), and Ph.D. (1947). He served on the staff of the U.S. Geological Survey (1942–45) and the Naval Research Laboratory (1945) before returning to Harvard (1945) as a junior fellow. He taught at Harvard from 1949 to 1953, when he became professor of geochemistry at the Institute of Geophysics and Planetary Physics at the University of California in Los Angeles. He received the Mineralogical Society of America Award in 1956, and in 1960 was elected to the American Academy of Arts and Sciences.

For background information *see* HIGH-PRESSURE PHENOMENA; HIGH-PRESSURE PROCESSES; ORE DEPOSITS, GEOCHEMISTRY OF in the McGraw-Hill Encyclopedia of Science and Technology. ☐

★ KETY, Seymour Solomon

*American physiologist, neurochemist, and re-
search psychiatrist*
Born Aug. 25, 1915, Philadelphia, Pa., U.S.A.

KETY'S FIELDS of research included the dynamics of the exchange of substances between capillary and tissue, the circulation and
metabolism of the brain, and the biochemical
aspects of mental state. His principal scientific
achievement was perhaps the measurement of
the blood flow and energy metabolism of the
human brain in health and disease. Although
reliable measurements of these functions had
been made in animals, knowledge of their magnitude in the human brain and their relationship
to normal and abnormal function in this unique
organ was lacking. Reasoning that a nonmetabo-
lized, diffusible substance would be taken up by
the brain as a function of the flow of blood
through it and independently of the rate of
cerebral metabolism, he developed a method
utilizing low concentrations of an inert gas (nitrous oxide) and requiring simple analysis of its
concentration in arterial and cerebral venous
blood during the short time in which it was
equilibrating with the brain. With Carl Schmidt,
he tested some of the theoretical assumptions
involved in the method, compared it with direct
measurement in the rhesus monkey, and, with
numerous collaborators, applied it in the study
of a large number of physiological, psychological, and pathological states in man.

It was found that the human brain receives
one-sixth of the cardiac output and accounts for
one-fifth of the body's oxygen consumption at
rest. Its rate of energy utilization, which is 20
watts in the normal conscious state, may fall
by 50% in anesthesia or in coma. Sleep,
which had been thought to be the result of a
generalized decrease in the activity of the brain,
was found to be associated with a normal rate of
cerebral energy metabolism, suggesting a redistribution rather than a general reduction in
cerebral functional activity in this condition.
In hypertension and cerebrovascular disease,
changes occur in the resistance within the vessels of the brain, which are at first reversible but
may lead ultimately to focal or generalized deficiencies in cerebral nutrition or function.

The inert gas method was applied to the study
of the action of many drugs and procedures used
therapeutically in cerebrovascular disorders.
Studies in man, without interference by pain,
surgery, or anesthesia, added significantly to an
understanding of the normal control of the cerebral circulation, the importance of intrinsic
mechanisms in adjusting blood flow to metabolic
demand, and the role of carbon dioxide in this
process of autoregulation.

From the specialized area of the brain, Kety
went on to examine the general principles involved in the exchange of inert, diffusible substances at the capillary, developing theoretical
formulations which found application in a number of areas. They permitted an explanation of
the differences in speed of induction and recovery in anesthesia by different agents on the
basis of the interactions between simple physical
and physiological factors, and became the basis
of several new techniques for studying regional
blood flow by uptake or clearance of inert,
diffusible tracers.

Kety's studies on the energy metabolism of the
brain led him to an interest in other biochemical
aspects of mental state and in the possible
contributions of biology to psychiatry. In 1959
he became the first editor in chief of the *Journal
of Psychiatric Research*, and he was one of the
founders of the Psychiatric Research Society.

Kety studied at the University of Pennsylvania
(B.A., 1936; M.D., 1940; honorary D.Sc., 1965).
As a medical student and intern, he investigated
the dissociation of the lead-citrate complex. His
application of this complex formation in the
treatment of lead poisoning was a forerunner of
the present use of powerful chelating agents in
the treatment of this condition. On the basis of
this, in 1942 he was awarded a National Research Council fellowship under Joseph Aub at
the Massachusetts General Hospital. He was
successively instructor and assistant professor
during 1943–48 in the department of pharmacology of the School of Medicine of the University
of Pennsylvania, and professor of clinical physiology in the department of Julius Comroe at the
Graduate School of Medicine in 1948–61. In
1951 he joined the National Institute of Mental
Health as its first scientific director, and in 1956
assumed the direction of the Laboratory of
Clinical Science in the Institute. In 1967 he was
appointed professor of psychiatry at the Harvard
Medical School and director of the Psychiatric

Research Laboratories of Massachusetts General Hospital. Recipient of the Theobold Smith Award in 1949, the Max Weinstein Award in 1954, the Stanley Dean Award in 1962, and the Distinguished Service Medal of the Department of Health, Education, and Welfare in 1958, Kety was elected to the National Academy of Sciences in 1962.

For background information *see* BLOOD VESSELS; CARDIOVASCULAR SYSTEM; CIRCULATION; METABOLISM; PHARMACOLOGY in the McGraw-Hill Encyclopedia of Science and Technology. □

★ KIHARA, Hitoshi

Japanese geneticist
Born Oct. 21, 1893, Tokyo, Japan

As a student of plant physiology in the botany department of the College of Agriculture, Hokkaido University, Sapporo, Kihara in 1918 wrote a thesis for his bachelor's degree on the relation between the germination of pollen grains and absorption of water. When his professor, Kwan Koriba, was appointed in 1918 chairman of the newly established Botanical Institute of Kyoto University, Kihara followed him there to become an assistant. Tetsu Sakamura, a pioneer in studies of the polyploid wheat series, was appointed successor of Koriba and was granted a 2-year sojourn abroad to prepare for his new position. Abandoning his chromosome studies in wheat, he gave his materials to Kihara. Work with wheat then became the object of Kihara's life.

Kihara started extensive cytogenetic studies on wheat in Kyoto. One of the earliest contributions in this field was his doctoral thesis, written in German, "Cytologische und genetische Studien bei wichtigen Getreidearten mit besonderer Rücksicht auf das Verhalten der Chromosomen und die Sterilität in den Bastarden" (1924). At that time, the heredity of species hybrids was scarcely investigated because of their sterility, and it appeared to be lawless and fortuitous. Using the fairly fertile pentaploid hybrid between tetraploid emmer and hexaploid common wheat (for example, *Triticum durum* × *T. vulgare*), Kihara discovered the laws governing the change in chromosome number and fertility in the F_2 and following generations. Briefly, in the first maturation division of the pentaploid hybrid, 14 bivalents and 7 univalents are found ($14_{II} + 7_I$). The 14 bivalents behave normally throughout the meiotic divisions. But the univalents split equationally in the first division, and are distributed at random in the second. The gametic chromosome number may be represented by $14 + i$, where i has values ranging from 0 to 7 with frequencies corresponding to $(a + b)^7$. The value of a and b is 0.5, if the distribution of univalents is at random and no loss of univalents occurs. There are some irregularities, such as lagging of the daughter halves of the univalents, which may cause elimination and fragmentation of the chromosomes. The value of a and b is therefore not equal. Also it seems that the univalents do not distribute at random. The actual frequency of the female gametes is somewhat different from that expected from $(0.7 + 0.3)^7$ or $(0.6 + 0.4)^7$. The frequency curve is very flat.

On the other hand, there is a selection of male gametes in favor of those with chromosome numbers approaching those of the parents. By selfing of the pentaploid hybrids, Kihara could obtain all possible chromosome numbers (28–42) in the F_2. Based on the combination of the numbers of bivalents and univalents, the F_2 plants were divided into two groups: one with viable and the other with nonviable chromosome combinations. The viable combinations were divided into two subgroups. One ranging in chromosome numbers from 28 to 34 (14_{II}, $14_{II} + 1_I$, $14_{II} + 2_I$, . . . $14_{II} + 6_I$) was the chromosome number diminishing group, because it reverts in the subsequent generations to 28; the other group, with chromosome numbers 36–42 ($15_{II} + 6_I$, $16_{II} + 5_I$, $17_{II} + 4_I$, $18_{II} + 3_I$, $19_{II} + 2_I$, $20_{II} + 1_I$, and 21_{II}) was called the chromosome-number increasing group, because their progeny returns to the 42-chromosome condition of the other parent. The nonviable (or sterile) chromosome combinations are those whose progeny cannot revert to the parental chromosome number (14_{II} or 21_{II}). Examples of such combinations are 15_{II}, 16_{II}, 17_{II}, and so on. They are rather rare in the progeny. If found, they are dwarf and highly or completely sterile. The same laws were later found to govern various other interspecific hybrids, for example, triploid *Avena* and *Allium* hybrids.

Kihara adopted H. Winkler's term "genome" for a set of chromosomes representing a fundamental genetic and physiological system whose completeness is indispensable for normal development and reproduction. A series of genome analyses in *Triticum* and *Aegilops* was undertaken in 1930 and was completed in 1951 with the concluding review of F. Lilienfeld (genome analysis X).

From 1935 on, Kihara investigated the hybrid between *Aegilops caudata* (female) and *T. vulgare erythrospermum* (male), which he successively backcrossed to the latter as the male parent. This series resulted in a substitution line having *caudata* cytoplasm and *vulgare* nucleus. This study opened a new field of nucleus substitution in wheat. Together with his collaborators, Kihara succeeded in producing many substitution lines, using various species of wheat and *Aegilops* as donors of cytoplasm, for example, *A. ovata*, *A. umbellulata*, *A. speltoides*, *T. monococcum*, *T. timopheevi*, and so on. They were called by Kihara cytoplasm-nucleus hybrids; they usually show male sterility but are morphologically almost identical to the pollen parents. However, abnormalities in morphology and physiology were recognized to a certain extent. Kihara found also male fertility restoration genes. Some of them he found to be very efficient; this opened up the possibility of hybrid wheat breeding.

In 1944 Kihara published his view that *Aegilops squarrosa* must be one of the ancestors of common wheat. This was proved beyond doubt by the synthesis of 6x strains from the selfing of a triploid hybrid, *T. dicoccoides* × *A. squarrosa* (Kihara and Lilienfeld, 1949).

Besides studies on the evolution of wheat and its relatives, Kihara used *Rumex*, *Fragaria*, *Citrullus*, *Celosia*, *Oryza*, and others for cytological and genetic materials. The discovery of sex chromosomes in a higher plant, *Rumex acetosa*, in 1923 and the classification of polyploidy into auto- and allopolyploidy in 1926 were both achieved with T. Ono. In 1966 Kihara returned to the interest of his youth in pollen grains and investigated the behavior of three nuclei in the germinating pollen grain.

Two years after his graduation in 1918 from the College of Agriculture, Hokkaido University, Kihara became associated with Kyoto University. From 1925 to 1927 he studied genetics in the department of Carl Correns, the director of the Kaiser Wilhelm Institute (now the Max Planck Institute) in Berlin-Dahlem. He held a full professorship at Kyoto University from 1927 until 1955, when he was appointed director of the National Institute of Genetics in Misima. He established the Kihara Institute for Biological Research in Kyoto in 1942. Later it was moved to Yokohama, where he remained its director. He was president of the Genetics Society of Japan in 1944–49. In 1955 he organized and led the Kyoto University Scientific Expedition to the Karakoram and Hindu Kush ranges in southern Asia. He collected wheat and related wild species in Afghanistan and Iran. The results of the expedition were published by Kyoto University in eight volumes. In 1943 he was awarded the Emporer's Medal by the Japan Academy for his cytogenetic studies in wheat, and the Order of Culture in 1948. He was honored by the Japanese government as a Man of Distinctive Merit in 1951. He received the Leonard H. Vaughan Award for his paper "Seedless Watermelons" from the American Society for Horticultural Science in 1952. He was elected a member of the Japan Academy in 1948 and a foreign associate of the U.S. National Academy of Sciences in 1958.

For background information *see* BREEDING (PLANT); CHROMOSOME THEORY OF HEREDITY; GENE ACTION; POLYPLOIDY in the McGraw-Hill Encyclopedia of Science and Technology. □

★ KING, Charles Glen

American biochemist and nutritionist
Born Oct. 22, 1896, Entiat, Wash., U.S.A.

KING'S FIRST independent research interest at the University of Pittsburgh related to the molecular structure and properties of fatty acid glycerides. Interest in the isomeric and homologous forms of the lipids led to comparative studies with the enzymes pancreatic lipase and liver esterase. Inspiration for this area of investigation was kindled by Emil Fischer's paper showing that nearly all of the earlier reports on the structure of fatty acid glycerides had been confused by unsuspected shifts from the beta to the alpha position during synthesis or comparable changes in the ring structure of intermediate compounds used to form esters.

Interest in vitamin C (ascorbic acid) developed during King's studies with H. C. Sherman at Columbia University in 1926–27, while on leave of absence from the University of Pittsburgh. King decided to undertake isolation of the active material upon returning to Pittsburgh. Sherman had specialized in developing vitamin bioassays so that nutritional values in foods could be established on a more quantitative basis. Five vitamins were recognized at that time on a biological basis, A, B_1, B_2, C, and D. None of the vitamins had been satisfactorily identified as a specific chemical. Assays were very time consuming and expensive, required large quantities of test material, and were only approximations at best. Although many laboratories were known to be working on the other vitamins, relatively few chemists had reported progress in attempts to isolate vitamin C because of its great tendency to lose its activity and the tedious requirement for conducting 90-day assays with about 50 guinea pigs. S. S. Silva in England and N. Bezssonoff in France, however, had published a few papers indicating that concentrates could be prepared in the laboratory. There was no indication that anyone in the United States was working on the problem, even though it was reasonably clear that the vitamin was an important agent in plant and animal metabolism and in public health—particularly among small children, military personnel, and explorers. (During World War I it was estimated that about 50% of the Russian army developed clinical evidence of scurvy.)

In cooperation with W. A. Waugh, the sixth graduate student to work with him in the vitamin C studies, King succeeded in isolating the crystalline vitamin in the fall of 1931 and established its identity with a "hexuronic acid" of unknown structure, which had been reported in the literature as a reducing material extracted from adrenal glands and two plant sources at Cambridge University.

There rapidly followed studies of chemical methods of analysis; distribution in human, animal, and plant tissues; effects upon specific enzymes and total respiration; effects of different intakes in relation to health; and sensitiveness to oxidation catalysis by ionic or protein-combined copper in synthetic or natural products (enzymes). In guinea pigs a wide margin was shown between the quantity of ascorbic acid required to prevent scurvy (0.5 mg/day) and the quantity (5–8 mg/day) that gave roughly maximum protection of the teeth and other tissues when animals were subjected to moderate stress by diphtheria toxin or placed on long-term tests for production of viable young.

In early investigations of the biosynthesis of ascorbic acid, rats were found to respond in a remarkable manner to the feeding of small quantities of a great variety of organic compounds and especially those that serve as nerve depressants, such as chloretone and the barbiturates. Urinary excretions rose to more than 100 times their initial quantities. This discovery later reached special usefulness in identifying precursors and end products of ascorbic acid metabolism and, most peculiar of all, a maximum quantity of synthesis and excretion when carcinogenic hydrocarbons were fed (J. J. Burns).

Biosynthesis of the vitamin from D-glucose without rupture of the carbon chain was shown clearly by feeding rats glucose with radiocarbon atoms in positions 1 or 6 or uniformly in all positions and then determining the position of each carbon in the C^{14} ascorbic acid formed. The successive steps then could be identified in relationship to glucuronic acid as an intermediate product. It was interesting to find in similar tests with guinea pigs that glucuronic acid was similarly formed but was eliminated instead of ascorbic acid—an enzyme essential to catalyze one step on the ascorbic synthesis was missing in the guinea pig, as shown later by B. C. Guha in man, in other primates, and in two additional animals identified in India. Chief end products of the vitamin, other than carbon dioxide, were found to be oxalate and a pentose, part of which is normally cycled back to form glucose and glycogen.

During the war years King's research dealt with aviation feeding, in which it was shown that preflight and in-flight meals or snacks relatively high in carbohydrate add about 3000 ft in altitude tolerance during the normal interval between meals, including tests with untrained volunteer subjects and experienced pilots. The effect generally is quite clear in the range of 15,000-ft elevation above sea level.

King received a B.S. (1918) at Washington State College. Subsequent to military service, he received an M.S. (1920) and a Ph.D. (1923) at the University of Pittsburgh, where he was invited to remain on the faculty; he advanced to a full professorship, later becoming director of the Buhl Foundation research programs in chemistry, physics, and biology and also chairman of the faculty council. In 1942 he became scientific director of the newly formed Nutrition Foundation, and was appointed visiting professor of chemistry at Columbia University, then full professor on a part-time basis; he became emeritus professor in 1962. At the Nutrition Foundation he advanced to executive director and then president before retiring in 1963. He was then appointed associate director of the Institute of Nutrition Science in the School of Public Health and Administrative Medicine at Columbia University and a part-time consultant on nutrition with the Rockefeller Foundation. Upon retirement from the Institute he was appointed director of grants management at the St. Luke's Hospital Center and special lecturer at the Institute. King's awards included the Pittsburgh Award and the Charles F. Spencer Award of the

American Chemical Society, the Nicholas Appert Award of the Institute of Food Technologists, the Bicentennial Award in Science of the City of Pittsburgh, and the Conrad A. Elvehjem Award of the American Institute of Nutrition. He was elected to the National Academy of Sciences in 1951.

For background information *see* ASCORBIC ACID; BIOASSAY; VITAMIN in the McGraw-Hill Encyclopedia of Science and Technology.   □

★ KING, Philip Burke

American geologist
Born Sept. 24, 1903, Richmond, Ind., U.S.A.

KING'S INTERESTS and methods of scientific inquiry were those of the field geologist, who obtains his data from the rocks exposed at the Earth's surface and from them derives inferences as to the history and behavior of the Earth. He was especially interested in the sedimentary rocks, and interpreted the environments in which they were originally laid down and the relation of these environments to tectonic movements that were taking place in the Earth's crust.

King did his early field work (1925) in the Marathon region, an area of about 1600 square miles in the trans-Pecos part of Texas, where varied rocks and structures that were formed during Paleozoic time have been stripped of the cover of younger strata that conceal them elsewhere in this part of the Southwest. Because of the semiarid climate the Paleozoic rocks are well exposed, making the Marathon region a virtual outdoor laboratory for the investigator.

His first field work in the Marathon region was on Permian marine strata that form a sequence about 7000 ft thick on its northern side in the Glass Mountains. In this work he was greatly assisted by his brother and collaborator, Robert E. King, who at that time was investigating the Permian fossils, many of which were new

to science. The Permian strata, they discovered, were quite differently arranged from those with which they had hitherto been familiar. Instead of an orderly sequence, whose component strata extended laterally for great distances, those of the Glass Mountains were a disorderly array of discontinuous bodies of carbonate rocks, shale, and sandstone, interspersed with lenses of gravelly conglomerate. As the work progressed, it became apparent that this array had been built on the southern margin of a former marine basin. The conglomerate clasts had been eroded from highlands farther south, the carbonate bodies had formed as reefs or banks in well-aerated waters on the edge of the basin, and the shales and sandstones were the deposits of the basin floor. Nevertheless, at the close of their investigation of the Glass Mountains, many features of the rocks were still imperfectly interpreted; some of these features are little understood even today.

An opportunity to clarify the Permian stratigraphy of western Texas came later (1934), when King began work in the southern Guadalupe Mountains, about 150 mi northwest of the Glass Mountains. There are about 4000 ft of Permian strata in the southern Guadalupes, much less disturbed by later movements than in the Glass Mountains and much more boldly exposed on steep mountain slopes and canyon walls, permitting three-dimensional reconstructions. Many features of the Guadalupe Mountains had by that time been described by a succession of geologists, but they had been puzzled by a disorderly arrangement of the strata that was much like that in the Glass Mountains. Drilling for oil to the east had demonstrated that the Guadalupe Mountains, like the Glass Mountains, lay on the margin of the former large marine basin referred to, but in this case on its northwestern rather than its southern side.

During King's field work much attention was given to the Capitan Limestone, which stands in lofty white cliffs at the summit of the mountains. The Capitan had already been interpreted as a barrier-reef deposit by other geologists, and many observations were made by King on its details—the marine organisms that built the growing parts at its summit, the talus and slide debris on its basinward flank, and the manner in which the reef rocks intertongue toward the basin with very different deeper-water deposits. Because of the steep mountainous relief, it was also possible to observe the structure of the strata beneath the Capitan and thus to determine its origin. During earlier parts of Permian time crustal movements downflexed the strata toward the basin, producing marked contrasts in depths of water, and reef deposits began to grow in shallower waters at the upper edge of the flexure. Once initiated by crustal forces, the reef became self-perpetuating, until the reef-building organisms were destroyed by an increase in the salinity of the waters of the basin; during the last part of Permian time the reef was buried by evaporite deposits.

Before working in the Guadalupe Mountains, however, King studied another aspect of sedimentary rocks and their structures—the interaction between sedimentation and mountain building. The southern part of the Marathon region is formed of Paleozoic rocks older than Permian and had undergone several periods of mountain building before Permian time. Erosion of these mountains produced the clasts that formed the conglomerates in the Glass Mountains. Field work in 1929–31 revealed a sequence extending from the Cambrian to the Pennsylvanian, laid down in a geosyncline. The older geosynclinal deposits (Cambrian, Ordovician, and Devonian) were laid down in deep water under quiet crustal conditions—thin deposits of shales, muddy limestones, and many siliceous beds (chert and novaculite). A dramatic change took place in Mississippian time, when clastic deposits (flysch) succeeded the novaculite and eventually filled the geosyncline to a thickness of 10,000 to 15,000 ft. Microscopic study of the flysch deposits showed that they were derived from heterogeneous sources—from granites and schists of the basement and from older Paleozoic deposits—and that the flysch was related to the initial orogenic pulses of the geosyncline, when tectonic ridges were raised and adjoining troughs were deeply depressed. High in the flysch sequence King discovered dramatic evidence of these early orogenic pulses—beds of giant boulders composed of earlier geosynclinal deposits, shelf carbonates, and Precambrian basement. These beds were derived from sources that had been sharply uplifted and from which the boulders had broken off and slid into the deep troughs.

Field work also revealed the structures of the geosynclinal deposits—a succession of folds and faults trending northeastward across the prevailing but much younger Cordilleran grain; these were a small-scale replica of the well-known "Appalachian structure" of the eastern states. The resemblance suggested, moreover, that these structures were a far-western prolongation of the Appalachian mountain system. Many details of the history of these structures could be deduced, beginning with low-angle thrusts that were later overwhelmed by folding and ending with the low-angle thrusts farthest northwest that had formed after the time of folding. These structural events could be correlated with the record of sedimentary strata that were being laid down in the region in the later part of the geosynclinal cycle.

In 1940–44 the wartime search for strategic minerals by the U.S. Geological Survey afforded King an opportunity to investigate the Appalachian Mountains in Virginia and Tennessee. The insights gained in the Marathon region made it possible to unravel and interpret the much larger and more massive folds and low-angle thrust faults of that region.

Throughout these investigations of sedimentary rocks and their structures, he was aware of their broader significance and developed many regional syntheses, resulting in publications of a general nature—on the Permian stratigraphy of the Southwest, on the Appalachian structure of the Southeast, and the like. Even broader in scope was *Evolution of North America* (1959), which evolved from a series of lectures. These larger concepts could also be represented on maps, so he made important contributions to the *Tectonic Map of the United States* (1944; 2d ed. 1962) and later compiled the *Tectonic Map of North America* (1968).

King's early years were spent largely in Iowa, where he graduated from the State University (B.A., 1924). His father, Irving King, was a professor of psychology and education, and provided his three sons with an environment of scientific and scholarly inquiry. After his graduation King went to Texas with an oil company, and was assigned to the Permian Basin region of the western part of the state (later to become one of the great oil provinces of the nation). Then he continued his studies at Yale University (Ph.D., 1929). Most of his career from 1930 onward was spent as a geologist with the U.S. Geological Survey, although he taught at universities for short periods (Texas, 1925–27; Arizona, 1929–30; University of California at Los Angeles, 1954–56). In the autumn of 1965 he was a visiting lecturer at the University of Moscow. In 1965 he was awarded the Penrose Medal of the Geological Society of America and the Distinguished Service Medal of the U.S. Department of the Interior. He was elected to the American Academy of Arts and Sciences in 1966.

For background information *see* GEOSYNCLINE; STRATIGRAPHY; TECTONIC PATTERNS in the McGraw-Hill Encyclopedia of Science and Technology.   □

KLUYVER, Albert Jan

Dutch biochemist
Born June 3, 1888, Breda, Netherlands
Died May 14, 1956, Delft, Netherlands

WHILE INVESTIGATING the biochemical activities of microorganisms, Kluyver enunciated the principle of unity in biochemistry. This principle became the cornerstone of bacterial biochemistry and had significant repercussions in microbiology as a whole.

The discovery of bacteria by Anton van Leeu-

wenhoek about 1683 led to the investigation of these and other microorganisms, providing the basis for the discipline of microbiology. Through the studies of Louis Pasteur, Robert Koch, and others the world of microorganisms evolved into a bewildering population of apparently unrelated microscopic life. Microorganisms were shown to play vital roles in a host of organic processes, such as fermentation and reduction, and each of these microbial activities constituted a phenomenon seemingly having nothing in common with any other. Kluyver believed, as had Pasteur before him, that this diversity in metabolic processes presented the opportunity for a unique trend of study to discover the unifying principle underlying the diversity. He coined the term "comparative biochemistry" to describe the methods by which such a study could be undertaken. He based his concept on studies of glucose fermentation by yeast that had shown this apparently complex process to be a series of relatively simple chemical changes. He was convinced that this process was a common feature of the metabolism of microorganisms and that a simplification would reduce to an underlying principle.

Kluyver began his investigations at the Technical University in Delft, Netherlands. By 1924, working with F. J. G. de Leeuw, he had discovered what he believed to be the first confirmation of his idea: When growing on a medium of glucose and calcium carbonate, *Acetobacter suboxydans*, an aerobic beer organism, deposited crystals of calcium-5-ketogluconate. Not only was the conversion virtually quantitative, but further investigation established that mixtures of numerous sugar alcohols and of glycerol were oxidized to corresponding keto compounds by *A. suboxydans* and other *Acetobacter* varieties. This and other evidence collected by Kluyver and by his students led him to propose that glucose was catabolized in a series of steps through gluconic and ketogluconic acids.

He and his students continued investigations along various lines. Among the areas of study were yeast fermentation, fermentation by coliform bacteria, and butyl alcohol–butyric acid fermentation. By 1926 Kluyver had obtained sufficient evidence to justify his postulation of the unity in biochemistry. However, it was not until 1930, as evidenced in a series of lectures at the University of London, that he began to consider the principle to be more than just a working hypothesis. In his proposal all catabolic reactions, both aerobic and anaerobic, were a series of related reactions; in addition, all biochemical changes—with the exception of hydrolysis—were considered to be one of four forms of hydrogen transfer.

The work of Kluyver and his students provided the starting point for the utilization of bacteria as tools in biochemical investigations. The studies of numerous details of biochemical processes with the aid of bacteria has helped elucidate the detailed mechanisms of the breakdown and synthesis of most of the important groups of substances.

Because of his involvement with the students at the Technical University, it is difficult to separate Kluyver's work from that of his school. Under his direction the school made a number of significant contributions to microbiology. For example, at Kluyver's instigation the university built the most comprehensive collection of yeasts in the world. From this has emanated a wealth of data on the morphology, physiology, and classification of yeasts.

The son of a professor of mathematics at the University of Leiden, Kluyver received his degree in chemical engineering from the Technical University in Delft in 1910. He accepted an assistantship to G. van Iterson, a professor of microscopical anatomy, at the university while continuing his studies. Although Kluyver received his degree of Doctor of Technical Science in 1914, he remained at the university as van Iterson's assistant until 1916. Then he was appointed a consultant for the Dutch East Indies to the Department of Agriculture, Industry, and Commerce, and moved to Buitenzorg, Java. In 1919 he resigned this post to accept a position as chemical adviser to Insulinde Ltd. in Bandoeng, Java. He remained in the East Indies until 1921, when he returned to Delft to assume the chair of general and applied microbiology and the directorship of the Microbiological Laboratory at the Technical University, which he held until his death. His awards include the Emil Christian Hansen Gold Medal from Denmark in 1946 and the Copley Medal of the Royal Society of London in 1954. He was elected a foreign associate of the U.S. National Academy of Sciences in 1950 and a foreign member of the Royal Society of London in 1952.

Kluyver wrote *Microbiologie en Industrie*

(1922); *The Chemical Activities of Micro-organisms* (1931); and *The Microbe's Contribution to Biology*, with C. B. van Niel (1956).

For background information *see* BACTERIAL METABOLISM; BACTERIOLOGY; BIOCHEMISTRY in the McGraw-Hill Encyclopedia of Science and Technology.   □

★ KNIPLING, Edward Fred

American entomologist
Born Mar. 20, 1909, Port Lavaca, Tex., U.S.A.

INSECTS AND related pests annoy and transmit diseases to man and animals and destroy plants grown for food, fiber, and timber. Scientists have developed ways to deal with insect pests through the use of chemical insecticides, by pitting useful insects against those that are destructive, by breeding insect-resistant plant varieties, and by applying cultural and sanitary measures. Such methods are often effective, and through their use it has been possible to compete with insects, even though these pests still take a large share of the world's potential food supply and the diseases they transmit are a continuing threat to man's health and welfare. Knipling made notable contributions to the welfare of mankind through research on various methods of controlling insects. During World War II he led a group of scientists in the development of DDT and various other insecticides and repellents for protecting military personnel from annoyance and disease-spreading insects. However, Knipling devoted most of his research efforts on biological and other more selective ways to deal with insects and other pest problems.

In 1938, while conducting research on the screwworm fly, a major livestock pest, Knipling conceived and proposed a new concept of insect population control, which involves the use of the insect for its own destruction. Observing the mating habits of the fly in laboratory cages, he noted that females of the screwworm fly appeared to be monogamous in mating habits. Also by drawing on information obtained by his colleagues on the biology, ecology, behavior, population dynamics, and methods of rearing the insect, he reasoned that it might be possible to control the pest by overflooding the natural population with reared flies that were sterile or that carried some conditional, lethal genetic traits. The potentialities of this approach to the control of an insect were first tested, theoretically, by establishing hypothetical screwworm population models and then calculating the effects to be expected by introducing sterile insects into such hypothetical populations. The results of such theoretical studies were so impressive that he consulted many biologists for their views regarding the feasibility of this approach to pest control and methods of achieving sterility or lethal genetic effects. His theories were met with general skepticism, but he persisted in his efforts to have the method investigated. Research to explore this approach to pest control was delayed because of his assignments on military entomology research during World War II. After the war he was placed in charge of the Department of Agriculture's research program on livestock insects. He urged his colleague, R. C. Bushland, to undertake investigations on the sterility approach to insect control and helped develop plans for the research. H. J. Muller, noted radiation biologist, had shown that fruit flies exposed to x-rays were rendered sterile without adversely affecting normal vigor and sexual behavior. Drawing on this information, R. C. Bushland determined the dosage of x-rays required to sterilize screwworm flies and demonstrated in laboratory cages that sterilized males would compete almost fully with normal males in mating with the females. Normal females mated to sterile males deposited sterile eggs. When sterile and fertile males were present in equal numbers, about half the normal females deposited sterile eggs. When the sterile males exceeded the fertile males by a ratio of 9:1, about 90% of the normal females in the population deposited sterile eggs.

The laboratory studies supported theoretical calculations. However, extensive and difficult field tests were required to demonstrate the effectiveness and practicability of the method.

Knipling arranged for a pilot field test to be conducted on the 170-sq-mi island of Curaçao in the Netherlands Antilles. This experiment demonstrated that the sustained release of reared and sterilized screwworm flies for about 6 months, or during a period spanning about four generations of the natural population, led to the complete elimination of the natural screwworm population. This successful demonstration led to the initiation of a screwworm eradication program in Florida and other southeastern states. The program, carried out jointly by the U.S.

Department of Agriculture and the Florida live-stock industry, involved techniques and procedures never before utilized in the annals of biology. A screwworm-rearing plant was constructed and put into operation in 1958. Flies were reared and sterilized at the rate of about 50,000,000 per week, and they were released in an area of about 75,000 sq mi. Twenty aircraft operating daily were required to disperse the flies. Within about 18 months the natural screwworm population in the southeastern United States was eliminated. A pest that cost the livestock industry in the Southeast up to $20,000,000 each year was eliminated at a cost of less than $10,000,000. It has been estimated that savings to the industry in the Southeast during the 10 years since the program was initiated would aggregate $200,000,000.

A larger, more difficult control program was subsequently initiated in the southwestern United States, starting in 1962. This program, still under way, requires the rearing and release of up to 150,000,000 sterile screwworm flies per week in an area involving more than 200,000 sq mi in southwestern United States and in northern Mexico. It is not possible to eliminate permanently the screwworm population in this region, because the insect ranges southward into Central America. However, the natural population of the insect is being held to virtually noneconomic levels by the continuous release of sterile screwworm flies in a 200-mi barrier zone. The cost of the program amounts to about $5,000,000 each year, but livestock growers estimate that losses by the insect are reduced by as much as $100,000,000 each year. Mexico and United States officials are now studying plans to undertake a joint program that would eliminate screwworms from all of the western United States and Mexico.

The sterility method involving the rearing and release of sterile insects has certain advantages as well as disadvantages in comparison with other insect control methods. Knipling pointed out that the method is not the answer to all insect problems. However, he believed that the method would help control or eliminate a number of highly destructive insects.

The theoretical trend of a natural insect population, subjected to competition with released sterile males and sterile females that are fully competitive in mating vigor and behavior, in comparison with the trend of a normal all fertile population may be noted in Tables 1 and 2.

Table 1. Characteristic trend of a normal all-fertile insect population with capacity to increase fivefold each generation

Generation	Number of fertile insects
1	1,000,000
2	5,000,000
3	25,000,000
4	125,000,000

As may be noted, the postulated effect on an insect population subjected to competition with a high ratio of released sterile insects is impressive. One unique feature of this approach to insect population suppression is the progressive increase in efficiency of the method as the natural population declines. When the natural population of an insect is high, it may be impractical to rear and release enough sterile insects to suppress the natural population. However, the sterility procedure might be the most effective and practical way to eliminate or suppress the same insect when the natural population is low. These features are in contrast with the efficiency of other methods of insect control. Insecticides, for example, may be highly efficient when the natural population is high. However, it requires the same dosage of insecticide to kill a given percentage of an insect population whether the population consists of a million insects or a hundred insects. Knipling stressed the point that these basic differences in the effects of different methods of suppressing insect populations open up many new possibilities for integrating the use of sterile insects with other methods of control for suppressing or eradicating insect populations.

Knipling's colleagues in the Entomology Research Division of the Department of Agriculture showed that the sterile insect release method is practical for suppressing or eliminating populations of several species of tropical fruit flies that are major pests of fruits and vegetables in many areas. Scientists are investigating ways of employing sterile insects to control a wide range of insects in many parts of the world. Substantial progress has been made in

Table 2. Characteristic trend of a natural insect population competing with an overwhelming but constant population of sterile insects released into the environment (insects reproducing produce a fivefold increase in progeny)

Generation	Number of fertile insects	Number of sterile insects	Ratio of sterile to fertile insects	Insects reproducing
1	1,000,000	9,000,000	9:1	100,000
2	500,000	9,000,000	18:1	26,316
3	131,625	9,000,000	68:1	191
4	9,535	9,000,000	942:1	10
5	50	9,000,000	180,000:1	0

developing the technique for controlling or eventually even eradicating populations of major harmful insects, such as the cotton boll weevil, tsetse fly, codling moth, tobacco hornworm, sugarcane borer, and gypsy moth.

The concept of managing pest populations by utilizing the sterility principle was broadened by Knipling in 1959, when he postulated the theoretical advantage of sterilizing rather than killing pests in the natural environment. He calculated that, if a high percentage of a pest population in the natural environment is sexually sterilized without adversely affecting sexual vigor and behavior, the adverse impact on reproduction of the pest population will be vastly greater than that produced by killing the same percentage by the conventional procedure. The advantages of this approach to pest population management should apply to vertebrate as well as invertebrate pests.

The suppression of natural vertebrate pest populations by this approach should be particularly useful and more acceptable to the public than the conventional killing method. The greater efficiency of the method can be explained by the following example. If a natural pest population consists of 1,000,000 individuals and 90% are killed with a pesticide, this leaves 100,000 to reproduce. If each reproducing pest gives rise to two progeny that reproduce in the second generation, and if half the parents survive, the total population in the second generation will consist of 250,000 individuals, all of which will be capable of reproducing. On the other hand, if 90% of 1,000,000 pests are sterilized by a chemical sterilant used in the same way as the pesticide, the population will consist of 900,000 sterile individuals and 100,000 potentially fertile individuals. By chance matings, only 10,000 of the potentially fertile individuals will actually produce progeny. Thus, only 20,000 progeny will be produced in comparison with 200,000 produced by the 100,000 survivors of the chemical pesticide treatment. The added advantage of the sterilization method does not stop with the first generation. If the pest is long-lived and if the sterilization procedure is permanent for the life of the pest, the surviving sterilized individuals will continue to affect adversely reproduction in subsequent generations. If half the 900,000 sterile individuals survive to mate in the next generation, 450,000 sterile individuals will compete with 50,000 fertile survivors of the original population plus the 20,000 fertile progeny. Thus, the ratio of sterile to fertile individuals in the second generation will be 450,000 to 70,000. Only about 19,000 progeny will be produced. In contrast, all of the population subjected to the killing agent, which theoretically will consist of 250,000 individuals in the second generation, will be capable of producing 500,000 progeny. The population containing the sterile organisms will continue to be influenced by the sterile individuals until all of the sterilized organisms disappear because of natural causes, whereas the population subjected to the killing agent will continue to reproduce to its maximum potential. Entomologists and vertebrate biologists throughout the world are now investigating ways of inducing sterility in pest animals in order to take advantage of the great potential of this approach to pest population management.

A farmer's son, Knipling attended Texas A & M University as an agricultural student, majoring in entomology. After receiving his B.S. in 1930, he enrolled as a graduate student in entomology and parasitology at Iowa State University, receiving his M.S. in 1932 and his Ph.D. in 1947. He became an employee of the U.S. Department of Agriculture in 1931, and for a number of years he conducted or directed research on the control of a variety of insects that affect the health of man and animals. His responsibilities and interests were broadened to include insects affecting crops when, in 1954, he was made director of the Entomology Research Division, Agricultural Research Service, U.S. Department of Agriculture, with headquarters at Beltsville, Md. He received worldwide recognition for his contributions to many aspects of entomology, but became best known for originating the sterility concepts of pest population control and for directing the research leading to its practical application. He received many awards, including the President's Medal for Merit (1958), the U.S. Army Typhus Commission Medal (1958), the U.S. Department of Agriculture Distinguished Service Award, the Hoblitzelle National Award (1960), the Rockefeller Public Service Award (1966), and the National Medal of Science (1966). He was elected to the National Academy of Sciences in 1966.

Knipling authored or coauthored over 150 scientific papers.

For background information *see* AGRICULTURAL SCIENCE (PLANT); INSECT CONTROL, BIOLOGICAL; INSECTICIDE; RADIATION INJURY (BIOLOGY) in the McGraw-Hill Encyclopedia of Science and Technology.   □

★ KNOPOFF, Leon

American geophysicist
Born July 1, 1925, Los Angeles, Calif., U.S.A.

KNOPOFF FORMULATED mathematical solutions in a general form to the equations of elastic-wave motion. Solutions to the problems of the scattering and diffraction of elastic waves were obtained for a number of specific geometries. By means of this catalog of solutions, many of the

complex wiggles observed on a seismogram could be correlated qualitatively with the physical processes that produced them. A number of these results proved valuable in the development of techniques for improving signal-to-noise ratios in seismic observation procedures. For example, it was found that one of the principal causes of seismic noise is the generation of Rayleigh waves by body waves incident upon topographic irregularities at the surface of the Earth. Further, it was found that the processes that govern the generation of scattered seismic shear waves are much more potent than those that generate scattered compression waves.

Knopoff launched an investigation into the nature of attenuation of seismic waves in the Earth's interior. Starting with the postulate that the nature of attenuation in the solid parts of the Earth's interior is similar to that found in solids in the laboratory, attenuation of elastic waves in solids in the laboratory was studied. For almost every material on which data could be obtained, it was found, for small oscillatory strains, that the attenuation factors are independent of the amplitude of the strain and increase as the first power of the frequency of excitation. Mathematical analysis showed that linear processes, such as viscoelasticity, were inadequate to account for the frequency dependence of the attenuation factors. A simple mechanism to account for the observations was proposed, involving a nonlinear frictional process. When the postulate concerning the frequency dependence was extended to the materials composing the mantle of the Earth, interpretation of available data on observations of the attenuation of seismic surface waves showed that the upper parts of the Earth's mantle attenuate seismic waves considerably more than do the lower parts.

With R. Burridge, Knopoff investigated the possibility that a mechanical process could be found that is responsible for the many-faceted types of earthquake statistics relating to the times of occurrence and the energy-frequency relationships. In studies on stick-slip friction, it was found that laboratory and theoretical models could be constructed that gave rise to statistical distributions of events similar to those observed in nature; even aftershocks following a catastrophic event were produced in the models. Basically, the models must have several degrees of freedom to account for the different magnitudes, must have nonlinear behavior, and, especially, must be unstable during the earthquake motion. It was found that small shocks are necessary preludes to larger shocks; small shocks produce stress concentrations at the termini of ruptured sections of fault structures. This circumstance provides a means by which energy is rapidly stored in parts of the structure in which the energy was formerly small. It was found that, even in large seismic events, only a part of the available potential energy is released as frictional heat and seismic radiation. Inhomogeneity plays a strong role in starting and stopping the seismic event. Aftershocks could be simulated by the introduction of viscosity into the system.

Interpretation of observations of distant seismic events with instruments located around the Alps and around the western basin of the Mediterranean led to the conclusion that the low-seismic-velocity channel of the upper mantle of the Earth, found more or less at depths of 80 to 225 km below the surface, was to be found in these regions as well. The velocity of shear waves in the channel varies significantly over short horizontal distances, and seems to be uncorrelated with the surface topography of mountainous and oceanic regions. This suggests that the forces that deform the Earth to create these surface features have their origin at rather shallow depths in the Earth, of the order of the depths to the top of the low-velocity channel. The presence of a first-order discontinuity in seismic velocity at a depth of the order of 225 km, suggested by I. Lehmann, was confirmed.

Following a suggestion of W. Elsasser, Knopoff studied the equations of state for solids at high pressures and, in particular, how to extend available laboratory data on solids to ultrahigh pressures where the Thomas-Fermi equation would hold. Using a model that requires that the equations of state for solids be asymptotic to the asymptotic form of the Thomas-Fermi equation, and postulating a model for the attractive term in the potential function, Knopoff predicted a relationship $K_0 Z^{-1} v_0^{7/3} = $ constant, relating the atomic number Z, the bulk modulus K_0, and the volume per atom v_0 at zero pressure and temperature. This relationship was verified for over 175 solid elements and compounds, with Z suitably defined for compounds. The density in the fluid outer core of the Earth was shown to be too great for silicates and too small for an iron-nickel composition. Thus, the outer core cannot be a phase transition of the material of the mantle. It was postulated that the core was mainly iron-nickel with a smaller amount of dissolved lighter elements in it. This was later supported by shock-wave studies.

Knopoff received his B.S. (1944), M.S. (1946), and Ph.D in physics (1949) from the California Institute of Technology. In 1950 he went to the University of California at Los Angeles in a postdoctoral capacity in the laboratory of L. B. Slichter. In 1957 he joined the professorial staff at UCLA, becoming professor of geophysics and physics and research musicologist (the last appointment in the Institute of Ethnomusicology). In this last capacity he studied the linguistic and communication content of music. He was elected to the National Academy of Sciences in 1963 and to the American Academy of Arts and Sciences in 1965.

For background information *see* EARTH INTERIOR; EARTHQUAKE; SEISMOLOGY in the McGraw-Hill Encyclopedia of Science and Technology.   □

KÖHLER, Wolfgang

American psychologist

Köhler died on June 12, 1967, in Hanover, N.H., U.S.A. See *McGraw-Hill Modern Men of Science,* Volume I.

★ KONDRATIEV, Victor N.

Soviet physicochemist
Born Feb. 1, 1902, Rybinsk, Russia

KONDRATIEV WORKED on the chemical mechanism of chain and radical reactions, in particular to determine rate constants for elementary steps of complex chemical conversions, to identify active particles, atoms, and radicals, and to measure their concentrations. Rapid development of the chain reaction theory in the late 1920s and the early 1930s brought forward many problems of primary importance for substantiation and further development of the theory. One of these was the mechanism of chemical chain reactions: The formal reaction scheme with its hypothetic elementary steps and active centers had to be replaced by a system of real reactions involving known particles. The chemical nature of these particles had to be established, and their contribution to the reaction mechanism had to be discovered. It was also necessary to measure, or at least to estimate, the concentrations of active particles and the rate constants for the main elementary reactions involving various particles.

In studying the combustion of hydrogen and of carbon monoxide by means of the spectroscopic technique, Kondratiev detected the OH radical in the combustion zone and measured its concentration. In both cases it appeared to be several powers higher than the equilibrium concentration. This was an indication that hydroxyl is no casual by-product of the reaction, but plays an essential part in its development. This role became quite evident when it was established in Kondratiev's laboratory that the overall reaction rate is the same as that of elementary steps involving hydroxyl: $OH + H_2 = H_2O + H$ for hydrogen combustion and $OH + CO = CO_2 + H$ for carbon monoxide. Later, using the catalytic probe technique, Kondratiev measured the concentration of hydrogen atoms in flames of hydrogen, carbon monoxide, and acetylene. These also appeared to be many powers higher than the equilibrium concentrations. For instance, the concentration of hydrogen atoms in hydrogen flame appeared to be co-measurable with that of molecular hydrogen, and amounted to several 10-percents of the initial hydrogen concentration. Finally, applying the technique based on nitrogen dioxide luminescence, Kondratiev determined the concentration of oxygen atoms in the carbon monoxide flame. The concentration of H and O atoms and of the OH radical in hydrogen flame was determined later in Kondratiev's laboratory by means of the electron spin resonance (ESR) technique. Confirmation was obtained of earlier conclusions on the huge amount of hydrogen atoms in hydrogen flame. At the same time it was found that the H-atom concentration would be considerably higher than that of O only at a sufficiently high content of hydrogen in mixtures of the latter with oxygen. An inverse ratio of H-to-O concentrations was observed for mixtures lean in hydrogen.

The techniques used by Kondratiev for identification of active particles, atoms, and radicals, and for measurement of their concentrations in hydrogen–oxygen–carbon monoxide systems were extended by him to other systems as well.

For instance, CS and S_2O radicals were detected spectroscopically in the zone of carbon sulfide combustion. It was found that the CS radical reacts with molecular oxygen, which was evidence for the active part played by this radical in chain propagation. The kinetic features of S_2O oxidation and decomposition were established. These results were of importance in finding out the chemical mechanism of the reaction between CS_2 and oxygen, because the detection of active centers in flames of hydrogen and carbon monoxide, as well as the determination of their concentrations, played a great part in establishing the mechanism of these reactions.

Another important contribution made by Kondratiev and his co-workers to the kinetics of combustion reactions was the investigation of emission spectra of flames. Measurement of the absolute emission yield for various flames in the visual and ultraviolet regions showed that the intensity of this emission is by many orders higher than that of thermal (equilibrium) emission. It followed that the concentrations of emission spectra carriers are far from being in equilibrium, just like the concentrations of particles that induce by their interaction the appearance of electronically excited molecules in the combustion zone. The excitation mechanism could be estimated from the emitted light quanta and from other flame emission characteristics.

Kondratiev also showed that the only carrier of the emission spectra in all "cool flames" is the formaldehyde HCHO molecule. A number of important conclusions on the mechanism of cool-flame combustion could be made from the mode of emission and the nature of the spectrum carrier. Continuous spectra are often observed along with discrete spectra. Under conditions of ordinary flames these spectra are emitted on recombination of atoms and radicals. A recombination luminescence of this kind was observed by Kondratiev for heated halogen vapor. It was shown that in this case luminescence accompanies recombination of atoms, $X + X = X_2 + h\nu$, which is a reverse reaction to photodissociation, $X_2 + h\nu = X + X$. On grounds of the microscopic equilibrium principle, it appeared possible to calculate from the absorption coefficient the rate constants for recombination reactions with release of excess energy as luminescence. This made possible the determination of atom concentrations from the intensity of recombination luminescence. The latter accounts for the intensive continuum of the carbon sulfide flame that seems to be related to reaction $O + SO = SO_2 + h\nu$, for that of the carbon monoxide flame that may be attributed to reaction $O + CO = CO_2 + h\nu$, and for those of many other flames.

Kondratiev graduated in 1924 from the Polytechnic Institute in Leningrad. As a student, he had started research in the laboratory of N. N. Semenov at the Leningrad Physico-Technical Institute under the directorship of A. F. Joffe. The Institute of Chemical Physics was created in 1931, and he went there together with Semenov as director; Kondratiev became vice-director of the Institute in 1948. He was professor at the Polytechnic Institute of Leningrad from 1934 to 1941 and at the Moscow Engineering Physical Institute from 1951 to 1957. He was elected a corresponding member of the Academy of Sciences of the Soviet Union in 1943 and full member in 1953. He was awarded the State Prize of the Soviet Union in 1945 for spectroscopic studies on gas reactions; the Lewis Gold Medal of the Institute of Combustion, Pittsburgh, in 1966 for research in the field of combustion, particularly in spectroscopy and kinetics of chain reactions; and the A. W. Hoffman Medal of the Society of German Chemists in 1967.

Kondratiev wrote, in Russian, *Electronic Chemistry*, with N. Semenov and Y. Khariton (1927); *Photochemistry* (1933); *Elementary Processes of Energy Exchange in Gases*, with M. Elyashevich (1933); *Elementary Chemical Processes* (1936); *Free Hydroxyl* (1939); *Spectroscopic Studies of Chemical Gas Reactions* (1944); *Structure of Atoms and Molecules* (1946; 3d ed. 1960; English transl. 1964; French transl. 1965); *Chemical Kinetics of Gas Reactions* (1958; English transl. 1964); and, with coauthors, *Chemical Bond Dissociation Energies, Ionization Potentials and Electron Affinity* (1962).

For background information *see* ATOMIC STRUCTURE AND SPECTRA; CHAIN REACTION, CHEMICAL: COMBUSTION; FREE RADICAL in the McGraw-Hill Encyclopedia of Science and Technology. □

★ KONORSKI, Jerzy

Polish neurophysiologist
Born Dec. 1, 1903, Łódź, Poland

AT THE beginning of the 20th century when the Russian physiologist I. P. Pavlov embarked upon the study of physiological mechanisms of acquired animal behavior, he proposed the conditioned reflex (CR) as the simplest model of this behavior. According to Pavlov, innate behavior is composed of a relatively limited number of unconditioned reflexes (URs), that is, instincts, elicited by the appropriate unconditioned stimuli (USs). But a multitude of indifferent stimuli, mainly from the distance receptors, may closely precede USs and become by repeated pairings their signals, or conditioned stimuli (CSs). This signaling is manifested by the CS eliciting the same response as the US—a

phenomenon denoted now as the classical, or type I, CR.

Konorski and Stefan Miller, in their early work started in 1928, proved that the Pavlovian CR fails to cover all forms of acquired animal behavior, because the greater part of motor performances cannot be explained by the formula of this reflex. They proposed the following models for learned motor behavior, which they called the CR type II. *Variety 1:* When an indifferent stimulus S is accompanied by a motor act R produced passively or reflexively, and this compound is followed by a "positive" US (such as presentation of food) and stimulus S alone is not, then the animal learns to perform the movement R in response to stimulus S (S → R). *Variety 2:* When the compound S + R is followed by a "negative" US (such as pinprick) and S alone is not, the animal learns to resist performing movement R in response to stimulus S (S → ∼ R). *Variety 3:* When stimulus S is followed by a "positive" US and the compound S + R is not, the animal learns to resist performing movement R in response to stimulus S (S → ∼ R). *Variety 4:* When stimulus S is followed by a "negative" US and the compound S + R is not, the animal learns to perform movement R in response to stimulus S (S → R). Konorski and Miller showed that all forms of motor responses ("habits") trained by trial-and-error methods in behavioristic studies can be satisfactorily reduced to these forms of CRs (now usually called instrumental CRs).

Before World War II Konorski and Miller described a number of properties of type II CRs and in particular analyzed their interrelations with type I CRs. On the basis of these studies, they proposed a hypothesis concerning the mechanism of type II conditioning: The essential role in type II conditioning was supposed to be played by the proprioceptive feedback (to use the modern term) generated by the performance of movement R; depending on whether the proprioceptive stimulus is the complement to the compound type I CS (in varieties 1 and 2) or is the conditioned inhibitor (in varieties 3 and 4), and whether the reinforcing US is positive (varieties 1 and 3) or negative (varieties 2 and 4), the animal learns to perform or to resist performing movement R in the presence of stimulus S.

After the war Konorski, with co-workers, resumed his work on type II conditioning. It was shown that the original theory proposed by Konorski and Miller, in which the feedback of the movement performed is the decisive factor in type II conditioning, cannot be retained. First, it was shown that deafferentation of the limb participating in the trained movement does not abolish the type II CR; second, the trained movement can appear even when it is not the complement of the type I compound CS. The new concept based on recent experimental data takes advantage of the better understanding of the physiological mechanisms of drives and is a modified version of the drive reduction theory.

Another line of research for Konorski was an attempt to establish a coherent neurophysiological theory of acquired animal behavior. In 1948 he tried to evaluate critically the Pavlov theory of higher nervous processes and to propose a theory that would be in better harmony with the achievements of modern neurophysiology. This work was later enlarged and extended not only to cover the phenomena of type I and type II conditioning, but also to account for the phenomena of perceptions and associations in humans.

Konorski graduated in medicine from the University of Warsaw in 1929. In 1928 he started, with his colleague Stefan Miller, research work on type II CRs, in a small self-organized laboratory. Pavlov became interested in their studies and invited them to come to Leningrad and work in his institute. Konorski spent 2 years in 1931–33 with Pavlov. After returning to Warsaw he established the laboratory on conditioned reflexes in the Nencki Institute of Experimental Biology, where he worked until 1939. During the war the Institute was destroyed and Miller was killed. After the war the Institute was reestablished and Konorski became its deputy director and head of the department of neurophysiology in 1946. He was professor of physiology at Lódź University from 1945 to 1955. He was elected a member of the Polish Academy of Sciences in 1956 and a foreign member of the U.S. National Academy of Sciences and the Roumanian Academy of Sciences.

Konorski wrote *Les Principes Fondamentaux de la Théorie Physiologique des Movements Acquis,* with S. Miller (1933); *Conditioned Reflexes and Neuron Organization* (1948); and *Integrative Activity of the Brain: An Interdisciplinary Approach* (1967).

For background information *see* LEARNING
THEORIES; REFLEX, CONDITIONED; SENSORY
LEARNING in the McGraw-Hill Encyclopedia of
Science and Technology.   ☐

★ KORZHINSKII, Dmitrii Sergeevich

Soviet geologist
Born Sept. 13, 1899, Saint Petersburg, Russia

KORZHINSKII MADE a geological survey and
topical field studies on the petrology of
micaceous, skarn, and other types of mineral
deposits in different areas of the Soviet Union.
These geological observations formed the basis
of his theoretical work in physicochemical
petrology.

During a study of the Precambrian metasomatic phlogopite deposits of eastern Siberia,
Korzhinskii was amazed to find that in the rocks
of these deposits the content of some ("perfectly
mobile") components, in particular H_2O, CO_2,
K_2O, and Na_2O, is a definite function of the
content of other ("inert") components. Such a
relationship turned out to be typical not only for
metasomatic formations but for metamorphic
and magmatic formations ("principle of differential mobility of components"). For a thermodynamic interpretation of such mineral equilibria,
Korzhinskii introduced the "open systems with
perfectly mobile components," in which the
equilibrium states depend on the masses of
the inert components and the chemical potentials (or concentrations in one of the phases) of
perfectly mobile components (1936). The greater
the degree of openness of the system, the greater
is the number of the components that becomes
perfectly mobile. The chemical potentials of the
perfectly mobile components (or of their concentrations) are determined by the conditions of the
outside medium and are independent of the inside
state of the system. From the viewpoint of the
Gibbs phase rule, every perfectly mobile component, under random outside conditions, introduces one degree of freedom and, for this reason,

does not increase the number of simultaneously
stable, coexisting phases. This explains the limitation of the number of coexisting minerals in
rocks, particularly in metasomatic rocks. The
Gibbs phase rule, with consideration of the differential mobility of the components, has been labeled the Korzhinskii rule in a number of papers.

In 1949 Korzhinskii introduced thermodynamic potentials of the systems with perfectly
mobile components, from which the basic
thermodynamic properties of such systems were
derived directly. The thermodynamic potentials
of systems in which the acidity and reduction
potential are set by outside conditions were also
derived (1963).

The concept of systems with perfectly mobile
components opened new possibilities for a
physicochemical analysis of mineral associations
("analysis of the parageneses of minerals"),
because its application was extended to formations which originate under conditions of open
systems. Such an analysis makes it possible to
reveal the relative mobility of the components
during the process of mineral formation and the
dependence of the mineral composition on the
conditions of temperature, pressure, and activity
of the mobile components in circulating
solutions.

These concepts about systems with perfectly
mobile components and their thermodynamic
potentials and the application of the phase rule
to rocks aroused lively and frequently bitter
discussions. For two decades the concepts received practically no support. But then they
found a wide application, and were further developed in the papers of a number of researchers.

Analysis of the parageneses of minerals in
metamorphic rocks made it possible for Korzhinskii to establish the specific features of the water
and carbon dioxide conditions during the metamorphism. With depth the pressure of carbon
dioxide during metamorphism increases (regardless of the presence of carbonate rocks), as a
result of which a number of silicates of calcium
and magnesium become unstable in a definite
sequence, being subjected to carbonation. On
this basis Korzhinskii derived a number of
"mineral facies of the depth of metamorphism"
(1937). Then the fully mobile behavior of K_2O
and Na_2O during magmatic processes was established, and the first diagrams were made of the
dependence of the mineral parageneses of the
magmatic and metasomatic rocks on the chemical potentials of K_2O and Na_2O (1945, 1946).

Korzhinskii developed the physicochemical
theory of bimetasomatic and infiltration-contact
processes in contacts of carbonate rocks (skarns,
pholopite rocks) and hyperbasites (1937, 1945,
1953), and then the general physicochemical
theory of different types of infiltration and diffusion metasomatic zonality. During metasomasis
a column of simultaneously growing metasomatic

zones is formed. Similar to chromatographic zones, they are divided by more or less sharp fronts of substitution, on each of which one of the minerals of the rock is subject to complete substitution. Prior to Korzhinskii's theory the formation of several zones was usually explained by the change of the acting solutions in a multistage, intermittent metasomatic process.

On the basis of geological data Korzhinskii predicted the acid filtration effect, later confirmed experimentally by L. N. Ovchinnikov, A. S. Shur, and V. A. Zharikov. During the filtration of a true solution, its components can move through the filter at different rates while the acids move faster than the bases. The acid filtration effect forms the basis of the hypothesis of the "outstripping acidity wave" in the flow of postmagmatic solutions (1957). The passage of this acidity wave explains the replacement of the postmagmatic acid leaching by the subsequent concentrated deposition of bases from solutions and, in particular, of ore components leached out from rock masses ("acid-base hydrothermal differentiation").

Korzhinskii formulated the "principle of acid-base interaction in solutions and melts" and gave its general thermodynamic derivation (1956, 1963). The overall activity coefficient of a base rises under the influence of a drop in the acidity of the solution or melt; the stronger (in other words more dissociated) the base, the stronger is the rise. The reverse is true for acid components. In accordance with this principle, a change in the concentration of some components in a melt changes in a definite manner the eutectic and cotectic relationships of all the other components.

Korzhinskii developed the hypothesis of granitization as a magnetic replacement, under the influence of rising "transmagmatic solutions" of deep subcrustal origin (1952). The concentration of the alkali metals in these solutions depends on the tectonic conditions (role of the abyssal fractures) and, in turn, determines the alkalinity and the eutectic compositions of the magmas which originate as a result of the debasification and selective melting of the rocks in the Earth's crust.

Son of a botanist who was a member of the Russian Academy of Sciences, Korzhinskii finished his studies in 1926 at the Mining Institute in Leningrad, where he specialized in geology. From 1925 to 1937 he worked as a scientific colleague in the Geological Committee (now the All-Union Geological Institute) in Leningrad, and in 1937 went to the Institute of Geology of Ore Deposits, Petrography, Mineralogy, and Geochemistry of the Academy of Sciences in Moscow. From 1929 to 1940 he taught in the Leningrad Mining Institute. He received his doctorate in geological-mineral sciences in 1938 and became a professor of petrography in 1940.

In 1943 he was elected a corresponding member and in 1953 an active member of the Academy of Sciences of the U.S.S.R. For his scientific work in petrology he received the State Prize of the Soviet Union in 1946 and the Lenin Prize in 1958.

Korzhinskii wrote in Russian *Bimetasomatic Phlogopite and Lazurite Deposits of the Transbaikal Archean* (1947), *Outline of Metasomatic Process* (1953; enlarged German ed. 1965), and *Physicochemical Bases of the Analysis of Parageneses of Minerals* (1957; 2d ed. 1959).

For background information *see* ACID AND BASE; EQUILIBRIUM PHASE; METAMORPHIC ROCKS; MINERAL; PETROLOGY in the McGraw-Hill Encyclopedia of Science and Technology.   ☐

★ KROGMAN, Wilton Marion

American physical anthropologist
Born June 28, 1903, Oak Park, Ill., U.S.A.

MAN LEAVES behind him many tangible evidences of his mortality: dwelling places and other structures, household implements, tools, weapons, and other miscellaneous artifacts. He also leaves behind him his own remains: bones and teeth. The hard parts of the human body form indelible records of individuality, of health, and of many diseases. Therefore the physical anthropologist joins hands with the archeologist in the total reconstruction of human history, with the physician and dentist in the study of human growth and development, with law enforcement agencies in forensic osteology and forensic odontology, and with the industrial designer in human engineering. In substance, the physical anthropologist is the interpreter of human body form and function in the biological panel of present-day biocultural social structure.

In this total picture Krogman focused his attention primarily on the human skeleton, studied not only grossly—actual bones dug up by archeologists or recovered in forensic cases—

but also radiologically—x-ray films of the living human body. In the late 1920s, while a graduate student in anthropology at the University of Chicago, he was field director of the archeological survey of Illinois, which was beginning the project of re-creating the prehistory of the Upper Mississippi Valley. Details of cultural development and migration, the emergence of discrete cultural patterns, and the interpretation of physical types (prehistoric Indian tribes) were contributions of the survey, which under other direction continued through the 1930s and 1940s.

In 1930–31 Krogman studied with Sir Arthur Keith at the Royal College of Surgeons, London, as a National Research Council fellow and began studies in the protohistory of the Near East. From 1935 to 1945, in cooperation with the Oriental Institute of the University of Chicago and the museum of the University of Pennsylvania, he studied skeletal material from Alishar, Chatal Huyuk, and Tell al-Judaidah in Anatolia, and from Tepe Hissar in Iran. Modern European and Asia Minor types—Nordic, Alpine, Mediterranean, Armenoid—were clearly distinguished in the time span represented, ca. 4000 B.C.–A.D. 500. Asia Minor, the east-west gateway to Europe via a circum-Mediterranean avenue, witnessed a commingling of peoples before and during their entrance into Europe through its southeast and southern regional components.

Contemporaneous with these skeletal studies, Krogman was associated, first as student and then as colleague, with T. Wingate Todd of Western Reserve University. It was here that Krogman set his feet on the major path he was to follow: the study of the physical growth and development of normal, healthy American children. It was here, too, that he was able to broaden his knowledge of human skeletal variability. In the field of growth the emphasis, via the Brush Foundation, was upon serial or longitudinal analysis, rather than cross-sectional sampling; the problem was not only how all children grow—and the computing of tables of averages—but how a single child grows—how an individual boy or girl pursues his or her own biogenetic pattern of growth progress. Study of this problem was facilitated by x-ray film standards, via hand films, which enabled the assessment of the child's rate of maturation, or biological growth timing. In the field of skeletal variability the contributing factor was the study of the Todd Collection of the bones and jaws of 3300 American men and women, white and colored, for each of whom age at death, sex, and race were known from clinical records. From these skeletons, norms were set up to be used in the identification and analysis of unknown human remains.

In 1947 Krogman moved to Philadelphia where, in cooperation with the School (now Division) of Graduate Medicine and the School of Dentistry (now Dental Medicine) of the University of Pennsylvania and the Children's Hospital of Philadelphia, he established the Philadelphia Center for Research in Child Growth. In cooperation with the Board of Public Education and the Archdiocese of Philadelphia, longitudinal research on the physical growth of normal, healthy Philadelphia children, boys and girls, white and colored, was begun. The "Philadelphia Standards," white and colored from ages 6 to 17 years, are now completed; corresponding standards from birth to 6 years will soon be available for white children.

In the development of these standards, complete measurement of head and face (cephalometry) and of trunk and limbs (somatometry) was undertaken. Tables of height, weight, head length and breadth, face height and breadth, trunk and limb dimensions, and so on were derived. Radiology of head, face, and jaws, of hand, knee, and foot, and of upper arm was employed. The data from these films were basic to serial cephalofacial growth studies, to assessments of "skeletal age," and to long-bone studies of cortex-medulla ratios during growth. Serial dental models were gathered for studies of tooth eruption and jaw (arch) growth. When these several approaches are combined, it is possible to study a child's growth progress from three major aspects of time: chronological, skeletal, and dental, the first being sidereal, the latter two biological.

The growth standards of Philadelphia children are applicable to a number of clinical problems in pediatric, orthopedic, endocrinologic, and serologic medicine and in pedodontic, orthodontic, and oral surgical dentistry. This study includes, for example, children with systemic or neurotrophic illnesses, endocrinopathies, bone diseases, blood dyscrasias (such as Cooley's anemia or sicklemia), faulty erupting or malposed teeth, cleft lip and/or palate, and genetic syndromes of various types, affecting body systems or parts, or bones, or teeth.

Son of a carpenter and housebuilder, Krogman went from Oak Park High School to the University of Chicago with a competitive scholarship in American history. He majored in the biological sciences with focus upon comparative and human anatomy and physical anthropology and received his A.B. in 1926, his M.A. in 1927, and his Ph.D. in 1929. After a year's instructorship, 1929–30, he studied with Sir Arthur Keith, 1930–31. From 1931 to 1938, he was associate professor of anatomy and physical anthropology at Western Reserve University and from 1938 to 1947 at the University of Chicago. In 1947 he became professor of physical anthropology, and in 1955 chairman of the department in the Graduate School of Medicine of the University of Pennsylvania and director of the

Growth Center. In 1950 he received the Viking Fund Medal and Award in Physical Anthropology. He was elected to the National Academy of Sciences in 1966.

Krogman wrote *Bibliography of Human Morphology, 1914–1939* (1941); *The Growth of Man*, Vol. 20 of *Tabulae Biologicae* (1941); *Syllabus of Roentgenographic Cephalometry*, with V. Sassouni (1957); *The Human Skeleton in Forensic Medicine* (1962); and *Human Mechanics*, with F. E. Johnston (1963).

For background information *see* ANTHROPOLOGY, PHYSICAL in the McGraw-Hill Encyclopedia of Science and Technology.   □

★ KUNO, Hisashi

Japanese geologist
Born Jan. 7, 1910, Tokyo, Japan

IN HIS study of a volcanic region southwest of Tokyo, started when he was an undergraduate student of the University of Tokyo, Kuno traced the course of crystallization of pyroxenes from magmas. The result enabled him to distinguish two rock series: the pigeonitic rock series formed from comparatively high-temperature, H_2O-poor magma, and the hypersthenic rock series formed from comparatively low-temperature, H_2O-rich magma, both covering the whole range from basalt to rhyolite. The two series are distinct from each other in chemical composition, especially in the degree of enrichment of $FeO + Fe_2O_3$ in their differentiation trends, although they appear to have been derived from a single parental basalt magma. For his study of pyroxenes in rocks, Kuno received the Japan Academy Prize in 1959.

Kuno also found the existence of the same two series among volcanic rocks in many regions of the world, especially in the circum-Pacific volcanic belt. Several different hypotheses were proposed regarding the origin of the basalt-rhyolite series of the circum-Pacific belt. The apparent absence of the rocks of this series in the oceanic regions led some petrologists to suppose that they originated through contamination of the continental crust or even through bodily melting of this crust. In 1957, however, Kuno found that a differentiation trend of some Hawaiian magma is quite similar to that of the pigeonitic rock series: conclusive evidence that this series can originate without presence of the continental crust.

Since the work of L. R. Wager and W. A. Deer in 1939 on the differentiation of basalt magma of Skaergaard intrusion, eastern Greenland, petrologists' attention was directed to the marked contrast between the differentiation trend with strong enrichment of $FeO + Fe_2O_3$ in the late stage, as exemplified by the Skaergaard intrusion, and that without enrichment of $FeO + Fe_2O_3$, as exemplified by the common basalt-andesite-dacite-rhyolite series of orogenic belts. But Kuno emphasized the existence of the two series with different degrees of iron enrichment even among rocks of orogenic belts. He showed in 1965 that there is a complete gradation from the trend with strong iron enrichment as in Skaergaard, through the trend with moderate iron enrichment as in the pigeonitic rock series, to the trend without iron enrichment as in the hypersthenic rock series. Kuno ascribed this to the difference in the stage of crystallization of magnetite from magmas, stating that higher oxygen partial pressure of magmas would favor earlier crystallization of magnetite which would remove much iron from the magma, resulting in the trend without iron enrichment. The H_2O-rich magma of the hypersthenic rock series may have high oxygen pressure as compared with the other magmas. However, the cause of H_2O concentration in magma of the hypersthenic rock series is not yet known.

The problem of the origin of the different primary basalt magmas—the SiO_2-rich, alkali-poor magma, which is called tholeiite magma, and the SiO_2-poor, alkali-rich magma called alkali basalt magma—has been discussed by petrologists since 1924. From his study of Hawaiian rocks and his consideration of the possible effect of pressure on the phase equilibrium relation relevant to basalt magma generation, Kuno concluded in 1957 that tholeiite magma is generated by partial melting of peridotite constituting the upper mantle at comparatively shallow depth, whereas alkali basalt magma is generated by partial melting of the same material at comparatively great depth. In 1959–60 Kuno showed that tholeiite occurs in Quaternary volcanoes lying in a zone on the Pacific side of the Japanese islands, whereas alkali basalt occurs in Quaternary volcanoes lying in a zone on the continental side of the same islands and also in Korea and Manchuria, and that these two zones are separated from each other by another zone where an intermediate magma called high-alumina basalt occurs. This kind of arrangement of different basalts is found in many other regions of the circum-Pacific belt and Indonesia. Kuno also found that in the Japanese islands the tholeiite, high-alumina basalt, and alkali basalt occur where earthquakes originate from depths of 100–150 km, 150–200 km, and 200–400 km, respectively. Such a close correlation supports his conclusion regarding the depth relation of different kinds of magma generation. I. Kushiro's high-pressure experiments carried out in 1965 gave results consistent with Kuno's hypotheses, although Kushiro showed that the different basalt magmas can be generated at depths much shallower than those inferred from the earthquake foci depths underneath the Japanese islands.

Born in the land of volcanoes and earthquakes, Kuno was first attracted to the science of geology when he was 16 years old. He graduated from the Geological Institute, University of Tokyo, in 1932, and was appointed assistant there in 1933, associate professor in 1939, and full professor of petrology and volcanology in 1955. During World War II he was drafted into the Japanese army and stayed in Manchuria for 5 years, managing to study some plateau basalt areas in eastern Manchuria that were little known to geologists. Kuno was a visiting research fellow at Princeton University in 1951–52 and a visiting professor at the University of Minnesota in 1964. He was elected foreign associate of the U.S. National Academy of Sciences in 1963 and president of the International Association of Volcanology, International Union of Geodesy and Geophysics, for the period 1963–67.

For background information *see* MAGMA; PETROGRAPHIC PROVINCE; VOLCANOLOGY in the McGraw-Hill Encyclopedia of Science and Technology. □

★ KURSANOV, Andrei Lvovitch

Soviet botanist
Born Nov. 8, 1902, Moscow, Russia

A PLANT physiologist having a wide scope of scientific interests, Kursanov took a biochemical approach to physiological processes. His first research works in 1926–28—suggested by his father, L. I. Kursanov, then a professor of mycology in Moscow University—were concerned with the physiology of a diseased plant (wheat infected by *Ustilago tritici*). Kursanov concluded that metabolic changes occurring under the influence of the fungus parasite in the host plant affect not only the tissues immediately invaded by the fungi but also the organs free from hyphae. This indicated the possibility of toxins being transported long distances.

Kursanov's interest was also attracted by vegetable substances of a polyphenol nature. While investigating the activity of enzymes in homogenized compounds, he encountered difficulties with plants rich in tannins. Therefore, he made a study in 1929 in collaboration with A. I. Oparin, in which an inactivating action of tannins on different enzymes was shown and a method for their protection by means of peptones and albumins was worked out. These findings were later used for establishing the biochemical theory on fermentation of tea, that is, the technological process during which intensive enzymatic reactions occur in the crushed leaf tissue, notwithstanding the plant's richness in polyphenols.

In 1933–52 Kursanov, in collaboration with Oparin, devoted his attention to the elaboration of biochemical fundamentals for all stages of tea production, which at that time was still at its initial stage of development in the Soviet Union. It necessitated detailed studies of the raw material used for preparation of black tea and of the transformations that initial components undergo at different phases of processing. This work resulted in improvement of black tea production in the tea factories of the Soviet Union and in the establishment of permanent biochemical laboratories to control the raw material for tea processing. Kursanov paid particular attention to tannins, which constitute the most valuable part of the product. In collaboration with M. N. Zaprometov, he isolated individual catechins from tannin contained in tea leaves of the Georgian tea varieties. Biosynthesis of these catechins and secondary transformations in the tea plant were investigated. A strong capillary-strengthening action of tea catechins was discovered in 1952. Based on these findings, com-

mercial production of vitamin "P" from side products of tea processing was organized.

During 1934–40, using a vacuum infiltration technique, Kursanov developed methods for determining enzyme activity in living plant tissues. Based on these methods, numerous investigations were carried out on the role of enzymes in living plants, depending on their development stage, nutrition, and specific features. This approach, known as the biology of enzymes, contributed considerably to drawing together plant physiology and biochemistry.

From 1949 on, Kursanov concentrated his attention mainly on the problem of the transport of organic matter in phloem, considering this process metabolic by its nature. He was one of the first investigators who, using C^{14}, measured the rate of transport of assimilates in plants and showed the predominance of sucrose over hexoses in movements at long distances. Detailed studies into the carbohydrates and nucleotide composition of conducting bundles, as well as into their respiration, enabled him to characterize these tissues as extremely active metabolically. It was shown that movement of assimilates from photosynthesizing cells of the leaf to the fine endings of conducting bundles is connected with overcoming the high concentration gradient that is accomplished with the help of adenosinetriphosphate energy. The studies of transport phenomena were carried out mainly with sugar beet plants. Investigations on assimilates transport were summarized in a number of review papers (1961, 1963) and reports for international congresses and symposia (1959, 1966, 1967).

In his 1954 report to the Eighth International Botanical Congress held in Paris, Kursanov expounded a hypothesis about the existence of turnover of organic substances in plants by means of which the exchange of metabolites between roots and above-ground organs is provided. This concept was further developed experimentally and was presented to various international meetings (1957, 1959, 1960). This led to the special study of roots participating with the help of their metabolites in assimilation of nutrient elements and in the overall turnover of substances in plants. The main attention was paid to NH_4, P, and K. This work, started as far back as 1954, made it possible to reveal the central role played by the cycle of dicarboxylic and tricarboxylic acids in the initial stage of assimilation of ammonium ions by roots. At the same time the studies indicate the high synthetic activity of roots, which synthesize many nitrogen compounds not only for themselves but for export to other organs. Among these compounds are physiologically active substances of the cytokinin type, initiating nucleic acid metabolism and protein metabolism in plant tissues. Early inclusion of inorganic phosphate in the composition of nucleotides during its absorption by roots was also established, and structural disorganization of mitochondria in the case of potassium deficiency was shown. Results of the studies in the field of biochemistry of root nutri-

tion were reported at the general meeting of the U.S.S.R. Academy of Sciences in 1962, as well as at various international scientific congresses and symposia.

In 1958–65 Kursanov, in collaboration with B. B. Vartapetyan, extensively used heavy oxygen (O^{18}) in physiological trials. As a result, a new approach to the studies of water balance in organisms was worked out. For example, using H_2O^{18}, Kursanov showed a ready mobility and exchangeability of water in plant and animal organisms and in yeasts. With the help of heavy oxygen (O^{18}), amounts of water synthesized by various organisms as the result of their own metabolism were measured, and it was shown that in silkworm or in cactus the major part of their water supply may be of metabolic (endogenous) origin. Using heavy oxygen, Kursanov demonstrated experimentally that in the process of plant respiration, at the expense of carbohydrates or fats, oxidation of these substrates takes place with the participation of oxygen from water but not by the direct addition of atmospheric oxygen.

During World War II, Kursanov, in collaboration with N. N. Dyatchkov, organized in various regions of the Soviet Union production of glucose from lichens (*Cetraria islandica* and others).

After completing his schooling in Moscow, Kursanov joined the Biological Faculty of Moscow University. After his graduation in 1926, he worked there in the department of plant physiology until 1929. He was a research worker on the staff of the Institute of Sugar Production during 1929–44, a lecturer on plant physiology at the K. A. Timiriazev Agricultural Academy during 1929–38, and a research worker and then a deputy director of the Bakh Institute of Biochemistry during 1934–54. In 1952 he was appointed director of the Institute of Plant Physiology, U.S.S.R. Academy of Sciences, and head of one of its laboratories. He received a candidate's degree in biological sciences in 1936 and a doctorate in 1940. In 1944 he received the academic rank of professor of plant biochemistry and physiology. He became a corresponding member of the U.S.S.R. Academy of Sciences in 1946 and a member in 1953. During 1957–63 he served on the presidium of the Academy of Sciences. He was elected a foreign honorary member of the American Academy of Arts and Sciences in 1962, and a member of the Academie d'Agriculture de France in 1964.

Kursanov was a founder and chief editor of the journal *Fiziologiya Rastenii* (*Plant Physiology*), published since 1954.

For background information *see* PLANT, WATER RELATIONS OF; PLANT METABOLISM; PLANT RESPIRATION in the McGraw-Hill Encyclopedia of Science and Technology.   □

★ LALLEMAND, André

French astronomer
Born Sept. 29, 1904, Cirey, Côte-d'Or, France

LALLEMAND'S RESEARCHES had as their principal aim the study, development, and use of receptors for luminous energy, intended for astronomical observations. With this in mind, he brought photomultipliers to a high degree of perfection, but it was chiefly with the development and use of the electronic camera that he greatly improved astronomical observations.

His first researches, carried out in the laboratory of Pierre Weiss at Strasbourg, were concerned with magnetism. He elucidated the question of the experimental magneton, which Weiss had introduced concurrently with the Bohr magneton (1934).

Lallemand's work in electronic photography began about 1934 with the appearance of electron optics. He then saw the possibility of developing an ideal receptor for photons, conceived in accordance with the quantum properties of radiation and with consideration of the discrete and independent particles which can be generated and utilized, starting with the photon. The photoelectric effect, for which Einstein provided the theory, permitted the exchange of photons for electrons and of particles for particles, using photoemissive layers, without any threshold effect and with a constant, well-defined yield. Electron optics permitted conservation with electrons of the initial image of photons formed on the photocathode without loss of definition. Finally, the special electron-sensitive photographic plate permitted the development of a veritable Wilson cloud chamber, in which each electron makes its own record in the form of a visible trace, hence without threshold effect. Lallemand announced these findings in two papers before the Academy of Sciences of Paris in 1936, and in an article in *l'Astronomie* in

1937, with a description of experiments showing that it was possible to construct such a receptor. This conception of a quantum receptor for reconstituting an image proved fruitful, with a 100-fold gain in sensitivity estimated thereby; today this order of magnitude is still accepted.

Lallemand's researches were interrupted during World War II, and it was not until a decade later that he was able to resume his experiments on the development of the ideal detector. Technically, this was a difficult problem to solve, and these difficulties had at times discouraged certain astronomers. But Lallemand always considered that the perfection of a receptor should be preserved as a goal, whatever the technical difficulties. Because the great discoveries in astronomy have always been made at the limit of possible observation, he concentrated on the development of a detector which would impair to the minimum extent the information collected by the telescope. This approach enabled him to show that the use of electronic photography is more interesting for the possibility of collecting the maximum of undistorted information from a celestial object than for the possibility of increasing the sensitivity of a photographic plate by a factor of 20 or 100. For example, one of his publications at the Academy of Sciences of Paris (1966) showed that in an electronic photograph of objects of very high magnitude it is possible to determine, in one wavelength region, the output of photons from that object, even if it is at the limit of detection. This is true for all of the objects present on the plate, and with no difficulties in identification. The bright stars are well known today since they are the easiest ones to study, but they are less numerous at a distance, and studies of very faint stars, at the limit of instrumental capabilities, are indispensable for attaining the most objective ideas of the universe. The results obtained by Lallemand have been confirmed by numerous observations carried out at the observatories of Haute-Provence and of Pic-du-Midi in France and by M. F. Walker at Lick Observatory.

Lallemand, Agrégé des sciences physiques, qualified as a Docteur ès sciences at the University of Strasbourg. After teaching at Haguenau, he became an astronomer at the Observatory of Strasbourg, then at the Observatory of Paris. He was appointed to the chair of practical astronomy at the Collège de France in 1961. Lallemand was named to the Academy of Sciences of Paris in 1961. Among the honors he received were prizes awarded by the Academy of Sciences of Paris and the French Astronomical Society, the Paul and Marie Stroobant Prize of the Royal Academy of Belgium (1962), and the Eddington Medal of the Royal Astronomical Society of London (1962).

For background information *see* ASTRONOMI-

CAL PHOTOGRAPHY; ASTRONOMY; ELECTRON MOTION IN VACUUM; RADIO ASTRONOMY in the McGraw-Hill Encyclopedia of Science and Technology.   ☐

★ LANDIS, Eugene Markley

American physiologist
Born Apr. 4, 1901, New Hope, Pa., U.S.A.

BEGINNING IN 1925, Landis used glass micropipettes with tip diameters of 2 to 20 microns to measure the blood pressure in single capillaries of several species of animals and, by 1930, in the cutaneous capillaries of man. He also measured the microscopic volumes of fluid filtered and absorbed by single capillaries of frogs, and he obtained the first filtration constants or coefficients of the capillary wall. These figures described in quantitative terms the permeability of the capillary wall to the fluid portion of blood plasma, first under normal conditions and then during injury or inflammation.

These studies were done because of the need for more data relating to a highly significant (but for 30 years much debated) hypothesis proposed in 1896 by Ernest H. Starling, an English physiologist. According to this hypothesis, the vitally important constancy of the circulating blood volume in animals and in man depends upon an average balance between the osmotic pressure of the plasma proteins (tending to produce absorption of fluid from the tissue spaces into the circulating blood) and capillary blood pressure (tending to produce filtration of fluid from blood plasma to the tissue spaces). The former pressure was known from Starling's measurements made in 1896, but accurate figures for capillary blood pressure were still lacking in 1925. Various calculations and indirect measurements had been tried, but these provided only rough estimates subject to serious criticism.

Direct measurements of capillary blood pressure by cannulation had also been attempted several times, beginning with studies by J. L. M. Poiseuille in 1827, but glass cannulas or hollow needles could not be made small enough to insert into capillaries, nor held in place long enough, to provide accurate results. By 1925, however, technically improved micromanipulators, micropipettes, and photomicrography made it appropriate to investigate the problem again. This time it could be shown clearly that the average pressure balance hypothesized by Starling is present in frogs, rats, rabbits, and man, though maintained at different average capillary pressure levels, lower in frogs (about 10 mm Hg) and more than twice as high in man (about 25 mm Hg).

Landis proceeded to measure capillary pressures, rates of filtration, and rates of absorption in more detail. He measured the gradient of capillary blood pressure from arterioles through capillaries to veins. Filtration and absorption were measured in terms of cubic microns of fluid per second per square micron of capillary wall per centimeter H_2O difference between capillary blood pressure and the osmotic pressure of the plasma proteins. The linear relationship between this pressure difference and fluid movement confirmed other evidence that the capillary wall retains protein and behaves as an inert, though living, membrane. There was no indication of secretory activity by the capillary wall. Fluid movement to and fro between capillary blood and the interstitial fluid outside the capillaries depends upon pressure differences. In later work the effects of interstitial fluid pressure and of the osmotic pressure of proteins in the interstitial fluid were studied. A commonly used expression of this relationship is shown in Eq. (1). Here + indicates filtration and − indicates ab-

$$\text{Fluid movement} = k(P_c - \pi_{pl} - P_{if} + \pi_{if}) \quad (1)$$

sorption; P is hydrostatic pressure, P_c in the capillary and P_{if} in the interstitial fluid; π is the osmotic pressure of proteins, π_{pl} in the blood plasma and π_{if} in the interstitial fluid; the proportionality constant k is the filtration coefficient.

Landis also studied the changes of capillary pressure and of filtration coefficients produced by a wide variety of functional conditions. For example, the contraction of a muscle produces metabolic products that dilate the arterioles carrying blood to the muscle being exercised, and blood flow then increases to several times above the resting level. Capillary blood pressure increases to as much as two or three times normal. Another illustration is that moderate warming and moderate cooling (for instance, of the skin of man) produce respectively vasodilatation and vasoconstriction, which in turn increase and decrease capillary blood pressure.

The permeability of the capillary wall to protein and fluid remains normal, and the changes in fluid movement are small. But severe grades of heat (burns) and severe cold (frostbite) both produce maximal vasodilatation, elevate capillary blood pressure to very high levels, and very quickly injure the capillary wall. At the moment this occurs, the filtration coefficient of the damaged capillaries rises sharply to as much as eight or nine times normal and, even more important, large molecules such as proteins can pass easily through the capillary wall. Plasma proteins and fluid in large volume leak rapidly from the blood in the capillaries into the tissue spaces. This leakage increases the volume of interstitial fluid and produces the local swelling or edema observed in frostbite or the blister following a burn. Motion-picture microscopy demonstrates that, as plasma is lost from the capillary blood, the blood cells are still retained because the openings or "leaks" in the capillary wall exceed the size of protein molecules but are still far smaller than the blood cells. The vitally important consequence is that the retained erythrocytes become packed in semisolid cylinders and blood flow ceases in all severely damaged capillaries. The death or recovery of the immediately adjacent tissue cells depends on how much time elapses before some blood flow and oxygen supply can be restored to the injured area.

The importance of the blood capillaries in the pathologic physiology of hemorrhage, surgical shock, inflammation, and some forms of edema led Landis and his associates in the 1930s to measure capillary filtration coefficients in the human forearm by means of a specially devised "pressure plethysmograph." This method provided quantitative information directly applicable to man. Other researches on related medical problems dealt with the use of skin temperature and induced vasodilatation in order to diagnose, measure, and treat insufficiency of blood flow in human peripheral vascular disease. Included also were studies on the pathophysiology of blood vessels in hypertension, renal diseases, heart failure, and edema.

The application by J. R. Pappenheimer and his associates of general "pore theory" to the capillary wall, coupled with the inability of electron microscopists to confirm the presence of any uniform, "small-pore" system in the capillary wall, has presented many new questions concerning capillary permeability at the molecular level. Technical advances in several scientific fields during the 1950s and early 1960s have presented new tools for problems that have resisted research efforts. For example, Landis had tried in 1927 and in 1931 to quantify certain molecular aspects of capillary permeability by photographing the passage of dyes through the walls of single capillaries during microinjection and microperfusion. He could conclude only that passage of dyes was unequal from capillary to capillary and differed greatly depending upon the colloidal nature of the dye molecule, capillary blood pressure, and capillary blood flow. In 1930 Peyton Rous injected dyes into whole animals intravenously and described, for slowly diffusible dyes, a gradient of capillary permeability, which was lower in arterioles and higher in venules, but this gradient could not be observed when rapidly diffusible dyes were used. Interpretations of these early results with dyes were limited and unsatisfactory, but recent concepts of dye chemistry, the development of more sensitive color motion-picture film, and improvements of micro-cinematography now present many interesting, new approaches.

In later studies Landis measured heteroporosity of the walls of arterioles, capillaries, and venules by combining motion-picture photography with the microinjection of dye-labeled macromolecules of different chemical compositions, graded molecular weights, sizes, and electrical charge. He proposed and began testing a theory that in most normal capillaries a system of "fenestellae" (little windows), few or none in arterioles and more in venous capillaries, must be added to the system of intercellular spaces or slits between the endothelial cells of the capillary wall, as proposed by Starling in 1896, by August Krogh in 1922, and by Pappenheimer in 1954. If correct, this theory or a modification of it may explain some of the perplexing problems that are still presented by the rapid or slow exchanges of molecules, small or large, through the walls of the capillary blood vessels, both normal and injured, for example, in burns, allergy, and inflammation.

Still needed in medicine and surgery are methods of arresting the dangerous losses of plasma proteins and fluid that occur whenever the capillary wall is injured, inflamed, or separated drastically from its supply of oxygen for prolonged periods. Eventually the intravenous injection of a suitable macromolecule may be found capable of doing this, either by generalized sieving on the inner surface of the capillary wall or by actual blockage of the large apertures or leaks that appear whenever the endothelial cells and other components of the capillary wall are damaged in any way.

Son of a biology teacher in a Philadelphia high school, Landis majored in zoology at the University of Pennsylvania, receiving a B.S. in 1922, an M.S. (protozoology) in 1924, and a Ph.D. (physiology) in 1927. His earliest papers, published during 1919–25, dealt with topics in zoology and protozoology. In 1922 he enrolled in the Medical School of the University of Pennsylvania, receiving his M.D. in 1926. With the aid of a National Research Council fellowship, the year 1926–27 was spent in the laboratory of Merkel H. Jacobs, professor of physiology in the Medical School of the University of Pennsylvania. After completing his medical internship, Landis was awarded a Guggenheim fellowship, which provided a year of work in the laboratory of Thomas Lewis in London and a year with Krogh in Copenhagen. Returning to the University of Pennsylvania in 1931, Landis was a research associate in pharmacology and, by 1939, assistant professor of medicine. From 1939 to 1943 he was professor of internal medicine and head of department at the University of Virginia, and then he moved to Harvard Medical School, becoming the George Higginson Professor of Physiology and head of the department until his retirement as professor emeritus in 1967. He was then appointed adjunct professor of biology at Lehigh University in Bethlehem, Pa. During World War II Landis was secretary of the Committee on Aviation Medicine of the Office of Scientific Research and Development and also chairman of the Subcommittee on Acceleration. His honors included medals for research done while in medical school, the Phillips Medal of the American College of Physicians in 1936, election to the National Academy of Sciences in 1954, and a Gold Heart Award by the American Heart Association in 1966.

Landis published over a hundred research papers and reviews. From 1962 to 1966 he was editor of *Circulation Research*, a journal of the American Heart Association.

For background information *see* CIRCULATION; CIRCULATION DISORDERS; OSMOREGULATORY MECHANISMS in the McGraw-Hill Encyclopedia of Science and Technology.   □

★ LARDY, Henry Arnold

American biochemist
Born Aug. 19, 1917, Roslyn, S.Dak., U.S.A.

L ARDY'S MAJOR research deals with the function and regulation of enzymes that derive energy from the oxidation of foodstuffs in living cells. In 1947 he discovered the role of biotin in synthesizing oxalacetic acid in bacteria and demonstrated that enzymes from animal tissues also require this vitamin for the synthesis of oxalacetate from pyruvate, arginine from ornithine, succinate from propionate, and acetoacetate from leucine. During the course of this work he reported that the presence of L-aspartate prevents the incorporation of radioactive bicarbonate into this amino acid in bacteria. This was one of the earliest demonstrations of "feedback" inhibition of a biosynthetic reaction.

In 1951 Lardy demonstrated that tissue oxida-

tions in mitochondrial particles are regulated by their need for energy in the form of adenosinetriphosphate (ATP). When either inorganic phosphate or adenosinediphosphate (ADP) is removed from the medium by oxidative phosphorylation, respiration drops to about one-tenth the rate achieved in the presence of these two compounds. The latter are derived from ATP when work is performed and are reconverted to ATP by energy derived from oxidations. Continuing the studies of oxidative phosphorylation, Lardy sought specific agents that might inhibit or alter the oxidative phosphorylation process. He chose to investigate antibiotics toxic to aerobic organisms but not to anaerobes. These studies led to the discovery that oligomycins, aurovertin, and venturicidin are potent inhibitors of the terminal reaction of oxidative phosphorylation; that nonactin, monactin, dinactin, and trinactin induce ion transport into mitochondria; and that nigericin and dianemycin are powerful inhibitors of the mitochondrial ion pump.

Early studies on CO_2 incorporation into four-carbon acids provided a background for later investigations of the path of carbon in gluconeogenesis—the synthesis of glucose in liver and kidney. Lardy and his students demonstrated that the oxalacetate formed in liver mitochondria does not diffuse to the soluble part of the cell where the enzymes catalyzing the remainder of the glucose synthesis pathway are located. Instead, oxalacetate is reduced to malate or transaminated to form aspartate, and these two substances move freely to the cytosol, where they are converted back to oxalacetate. The latter is a precursor of phosphopyruvate, and the enzyme

that catalyzes this conversion is subject to several types of control mechanisms. It can be allosterically activated to approximately twice its normal catalytic potency, and physiological conditions that are conducive to glucose synthesis (fasting, feeding a carbohydrate-free diet, administering the hormones glucagon or hydrocortisone, diabetes) cause greater quantities of this enzyme to be formed in liver. The synthesis of malate in mitochondria is regulated by the availability of reducing equivalents, and both malate and aspartate (the latter via fumarate and malate) in turn supply reducing equivalents to the cytosol, where phosphoglycerate is reduced to triose phosphate in carbohydrate synthesis. Thus pyruvate, CO_2, and sources of ATP and electrons are necessary to sustain glucose synthesis in liver and kidney.

Lardy earned a B.S. with a major in chemistry (1939) from South Dakota State University and an M.S. (1941) and a Ph.D. (1943) from the University of Wisconsin, where his major study was biochemistry and his minor was medical sciences. His thesis work dealt with the preservation of viable, fertile spermatozoa for artificial insemination of livestock and with the metabolism of mammalian spermatozoa. He spent 1 year as a National Research Council posdoctorate fellow with Hermann Fischer at the Banting Institute, University of Toronto, and then returned to a staff position in the department of biochemistry at the University of Wisconsin. In 1950 he was promoted to a full professorship and named chairman of a research department in the Institute for Enzyme Research at Wisconsin, but he continued to teach graduate courses in biochemistry. Most of Lardy's research was conducted in collaboration with graduate students being trained for careers in biochemistry. In 1966 Lardy was named Vilas Research Professor in Biological Sciences. Recipient in 1949 of the American Chemical Society's Paul-Lewis Award in Enzyme Chemistry, he was elected to the National Academy of Sciences in 1958 and to the American Academy of Arts and Sciences in 1965.

Lardy coedited *The Enzymes* (8 vols., 2d rev. ed. 1959–63).

For background information *see* ENZYME; METABOLIC DISORDERS in the McGraw-Hill Encyclopedia of Science and Technology.   □

LARSEN, Esper Signius, Jr.

American geologist
Born Mar. 14, 1879, Astoria, Ore., U.S.A.
Died Mar. 8, 1961, Washington, D.C., U.S.A.

THE VOLCANICS of the San Juan Region of southwestern Colorado, the igneous rocks of the Highwood Mountains of Montana, and the batholithic rocks of southern California were the major objects of Larsen's studies. Not only did he contribute significantly through such regional

studies, but his results in two different branches of laboratory research stand out as classics: He determined the optical properties of over 600 minerals, and he devised the "Larsen method" for the age determination of rocks, based on the lead-uranium ratio of zircons separated from them.

Larsen began his career as assistant petrographer at the Geophysical Laboratory of the Carnegie Institution in Washington, D.C., where he and F. E. Wright worked together and published the classic paper "Quartz as a Geologic Thermometer" (1909). Their results suggested a temperature of around 573°C, plus allowance for pressure effects, for the formation of normal granite pegmatite—a figure which still stands. The principle of determining the index of refraction of a mineral by immersion in a liquid had been demonstrated in the 1890s, but the method for routine exploitation of the principle was developed at the Geophysical Laboratory by Wright. It consisted simply in having available a whole series of liquids whose predetermined index was known. The method, however, required that the indices of refraction of minerals be known. This necessity stimulated Larsen to secure the requisite data and compile his monumental work on the optical determination of the nonopaque minerals when he was a member of the U.S. Geological Survey. His extensive and intensive review of the optical properties of over 600 minerals for his book on their microscopic determination gave him an unusually fine background for the recognition of new minerals. He was author or coauthor in the description of 24 new mineral species.

The study of rocks and minerals based on field work, however, was what really appealed to

Larsen, and in 1909 he joined the U.S. Geological Survey; from 1918 to 1923 he was in charge of the petrology section. His field work while with the Survey was concerned largely with a

study of the San Juan Region of Colorado and New Mexico, one of the world's greatest areas of unmetamorphosed volcanic rocks. The most outstanding results were the papers entitled "Petrologic Results of a Study of the Minerals from the Tertiary Volcanic Rocks of the San Juan Region, Colorado" (1936, 1937, 1938), written by Larsen with several associates. For the first time in the history of petrology, these papers presented a superb, unified systematic study of the phase petrology of a wide variety of volcanic rocks of a single region, correlated with their bulk composition and interpreted by one thoroughly familiar with the geological relationships and history as revealed by personal field studies. The data, including 23 chemical analyses of rock-making minerals, are a permanent contribution to the literature.

The interpretations of the chemical relationships of the volcanic rocks were based on more than 100 chemical analyses. As a result of his studies, Larsen found that in the lavas of the San Juan Mountains there are probably more tridymite and more cristobalite than quartz. The tridymite was especially prevalent in the groundmass of rhyolitic volcanics. His studies of the phenocrysts in relation to the composition of the groundmass in which they occur led Larsen to conclude that most of the plagioclase phenocrysts did not crystallize from a magma of the composition of the lavas in which they were found. Similarly, many of the other kinds of phenocrysts were also of foreign origin. He concluded that, whereas some phenocrysts may be due to sinking or floating, most are the result of thorough mixing of two partly crystallized magmas or by reaction on solidified rock.

On essential completion of work in the San Juan Region in 1930, Larsen, then professor of petrography at Harvard, turned to the Corona quadrangle of southern California and the adjacent Elsinore and San Luis Rey quadrangles. His prime interest here was a study of a part of the southern California batholith. Several of his students assisted him in this work, which required about 22 months (1930–32, 1936, 1938) in the field. He was able to demonstrate that in the area studied the batholith was complex and emplaced by more than 20 separate injections, largely by stoping. From a study of the San Juan lavas Larsen had concluded that they were largely the product of fractional crystallization of basaltic magma. Similarly, he concluded that the different rocks of the batholith—the gabbros, tonalites, granodiorites, and a little granite— were formed from an intermediate gabbro magma by crystal differentiation modified by assimilation in depth.

The last three decades of Larsen's active research were a period of intense discussion and controversy among petrologists concerning the origin of granite: To what extent were the great bodies of granite rock emplaced as magma? To what extent were they the product of granitization of solid rock or the result of metamorphic recrystallization of suitable sedimentary or volcanic rocks? The tremendous volume of lavas and volcanics studied by Larsen in the San Juan Region was unequivocally of magmatic origin. Associated with them were bodies of rock showing the same range of chemical composition as the effusive lavas but with such size and structural relations to the surrounding rocks that they were called dikes, sheets, sills, laccoliths, and stocks. Yet similar textures could be found in their chill facies, and these masses, too, were reasonably considered to be of magmatic origin. With such a background it was only a further step, long as it might be, to interpret the great southern California batholith and later the Idaho batholith as composite bodies built up by successive magmatic intrusions. This problem continues to be one of active debate.

During the last decade before his retirement from Harvard, Larsen became interested in the measurement of geologic time, and more than a third of his publications from then on dealt with this problem. Although he had long been interested in the subject, his active participation began while determining the rare elements in the rocks of the southern California batholith, in which he found that the radioactivity was concentrated in the zircon and a few other rarer accessory minerals. He questioned whether it would be possible to separate the zircon and determine its radioactivity by the measurement of alpha emanations and its content of radiogenic lead by spectroscopic means. If a lead-uranium ratio could thus be obtained, the age of the rock could be determined. Aided by a generous grant from the Geological Society of America and after 10 years of painstaking and often frustrating work by Larsen and several assistants, this supposition was confirmed. The Larsen method is today one of the standard procedures of age determination of rocks.

Larsen received his B.A. in 1906 and Ph.D. in 1918 at the University of California, Berkeley. From 1907 to 1909 he was a member of the staff of the Geophysical Laboratory of the Carnegie Institution in Washington. After 14 years with the U.S. Geological Survey (1909–23), he was appointed professor of petrography at Harvard, retiring in 1949. He received the Roebling Medal of the Mineralogical Society of America in 1941 and the Penrose Medal of the Geological Society of America in 1953. He was elected to the National Academy of Sciences in 1944.

Larsen wrote *The Microscopic Determination of the Nonopaque Minerals* (1921; 2d ed. with

Harry Berman 1934) and *Geology and Petrology of the San Juan Region of Southwestern Colorado,* with Whitman Cross (1956). He was the author or coauthor of 130 papers.

For background information *see* MINERALOGY; PETROGRAPHY in the McGraw-Hill Encyclopedia of Science and Technology. □

★ LE GROS CLARK, Sir Wilfrid (Edward)

British anatomist and anthropologist
Born June 5, 1895, Hemel Hempstead, England

LE GROS CLARK'S academic and research career had its initial inspiration in Borneo, where he spent 3 years in 1920–23 as principal medical officer of Sarawak. In the course of expeditions on medical duties, he made observations on the tarsier and the tree shrew, small mammals then being discussed by those interested in the early evolution of the Primates. After his return to England he was appointed professor of anatomy at London University, and in 1934 professor of anatomy at Oxford University. His first work was in the field of comparative anatomy, with special reference to tarsiers, tree shrews, and insectivores. He was able to list a large number of anatomical characters in which the tree shrews resemble lower Primates rather than the Insectivora, with which they had commonly been classified. This fresh examination led to a reappraisal of the taxonomic position of the tree shrews (Tupaiidae) and their reallocation by most taxonomists to the order Primates. A relationship with the Primates had been suggested by some zoologists previously, but on evidence too slender to be generally accepted.

The study of the brain of these small Primates, particularly the visual system and the thalamus, led Le Gros Clark into neurological research by the application of experimental methods. He confirmed and extended the observation of O. Minkowski that in the higher Primates crossed and uncrossed optic fibers from the retina of each eye undergo a complete segregation when, by way of the optic tract, they reach their termination in the geniculate nucleus. The latter consists of six layers, the crossed fibers ending in three of these and the uncrossed fibers in the other three, without any overlap. These studies were pursued further by making small, discrete lesions in different parts of the retina and tracing the degeneration resulting from the fibers involved in each experiment. It then was found that from the central area of the retina each small locus sends back three sets of optic fibers that end locally in all the three corresponding cell layers of the geniculate nucleus. One result of this study was the demonstration that the topical localization of the retina in the geniculate nucleus is much more precise and sharply circumscribed than had formerly been recognized. The experiments also led to the inference that the conducting unit from the retina is a three-fiber unit such as had been postulated by the trichromatic theory of color vision. It is now know that the three cell layers of the geniculate nucleus in the monkey, corresponding to crossed or uncrossed optic fibers, do show different patterns of electrical activity following stimulation of the retina; however, it has yet to be demonstrated that these different patterns are related to color discrimination. A further observation by Le Gros Clark established that, in their course along the optic tract, crossed and uncrossed retinal fibers appear to be completely mixed up in a random disarrangement; it is only when they reach the geniculate nucleus that they become unraveled and segregated from each other. Thus the geniculate nucleus is more than a relay station through which retinal impulses are conveyed to the visual cortex; it is a sorting station concerned with the sorting out of fibers carrying impulses of different functional significance. This "sorting principle in sensory analysis" has come to be recognized as an important phenomenon in the organization of the nervous system.

The geniculate nucleus is but one element of the thalamus, and to the analysis of this sensory mass of gray matter Le Gros Clark next turned his attention. By making small, circumscribed lesions in various parts of the cerebral cortex and studying the resultant retrograde degeneration in the thalamus, he mapped out the cortical projection areas of various thalamic nuclei and followed this up by tracing the termination in the latter of some of the ascending tracts of the spinal cord and brainstem. He also charted the nuclear elements of the hypothalamus as a preliminary to the investigation of their fiber connections. During World War II he engaged in an experimental study of the regenerative capacity of fiber tracts in the central nervous system and of voluntary muscle tissue following vascular injuries. In regard to the first of these, carefully controlled experiments failed to show any positive evidence of the regeneration of nerve fibers of brain tissue following their interruption by local lesions, even when small pieces of predegenerated peripheral nerves containing abundant Schwann cells were implanted in the lesions. Newly growing nerve fibers were indeed present at the site of the lesions, but they were found to be derived from the ingrowth of extrinsic fibers from the overlying dura mater or skin or from the regeneration of vasomotor fibers. Following the implantation of proximal stumps of cut facial nerves into the brain, regenerating fibers from this nerve penetrated into the brain tissue with vigorous growth, indicating that there is nothing in the inherent constitution of brain tissue that inhibits nerve fiber regeneration. Yet the immediately adjacent intrinsic fibers of the brain interrupted by the operational procedure showed no sign of regenerative activity. The experimental study of muscle regeneration demonstrated that a partial devascularization of a muscle leads to a complete necrosis of the affected area, but new muscle fibers rapidly extended down from the remains of fibers obtaining their blood supply from other sources, replacing the necrotic tissue. Later neurological studies by Le Gros Clark included an examination of the nervus conarii of the pineal body and the pattern of olfactory innervation. The results of the latter were presented in the Ferrier Lecture of the Royal Society of London under the title "Inquiries into the Anatomical Basis of Olfactory Discrimination."

Throughout his academic career Le Gros Clark continued to take an interest in the comparative anatomy of the Primates and more particularly in the fossil evidence for human evolution. Sceptical of the claims advanced by Raymond Dart and R. Broom for the hominid affinities of the Early Pleistocene genus *Australopithecus*, Le Gros Clark visited South Africa in 1946 to examine the relevant fossil material. As a result, he was able to confirm Dart and Broom's main conclusions; that is, *Australopithecus* was on, or close to, the main line of hominid evolution and quite distinct from the line of evolution of the anthropoid ape family. His observations were published in a series of monographs in scientific journals and, although the inferences he drew from these were controverted by some anthropologists (partly on the basis of statistical data later shown to involve a serious error in the calculation of standard deviations), they were substantiated by further discoveries of fossil remains in Africa. He also took part, with K. P. Oakley and J. S. Weiner, in the exposure of the Piltdown forgery by demonstrating the anatomical evidence for the fradulent fabrication of the teeth of an orangutan jaw to make them simulate the teeth of a primitive type of man.

Le Gros Clark took degrees at London, Durham, Manchester, and other universities. He was captain in the Royal Army Medical Corps in 1916–18, principal medical officer in Sarawak, Borneo, in 1920–23, and reader in anatomy at London University in 1924–27. He was professor of anatomy at St. Bartholomew's Hospital (1927–29) and at St. Thomas's Hospital (1929–34), both divisions of London University, and at Oxford University during 1934–62. Recipient of the Viking Fund Medal in physical anthropology in 1951 and a Royal Medal of the Royal Society of London in 1961, he was elected a fellow of the Royal Society of London in 1935 and a foreign associate of the U.S. National Academy of Sciences in 1963. He was knighted in 1955.

Le Gros Clark wrote *The Tissues of the Body* (1939; 5th ed. 1965), *The Fossil Evidence for Human Evolution* (1955; 2d ed. 1964), *History of the Primates* (8th ed. 1962), *The Antecedents of Man* (1959; 2d ed. 1962), and the sections on the central nervous system in D. J. Cunningham's *Text-Book of Anatomy* (1902; 9th ed. 1956).

For background information *see* ANIMAL EVOLUTION; PRIMATES; PRIMATES (FOSSIL) in the McGraw-Hill Encyclopedia of Science and Technology.   □

☆ LEHNINGER, Albert Lester

American biochemist
Born Feb. 17, 1917, Bridgeport, Conn., U.S.A.

AT THE University of Chicago in 1948 Lehninger and the biochemist Eugene P. Kennedy discovered that the subcellular body known as the mitochondrion is the main site of cell respiration, the process whereby metabolically useful energy is extracted from nutrient raw materials. Lehninger showed that most of the enzyme molecules involved in respiration are located along the walls or within the interior of the mitochondria. This discovery was an important step forward in the elucidation of cell structure and function.

By the end of the 19th century it was known that energy is obtained in the living cell by the degradation of complex nutrient substances (sugars, fats, and amino acids) with the subsequent release of water and carbon dioxide. By the middle of the 20th century many of the basic aspects of this process, to which the comprehensive name "respiration" was given, had yielded to intensive research. It was found that respiratory reactions require a great many steps; that each step involves specific enzymes ("carriers") and intermediate reaction products; and that the resulting energy is stored in an organic molecule, adenosinetriphosphate (ATP), universally present in cells. The whole process was divided into three stages. The first, glycolysis, involves (in the case of sugars) the breakdown of a six-carbon sugar such as glucose to a three-carbon compound, pyruvic acid. The second, called either the "citric acid cycle" or the "Krebs cycle" (for the English biochemist Sir Hans Krebs, who first postulated it in 1937), is an endless belt affair that transfers the energy from pyruvic acid to various carrier enzymes by reducing them, that is, by adding to them either a hydrogen ion or an electron. It is here that one of the waste products, carbon dioxide, is released. Finally, in the last stage, a chain of electron carriers releases most of the energy in the form of molecules of ATP, and also the second waste product, water.

From the complexity of respiration and the number of substances required, it was clear that the process would be inefficient, not to say impossible, if the needed materials are simply scattered at random throughout the cell. Further evidence for the existence of enzyme complexes in the cell came in the mid-1940s, when the American biochemist David E. Green found that the various enzymes involved in the respiratory process are tightly associated together in granules.

In 1948 Lehninger and Kennedy were working with mitochondria in the hope of discovering their function in the cell's economy. Nothing was then known of the internal structure of these particles, but it was known that some hundreds or thousands of them are present in almost all cells, and that they are generally globular or rod-shaped. (Mitochondria are just barely visible under the light microscope.) The experimenters obtained mitochondria by successive centrifugation of disrupted cells, usually from rat liver. They incubated the particles with pyruvic acid

and other intermediate products of respiration in the presence of oxygen. They found that all the reactions involved in the citric acid cycle and electron transport were taking place at a rate and with an efficiency approaching those observed in the intact cell. They found, in contrast, that cell nuclei and other subcellular structures are unable to carry on these reactions under the same circumstances. (Some other investigations showed that the usual first stage of respiration, glycolysis, does not in fact take place in the mitochondria. However, because the last two stages of the process liberate over 90% of the energy involved, the usual statement that the mitochondria are the "powerhouse of the cell" is quite justified.)

In other experiments Lehninger was able to pinpoint the location of the citric acid and respiratory cycles more precisely. He took advantage of the fact that mitochondria can be broken up by intense sound waves or chemicals such as detergents. In the process the particles rupture, the liquid "matrix" within them escapes, and the insoluble outer membrane is reduced to fragments. The two fractions may then be separated by centrifugation and investigated separately. Lehninger concluded that the enzymes involved in the citric acid cycle come from the matrix, while those involved in the respiratory chain are located in the mitochondrial membrane. These findings suggested that the mitochondrion has a complex and orderly internal structure (which began to be revealed in 1952 when the first electron micrographs of mitochondria were made).

Another finding, made by Lehninger in 1949, was that the mitochondria also are the site of oxidative phosphorylation, the reaction in which a phosphate group is added to energy-poor adenosinediphosphate (ADP) to produce energy-rich ATP. Up to this point there had been no conclusive evidence to connect this process with the oxidative and electron-transfer cycles of respiration, and the discovery that the three basic mechanisms of energy transfer in the cell are intimately connected was a significant one. Lehninger and a research group at the University of Chicago discovered that at three points in the respiratory chain (third stage), there are present, in addition to the enzymes necessary for oxidation and electron transfer, other enzymes that utilize the energy liberated in electron transfer to phosphorylate ADP to ATP. Lehninger envisioned the respiratory chain as a row of interlocking loops or gears of various sizes, each centering on a particular intermediate product. At each "turn" of a gear an electron is transferred from one stage to the next. At some intermediate point the energy is utilized by one of the three enzymes or "coupling factors" to add a phosphate group to ADP and thus help restore the balance of ATP in the cell. This discovery led to a great deal of further research, including a model of the electron-transfer process which modifies some details, though no essentials, of Lehninger's original model.

In addition to these discoveries, Lehninger found that the transport of ions across the mitochondrial membrane, which involves high-energy intermediate compounds of a type similar to those involved in ATP production, is a process that is alternative to formation of ATP, and that the number of ions accumulated by mitochondria is related to the number of electrons flowing from the Krebs cycle to oxygen. Lehninger also demonstrated that the shape or internal structure of the mitochondria may undergo reversible permeability and structural changes accompanying electron transport. These changes he associated with metabolic control of the activity of mitochondria.

Lehninger received his B.S. (1939) at Wesleyan University and his M.S. (1940) and Ph.D. (1942) at the University of Wisconsin, where he remained as an instructor until 1945. From 1945 to 1952 he was assistant, then associate, professor at the University of Chicago, and in 1951 he was an exchange professor at the University of Frankfurt. From 1951 to 1952 he was also a Guggenheim fellow and Fulbright research professor at the University of Cambridge, England. In 1952 he went to Johns Hopkins University as DeLamar Professor of Physiological Chemistry and director of the department of physiological chemistry. Recipient of the American Chemical Society's Award in Enzyme Chemistry in 1948, Lehninger was elected to the National Academy of Sciences in 1956 and to the American Academy of Arts and Sciences in 1959.

For background information see BIOLOGICAL OXIDATION; MITOCHONDRIA in the McGraw-Hill Encyclopedia of Science and Technology.   □

★ LELOIR, Luis Federico

Argentine biochemist
Born Sept. 6, 1906, Paris, France

SOON AFTER graduation with an M.D. in 1932, Leloir started on his thesis under Bernardo A. Houssay, then head of the Institute of Physiology of the Faculty of Medicine of the University of Buenos Aires. After Leloir had worked about 2 years on the role of the adrenals on carbohydrate metabolism, Houssay advised him to go abroad to improve his background. The place selected was the Biochemical Laboratory of Cambridge University, England, which was directed by Frederick Gowland Hopkins and was one of the most active centers of biochemical research. During the fruitful year he spent there, Leloir collaborated with Malcolm Dixon, N. L. Edson, and D. E. Green. On returning to the Institute of Physiology, Leloir began to work with J. Muñoz on fatty acid oxidation. (At the time this process was believed to be dependent on intact cell structure.) They prepared liver homogenates and found that in order to oxidize butyric acid these homogenates had to be complemented with C_4 dicarboxylic acids, adenosinephosphates, and cytochrome c.

In the meantime J. C. Fasciolo had been working on the effect of renal artery constriction on blood pressure, and it seemed that a pressor substance was liberated. Leloir and Muñoz joined Fasciolo, with E. Braun Menéndez, and set to work on the problem. It was known that there is a protein in kidney that increases blood pressure. However, this protein, called renin, is thermolabile, and Fasciolo had evidence that his substance was thermostable. After many trials Leloir and co-workers found that incubation of renin with a blood protein led to the formation of a pressor substance, which they named hypertensin. They called the blood protein hypertensinogen. (D. M. Helmer and I. H. Page had independently reached similar conclusions, naming the substance angiotonin. Several years later Braun Menéndez and Page agreed to use the hybrid name angiotensin.) All their work on hypertensin was summarized in the book *Hipertensión Arterial Nefrógena* (1943; English transl. 1946).

In 1943 political events in Argentina affected the university so that Houssay and many other professors were dismissed. Leloir resigned his university position and went to work in the United States, where he spent some time in Carl F. Cori's department in Washington University, St. Louis, and with David E. Green at College of Physicians and Surgeons, Columbia University.

Leloir was back in Buenos Aires in 1946, when a wealthy textile manufacturer, Jaime Campomar, consulted Houssay as to who might take charge of a biochemical research laboratory there. Houssay mentioned Leloir, and the Instituto de Investigaciones Bioquimicas "Fundación Campomar" was started. The group was organized with Ranwel Caputto, who had just returned from a fellowship spent in the Biochemical Laboratory at Cambridge, Raúl Trucco, who had been trained as a microbiologist, Carlos E. Cardini, and Alejandro C. Paladini. An important contribution of this team was the discovery of uridine diphosphate glucose and other sugar nucleotides. This finding led to the elucidation of the mechanism of synthesis of many oligosaccharides and polysaccharides.

Caputto had done some experiments with mammary gland extracts that led him to believe he might have obtained the synthesis of lactose (the sugar of milk) in vitro. Leloir's team decided to follow this line of work but soon got discouraged with animal tissue extracts and reasoned that in studying the process of lactose degradation they might find out how it is synthesized. At the time it was thought that the same reactions could be involved in both synthesis and degradation. Leloir and co-workers obtained a yeast (*Saccharomyces fragilis*) that grows well on lactose-containing media and acquires the property of utilizing lactose at a higher rate than the sum of its constituent hexoses, glucose and galactose. They first found a lactose-hydrolyzing enzyme in *S. fragilis* extracts and afterward an enzyme that catalyzes galactose phosphorylation to give galactose-1-phosphate. The next obvious step was the study of the transformation of galactose-1-phosphate. It was found to yield glucose-6-phosphate, and the study of this process was very rewarding since two thermostable cofactors were found to be involved. The results were very confusing at first, but it was eventually observed that the reaction has two steps, each requiring a cofactor. One step is the conversion of galactose-1-phosphate to glucose-1-phosphate, which requires uridine diphosphateglucose (UDPG), and another step is the isomerization of glucose-1-phosphate to glucose-6-phosphate. In the latter step Leloir found that glucose-1,6-diphosphate is required. Present-day methods for the separation were not available in those times, so that the isolation of substances found in fairly small amounts was a laborious task, especially where laboratory facilities were very poor.

The isolation of UDPG from yeast extracts led to the discovery of two similar substances, UDP-acetylglucosamine and GDP-mannose. Another compound, UDP-galactose, was found to be formed from UDPG by enzyme action. With these findings it seemed likely that many different sugar nucleotides occur in natural products and that they have some important metabolic role. The first transfer reaction to be detected (with E. Cabib in 1953) was the formation of trehalose phosphate from UDPG and glucose-6-phosphate. Soon (with Cardini and J. Chiriboga in 1955) Leloir's team detected enzymes in plants that form sucrose or sucrose phosphate from UDPG. Many other reactions of the same type were discovered by other workers, especially by W. Z. Hassid of the University of California.

Another finding of some interest was the role of UDPG in glycogen metabolism. Carl and Gerty Cori had carried out important work on phosphorylase, the enzyme that catalyzes the conversion of glycogen to glucose-1-phosphate. Since this reaction is reversible, it was believed that both glycogen synthesis and degradation were catalyzed by phosphorylase. When Leloir's team found (with Cardini in 1957) a liver enzyme that uses UDPG as a glucose donor for glycogen synthesis, it was realized that there are two different pathways, one for synthesis, with UDPG as donor, and another for degradation, in which glucose-1-phosphate is the product. Glycogen is a reserve polysaccharide in animals as starch is in plants, so Leloir's team directed their attention to plant enzymes. They found (with Cardini and M. Fekete in 1960) an enzyme in several plant tissues that catalyzes starch synthesis from UDPG. Later (with E. Recondo in 1961) they found that ADP-glucose is more likely to be the natural donor in plant tissues.

Leloir graduated from the University of Buenos Aires with an M.D. in 1932. He was assistant to B. A. Houssay at the Institute of Physiology, Buenos Aires, in 1934–35, worked in 1936 at the Biochemical Laboratory of Cambridge University, England, and in 1937 returned to the Institute of Physiology, where he did research until 1943. He was research associate in the department of pharmacology at Washington University in 1944 and in the Enzyme Research Laboratory of the College of Physicians and Surgeons, Columbia University, in 1944–45. In 1946 he took charge of the Instituto de Investigaciones Bioquimicas "Fundación Campomar" in Buenos Aires. Leloir's honors included the T. Duckett Jones Memorial Award of the Helen Hay Whitney Foundation in 1958, the Gairdner Foundation Award in 1966, and honorary degrees from the universities of Paris, Granada (Spain), and Tucumán (Argentina). He was elected a foreign member of the U.S. National Academy of Sciences in 1960 and the American Academy of Arts and Sciences in 1961.

For background information *see* CARBO-HYDRATE METABOLISM; ENZYME in the McGraw-Hill Encyclopedia of Science and Technology. □

★ LEONARD, Nelson Jordan

American chemist
Born Sept. 1, 1916, Newark, N.J., U.S.A.

IN AN era of general progress in the synthesis of organic compounds by rational methodology and for particular illustration of function, property, stereochemistry, or some new phenomenon, Leonard made frequent and timely contributions. These are exemplified by innovations in reductive cyclization, oxidative cyclization, rearrangements of aminoketones and thiaketones, transannular interactions and reactions, synthesis and reactions of enamines and iminium and aziridinium salts, and synthesis of adenine derivatives possessing biological activity. For his contributions to organic synthesis he received in 1963 the American Chemical Society Award for Creative Work in Synthetic Organic Chemistry.

His first large-scale endeavor in organic synthesis was at the University of Illinois, where he initially concentrated in 1944–46 on the synthesis of antimalarial drugs, including assistance (with C. C. Price and H. R. Snyder) in the development of a commercially feasible synthesis of 4-(4'-diethylamino-1'-butylamino)-7-chloroquinoline, a compound adopted by the U.S. Armed Forces. From an interest in heterocyclic nitrogen compounds he developed a method of synthesis of compounds containing bridgehead nitrogen, such as are present in a wide variety of alkaloids isolated from plants of the *Senecio* and *Lupinus* genera. General methods of reductive cyclization were developed for closing rings to yield bicyclic, tricyclic, and tetracyclic nitrogen compounds, including the lupin alkaloid sparteine. These methods provided specific compounds that aided in the delineation of the

stereochemistry of the necine portions of the *Senecio* alkaloids and (with L. Marion) that of the entire family of C_{15} lupin alkaloids. The availability of bicyclic bridgehead nitrogen compounds permitted a thorough investigation of the reduction, with rearrangement, of a series of α-aminoketones. During this investigation, and specifically in the electrolytic reduction of bicyclic α-aminoketones (with S. Swann), a new method was discovered for the synthesis of rings of medium size (8–11 members) containing nitrogen.

In this and in other synthetic approaches to medium-ring compounds, he and his students accumulated several series of compounds (Fig. 1) in which unusual combinations of organic functionality could be identified (Formulas I-VII). The combinations were made possible by incorporating electron-donating and electron-accepting groups in eight-membered rings (Formula VIII), on opposite sides of the ring but actually in close proximity, and then, in most cases, treating the medium-ring compound with a protonic acid to effect transannular bond formation. The result is actually a spatial control of organic functionality, since the functional combinations represented have not been realized in open-chain analogs or in reactions between

Fig. 1. Formulas I–IX.

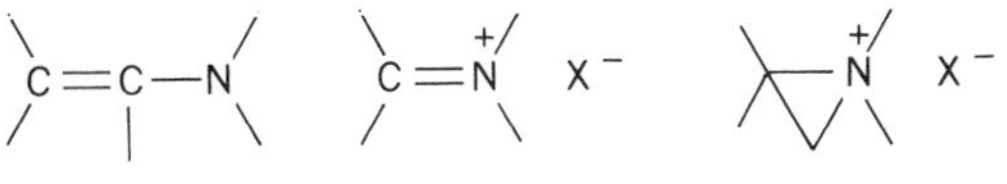

Fig. 2. (a) Enamine grouping. (b) Iminium salt grouping. (c) Aziridinium perchlorate and fluoborate grouping.

separate molecules possessing the reactive groups. Structures having these unusual combinations were established by infrared, nuclear magnetic resonance, and ultraviolet spectra, by basicity studies, by kinetics of hydrolysis, and by isotopic labeling experiments. These functional combinations offer new directions for organic reactions and suggest possible consequences of fixation of intermolecular geometrical relationships in more complicated systems, such as enzyme systems.

In further investigations of basic nitrogen compounds, Leonard and his students developed diagnostic methods for the detection of double-bond unsaturation adjacent to an amino nitrogen, that is, an enamine (see Fig. 2a), and oxidative methods for the introduction of such unsaturation into a saturated tertiary amine or alkaloid system. Among the oxidation methods the use of mercuric acetate provided a new synthetic route to substituted piperidines, tetrahydropyridines, tetrahydroanabasines, and—by oxidative cyclization—to oxazolidines. The enamines were found to be protonated on β-carbon where this is not sterically prevented, and the chemistry of the resulting iminium salts (see Fig. 2b) was thoroughly investigated. Moreover, a direct method of synthesis of compounds having this functionality was discovered by Leonard in the reaction of aldehydes and ketones with the secondary amine perchlorates and fluoborates. The reaction of diazomethane with iminium salts was discovered and found to be a widely applicable method for the synthesis of aziridinium perchlorates and fluoborates (see Fig. 2c). Many new reactions were then uncovered in Leonard's laboratory that are now considered to be typical of the strained, charged ring in the aziridinium salts, the most remarkable being a series of ring enlargement reactions involving ketones, aldehydes, nitriles, and nitrones.

Following the determination of the structure of the alkaloid triacanthine and the investigation of its chemistry, new facts were uncovered by Leonard and his students concerning the alkylation of purine compounds. Moreover, the synthesis of an isomer of triacanthine, 6-(γ,γ-dimethylallylamino)purine (IX), provided the most active cytokinin known, as determined by the promotion of growth of tobacco cells (F. Skoog). This compound was later isolated in

Skoog's laboratory from the plant pathogen *Corynebacterium fascians* and identified at Illinois as IX. It was also found that cytokinin activity could be developed by the rearrangement of 1-substituted adenines to N^6-substituted adenines, a research project that included the synthesis of 6-(γ,γ-dimethylallylamino)-9-β-D-ribofuranosylpurine, having, as IX, the property of cell division and differentiation. The ribosyl derivative of IX was isolated in other laboratories from serine tRNA and from yeast and calf liver sRNA. The determination of the preferred site of alkylation of adenine prompted the synthesis at Illinois of 3-isoadenosine, the isomer of adenosine in which the ribose is attached to the 3-position rather than the usual 9-position, and the determinatoin of the biological activities of analogs of ADP, ATP, and NAD derived from this nucleoside isomer.

Leonard received a B.S. from Lehigh University in 1937. As a Rhodes scholar, he attended Oxford University during 1937–39 (B.Sc., 1940). He received his Ph.D. from Columbia University in 1942, when he joined the faculty of the University of Illinois. He was elected to the National Academy of Sciences in 1955 and to the American Academy of Arts and Sciences in 1961.

Leonard published more than 175 papers in the chemical journals and edited *Organic Syntheses* (Vol. 36, 1956). He was also granted six patents.

For background information *see* ORGANIC CHEMICAL SYNTHESIS; ORGANIC CHEMISTRY in the McGraw-Hill Encyclopedia of Science and Technology.   □

☆ LIM, Robert Kho-Seng

American physiologist
Born Oct. 15, 1897, Singapore

UNTIL FAIRLY recently, medical teaching concerning the cause of pain and the manner in which pain-relieving drugs act was based upon misconceptions. Lim, a senior research fellow and director of the Medical Sciences Research Laboratory at Miles Laboratories, showed that pain can be produced anywhere in the body, without physical injury, by a variety of chemical agents. The discovery that the receptors which mediate pain are chemosensitive has altered the classical concept of the pain receptor as an injury-sensitive organ. Pain is signaled whenever the nerve fibers from these receptors or the receptors themselves are injured, but the proper biological stimulus is chemical, usually an increase of hydrogen ions associated with any local impairment of blood flow, or the chemical changes associated with the processes of tissue

removal and repair which follow injury and which constitute inflammation. During the inflammatory process pain-producing agents, such as the bradykinin peptides, are formed. Being chemosensitive, the pain receptors are receptive not only to pain-producing agents, but also to substances that resemble them although they do not cause pain. By occupying the pain receptors, these substances prevent the agents from causing pain. The well-known pain reliever aspirin acts in this way, relieving pain by combining with the pain receptor and denying it to the pain-provoking agents. Lim proved experimentally that aspirin and like analgesics act peripherally, not in the brain, whereas morphine and other narcotic analgesics act on the central nervous system.

In his earlier career in Peking, Lim worked in two main areas: gastroenterology and the central mechanisms concerned with the regulation of autonomic functions. He and his co-workers demonstrated that gastric secretion could be stimulated locally by mechanical means, and that it is inhibited by a humoral agent, enterogastrone, which was isolated in crude form from the intestinal mucosa. He showed that the sympathetic reflexes could be obtained in the decerebrate animal and that all the sympathetic responses could be evoked by stimulation of the medulla. He and his group were among the first to show that acetylcholine is liberated in the central nervous system and that the posterior pituitary (vasopressor, antidiuretic, and oxytocic) hormones could be liberated reflexly on vagal stimulation.

Born a British subject of Chinese parentage in the Crown Colony of Singapore, Lim studied in Scotland, then served during World War I in the Indian Army Medical Service. He earned his M.B. and Ch.B. (1919), his Ph.D. in physiology (1920), and his D.Sc. (1924) from Edinburgh University. He was a lecturer in physiology at Edinburgh from 1919 to 1923. In 1923 he was awarded a Rockefeller Foundation fellowship to the University of Chicago, and in 1924 he became professor of physiology at the Peking Union Medical College. While there, he established the Chinese Physiological Society and its journal. He organized the first reserve officers training corps for medical officers in North China, was president of the Chinese Medical Association, founded the Red Cross Medical Relief Commission in North China and served as its field director, and was chairman of the North China Council for Rural Reconstruction. In World War II Lim was called on to organize the Chinese Red Cross Medical Relief Corps in support of the Chinese army. In 1942 he was assigned to the Chinese Expeditionary Force in Burma under General J. W. Stilwell. Shortly thereafter, he led his medical group with miscellaneous allied personnel to safety in a gruelling 26-day march through the roadless, Japanese-controlled jungles of Burma to India at the start of the monsoon. For this action he received the U.S. Legion of Merit, Officer Grade, in 1942. After the war Lim, as surgeon general of the Chinese Nationalist army, organized the National Defense Medical Center, set up 10 general hospitals, and initiated a program of postgraduate training of Chinese medical service personnel in the United States. In 1949 he went to the United States and in 1952 joined Miles Laboratories. Lim was elected an honorary member of the Deutsche Akademie der Naturforscher, Halle, in 1932, a foreign associate of the U.S. National Academy of Sciences in 1942, an honorary member of the American Gastroenterological Association in 1946, and an honorary fellow of the American College of Surgeons in 1947.

For background information *see* ANALGESICS; PAIN, CUTANEOUS; PAIN, DEEP; SYMPATHETIC NERVOUS SYSTEM in the McGraw-Hill Encyclopedia of Science and Technology.   □

★ LINDAUER, Martin

German zoologist
Born Dec. 19, 1918, Wäldle (Oberammergau), Bavaria, Germany

WHEN BEES communicate with each other by means of a tail-wagging dance about the direction, distance, quality, and productivity of a goal, they use coded signals that are valid for all bees of the same species. Between members of different species small misunderstandings exist because they speak their own "dialects."

A grant from the Rockefeller Foundation en-

abled Lindauer to travel to Ceylon in 1952 in order to study the language of the Indian bees. In southeastern Asia, the ancestral home of the European honeybee, *Apis mellifera,* there are three other species of honeybees, *A. indica, A. florea,* and *A. dorsata.* The dances of these Indian bees have such different characteristics that they can no longer communicate with the European bees. While the latter can indicate precisely a goal's direction and distance only after 30 or 70 m, the *A. indica* communicates after a distance of 2 m the exact location of a feeding place. Therefore, the communication among the Indian bees is more exact. The dance of the dwarf honeybee, *A. florea,* is especially interesting. It is more primitive than the dances of the other species because the compass direction to the goal is not transposed with respect to gravity; in order to communicate, *A. florea* needs a horizontal dance floor under a clear sky because that is the only way it can indicate in a compass-true fashion the angle between the Sun and the goal. For the same reason the dwarf honeybee is forced to build its nest in the open—it cannot withdraw into a sheltering cave because it cannot communicate in the dark by way of gravity. Thus was discovered a phylogenetically more primitive step of the bee's language which, in turn, lets one anticipate how the intermediary stages of this highly organized communication method have developed.

Other comparative "language studies" led Lindauer to Brazil, the home of the stingless bees. There are several hundred species of stingless bees, and they show both in their social organization and in their communication system all stages of development from the most primitive beginnings to the most effective alarm and goal indications. In common with honeybees all these stingless bees have the most elementary components of the bee dance, such as the excited zigzag walk to alarm the other hive members to congregate and to inform them by the perfume sticking on their hairy bodies which blossom locations offer nectar. Concerning other goal indications, the Brazilian bees have evolved their own methods: The most organized species send their novices in front of the flight hole by means of a zigzag alarming walk; in the meantime several scout bees have laid a scent trail between hive and goal by leaving a scent secretion from their upper jaw gland on small stones or grass blades. The alarmed swarm at the flight hole is then lured along the scent path—a most effective goal indication, but in comparison with *A. mellifica,* a much more primitive communication method. The novices are not given coded, indirect information since they cannot find the goal independently.

Another area of communication is in the establishment of new colonies by a process called swarming. When the bees separate from their hive in a swarm, the queen and accompanying cluster of workers are homeless. Scouts go house hunting, and those which find a suitable nesting site (such as a hollow tree or a hole in the ground) return to the swarm and inform their colleagues, again by way of the tail-wagging dance. Lindauer marked these dancers with paint dots and discovered to his great astonishment that a number of nesting sites were announced, up to 20 and more. It is clear, of course, that the swarm, having only one queen, can accept only one of these offers. How is an agreement reached among 20,000 individuals of a swarm? Looking for a solution, Lindauer moved bee swarms to deserted islands where there were no nesting sites and no other bees and offered artificial nesting sites. The bees found a simple solution to this serious dilemma: They agreed on the best of the nesting sites offered. The tail-wagging dance of the scouts showed not only the location, but also the quality of the prospective home and thus enlisted the interest of the bees of the swarm in the best nesting sites. These sites were inspected, even by the reconnaissance bees that had previously announced other sites. Agreement on the new home site is essential because only then can the swarm relocate.

Besides hunting for food and home, the bee dance is also used as an SOS signal in dangerous situations. During the hot season, if a beehive remained in the strongest sunlight, the honeycombs would melt through overheating. Countermeasures are taken by the water carriers. Water is squirted in millions of tiny puddles everywhere in the hive and cells and is brought to fast evaporation by fanning of the wings. The preservation of the bees depends on how quickly the water is brought to the hive, and that is possible only when all available forces are sent to the water place by an alarm, that is, again, by the dancing bees.

Since his student days Lindauer was fascinated by the harmony that exists in the division of labor of bees. As Gustav A. Rösch discovered in 1925, every bee has a work calendar which determines its role in the social system. But this does not explain the perfect harmony of a beehive. Lindauer undertook, therefore, constant observations of several bees from the cradle to the grave, and these observations showed that the work calendars are only a general guideline for the individual bee and that the social needs of the society determine the individual's activity.

In recent years, with his colleagues, Lindauer investigated the orientation abilities of bees and their physiological basis in the optical, olfactory, and statoreceptive spheres. The hair tufts on the neck, abdomen, and leg joints of the bee were discovered to serve as receptors for gravity; they control, among other things, the transposition of the Sun's angle into the field of gravity during the tail-wagging dance. The bee's bipolar movable antennae, on which are found closely united chemical and mechanical receptors, were individually analyzed for their unique topochemical perception ability. And Lindauer found on the antennae's points three specific sensory pads in the shape of hooked bristles, circularly arranged, which are used by the building bees to control precisely the thickness of the comb walls (which are uniformly 72 microns). With its upper jaws the building bee punches a dent in the wall, which swings back to its previous state because of its elasticity; the extremely pressure-sensitive bristles on the antennae's points control the dynamic transformation and the intensity of the counterpressure. Because both parameters of temperature and wax material remain constant, the thickness of the walls can in this way be measured.

Returning wounded to Germany from the Soviet Union in World War II, Lindauer studied with Karl von Frisch at the University of Munich, where he received his doctorate in 1948. He became scientific assistant in Graz and Munich, then professor extraordinarius in Munich in 1960, and in 1963 was made director of the Zoological Institute in Frankfurt am Main. Lindauer was elected a member of the Deutsche Akademie der Naturforscher Leopoldina in Jena and the American Academy of Arts and Sciences.

Lindauer wrote *Communication among Social Bees* (1961), awarded the Phi Beta Kappa Prize of Harvard University.

For background information *see* BEE AND BEE-KEEPING; HYMENOPTERA; INSECT PHYSIOLOGY in the McGraw-Hill Encyclopedia of Science and Technology.   □

★ **LINGANE, James Joseph**

American analytical chemist
Born Sept. 13, 1909, Saint Paul, Minn., U.S.A.

LINGANE'S CAREER in analytical chemistry began in 1931, when he was employed as a student assistant by I. M. Kolthoff at the University of Minnesota. While still an undergraduate under Kolthoff, he published six research papers. One of these described a precise method for determining uranium by titration from the +4 to the +6 state with dichromate, which a decade later, after the advent of atomic energy, became the standard method of uranium determination.

Beginning graduate study in 1935, Lingane was attracted to polarographic analysis with the dropping mercury electrode, a technique invented a dozen years earlier by Jaroslav Heyrovsky in Prague, but which at that time was still virtually unknown in the United States. Polarography depends on the fact that, when solutions of electroactive substances are electrolyzed with an electrode consisting of mercury flowing drop by drop from a capillary glass tube, the resulting current-potential curves show increases in current at potentials which are characteristic of the particular electroactive substances. Under optimum conditions the current due to each substance attains a constant value over a certain range of applied potential. This limiting current usually is governed by the rate of diffusion of the substance to the electrode surface and consequently is directly proportional to its concentration.

Lingane undertook as his Ph.D. thesis a systematic investigation of the many phenomena that underlie current-potential relationships under polarographic conditions. This investigation provided the first conclusive experimental verification of a theoretical relation for the diffusion-controlled limiting current which had just been proposed (1935) by D. Ilkovic. It also yielded new information about the influence of electrical migration on the limiting current, maxima in polarographic waves, the background current caused by the capacitive charging of the ionic "double layer" at the mercury-solution interface, and the current-potential function of a polarographic wave. During these studies Lingane invented the technique, now known as "three-electrode polarography," of using a separate reference electrode to monitor the potential of the dropping electrode. The results of this study published, with Kolthoff, in 1939 in *Chemical Reviews* comprised the first critical and thorough exposition of polarography in an American journal. Further published studies helped guide polarography to its present sophisticated state.

Heyrovsky had originally pointed out that the position of a polarographic wave on the voltage axis is best defined by the potential at which the current is one-half its limiting value, since this half-wave potential, being closely related to the standard potential of the electrode reaction, is independent of concentration. During 1939–41 Lingane pursued studies which clarified the thermodynamic significance of the half-wave potential and which, in particular, paved the way for the fruitful application of polarography to the determination of the formulas and instability constants of metal ion complexes. At this time he also initiated the use of dropping amalgam electrodes.

Successful application of polarography (or any physicochemical technique) to analytical problems depends not merely on understanding the principles of the method, but equally on an intimate knowledge of the chemical and electrochemical properties of the substances concerned. Thus, Lingane and his students were drawn to systematic investigations of the electrochemistry of many elements as necessary groundwork to the development of polarographic analytical methods. These researches contributed to better understanding of the redox chemistry of such elements as rhenium, vanadium, tungsten, titanium, chromium, selenium, and tellurium, especially in their less familiar oxidation states.

Phenomena encountered in polarography emphasize the principle first recognized by Fritz Haber in the 1890s, but long ignored, that the potential of the electrode is the cardinal factor in determining which of several possible electrode reactions will occur. Lingane vitalized this method of "controlled potential electrolysis" both by developing automatic instrumentation to render its application convenient and by demonstrating a variety of practical applications to the electrogravimetric determination of metals and to the separation of substances prior to polarographic (or other) determination. Observing in these studies that 100% current efficiency is easily achieved when the potential of the working electrode is controlled, and hence that the total quantity of electricity passed (coulombs) can be equated using Faraday's law to the quantity of substance reacted, he was led to the development of "coulometric analysis at controlled potential." In addition to its utility as an analytical procedure, coulometric analysis has since become a powerful tool in the elucidation of the pathways (mechanisms) of electrode reactions. Controlled potential electrolysis, when guided by polarography, can be employed with remarkable effectiveness in preparative chemistry. Because the reducing or oxidizing condition is controlled precisely, this method is especially valuable when the desired product is an intermediate in a sequence of possible reduction or oxidation reactions.

Stimulated by polarography, various other electrochemical analytical methods were invented, such as coulometric titration with constant current, amperometric titrations, and chronopotentiometry. Lingane and his students contributed significantly to these innovations. Lingane always maintained interest in applied analytical chemistry, and while pursuing fundamental research on the principles of electroanalytical techniques, he also invented many practical analytical methods.

After completing both his undergraduate and graduate education at the University of Minnesota (Ch.B., 1935; Ph.D., 1938), Lingane remained there for a year (1938–39) as an instructor in chemistry. This was followed by 2 years of teaching at the University of California at Berkeley. In 1941 he joined the faculty of Harvard University, where he became professor of chemistry. Lingane received the American Chemical Society's Fisher Award "for outstanding contributions in analytical chemistry" in 1958. He was elected a fellow of the American Academy of Arts and Sciences in 1949 and an honorary member of the Society for Analytical Chemistry, London, in 1965.

Lingane wrote *Polarography*, with I. M. Kolthoff (2 vols., 1941; 2d rev. ed. 1952); *Electroanalytical Chemistry* (1953; 2d rev. ed. 1958), which has served as both a textbook and reference monograph in this field; *Analytical Chemistry of Selected Metallic Elements* (1966); and about 140 research papers. He served on the editorial advisory boards of the *Journal of the American Chemical Society*, *Analytical Chemistry*, and the *Journal of Electroanalytical Chemistry*.

For background information *see* COULOMETRIC ANALYSIS; POLAROGRAPHIC ANALYSIS in the McGraw-Hill Encyclopedia of Science and Technology. □

⋆ LIPSCOMB, William Nunn

American chemist
Born Dec. 9, 1919, Cleveland, Ohio, U.S.A.

THE RELATION of geometrical and electronic stuctures of molecules to their chemical and physical behavior was the unifying interest throughout studies by Lipscomb and his students.

Electron-deficient compounds, especially the boron hydrides and their derivatives, are not readily described in the electron-pair bonding approximation, which describes well so much of chemistry. Recognizing that most earlier ideas on these compounds were based on incorrect geometrical structures, Lipscomb embarked upon the development of low-temperature x-ray diffraction methods for the study of single crystals and, together with his students, established most of the presently known chemical structures of these compounds. The relations among these structures, and to those of polyhedrons in the borides established by other research workers, led to the general recognition of polyhedral structures, fragments of these polyhedrons, and cooperative rearrangement properties of these molecular structures. For these studies Lipscomb received the Harrison Howe Award in 1958.

From the simpler members of the series, W. H. Eberhardt, B. L. Crawford, Jr., and Lipscomb developed several types of three-center two-electron bonds in order to describe these molecules as filled electronic shells in a way that preserves some common features. Molecular orbital descriptions, in which bonding electrons are delocalized over the whole molecule, were also developed. About the same time H. C. Longuet-Higgins and M. de V. Roberts also investigated theoretically the polyhedral ions $(B_{12}H_{12})^{-2}$ and $(B_6H_6)^{-2}$, which were later discovered. The successful description of closed electronic shells and the subsequent studies by R. Hoffmann and Lipscomb on sites of electrophilic and nucleophilic attack on the carboranes, $C_2B_{10}H_{12}$, are among the predictive successes.

These studies stimulated research in several directions. The nuclear magnetic resonance spectra of these molecules led to a general theory of the chemical shift in these spectra by R. M. Stevens, R. M. Pitzer, and Lipscomb. These calculations are the first accurate a priori results for the constants that describe the behavior of several types of molecules in a magnetic or electric field. Also, a sound theoretical basis for the application of quantum mechanical methods to complex molecules was developed, with wide applications to organic and inorganic chemical problems. The objective here is to establish firm relations and new atomiclike parameters so that approximate theories for complex molecules can be obtained from relatively more exact theories for simpler, but chemically closely related, molecules. In the earlier stages of these studies, Pitzer and Lipscomb made the first accurate calculation of the barrier to internal rotation about the C-C bond in ethane. These and other studies of transferability of atomic properties among closely related molecules were greatly facilitated by the use of high-speed digital computers.

The x-ray diffraction method, which serves so well to establish geometrical structures firmly, was further developed in Lipscomb's laboratory for the studies of single crystals of such low-melting substances as nitrogen, oxygen, fluorine, and other substances which are solid only below liquid nitrogen temperatures. The need to solve complex borane structures led to a number of structure determinations of inorganic complexes, such as cyclooctatetraene iron tricarbonyl complexes, and of natural product structures. The most interesting of these is the establishment by J. W. Moncrief and Lipscomb of the structure and stereochemistry, by new methods, of leurocristine, which is presently employed in leukemia therapy.

In recent years Lipscomb's research group was concerned with the elucidation of the three-dimensional structure of the pancreatic enzyme carboxypeptidase A, which has reached the resolution of 2.0 A. At a molecular weight of 34,400, it is the largest globular protein yet to be studied at higher resolution. An investigation of an enzyme-substrate complex was carried out, with the expectation that a three-dimensional description of the mechanism of action of this enzyme would emerge.

Lipscomb graduated from the University of Kentucky (B.S., 1941) and the California Institute of Technology (Ph.D., 1946). During World War II he was associated with Office of Scientific Research and Development projects. He taught at the University of Minnesota from 1946 to 1959 and at Harvard University after 1959. He was elected to the American Academy of Arts and Sciences in 1960 and to the National Academy of Sciences in 1961.

Lipscomb wrote *Boron Hydrides* (1963).

For background information *see* BORANE; MOLECULAR STRUCTURE AND SPECTRA; NUCLEAR STRUCTURE; X-RAY DIFFRACTION in the McGraw-Hill Encyclopedia of Science and Technology. □

★ LOEB, Robert Frederick

American physician
Born Mar. 14, 1895, Chicago, Ill., U.S.A.

LOEB'S INTEREST in electrolyte and water metabolism began in 1920 while working in the laboratory of his father, Jacques Loeb, at Woods Hole. Problems in this area of physiology were a continuing subject of his attention in subsequent years in association with Dana W. Atchley and other collaborators.

In 1932 Loeb made clinical observations on a small series of patients with Addison's disease suffering from acute adrenal insufficiency. These patients exhibited the manifestations characteristic of acute salt and water depletion, as Loeb noted in his studies with Atchley on electrolyte and water losses in diabetic acidosis and severe diarrheal states. These observations in patients in adrenal crisis led to studies in which the mechanisms of the physiological disturbances encountered and the means of their correction were established. Joseph W. Ferrebee, Charles A. Ragan, Jules Stahl, Daniel Kuhlmann, and others participated for the next 8 years in the extension of these investigations.

Blood studies on patients observed clinically in Addisonian crisis revealed a sharp decrease in the serum sodium concentration with elevation of potassium and hemoconcentration, as well as certain additional abnormalities previously observed by others, such as azotemia and (occa-sionally) hypoglycemia. It was demonstrated that the simple administration of large amounts of sodium chloride and water usually restored patients dramatically, without the use of the essentially inert adrenal cortical extracts available at that time. Many patients who might have been expected to die in less than a year after the establishment of the diagnosis of Addison's disease returned to full activity for many years as a result of the daily ingestion of some 15 g of table salt without other therapeutic aids. In these clinical studies it was further shown that the withdrawal of salt from the diet of most individuals with overt Addison's disease would, in the course of 1 to 5 days, precipitate a crisis of alarming severity. This in turn would be promptly alleviated by the readministration of salt and water.

The effects of adrenalectomy on the dog confirmed the clinical observations on patients with adrenal insufficiency: Adrenal crisis in these animals was also associated with dehydration, hyponatremia, hyperkalemia, and azotemia. It was further demonstrated that the excessive excretion of sodium noted in the urine was not dependent upon the development of acidosis nor upon any significant decrease in ammonia formation by the kidneys. It was inferred in these early studies that the adrenal cortex exerts on the renal tubules a vital influence in the control of the excretion of sodium, potassium, and water. The validity of this concept was subsequently established experimentally by others.

Later, long-term toxicity studies of deoxycorticosterone acetate (the first salt- and water-regulating hormone to be synthesized) were performed in the normal dog. This compound was found to increase the sodium concentration of the blood serum and to decrease the potassium through its effects on the kidneys. Deoxycorticosterone also caused striking replacement of potassium by sodium in skeletal and heart muscle. It also caused some increase in blood pressure, as it does in man. The changes in sodium and potassium, which were the converse of those present in hypoadrenalism, were associated with extraordinary intermittent muscle weakness and an intense and salt-dependent diabetes insipidus–like syndrome. In later years J. W. Conn described similar clinical and chemical changes in man in association with excessive secretion of aldosterone caused by tumors of the adrenal glands.

Loeb attended the University of Chicago for 2 years and received his M.D. magna cum laude from Harvard Medical School in 1919. He was an intern in medicine at the Massachusetts General Hospital and a resident physician at the Johns Hopkins Hospital and the Presbyterian Hospital in New York for 4 additional years. A teacher of clinical medicine at the Columbia

University College of Physicians and Surgeons for 39 years, and chairman of the department for 13 years, he became Bard Professor of Medicine Emeritus in 1960. He retired as director of the Medical Service of the Presbyterian Hospital in 1959. Loeb received numerous honorary degrees, and was elected to many scientific societies, including the National Academy of Sciences (1946) and the American Academy of Arts and Sciences (1949), and to the American Philosophical Society (1951). He served on the President's Science Advisory Committee and the Board of the National Science Foundation, and was chairman of the Board of Review for Biology and Medicine of the Atomic Energy Commission. He was president of the Association of American Physicians, the Society for Clinical Investigation, and the Harvey Society, and served as a trustee of the Rockefeller Foundation and the Rockefeller University, and as an overseer of Harvard University.

Loeb has a lengthy bibliography on problems in electrolyte physiology and various metabolic disorders. He was coeditor of the *Cecil-Loeb Textbook of Medicine*, with Russell L. Cecil (11th ed. 1963); and of Paul Martini's *Principles and Practice of Physical Diagnosis*, with Y. Kneeland (3d rev. ed. 1962).

For background information *see* ADDISON'S DISEASE; ADRENAL CORTEX STEROID; ADRENAL GLAND; OSMOREGULATORY MECHANISMS in the McGraw-Hill Encyclopedia of Science and Technology.   □

★ **LONDON, Heinz**

British physicist
Born Nov. 7, 1907, Bonn, Germany

LONDON'S INTEREST in the electrodynamic and thermodynamic behavior of superconductors and in the properties of superfluid helium dated from his undergraduate days. The subject of his Ph.D. thesis, suggested to him by Professor F. E.

(later Sir Francis) Simon in 1931, was to find out whether superconductors offer resistance to alternating current. In trying to find a possible cause for such a resistance, he started from the concept of frictionless motion of the electrons. Taking into account the effect of the mass of the electrons which have to be accelerated when a supercurrent is initiated, he concluded that an applied magnetic field is not completely screened by the induced supercurrents, but penetrates to a depth of about 10^{-6} cm. If the magnetic field alternates, an electric field would appear within the penetration layer, and if some normal electrons are present, these will be set in motion and produce Joule heating, thus giving rise to a resistance. This resistance would become observable only at frequencies of about 1000 megacycles per second. It was not until 1938 that he succeeded in demonstrating this effect experimentally.

Meanwhile, the discovery of the Meissner effect in 1933 showed superconductivity in a new light. It had been known for a long time that superconductivity is destroyed when an applied magnetic field exceeds a certain critical value, and that the magnetic field previously excluded from the interior enters the metal as the screening currents fade away. When "infinite conductivity" is restored by reducing the field below the critical value, it was thought that the magnetic flux would be frozen in. W. Meissner found that in actual fact the magnetic flux is expelled when the field is lowered—in other words, that the screening currents are reestablished. Thus superconductivity was not infinite conductivity but an extreme form of diamagnetism.

Soon after the discovery of the Meissner effect, the Nazi upheaval in Germany brought Simon, Heinz London, and his elder brother, Fritz, together at the Clarendon Laboratory in Oxford. Fritz London, a theoretician who had made his name, together with Walter Heitler, by the quantum mechanical explanation of the chemical bond, became interested in superconductivity. This was the beginning of a period of close collaboration between the two brothers, in which the deep theoretical understanding and mathematical expertise of Fritz interacted fruitfully with the more intuitive and practical approach of Heinz.

The problem was to formulate the diamagnetism revealed by the Meissner effect in such a way that it included the case of a current flowing through a wire. The Meissner effect meant that there must be a unique relation between the local magnetic field and the current density. This relation was obtained from the above-mentioned acceleration concept, taking as initial condition a zero magnetic field. The essential step was to exclude all frozen-in magnetic fields *on principle*. Then the supercurrents appear as the inevitable consequence of the magnetic field that is in turn partly or wholly determined by the supercurrent itself. The same current-field relation is found in a diamagnetic atom, where it is due to the rigidity of the wave function in relation to a magnetic field. To find a similar rigidity in the wave functions of the superconducting electrons was recognized by Fritz London as the object of any future microscopic theory.

Applying C. J. Gorter's thermodynamics to the new theory, Heinz London showed that thin films should have a higher critical magnetic field than the bulk metal, as was soon confirmed experimentally by him and by others. This posed a new problem. Why does the bulk metal not split up into superconducting domains separated by normal regions when it is placed in a supercritical field? This question led to the postulate of an interfacial energy at the superconducting-normal boundary. The further development of these ideas by L. D. Landau and V. L. Ginzburg led A. A. Abrikosov to the recognition of a new type of superconductor in which the interfacial energy is small enough to make domain formation energetically favorable. These "type 2 superconductors" retain some superconductive properties in high magnetic fields.

In 1938 the fountain effect of superfluid helium was discovered by J. F. Allen and H. Jones. Fritz London suggested that superfluidity might be understood as the condensation phenomenon of a gas that obeys Bose-Einstein statistics. L. Tisza developed these ideas further in his "two-fluid model." Heinz London applied the second law of thermodynamics to this model and obtained a relation between the entropy and the fountain pressure and predicted the existence of a mechanocaloric effect. He showed that these effects explain the high heat conduction of superfluid helium as a convection mechanism involving the relative motion of the two fluids.

The discovery of the rare isotope helium-3 led to new advances in low-temperature physics. Dissolved in superfluid helium-4, the lighter isotope behaves like an ideal Fermi gas which can be compressed or expanded by withdrawing or adding superfluid helium-4 through a "superleak," a narrow channel which is permeable to helium-4 only. Whereas the heat content of liquid helium-4 below 1°K is practically zero and that of pure helium-3 is fairly low, the heat context of dilute helium-3 is still considerable. When these facts became known, Heinz London suggested in 1951 the use of solutions of helium-3 in helium-4 for the production of very low temperatures. In analogy to the cooling observed in a gas that is expanded in an engine, a helium-3 solution should cool when it is diluted with helium-4 admitted through a superleak. In 1956 it was found by G. K. Walters and W. M.

Fairbank that below 0.8°K the two helium isotopes are only partially soluble in each other. This seemed to make the 1951 suggestion impracticable, but opened up the possibility of basing a continuous refrigeration process on the transfer of helium-3 from the concentrated phase into the dilute phase. A refrigeration cycle of this kind was proposed in a paper by H. London, E. Mendoza, and G. R. Clarke in 1963, and refrigerators working on this principle have reached temperatures as low as 0.02°K.

The son of a mathematics professor, Heinz London was educated in Germany, where he received his Ph.D. at the University of Breslau in 1934. He then immigrated to England and worked first at the Clarendon Laboratory, subsequently at Bristol University. During the war he was engaged in work on isotope separation under Sir Francis Simon. From 1946 he was employed by the Atomic Energy Research Establishment, where he became deputy chief scientist. In 1959 he was awarded the Simon Memorial Prize of the Institute of Physics and the Physical Society. He was elected to the Royal Society of London in 1961.

For background information *see* CRYOGENICS; DIAMAGNETISM; MEISSNER EFFECT; SUPERCONDUCTIVITY in the McGraw-Hill Encyclopedia of Science and Technology.   □

★ LONG, Franklin Asbury

American chemist
Born July 27, 1910, Great Falls, Mont., U.S.A.

LONG'S CAREER combined academic science and scientific administration. To a considerable degree the latter was a consequence of World War II experiences, when he administered large programs of applied research and development.

In 1932, when Long started his graduate work at the University of California, Berkeley, a type of chemistry now known as physical-organic was just developing. The great names in the field at that time were Robert Robinson and C. K. Ingold in Britain and J. B. Conant and L. P. Hammett in the United States. However, there were several very able people at Berkeley who would now be called physical-organic, and Long worked with one of the most interesting of these, Axel Olson. Long's thesis was on a well-known and perplexing problem in organic chemistry, that of the Walden inversion. The kinetic analysis that Olson and Long made showed conclusively that the normal act of substitution of a group on a tetrahedral carbon atom leads quantitatively to inversion of the configuration of the molecule. Put another way, substitution is from the "back side" of the tetrahedron. These initial studies generated a deep interest in physical studies of organic reactions, an interest which sparked the majority of Long's research during the subsequent 35 years.

Still another area of vigor at Berkeley in the 1930s was nuclear physics and chemistry, and during his graduate student days Long developed an appreciation of the utility to chemistry of isotopic tracers and isotope effects. As one example, the short-lived C^{11} isotope was used by Long at Cornell in 1938 to demonstrate fundamental differences in the properties of the tri-oxalato complex ions which are formed by trivalent metal ions. Chromium complex ions in aqueous solution showed no exchange of their oxalates with added free oxalate ion; in contrast, tri-oxalato complexes of ferric and aluminum ions showed instant exchange. These results could then be rationalized in terms of the different types of bonding involved.

Kinetic analysis of the reaction of organic molecules continued and led Long, in collaboration with William McDevit, Mary Purchase, Frances Dunkle, and Donald McIntyre, to a fruitful set of studies of hydrolysis of lactones, esters, and acetals. The pronounced differences in the hydrolytic behavior of β- and γ-lactones in concentrated aqueous electrolyte solutions led to a number of studies of salt effects and of acid catalysis in concentrated solutions of strong acids. The highly specific salt-effect behavior of individual ions in solution led McDevit and Long to their 1952 "free volume" theory of salt effects, a theoretical approach which still remains very useful.

These various studies culminated in two important summary and review papers: "Salt effects on the acid-catalyzed hydrolysis of gamma butyrolactone," with W. McDevit (1951) and "Applications of the H_0 acidity function to the kinetics and mechanism of acid catalysis," with M. Paul (1957).

In the hands of several graduate students and postdoctoral research collaborators, these kinetic and mechanistic studies proceeded in a number of interesting directions. Long and John

Pritchard studied the mechanisms of the epichlorohydrin hydrolysis and did a number of related studies on the opening of epoxy rings. Labeling with O^{18} was used to obtain information on the position of the ring opening. Long and Peter Ballinger devised a conductometric method to measure the acidity of very weak acids and reported on the acidities of a series of aliphatic alcohols. They also studied the kinetics of base attack on an acetylenic hydrogen, a reaction which Emil Halevi and Long later demonstrated to be subject to general base catalysis. Long, D. Watson, and T. Riley studied the deuterium kinetic isotope effect on the base-catalyzed enolization of beta diketones and were able to determine kinetic isotope effects for the individual steps of the reaction. Parallel studies of the deuterium solvent isotope effects, that is, for rates and equilibria in D_2O as compared to H_2O, gave evidence that the lower acidity of D_2O relative to H_2O is due almost entirely to the lower acidity of the particular species, D_2O.

These earlier studies led to a continuing interest in deuterium solvent isotope effects and their use in studying the properties of water and reactions in water. One of the more interesting aspects of these studies was a reconsideration of the Gross theory for the behavior of acids in mixed H_2O-D_2O solvents, and a generalization of this theory to cover acid-base properties of species with more than one exchangeable proton was developed by Pentii Salomaa, Larry Schalager, and Long. Concurrently, with Halevi, David Goodall, and others, Long showed that the normal assumption of complete ideality for the H_2O-D_2O solvent mixture is inadequate and that medium effects or, more precisely, free energies of transfer must be considered.

In recent years much of Long's research went into the properties of highly basic aromatic systems, such as the azulene molecule, and of the conjugate acids formed by protonation of these on a carbon atom. The experimental procedures involve tritium labeling to follow the proton exchange reactions, indicator measurements to determine the acid-base properties, and "fast flow" techniques to follow the kinetics of the proton transfer, a transfer which is notably slow compared to that for protons on oxygen or nitrogen. The proton transfer reaction is generally acid catalyzed and is the slow step in the proton exchange reaction. As would be expected, the rate of proton transfer depends markedly on the base strength of the aromatic system. In addition, there is evidence for significant steric effects on the rates.

Long's research exhibited three substantial variations from the physical-organic area. One group of papers involved surface chemistry and included an important demonstration that the famous Jones-Ray effect in the surface tension of aqueous electrolyte solutions is primarily instrumental, as Irving Langmuir hypothesized. Interest in these phenomena was a consequence of a year's postdoctoral study with W. D. Harkins of Chicago, a notably vigorous and influential chemist. A second variant set of studies, done in conjunction with Lewis Friedman and Max Wolfsberg of the Brookhaven Laboratory, dealt with the theory and mechanisms of the gas-phase decomposition of organic positive ions. These studies, which were among the first in the field, were a direct consequence of curiosity aroused by analytical use of a mass spectrometer to determine the position of an O^{18} label on organic molecules. The third group of studies, done in collaboration with Leo Mandelkern, S. Prager, R. Kokes, D. Richman, and others, dealt with the diffusion of vapors of small molecules into polymeric substances. During these studies it was determined, for example, that for "non-glassy" polymers, say polyisobutylene, the diffusion of such molecules as water, methanol, and carbon tetrachloride obeys Fick's general law of diffusion with, however, a concentration-dependent diffusion coefficient. Below the glass transition of the polymer the behavior is usually very different, and an important rate-determining process is the slow structural rearrangement of the polymer network. Long's interest in this area of research came from some highly applied studies on the production and properties of "double-base" and "single-base" nitrocellulose rocket propellants during World War II, when it became clear that slow, diffusion-controlled processes were of great consequence.

Long received his B.A. from the University of Montana in 1932 and his Ph.D. from the University of California, Berkeley, in 1935. He taught at California and the University of Chicago before joining the faculty at Cornell University in 1937. He became a full professor in 1946, served as chairman of the department of chemistry from 1950 to 1960, and in 1963 was named the university's vice-president for research and advanced studies.

During and since World War II Long served on numerous advisory committees to federal agencies and participated in several study efforts on military and technical problems. He organized and directed a 6-month study for the Atomic Energy Commission on characteristic materials and products associated with the various operations involving the production of nuclear energy. In 1962 and 1963 he served as assistant director for the U.S. Arms Control and Disarmament Agency and during this period was a member of the Harriman group, which successfully negotiated in Moscow the Partial Test Ban Treaty. He served as a member of the President's Science Advisory Committee (PSAC) in 1961–62 and again from 1963 to 1967. During this second period he chaired the PSAC group which produced the 1967 report "The Space Program in the Post Apollo Period." Long was elected to the National Academy of Sciences in 1962 and to the American Academy of Arts and Sciences in 1965.

For background information *see* AROMATIC HYDROCARBON; DEUTERIUM; STEREOCHEMISTRY in the McGraw-Hill Encyclopedia of Science and Technology. ☐

★ LONGUET-HIGGINS, Hugh Christopher

British chemist
Born Apr. 11, 1923, Lenham, Kent, England

LONGUET-HIGGINS'S first contribution to theoretical chemistry, in his twentieth year, was to overthrow the currently accepted view of the structures of some very strange molecules, the boron hydrides. The simplest of these is diborane, B_2H_6, which had for nearly 20 years been assigned a structure like that of ethane, C_2H_6. He pointed out to his tutor, R. P. Bell, that there was good chemical evidence in support of an alternative structure containing "hydrogen

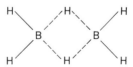

bridges." They showed in 1943 that the infrared and Raman spectra of diborane, which were difficult to reconcile with the ethane-like structure, gave very strong support to the bridged structure. This structure was later confirmed beyond doubt by W. C. Price's analysis of the rotational fine structure and by R. Ogg's study of the nuclear resonance spectrum, but not before Longuet-Higgins had used the "hydrogen bridge" hypothesis for predicting the structures of the volatile borohydrides $M(BH_4)_n$, the polymeric alkyls, and the (then unknown) hydride of beryllium, predictions which were all subsequently confirmed. This work was published in 1945.

In 1945–47 he studied for his D.Phil. at Oxford University with C. A. Coulson, an old student of J. E. Lennard-Jones, who had been associated with F. Hund and R. S. Mulliken in the creation of the molecular orbital theory. Coulson and Longuet-Higgins developed the orbital theory of conjugated organic molecules, basing their analysis on the approximations originally introduced by Ernst Hückel. The novel feature of this work was the generality of the results—for example, a rigorous derivation of the law of alternating polarity, which had been known experimentally for many decades—and the use of quantum mechanical perturbation theory for describing the effects of substituents and the approach of reagents upon the electrons of the conjugated system. At the same time he was able to translate the "hydrogen bridge" concept into molecular orbital terms and to formulate the structure of diborane in terms of two "3-center bonds," one on each side of the bridge. The concept of the "many-center bond" was used to great effect later by W. N. Lipscomb and his colleagues in rationalizing the structures of the higher boron hydrides.

In 1948–49 Longuet-Higgins spent a year in Chicago with Mulliken, who introduced him to molecular spectroscopy, a subject to which he later contributed some ideas, particularly about the spectra of molecules in electronically degenerate states. While in Chicago he investigated the properties of "alternant" hydrocarbons and produced a series of papers showing that many properties of conjugated systems could be very simply deduced from a study of the "nonbonding orbitals" of odd alternant hydrocarbons. M. J. S. Dewar incorporated this idea into his LCMO (linear combination of molecular orbitals) theory, and later he and Longuet-Higgins collaborated to show how nonbonding orbitals could be used for comparing the chemical predictions of the molecular orbital theory with those of the more fashionable resonance theory. The comparison enabled Longuet-Higgins to find a case in which the two theories made contrary predictions, namely, biphenylene, for which the relevant facts were not known. He drew attention to this discrepancy in his Chemical Society Tilden Lecture in 1957, and a few years later M. K. Zimmermann confirmed experimentally the molecular orbital prediction.

From 1949 to 1952 Longuet-Higgins worked in the University of Manchester and turned to statistical mechanics. In 1950 he constructed the theory of "conformal solutions," which provides a rigorous connection between the various excess thermodynamic properties of mixtures in which the intermolecular potentials are all of the same form. In 1952–54 in London he extended these ideas to polymer solutions and also worked on the optical rotation of helical molecules, but was anticipated in publication by William Moffitt. He also collaborated with Dewar and with J. A. Pople on the electronic spectra of alternant hydrocarbons and first showed how the π-to-π transitions could be interpreted by using the pairing properties of the orbitals.

This work was continued at Cambridge University from 1952 onward. It led indirectly to a paper with L. Salem in which they demonstrated the instability of an infinite polyene against an alternation in the bond lengths, again indicating the dangers of too literal an interpretation of the resonance theory. In 1956 M. de V. Roberts and Longuet-Higgins predicted the existence of a regular icosahedral borohydride ion, $B_{12}H_{12}^{--}$, and several years later the stability of this ion was strikingly verified. Another prediction, with L. E. Orgel, was that cyclobutadiene, which had defeated all attempts at preparation, would be capable of existence as a ligand (like C_5H_5) attached to a transition metal atom; this was confirmed 3 years later. His other interests during that period included the transport properties of rigid sphere assemblies, which led to the derivation of a statistical expression for any transport coefficient; the spectra of electronically degenerate molecules, for which some of the basic problems had been formulated earlier by Edward Teller, A. K. Jahn, and M. S. Renner, and the application of group theory to nonrigid molecules.

Rigid symmetrical molecules such as CO_2 or CH_4 had long been treated by group theory; their symmetry groups have an obvious geometrical interpretation. But how was one to define the elements of symmetry of a molecule such as hydrazine, N_2H_4, which keeps changing its shape? Longuet-Higgins found the answer in the allowable permutations of identical nuclei, some of which require a simultaneous inversion of the whole molecule. These elements form a group which for a rigid molecule is essentially the geometrical point group, but for a nonrigid molecule is often—indeed usually—much larger and richer in structure. With such a group P. R. Bunker and he were able to classify the individual quantum levels of dimethylacetylene, CH_3CCCH_3, and to use its spectrum to set an upper limit to its torsional barrier.

Questions which have long interested organic chemists are: Why are many electronic rearrangement reactions stereospecific, and what determines the geometry of the transition state? Introduced by R. B. Woodward to some of the more startling characteristics of "electrocyclic" reactions, Longuet-Higgins was able, with E. W. Abrahamson, to discover symmetry principles which, together with the noncrossing rule, enable one to make clear predictions about the outcome of not only thermal but also photochemical reactions of this type; the principles are based on the molecular orbital theory and the relative unimportance of configurational interaction when one is dealing with a nondegenerate state.

Having worked occasionally on biological problems, such as the uncoiling of DNA (with B. Zimm) and the transport of water across membranes (with G. Austin), Longuet-Higgins turned in 1967 to the study of information-processing systems, which he thought has a closer bearing on true biology than on purely physicochemical studies. In the late 1960s he was at the University of Edinburgh in the newly founded department of machine intelligence and perception.

Longuet-Higgins was educated at Winchester College and Balliol College, Oxford (M.A., D.Phil.), where he also held a research fellowship from 1946 to 1948. He spent 1949 with R. S. Mulliken as a research associate at the University of Chicago; from 1949 to 1952 he lectured at the University of Manchester, and from 1952 to 1954 was professor of theoretical physics at King's College, London. From 1954 to 1967 he was professor of theoretical chemistry at the University of Cambridge. He received the Harrison Memorial Prize of the Chemical Society in 1952 and became a fellow of the Royal Society in 1958 and a foreign member of the American Academy of Arts and Sciences in 1961.

Longuet-Higgins was editor of *Molecular Physics* in 1958–61.

For background information *see* COORDINATION CHEMISTRY; HYDROCARBON; STATISTICAL MECHANICS in the McGraw-Hill Encyclopedia of Science and Technology.   □

★ LUNDEGÅRDH, Henrik Gunnar

Swedish botanist
Born Oct. 23, 1888, Stockholm, Sweden

LUNDEGÅRDH STARTED his scientific work in the area of cytology, and he wrote in 1909–12 a series of 10 papers dealing with the mechanism of nuclear division in cells. Special attention was paid to cytological technique, including observations of live material and the effects of different agents of fixation. In 1910–11 his interest turned to plant physiology, and he published in 1911 a paper on the permeability of the roots to various salts. The results were discussed in the light of recent work in zoological cell physiology

and in colloidal chemistry (Kapillarchemie). The physiological aspects were pursued during studies in the laboratories of Georg Klebs in Heidelberg and Wilhelm Pfeffer in Leipzig (1912–13).

Lundegårdh moved to the University of Lund in 1915 and continued his work in experimental morphology and ecology. His approach in experimental ecology of plants implied moving the physiological laboratory out in the open field. He leaned more heavily than his predecessors on the exact laboratory side of the investigations. To this end he erected in 1915–17 an ecological station on the island Hallands Väderö in Kattegat, off the west coast of southern Sweden. This island is famous for its vegetation, which includes all types of associations. He invented and introduced new instruments for the study of the main ecological factors in photosynthesis (light, CO_2, humidity, and so on). The dominating ecological factors and processes were thus studied simultaneously in the environment of the plants and in the laboratory. Also the salt content of the soil and its biological activity was studied. The research work at the ecological station covered the period from 1917 to about 1931, during which a large number of co-workers from Europe, America, and Asia participated in this new line of ecology. Lundegårdh summarized the leading ideas of his work in the book *Klima und Boden in ihrer Wirkung auf das Pflanzenleben* (German ed. 1925, 5th ed. 1957; 2d English ed. 1930). The book arose from lectures at the University of Brno (Czechoslovakia) in 1923–24. A separate book was also written, *Der Kreislauf der Kohlensäure in der Natur* (1924).

During his activity at the laboratory of plant physiology in Lund (1915–26), Lundegårdh devoted his time largely to the movements of plants, primarily to geotropism and phototropism. In a series of his papers attention was paid also to the problems of plagiotropism of side roots and aerial shoots. It was shown that all orthotropic organs develop two opposite reactions, one positive and one negative, with different sensitivity and time course, and that the mutual intensity of the inductions can be experimentally regulated by the intensity and time of action of gravity (or centrifugal force) and light. A third important factor was autotropism. The fourth and fifth elementary processes were inductions in the longitudinal direction of the organs regulating growth activity, factors consequently determining also the orientation of the plagiotropic organs. These studies implied the development of a cinematographic technique of recording and special arrangements for testing the cooperation of the elementary tropistic reactions. These studies were performed before the era of auxins, but the large amount of experimental observations in many ways illustrate the movements and activities of auxins and antiauxins discovered later on. When in a later period he focused his attention on the importance of the surface potentials of cells and tissues for the movement and distribution of ions, he emphasized the importance of these factors for explanation of tropistic and growth phenomena, pointing to the fact that auxins always appear as easily movable anions.

In 1926 Lundegårdh became professor and head of the Botany Division of the Central Institution for Agricultural Research at Experimentalfältet, near Stockholm. During his visit to Brno he had already approached the problems of absorption and accumulation of salts in the roots, but these problems were further developed and during the following 25 years occupied the overwhelming part of his efforts as plant physiologist. From the days of Liebig mineral nutrition of plants had a central position in plant physiology, but little was known about the physicochemical mechanism of uptake and accumulation and its connection with the life of the protoplast. Even the pioneers of permeability problems had as a rule little to say here. Lundegårdh realized that one reason for this stagnation of the salt problem was the lack of sensitive and rapid chemical methods for quantitative determination of salts, primarily the cations. To fill this gap, he investigated spectral emission analysis.

Before and during World War I attempts had been made in France and England to use the electric spark as a source for emission spectra of introduced samples and to estimate the quantity of involved elements from the degree of blackening of the photographed lines. The accuracy was low, and the spark method could not be applied to the alkali and earth-alkali metals that belong to the chief plant nutrients. Attempts had also been made without success to use the old Kohl-rausch flame method for this purpose. Lundegårdh developed a sensitive and accurate flame spectrophotometer, using an acetylene-air flame in combination with an efficient atomizer. This flame photometer has now been universally accepted as a standard instrument for quantitative spectral analysis (*Die quantitative Spektralanalyse der Elemente*, 1929–34). An "analytic robot" was constructed for large-scale investigations on leaf analysis as a tool for determination of soil fertility (*Leaf Analysis*, 1951). The methods of spectral analysis were extended by introduction of exact photometry of the spectral lines, internal standards for elimination of disturbing factors, and application of more suitable arrangements for introduction of solutions in electric sparks and bows. Incisive studies of uptake, exchange, and distribution of salt cations in the plant illustrated the universal importance of the colloidal properties of the living protoplasm (*Die Nährstoffaufnahme der Pflanze*, 1932).

A complete determination of absorbed and exchanged cations and anions of neutral salts simultaneously with the consumption of O_2 and production of CO_2 revealed the important fact that a quantitative relation exists between the active absorption of salt anions and one fraction of the total respiration that is sensitive to cyanide and CO (the anion or salt respiration), whereas the remaining ground respiration does not actively transport salts. This discovery, made in 1933–35, was followed by a large number of papers. It also aroused an increasing flow of work and intense discussions from other investigators. The discovery of a causal connection between active salt transport and the cyanide-sensitive fraction of plant respiration led to an incisive analysis of the respiratory enzymes. It was shown that cytochrome oxidase $(a + a_3)$ in cooperation with cytochrome b and succinodehydrogenase conducts the salt respiration, whereas the ground respiration runs through cytochrome b_3. For determination of the state of oxidation-reduction of the cytochromes, Lundegårdh developed a special spectrophotometric technique for rapid and sensitive recording of living material. This new line of work led finally back to the field of photosynthesis, now from the viewpoint of its physicochemical mechanism.

In 1947 he built a private, nonprofit research laboratory at Penningby, 70 km east of Uppsala, mainly to avoid electrical disturbance of the very sensitive instruments. The equipment of this laboratory includes four recording spectrophotometers of his own construction. One of the instruments rapidly scans a spectrum down to a fraction of a second, and is combined with a special device for electric flashes.

As shown by R. Hill, chloroplasts contain a characteristic cytochrome f and one or two cytochromes *b*. Lundegårdh discovered in 1954 that cytochrome *f* is oxidized by light and again reduced in the dark. This discovery was the incitement for the now generally accepted idea of the existence of a chain of electron transport between the photically excited pigments and a complicated system of redox reactions in which the photic energy is transferred to reduced pyridine nucleotide (TPNH) and adenosinetriphosphate (ATP), the latter process first shown by D. I. Arnon. Lundegårdh devoted his time in the 1960s to a detailed study of the involved enzymes and pigments, among other things the importance of the carotenoids as primary photoreductones and a counterpart to the oxidoreduction between cytochrome *f* and chlorophyll.

Lundegårdh gained his Ph.D. in 1912 and his D.Bot. in 1913 at the University of Stockholm. He worked in the laboratory of plant physiology at the University of Lund in 1915–26. Then he became professor and head of the Botany Division of the Central Institution for Agricultural Research near Stockholm. He was professor of plant physiology at the Royal Agricultural Technical University at Uppsala during 1935–55. In 1947 he opened his own laboratory in Penningby. Lundegårdh was elected a foreign member of the American Academy of Arts and Sciences in 1950 and of the U.S. National Academy of Sciences in 1964.

For background information *see* CYTOCHROME; CYTOLOGY; PLANT MOVEMENTS; PLANT PHYSIOLOGY in the McGraw-Hill Encyclopedia of Science and Technology. □

★ LUYTEN, Willem Jacob

American astronomer
Born Mar. 7, 1899, Semarang, Netherlands East Indies (Indonesia)

LUYTEN'S INTEREST in astronomy was first aroused when, as a small boy in the East Indies, he was waked by his uncle early one morning to look at Halley's comet. To see this comet, with its tail 110 degrees long and so bright that it cast a shadow, was an unforgettable experience.

While still in high school in the Netherlands, he began his observing career with variable stars. The observations made during that period formed an integral part of his doctoral thesis in 1921. But, as is so often the case with careers in science, Luyten's main interests soon switched to other fields. Shortly after receiving a fellowship at the Lick Observatory in California, he became interested in stellar motions and especially in the determination of spectra of stars of large motion in the hope of finding more white dwarfs. These objects, then newly discovered, are among the most exotic of the stellar species, for with their planetlike diameters, their solarlike masses, and resulting densities of many tons per cubic inch they represent matter in the raw under conditions that one cannot hope to approximate on Earth. During the year at Lick it became evident that the then existing spectroscopic equipment was hardly powerful enough for the detection of further white dwarfs, and that large numbers of faint, nearby stars must first be discovered. White dwarfs are stars of such small size that, in spite of their often very high temperatures and intense surface brightness, their total luminosity (light-giving power) is quite small. Hence such stars can be discovered and observed in detail only if they are nearby, and the problem therefore resolves into a search for nearby stars. To do this directly by determining distances is impractical—it is far too slow. But, fortunately, nearby stars reveal their presence very easily by their very large angular motions. To find moving stars is relatively simple, though rather tedious—all one needs to do is to compare plates taken many years apart but with the same telescope.

For 30 years Luyten compared plates and published motions for more than 120,000 stars. Out of this work came a new determination of the distribution of stellar luminosities and his evaluation of that "luminosity function," which is quite important in all theoretical investigations dealing with the origin of stars (although done in 1939, it is still the only determination

available). Once the motions are known, it becomes a simple matter to find the white dwarfs: One takes plates in blue and red light, thus easily revealing which stars, having large motion, are blue or white in color—in other words, which are the white dwarfs. These objects are now generally considered to be one of the end products of stellar evolution—the dying stars—and for this reason Luyten, having found more than 90% of the known white dwarfs, was referred to by his colleagues as the "stellar mortician."

At the same time, largely to relieve the tedium of these slow, routine searches for moving stars and white dwarfs, Luyten occupied himself with the problems of double stars and especially with that of the origin of the solar system. In the 1930s he was one of the first to criticize and help bring about the downfall of the then accepted theory that the Earth originated through a stellar collision and that hence life in the universe could hardly exist outside the Earth.

In the early 1950s he began to apply the technique developed for finding white dwarfs to the search for "faint blue stars," then newly discovered, and quickly began to find large numbers of them. He indicated that some of them must lie at great distances from our galaxy in regions of space hitherto believed to be almost empty. While largely neglected by astronomers for 15 years, these faint blue stars have now suddenly been catapulted into prominence, since it appears that through them lies the easiest way of discovering quasi stellars (quasars).

In the mid-1960s, when the plates taken for the Palomar–National Geographic Survey became old enough to be repeated, Luyten embarked on an ambitious program of completing another proper motion survey on these plates, which represent the ultimate now available and should produce a great deal of new knowledge on the stars of lowest luminosity and the faintest white dwarfs. But now the problem is so formidable that the old manual–human-eye method of plate examination must be replaced by an automated laser-beam scanner, which feeds its information into a computer for evaluation and produces the final data directly on punched cards.

Since he spent most of his career at the University of Minnesota, which possesses no observational equipment, Luyten enlisted the help of a multitude of observatories, not only in the United States but in France, England, Argentina, Australia, and South Africa as well, and he often described himself as the most successful parasite in astronomy. He felt that international cooperation is the lifeblood of science and especially of astronomy.

Luyten received a B.A. at the University of Amsterdam in 1918 and a Ph.D. in astronomy at the University of Leiden in 1921. A fellow at the Lick Observatory of the University of California in 1921–23, he was astronomer at the Harvard Observatory in 1923–26 and assistant professor of astronomy at Harvard in 1927–30. At the University of Minnesota he became assistant professor of astronomy in 1931, associate professor in 1934, and professor in 1937. Elected to the American Academy of Arts and Sciences in

1925, he was awarded the Watson Medal of the National Academy of Sciences in 1964.

Luyten wrote *The Pageant of the Stars* (1929) and *Proper Motions of 28,535 Stars* (1939).

For background information *see* ASTROMETRY; RADIO SOURCES (ASTRONOMY); STAR; VARIABLE STAR; WHITE DWARF STAR in the McGraw-Hill Encyclopedia of Science and Technology. □

★ LYTTLETON, Raymond Arthur

British astrophysicist

LYTTLETON'S FIRST significant contribution to science was made in 1936, while he was a visiting research fellow at Princeton University, working in close association with H. N. Russell. This contribution concerned the origin of the solar system at a time when all such hypotheses seemed to suffer from fatal objections. In this paper Lyttleton showed how the angular momentum difficulty (pointed out by Russell) could be overcome by a mechanism of formation of the planets from a distant binary companion star to the Sun.

It is a perennial problem of cosmogony to decide what features may be significant and what merely peculiar where clues to the origin of the solar system are concerned. In a study of the rotations of the planets and the motions of satellites, Lyttleton was the first to propose and develop the hypothesis that Pluto is in reality an escaped satellite of Neptune, a conclusion that in recent years has been rediscovered and advocated by others.

In 1938 Lyttleton became acquainted with Fred Hoyle, who was beginning to make his mark in the field of theoretical physics, and he soon realized that Hoyle possessed the analytical power and knowledge of physics to tackle the sort of astronomical problems then engaging his own attention. The central problem of astrophysics at that time was the constitution of the stars, a subject in a highly controversial state owing to the divergent views of A. S. Eddington, J. H. Jeans, and E. A. Milne. One of the basic causes of the confusion was the lack of knowledge of the processes of release of stellar energy; the theory was an equation short, so to speak, and this was made up for in various ways by unrecognized or tacit assumptions. However, by 1938 nuclear physics had progressed sufficiently for a fairly clear-cut law of energy generation to be formulated, and Lyttleton and Hoyle were the first to perceive how this long-awaited information could be utilized to construct the theory anew. They showed how both the luminosity and the radius of a star might be calculated in terms of its mass and composition. One of the first triumphs of this work was to make clear the precise theoretical status of Eddington's important but hitherto obscure "mass-luminosity relation" by showing how that particular combination of their mass-luminosity and mass-radius relations was independent of the energy-generation law.

Lyttleton and Hoyle further demonstrated the power of their formulation of the theory by going on to produce the first viable theory of the structure of the red giant stars. In the field of stellar evolution they were also the first to recognize and insist upon the existence of interstellar gas on a scale far in excess of anything hitherto thought possible. They arrived at this conclusion from purely theoretical considerations.

All this astrophysical work by Lyttleton was in collaboration with Hoyle, but over a period of some 20 years Lyttleton had also been interesting himself in the great classical problem of the stability of rotating liquid masses. Here again, despite the efforts and contributions of G. H. Darwin, A. M. Liapounov, and H. Poincaré, and more recently E. Cartan and J. M. Jeans, there remained an unsettled question of much importance to astronomy as to the precise nature of the instability that ultimately enters. Lyttleton showed how the conclusion by Cartan that the instability is of the ordinary kind when the Jacobi ellipsoidal series first becomes unstable would have entirely different consequences from the mere secular instability demonstrated by Liapounov and confirmed by Jeans. His protracted study of this recondite matter resulted in a celebrated monograph, *The Stability of Rotating Liquid Masses* (1953).

A few years earlier Lyttleton had shown how the application of the accretion mechanism to the passage of the Sun through interstellar dust clouds led in a perfectly natural way to an explanation of the formation and capture of comets; he made clear why they move in almost parabolic orbits, why they are so numerous, and why they consist of vast irregular swarms of tiny dust particles—a conclusion long since

arrived at by almost all comet workers on observational grounds. This theory could be developed in numerous directions, and all the early work based on the accretion hypothesis was put together in his book *The Comets and Their Origin* (1953). Since then further important work on cometary theory was carried out by Lyttleton and his collaborators, notably J. A. Tyror's analysis of the distribution of cometary perihelion points and J. M. Hammersley's statistical and mathematical study of the escape of long-period comets from the solar system.

Lyttleton's researches also took him into the realm of geophysics and planetary physics, in particular the structures of the terrestrial group of planets. He was the first to appreciate that the motion of the liquid core of the Earth must be considered on the fullest basis of hydrodynamical theory, and in collaboration with H. Bondi, he conducted extensive mathematical investigations on the effect of tidal friction and of precession on motions within the core. Where the planetary interiors are concerned, the hypothesis advocated by W. H. Ramsey about 1950 that the liquid core of the Earth represents a phase-change produced by high pressure, and not a difference of composition from the mantle, was again advanced by Lyttleton but with the additional feature that the combined effect of pressure and temperature was concerned in bringing the phase-change about. As internal temperature rose through the release of radioactive energy, the extent of the liquid core in the Earth would grow and evolution of the planet would take place. The associated change of phase was shown by Lyttleton to be to a so much denser liquid form that the Earth as a whole would undergo overall decrease of volume. The amount of this decrease would imply contraction of the surface area on a scale far greater than anything attainable on the old thermal contraction hypothesis, and it gave results meeting in order of magnitude the requirements long since regarded by geologists as inescapably associated with the several periods of mountain-building and the extents of each of these.

The theory could also be applied to the other terrestrial planets and the Moon, and led to the important predictions that Venus would have a liquid core and hence mountain ranges of the thrusted and folded types; Mars would be without any such core and would have no such mountains at its surface. The 1965 *Mariner IV* photographs of Mars, which covered a band containing about 1% of the surface, showed no signs of mountain ranges. Moreover, the absence of a liquid core would imply the absence of any strong magnetic field, and this prediction too was confirmed by *Mariner IV* measurements. The predictions for Venus remain as yet unconfirmed as a result of the extreme difficulty of making detailed observations of the surface structure.

Lyttleton received his Ph.D. from Cambridge University in 1937. He was an assistant lecturer in mathematics there during 1937–45 and university lecturer in mathematics during 1945–59. During World War II he was engaged in scientific work at the British War Office, where he served with Sydney Chapman. He was elected to the Royal Society of London in 1955, and his other honors included the Hopkins Prize of the Cambridge Philosophical Society in 1953, the Gold Medal of the Royal Astronomical Society in 1959, and a Royal Medal of the Royal Society in 1965. In addition to his duties as Reader in theoretical astronomy at Cambridge, Lyttleton in 1960 became a research associate of the Jet Propulsion Laboratory in California.

In addition to the works cited, Lyttleton wrote *The Modern Universe* (1956), *Rival Theories of Cosmology* (1960), and *Man's View of the Universe* (1961).

For background information *see* COSMOGONY; GEOPHYSICS; INTERSTELLAR MATTER in the McGraw-Hill Encyclopedia of Science and Technology.   □

☆ **MacDONALD, Gordon James Fraser**

American geophysicist
Born July 30, 1929, Federal District, Mexico

CONCERNED WITH the dynamics and evolution of the solar system, MacDonald studied the evolution of the Earth-Moon system and its consequences with regard to the origin of these two bodies. As a result of these studies, he suggested that the Moon evolved from a conglomeration of several moons.

Three general mechanisms have been proposed to explain the origin of the Moon. One, first enunciated by the English astronomer George Howard Darwin about 1879 as a result of his pioneering studies of tidal friction, is that the Moon is a portion of the Earth's crust that was thrown off by centrifugal action; this fission hypothesis was extended by some to suggest that the Pacific Ocean is the vast hole that marks where the Moon was lost. The second mechanism, proposed by the Dutch-American astronomer Gerard Peter Kuiper about 1950, is that the Earth and Moon originated as a binary system by condensation from the same region of the initial solar cloud. The third, proposed with minor variations by a number of independent investigators, is that the Moon was formed independently of the Earth and at a great distance from it, then was captured by it during the early history of the solar system.

During the early 1960s, working at the University of California at Los Angeles, MacDonald became interested in the origin of the Earth-Moon system. He began with the premise that, since the present motion of the Moon and rotation of the Earth are specified by a finite set of parameters which because of tidal friction change with time, it is possible to determine the range of initial conditions that could yield the present state of the Earth-Moon system. The history of the Moon can be described in terms of the orbital elements connected with the energy and angular momentum of the orbit. Furthermore, changes in the rotational parameters of the Earth accompany changes in the orbital motion of the Moon.

In calculating the variation of the orbital elements, MacDonald departed from Darwin's theory. In its place he developed a theory in which the time derivatives of the orbital elements are expressed in terms of the forces due to the frictionally produced tidal potential. The theory required no restrictions regarding the internal constitution of the Earth and took into account the effects of the solar tides and of the tides raised by the Earth on the Moon. MacDonald coupled his equations for the orbital elements to those of the Swiss mathematician Leonhard Euler, which describe the change in the rate of the Earth's rotation, and then solved the coupled equations by numerical methods.

His calculations showed that (1) the eccentricity of the present Moon's orbit is inconsistent with the hypothesis that the Moon was captured, (2) the present configuration of the Earth and Moon is inconsistent with the hypothesis that the Moon originated from the Earth by fission, and (3) the present configuration of the Earth-Moon system with the present rate of energy dissipation is inconsistent with a Moon of 4,500,000,000 years of age. The latter conclusion presents difficulties for the binary-evolution theory.

As an alternative mechanism, MacDonald theorized that the Earth, like the major planets, once had several satellites—at least three or four. The time scale in such a situation would be determined entirely by the mass of the largest satellite. If the most massive satellite were nearest the Earth, it would move outward the most rapidly. In moving out it would collide with the smaller outer satellites and in this way form the present Moon. In MacDonald's hypothesis the surface of the Moon, the features of which would be the result of the final collapse of the collision fragments, would be relatively young, having formed no more than 1,500,000,000 years ago.

This hypothesis permits a theoretical dynamical history consistent with the orbital-element, energy, and time-scale requirements. However, the origin of the several satellites cannot yet be explained. The density of the Moon is evidence against a local accumulation of the primitive satellites. Furthermore, no detailed calculations have been made concerning the capture of small satellites by the Earth, thus leaving this avenue unexplored.

A second area of interest to MacDonald was the physics of the Earth's interior. He investigated the internal thermal structure with special emphasis on the thermal constitution. One result of his studies was to show that the continents extend to far greater depths than the usual seismologic criterion (the Mohorovičić disconti-nuity, or Moho).

His analysis of the gravitational figure of the Earth, coupled with considerations of the rotational history, gave new evidence regarding the mechanical properties of the deep interior. In particular, MacDonald showed that the average viscosity of the Earth's mantle is 10^{26} cgs (centimeter-gram-second). This makes impossible any hypothesis of deep-seated convection within the mantle. However, convection in the upper portions of the mantle is not ruled out.

Models for the development of thermal stress leading to earthquakes were also studied by MacDonald. In particular, he showed that the relative distribution of heat will lead to a concentration of thermal stress on the boundaries of continents and oceans. This thermal stress can give rise to breaks, along which are concentrated tectonic stresses of varying origins.

From these studies, MacDonald developed a new theory for the internal figure of the Earth. He also carried out studies on the internal constitution of the Moon and the terrestrial planets. His detailed investigations substantiated the earlier conclusion that the inner planets must differ in chemical composition.

Still another area of investigation was the propagation of energy in the upper atmosphere. These studies included determination of the characteristic modes of hydromagnetic propagation and evaluation of the contribution of acoustic modes of the cloud balance of the high atmosphere. The long-term stability of the atmosphere to the loss of gases was also studied.

New methods of analyzing time series, in which linear processes played an important part, were developed by MacDonald. Atmospheric pressure records, ocean wave records, and tidal records were studied in this way.

Son of a Scotsman who had gone to Mexico to work as a bookkeeper for a smelting and refining company, MacDonald attended Mexican schools before going to the United States in 1941. He received his B.S. (1950), A.M. (1952), and Ph.D. (1954) at Harvard. He taught at the Massachusetts Institute of Technology, first as an assistant professor of geology and geophysics and later as an associate professor of geophysics. In 1958 he became a full professor at the University of California at Los Angeles. There he served also as associate director of the Institute of Geophysics and Planetary Physics, director of the Atmospheric Research Laboratory, and chairman of the Department of Planetary and Space Science. In 1966 he became vice-president for research at the Institute for Defense Analyses in Washington.

MacDonald was elected to the American Academy of Arts and Sciences in 1958 and the National Academy of Sciences in 1962. In 1965 he received the James B. Macelwane Award of the American Geophysical Union.

Editor of the *Journal of Atmospheric Sciences* and the *Review of Geophysics* and associate editor of five other journals, MacDonald wrote *The Rotation of the Earth*, with Walter Munk (1960).

For background information *see* COSMOGONY; EARTH (ORBITAL MOTION); MOON in the McGraw-Hill Encyclopedia of Science and Technology.   □

★ MacLEOD, Colin Munro

American physician and microbiologist
Born Jan. 28, 1909, Port Hastings, Nova Scotia, Canada

MACLEOD'S RESEARCH activities covered a number of areas in the field of microbial genetics, infectious diseases, and immunology.

With Oswald T. Avery and Maclyn McCarty, he discovered the role of DNA (deoxyribonucleic acid) in the genetic transformation of pneumococcal types, a finding which was to usher in the modern era of microbial genetics and molecular biology. Prior to the publication of these results in 1944, the nature of the genetic material in cells was unknown. These investigators showed that type transformation in pneumococcus is due to DNA in highly polymerized form and that the specific activity is destroyed upon depolymerization as by the action of the enzyme DNase (deoxyribonuclease). MacLeod's subsequent studies on genetic transformation were concerned chiefly with reactions between pneumococcus and various strains of streptococci of the viridans group.

During World War II his studies on microbial genetics were interrupted, and he devoted his attention to problems of infection in military personnel as director of the Commission on Pneumonia of the Army Epidemiological Board. The type-specific, capsular polysaccharides of pneumococcus had been known for some time as the antigenic components most concerned in specific immunity to pneumococcal infections in animals and in man. MacLeod showed that immunization of man by injection of the purified capsular polysaccharides of pneumococcus protects against the natural disease, lobar or pneumococcal pneumonia, under epidemic conditions.

In a study of the antigenicity of pneumococcal polysaccharides in mouse, rabbit, and man, MacLeod showed that the polysaccharides are antigenic for the rabbit and not merely haptenic as had previously been believed. In the rabbit the polysaccharides are weakly antigenic if used in appropriately small dosage. The appearance of antibodies can be prevented (so-called immune paralysis) if the critically small dosage of polysaccharide is exceeded.

Other studies by MacLeod in infectious diseases centered on the action of chemotherapeutic drugs. He demonstrated the development of sulfonamide resistance in pneumococcus both experimentally and during the course of treatment of the disease in man and the conditions most likely to lead to the emergence of resistant mutants. The essentiality of the specific immune response in successful therapy of pneumococcal infections by sulfonamides was also shown by him in studies carried out in 1937–40.

His studies on the toxicity of silicates for bacteria and red blood cells demonstrated that the degree of polymerization of silicate determines the toxic action in large measure. Monomers of silicate do not combine with red cells and do not affect their lytic properties. During early polymerization the small polymers become fixed to red cells and, if complement is present, the cells are lysed. Larger polymers also combine with the red cell membrane, and are directly toxic since they produce lysis even though no complement is present.

MacLeod received his M.D. at McGill University in 1932. He interned at the Montreal General Hospital and joined the staff of the Rockefeller Institute for Medical Research in 1934. He was chairman of the department of microbiology at New York University College of Medicine from 1941 to 1956, when he went to the University of Pennsylvania as professor of research medicine. He returned to New York University as professor of medicine in 1960. He served as president of the Armed Forces Epidemiological Board from 1946 to 1955, and was deputy director of the Office of Science and Technology, Executive Office of the President, in 1963–66. He became vice-president for medical affairs of the Commonwealth Fund in 1966. He was elected to the National Academy of Sciences in 1955 and to the American Academy of Arts and Sciences in 1965.

For background information *see* CHEMO-THERAPY; MOLECULAR BIOPHYSICS; NUCLEIC ACID; PNEUMOCOCCUS in the McGraw-Hill Encyclopedia of Science and Technology.   □

★ MAIMAN, Theodore Harold

American physicist
Born July 11, 1927, Los Angeles, Calif., U.S.A.

FOR HIS conception and development of the first operating laser Maiman received a number of awards, including the Stuart Ballantine Medal of the Franklin Institute in 1962, the Oliver E. Buckley Solid State Physics Prize of the American Physical Society in 1966, and the Fannie and John Hertz Foundation Award for Applied Physical Science in 1966—the latter presented by President Lyndon B. Johnson.

In his studies of stimulated emission of microwave energy, Maiman emphasized the three-level, solid-state maser (conceived by Nicolaas Bloembergen). He concentrated his efforts on the use of chromium-doped corundum (ruby) in these devices (first demonstrated by Chihiro Kikuchi). During the course of this work he came up with a filled-cavity innovation in which the microwave cavity was formed directly on the ruby crystal. This resulted in a unity-filling factor, and consequently a 10-times-greater maser gain-bandwidth product than had previously been attainable. It also allowed maser operation at much higher temperatures than the prior restriction to liquid helium. The high dielectric constant of ruby resulted in a large reduction in the size of the cavity and allowed a small, internal permanent magnet to be used. This development was instrumental in making the solid-state maser a practical device.

Maiman later developed a parallel-plate maser cavity design, again filled with ruby, and it was this cavity concept which led him to consider the generation of stimulated emission at much higher frequencies.

In the meantime, A. L. Schawlow and C. H.

Townes had proposed the idea of making a stimulated emission amplifier in the optical region of the spectrum, basing their concept around an alkali vapor system in a Fabry-Perot resonator. Maiman, however, having been successful with the parallel-plate cavity at microwave frequencies and having a familiarity with the work of Satoru Sugano and Yukito Tanabe and also of I. Wieder, was led to pursue the approach of using optical fluorescence in solids as the basis for a laser. He decided to consider ruby in this connection, even though the results indicated by Wieder's work were discouraging because of a reported low fluorescent quantum efficiency. It should be noted that it was a complete coincidence that ruby, which had worked so well as a maser, was now a candidate for laser action. Schawlow considered the ruby system briefly and concluded that it would be impossible to depopulate the ground state of a solid by means of optical pumping. Maiman persisted, however, in pursuing the material further.

First, he set up a series of experiments to measure carefully the losses in each step of the fluorescent process in ruby in an attempt to find out where the bottleneck responsible for the low quantum efficiency lay. He was searching for a guide for finding a more suitable material. In checking the fluorescent process step by step, he found that no such bottleneck existed and that Wieder's results were in fact in error by approximately two orders of magnitude. That is, the fluorescent quantum efficiency of ruby was actually fairly close to unity.

With this limitation removed, Maiman set up a series of kinetic equations to describe the various processes involved in the optical pumping of a fluorescent solid. Solving these equations and using the appropriate parameters which he had measured to be applicable to ruby, he found that the optical pump to provide laser action in ruby would need to be extremely intense. After studying the spectral properties and intensities of very bright lamps, he concluded that the best continuous pump would be a mercury arc, since it would provide both a good spectral match to the ruby and also the needed brightness. However, he further reasoned that the best available lamps would be somewhat marginal and therefore decided to use a very intense, pulsed xenon lamp for the initial measurement in order to provide a much larger margin for possible experimental success.

To test his hypotheses before proceeding to the final configuration, Maiman devised a microwave-optical experiment. He fabricated a cube of ruby and placed it between parallel metal plates, thereby forming a microwave resonator. The cavity was so designed as to have the same resonant frequency as the paramagnetic reso-

nance of the zero field splitting in the ground state of the ruby (11.3 GHz). The reflection coefficient of the cavity was monitored on an oscilloscope, while a short pulse of radiation from the xenon lamp was coupled to the crystal with a light pipe. From the magnitude of the change in the microwave absorption, Maiman was able to deduce that a sizable depletion in the ground state had indeed been produced, which gave him encouragement to continue further.

He then proceeded to the final configuration. It consisted of a ruby cylinder carefully ground flat and parallel, with silver coatings at each end (parallel-plate cavity). The ruby was surrounded by a helical-shaped flashlamp and that in turn by a polished aluminum reflector. The lamp was fired by discharging a capacitor through it, and in May, 1960, the ruby indeed emitted stimulated radiation at a wavelength of 6943 A. Coherent light was produced for the first time.

Maiman was motivated and guided into the world of science by his father, a creative electrical engineer who developed the first automobile vibrator power supply. In his teens Maiman earned college money by repairing electrical appliances and radios. He attended the University of Colorado and received a B.S. in engineering physics in 1949, then went on to do graduate work at Stanford University, where he received an M.S. in electrical engineering in 1951 and a Ph.D. in physics in 1955. His doctoral thesis, under W. E. Lamb, was a series of spectroscopic measurements in helium, using microwave-optical techniques. Maiman did his maser and laser work while associated with Hughes Research Laboratories. In 1962 he founded his own company, Korad Corp., which is devoted to the research, development, and manufacture of lasers.

For background information *see* LASER; MASER in the McGraw-Hill Encyclopedia of Science and Technology. □

★ MANTON, Sidnie Milana

British zoologist
Born May 4, 1902, London, England

Zoological interests in the early decades of this century largely centered around piecing together evolutionary histories, using the stock lines of investigation—comparative anatomy and embryology. Knowledge of the invertebrates lagged far behind that of the vertebrates in these respects. Physiological studies on invertebrates were starting, but a comprehensive functional approach to the invertebrates had hardly begun. Comparative behavior studies and ecology were yet to come.

Manton's initial work centered on the embryology and functional morphology of Crustacea and Onychophora. Her work on the development of *Hemimysis* (1928) and *Nebalia* (1934) represented the first application of modern methods to the "higher" Crustacea, following that by H. G. Cannon on the Branchiopoda. The fundamental pattern of malacostracan development thereby disclosed showed that the Leptostraca are in no way an intermediate group between Malacostraca and other crustaceans, as was then supposed, but thoroughly malacostracan in affinity. This conclusion was substantiated by studies on crustacean feeding mechanisms (Cannon and Manton, 1927, and Manton, 1930) and by work on segmental excretory organs (1927, 1931). A fundamental basis was thus formed for the many later studies on crustacean development by workers all over the world.

Membership in the Great Barrier Reef Expedition (1928–29) provided her with the opportunity for study of syncarid Crustacea in Tasmania (1930). Ecological surveys of reefs and a particular study of the manner of growth of one species of coral (*Pocillopora*) constituted her contribution to the coordinated work of the party (1932, 1935).

Research on crustacean embryology led to a similar study of the Onychophora (1949). Her work on the early development of four South African species corrected many previous, rather fundamental. misconceptions and provided the opportunity for reviewing many topics of essential importance to arthropodan understanding. A series of functional studies were also completed on onychophoran feeding, digestion, growth, life cycle, and so on (1937, 1938).

But it was the analysis of the locomotory mechanism used by the Onychophora (1950) that set in train the largest project ever made on invertebrate functional morphology, and the most rewarding. This work occupied 17 years before an end came in sight. A comparative

analysis of the locomotory mechanisms of terrestrial and of some aquatic arthropods and worms led to the inclusion of other patterns of behavior found to be fundamental to the evolution of arthropodan classes and orders. It was possible to show in great detail how the internal and external structure forms a functionally integrated whole, and morphology, which hitherto held no functional or evolutionary significance for us, could now be understood. The correlations between the structure of the larger groups of arthropods and their habits show how the habits and the structure must have evolved together. The evolutionary differentiation of classes and orders of arthropods has been associated with morphological progress which facilitates habits. This type of progress enables animals to live better in the same or in a wide variety of habitats, and it is the antithesis of the well-known adaptive radiations within more limited taxa which lead to detailed adaptation to various environmental niches.

The comparative approach for this type of work cannot be overestimated, since detailed study of structure and possible function in one animal alone cannot be properly interpreted. The habits of greatest evolutionary importance in present-day morphology vary greatly in their ease of recognition, and the fullest use has had to be made of modern methods in elucidating anatomy and movements. It was shown how a divergence of habits among early terrestrial arthropods must have accompanied the evolution of the trunk characteristics of the several classes of myriapods and of hexapods. Pushing into the substratum (in a variety of ways) by the motive force of the legs led to the Diplopoda and their component orders (1954, 1956, 1961). Faster running, and a moderate ability to thicken and shorten the body momentarily, led to the Chilopoda, the former habit being further advanced by the Scolopendromorpha, Lithobiomorpha, and Scutigeromorpha and the latter by the Geophilomorpha, together with an abundance of facilitating morphology (1953, 1965). Penetration of small and awkward crevices by body twisting and turning, without pushing, led to the Symphyla and their diagnostic structure (1966). Penetration of crevices by smallness of size combined with hydrostatic and muscular rigidity of a short body and fast patterns of gait resulted in the Pauropoda (1953, 1966). The essential arthropodan nature of the Onychophora was confirmed and the peculiarities in structure of these animals shown to be related to their habit of greatest evolutionary significance, that of penetrating crevices by extreme body deformations without pushing (1958).

A detailed study of jaw mechanisms throughout the Arthropoda (1964) and of leg mechanisms within the myriapods and hexapods (1958,

1965, 1966) showed that the myriapod classes do indeed form a natural group, and that the hexapod classes must have had a different origin from those of any extant myriapods, thus disproving the supposed symphylan theory of insect origin. The "Apterygota" and the "Entognatha" do not constitute natural groups but are convergent assemblages, and only the Thysanura approach at all closely to the Pterygota in their functional morphology and relationships. The Onychophora were shown to be related to the myriapod-hexapod animals in contrast to the rest of the Arthropoda. The category "Mandibulata" was proved to be fictitious, and abundant evidence was presented to show that a simple monophyletic scheme for arthropodan relationships is untenable, and that the Onychophora-Myriapoda-Hexapoda evolved parallel with, and independently from, the Crustacea. The limb mechanisms of Crustacea and of Chelicerata show a fundamental absence of uniformity, which again indicates parallel evolution of these superclasses. The concept of grades was clarified in its application to the Arthropoda, and some evidence was advanced concerning the origin and functions of the arthropodan hemocoel (1961, 1965, 1967).

Manton was awarded an M.A., Ph.D., and Sc.D. at Cambridge University, where she was a demonstrator in comparative anatomy in 1927–35 and director of studies in natural sciences at Girton College in 1935–42. At the University of London she was visiting lecturer in 1943–46, assistant lecturer in 1946–49, and reader in zoology in 1949–60. Elected to the Royal Society of London in 1948, one of the first women to be so honored, she received the Gold Medal of the Linnean Society of London in 1963.

For background information *see* ARTHROPODA; INVERTEBRATE EMBRYOLOGY in the McGraw-Hill Encyclopedia of Science and Technology.   □

★ MARSDEN, Sir Ernest

New Zealand nuclear physicist
Born Feb. 19, 1889, Rishton, Lancashire, England

WHILE HOLDING the John Harling fellowship at Manchester University (1911–14), Marsden worked under Ernest Rutherford during the early experimental stages of atomic physics. J. J. Thompson's work on ionization and Rutherford's on disintegration of radioactive substances had shown that the atom was not a finite particle but a highly complex energy unit. The atomic model then suggested comprised a sphere of uniform positive charge containing electron "shells." While investigating atomic structure, Rutherford and Hans Geiger observed scattering of alpha particles, and Marsden was asked to experiment further. Using radium emanation striking metal reflectors and counting scintillations visually, Geiger and Marsden showed (*a*) that while most of the alpha particles passed through the metal atoms unhindered, a few were deflected at an angle wide enough to emerge from the incident side; (*b*) that the relative amount of deflection varied with different metals, decreasing with the atomic weight of the reflector; and (*c*) that results from use of metal reflectors of varying thickness proved conclusively that deflection was not a surface phenomenon but a volume effect due to scattering by some hitherto unsuspected force. Rutherford then put forward the theory (1911) that the atom consisted of a central nucleus of massive positive charge with outer electron shells. Further work (1912–13) by Geiger and Marsden proved conclusively that a central nucleus existed and that the amount of large-angle alpha scattering from different metal reflectors varied as half the atomic weight.

In 1914 Marsden went to New Zealand as professor of physics at Victoria University College, Wellington. There he began his own experiments on radioactivity, producing evidence of the possibility of induced transmutation of the elements. This evidence was that alpha-particle bombardment of nitrogen nuclei resulted in a scattering in which the scattered particles had a greater velocity than the original alphas. Marsden's work was interrupted by military service in World War I, but his results were communicated to Rutherford. At the conclusion of the war Marsden was working with him at the Cavendish Laboratory when these early results

were confirmed and extended with the now famous transmutation

$$N_{14} \xrightarrow{\ aP\ } O_{17}$$

Marsden then returned to the Victoria University of Wellington. He was appointed assistant director of education in 1922 and laid the foundation for the New Zealand Technical Education Institute. In 1926 Marsden was appointed the first permanent secretary of the newly constituted Department of Scientific and Industrial Research. During his 20-year term the few research units in chemistry, geology, and agriculture were expanded, and laboratories were established to foster development of New Zealand's resources, notably the Physical Testing Laboratory, the Radar Development Laboratory, and laboratories for geophysics and soil science.

Research in the 1930s showed a strong correlation between the regional incidence of goiter and natural radiation. Marsden was interested in the suggestion that a goiterous condition was not altogether determined by the availability of iodine ingested, but might be connected with regional types of rock, the natural emanation from which intensified ionization of fluids within the body, thus interfering with natural metabolism. Marsden also knew that goiter was prevalent in the Himalaya Mountains, composed of ancient granites, and highest for graywackes. in New Zealand, which exhibit a high natural background of radioactivity. He began comparative studies of background radiation from rocks occurring in all parts of New Zealand. World War II interrupted this program, but results published with C. Watson-Munro (1944) established a comparatively low alpha activity for alkaline rocks, moderate for recent volcanics, such as basalts, rhyolites, and andesites, high for ancient granites, and highest for graywackes. The background radiations for soils were related to parent rock rather than to soil type.

Marsden retired from the Department of Scientific and Industrial Research in 1954. Thus he was able to undertake a series of studies into bioeffects of natural radioactivity. He suspected a link between the high radioactivity levels in shellfish-eating communities and stomach cancer. Earlier work carried out on New Zealand Tertiary sediments with Paul Vella had shown that in some marine beds fossil diatoms had a high level of alpha radioactivity. In view of the fact that observed incidence of stomach cancer for the white population of New Zealand was only half that of the shellfish-eating Maori, Marsden began a detailed survey of the origin of radioactivity in foodstuffs and its effects. Observations on plankton collected from a ship en route to the United Kingdom (1963) had shown these to possess a high alpha activity, almost all due to polonium. Marsden also tested New Zealand shellfish, finding that those types which feed on plankton were also high in radioactivity. He ascribed the higher incidence of stomach cancer in Maori communities to their shellfish diet. He also suggested that the several-fold-higher incidence of congenital impairments, such as clubfoot and albinism, found among Maoris and Hawaiians could be related to muta-

genic effects of this activity. A soil survey of Niue Island recording exceptionally high levels of natural radiation (1962) led him to carry out a detailed investigation of local radioactivity. He correlated regional increases in alpha radiation with higher incidence of cataract, albinism, and deformities, together with an exceptionally high sterility rate among the islanders. Measurements of radiation from local foodstuffs showed astonishingly high levels due to radium. For a day's average intake of taro, locally the staple food, the ingestion of alpha-radiating nucleides was a hundred times that of a normal European carbohydrate diet. However, Marsden found a significant difference between species: A certain variety of taro showed very little activity. This led him to comparative investigations for other plants.

The correlation suggested by many health authorities between cigarette smoking and lung cancer led Marsden in the 1960s to examine radioactivity in tobaccos. Results from ashed tobaccos revealed that stable active radicals were carried over by smoke and retained in tar condensates, different varieties of tobacco showing a range of 30:1 in polonium activity. Controlled experiments made with the assistance of the U.S. Department of Agriculture and the U.S. Atomic Energy Commission in 1966 showed that a high radioactive level characterized tobaccos grown on soils of low pH derived from ancient granites or granodiorites, or those grown on soils of low activity fertilized with uranium ores. This effect was little influenced by variety, species, or by natural fallout.

Marsden also investigated phosphate fertilizers of different origins. He found these differed widely in alpha radiation, as reflected in Graminaceae grown on test plots. Comparative studies on cereal grains showed that wheat grown in acid soils in various parts of the world was eight times higher in alpha activity than the same varieties grown in less acid soils. Some of this activity was retained when cereals were processed, and certain breakfast foods were shown to have a particularly high polonium activity.

Among subjects of other comparative studies were potable waters from many regions in New Zealand (graywacke districts showed relatively high activity from radon); radioactivity of bones from a wide range of animals; and the possible carcinogenic effects of tetraethyl lead (Marsden recorded polonium activity from automobile exhaust pipes).

Marsden was educated at Queen Elizabeth Grammar School, Blackburn, and the University of Manchester. In 1911–14 he was a fellow at Manchester, after which he was professor of physics at Victoria University College, Wellington, New Zealand, until 1922. In 1922–26 he was assistant director of education for New Zealand,

and in 1926–46 he was secretary of the government's Department of Scientific and Industrial Research. President of the Royal Society of New Zealand in 1947, Marsden was elected to the Royal Society of London in 1946. He was chairman of the New Zealand Defence Science Advisory Council in 1956. In addition to honorary degrees from Manchester, Oxford, and Victoria University (Wellington), he received the U.S. Medal of Freedom (1947) and the Rutherford Medal of the Institute of Physics and Physical Society (1948). He was knighted in 1958; he was made a Commander of the North Star in Sweden in 1966.

Marsden wrote papers on the more important aspects of his research; some 15 years' results of radiation research are summarized in the Proceedings of the First International Symposium on Natural Radiation Environment, held at Rice University, in Texas, in 1963.

For background information *see* ATOMIC STRUCTURE AND SPECTRA; RADIATION BIOCHEMISTRY; RADIATION INJURY (BIOLOGY); RADIOACTIVITY in the McGraw-Hill Encyclopedia of Science and Technology.   □

★ MARSHAK, Robert Eugene

American physicist
Born Oct. 11, 1916, New York, N.Y., U.S.A.

MARSHAK STARTED his scientific career by assisting Hans Bethe in his pioneering work on the thermonuclear sources of stellar energy. For his thesis, Marshak studied the internal constitution and energy sources of the class of extremely dense stars known as white dwarf stars. For this work he was awarded the A. Cressy Morrison Prize of the New York Academy of Sciences in 1940. An important prediction in Marshak's thesis, dealing with the radius of Sirius B, the white dwarf companion to the brightest star in the sky, is now being tested after a lapse of more than a quarter of a

century; preliminary results are encouraging for the theory. During the war years Marshak served in the theoretical physics division at the Los Alamos laboratory. There he developed several powerful methods (spherical harmonic, variational, and Laplace transform) for solving problems in neutron diffusion that were widely used during and after the war. He also worked on the theory of shock waves, concentrating on the effect of high temperatures on shock hydrodynamics; he discovered a new type of shock wave, sometimes called the "Marshak wave."

After the war Marshak became interested in the newly developing subject of meson physics. As early as 1935 Hideki Yukawa had suggested the existence of a particle of intermediate mass, called the meson, which would be exchanged between the proton and neutron and give rise to the nuclear force between them. The discovery in 1937 of a particle in the cosmic radiation with a mass about 200 times that of the electron mass seemed to support Yukawa's theory. During the next decade, however, experiments on the interaction of these mesons with matter at sea level and underground, culminating in the experiment of M. Conversi, E. Pancini, and O. Piccioni in 1947, raised strong doubts about Yukawa's theory. From the latter experiment one could conclude that, when negatively charged cosmic-ray mesons stop in ordinary solid materials like carbon, they prefer the slow process of decay to the rapid process of absorption—in disagreement with the Yukawa theory by the startling factor of 10^{12}.

In order to save the Yukawa theory, Marshak proposed the two-meson hypothesis, according to which the cosmic-ray mesons observed at sea level are not Yukawa mesons but rather weakly interacting decay products of the true Yukawa meson, which is produced copiously in nuclear collisions of cosmic rays high in the atmosphere. Within weeks after the two-meson theory was proposed (at the famous Shelter Island Theoretical Conference organized in June, 1947, by Robert Oppenheimer), the first photographs of the heavy mesons (now called pions) decaying into the lighter mesons (now called muons) were published. These cosmic-ray photographs were soon followed by more precise experiments with high-energy accelerators, and the essential features of the two-meson theory were confirmed.

Once the chief properties of the pion were known, a large number of calculations were undertaken to work out the implications of Yukawa's meson theory of nuclear forces. Unfortunately, the huge strength of the pion-nucleon interaction created formidable computational difficulties in this endeavor. Indeed, after 10 years of experimentation on proton-proton and neutron-proton scattering with the high-energy accelerators, even a good phenomenological theory of the force between two nucleons did not exist. In 1957 Marshak and his student P. S. Signell introduced a spin-orbit term into the nuclear potential otherwise taken from meson theory, and they showed that all the nucleon-nucleon scattering data up to several hundred million electron volts could be quantitatively described by a potential of this form. The Signell-Marshak potential was the beginning of a highly successful semiphenomenological theory of the two-nucleon potential.

A major research interest through all of Marshak's career was the subject of weak interactions among elementary particles. As early as 1942 Marshak published a paper in which he proposed some incisive tests of Enrico Fermi's theory of nuclear beta decay first suggested in 1934. Marshak considered the capture of electrons by nuclei from the L atomic shells, as well as the conditions under which highly forbidden transitions from nuclei like Be^{10} and K^{40} would yield unique shapes of electron spectra. The Fermi theory passed both tests in measurements carried out after the war. However, with his student E. C. G. Sudarshan, the most significant accomplishment of Marshak in the field of weak interactions was the development in 1957 of the universal V-A (vector–axial vector) theory of weak interactions.

As early as 1948, only a year after the discovery of the pion, it was noted by several authors that the observed decay processes $n \rightarrow p + e + \nu$, $\pi \rightarrow \mu + \nu$, and $\mu \rightarrow e + \nu + \nu$ (n is neutron, p proton, e electron, ν neutrino, π pion, μ muon) might be governed by forces of comparable strength. The search for the universal law of weak interactions thereby became a major goal of theoretical particle physics. By 1957 a great deal of experimental work on the weak decays of the nucleon, pion, and muon—including the parity-breakdown experiments suggested by T. D. Lee and C. N. Yang in 1956—appeared to exclude the possibility of a universal law of force for all these decays. The nuclear beta-decay experiments seemed to favor one type of weak force, the muon decay another, and the pion decay still a third.

In such a confused experimental situation Sudarshan and Marshak argued that the only hope for a universal law of force lay in one particular type of weak force, called the V-A interaction, and that a new principle, called "chirality invariance," would predict this V-A interaction. The same theory was developed independently somewhat later by R. P. Feynman and M. Gell-Mann, using a different argument. But Sudarshan and Marshak pointed out that four experiments contradicted the theory and that, if any of these experiments was correct, it would be necessary to abandon the hypothesis of

a universal weak force. Within 2 years all four experiments were redone and found to be incorrect, and the new results were in agreement with the V-A theory. This theory was not only successful in supplying a unified explanation of the weak decays of nucleon, pion, and muon. In its very first formulation in 1957, it was suggested that the same law of force should govern the weak decays of the strange particles, such as the K-meson and the various types of hyperons. The hundreds of measurements which have been made of both strange and nonstrange particle decays in recent years on the large accelerators have all tended to confirm the essential correctness of the universal V-A theory of weak interactions.

A graduate of New York City high schools, Marshak studied at Columbia University (A.B., 1936) on a Pulitzer scholarship and took his Ph.D. in physics at Cornell in 1939. He then went to the University of Rochester, where he became chairman of the department of physics and astronomy in 1950 and Distinguished University Professor in 1964. Marshak was twice Guggenheim fellow, at the University of Paris (1953–54) and at CERN, Geneva (1960–61). He was elected to the National Academy of Sciences in 1958, and served as chairman of its Advisory Committee on the Soviet Union and Eastern Europe in 1963–66, during which time he negotiated scientific exchange agreements with the science academies of Poland, Yugoslavia, and Czechoslovakia. He was elected to the American Academy of Arts and Sciences in 1961.

Marshak wrote *Our Atomic World*, with E. C. Nelson and L. I. Schiff (1946); *Meson Physics* (1952; paper 1959); and *Introduction to Elementary Particles*, with E. C. G. Sudarshan (1961; translated into French, German, and Russian).

For background information *see* ELEMENTARY PARTICLE; MESON; STELLAR EVOLUTION in the McGraw-Hill Encyclopedia of Science and Technology.   □

★ MARTYN, David Forbes

Australian physicist
Born June 27, 1906, Cambuslang, Lanarkshire, Scotland

IN 1935 Martyn was engaged with O. O. Pulley in an experimental study of the characteristics of the ionosphere above Australia. The results obtained led to an intensive study of all characteristics of the high atmosphere, especially its temperature and composition. This led him to the firm conclusion that, although there is a warmer region above the stratosphere, the temperature must drop again to a very low value

(about 160°K) at about 82 km and then rise again to extremely high values (about 1000°K) at heights above 250 km. He also concluded that the atmosphere at such heights still consists mainly of nitrogen and that strong winds and turbulence prevent any settling out of gases in diffusive equilibrium, as had been previously supposed. All these conclusions have been amply confirmed in recent years by rocket probes.

In 1933 Martyn joined with V. A. Bailey in working out the theory of interaction of radio waves in the ionosphere. Their work was developed to explain the experimental discovery by Tellegen that a powerful long-wave transmitter (Radio Luxembourg) was able to impress its program upon that of medium-wave transmissions passing through the ionosphere above Luxembourg; their theory is now accepted as the classical explanation of all major features of the phenomenon.

In the postwar years Martyn continued his studies of the ionosphere, discovering the existence of large semidiurnal lunar oscillations in the height and peak electron densities of the F region of the ionosphere. He showed that these oscillations are due not to local winds, but to electric fields generated by polarization in the lower "dynamo" or E region of the ionosphere and communicated upward along the highly conducting geomagnetic field lines. Martyn also was first to give a clear outline of the morphology of the perturbations of the F region which are associated with geomagnetic storms. He showed that these pertubations do not travel relatively slowly from polar regions, as had previously been supposed, but developed almost simultaneously all over the globe according to a relatively simple pattern when expressed in *geomagnetic* storm time.

In 1948 Martyn turned his attention to the dynamo theory of the daily geomagnetic variations, originally proposed by Balfour Stewart and developed later in quantitative detail by A.

Schuster and S. Chapman. At that time it was already clear that the known tidal velocities and conductivity in the ionosphere are inadequate to account for the magnitude of the observed geomagnetic variations. Martyn suggested that Hall conductivity might overcome the quantitative difficulty, and in 1952 he went on with W. G. Baker to reexamine the dynamo theory, taking account of this conductivity. As a result of their work, Stewart's original hypothesis was vindicated quantitatively; as a by-product of this investigation, they also accounted for the equatorial electrojet, which had recently been discovered above the geomagnetic equator. Martyn also used the theory (1953) to explain the anomalous depression of F-region electron densities near the geomagnetic equator; the electrons in this region are lifted upward by "motor" action and diffused downward and poleward to form two anomalous peaks lying some 10° on each side of the equator.

In 1946 Martyn turned his attention to solar radio astronomy. After showing experimentally that the radiation from sunspot areas has a large component which is circularly polarized, he went on to study the theoretical problem of the radio radiation to be expected from the Sun at meter and centimeter wavelengths. He showed that on meter wavelengths the corona should give out blackbody radiation corresponding to a temperature of 1,000,000°, and that at centimeter wavelengths the temperature of the radiation should drop to about 10,000° with a markedly hotter halo. These predictions were rapidly confirmed by experimentalists.

Son of an ophthalmologist, Martyn took his B.Sc. and A.R.C.Sc. from the University of London (Royal College of Science) in 1926, Ph.D. in 1928, and D.Sc. in 1936. He joined the staff of the Radio Research Board in Australia in 1929, working there in association with the Commonwealth Scientific and Industrial Research Organization. In 1939 he initiated radar research and development in Australia, setting up the Radiophysics Laboratory in Sydney for this purpose. Later, during World War II, he was director of operational research for the Australian armed services. With a strong interest in various unions of the International Council of Scientific Unions, he served successively as chairman of the Radio Astronomy Commission of the Union Radio Scientifique Internationale, then as chairman of that body's Ionosphere Commission. Along with Sir Mark Oliphant he took a leading role in founding the Australian Academy of Science and in drafting its constitution. He also took a keen interest in Australia's Antarctic and space research work, serving as chairman of the relevant national committees. In 1962 he became chairman of the United Nations Scientific and Technical Committee on the Peaceful Uses of

Outer Space. Martyn was elected a fellow of the Royal Society of London in 1950, and in 1955 he was awarded the Chree Medal of the Institute of Physics and the Physical Society.

For background information *see* ATMOSPHERE; GEOMAGNETIC STORM; IONOSPHERE; SUN in the McGraw-Hill Encyclopedia of Science and Technology.   □

★ **MATHER, Kenneth**

British geneticist
Born June 22, 1911, Nantwich, Cheshire, England

FOR HIS genetical studies of quantitative characters and their significance in evolution and development, Mather received in 1964 the Darwin Medal of the Royal Society of London.

From 1931 to 1938, Mather's interest in chromosome behavior and the mechanism and consequences of crossover reflected his initial association with C. D. Darlington. During this period Mather's studies of interlocking among chromosomes threw light on the mechanism of crossover, and he worked out the first comprehensive theory of segregation in autotetraploid plants, which carry four sets of chromosomes instead of the customary two and therefore do not show simple regular mendelian ratios. He was also among the first to study the damaging action of x-rays on chromosomes and by this was able to determine experimentally the time at which the chromosomes become functionally double during the cycle of nuclear division.

In 1938 he turned his attention to the genetical study of quantitative or metrical variation in which characters, instead of showing clear mendelian segregation, display every grade of expression between wide limits. This is the variation which Darwin had seen as the raw material of evolution, and a stay at the plant breeding institute at Svalöf, Sweden, during 1933–34 had convinced Mather of its basic importance in the applied genetics of plant and animal breeding.

This interest was confirmed by a subsequent association with R. A. Fisher, who had earlier been responsible for fundamental developments in the genetical interpretation and analysis of quantitative variation. The basic genetical postulate had already been made that this variation depends not on the segregation of genes of individually large and distinctive effect, but on the simultaneous action of systems of genes each of relatively small effect, yet capable of reinforcing and balancing one another's actions—polygenic systems, as Mather was to call them. These systems of genes, however, had been subjected to very little experimental investigation or theoretical analysis.

Principally by practicing selection on hybrid populations of *Drosophila melanogaster*, following the progress of change in appropriate characters under this selection and analyzing its products genetically, Mather showed that such polygenic systems contribute to quantitative variation and that they were responsible for all the heritable variation of this kind displayed by the character he followed. It became clear that the variation observable as differences between individuals is but a small fraction of the genetic variation the population contains, the rest lying hidden in the genotypes in the form of combinations of genes which balance out one another's effects. This hidden variation is released or uncovered by segregation and recombination of the genes following crossing, with the result that, as it picks out recombinant groups of genes, selection can quickly push the expression of a character well beyond the limits of its manifestation in the original population in which the selection is initiated. Furthermore, selection for the primary character was found to change the expression of other characters for which no selection is practiced, not because of any direct developmental relations between them but because the polygenic systems mediating the different characters are mingled in their distribution along the chromosomes.

The frequencies of natural crossing between individuals in a population and of recombination within their chromosomes govern the behavior of variability and hence the response to natural selection. Crossing and recombination are thus themselves key characters of a species, and it was shown that they are subject to adjustment by natural selection in ways related to the general biological properties of the species and their life cycles.

Quantitative variation cannot be investigated and measured by the conventional segregation ratios of genetics. They require a biometrical approach by the use and manipulation of statistical quantities—means, variances, and covariances. Mather and his associates, notably J. L. Jinks, devised methods, experimental and biometrical, for analyzing quantitative variation so as to reveal the properties of the underlying polygenic systems in the action, interaction, and linkage relations of their member genes. This branch of genetics has now come to be known by Mather's name for it: biometrical genetics. The methods of biometrical genetics are being used not only in breeding improved strains of domestic plants and animals but also in other ways, such as the investigation of behavioral characters in rats.

Natural selection can act in a number of ways, of which Mather recognized three, each with its special impact not only on the overall behavior of the populations subject to its action, but also on the genetical architecture (the way the genes dovetail with one another in exerting their effects) of the characters each individual shows. The history of selection is in fact reflected in a character's genetical architecture, which also governs its future responses to selection. In other words, genetic structure is determined by what natural selection has done in the past, and at the same time it determines what selection can do in the future.

Mather received his B.Sc. (1931) from the University of Manchester and Ph.D. and D.Sc. (1940) from the University of London. He was lecturer in Galton Laboratory, University College, London, during 1934–37, and head of the genetics department, John Innes Horticultural Institution, during 1938–48. He was professor of genetics in the University of Birmingham for 17 years until 1965, when he became vice-chancellor of the University of Southampton. He was elected to the Royal Society in 1949.

Mather wrote *The Measurement of Linkage in Heredity* (1938; 2d ed. 1951); *Statistical Analysis in Biology* (1943; 5th ed. 1964); *Biometrical Genetics* (1949); *The Elements of Genetics*, with C. D. Darlington (1949); *Genes, Plants and People*, with C. D. Darlington (1950); *Human Diversity* (1964); and *The Elements of Biometry* (1967).

For background information *see* BIOMETRICS; GENE ACTION; RADIATION CYTOLOGY in the McGraw-Hill Encyclopedia of Science and Technology.   □

★ MATHER, Kirtley Fletcher

American geologist
Born Feb. 13, 1888, Chicago, Ill., U.S.A.

SUCCESSFULLY CARRYING forward into the mid-20th-century specialization of science something of the spirit of the 19th-century naturalists, Mather was best known as a general geologist and educator. His contributions to scientific knowledge stemmed from his field studies rather than from the laboratory. His interests covered the entire area of the earth sciences, with emphasis upon glacial geology, geomorphology, petroleum geology, and structural geology.

From 1910 to 1916 he was associated with Wallace W. Atwood in the study of the geomorphology and glacial geology of the San Juan Mountain area of Colorado and New Mexico, under the auspices of the U.S. Geological Survey. During World War I the USGS transferred Mather to field studies related to the provision of fuel oil for the Navy, and he spent the summers of 1917 and 1918 mapping potentially petroliferous geologic structures in Allen County, Ky., and Osage County, Okla. In 1919 he went to South America for Richmond Levering and Company to make an exploratory study of petroleum resources in the eastern foothills of the Bolivian Andes. This pioneer work continued through 1920, and Mather's interpretation of the geologic structure and history of the Pre-Cordillera was generally verified by geologists who were subsequently involved in the development of the oil fields of eastern Bolivia. Returning to field studies in the San Juan area in 1922, he introduced to geomorphologists a technique of petroleum geologists by depicting with contour lines the restored surface of the deformed San Juan peneplain. This work also revealed the frequently renewed upward movement of the San Juan "dome" as it underwent erosion and the contemporary downward movement of the adjacent San Luis Valley, in which much debris from the mountains was deposited, the crustal movements apparently being a result of isostatic adjustment.

Mather spent the summer of 1923 as a geologist in a USGS party that surveyed a part of the

Alaska Peninsula between Kamishak Bay and the Valley of Ten Thousand Smokes. His activities in subsequent field seasons included study of the petroleum possibilities of northeastern Colorado under USGS auspices in 1924; on

Cape Breton Island, Nova Scotia, for the Gulf Oil Corporation in 1925; and assignment as government geologist in connection with litigation concerned with the Navy Fuel Oil Reserve in the Elk Hills of California in 1926–27. He conducted a party of Harvard and Radcliffe students through France, Switzerland, Italy, and Spain in the summer of 1928, and was with another party of geology students, most of them from Harvard, in the Canadian Rocky Mountains in the summer of 1929. During subsequent years he had field consultations with Harvard Ph.D. candidates in Tennessee, Colorado, and elsewhere, and he conducted the detailed mapping of the glacial and postglacial formations of the Buzzards Bay area in the western part of Cape Cod, Mass. His latest systematic field studies were in southwestern Colorado, where he found that a glacial deposit previously believed to be Eocene in age was in reality a Pleistocene moraine overlain by remnants of a gigantic landslide containing huge slabs of Early Tertiary volcanic agglomerate.

A descendant of the Reverend Richard Mather, who migrated from England to the Massachusetts Bay Colony in 1635, Mather received the B.S. in 1909 from Denison University and the Ph.D. in 1915 from the University of Chicago, where he studied under Thomas C. Chamberlin, Rollin D. Salisbury, Wallace W. Atwood, and Albert Johannsen, and completed his doctoral dissertation under Stuart Weller. He taught geology in the University of Arkansas from 1911 to 1914, in Queen's University, Kingston, Ontario, from 1915 to 1918, and in Denison University from 1918 to 1924. He went to Harvard in 1924, retiring as professor emeritus in 1954. He was president of the Ohio Academy of Science in 1923–24, of the American Association for the Advancement of Science in 1951, and of the American Academy of Arts and Sciences from 1957 to 1961. Besides several honorary degrees, Mather received the Distinguished Service Medal of the University of Chicago in 1941; the Abraham Alper Award of the Civil Liberties Union of Massachusetts in 1961; the Bradford Washburn Medal of the Boston Museum of Science in 1964; the Publication Award of the Geographical Society of Chicago and the Thomas Alva Edison Foundation Award, both conferred for his book *The Earth Beneath Us* (1964); and the Cullum Medal of the American Geographical Society in 1965.

Mather also wrote *Old Mother Earth* (1928); *Science in Search of God* (1928); *Source Book in Geology*, with S. L. Mason (1939); *Enough and to Spare* (1944); and *Source Book in Geology, 1900–1950* (1967).

For background information *see* GEOMORPHOLOGY; GLACIATED TERRANE; PETROLEUM GEOLOGY in the McGraw-Hill Encyclopedia of Science and Technology. □

★ MAYNARD, Leonard Amby

American nutritional scientist
Born Nov. 8, 1887, Hartford, N.Y., U.S.A.

MAYNARD'S RESEARCH in the field of nutritional science began immediately following the initial discoveries that ushered in the "newer knowledge of nutrition." In 1913 years of research had culminated in the establishment of the essentiality of the first vitamin. In 1914 clear evidence was obtained that adequate protein nutrition depended upon the amino acid makeup of the protein. About this same time more specific research began on the role of certain minerals in the diet. Thus it became established that adequate nutrition required the presence in the diet of specific amino acids, vitamins, and minerals, as well as proteins and the energy-yielding fats and carbohydrates.

In 1915, following the completion of his studies for a Ph.D. in chemistry, Maynard began his research activities in the Laboratory of Animal Nutrition, which he designed and equipped for chemical and biological studies in the department of animal husbandry at Cornell University. Since the initial discoveries resulting in the "newer knowledge" had been made with small laboratory animals receiving diets made up of purified ingredients, his first efforts were directed to the establishment of a rat colony. Although aware that the use of purified diets with laboratory animals had solved nutritional problems which had baffled solution by other techniques, he recognized that it was not feasible to use the purified-diet method with large animals. He conceived the idea of integrated small and large animal studies for the solution of a given problem, using semipurified diets with rats in pilot experiments to guide the studies with farm animals.

Using this concept, Maynard began in 1916 a program to develop a "milk substitute" for weaning young calves. Such a substitute, if nutritionally satisfactory and reasonable in price, would enable the farmer to increase his net income by marketing the milk thus replaced. Various ingredients and combinations of them were tested in rat growth studies, and the more promising combinations were fed to various groups of calves. These studies were interrupted from 1917 to 1919 while Maynard served in the Army. After the war Maynard continued his former studies; he also conducted some basic biochemical studies of digestive upsets in young calves fed diets other than milk. The comparative rat and calf experiment resulted in 1923 in the development of a "calf meal" that found wide use on dairy farms. It was marketed by one commercial concern for about 25 years with sales amounting to 1200–15,000 tons annually.

In 1922 a study was begun, in cooperation with S. A. Goldberg, a pathologist, of an ailment in growing pigs of unknown cause but referred to as "lameness" and "posterior paralysis" because of the physical symptoms. By various experimental supplementations of the diet known to cause it, the ailment was found to be due to a dietary calcium deficiency. This specific finding was obtained through chemical and histological studies of the bones, and proved that the better growth obtained when calcium supplements were added to deficient rations was due to improved bone nutrition. It was shown that the physical symptoms of the trouble were reflected in an abnormal chemical and histological structure of the leg bones. An accompanying study (1923–24) demonstrated why pigs were more susceptible to these same troubles when housed indoors, and thus the beneficial effect of sunlight in producing normal bones was established. At the time he undertook this study Maynard was aware of the discovery by M. Huldinsky in 1919 that ultraviolet rays (present in sunlight) improved calcium deposition in rachitic children. Maynard's studies extended this finding to pigs and contributed to the later explanation that sunlight produced the antirachitic vitamin (discovered in 1922) in the body of the animal.

In 1928 Maynard began a series of studies on the biochemistry of lactation to learn more about the basic processes involved in order to contribute to the better nutrition of the young during the nursing period and, in the case of commercial milk production, to improve its efficiency. Here again purified diet studies with rats were combined with experiments on goats and cows, because the milk output could be definitely measured and blood samples of a size needed for the analytical methods then available could be readily obtained. In this series of experiments major emphasis was placed on the lipids. Studies were made of the fatty acids, phospholipids, and cholesterol in the blood prior to parturition, and during the lactation period in relation to the yield and composition of the milk. The changes taking place in these blood constituents were thus established. It was found that the fat content of the diet was a factor governing milk yield.

Maynard was born on a farm and received the first years of his education in a "little red schoolhouse." He obtained his A.B. from Wesleyan University in 1911 and his Ph.D. in chemistry from Cornell University in 1915. In the 1920s he pursued postdoctoral studies at Yale University, and in France at the University of Strasbourg and the Ecole Veterinaire in Lyon. His entire academic career was spent at Cornell University, following his appointment in 1915 as assistant professor. From 1939 to 1945 he served part time as the first director of the U.S. Plant, Soil and Nutrition Laboratory at Ithaca. In 1941 he became director of the newly established School of Nutrition and in 1944 head of the department of biochemistry at Cornell. He held both of these positions until he retired in 1955, and was then appointed emeritus professor of nutrition and biochemistry. Elected to the National Academy of Sciences in 1944, he served as chairman of the Academy's Division of Agriculture and Biology from 1955 to 1958. He received the Osborne and Mendel Award of the American Institute of Nutrition in 1954.

For background information *see* ANIMAL-FEED COMPOSITION; FOOD; NUTRITION; PROTEIN; SKELETAL SYSTEM in the McGraw-Hill Encyclopedia of Science and Technology.   □

★ MAYR, Ernst

American biologist
Born July 5, 1904, Kempten, Bavaria, Germany

EVEN THOUGH Charles Darwin called his classic *On the Origin of Species*, it was a treatise on evolutionary change as such and he failed to solve the problem of the multiplication of species. The endeavor to explain the problem of the division of one species into several daughter species, a phenomenon designated as speciation, occupied much of Mayr's research career. He demonstrated far more decisively than M. Wagner, Henry Seebohm, K. Jordan, and B. Rensch that the geographic isolation of populations in higher animals is a normal prerequisite of speciation. Instantaneous speciation through polyploidy and sympatric speciation are decidedly rare in animals and apparently altogether absent in many, if not most, groups.

The biology and systematics of birds were the

areas of Mayr's earlier researches after he obtained his Ph.D. in 1926 at the University of Berlin. In 1928–30 he led three expeditions to various parts of New Guinea and the Solomon Islands, where he acquired not only a thorough knowledge of tropical biology but also, particularly in the Solomon Islands, an impressive documentation of the great importance of geographic variation. Nothing demonstrated so conclusively the error of the evolutionary thesis of the early mendelians as did the phenomena of geographic variation. The claims of Hugo DeVries, William Bateson, and their followers that new species and other new types originate by mutation, that natural selection is irrelevant except as a device for the elimination of deleterious mutants, and that therefore the environment plays no role whatsoever in evolution are clearly negated by the regularities in geographic variation and the evident importance of geographic barriers.

The mere fact of geographic variation is not enough. The particular population structure of each species is of decisive importance for its role. Peripheral populations have a different evolutionary potential than central populations have. Gene flow between contiguous populations maintains genetic cohesion within a species. In contrast, peripherally isolated populations can pursue an independent evolutionary path. Mayr broke new ground in the study of "founder populations," that is, new populations established by a few founders. Such populations are not only genetically impoverished, but they are also far better able to respond to local selective influences because of their protection against gene flow. Sometimes they undergo regular "genetic revolutions," leading to dramatic changes in adaptation and niche occupation.

Along with Theodosius Dobzhansky, J. S. Huxley, and G. G. Simpson, Mayr was one of the founders of the modern evolutionary synthesis. He assumed the initiative in the founding of the

Society for the Study of Evolution in 1946 (as its first secretary), and he founded in 1947 the journal *Evolution*, of which he was the editor until 1949.

Concurrently he advanced the theory of zoogeography by his emphasis on the historical components of faunas rather than on the geographic borders of faunal regions. These ideas were utilized in novel analyses of the biological significance of Wallace's line as well as of the faunal composition of the bird life of Central America. The scantiness of the fossil record of birds (compared to mammals) places a special premium on the development of new analytical methods. Special attention was given to the question of why certain groups of birds disperse readily across geographic barriers while others do not. A careful evaluation of the dispersal facility of various taxa and of the area of distribution of their nearest relatives permitted inferences on the area of origin of taxa.

The species concept was also a concern of Mayr for many years. He showed that it is quite inappropriate to apply typological (essentialist) and nominalist concepts to the biological species, and he proposed in 1940 a species definition which is now widely adopted: Species are groups of interbreeding natural populations which are reproductively isolated from other such groups. Individuals are members of a species because they share in the same (historically evolved) genetic program, which determines their isolating mechanisms and ecological properties (niche occupation). Not degree of difference but reproductive distinctness is the earmark of the biological species. This revision of the species concept led to the recognition (and indeed often discovery) of numerous cryptic or sibling species.

The author of more than 100 papers on avian taxonomy, Mayr became increasingly interested in the theory and methodology of taxonomy; with E. G. Linsley and R. L. Usinger, he published in 1953 a textbook in this field. More recently he pointed out the fundamental differences between the classification of inanimate objects and of organisms. The rational approach of the classifier is paramount in the classification of artifacts and inanimate objects, and many alternate classifications are possible in most cases. Natural groups of organisms, like birds or beetles, however, are not arbitrary assemblages, but products of evolution. Members of such a natural group share much of their genetic program, which is derived from a common ancestor. Biological classification thus must utilize entirely different principles than those of object classification. This analysis of the principles of classification, together with his evolutionary studies, led Mayr to an interest in the underlying concepts of biology. Essentialist thinking (from Plato to idealistic philosophy) and nominalism have been among the early dominant influences of conceptualization in biology. The role these underlyling concepts have played in the later philosophies of Descartes, Locke, Hume, Kant, and their followers in biology is not yet properly understood; this became Mayr's most recent major interest.

From 1926 to 1932 Mayr was assistant at the Zoological Museum of the University of Berlin. From 1932 to 1953 he was curator of birds at the American Museum of Natural History, New York. In 1953 he went to Harvard as Alexander Agassiz Professor of Zoology at the Museum of Comparative Zoology (director from 1961). Among his honors were the Leidy Medal (1946), the Darwin-Wallace Medal (1958), the Brewster Medal (1965), and the Verrill Medal (1966). He was awarded honorary degrees by Uppsala (1957), Yale (1959), Melbourne (1959), and Oxford (1966). He was elected to the National Academy of Sciences and to the American Academy of Arts and Sciences in 1954.

Among the nearly 400 publications that Mayr wrote are *Systematics and the Origin of Species* (1942); *Birds of the Southwest Pacific* (1945); *Birds of the Philippines*, with J. Delacour (1946); *Methods and Principles of Systematic Zoology*, with E. G. Linsley and R. L. Usinger (1953); *The Species Problem* (1957); and *Animal Species and Evolution* (1963). He edited Darwin's *On the Origin of Species* (facsimile ed. 1964).

For background information *see* Aves; Evolution, organic; Speciation; Species concept; Zoogeography in the McGraw-Hill Encyclopedia of Science and Technology. □

★ MAZIA, Daniel

American biologist
Born Dec. 18, 1912, Scranton, Pa., U.S.A.

THE PROCESS of mitosis, by which reproducing cells transmit chromosomes to their progeny, involves both the entire life history of the cell and the special structures participating in the process: the chromosomes, centrioles, and mitotic spindle. Mazia was deeply involved in the exploration of all of these aspects of cell reproduction. Perhaps his most conspicuous contribution was his participation, with Katsuma Dan, in 1952 in the first isolation of the mitotic apparatus, which was followed by a long series of studies dealing with the chemistry of mitosis.

Beyond the technical feat of the isolation, Mazia and Dan reported that the mitotic apparatus, a complex structure, seemed to be composed predominantly of a single kind of protein. The meaning of that observation for the process of mitosis became clear only recently. The protein turned out to be the molecular unit of the "spindle fibers," which had been thought, since the era of classical microscopy around the turn of the century, to be the devices whereby the chromosomes are moved or at least guided during cell division. The electron microscope had revealed that the "spindle fibers" seen by the ordinary microscope were composed of finer "microtubules." Now it appears that the microtubules are composed of filaments, which in turn are composed of molecules of the "major protein" that was revealed in the first work of Mazia and Dan. In that work they also found evidence suggesting that sulfur-to-sulfur bonds between protein molecules might play an important role in the formation of the mitotic apparatus. The role of such bonds has been the subject of many investigations. It appears that the S-S bonds may function to hold together the subunits of which the major protein is composed.

While an undergraduate at the University of Pennsylvania, Mazia was encouraged toward the study of the cell by L. V. Heilbrunn. As is true for so many American biologists, the scientific climate of the Marine Biological Laboratory at Woods Hole was a potent formative influence. Mazia's doctoral thesis was a demonstration of the liberation of ionized calcium in the sea urchin egg at the time of fertilization, a result which had been predicted by Heilbrunn's theories.

Mazia joined the department of zoology at the University of Missouri in 1938. Stimulated by L. J. Stadler and Barbara McClintock, he did in 1939 his first work on chromosomes, a study of the role of DNA and proteins in the structure of chromosomes. One of the early chemical studies of chromosomes, it employed the then novel method of enzymatic digestion. In the late 1940s he turned his attention to the role of the nucleus in cell function, another old problem that seemed ripe for attack by modern methods. A series of investigations of the functions of cells with and without nuclei led to the hypothesis that the nucleus served a "replacement" function and to the anticipation of the current view that the main output of the nucleus is RNA.

The isolation of the mitotic apparatus, which was accomplished shortly after Mazia's move to Berkeley in 1951, raised new questions about the cell as the theater of mitosis. The formation of the mitotic apparatus calls for a considerable investment of proteins; the question was whether these were provided as a preparation for mitosis or as part of the mitotic process itself. Experiment showed that the proteins are synthesized in advance of actual mitosis. The timing of another important event, the replication of the centrioles, also was shown to be an anticipation of mitosis. These and related studies led to the formulation of a theory of "parallel pathways," according to which the onset of mitosis depends on the completion of a number of preparations for division, each preparation being relatively independent of the other and independent of other processes belonging to the general growth of the cell between divisions.

A large group of graduate students, fellows, and visiting workers in Mazia's laboratory made important contributions to the study of the cell cycle and cell reproduction, including early data on the growth curves of cells, studies of the effects of enucleation on biosynthesis, the demonstration that RNA passes from nucleus to cytoplasm, the electron microscopic study of the mitotic apparatus, fine-structural studies of kinetochores and their behavior in mitosis, and the characterization of DNA polymerase in cell nuclei.

The son of a jeweler who had emigrated from Russia, Mazia was educated in the public schools of Philadelphia and did his undergraduate and graduate work at the University of Pennsylvania (Ph.D., 1937). He did a year of postdoctoral work at Princeton as a National Research Council fellow under E. Newton Harvey, then joined the zoology department at the University of Missouri. He remained in that department from 1938 to 1951, with a 3-year interruption for military service. In 1951 he joined the zoology department at the University of California, Berkeley. He was active at the Marine Biological Laboratory, serving as head of the physiology course there from 1951 to 1955. In recent years he did summer work at the Scripps Institution of Oceanography at La Jolla. Mazia was elected to the American Academy of Arts and Sciences in 1954 and to the National Academy of Sciences in 1960.

Mazia edited *The General Physiology of Cell Specialization*, with Albert Tyler (1963). He served as an executive editor of the journal *Experimental Cell Research*.

For background information *see* CELL DIVISION; MITOSIS; NUCLEIC ACID in the McGraw-Hill Encyclopedia of Science and Technology. □

★ McCARTY, Maclyn

American medical scientist
Born June 9, 1911, South Bend, Ind., U.S.A.

IN COLLABORATION with Oswald T. Avery and Colin M. MacLeod, McCarty published in 1944 the first experimental evidence to suggest that the genetic material of living cells consists of deoxyribonucleic acid (DNA). These studies were concerned with the phenomenon of transformation of pneumococcal types, discovered by F. Griffith of England in a series of classic animal experiments reported in 1928. Subsequent studies by others, notably M. H. Dawson and L. Alloway, made it possible to carry out transformation experiments in the test tube, using cellfree extracts as the transforming material. In essence, transformation involved the capacity of material extracted from one specific type of pneumococcus to induce a second pneumococcal strain to produce a capsular polysaccharide characteristic of the donor type. The transformed organisms retained this new property on repeated subculture, indicating that the transforming substance had brought about a heritable and predictable change involving the directed synthesis of a new cellular constituent not previously produced by the cells. The studies with Avery and MacLeod indicated that the substance in the extracts responsible for transformation is DNA.

The identification of the pneumococcal transforming substance as DNA depended on biochemical fractionation of crude bacterial extracts, culminating in the isolation of a purified preparation of DNA possessing a high degree of biological activity. A variety of biochemical and physicochemical studies supported the view that transforming activity is indeed a property of the DNA molecule. To obtain more definitive evidence on this point, McCarty prepared a deoxyribonuclease (DNase) from beef pancreas and defined certain of its properties. Minute amounts of this magnesium-activated DNase rapidly destroyed the biological activity of transforming DNA. Later, M. Kunitz succeeded in crystallizing pancreatic DNase, and the crystalline material proved to be a still more potent inactivator of the transforming substance. Thus, the enzymatic evidence confirmed the other findings on the DNA nature of the active material.

Knowledge of the DNase also facilitated further studies on transforming DNA, since the pneumococcus was found to contain a similar enzyme which complicated extraction procedures. Inhibition of this enzyme through chelation of the magnesium ion activator greatly increased the efficiency of isolation of intact DNA from pneumococcal cells.

The demonstration of the DNA nature of the pneumococcal transforming substance was the initial step leading to the current concept that the genetic information of all living organisms resides in nucleic acids. At the same time the technique of transformation became an important factor in the emerging field of bacterial genetics. Through the work of many investigators, the use of bacterial transformation was extended to the study of numerous genetic characters both in pneumococci and in several other bacterial species.

In 1946 McCarty succeeded Homer F. Swift as head of a laboratory concerned with a family of organisms related to pneumococci, the hemolytic streptococci, in studies with the ultimate aim of elucidating the role of streptococcal infection in acute rheumatic fever. His work was then directed primarily toward the biology of streptococci, particularly those of serological group A, which had earlier been defined by his colleague Rebecca C. Lancefield as the causative agents of most human streptococcal disease. The importance of surface constituents of the cell was emphasized, and from this approach came the isolation of the streptococcal cell wall and a detailed analysis of several components composing this structure. The use of enzymatic reagents proved as valuable in this analysis as in the study of the pneumococcal transforming substance. Thus, an enzyme complex obtained from a strain of *Streptomyces albus* provided the means of breaking up the essentially insoluble cell wall, and led to the demonstration that the major single constituent of the wall is the group-specific antigen, a carbohydrate composed of N-acetylglucosamine and rhamnose. Further investigation of this carbohydrate was similarly facilitated by the preparation of induced enzymes isolated from soil bacteria which were

capable of degrading the carbohydrate. In this way the chemical basis for the serological specificity of this antigen was elucidated.

The nature and interrelationships of the several components of the streptococcal cell wall, and of the lipoprotein membrane which underlies it, were the subject of continuing study in McCarty's laboratory. The possible role that individual components might play in the genesis of rheumatic fever was explored in associated clinical studies.

After receiving his early education in Oregon, Indiana, and Wisconsin, McCarty went to Stanford University, where he majored in biochemistry and received his A.B. in 1933. He received his M.D. in 1937 at the Johns Hopkins School of Medicine, then spent 3 years as a house officer in pediatrics at the Johns Hopkins Hospital. His first full-time laboratory position came in 1940 as a fellow with W. S. Tillett at New York University. Tillett introduced him to the study of pneumococci and, as a former colleage of O. T. Avery, arranged the opportunity to work in Avery's laboratory at the Rockefeller Institute when McCarty was awarded a National Research Council fellowship in 1941. He became a member of the Institute (now the Rockefeller University) in 1950 and vice-president and physician in chief in 1965. McCarty received the Eli Lilly Award in Microbiology and Immunology in 1946. He was elected to the National Academy of Sciences in 1963.

For background information *see* DEOXYRIBONUCLEIC ACID; NUCLEIC ACID; PNEUMOCOCCUS; STREPTOCOCCUS in the McGraw-Hill Encyclopedia of Science and Technology.   □

★ McCONNELL, Harden Marsden

American chemist
Born July 18, 1927, Richmond, Va., U.S.A.

MANY OF McConnell's contributions involved the application of electron and nuclear magnetic resonance to the solution of fundamental problems in theoretical chemistry, chemical kinetics, radiation chemistry, solid-state physics, and biophysics.

The motion of electrons in unsaturated hydrocarbons has been a subject of great interest to theoretical chemists since the pioneering contributions of E. Hückel, R. S. Mulliken, J. C. Slater, and L. C. Pauling, in much the same way that the motion of electrons in metals has been an active topic in theoretical physics since the original studies of E. Fermi and F. Bloch. McConnell was one of the first to recognize that the discovery of nuclear hyperfine interactions in aromatic free radicals, by C. A. Hutchison, Jr., and S. I. Weissman in 1952–53, represented a

major breakthrough in the study of electronic motion in unsaturated hydrocarbons. McConnell's theoretical and experimental studies of the mechanism of nuclear hyperfine interaction during 1955–62 showed conclusively that this interaction can be used to measure the odd electron density (spin density) on carbon atoms in these molecules. McConnell's equation relating carbon atom spin density and isotropic proton hyperfine splittings in unsaturated molecules has been used in a large number of theoretical and experimental studies of the electronic structure of unsaturated hydrocarbons and metal-organic compounds. The validity of this equation was established by many studies, including the independent work of McConnell and D. M. Whiffen that verified the theoretically predicted anomalous sign of the (π-electron)-(σ-proton) proton hyperfine interaction, as well as extensive experimental and theoretical studies of spin distributions in unsaturated systems by Weissman, G. K. Fraenkel, A. Carrington, A. D. McLachlan, G. J. Hoijtink, J. H. van der Waals, Hutchison, R. W. Fessenden, and others.

One significant general theoretical result derived from these studies was a convincing demonstration of the adequacy of the simple molecular orbital theory as a first approximation for large unsaturated molecules, especially the theory as developed extensively by H. C. Longuet-Higgins. The studies, as well as McConnell's further theoretical and experimental investigations of the anisotropic parts of nuclear hyperfine interactions, laid a firm foundation for the analysis of the paramagnetic resonance spectra of organic free radicals in molecular crystals in terms of the molecular electronic structure of the radicals. Thus in 1959 McConnell and co-workers showed that radiation damage in malonic acid crystals produces an oriented radical with the formula $CH(COOH)_2$, and that the anisotropic proton hyperfine interactions in this radical can be accounted for quantitatively in terms of a π-

electron "CH fragment," in which the proton is in the nodal plane of the $2p\pi$ orbital that holds the odd electron. This work also provided the first experimental demonstrations of a negative spin density at a σ-proton. This analysis of the proton and C^{13} hyperfine interactions in $CH(COOH)_2$ led McConnell and co-workers to a study of hyperfine interactions in $C^{13}H_3$, from which they obtained one of the first pieces of strong evidence that the methyl radical is planar, or nearly planar. These studies, and other work by Whiffen and by W. Gordy, were the starting point for many subsequent investigations of the effects of high-energy radiation on organic materials using paramagnetic resonance.

In 1961 McConnell showed that the remarkable paramagnetic resonance spectra first observed in certain solid free radicals by D. B. Chestnut and W. D. Phillips are due to "triplet excitons," a propagating spin excitation. During 1961–66 McConnell and collaborators carried out an extensive theoretical and experimental study of these spin excitations. In this work they showed that at least in certain solids the unpaired electrons of the propagating triplet state are on neighboring molecules in the crystal lattice, and that a crystal distortion accompanies the moving electronic excitation. The theory accounts for many of the properties of triplet excitons, including the magnitude and orientation of the triplet state fine structure interactions, the absence of nuclear hyperfine structure, the quantum chemical origin of the exciton creation energies, and the nature of phase changes in exciton-containing molecular crystals.

In 1964–67 McConnell and co-workers introduced spin labeling, a new spectroscopic technique for studying biological systems. A spin label is a stable synthetic (paramagnetic) organic free radical that can be selectively attached to, or incorporated in, molecules of biological interest such as enzymes, substrates, nucleic acids, biological membranes, and so forth. Since the great majority of molecules normally present in a living system are not paramagnetic, the paramagnetic resonance of a spin label incorporated in a biological system is essentially free from interference. The resonance of spin labels can yield information on molecular conformation of proteins in solution and in single crystals. Spin-labeled protein crystals can, for example, be used to determine the symmetry of protein molecules built up from equivalent subunits. Conformational changes in mammalian hemoglobin in solution associated with the cooperative uptake of oxygen ("heme-heme" interaction) were studied extensively by McConnell and S. Ogawa, using spin labels. In this work evidence was obtained that each β-subunit of hemoglobin undergoes a conformational change when oxygen binds to its heme group, and that this conformational change is important for the heme-heme interaction.

McConnell also made contributions to nuclear magnetic resonance spectroscopy, including the development of basic theoretical relations between nuclear magnetic resonance spectra and molecular conformation, molecular electronic structure, and chemical kinetics. He introduced the use of group theory for the analysis of high-resolution nuclear resonance spectra, made early theoretical studies of the origin of spin-spin couplings in complex molecules, and showed how the Bloch equations for nuclear magnetic resonance can be modified to include chemical kinetic effects, including fast electron exchange. Other original contributions include research in optical spectroscopy and superconductivity.

McConnell received his B.S. from the George Washington University in 1947 and his Ph.D. from the California Institute of Technology in 1951. During 1950–52 he was a National Research Council fellow at the University of Chicago, and was then employed by Shell Development Co. (1952–56). He taught at the California Institute of Technology from 1956 to 1964, when he moved to Stanford University. McConnell received the California Section Award of the American Chemical Society in 1961 and the American Chemical Society Award in Pure Chemistry in 1962. He was elected to the National Academy of Sciences in 1965.

For background information *see* AROMATIC HYDROCARBON; ELECTRON PARAMAGNETIC RESONANCE SPECTROSCOPY; MOLECULAR STRUCTURE AND SPECTRA in the McGraw-Hill Encyclopedia of Science and Technology.   □

★ McFARLAND, Ross Armstrong

American physiological psychologist and aerospace scientist
Born July 18, 1901, Denver, Colo., U.S.A.

IN AN attempt to obtain a better understanding of the relationship between human performance and the underlying physiological mechanisms, McFarland began a series of investigations in physiological psychology during 1927–28 at Cambridge University, England, in collaboration with Joseph Barcroft and Frederic Bartlett. The primary objective of this and his subsequent research was to analyze the adjustments of the mind and body to the stresses of the environment.

Early in his academic career McFarland was impressed by the dramatic changes in sensory and mental functions resulting from oxygen want at high altitude observed by Paul Bert and the early balloonists and mountaineers. He became interested in making precise measurements of the deterioration in sense perception and mental functions while exposed to various environmental stresses, and at the same time in determining the blood gases or other relevant biochemical or physiological measurements. Special attention was given to the effects of high altitude, extremes of environmental temperature, and to variations in blood sugar. Thus he provided quantitative data for the earlier prediction of Claude Bernard that the development of the central nervous system is completely dependent upon the constancy of the internal environment. In the studies at Cambridge University on RAF student pilots he showed how the lack of oxygen during simulated flights can impair complex reaction times and mental functions, leading to impaired behavior, lack of insight, and loss of judgment. These findings and subsequent studies had direct implications for understanding not only aviation accidents resulting from lack of oxygen but also fatigue, certain forms of mental illness, and the aging process.

From 1929 to 1937, in the department of psychology and the College of Physicians and Surgeons at Columbia University, he continued to investigate the ways in which the central nervous system is completely dependent upon a normal supply of oxygen, glucose, and other organic constants. In one investigation for the federal government on the effects of high altitude, a large number of subjects from 16 to 60 years old were studied individually in low-oxygen chambers at simulated altitudes of 10,000 to 18,000 ft. In other studies, using visual tests of differential light sensitivity, McFarland demonstrated for the first time that impairment may be present at altitudes as low as 4000 ft in unacclimatized subjects. The novelty of the approach was the development of nomograms from

which the combined effects of altitude and other variables such as carbon monoxide (as from engine exhaust or cigarette smoke) can be precisely estimated or predicted. In this way simultaneous data from the visual mechanism and from the blood gases were used to determine a subject's true *physiological* altitude as contrasted with the effects of one variable such as pressure altitude. These and other findings led to regulations for the use of oxygen by pilots in civil aviation and by military pilots during night combat. McFarland also contributed significant physiological data in the development of pressurized cabins for air transports.

As a member of the International High Altitude Expedition sponsored by the Harvard Fatigue Laboratory in 1935, he was able to extend his psychophysiological observations on the effects of oxygen want on acclimatized subjects. On this expedition the members were compared with natives of Chile and Peru who lived at altitudes up to 20,000 ft, the highest permanent mining camps being at about 18,500 ft. In 1937 McFarland became a member of the Fatigue Laboratory at Harvard University, where he worked with physiologists L. J. Henderson, D. B. Dill, and W. H. Forbes. A wide variety of stressful conditions on human performance were studied, sometimes in the laboratory and at other times on expeditions to mountainous or desert areas, on flights to high altitudes, or in diverse industrial situations.

During the initial flights in the opening of air routes over the Pacific and Atlantic oceans in 1937 and 1939, McFarland was asked to make studies of the fatiguing effects of these long flights. For the first time the results of sensory and mental tests were correlated with blood gases and other biochemical determinations obtained in flight. In 1940 he was an advisor to Pan American Airways in opening air routes across Africa, and he served as an operations analyst, 13th Air Force, in the Solomon Islands campaign (1943–44), studying combat fatigue in the air and ground forces. During these investigations he became interested in the problems of designing equipment to meet human capabilities. His work in the field of human factors engineering formed the background for additional studies relating to the more effective integration of men and machines in World War II. He was one of the leaders in developing this field as a new discipline and wrote one of the first textbooks on the subject for engineers, *Human Factors in Air Transport Design* (1946). A volume for physicians, *Human Factors in Air Transportation: Occupational Health and Safety* (1953), aided greatly in the development of health and safety standards in civil aviation. His latest book, *The Human Body in Equipment Design*, with A. Damon and H. W. Stoudt (1966), is being widely used by engineers and industrial designers.

With the outbreak of World War II it was apparent that many older persons would be required to work in industry. Through experimental studies of the aging process, McFarland was able to show that with proper supervision and placement men and women can work productively much longer than originally believed. Qualitative studies of sensory and mental functions of older subjects brought out the close relationship between skill and age. The necessity for job reassignment with increasing age is now generally accepted, especially where time-complexity stresses are involved. He also pointed out the close relationship between the oxidative processes and certain functions of the central nervous system. These relationships were revealed to be closely parallel in tests of light sensitivity, immediate memory, and the loss of insight. Other studies during the war concerned the visual problems of fire control and fatigue. In the former studies it was shown that the human eye is capable of great accuracy in making visual judgments and that the range finder itself was accurate, but when the eyes were coupled to the instrument, the errors were great. This led to the redesign of various types of instruments to meet human requirements.

During 1939–40 McFarland became interested in pilot selection and the development of better tests for predicting success or failure. Because of the high failure rates in the military services, McFarland and a group of his colleagues at Harvard were asked to make a comprehensive analysis of this problem. Their efforts resulted in the "Pensacola Study of Naval Aviators." Follow-up studies were begun 25 years later of the 1000 Naval aviators in the original group and of other pilots studied during the war period. The results are proving to be of use not only in selection but also in a better understanding of the aging processes.

In 1947 McFarland became a member of the faculty of the Harvard School of Public Health. Here it was possible to develop a new approach to some of the increasingly difficult problems of health and safety not only on the ground but also in the air and outside the Earth's atmosphere, including the complex human factors of space flight. He was one of the first to emphasize the multiple causes of accidents and to apply the methods of epidemiology in the study of highway injuries and fatalities. Thus, what had been learned in aviation and aircraft design was applied to automotive design and safety. If accident preventive measures are to be effective, he and his colleagues demonstrated through many investigations not only that attention must be given to the control of human behavior, but also that the mechanical forces reaching the body must not exceed the threshold of resistance to injury. Many of the principles advocated are beginning to be incorporated into federal regulations relating to air and highway safety. This new approach attracted many young physicians and engineers for advanced study at the Harvard School of Public Health under his direction. He served as a technical adviser to many governmental agencies, most recently participating in a research project with NASA on the environmental parameters for astronauts in the Apollo mission.

In 1962 the Guggenheim Foundation endowed a teaching and research center at Harvard, with McFarland becoming the first to occupy the Daniel and Florence Guggenheim Chair of Aerospace Health and Safety. More than 200 young scientists trained by McFarland and his colleagues at the Harvard School of Public Health became leaders in the fields of aerospace medicine, occupational health, and highway safety.

McFarland received his A.B. from the University of Michigan in 1923 and his Ph.D. from Harvard University in 1928. He taught at Columbia University from 1928 to 1937, when he moved to Harvard. Besides three honorary degrees, McFarland received the Longacre Award of the Aero Medical Association in 1947; the Flight Safety Foundation Award in 1953; the John Jeffries Award of the Institute of Aeronautical Sciences in 1956; and the Walter M. Boothby Award of the Aerospace Medical Association in 1962. He was elected to the American Academy of Arts and Sciences in 1953.

For background information *see* DECOMPRESSION ILLNESS; GERONTOLOGY; RESPIRATION; SPACE BIOLOGY in the McGraw-Hill Encyclopedia of Science and Technology.   □

★ McMICHAEL, Sir John

British clinical scientist
Born July 25, 1904, Gatehouse-of-Fleet, Scotland

A FTER EARLY hospital experience in medicine and surgery, McMichael began laboratory work in 1929 as Goodsir research fellow at Edinburgh University. His first efforts were devoted to the then disorderly subject called "splenic anemia" or "Banti's disease." By careful classification of the pathological appearances he concluded that a major determinant of the condition was hypertension in the portal venous system, often but not always the result of cirrhosis of the liver. This led him to physiological studies on the regulation of pressure in the portal veins and the complexities of the double vascular supply of the liver. Throughout his career he was a physician actively engaged in the teaching of medicine, to which he brought a physiological outlook. After his early work on portal venous congestion, he turned his attention to the causes and consequences of congestion of the systemic veins. The major cause of the latter

being failure of the heart, he devoted the years 1935–39 in Edinburgh to studies on the output of the heart by the acetylene method and to the elaboration of a method of measuring the volume of air in the lungs by hydrogen dilution and electrical recording in order to approach the allied problem of breathlessness and associated lung disorders.

Before the outbreak of war in 1939 he had already noted that the resting output of the heart is often well sustained in the earlier stages of heart failure and that early elevations of venous pressure are not necessarily due to "damming back" but could be considered as venomotor mechanisms on the Starling principle. The establishment of cardiac catheterization for studies on the human heart provided an opportunity to accelerate these studies. McMichael and E. P. Sharpey Schafer confirmed the earlier observations and especially noted that with heart failure due to severe anemia, or hypoxia from emphysema, the resting output of the heart can be normal or even high. Fundamentally the cause of most heart failure is overwork of the heart, however imposed, but even this simple idea appeared to be revolutionary at the time. Studies made with right atrial catheters on the action of digitalis gave confusing results. The most constant action was a fall in filling pressure of the heart irrespective of changes in cardiac output, which could rise, fall, or remain unchanged. At first this suggested a primary effect of digitalis on venous tone, but a few years later, with optical intraventricular pressure measurements, the variety of digitalis responses was more acceptably explained by the state and degree of failure of the right or left ventricle, modified by the degree of valvular disease or other pathological change.

During the war special problems arose which attracted investigation. Attempts to produce experimental hemorrhagic shock in volunteer blood donors was usually accompanied by a vasovagal faint with slowing of the heart and profound fall of arterial pressure. With Barcroft, Edholm, and Sharpey Schafer, McMichael showed the vascular component of this to be mediated by sympathetic vasodilator nerves to the limb muscles.

Another contribution was made by needle biopsy of the liver, showing the pathology of epidemic jaundice and its similarity to serum and syringe (arseno-therapy) hepatitis. This led in 1943 to the recognition of human serum as a cause of hepatitis.

After 1950 McMichael studied the problems of hypertension and evaluation of the mode of action of blood pressure–reducing drugs. Long-term studies were made on malignant hypertension, its natural history and pathology, and its amelioration by blood pressure reduction. The most recent phase of this work began in 1960 with detailed analysis of the human retina's vascular and exudative changes, which are a prominent feature of this group of disorders. The work was later carried on by his associate C. T. Dollery.

McMichael graduated in medicine from Edinburgh University in 1927. After junior teaching appointments in Aberdeen and University College, London, he was lecturer in human physiology in Edinburgh from 1934 to 1937. From 1939 to 1966 he was director of the department of medicine at the Postgraduate Medical School of London University, then was put in administrative charge of this and other specialist institutes as director of the British Postgraduate Medical Federation, a section of the University of London. Elected a fellow of the Royal Society in 1957, he received a Gairdner Foundation Award in 1960.

For background information *see* HEART DISORDERS; HYPERTENSION; LIVER in the McGraw-Hill Encyclopedia of Science and Technology. □

★ MEHL, Robert Franklin

American metallurgist and physical chemist
Born Mar. 30, 1898, Lancaster, Pa., U.S.A.

IN THE early 1920s there was very little scientific information concerning reactions in the solid state. Practical knowledge abounded, especially in the field of physical metallurgy, and more especially with respect to the ancient art of the heat-treatment of steel. It had been surmised, since Réaumur in 1722, that a solid-solid reaction was involved in the quenching of steel, and at about the turn of the century, following the application of Gibbs phase rule to the constitution of alloys, it became clear that steel during heat-treatment does indeed undergo a change in phase.

The Widmanstätten structure in iron-nickel meteorites, discovered at the beginning of the 19th century, was recognized toward the end of the century to be the result of a solid-solid transformation, akin to that occurring in steel. It was then thought of merely as a structure in which a new phase had precipitated during cooling in the "cleavage planes" of the matrix crystal. This beautiful structure fascinated all metallographers, especially as it was observed in ordinary alloys once metallurgical microscopy was developed. Mehl spent 1925–27 in the laboratory of Albert Sauveur at Harvard and inherited Sauveur's enthusiasm for this subject. During the following 4 years at the Naval Research Laboratory, Mehl conceived the idea that a precipitated phase in alloys generally must have an orientation relationship to the matrix phase, and in a series of a dozen papers demonstrated this principle for a large number of metallic systems. With this work as basis he elucidated the atomic-crystallographic mechanism of the process and also the habit plane, that is, the crystal plane in the matrix crystal along which a platelet of the precipitate crystal lies parallel. In his later research at the Carnegie Institute of Technology, it was shown that these same orientation relationships obtain no matter what type of reaction creates a new phase from an old one; the first demonstration of the orientation relationship between metals and oxides formed on them (and among the several oxides on iron) was accomplished.

All alloy systems which exhibit a Widmanstätten structure, including such familiar alloys as the airplane alloy Duralumin, respond to an age-hardening treatment; that is, on quenching and subsequent aging they harden and strengthen. It had been known since 1919 that this involved precipitation in the solid state. It seemed likely that a knowledge of the crystallographic mecha-

nism of atom movement, developed from the study of the Widmanstätten structure in age-hardening alloys, should offer a basis for a general theory of the aging process. This theory was demonstrated in a series of papers: At an early stage of the precipitation process the new lattice is observed to be coherent with the matrix, that is, strained to fit the atom positions in the matrix, thus strengthening the alloy; and as the precipitate grows larger, this coherency is lost, resulting in ultimate softening. This remains the current theory of age hardening.

Mehl had translated and published Gustav Tammann's *Aggregatzustände* in the mid-1920s, and from this became deeply interested in nucleation and growth phenomena and theory, a subject obviously basic to precipitation in the solid state. In teaching this subject in the early 1930s at the Carnegie Institute of Technology, he became dissatisfied with its qualitative nature and elected to undertake a long research project. Steel was selected for primary attention, partly because the crystallographic structures of its constitutents were known and partly because of the overriding engineering importance of steel. First, a generalized reaction equation for the rate of a nucleation and growth process was derived. Then, by using the recently developed isothermal reaction technique, the rate of nucleation and the rate of growth of the major reaction products were measured, especially of the lamellar product pearlite (from which railroad rails and many other industrial products are made). It shortly became apparent that, if the measured rates were to be explained, careful measurement of a number of quantities would be required—for example, the interlamellar spacing in pearlite, the rates of diffusion of carbon and of alloying elements, the specific internal surface free energies in pearlite, and the bulk free-energy change of the reaction. These were all measured, and the beginning of a theory was constructed. During these studies the crystallography of the bainite reaction in steels was determined; the hardening constituent in steels, martensite, was shown to form with a linear velocity near that of sound in steel; finally the generalized reaction rate equation was applied to the phenomenon of recrystallization of cold-worked metals. It was obvious that in many of the reactions studied the diffusion rates were of critical importance, and thus a program emerged of measuring diffusion rates in a series of alloy systems, including an analysis of the Kirkendall effect. This lengthy study in time turned to the related study of the rates of oxidation of metals and alloys, which often depend directly upon diffusion rates.

Mehl graduated with a B.S. in chemistry from Franklin and Marshall College in 1919, and was awarded the Ph.D. in chemistry at Princeton University in 1924. He taught chemistry at Juniata College from 1923 to 1925, when he went to Harvard University as a National Research Council fellow. In 1927 he became the first superintendent of the division of physical metallurgy at the Naval Research Laboratory (during this period he invented gamma-ray radiography, now widely used), and in 1931 he became assistant director of research at the Armco Steel Company in Middletown, Ohio. He accepted a professorship at the Carnegie Institute of Technology in 1932, and was progressively director of the Metals Research Laboratory, chairman of the department of metallurgical engineering, and dean of graduate studies. During World War II he and his associates conducted an extensive research program on gun steels for the U.S. Army. He spent 1960 to 1966 in Zurich as scientific liaison officer for the U.S. Steel Corporation. In 1966 he was appointed Distinguished Visiting Professor of Metallurgy at the University of Delaware. Elected to the National Academy of Sciences in 1958, Mehl was awarded a number of honorary degrees and medals in the United States and abroad.

Mehl published some 200 papers, translated *States of Aggregation* by Gustav Tammann (1925), and wrote *A Brief History of the Science of Metals* (1948), and *Metallurgy of Iron and Steel* (in Portuguese).

For background information *see* CRYSTAL GROWTH; HEAT-TREATMENT (METALS AND ALLOYS); SOLID-STATE CHEMISTRY; STEEL in the McGraw-Hill Encyclopedia of Science and Technology.   □

★ MEISTER, Alton

American biochemist
Born June 1, 1922, New York, N.Y., U.S.A.

MEISTER'S CONTRIBUTIONS were mainly in the field of amino acid and protein biochemistry. In 1954 he received the American Chemical Society's Paul-Lewis Award in Enzyme Chemistry for his studies on the enzymology of the transamination reaction. This work stemmed from an attempt to explain the previously known accelerating effect of α-keto acids on the deamidation of glutamine catalyzed by preparations of liver and kidney. Meister discovered that glutamine transaminates with many α-keto acids to give the corresponding amino acids and α-ketoglutaramic acid, which undergoes enzymatic hydrolysis to α-ketoglutarate and ammonia. These studies demonstrated new pathways of glutamine and ammonia metabolism and showed that the scope of enzymatic transamination is very broad and not limited, as thought earlier, to aspartate, glutamate, and alanine.

With Daniel Rudman, Meister showed the existence of separate transaminases and discovered valine-alanine transaminase; the existence of this enzyme in mutants of *Escherichia coli* lacking glutamate-valine, isoleucine transaminase, explains the ability of these cells to grow in valine-free media. With Elbert Petersen and Herbert Sober, crystalline pyridoxal 5′-phosphate and pyridoxamine 5′-phosphate were synthesized, and pyridoxamine 5′-phosphate was shown to be an enzyme-bound intermediate in enzymatic transamination, substantiating E. E. Snell's hypothesis of transamination. Meister prepared by enzymatic and other procedures a series of α-keto acids, whose study led to finding of new enzymatic reactions (for example, desulfuration of β-mercaptopyruvate) and to the observation that lactic dehydrogenase possesses a very broad specificity. A new vitamin B₆ enzyme, aspartate β-decarboxylase, was discovered and later (with Abraham Novogrodsky) the transamination control mechanism by which this enzyme is activated by keto acids and inhibited by aspartate and other amino acids was worked out. This pyridoxal phosphate enzyme thus catalyzes two reactions, one of which can destroy (or regenerate) the coenzyme needed for the other.

About 1957 Meister began a series of studies aimed at understanding enzymatic reactions in which synthesis reactions are coupled with the cleavage of ATP. With Kivie Moldave, he investigated the enzymatic synthesis of hippuric acid and phenylacetylglutamine and showed that the corresponding acyladenylates are enzyme-bound intermediates; later (with Paul Castelfranco and Marvin Karasek) direct evidence for an enzyme-bound aminoacyladenylate in amino acid activation was obtained and (with Govind Kalyankar) β-alanyladenylate was shown to be an intermediate in carnosine synthesis.

Meister studied enzymes of the group that catalyze synthesis coupled with cleavage of ATP to ADP and inorganic phosphate. With Leon Levintow, he showed that the synthesis of glutamine is freely reversible, and from the equilibrium constant determined for the reaction in Eq. (1) the value was obtained for the standard

$$\text{Glutamate} + \text{ammonia} + \text{ATP}$$
$$\rightleftharpoons \text{glutamine} + \text{ADP} + \text{P}_i \quad (1)$$

free energy for hydrolysis of ATP. With P. R. Krishnaswamy and Vaira P. Wellner, he showed that the synthesis of glutamine involves an activation step in which ATP is split and glutamic acid becomes bound to the enzyme. The activated intermediate can react with ammonia to form glutamine or can be converted to pyrrolidone carboxylate in the absence of ammonia. It was shown, with Ezra Khedouri, that β-glutamic acid is also a substrate of glutamine synthetase and that β-aminoglutarylphosphate is enzymatically utilized by the enzyme. The surprising findings that the enzyme converts β-glutamic acid to D-β-glutamine, that it acts stereospecifically in the L sense on α-methylglutamic acid, and that it acts on the L- and D-isomers of glutamic acid led to studies, with Herbert Kagan, on the stereochemical mapping of the active site of glutamine synthetase. It was proposed that L-glutamic acid is oriented on the enzyme in an extended conformation in which the α-hydrogen atom is directed away from the active site. This hypothesis, which was substantiated by studies with the isomers of various glutamic acid derivatives, explains the inhibition of the enzyme by substrate analogs and leads to conclusions concerning the relative orientations on the enzyme of glutamic acid, nucleotide, and ammonia.

In related work with Jonathan Nishimura and Elizabeth D. Mooz, it was established by direct isolation that an enzyme-bound acylphosphate intermediate is formed in the synthesis of glutathione and related γ-glutamyl dipeptides, and evidence also was obtained that succinyl phosphate is an enzyme-linked intermediate in the succinyl thiokinase reaction. With Paul Anderson, Meister found a similar activation of carbon dioxide by carbamyl phosphate synthetase and adduced the series of intermediate steps that follow the activation reaction.

Meister worked on the flavoprotein amino acid oxidases and, with A. N. Radhakrishnan, demonstrated the reversibility of the reactions catalyzed by these enzymes. Studies on L-amino acid oxidase (crystallized in Meister's laboratory by Daniel Wellner in 1957) led to elucidation of its unusual substrate inhibition and to discovery of a new form of the enzyme. Meister also worked on collagen biosynthesis, acyl RNA compounds, the D-serine of insects, phenylketonuria, gas-liquid chromatography of amino acids, γ-glutamyltranspeptidase, and lysine metabolism.

Meister received his B.S. in 1942 at Harvard, where he worked on myosin with H. O. Singher in J. T. Edsall's laboratory. He attended Cornell University Medical College and received his M.D. in 1945. After serving as an intern and assistant resident in medicine at New York Hospital, he went to the National Institutes of Health, where he worked on the enzymology of tumors and on amino acid and peptide chemistry in the laboratory of J. P. Greenstein at the National Cancer Institute. In 1951 he was appointed head of the Institute's Clinical Biochemical Research Section. He was appointed professor and chairman of the department of biochemistry at Tufts University School of Medicine in 1956. He was visiting professor of biochemistry at the University of Washington in 1959 and at the University of California, Berkeley, in 1962. He became professor and chairman of the department of biochemistry at Cornell University Medical College in 1967. He was elected to the American Academy of Arts and Sciences in 1958.

Meister wrote *Biochemistry of the Amino Acids* (1957; 2d ed. 1965).

For background information *see* AMINO ACID; ENZYME in the McGraw-Hill Encyclopedia of Science and Technology.   □

MEITNER, Lise

Austrian physicist
Born Nov. 7, 1878, Vienna, Austria

A PIONEER in many areas of nuclear physics, Meitner made particularly important contributions which led to the liberation and control of nuclear power. Her experiments with the properties of uranium from 1934 onward culminated in 1939 when she and her nephew, the physicist Otto Robert Frisch, attributed the behavior of uranium under neutron bombardment to the fission—the term is their invention—of the uranium nucleus. The work of Meitner and Frisch, marking the decisive juxtaposition of theory and experiment, was one of the most important steps toward the generation and control of energy from the atomic nucleus. In recognition of this and many other discoveries, Meitner and her co-workers, the German chemists Otto Hahn and Fritz Strassmann, received the U.S. Atomic Energy Commission's Fermi Award in 1966.

Meitner's work with neutrons began in 1932 at the Kaiser Wilhelm Institute, and by 1935 she and Hahn were studying the neutron-induced activity

of uranium. Among other things, Meitner was able to show in 1938 that one of the products of this activity was the short-lived isotope U^{239}. An isotope resembling radium was also found among the products; but before the situation could be elucidated, Meitner left Nazi Germany for Sweden. Hahn and Strassmann remained to continue the work and, later that year, communicated to Meitner some of their findings. Since contemporary atomic theory made no provision for the fragmentation of atomic nuclei at the relatively low energy levels involved in their experiments, Hahn and Strassmann had first assumed that any radioactive substance formed must be an element such as thorium or protactinium, whose Z (atomic number) would be close to the $Z = 92$ of uranium. However, their attempts to identify their "radium" showed, to their surprise, that the substance in question was barium, which stands directly above radium in the periodic table. But this would mean that, since barium has $Z = 56$, the uranium nucleus must have been divided into much smaller parts —a conclusion unpalatable to contemporary theory, which had inferred from the observed results of the bombardment of stable atoms that the energy required would run into hundreds of millions of electron volts (far more than Hahn and Strassmann had employed).

The explanation of these results, as developed by Meitner and Frisch at the Nobel Institute for Physics at Stockholm, was published in the British journal *Nature* in January, 1939. Assuming that the mysterious radium-like isotope was indeed barium, the two employed the liquid-drop model (suggested earlier by Niels Bohr) to explain the implied fission of the uranium nucleus. The behavior of the heavy, unstable uranium nucleus was likened to that of a drop of water: When left to itself, the collective motion of the molecules in the drop is insufficient to disturb its overall shape; but when enough energy is introduced into the system (in the case of U^{235} a single slow neutron is sufficient), the particles in the drop become so agitated that a new equilibrium state may be attained through its fission into smaller drops. Meitner and Frisch assumed that in the case of uranium the resulting fragments would be of about equal mass. If one was indeed barium ($Z = 56$), then the other ought to be krypton ($Z = 36$, that is, $92 - 56$). Hahn, Strassmann, and others later confirmed the presence of krypton and many other elements among the fission products. According to Meitner and Frisch, the energy released could be expected to be about 200 Mev, being composed of some fast neutrons, kinetic energy of the fission products (whose high ionizing ability soon enabled Frisch to detect them with an ionization chamber), and subsequent beta and gamma radiation. Finally, they pointed out that, because of the close packing of the uranium atoms, a "chain disintegration" would likely result as the fast neutrons released by a fissioning uranium atom encountered neighboring atoms.

The contents of this paper were by no means wholly unprecedented. Others had predicted the possibility of chain reaction and had shown that such a process could yield a net gain in energy. But because of the cogency of its arguments, the specific nature of its predictions, and the historic juncture at which it appeared, the paper of Meitner and Frisch was to exercise an influence upon later developments whose importance could scarcely be overstated.

Meitner made numerous other contributions to physics. From 1907 to 1925 she was concerned mainly with interpreting the physical properties of radioactive substances. At first, absorption methods were used; later, magnetic deflection techniques permitted the establishment of the beta line spectra of a number of radioactive elements and isotopes. These experiments, conducted together with Hahn, were crowned in 1918 with the identification of the new element protactinium (number 91), which the investigators isolated from pitchblende.

In 1909 Meitner and Hahn were responsible for an important technical advance. Hahn had previously shown that the apparent migration of some radioactive substances was due to the recoil of individual atoms as they emitted alpha particles. In their joint paper Meitner and Hahn suggested that this effect be employed to produce clean specimens of some radioactive materials, a procedure widely adopted thereafter.

Meitner was the first to propose that the beta line spectra of many radioelements are produced when a gamma ray from the nucleus ejects electrons from the K, L, and H-shells. She also proved (in 1925) that the process follows, rather than precedes, radioactive disintegration. She was the first to describe the ejection of Auger electrons, a process in which (for example) an L-electron upon dropping into a vacancy in the K-shell brings about, not the emission of an x-ray quantum, but the ejection of an electron from the same atom.

From 1925 on, Meitner and her students worked more and more on purely physical problems. In 1929–30 she confirmed that in beta decay the continuous energy spectrum of the primary beta particles is not due to secondary energy losses.

Meitner was a pioneer in using the Wilson cloud chamber. In 1926 she was able to measure the true track length of slow electrons, and in 1933 she used a chamber to photograph the tracks of positrons arising from pair-production caused by gamma rays.

After 1939 Meitner continued to investigate the nature of fission products. In 1950, independently from the physicist Maria Goeppert Mayer, Meitner advanced the idea that the asymmetry of uranium fission is caused by the preferential formation of closed nucleon shells in the fragmentary fission products. She also worked on the relationship of various aspects of fission to the shell model of the nucleus, developed about 1950.

The third of eight children of a lawyer, Meitner received a doctorate in physics at the University of Vienna in 1906. She then went to the University of Berlin, where she studied under Max Planck and began her 30-year collaboration with Hahn. In 1912 she became an assistant to Planck at the Berlin Institute for Theoretical Physics, and in the following year joined the Kaiser Wilhelm Institute for Chemistry. Together with Hahn, Meitner was named joint director of the Kaiser Wilhelm Institute in 1917 and in the same year was made head of the physics department there. In 1926 she became extraordinary professor of physics at the University of Berlin. In 1938 she fled to Sweden and resumed research, first at the Nobel Institute for Physics, Stockholm, and later at the Atomic Energy Association, from which she retired in 1960, when she left Sweden for Cambridge, England.

Among her awards, apart from the Fermi Award, were the Prize of the City of Vienna (sciences), the Max Planck Medal, and the Otto Hahn Award. She was elected a foreign member of the Royal Society of London in 1955 and of the American Academy of Arts and Sciences in 1960.

For background information *see* FISSION, NUCLEAR; NUCLEAR REACTION; URANIUM in the McGraw-Hill Encyclopedia of Science and Technology. ☐

★ MENZEL, Donald Howard

American astrophysicist
Born Apr. 11, 1901, Florence, Colo., U.S.A.

MENZEL'S WORK ranges over the broad field of astronomy and astrophysics, with occasional ventures into pure physics. Most of his studies were concerned in some way with the interpretation of the spectra of various celestial objects: stars, the Sun, planets, and the gaseous nebulae. His doctoral research, carried out at Harvard Observatory under a fellowship from Princeton University, dealt generally with the relationship between stellar spectra and the surface temperature of the stars. British scientists R. H. Fowler and E. A. Milne had developed the theory of stellar spectra. Menzel used the extensive Harvard collection of spectroscopic records to test and extend the theory.

Menzel early became interested in the radiations of planets. From the spectra of Jupiter, Saturn, Uranus, and Neptune, he deduced that the planets must be very cold, and not hot, substars as astronomers then generally supposed. Using infrared measurements made by W. W. Coblentz and C. O. Lampland at the Lowell Observatory, Menzel confirmed his conclusions about the temperatures of the major planets and derived the first quantitative figures for the temperatures of Mars, Venus, and the Moon.

In a further study of Venus, F. L. Whipple and Menzel challenged the opinion then current that the clouds of Venus were some form of dust. They showed that the observed low temperature of the upper atmospheric layers was consistent with clouds of ice crystals. J. Strong, in observations made from a high-altitude balloon, later detected an amount of water vapor substantially agreeing with that predicted by Whipple and Menzel. A collaborative study by G. de Vaucouleurs, H. Ingrao, and Menzel of data recorded at a rare event, an occultation of the bright star Regulus by Venus, gave new determinations of the temperature and density of the Venusian atmosphere.

At Lick Observatory, Menzel fell heir to the flash spectra taken by W. W. Campbell and his colleagues at various eclipses. These were spectra of the Sun's atmosphere. Menzel's analysis of the data, interpreted by astrophysical theory, led to many new discoveries about the Sun's outer layers. He measured quantitatively the temperature and pressure of the chromosphere, as well as its chemical composition. Of special impact was the fact that the upper atmosphere attained temperatures of 15,000–20,000°K, several times higher than that of the photosphere, the Sun's shining surface. Menzel's determinations of the low density gradient furnished the chief clue that hydrogen was the dominant element on the Sun.

Studies of eclipse spectra and of eclipses in general led Menzel to observe some 12 eclipses through 1966, of which 9 were clear. He was a member of two Lick Observatory expeditions in 1930 and 1932. In 1936 he led the Harvard–MIT expedition to Kazakhstan in the Soviet Union. One by-product of the spectral data obtained from such eclipses was the fact that the temperature of the Sun's corona must be very high and that the coronal lines, whose origin was then unknown, must originate in high stages of ionization of some well-known element. B. Edlén later showed that the green coronal line comes from iron atoms that have lost half of their normal complement of 26 electrons.

Frustrated by the infrequency and the shortness of eclipses, Menzel began experimenting with artificial eclipses in an attempt to get more observations of the corona. J. H. Moore and Menzel had earlier called attention to this possibility. The French astronomer B. Lyot invented and brought the coronagraph to perfection. Menzel designed the first coronagraph in the United States and established it at Climax, Colo., at an altitude of 11,500 ft. This instrument furnished many valuable observations of solar activity. He later established a second and more advanced coronagraph station at Sacramento Peak, N.Mex. From studies made at these observatories Menzel developed new theories of solar structure. He showed that the intense magnetic fields existing in sunspots directly caused the lower temperatures. He further demonstrated that solar flares result from the same general cause, an instability associated with the magnetic field of a bipolar spot.

Working with students and colleagues, Menzel performed a detailed study of physical processes in gaseous nebulae. The results appeared as a long series of papers in the *Astrophysical Journal*. To solve such problems, he had to carry out parallel research in atomic physics, with the aid of quantum mechanics. He also made a special study of radiation from atomic hydrogen, including emission in the radio range, from levels with very large quantum numbers.

During World War II Menzel served as a commander in the U.S. Navy, where he directed the section on research in mathematics and physics for naval communications. His studies of the propagation of radio waves prompted the writing of a technical manual on the subject.

Menzel attended public school in Leadville and Denver, Colo. After receiving his A.B. (1920) and A.M. (1921) from the University of Denver, he went to Princeton, where he received another A.M. in 1923 and the Ph.D. in 1924. He taught at the University of Iowa in 1924–25 and Ohio State University in 1925–26. From 1926 to 1932 he was at Lick Observatory, with two semesters at the Berkeley campus. He went to Harvard University in 1932 as an assistant professor of astronomy, and was appointed associate professor of astrophysics in 1935 and full professor in 1938. In 1952 he became acting director and in 1954 director of Harvard College Observatory, a post he held until 1966. He became Paine Professor of Practical Astronomy at Harvard in 1956. In 1959 he became chief scientist of the Geophysics Corporation of America and in 1966 senior scientist of the Smithsonian Astrophysical Observatory. He was president of the American Astronomical Society from 1954 to 1956. Menzel was elected to the American Academy of Arts and Sciences in 1934, to the American Philosophical Society in 1940, and to the National Academy of Sciences in 1948.

Menzel wrote or edited many books, including *Stars and Planets* (1931; 3d ed. 1938), *Our Sun* (1949; 2d ed. 1959), *Mathematical Physics* (1953; paper 1961), *Fundamental Formulas of Physics* (1955; 2d ed., paper 1960), *The Radio Noise Spectrum* (1960), *Field Guide to the Stars and Planets* (1964), and *Papers on Radiative Transfer* (paper 1966). His interest in good writing led him to coauthor *Writing a Technical Paper*, with H. M. Jones and L. G. Boyd (1961). He also wrote *Flying Saucers* (1953) and coauthored *The World of Flying Saucers*, with L. G. Boyd (1963), to show that UFOs are natural phenomena and not vehicles from outer space. He also wrote extensively for young people, especially in the magazine *Highlights for Children*.

For background information *see* ASTRONOMICAL SPECTROSCOPY; CORONAGRAPH; ECLIPSE, ASTRONOMICAL; SUN in the McGraw-Hill Encyclopedia of Science and Technology. □

MESELSON, Matthew Stanley

American molecular biologist
Born May 24, 1930, Denver, Colo., U.S.A.

IN EXPERIMENTS performed with the molecular biologist Franklin W. Stahl, Meselson showed that the inheritance of deoxyribonucleic acid (DNA, the genetically active macromolecule of the cell, usually in the nucleus) in bacteria was "semiconservative." This means that when a DNA molecule duplicates itself, the intertwined double-helix structure splits up so that each of the two "offspring" molecules possesses a single strand of the "parent" molecule; this strand then serves as a "template" for the manufacture of a complementary strand from raw materials, and the result is two DNA molecules, each "conserving" one-half of the original molecule. This process had been predicted in 1954 by the Watson-Crick theory of DNA structure; its experimental demonstration served as a major confirmation of that theory,

central to modern molecular biology, as well as an important advance in the understanding of the living cell.

In 1954 Meselson and Stahl began to contemplate a type of experiment to determine the nature of DNA transmission. Some virus particles would be labeled with deuterium and centrifuged in a density-gradient medium so that they would separate from unlabeled particles of lower density. This idea of using a density gradient within an ultracentrifuge, later to be so useful in molecular biology and many other fields, was original with Meselson, Stahl, and the biologist Jerome R. Vinograd. For various reasons, however, the idea was not implemented, and the experiments remained in the planning stage until 1957. Then it was shown clearly by the biologists J. Herbert Taylor, Walter L. Hughes, and Philip S. Woods that transmission of DNA was semiconservative in the cell-duplicating process of mitosis; and in the same year Meselson and Stahl again took up at the California Institute of Technology their idea of ultracentrifuge experiments.

The first efforts involved 5-bromouracil (5BU). It had recently been shown by the biologist Rose Litman that T4 viruses massively incorporate the pyrimidine analog of this polymer into their DNA. The plan was to label viruses with 5BU, allow a few cycles of reproduction, and then centrifuge virus samples in a water solution of the salt cesium chloride, CsCl, in which a density gradient had been established. It was hoped that virus particles containing different amounts of 5BU would separate to a measurable degree. As a first step, Meselson and Stahl, using an analtyical ultracentrifuge, investigated the centrifugation rate of unlabeled

T4 in the CsCl solution. They found that the rate was reasonably homogeneous, so that they should easily be able to detect the 3% difference in sedimentation rate expected for labeled and unlabeled T4.

After several attempts sedimentation bands were observed in the T4 solution. But despite this encouragement a number of difficulties arose, the most problematical being the experimenters' inability to detect phage particles or DNA molecules with distinctly intermediate amounts of "parental" 5BU.

For this and other reasons Meselson and Stahl abandoned the use of T4 and 5BU and turned to the bacterium *Escherichia coli*, with the heavy nitrogen isotope N^{15} as a labeling substance. The bacteria were grown in a medium containing N^{15} so that they would incorporate the isotope into the nitrogen-base compounds of their DNA. Then they were transferred to a medium containing the more common, lighter nitrogen isotope N^{14}, where they remained for several reproductive cycles. Samples of bacteria were then removed from this culture, as in the previous experiments, and placed in a density-gradient ultracentrifuge. The solution was again CsCl. This time, however, analysis of ultraviolet absorption photographs and microdensitometer tracings showed unequivocally the presence of three types of bacterial DNA in the centrifugate, occupying different equilibrium positions. One type contained only N^{14}, one only N^{15}, and the third a mixture of N^{14} and N^{15}. Further experiments showed that this last "hybrid" variety was made up of equal amounts of DNA containing either only N^{14} or N^{15}. Moreover, Meselson and Stahl found that, when they heated this hybrid DNA, it separated into DNA containing only N^{14} or N^{15}.

These experiments demonstrated clearly that the hybrid DNA comprised two halves, one of which had been transmitted from "parental" DNA and the other newly synthesized. But there was still some question whether the two fractions of hybrid DNA which had been obtained by heating were in fact made up of single DNA strands, because at the time of the experiments (1958) it had not been shown that *E. coli* unquestionably possessed DNA with the Watson-Crick double-helix structure. Indeed, Meselson and Stahl were at first somewhat reluctant to conclude that they had separated DNA into single strands, because various experiments had seemed to indicate that single strands of DNA were not separated by heat denaturation. Within a few years, however, the molecular biologist John Cairns showed, in experiments where radioactivated DNA molecules took their own photographs by autoradiography, that the process of DNA replication actually involves the separation of the double helix into two strands. Cairns also demonstrated that the double-helix model exactly predicts the mass per unit length of the chromosomes of bacteria and viruses already known to duplicate semiconservatively.

Meselson's other work covered considerable ground in molecular biology. In 1961, together with biologists Sidney Brenner and François Jacob, Meselson in a series of experiments showed that, when the T4 virus invades a bacterial cell, the viral DNA releases messenger RNA which, on reaching the cell's ribosomes, "instructs" them to manufacture viral protein instead of the various bacterial proteins these bodies usually produce. These experiments shed light on the role of messenger RNA, showed that ribosomes must have "instructions" to be able to make proteins, and also demonstrated that ribosomes could produce proteins different from those "native" to the cell in which they occur. (Independent work along different lines by many other investigators also supported these conclusions.)

Other work by Meselson dealt with the following subjects: the behavior of macromolecules in density-gradient solutions, a venture into physical chemistry provoked by the first (1957) series of experiments with 5BU and T4; the techniques of density-gradient ultracentrifugation; the genetic recombination in viruses proceeding through breakage of DNA; the density variations in viruses involved in the phenomenon of bacterial transduction; and various aspects of genetic replication, transformation, and recombination.

Meselson received a Ph.B. in liberal arts at the University of Chicago in 1951 and a Ph.D. in physical chemistry at the California Institute of Technology in 1957. At the latter institution he was successively a research fellow in 1957–58, assistant professor of physical chemistry in 1958–59, and senior research fellow in chemical biology in 1959–60. He went to Harvard University, where he was associate professor of biology from 1960 to 1964 and then professor of biology. Meselson received a special National Academy of Sciences Award for Molecular Biology in 1963 and the Eli Lilly Award in Microbiology and Immunology in 1964.

For background information *see* CENTRIFUGATION (BIOLOGY); DEOXYRIBONUCLEIC ACID; NUCLEIC ACID; VIRUS in the McGraw-Hill Encyclopedia of Science and Technology.   □

★ METZ, Charles William

American zoologist
Born Feb. 17, 1889, Sundance, Wyo., U.S.A.

EXCEPT FOR some early taxonomic studies, Metz's investigations centered largely on chromosomes. These investigations began when he was a graduate student at Columbia University, under E. B. Wilson and in association with T. H. Morgan's *Drosophila* group. At that time, 1912–14, the chromosome theory of heredity,

with its basic concepts of "individuality and continuity" of chromosomes, was in dispute. Through cytological study of different species of *Drosophila*, Metz in 1914 helped to establish the validity of these concepts and to throw light on the evolution of chromosomes. Strong evidence was provided that individually identifiable chromosomes were qualitatively different from others and maintained their characteristics from generation to generation. It was also found that long, V-shaped chromosomes in some species were each represented in other species by two short rod-shaped chromosomes, each comparable to one arm of a V. Based on this principle, the different types of groups could readily be arranged in series suggesting evolutionary sequence.

If these interpretations were correct, it followed that similar genes should be present in homologous chromosomes, or chromosome arms, of different species, and that these might be detected genetically by securing and comparing mutant characters. Progress in such comparative genetic studies was made possible largely because the work of Morgan and his associates on *D. melanogaster* provided evidence about mutants and their linkage relations in this species which could be used for comparison. The cooperation of A. H. Sturtevant in securing specimens and in discussions also helped materially. Significant results were secured by 1915–16 and, with the aid of assistants, the work was extended to include cytological study of 26 species and genetic study of 3 species in addition to *D. melanogaster*. The results gave strong support to the initial interpretations. Genes for similar mutants appeared to be not only in corresponding chromosomes but in some cases arranged in similar sequence. Evidence of less conspicuous changes was also found. While these studies were under way, D. E. Lancefield in 1922 secured similar genetic results in studies on another species of *Drosophila*, and Sturtevant in

1920, by securing hybrids between *D. melanogaster* and a very similar species, *D. simulans*, demonstrated the presence of homologous genes in homologous chromosomes of these species.

At this stage, about 1923, the main purposes of Metz's studies had been accomplished. The field of cytogenetics had advanced greatly, with the fundamental importance of chromosomes recognized. Now it became desirable to learn as much as possible about the nature, behavior, and function of these bodies. Metz chose to approach this problem through study and comparison of chromosome behavior in organisms that diverge widely in their genetic and developmental behavior. Eminently satisfactory material was found in the "fungus gnats" of the genus *Sciara*. Using these, Metz, with his collaborators (especially H. V. Crouse), began a series of investigations.

In comparison with *Drosophila* and most other genetically known organisms, *Sciara* was found to deviate so widely as to reveal chromosome potentialities not formerly suspected, and to require revision of some supposedly well-established principles of chromosome behavior. Indeed, some processes were found which still defy explanation, especially in connection with sex determination, with interactions between chromosomes and cytoplasm in development and differentiation, and with the control and mechanism of chromosome movements in mitosis and meiosis. For example, in *Sciara* the males produce only one kind of sperm, all of which carry two sister sex (X) chromosomes. The sex of the offspring is then determined, after intervening events, by an accurate process of elimination, which removes either both of these sister chromosomes (in male production) or only one (in female production) from the somatic cells during development of the embryo. This process is influenced by the cytoplasm, which is preconditioned by the sex chromosomes of the mother (there are two types of mothers). Separations are thus made between three homologous X chromosomes—one from the mother, which is not affected, and two sisters from the father. How can one of two presumably identical sister chromosomes be thus influenced without the other and why are only the paternal ones affected? In the germ line an elimination also occurs, but by an entirely different process (as shown by the work of A. M. DuBois for the soma and R. O. Berry for the germ line). One of the two paternal sister X chromosomes is removed from all cells, in both sexes alike. The nature of the gonads is determined, not by the germ-line chromosomes, but by those of the somatic tissue (XX female, XO male).

Another example is seen in spermatogenesis. The expected random segregation of chromosomes does not occur. Instead, during a peculiar cell division process, all four chromosomes from the father move in one direction, their maternal homologs in the opposite direction. The former move backward in apparent opposition to forces that should typically tend to pull them forward. This behavior strongly suggests that chromosomes in general have a power of locomotion, acting but not manifest in ordinary mitosis. Direction of movement of chromosomes here is controlled by a mutational influence of sex of parent on each chromosome, regularly reversible in successive generations. The chromosomes which go backward did just the opposite in the preceding generation. Males in *Sciara* transmit only the chromosomes derived from the mother. Metz and his collaborators also found *Sciara* very favorable for other types of work, including studies on the giant salivary gland chromosomes. (This and the preceding references to *Sciara* do not take into consideration a peculiar type of chromosome found in some species of the organism and limited to the germ line.)

Metz received his B.S. at Pomona College in 1911 and his Ph.D. at Columbia University in 1916. He was a staff member in the Carnegie Institution of Washington's Department of Genetics during 1914–30 and Department of Embryology during 1930–40, also acting as part-time visiting professor at Johns Hopkins University in 1930–37. In 1940 he became chairman of the zoology department at the University of Pennsylvania, withdrawing from the chairmanship in 1955 to have more time for research. After his academic retirement in 1959, he continued research at the Marine Biological Laboratory, Woods Hole, Mass. Metz was elected to the National Academy of Sciences in 1948 and to the American Academy of Arts and Sciences in 1951.

For background information *see* CHROMO-SOME; CHROMOSOME THEORY OF HEREDITY; GENE ACTION in the McGraw-Hill Encyclopedia of Science and Technology.   □

★ MEYER, Karl

American biochemist
Born Sept. 4, 1899, Kerpen, Germany

MEYER WAS primarily interested in the ground substance of connective tissues, specifically in the acidic mucopolysaccharides which are responsible for the histological staining typical for the ground substances of connective tissues. The acidic mucopolysaccharides are polymers containing hexosamine and, as anionic groups, either hexuronic acid or sulfate ester group or both. The start of these investigations was the isolation of hyaluronic acid from vitreous humor in 1935 and from umbilical cord the following year. Subsequently Meyer and his associates

isolated a second mucopolysaccharide from umbilical cord, characterizing it as a chondroitin sulfate, and isolated hyaluronic acid from synovial fluid, from a malignant tumor, and from skin. Almost simultaneously with the isolation of hyaluronic acid a search was begun for enzymes with which specifically to degrade hyaluronic acid. Such enzymes, the hyaluronidases, were found first in pneumococci and later in streptococci and in some species of *Clostridium*. The interest in these enzymes and their substrate, hyaluronic acid, was greatly enhanced by the report of E. Chain and E. S. Duthie in England that the so-called spreading factors described by F. Duran-Reynals were identical with the hyaluronidases. These spreading factors had been found in various microorganisms, in snake venoms, in the leeches, and especially in mammalian testes. The mechanism of action and the chemical structure of the products of the different hyaluronidases were finally elucidated between 1950 and 1960. Meyer, with Bernard Weissman, showed testicular and snake venom hyaluronidases to be endohexosaminidases, with the end products being about 15% disaccharide and the rest being tetrasaccharide. The microbial hyaluronidases, studied with Alfred Linker, also proved to be endohexosaminidases. The end products, however, were unsaturated disaccharides with the double bond between carbon 4 and 5 of the glucuronosyl moiety formed by an elimination reaction between the *N*-acetylhexosaminyl and the following glucuronosyl group. The third type of hyaluronidase, the leech enzyme, was shown to be a specific endoglucuronidase. Studies on the chemical structures of mucopolysaccharides

originated with the isolation, with Maurice Rapport and B. Weissman, of the crystalline disaccharide hyalobiuronic acid in high yield. The structure of hyalobiuronic acid was proven as β-glucuronido 1 → 3 glucosamine by Weissman and Meyer by chemical degradation to a β-glucusido 1 → 2 arabinose of known structure.

The β 1 → 4 linkage of the hexosaminyl group was first postulated from the enzymatic degradation by bacterial hyaluronidase and later proven chemically by S. Hirano and P. Hoffman.

Research indicating the presence of three distinct types of chondroitin sulfate started with the isolation from skin of chondroitin sulfate B in 1941 by Meyer and E. Chaffee. The presence of three distinct isomers of chondroitin sulfate was first reported by Meyer and Rapport in 1951. The presence of iduronic acid in chondroitin sulfate B instead of glucuronic acid in chondroitin sulfates A and C was shown by P. Hoffman, A. Linker, and Meyer. The identity of the disaccharide repeating units of chondroitin sulfate A and C was demonstrated by E. Davidson and Meyer by the isolation and characterization of crystalline chondrosine from both. Hoffman and Meyer in 1958 showed the sulfate ester group of chondroitin sulfate A in the 4 position and chondroitin sulfate C in the 6 position of the galactosamine.

In 1953 Meyer and Davidson isolated from cornea a sulfated mucopolysaccharide, keratosulfate, composed of N-acetylglucosamine, galactose, and sulfate in equimolar quantities. Keratosulfate was further isolated from cartilage by Meyer, Hoffman, and Linker. Its structure was determined by S. Hirano, Hoffman, and Meyer for keratosulfate of cornea and was confirmed later by Bhavanandan and Meyer for keratosulfate of cartilage.

Beginning in 1963, the nature of the linkages between mucopolysaccharides and the protein or peptide backbone was investigated, first with Bonnie Anderson and later with N. Seno and Hoffman. The known alkali lability of some of these linkages was shown to be an elimination reaction of the O-glycosidic bond to the hydroxyl of serine in the case of chondroitin sulfate A and C, and to the hydroxyl of serine and threonine for keratosulfate, for submaxillary mucin, and for blood group substances. These reactions were subsequently studied extensively in other laboratories.

Meyer was also interested in the biology of mucopolysaccharides, a field which still is largely unknown. With H. Grossfeld he demonstrated the production of hyaluronic acid by fibroblasts in tissue culture in 1955 and the distribution of mucopolysaccharides in typical patterns in various tissues in 1956. Also shown were the changes of the pattern with aging in skin by G. Loewy and Meyer and in cartilege by D. Kaplan and Meyer. Basing their work on studies from other laboratories, Meyer and M. Grumbach reported in 1958 and 1959 the involvement of two mucopolysaccharides, chondroitin sulfate B and heparitin sulfate, the varying distribution in different tissues, and the pattern of excretion in urine in Hurler's syndrome, an inherited disease of connective tissues. In another, inherited generalized disease of connective tissue, Marfan's syndrome, the presence of keratosulfate in cartilage in very large amounts was reported by Meyer in 1963.

In recent years Meyer and his associates were mainly interested in the linkage region of chondroitin sulfates and especially of keratosulfates. The complexity of keratosulfates which was found in these studies is still being investigated.

Meyer took an M.D. at the University of Cologne in 1924 and a Ph.D. at Berlin University in 1928. He was assistant professor of experimental biology at the University of California, Berkeley, in 1930–32. At the College of Physicians and Surgeons, Columbia University, he was assistant professor of biochemistry during 1933–42, associate professor during 1942–54, and professor beginning in 1954. Meyer was awarded the Claude Bernard Medal of the University of Montreal in 1952, the Lasker Award of the American Public Health Association in 1956, the T. Duckett Jones Award of the Helen Hay Whitney Foundation in 1959, and the Gairdner Foundation Award in 1960. He was elected to the American Academy of Arts and Sciences in 1965 and to the National Academy of Sciences in 1967.

For background information *see* CONNECTIVE TISSUE; HYALURONIC ACID; HYALURONIDASE in the McGraw-Hill Encyclopedia of Science and Technology.   □

★ MICHENER, Charles Duncan

American biologist
Born Sept. 22, 1918, Pasadena, Calif., U.S.A.

ALTHOUGH MICHENER worked extensively on the taxonomy of bees, moths, and chigger mites and devised in 1944 the system now generally used for classifying the approximately 20,000 species of bees, his work of more general interest concerns the principles of classification and the origin and evolution of social behavior. The classification of organisms has always been as much an art as an exact science. The "new systematics," arising from the meeting of genetics and systematics and developed by such men as J. S. Huxley and Ernst Mayr, had by 1942 provided a basis, sometimes subjective in actual practice, for understanding species and infraspecific variation in nature; but at levels such as orders, families, and genera, classificatory methods and understanding were little better than those of the preceding century. Using data from bee taxonomy, Michener in 1957 helped to develop, with R. R. Sokal, statistical approaches (called numerical taxonomy)

to try to increase objectivity in taxonomic work. Although different characteristics and different coding and statistical methods still produce different classifications, numerical taxonomy has at least been successful in permitting a taxonomist to show clearly how he reached his conclusions. Moreover, it has reemphasized the subjectiveness of the phylogenies on which classifications are often based and has emphasized the obvious differences among classifications based on lines of descent (cladistics), degree of difference or similarity (phenetics), and some combination of the two (phylogeny). Most important, it has led to serious discussion of principles which should lead to the development of a firmer conceptual basis for taxonomy.

Michener's study of social behavior began when, while coauthoring a semipopular book on social insects in 1951, he realized how little was known of the origin and evolution of such behavior. The great majority of bees are solitary; each nest, usually in the ground, is made by a single female working alone. One can learn the major features of the nesting behavior of such bees merely by digging a series of nests of various ages. Much information has been obtained over centuries on the honeybee and other thoroughly social species. But the intermediates, the primitively social bees living in colonies of two to a very few hundred, usually less than two dozen, were very little known, partly because they are hard to study. The sweat bees (Halictidae) are the only group which shows a rich spectrum of intermediates between solitary and thoroughly social forms, a range which was previously only suggested by work of such men as H. Fabre and H. Legewie.

Since in primitively social bees there are no external differences between workers and queens, a first step was to learn how to recognize these castes when present. Working with halictine bees of Kansas, Michener, with A. Wille and others, showed that queens, in contrast to

workers, are relatively long-lived, are inhibited from leaving the nest by the presence of workers, mate, and have enlarged ovaries. Among females old enough to have worn wings and jaws, queens have sperm cells in the spermatheca and enlarged ovaries; workers have not mated and have slender ovaries.

After studying certain Kansas species, Michener worked in Brazil, Costa Rica, Australia, and Africa to obtain information on the social levels of as wide a variety of halictine bees as possible. He found many nonsocial or solitary species and some that live in groups where each female lays eggs and performs all the functions of solitary bees. He also found species which, although often solitary, can facultatively develop colonies. Certain species with colonies of females belonging to a single generation, commonly sisters, he termed semisocial, as distinguished from the numerous truly social species in which queens and workers are of different generations (mothers and daughters). He considered social behavior of different bees to have risen in two ways, through grouping of either unrelated or sibling individuals or through development of family (mother-daughter) groups.

Social behavior was shown to have arisen independently in numerous groups of halictine bees. In various genera and even subgenera, both solitary and social species exist. While body structure and nest architecture seem conservative, differing little among related species, the degree of social evolution varies greatly. One might expect social evolution in insects to be conservative, as it would seem to require some sort of communication to provide for cooperative activity—that is, each individual should respond to cues provided by others. Communication would seem to require an evolution more complex than that of responses to the inanimate environment; yet the data suggested the reverse.

To study communication and other behavior, bee rooms were constructed at the University of Kansas and halictine bees were cultured indoors for the first time, with the help of K. A. Stockhammer and S. W. T. Batra. Bees were induced to nest with their cells exposed to view through glass or plastic. It was seen that lone females seem to use both chemical and physical features of their own partially finished nests as cues stimulating and limiting further construction or provisioning. In other words, the bee "communicates with itself." When several bees jointly occupy a nest in a semisocial or social group, the same cues appear to stimulate or limit further work, irrespective of which bee responds to the cues. Thus without any complicated or specially evolved system of communication, but using merely the methods that a lone halictid uses, a group is able to act in a cooperative and mutually advantageous manner because any one bee is able to omit from its work the jobs already performed by others.

Michener's father was an electrical engineer and amateur ornithologist; his mother was trained as a zoologist. His interest in biology began in childhood when he painted many native flowers of California and drew insects. He studied at the University of California, where he received the B.S. in entomology in 1939 and the Ph.D. in 1941. He joined the staff of the American Museum of Natural History in 1942, moving to the University of Kansas in 1948 as associate professor. He served as chairman of the department of entomology from 1949 to 1961, during which time he was also state entomologist. In 1959 he was appointed Watkins Distinguished Professor at the University of Kansas. As an army officer during World War II, he worked in mosquito control and research on chigger mites. He was elected to the American Academy of Arts and Sciences in 1963 and to the National Academy of Sciences in 1965.

Michener wrote *American Social Insects*, with Mary H. Michener (1951); *Nest Architecture of the Sweat Bees: A Study of Comparative Behavior*, with S. F. Sakagami (1962); and *Bees of the Australian and South Pacific Regions* (1965). He served as editor of *Evolution* and American editor of *Insectes Sociaux*.

For background information *see* ANIMAL SYSTEMATICS; BEE AND BEEKEEPING; SOCIAL INSECTS in the McGraw-Hill Encyclopedia of Science and Technology.   □

★ MILLER, Charles Phillip

American physician
Born Aug. 29, 1894, Oak Park, Ill., U.S.A.

A CLINICIAN with a special interest in the infectious diseases, Miller devoted his laboratory investigations principally to the study of bacterial infection in experimental animals, the action of antibiotics, and the effect of ionizing radiation on resistance of animals to bacterial infection. He produced the first experimental meningococcal infection in mice by inoculating them intraperitoneally with meningococci suspended in mucin; he was also the first to show that by the same method it was possible, by repeated passage through mice, to raise the virulence of a strain of *Gonococcus* to a very high level.

As soon as penicillin became available, Miller began a long series of studies on the action of antibiotics on susceptible bacteria. He showed that penicillin killed meningococci only when they were in the process of active multiplication. In a small group of patients with acute gonococcal urethritis, he demonstrated by hourly culture and microscopic examination that the infection was rapidly cured by penicillin introduced into the blood stream, but not by direct intraurethral application to the infected tissues.

In a series of studies on the development of bacterial resistance to the action of antibiotics, Miller showed that strains of meningococci initially susceptible to penicillin gradually acquired resistance during repeated cultivation in media containing increasing concentrations of the drug. This gradual, stepwise development of penicillin resistance was due to the appearance of mutants only slightly more resistant than their antecedents in the bacterial population. Similar observations were made contemporaneously by other investigators working with other organisms, but Miller was the first to demonstrate that the same phenomenon could occur in vivo, that is, during the course of a long series of experimental meningococcal infections in mice treated with subcurative doses of penicillin.

In experiments with streptomycin Miller showed that two types of mutants appeared in cultures of meningococci, one highly resistant, the other actually requiring streptomycin to multiply, for in the absence of the drug this streptomycin-dependent variant promptly died. Inoculated into mice, the streptomycin-dependent strains produced no disease unless the mice were treated with streptomycin, in which case fatal meningococcal infections developed.

At the end of World War II, when there was general concern about suitable means of treating persons who might be exposed to lethal doses of ionizing radiation, Miller undertook an experimental study of the problem in mice. He found that the early deaths among mice exposed to mid-lethal doses of x-radiation or gamma radiation were commonly due to generalized infection caused by bacteria normally present in the animals' intestines. By controlling the development of fatal infections with injections of streptomycin, the 30-day mortality of such mice was sharply reduced. Similar observations were made on mice exposed to fast neutrons and on mice poisoned with nitrogen mustard. Other studies on the injury caused by ionizing radiation dealt with its effect on the natural antibodies in the mouse's blood serum and on the ability of the animal's fixed tissue phagocytes to dispose of bacteria filtered from the blood stream.

As the use of antibiotics in the treatment of patients became more general, Miller's interest was aroused by a clinical problem which was appearing with increasing frequency. This was the development of a troublesome, sometimes serious complication—infection of the bowel caused by microorganisms resistant to the drug being administered. The offending microorganisms were often members of the human intestinal flora, quite harmless under normal conditions. Miller undertook to investigate the problem experimentally in mice, using as inoculum a strain of *Salmonella enteriditis* of such low virulence that several millions of the bacilli introduced by mouth were required to infect normal mice. Less than 10, however, sufficed to initiate fatal *Salmonella* infections in mice which had been treated by mouth with a single large dose of streptomycin or penicillin. This marked increase in the mouse's susceptibility to *Salmonella* infection was found to be due to the action of the antibiotic on the microbial population within the large intestine. In the normal, untreated mouse, that population inhibited multiplication of the orally inoculated *Salmonella* and thereby prevented the development of *Salmonella* infection. The selective elimination of some of its components by the antibiotic converted the bowel content into an environment within which *Salmonella* could multiply unhindered and produce generalized infection. The ultimate solution of the problem required years of intensive effort because the bacteria which antagonized the *Salmonella* proved to be difficult to isolate and cultivate. They were eventually found to be anaerobes belonging to the genus *Bacteroides* and their protective effect to be caused by the production of butyric and acetic acids which inhibited multiplication of *Salmonella*, thereby preventing the development of infection by oral inoculation.

Miller received his B.S. in 1916 from the University of Chicago and his M.D. in 1919 from Rush Medical College. He served an internship in the Presbyterian Hospital of Chicago under James B. Herrick, then earned an M.S. in pathology at the University of Michigan in 1920. He went to the hospital of the Rockefeller Institute, where he worked for 4 years with Homer F. Swift on studies of rheumatic fever. He spent the following year in the laboratory of Karl Landsteiner at the Rockefeller Institute, collaborating in several immunological investigations of the relationships of the bloods of primates.

Miller then went to Europe for 18 months to study developments in his field, working for half a year as volunteer research assistant at the Institut für Infektions-Krankenheit "Robert Koch" in Berlin. He returned to the University of Chicago as assistant professor of medicine, and was appointed successively associate professor and professor, becoming professor emeritus in 1960. He continued his research activities until 1965, when he retired. He was elected to the National Academy of Sciences in 1956 and to the American Academy of Arts and Sciences in 1961.

For background information *see* ANTIBIOTIC; BACTERIA; RADIATION INJURY (BIOLOGY) in the McGraw-Hill Encyclopedia of Science and Technology.   □

★ **MILLER, George Armitage**

American psychologist
Born Feb. 3, 1920, Charleston, W.Va., U.S.A.

MILLER'S PRINCIPAL research was motivated by his desire to understand the psychological implications of communication in general and of language in particular and to represent that understanding in some appropriate formal notation. During World War II, as a graduate student under S. S. Stevens at Harvard, Miller worked on the design of jamming signals to interfere with voice communication. As expected from acoustic considerations, optimal masking was found to be produced by an uninterrupted noise having a constant signal-to-noise ratio per cycle over the speech bandwidth. He was impressed, however, by the fact that some types of spoken messages (such as digits) were consistently harder to hear than others (such as nonsense syllables). The experimental data seemed to demand a psychological explanation, and after the war Miller returned to the problem.

The appearance in 1948 of C. E. Shannon's and Norbert Weiner's statistical measure of amount of information suggested the answer. Miller and his collaborators verified that the larger the set of alternative messages that might have been sent, the better the signal-to-noise ratio (that is, the greater the amount of information) that a listener required on the average to identify a particular message correctly. For example, when the word "stop" is expected as one of two alternative possible messages, it can be heard correctly at much poorer signal-to-noise ratios than when it is expected as one of several thousand alternative words. Thus the phenomenon could be explained in terms of the required accuracy of discrimination: If two words are selected at random from the English lexicon, they will probably differ phonetically in many significant features; as more words are selected, however, the probability will increase that some of them will resemble one another more closely, so that a clearer signal (more information) will be required to discriminate among them correctly. Miller and his co-workers measured perceptual confusions among speech sounds as a function of signal-to-noise ratio and analyzed the results in terms of the distinctive phonemic features involved in the confusions. Some features (such as vocalization and nasality) were resistant to masking, but others (such as place of articulation) were easily disrupted.

It was also observed that any given word spoken in the context of a simple English sentence could be heard at poorer signal-to-noise ratios than when spoken in isolation. Miller said that the context of the sentence provided information that enabled a listener to narrow the range of expected words, so that he could identify the word correctly under less favorable conditions. The effect of this contextual information, which Shannon had named "redundancy," was also shown to be important for remembering a message correctly, and in 1950 Miller suggested that the greater ease of memorizing meaningful materials (as compared, say, with lists of unrelated words) might be largely, if not wholly, attributable to the smaller amount of information per word conveyed by redundant messages.

Attempts to test these arguments uncovered several complications. Miller's further research led him to recognize that the psychological mechanism which enables a listener to take advantage of sequential redundancy is much more complicated than a simple reduction of the expected number of alternatives, even though that seemed to be its ultimate effect. Instead, Miller attributed the effects of sequential redundancy to the fact that listeners are able to organize a grammatical message into functional units longer than individual words. These longer units are easier to hear than are individual words spoken in isolation because they differ from one another in more distinctive features; moreover, because a sentence n words long contains fewer than n functional units, it is effectively shorter and easier to remember than a list of n unrelated words. (The psychological advantage that can reward recoding is illustrated by a trick well known to all computer scientists: The binary sequence 101001011100, for example, is difficult for most people to remember because its 12 digits exceed their span of immediate memory, but if it is grouped by triplets into the "functional units" 101 001 011 100 and then recoded from binary to octal to obtain 5134, the shorter, recoded version is easily remembered.)

If it is true that meaningful sentences are ordinarily perceived, understood, and remembered in terms of functional units larger than individual words, how is this psychological grouping and recoding accomplished? Can the necessary information processing be characterized in any detail? The answers obviously require a detailed specification of the grammatical competence of language users. In approaching this formidable problem, Miller was again fortunate in finding a newly developed theory—this time the theory of syntax formulated in 1956 by Noam Chomsky—that could be exploited for psychological research. There followed a period of mathematical work with Chomsky and a series of experiments, with both natural and artificial languages, testing the psychological reality of the phrase structure and the grammatical transformations postulated in Chomsky's theory.

Miller tried repeatedly to generalize theoretical and methodological ideas from psycholinguistic research into other areas of psychology. He suggested that the functional units found in grammatical utterances might have suggestive analogs in the functional organization of nonverbal behavior, and he tried to develop the notion that the meaning underlying a sentence and the plan underlying purposive behavior have much in common. In 1960 his interest in extending psycholinguistic theories to other cognitive processes led him to collaborate with Jerome S. Bruner in creating the Harvard Center for Cognitive Studies.

Miller received his B.A. in 1940 and his M.A. in 1941 from the University of Alabama, where he majored in speech. In 1941 he was appointed instructor in psychology at Alabama, a position he held for 2 years. During the summer of 1942 he attended Harvard and in 1943 enrolled there as a graduate student in psychology. From 1944 to 1948 he worked at the Psychoacoustic Laboratory on the evaluation of radio-telephone communications for the armed services; some of this work was submitted in February, 1946, as his Ph.D. thesis. He was assistant professor of psychology at Harvard from 1948 until he went to MIT as associate professor in 1951. In 1953 he became a group leader at the MIT Lincoln Laboratory, where he worked on human engineering problems in air defense systems until February, 1955, when he returned to Harvard. In 1958 Harvard promoted him to professor of psychology. He was elected to the American Academy of Arts and Sciences in 1957 and to the National Academy of Sciences in 1962.

For background information *see* PSYCHOACOUSTICS; SIGNAL-TO-NOISE RATIO in the McGraw-Hill Encyclopedia of Science and Technology. □

★ **MITCHELL, John Wesley**

American physicist
Born Dec. 3, 1913, Christchurch, New Zealand

MITCHELL BEGAN his researches at the University of Canterbury in New Zealand in 1933. His first work was on the electrode potential of zinc and on the electrical conductivity of zinc bromide solutions. Always an enthusiastic climber and photographer, he satisfied these interests while carrying out one of the first petrographic surveys of the metamorphic rocks of the high mountain areas of the southern Alps. His awareness of the imperfections of apparently perfect crystals and of the lack of understanding of the science of photographic processes was aroused during this period.

Awarded an Overseas Science Research Scholarship by the Royal Commission for the Exhibition of 1851, Mitchell proceeded to Oxford in 1935 and worked for three years on the kinetics of homogeneous gas reactions in the Trinity College Laboratory with C. N. Hinshelwood. During World War II he developed methods of high-speed photography that were applied to the study of a wide range of problems, including armor penetration and shock waves

associated with the detonation of high explosives. This work brought him into contact with N. F. Mott, whose team of theorists was concerned with the analysis of physical phenomena. As a consequence of the collaboration which developed, Mitchell was invited to join the group of solid-state physicists that Mott was forming at the University of Bristol. Between 1945 and 1954, when Mott was appointed Cavendish Professor of Experimental Physics at Cambridge, this enthusiastic group, which included N. Cabrera, F. C. Frank, and F. R. N. Nabarro, was responsible for many advances in the knowledge of the mechanisms of crystal growth and of the role of imperfections in the mechanical deformation of crystals. Mitchell's contribution during this period, and from 1954 until 1959, when he joined the faculty of the University of Virginia, arose from his detailed experimental investigation of the photochemical and physical properties of single crystals of silver halides.

Stimulated by the theory of the formation of the latent image advanced by R. W. Gurney and Mott in 1937, and yet realizing that this theory left many fundamental questions unanswered, Mitchell started to work in 1947 to try to understand the role of crystal imperfections and of chemical sensitization in the formation of the latent image. Many difficulties had to be overcome before Mitchell and his graduate students, including T. Evans, J. M. Hedges, and H. D. Keith, were able to make thin fog-free disks of silver halides whose properties closely reproduced those of the microcrystals of photographic emulsions. With the new and powerful research techniques they developed, Mitchell was able to establish unequivocally that one of the important roles of the chemical sensitizer is to undergo a chemical change in which reaction with a positive hole results in the liberation of a silver ion. This possibility had not been envisaged by Gurney and Mott, whose theory could not account for the remarkably high quantum efficiency of the photochemical process, nor for the fact that the most sensitive grains of photographic emulsions require the absorption of only four quanta of visible light in order to be reduced to silver in a photographic developer. These and many other facts were explained by a new theory of photographic sensitivity worked out and presented in a series of publications by Mitchell during 1957–59. This theory was directly based on the results of a considerable number of carefully designed, yet essentially simple experiments carried out with thin-sheet crystals of silver halides. Unlike the theory of Gurney and Mott, Mitchell's theory does not assume that deep traps for electrons are produced by the chemical sensitization of the silver halide microcrystals. Rather, Mitchell proposed that such traps, at which the liberated silver atoms are concentrated, are first formed during or following exposure. According to Mitchell, the products of chemical sensitization react with the chemically equivalent number of positive holes, which would otherwise attack photochemically produced groups of silver atoms. This theory stimulated research in photographic science in many countries, and the new research techniques developed at Bristol were extensively adopted, notably by W. West of the Eastman Kodak Research Laboratories at Rochester, N.Y. They have contributed substantially to the advancement of the knowledge of the physics and chemistry of photographic processes.

In October, 1952, during the course of the study of the physical properties of the thin-sheet crystals of the silver halides, Hedges and Mitchell found that the distributions of dislocations in these crystals can be made visible by exposure to light. This was a discovery of fundamental importance. In the days before the development of transmission electron microscopy, Mitchell and his graduate students were able to make detailed studies of the dislocation structure of the subboundaries of the mosaic blocks in single crystals and of the generation and propagation of dislocations under the action of shear stresses. The validity of much of the theoretical analysis of the probable behavior of dislocations in single crystals was demonstrated for the first time during this work. One of Mitchell's main objectives was to produce single crystals of silver halides free from imperfections. He accomplished this in 1958, when crystals of remarkable perfection and photochemical insensitivity were first produced. Having worked for 12 years on the photochemical and mechanical properties of silver halides, which provide a transparent model system for the study of the processes of plastic deformation in single crystals of metals, Mitchell began to study the mechanical properties of metals themselves.

In 1959 he moved to the University of Virginia and, with Cabrera, began building up another research group. He studied the mechanical properties of single crystals of copper-aluminum and cadmium-zinc alloys and of the four pure metals. As in his studies of the silver halides, Mitchell had to produce single crystals of the highest possible perfection. With J. C. Crump, III, Mitchell showed that apparently perfect single crystals of cadmium do not fail until the theoretically predicted limiting shear stress has been established on their glide planes. This work provided the first confirmation of the soundness of the theoretical analysis of the strength of crystals and showed that failure usually results from the nucleation of dislocation loops. The dynamics of the dislocation phenomena, which occur during the earliest stages

of the plastic deformation of single crystals of copper-aluminum alloys, also was studied intensively, and new experimental techniques were developed for this work.

Mitchell received his B.Sc. in 1933 and M.Sc. in 1934 at the University of Canterbury, New Zealand. He went to England in 1935, and at the University of Oxford he received a Ph.D. in 1938 and a D.Sc. in 1960. He was a research physicist with the British Ministry of Supply during 1939–45 and was reader in experimental physics at the University of Bristol during 1945–59. He went to the United States in 1959, and at the University of Virginia was professor of physics from 1959 and William Barton Rogers Professor of Physics from 1965. Awarded the Boys Prize of the Institute of Physics and the Physical Society, London, in 1955, Mitchell was elected in 1956 a fellow of the Royal Society of London.

For background information *see* CRYSTAL DEFECTS; CRYSTAL GROWTH; CRYSTAL STRUCTURE; PHOTOCHEMISTRY in the McGraw-Hill Encyclopedia of Science and Technology. ☐

★ MOORE, John Alexander

American biologist
Born June 27, 1915, Charles Town, W.Va., U.S.A.

THROUGHOUT HIS scientific career Moore studied problems of evolution. He began his studies when he was a college student engaged in collecting frog embryos for use in the zoology department at Columbia University. In the New York City area there are five species of frogs, which breed in succession from early spring to summer. Because the frog embryos were used for class instruction, as well as for the research of several professors, it was important to learn how rapidly the embryos develop and the proper conditions for normal growth. Experiments showed that each species has a different rate of development and a different range of temperature tolerance. Furthermore, these differences are strictly correlated with the time that the adults breed. Thus, the first species to breed has the fastest development and is the most resistant to low temperatures, but is the least resistant to high temperatures. In the species that breed progressively later, there is a gradual decrease in the speed of development, a decrease in resistance to low temperatures, and an increase in resistance to high temperatures. In these and many other characteristics the five species show obvious adaptations to the special environmental conditions to which their embryos are subjected.

Not only are these embryonic adaptations related to the life of the five species in the New York region, but they are also correlated with geographic distribution. For example, the species that breeds first in the New York area has the fastest rate of development and the lowest range of temperature tolerance and also has the most extensive northern range; it almost reaches the Arctic Ocean. The sequence in which the other species breed is the sequence of decreasingly extensive northern distribution. This same relation is observed, with one exception, for southern distribution. That is, the more the embryos are adapted to high temperatures, the more extensive the distribution of the species to the south.

The one exception to the pattern of southern distribution is the meadow frog, *Rana pipiens*. On the basis of the embryonic adaptations of the individuals occurring in the New York region, one would have predicted a southern limit for this species at the latitude of northern Georgia. Instead the limit falls in Panama. This unexpected result raised very interesting questions: What is the nature of the populations of *R. pipiens* south of the latitude of Georgia? What would be their rates of development, their embryonic temperature tolerances? Experiments showed that they differ from northern populations of their species in just the same way that southern species differ from northern species.

Moore also wanted to learn about the genetic relationships of the various populations. He obtained some information by carrying on an extensive series of hybridization experiments. He discovered that individuals from some southern localities, such as Florida or Texas, are quite different from individuals from New England or Wisconsin. Thus, when individuals from the northern localities are crossed with those from the southern localities, the embryos are highly defective. Later experiments provided additional measures to indicate relationships between individuals of the same species but coming from different localities. This research consisted of studies of haploid hybrids, prepared by removing the egg nucleus just after a sperm has entered, after which the embryo grows with the paternal

chromosomes only. Experiments of this sort test the abilities of genes of one population to function in a cytoplasm formed under the direction of genes of another population. These experiments were conducted over a period of nearly 30 years and were described in approximately 35 scientific papers.

A lawyer's son, Moore received his A.B. (1936), M.A. (1939), and Ph.D. in zoology (1940) from Columbia University. He taught at Brooklyn College in 1939–41 and Queens College in 1941–43, but spent most of his academic life at Columbia, where he was appointed professor of zoology in 1950. In 1940 he became a research associate at the American Museum of Natural History. He was elected to the American Academy of Arts and Sciences in 1960 and to the National Academy of Sciences in 1963. He was also a member of the American Academy of Arts and Sciences and of the Royal Danish Academy of Sciences and Letters.

Greatly interested in biological education at all levels, Moore wrote two books for college students, *Principles of Zoology* (1957) and *Heredity and Development* (1963). He was active in the Biological Sciences Curriculum Study, started in 1959, and was the supervisor of the BSCS "Yellow Version," *Biological Sciences: An Inquiry into Life* (1963), for high school students. A little book, *The Wonder of Life* (1961), is for younger children.

For background information *see* ANIMAL GROWTH; EVOLUTION, ORGANIC; GENE ACTION; ZOOGEOGRAPHY in the McGraw-Hill Encyclopedia of Science and Technology.   □

★ MORGAN, William Wilson

American astronomer
Born Jan. 3, 1906, Bethesda, Tenn., U.S.A.

MORGAN DEVELOPED methods for investigating more precisely the structure of our galactic system and, in later years, the structure of other galaxies. His papers fall under the general heading of astronomical morphology. His doctoral thesis dealt with the discovery of several groups of peculiar stellar spectra; although isolated examples of "rare-earth stars" and other spectral peculiarities had been known earlier, he demonstrated that such peculiarities are not unique but are, in fact, shared by considerable numbers of stars in the solar neighborhood.

The most significant work in his earlier period (1936–43) was the development of a general, two-dimensional classification scheme for small-scale stellar spectra. This scheme, which made possible the determination of the distances (or "parallaxes") of large numbers of stars from

a successful classification of the form families of galaxies which are also strong radio sources. At about the same time Morgan called attention to the existence of supergiant galaxies in some galaxy clusters; these are probably the largest single optical structures known.

The determining influence in Morgan's earlier years was that of the papers and personality of the Danish astronomer Ejnar Hertzsprung. The simplicity of the approach to a problem, the care in defining the experimental situation, the distrust of complicated lines of reasoning, and the realization that there is no such thing as a truly definitive investigation are all implicitly present in the work of this great observational astronomer. In later years a strong influence was Walter Baade, whose near-superhuman use of telescopes, powerful drive and imagination, and touch of the artist were unique.

To the morphologist the discoveries of new regularities, new groupings, and new relationships are the ends continually sought. But comparable to these is the realization that, as researchers dig deeper, they generally find not final answers but new problems; the number of such problems increases with increasing investigation.

Morgan received his B.S. (1927) and Ph.D. (1931) from the University of Chicago. Thereafter he remained in residence at the University's Yerkes Observatory. He was elected to the National Academy of Sciences in 1956, awarded the Bruce Gold Medal of the Astronomical Society of the Pacific for 1958, and elected to the Pontifical Academy of Sciences in 1964.

Besides the *Atlas of Stellar Spectra*, Morgan wrote approximately a hundred research papers.

For background information *see* ASTRONOMICAL SPECTROSCOPY; COSMOLOGY; PARALLAX (ASTRONOMY); STAR in the McGraw-Hill Encyclopedia of Science and Technology.   □

their spectra, was published in 1943, jointly with P. C. Keenan and Edith Kellman, as the Yerkes *Atlas of Stellar Spectra*. It was based on earlier investigations of Walter S. Adams and Bertil Lindblad.

During 1946–51 Morgan carried out extensive investigations of the arrangement in space of the blue giant stars in the solar neighborhood by means of the new classification system; some of these were done jointly with J. J. Nassau at the Warner and Swasey Observatory. This work culminated in 1951 in the discovery—with graduate students Stewart L. Sharpless and Donald E. Osterbrock—of the first definite evidence of the spiral structure of our galaxy. Segments of two spiral arms similar to those observed in the Andromeda Nebula were located, and a probable third arm was found. This discovery, confirmed by Guido Münch from observation of the motions of interstellar gas in the spiral arms, was extended by means of radio astronomy.

The problem of correcting for the dimming of the light of stars by dust clouds in interstellar space led Morgan to devise a more precisely defined system of star brightness and star colors in 1953; this was a joint investigation with Harold L. Johnson. Also in 1953 Morgan and G. Haro at the Tonantzintla Observatory discovered several "flash" variable stars in the cluster associated with the Orion Nebula; the light of such stars may flash up in a matter of minutes.

In 1956 Morgan and N. U. Mayall (then of the Lick Observatory) devised a spectral classification of galaxies that made possible the determination of the principal contributors to the light of a galaxy from spectra of the blended light of millions of stars. Later Morgan constructed a new classification of the forms of galaxies which could be interpreted directly in terms of the stellar population of the galaxy concerned. In 1963 he and T. A. Matthews (then of the California Institute of Technology) made

★ MORSE, Philip McCord

American physicist
Born Aug. 6, 1903, Shreveport, La., U.S.A.

THE APPLICATION of new mathematical techniques to many areas of science was the connecting thread in Morse's research. Studying as an undergraduate at Case Institute under Dayton Miller in the early 1920s, Morse became familiar with the solutions of the acoustical wave equation. As a graduate student at Princeton in 1926, he learned of the revolutionary developments in quantum theory then being initiated by Louis de Broglie, Werner Heisenberg, and Erwin Schrödinger. The wave-mechanical formulation of the theory, with its close analogies to wave

acoustics, inspired Morse to utilize his skills in this new field. He published several papers on the structure of the hydrogen molecule ion and on an approximate form of internuclear attraction in diatomic molecules, now called the Morse potential, while still a graduate student. *Quantum Mechanics* (1929) by E. U. Condon and Morse was the first text on the newly evolving subject to be published in the United States.

In collaboration with C. J. Davisson at the Bell Telephone Laboratories, Morse wrote a paper on the quantum mechanics of electrons in metallic crystals, giving special attention to the measurements of Davisson and Germer on the diffraction of electrons from metal surfaces, one of the experiments which had demonstrated the need for wave mechanics in the first place. Work under A. J. Sommerfeld in Munich in 1930 was concentrated on wave scattering, rather than resonance, and in collaboration with W. P. Allis, Morse wrote a paper on the scattering of electrons from atoms. The anomalous scattering of slow electrons, called the Ramsauer effect, was shown to be a variety of incipient resonance, later to be more strikingly exhibited in the scattering of particles from nuclei. A later paper with Allis, after he and Morse had joined the physics department at MIT in 1931, dealt with the effects of electron interchange on the scattering of slow electrons from helium; the Bush differential analyzer, an early form of analog computer, was used to carry out the calculations. Morse then worked with L. A. Young on the application of variational techniques to the calculation of wave functions for atoms in the first row of the periodic table.

The first measurements of the energy of binding of the deuterium nucleus and the scattering of neutrons by protons, both of which depend on the nature of the neutron-proton binding force, were made in the early 1930s. Attempts to calculate the form of this force from the mea-

surements were carried out by Morse and two of his students, J. B. Fisk and L. I. Schiff, but the measurements were not complete enough to verify the theoretical assumptions; it was not until the 1950s that this problem could be more successfully attacked.

Astrophysics was another wide-open field for investigation. An informal study group of faculty and students from the Harvard Observatory, among them Donald Menzel, Leo Goldberg, and Laurence Aller, took up the applications of quantum mechanics to this field, particularly to the theory of stellar interiors. Morse's contribution, reported in the *Astrophysical Journal*, was to combine quantum mechanics and statistical mechanics in a computation of the opacity of mixtures of gases at high temperatures and pressures, an important ingredient in the calculation of the distribution of pressure, density, and temperature in the star's interior. Together with the theory of H. A. Bethe on nuclear energy generation at the star's core, a consistent model of a star could be constructed. These computations, with unpublished tables of the equation of state of the mixture, were later used in Los Alamos to predict the behavior of the fireball of atomic bombs.

Concurrently, Morse taught a course in acoustics, which induced his return to the theory of sound waves. In a series of papers in the *Journal of the Acoustical Society of America*, and in the book *Vibration and Sound* (1936; 2d ed. 1948), he applied the newer techniques, developed for the calculation of electron waves, to the calculation of acoustical resonance and scattering. Collaborating with F. V. Hunt, R. H. Bolt, L. L. Beranek, R. D. Fay, Cyril Harris, and other colleagues at MIT and Harvard, Morse wrote a series of papers on acoustic impedance, its measurement, and its relation to the acoustical properties of enclosures.

At the start of World War II this Harvard-MIT group turned to the application of acoustics to problems of defense, to problems of noise generation in aircraft and tanks, and to problems of underwater sound posed by the threats of submarines and acoustically actuated mines and torpedoes. Several projects established at Harvard and at MIT were headed by various members of the group. By the time the United States entered the war, these projects were already busy and growing in numbers of participants, and they remained active throughout the war years.

The activity of U-boats along the United States coast in the early months of 1942 made it clear that scientific measurement and analysis could not be confined to the design and development of defense weapons, but must also be used to assist in the weapons' employment. Morse was requested to organize a group of scientists to analyze antisubmarine tactics and to assist in making them more effective. Among the colleagues and former students he recruited were William Shockley, George Kimball, Arthur Kip, and John Pellam, and the group began the development of what came to be called operations research. An early activity was the development of a theory of search, using geometry and probability to optimize the hunt for the submarine. By the end of the war the U.S. Navy Operations Research Group (later known as the Operations Evaluation Group) had over 100 scientists, some at headquarters in Washington, D.C., and others at various Naval headquarters around the world. For his services in organizing and directing the group, Morse was awarded the Presidential Medal for Merit (the highest United States award to civilians). The scientific results of this development of operations research were recorded in a series of volumes, first published by the Office of the Chief of Naval Operations but later, in part, reprinted commercially and in the *Journal of the Operations Research Society of America*. The volume *Methods of Operations Research*, with George Kimball (1951) is still a standard reference.

Morse's return to MIT after V-J Day was interrupted by two additional leaves of absence, one to start Brookhaven National Laboratory on its career as a center for research in the peaceful uses of atomic energy, the other to organize an operations research group for the U.S. Joint Chiefs of Staff, called the Weapons Systems Evaluation Group. In the meantime he completed some work left unfinished since 1940. In 1936 Morse had initiated an advanced course in theoretical physics, which gained the reputation of being the most arduous in the curriculum. A set of these notes were mimeographed, and copies can still be found on physicists' bookshelves. The course was taken over by Herman Feshbach during the 1940s, and the expanded notes by Morse and Feshbach resulted in *Methods of Theoretical Physics* (2 parts, 1953, 1954).

Thereafter Morse's research and teaching were about equally divided between theoretical physics and the applications of operations research to industrial and municipal operations. Fruits of the former activity included papers on waves in lattices and a textbook on thermodynamics and statistical mechanics, *Thermal Physics* (paper 1962; rev. ed. 1964; 2d printing 1965). Acoustic research done in collaboration with K. Uno Ingard resulted in a section of Volume XI of the *Handbuch der Physik* entitled "Linear Acoustic Theory" and, more recently, the volume *Theoretical Acoustics* (1968). Research in the latter field was in the theory of queues, resulting in the book *Queues, In-*

ventories and Maintenance (1958), in the development of models representing automobile traffic, and in various aspects of library operations, among them the development of methods for predicting book circulation.

Son of a telephone engineer, grandson of a civil engineer, and great-grandson of an architect and builder, Morse grew up in Cleveland, Ohio, received his B.Sc. in 1926 from Case Institute and his Ph.D. from Princeton in 1929. He joined the physics department at MIT in 1931 as assistant professor and became associate professor in 1934 and professor in 1939. From 1955 he was director of the MIT Computation Center and from 1958 director of the MIT Operations Research Center. He was council member of the American Physical Society in 1946–50, president of the Acoustical Society of America in 1950–51, and founding president of the Operations Research Society in 1951–52. He was an associate editor of the *Technology Review*, *Physics Today*, and *Bulletin of the Atomic Scientists* and was editor of the *Annals of Physics* from its inception in 1957. Morse was elected to the American Academy of Arts and Sciences in 1934 and to the National Academy of Sciences in 1955.

For background information *see* QUANTUM MECHANICS; RESONANCE (ACOUSTICS AND MECHANICS); STATISTICAL MECHANICS; UNDERWATER SOUND; VIBRATION in the McGraw-Hill Encyclopedia of Science and Technology.   □

★ MORUZZI, Giuseppe

Italian physiologist
Born July 30, 1910, Campagnola, Reggio Emilia, Italy

DURING THE 1930s Moruzzi's neurophysiological work was concerned with the cerebellum and the cerebral cortex. He investigated the influence of the cerebellar anterior lobe on postural tonus, phasic movements, and autonomic reflexes. The electrophysiology of the motor cortex was the main subject of the work he performed in the late 1930s. In 1939 E. D. Adrian and Moruzzi reported that the Betz cells of the motor cortex fired during the synchronous EEG waves produced by barbital anesthesia. The rate of this tonic, subliminar corticospinal discharge was found to increase strikingly during normal movements, while convulsive high-frequency outbursts occurred after local application of strychnine on the motor cortex. The well-known chloralose jerks were found to be associated with the reflex pyramidal discharges of the hyperexcitable motor cortex.

These two lines of work converged in the early

1940s in a study of the cerebellocerebral relationships, which was made possible by the paradoxical properties of chloralose anesthesia. Moruzzi reported in 1941 that cortically induced movements could be blocked at spinal levels by the stimulation of the anterior lobe of the cerebellum. However, in a group of experiments on cats under light chloralose anesthesia, he found that the the clonic twitch produced by local strychnine on motor cortex remained blocked for several seconds after the end of the cerebellar stimulation, an aftereffect obviously too long to be explained by inhibition occurring at segmental levels. Moruzzi then suggested that impulses arising in the paleocerebellum might influence the activity of the neurons of the motor cortex. This hypothesis, however, postulated the existence of an ascending anatomical pathway arising in the fastigial nuclei, one that was unknown at that time, because the cerebello-rubro-thalamo-cortical system is purely neocerebellar in nature.

The discovery by H. W. Magoun (1944) of an inhibitory reticulospinal system and the demonstration by him and his colleagues (1947, 1949) of a fastigio-reticulo-spinal pathway provided a satisfactory explanation of the segmental aspect of the paleocerebellar inhibition of cortically induced movements. A fastigio-reticulo-cortical pathway was demonstrated in 1949 by Moruzzi and Magoun, who showed that the chloralose EEG waves were suddenly disrupted by electrical stimulation of both fastigial nuclei and the brainstem reticular formation. This EEG effect was not limited, however, to the sensory-motor cortex but could be observed on all neocortical areas; it could be elicited, moreover, by stimulating reticular regions outside the well-defined bulboreticular district, which has an inhibitory influence on the spinal cord. Finally, on the unanesthetized cerebral cortex the effect turned out to be a reproduction of the classical EEG arousal. The demonstration that the ascending

flow of impulses courses through the core of the brainstem, independently from the classical specific projection pathways, led to the discovery of the ascending reticular system.

As Moruzzi and Magoun pointed out in their original paper, the concept of a waking influence arising in the brainstem reticular formation has important physiological (EEG arousal, sleep and wakefulness), pharmacological (barbital anesthesia), and pathological (coma, sleeping sickness) implications. It remained for Lindsley, Magoun, and their colleagues to show that the EEG synchronization of Frédéric Bremer's *cerveau isolé* is due to the withdrawal of the tonic waking influence of the ascending reticular system. Subsequent work carried out in Pisa by Moruzzi and his colleagues led to a microelectrode analysis of the tonic discharge of single reticular units and of the effect thereon of converging sensory, cerebellar, and cortical impulses and to a study of the reticular effects on single pyramidal units and on cortical dc potentials. The demonstration of a blockade of cortical strychnine "spikes" and related pyramidal discharges elicited by reticular stimulation gave a satisfactory explanation of the cerebellar experiment of 1941. Finally, Moruzzi and his colleagues showed in 1959 the existence in the lower brain stem of EEG-synchronizing and possibly sleep-inducing structures, antagonistically oriented with respect to the ascending reticular system. The works carried out in the last years at Pisa were mainly concerned with the physiology of sleep.

The son of a physician, Moruzzi graduated M.D. at the University of Parma. As a Rockefeller fellow, he worked in the laboratories of Bremer (Brussels) and Adrian (Cambridge) from 1937 to 1939. He was appointed acting professor of physiology at the universities of Siena (1942) and Parma (1945). As full professor of physiology, after a short period at the University of Ferrara, he was called to the University of Pisa in 1948. He spent 1948–49 as a visiting professor at Northwestern University. Moruzzi received honorary degrees from the universities of Pennsylvania (1963), Lyon (1963), Louvain (1964), and Oslo (1965). He was elected a member of the Accademia dei Lincei (1953) and of the American Philosophical Society (1961), and honorary member of the American Physiological Society (1959), of the American Academy of Arts and Sciences (1965), and of the American Neurological Association (1965).

Moruzzi wrote *L'epilessia sperimentale* (1946), *Problems in Cerebellar Physiology* (1950), and *Physiology and Pathology of the Cerebellum*, in collaboration with R. S. Dow (1958).

For background information see BRAIN; ELEC-

TROENCEPHALOGRAPHY; PSYCHOLOGY, PHYSIO-
LOGICAL AND EXPERIMENTAL in the McGraw-Hill
Encyclopedia of Science and Technology.   □

MULLER, Hermann Joseph

American biologist

Muller died on Apr. 5, 1967, in Indianapolis,
Ind., U.S.A. See *McGraw-Hill Modern Men of
Science*, Volume I.

★ MUNK, Walter Heinrich

American geophysicist
Born Oct. 19, 1917, Vienna, Austria

MUNK WORKED in two broad areas: the study
of wave motion in the oceans on a very
broad spectrum of scales, from millimeters to
thousands of kilometers; and the geophysical
exploitation of the astronomically observed
irregularities in the rotation of the Earth.

Munk's fascination for ocean waves arose from
a wartime need to predict sea and swell for
amphibious landings. He decided that ocean
waves are fascinating because they are moderately confused. Pure sine waves are predictable
from wave to wave and therefore dull; highly
chaotic processes are unpredictable and disturbing. Ocean waves fall nicely between these extremes; their pattern is ever changing, yet an
experienced surfer can anticipate a good breaker
one or two waves in advance. In 1940 no one
knew how to give a quantitative description of
waves which included their irregularity as part
of the description even though the tools were
available through previous work on optical and
sonic spectra. Irregularity and unpredictability
increase with spectral bandwidth, from zero
bandwidth (line spectra) for complete predicta-
bility to a "white noise" at the other extreme.
Ocean-wave spectra are typically an octave wide,

which seems to be a nice compromise. Because it
proved impossible to apply wave research to
geological processes such as beach erosion and
sand movements, Munk became interested in
simpler problems.

One way to study the planet Earth is to
observe irregularities in its rotation. In this
manner one can learn about the growth of the
core, the variable distribution of glaciation, air
mass, global winds, bulk viscosity, and so forth.
In each case the information is related to certain integral quantities (moments) taken over
the entire globe. This is the weakness of the
method—and its strength. Astronomers were the
first to attempt to exploit, for geological purposes, the irregularities they had discovered.
They did this in the naïve faith that the simplicity of celestial mechanics could be carried
over to messy objects like the Earth. So they
applied their astronomic jargon and spoke of
the "proper motion" of observatories, and they
suddenly raised the Himalayan complex by one
foot. There was a curious dichotomy between
those who measured latitude and so inferred the
wobble of the Earth relative to a rotation axis
fixed in space and those who compared sidereal
time to ephemeral time (later to atomic time)
and thus inferred the variable spin. But wobble
and spin are the three components of one vector,
and for geophysical processes the observations of
latitude and time had better be discussed together. Here were wonderful opportunities for
learning new things about the planet Earth.

In the meantime, Munk continued to work on
ocean waves. With Charles Cox he photographed
the glitter of the Sun on the water and from that
pattern learned something about the statistics of
surface slope. These statistics are largely governed by short gravity waves and ripples, and
for a while Munk's interest was in the micro
scale of surface disturbances.

Subsequently, Munk and Frank Snodgrass
undertook a study of waves of ever decreasing
frequencies. They observed very long swells in
the Pacific which they estimated must have come
from a distance of 12,000 km. The Pacific being
too small, they surmised that the source of the
swells was in the Indian Ocean and that the
waves had entered the Pacific along a great-
circle route through the Tasman Sea. They then
built a simple array for measuring wave direction that confirmed the direction of this antipodal swell. Later they established six stations
along a great-circle route extending from Australia to Alaska and were able to follow the
propagation of a disturbance across the entire
Pacific.

At the frequency of a few cycles per hour
ocean waves are low, but they have the fascinating characteristic of being trapped by the continental shelf in the manner of a wave guide. At

still lower frequencies the effect of the tide-producing forces becomes dominant. With Dave Cartwright, Munk attempted to improve the means of tide prediction, a subject little developed since the days of Lord Kelvin and Sir George Darwin. Munk planned to make direct measurements of tides in the open sea by means of self-contained capsules that are dropped to the sea floor, record there, and subsequently transmit their data acoustically to a surface vessel.

At even lower frequencies one gets into oscillations of the ocean more akin to variable ocean currents than ordinary waves, with the effect of the Earth's rotation being dominant. At still lower frequencies, recorded fluctuations in sea level appear to be associated with climatic fluctuations, including the melting and freezing of ice, and to the up and down movements of the continents.

Munk came to the United States in 1932. He received a B.S. in applied physics from the California Institute of Technology in 1939. Summer work with Harold Sverdrup and Roger Revelle at the University of California's Scripps Institution of Oceanography turned his interests toward the ocean. He received an M.S. in geophysics in 1941 from Caltech and a Ph.D. in oceanography in 1947 from the University of California. He was appointed assistant professor (1947), associate professor (1949), and professor of geophysics (1954) at the Scripps Institution. From 1959 he served also as associate director of the University of California's Institute of Physics and Planetary Physics and as director of its La Jolla Laboratories. He was elected to the National Academy of Sciences in 1956, to the American Academy of Arts and Sciences in 1957, and to the American Philosophical Society in 1965.

Munk wrote *The Rotation of the Earth: A Geophysical Discussion*, with G. J. F. Macdonald (1961).

For background information *see* EARTH (ORBITAL MOTION); OCEAN WAVES in the McGraw-Hill Encyclopedia of Science and Technology.   □

★ MURRAY, Robert George Everitt

Canadian bacteriologist
Born May 19, 1919, Ruislip, England

THE BACTERIA, although small and seemingly simple in structure, have yielded information to the cytologist about cell organization, and the correlation of structure and function, that is of considerable significance in modern approaches to fundamental biology. Not least among the consequences of cytological observa-

tions on these microbes has been a clear definition of the unique properties of the bacteria in the realm of living things. It is in the consolidation of the diverse observations necessary to these ends that the studies made by Murray and his close colleagues had their greatest impact.

Murray spent virtually his whole academic life in the University of Western Ontario in a small department of bacteriology and immunology within the Faculty of Medicine. Pressures to provide consultative and diagnostic services in clinical bateriology in a busy general hospital were not particularly encouraging to academic research. However, such pressures made the diversion of microscopic cytology, and observations on the nature and morphology of a wide range of bacteria, an attractive recreation. Murray was joined in 1949 by a pioneer in the field, Carl F. Robinow, and shortly after by a former student, P. C. Fitz-James; they have worked closely together since then with quite individual interests but with a common interest in cytology to hold them together. Murray's initial research centered on bacteriophage infection, a pursuit prompted by his first chief, I. N. Asheshov, and the cytological events following infection with virulent bacterial viruses. This research put into practice some simple cytochemical methods so that biochemical and morphological events could be correlated. The 1940s were a time of great excitement and development in studies on bacteriophage, and the cytological studies added a minor but illuminating perspective to complex intracellular processes. With J. F. Whitfield, Murray explored the comparative cytology of phage infection, including the process of temperate infections (lysogeny).

It was apparent that knowledge of the intimate structure of the surface of bacterial cells, and of a clear definition of the presence, nature, and function of the surface membranes, was deficient. Murray's colleague Robinow pioneered in the definition of structures, using light microscopy, and they collaborated (1953) on an effective demonstration of the plasma membrane and cell wall behavior, using the very best possibilities of fixation and preparation, staining, and photomicrography. At this time electron microscopy was beginning to show its possibilities; embedding (after E. Borysko) and sectioning (after G. B. Chapman, J. F. Hillier, and F. Sjöstrand) for studying internal cellular details in profile were adding a new dimension to the preparations of whole cells and cell fragments (after T. F. Anderson and S. Mudd). Also coincident were the studies in England of the chemistry and electron microscopic structure of isolated wall fragments (M. R. J. Salton and R. W. Horne) and the observations in Holland on superficial macromolecular arrays on cell walls (A. L. Houwink). Murray acquired for his department an electron microscope in 1953, an instrument that served him and his colleagues effectively ever since.

At first a few organisms were exemplary objects for exploratory research (for example, in the demonstration of the plasma membrane in profile), but soon the need to compare structure and arrangement in a wide range of bacteria forced diversification. Correlation with light microscopy was always attempted, and much effort was directed toward lifelike preservation of the form of cells, as well as components such as elaborations of plasma membrane (for example, the "mesosomes" described by his colleague Fitz-James) or the nucleoids and their behavior according to the cation balance.

Murray's comparative studies led to generalizations concerning the profile of cell walls and particularly the distinctions between those of gram-positive and gram-negative bacteria. This interest led naturally to attempts to perceive more of the plan view of layers of wall and the arrangement of the component macromolecules (especially of rewarding objects such as *Micrococcus radiodurans, Spirillum serpens, Lampropedia hyalina,* and *Bacillus polymyxa* with various colleagues).

The burgeoning knowledge of cell wall chemistry and interference with the behavior of individual components by reagents such as antibiotics led naturally to Murray's interest in the localization of component polymers in profile and in plan. He made some effective observations on the early lesions in the developing cell wall septum (a "growing point" for the wall) due to the action of penicillin. More recently he focused his attention on the localization of the mucopeptide (murein) in complex gram-negative walls, the differential behavior of these layers and the equally complex but more superficial wall components, and the processes of cell wall septum formation and cell division. The old problems continued to interest Murray: the preservation of cells in lifelike state for cytological study and the detection of artefact.

As a corollary to the wide range of his cytological inquiries into the bacteria and their relatives, Murray was led into taxonomy, with a deep curiosity concerning the nature of bacteria. He discussed their systematic position and, coincidentally with an essay by R. Y. Stanier and C. B. van Niel, tried to describe them in modern terms. These descriptions helped to crystallize modern opinion that the bacteria and the other blue-green algae are procaryotic organisms and that they are distinct in nuclear organization and some other respects (such as the nature of the cell walls) from all other living things.

Murray was the son of a distinguished professor of bacteriology, Everitt G. D. Murray, who made pioneer studies of dysentery bacilli, meningococci, and *Listeria monocytogenes,* and who was among the first to undertake serological typing of a bacterial species. Murray studied zoology at McGill University and received his B.A. in 1941 and his M.A. in pathology and bacteriology in 1946 from Cambridge University. He received an M.D., C.M. from McGill University in 1943. After an internship and a period as a medical officer (captain) in the Royal Canadian Army Medical Corps, he became in 1945 lecturer in bacteriology and immunology in the University of Western Ontario. In 1949 he became professor and head of the department as well as chief of the bacteriology service, Victoria Hospital. This direct hospital association continued until 1965, when the department took up new quarters. He played a part in the founding of the Canadian Society of Microbiologists in 1950, and was its first president in 1951–52. He was awarded the Harrison Prize of the Royal Society of Canada in 1957 and the Award of the Canadian Society of Microbiologists in 1963.

Murray was an associate editor of the *Journal of Bacteriology* during 1950–56 and *Bacteriological Reviews,* beginning in 1965. He was the first editor of the *Canadian Journal of Microbiology* during 1954–60.

For background information *see* BACTERIAL CELL CHEMISTRY; BACTERIOPHAGE; CELL (BIOLOGICAL); CELL MEMBRANES AND MONOLAYERS in the McGraw-Hill Encyclopedia of Science and Technology.   □

★ NACHMANSOHN, David

American biochemist
Born Mar. 17, 1899, Jekaterinoslav, Russia

Nachmansohn's work presents the first breakthrough in the understanding of the chemical reactions controlling the permeability cycle in excitable membranes during electrical activity. Knowledge of these reactions is essential to understand the mechanism by which nerve impulses are propagated along nerve and muscle fibers. When he became interested in 1936 in the role of acetylcholine (ACh) in nerve activity, Nachmansohn introduced the notions and principles of biochemistry into a field which until then was nearly exclusively the domain of classical electrophysiology and pharmacology. Observations with these classical methods suggested the hypothesis that ACh is a neurohumoral transmitter of impulses across junctions, that is, between nerve and nerve or nerve and effector cell. The biochemical data very early suggested a much more general role of ACh. During the past two decades Nachmansohn and his associates accumulated evidence supporting the assumption of the essential role of ACh in the permeability cycle of excitable membranes. The action of ACh on a receptor protein apparently induces conformational changes with a shift of charge, involving probably the release of Ca^{++} ions and leading to a breakdown of the barriers for ion movements; the enzyme ACh-esterase rapidly, in a few millionths of a second, hydrolyzes and thereby inactivates the ester; the receptor returns to its resting state, and the barrier for the ion movements is reestablished. While it was widely recognized since the turn of the century that ions must be the carriers of bioelectricity in a fluid system, such as the living cell, Nachmansohn insisted emphatically that such a process in cellular membranes must involve the action of proteins and enzymes. This view, shared by most biochemists, has been accepted in recent years by many biologists. His contributions provided not only pertinent information about the macromolecules involved in the elementary process of conduction but also initiated several developments in the field of biochemistry and enzyme chemistry in general.

In 1937 Nachmansohn introduced the use of electric organs from electric fish to investigate the biochemical basis of bioelectrogenesis. These organs are the most powerful bioelectric generators created by nature; in addition, they are highly specialized for this function. They are capable of splitting 2 to 4 kg of ACh/kg tissue (fresh weight), although they contain only 3% protein and 92% water. In 1938 the enzyme ACh-esterase was for the first time isolated from electric tissue and subsequently purified several-hundred-fold. The active enzyme preparation obtained was instrumental in the studies of the molecular forces in the active site. The notions developed by Nachmansohn and his collaborators about the enzymatic mechanism of ester hydrolysis were borne out during the last decade by studies of many other ester-splitting enzymes. Recently, W. Leuzinger and L. A. Baker crystallized ACh-esterase from electric tissue and thus opened the way for studying the properties and structure of the enzyme protein.

Nachmansohn's studies with ACh-esterase also provided much insight into the mechanism of the action of inhibitors. This information was of particular importance in the case of organophosphates, to which belong the famous nerve gases, powerful potential chemical warfare agents, and also many widely used insecticides. The lethal action of these compounds is due to the irreversible inhibition of ACh-esterase. The understanding of the mechanism of organophosphate poisoning led to the development of an efficient antidote in Nachmansohn's laboratory: pyridine-2-aldoxime methiodide (2-PAM). This compound, synthesized by I. B. Wilson and S. Ginsburg, and independently and simultaneously by English investigators, reverses the action of many insecticides in vitro; it was shown by H. Kewitz to be a powerful antidote in animals. It is used today all over the world to treat cases of insecticide poisoning. It has saved many lives, especially in countries such as Japan where large-scale use of insecticides is vital for food protection.

Nachmansohn's studies on the sequence of energy transformations associated with electrical activity led in 1943 to the discovery of the enzymatic acetylation obtained in solution and ACh. The acetylation of choline was the first enzymatic acetylation obtained in solution and the first in which ATP hydrolysis was shown to provide the energy; the requirement of a coenzyme in this reaction was also recognized. These observations initiated a decade of intensive studies on acetylation and the role of the coenzyme, referred to by F. A. Lipmann as coenzyme A, in intermediary metabolism and the reaction mechanisms involved.

Nachmansohn's theory of the essential role of ACh in the excitable membranes during electrical activity was first based on the evidence that powerful specific and competitive inhibitors of ACh-esterase or of ACh-receptor block electrical activity. In the last few years strong new evidence for this view was offered by his associates, in particular W.-D. Dettbarn, F. C. G. Hoskin, and P. Rosenberg. Direct actions of ACh and curare, long believed to act on junctions only, were obtained on excitable membranes of nerve fibers. These results were obtained either by using suitable preparations or after chemical treatment, for instance, with snake venoms, by which the structural barriers are reduced, thereby permitting the compounds to act on the receptor protein in the excitable membrane; before treatment they are unable to penetrate and reach the receptor. Studies with electron microscopy combined with histochemical staining techniques made by several investigators showed recently that ACh-esterase is strictly localized in excitable membranes of nerve fibers, as well as in the membranes at the two sides of the junctions. These developments substantiated the unified concept according to which the action of ACh in axonal conduction and synaptic transmission is similar. Many of the differences between these two events were explained in terms of structure and organization.

Nachmansohn was brought up in Germany and attended a gymnasium with strong emphasis on Greek, Latin, and the humanities. He received an M.D. from the University of Berlin in 1926. After his medical training he studied biochemistry and enzyme chemistry in P. Rona's laboratory at the University of Berlin from 1924 to 1926. His scientific development was decisively influenced by the years spent in the Kaiser Wilhelm Institute of Biology in Berlin-Dahlem with Otto Meyerhof. In 1933 he left Germany and spent 6 years at the University of Paris. He went to the United States on an invitation from Yale University and then joined Columbia University in 1942, where he became a professor of biochemistry. During the war he helped the Army Chemical Center in the work on organophosphates. He was elected to the American Academy of Arts and Sciences in 1964 and to the National Academy of Sciences in 1965. Among other honors, he received the Pasteur and Nicloux Medals from the Society of Biological Chemistry in Paris.

Nachmansohn's work and that of his associates resulted in more than 300 papers in English, French, and German. He wrote *Chemical and Molecular Basis of Nerve Activity* (1959).

For background information *see* ACETYLATION; ACETYLCHOLINE; BIOELECTRIC MODEL;

NERVOUS SYSTEM in the McGraw-Hill Encyclopedia of Science and Technology. □

★ NEEL, James Van Gundia

American geneticist
Born Mar. 22, 1915, Hamilton, Ohio, U.S.A.

SHORTLY AFTER completing his training in both genetics and medicine, Neel found himself in 1946 on the verge of military service. The possible genetic consequences of the atomic bombings of Hiroshima and Nagasaki were then a topic of lively discussion, and the need for appropriate studies was clear. A fortuitous chain of circumstances resulted in military orders assigning him to a group considering the feasibility of long-range investigations on the bombs' effects —and thus began a series of studies in human population genetics, which continued over the years.

The population geneticist is interested in the factors which determine both the genetic similarities and differences between various ethnic groups. These similarities and differences are based on the frequency of occurrence in these populations of specific genes. Thus, one population, such as eastern Europeans, may have a high frequency of persons of blood type B, while another population, such as the American Indian, may lack the gene responsible for that trait. These differences are thought to result from the interplay of opposing forces, namely, mutation, which introduces new genes into populations, and selection and random loss, which tend to eliminate genes which do not serve a useful function in that particular population.

Experimental geneticists documented the occurrence of spontaneous mutation early in the history of genetics, and in 1927 H. J. Muller demonstrated that the rate of occurrence of mutations could be greatly accelerated in fruit flies exposed to x-irradiation. However, in 1946 little was known about spontaneous mutation rates in man and still less about the effects of exposure to radiation. The scientific challenge in Japan was to organize a system to collect highly accurate data on the kinds of children being born to exposed survivors, as well as to a suitable control group, the latter similar to the former in all respects except for exposure to atomic bombing. The possible indicators of bomb effects which it seemed feasible to study in postwar Japan were sex ratio, frequency of stillbirth, birth weight, frequency of congenital defect, and survival rates and developmental characteristics of live-born children. Since all of these indicators are influenced by many factors in addition to radiation, good control data on the offspring of similar but unexposed persons were crucial.

The resulting study, which extended over 20 years and involved many collaborators, was part of the total program of the Atomic Bomb Casualty Commission. From the earliest days W. J. Schull was a principal colleague in the study. Differing numbers of children born to both the exposed and the unexposed (control) parents were recorded for the various indicators, 73,362 with respect to congenital defects and birth weight, but 140,542 for the sex ratio. Thus far no conclusive effects of the exposure have been demonstrated. Since, however, radiation of this type has produced mutations in all properly studied experimental organisms, it cannot be concluded that there were no ill effects from the exposure in Hiroshima and Nagasaki, but only that those effects cannot be demonstrated under these circumstances. On the other hand, this lack of statistically significant effects can be used to set upper limits to the genetic effects of radiation—Schull and Neel calculated that the minimum amount of radiation to produce the same frequency of mutations as occurs spontaneously each generation (a critical figure in many attempts to understand radiation effects) is about 100 roentgens. This is a significantly higher estimate than that previously used as a reference point.

Early in the planning of the Hiroshima-Nagasaki studies, it became apparent that in these two cities some 7% of all the married couples were cousins. By virtue of the insertion of a question into the basic questionnaire used, 5129 births to cousins were registered in the course of the study, of which 4526 were to parents receiving little or no radiation. Since the outcome of cousin marriages is one of the best indices to the kinds of hidden recessive genes human populations carry, this was most unusual material. It had the particular advantage that each pregnancy was ascertained before the child was born, so that it was a prospective study rather than a retrospective one, without the opportunities for concealment and bias in the latter. When the bulk of the studies on atomic bomb effects were completed, Neel, in association with Schull and Japanese colleagues T. Yanase, N. Fujiki, and K. Ohkura, engaged in follow-up studies of these children—the most extensive on this subject to date. The study demonstrates that in the children of first-cousin marriages, the death rate up to an average age of 8 years was 1.5% greater than in control children, and that significant medical conditions were 3.0% more common. These effects are smaller than in many previous studies, quite possibly because the way the material was collected eliminates many of the biases of previous studies. From these findings it could be calculated that the average Japanese carries the equivalent of one gene which when homozygous would cause death.

Another outgrowth of these studies was the collection from the control material of extensive data on congenital defects in Japan. Interestingly, despite the differing diet and disease experience of the Japanese, the total frequency of congenital defect in Japan is about the same as in the United States, although there were significant differences (in both directions) in the frequency of a number of specific defects. These studies, with others, point to many congenital defects being due to a combination of a complex genetic background and a variety of environmental and physiological variables.

While the accumulation of much of these data was in progress, Neel was involved in a series of studies at the University of Michigan on the spontaneous rate of mutation of human genes; these studies were designed to provide a base line for comparison with the Japanese findings. He also engaged in studies of the genetic basis for sickle-cell anemia. At the same time that L. C. Pauling and colleagues were showing that the ultimate basis for the disease was a defective hemoglobin molecule, Neel was demonstrating that the anemia was under the control of a single "incompletely recessive" gene. The two studies thus complemented one another in the demonstration that genes control the genetic structure of proteins, a demonstration extended by V. Ingram in 1958 with the discovery that the ultimate basis for the anemia was the substitution of just one amino acid (valine) for another (glutamic acid). In other studies Neel, in collaboration with H. Itano and W. Zuelzer, discovered several additional hemoglobin abnormalities and developed a theory of the localization of the genes controlling hemoglobin synthesis in a single chromosome.

In recent years Neel's interests increasingly turned toward the study of some of the relatively few surviving populations of primitive American Indians, on the thesis that an understanding of the mating structure and agents of natural selection at this cultural level might shed light on a number of aspects of modern man. These studies, carried out in the remote jungles of Brazil and Venezuela, with the cooperation of F. Salzano and M. Layrisse, raised the possibility that many of the genetic differences between ethnic groups of modern man may depend as much on chance as on the operation of natural selection.

Neel received his A.B. (1935) from the College of Wooster and his Ph.D. (1939) at the University of Rochester. He was instructor of zoology at Dartmouth College in 1939–41, then returned to Rochester for his M.D. (1944). He was an intern in 1944–45 and assistant resident in medicine in 1945–46 at Strong Memorial and Rochester Municipal hospitals and was director of field studies for the Atomic Bomb Casualty Commission of the National Research Council in 1947–48. At the University of Michigan Medical School he was assistant professor of internal medicine (1949–51) and associate professor (1951–56). He became professor of human genetics and chairman of the department of human genetics in 1956, and in 1957 was also appointed professor of internal medicine. He received the Lasker Award of the American Public Health Association in 1960 and the Allan Award of the American Society of Human Genetics in 1965. He was elected to the National Academy of Sciences in 1963 and to the American Philosophical Society in 1965.

For background information *see* GENE ACTION; HUMAN GENETICS; LETHAL GENE; MUTATION; RADIATION INJURY (BIOLOGY) in the McGraw-Hill Encyclopedia of Science and Technology. □

★ NÉEL, Louis Eugène Félix

French physicist
Born Nov. 22, 1904, Lyon, France

IT HAS been known since 1927, from the work of W. Heisenberg, that the actions between the atomic magnetic moments which give rise to ferromagnetism are actions at a very short distance between closely neighboring atoms: At very low temperature the magnetic moments of neighboring atoms align parallel to each other. About 1930 Néel suggested that there should likewise exist interactions capable of bringing about antiparallel alignment of the magnetic moments of two closely adjacent atoms. It could then be imagined that at very low temperature the atoms of a crystal divide into two families, termed sublattices, crystallographically identical, so that the magnetic moments of the atoms of one of the two sublattices are directed in a certain direction and those of the other in the inverse direction. The atoms closely neighboring a given atom of one of the sublattices belong

totally or predominantly to the other sublattice. When the temperature is raised, the ordered orientation of the magnetic moments disappears at a certain temperature θ_N, called the Néel temperature, denoted by anomalies in the specific heat and analogous in expansion to those of ferromagnetic substances. The spontaneous magnetizations of the two sublattices are oriented in opposite directions and thus mutually cancel each other; the action of a magnetic field slightly deforms the antiparallel arrangement, giving rise to a paramagnetism which is independent of temperature. Thus a new category of magnetic substances, termed antiferromagnetic, made its appearance in science. The first examples (NiO, MnO) were subsequently discovered in 1937 by Bizette and Tsai.

In 1947 Néel generalized these concepts by supposing that the two sublattices may not be equivalent and that their spontaneous magnetizations, always aligned in opposite directions, are unequal. In this way a new class of substances is obtained whose properties share at the same time those of the ferromagnetics and the antiferromagnetics. They are the ferrimagnetics. Generalizing the notion of P. Weiss regarding the molecular field and introducing three molecular fields characterizing the magnetic interactions in the interior of each of the two sublattices and between the two sublattices, Néel showed that the reciprocal of the magnetic susceptibility of a ferrimagnetic varies as a function of temperature according to a hyperbolic law, and no longer according to the linear Curie-Weiss law for ferromagnetics. Thus the properties of the spinel ferrites and the magnetite

ferrites were explained. These are the longest-known ferromagnetic substances, which up to this point constituted an enigma. In 1956 these concepts inspired the discovery by Bertaut and Forrat, and the interpretation by Pauthenet, of the garnet ferrites of the rare earths, which today have very important technological applications. These substances possess not two but three sublattices.

Another important series of researches by Néel was based on the importance of the role of the internal demagnetizing fields in the properties of ferromagnetic substances. For example, in supposing simply that the internal demagnetizing fields are null for energetic reasons, he was able to develop a theory of magnetization of monocrystals based on the existence of modes and phases, which permit the interpretation of a great number of hitherto unexplained results. Indeed, in a perfect crystal a certain number—variable depending on external conditions—of phases coexist. Each phase is made up of elementary domains whose spontaneous magnetizations are parallel. Similarly Néel was able to specify in simple cases the details of the subdivision of a ferromagnetic substance into elementary domains, the formation of domains having a special form (Néel's spikes) around inclusions or cavities, and the formation in very thin layers of walls of separation between the elementary domains of a special type, the Néel walls, whose structure is very different from the ordinary Bloch walls.

Néel gave special attention to magnetic creep, that is, to variations in the magnetization of ferromagnetic substances with time, and showed that it is necessary to distinguish two classes of creep. These are, on the one hand, creep due to thermal fluctuations, common to all ferromagnetic substances, and on the other hand, diffusion creep, associated with changes in the distribution of certain atoms in the crystal accompanying the variations in orientation of the spontaneous magnetization, for example, of the atoms of carbon in an iron crystal. This creep, moreover, constitutes one of the aspects of directional order, that is, a particular order at short distance which becomes established in an alloy composed of atoms A and B: The frequency of a bond AB between closely neighboring atoms A and B depends on the angle formed by the direction AB with the local direction of spontaneous magnetization. These phenomena play a major role in the magnetic orientation and in the improvement of magnetic properties by annealing in a magnetic field.

Néel likewise studied the special properties of very fine grain ferromagnetics and explained the remarkable "magnetic memory" exhibited by bricks, basalts, lavas, and so forth. This memory made it possible to retrace the history of the terrestrial magnetic field during the course of geological eras. In the same way, and with the collaboration of L. Weil, Néel discovered and developed in 1941 a new class of permanent magnets whose properties are due essentially to the subdivision of the ferromagnetic substance into very fine grains. Néel likewise showed that the antiferromagnetic substances in very fine grains should possess extraordinary properties, even as far as following the Curie law like isolated magnetic atoms.

At the start of World War II, Néel was charged with the protection of French fighting ships against magnetic mines. He invented and developed, with excellent results, a procedure termed neutralization, which consisted in giving to the ship a permanent magnetization in a direction opposite to the terrestrial magnetic field.

After studies at the Ecole Normale Supérieure (Agrégé de l'université, 1928; Docteur ès sciences, 1932), Néel was professor at the University of Strasbourg, where he succeeded to the chair of Pierre Weiss in 1937. In 1947 he became a professor at the University of Grenoble and gave great impetus to the research institutions of that city. He served also as director of the Polytechnic Institute and of the Center for Nuclear Studies of Grenoble and represented France on the NATO Scientific Council. A Grand Officer of the Legion of Honor, he was awarded the Gold Medal of the National Center for Scientific Research, the Holweck Medal of the Institute of Physics, London, and numerous honorary degrees. He was elected a member of the Academy of Sciences of Paris and foreign member of the academies of science of Moscow, Amsterdam, Halle, and Bucharest, of the Royal Society of London, and of the American Academy of Arts and Sciences.

For background information *see* ANTIFERROMAGNETISM; FERROMAGNETISM; MAGNETIC THIN FILMS; MAGNETIZATION in the McGraw-Hill Encyclopedia of Science and Technology.   □

★ NESMEYANOV, Alexander Nikolaevich

Soviet chemist
Born Sept. 9, 1899, Moscow, Russia

NESMEYANOV'S RESEARCH was concerned with three fields of organic chemistry: organometallic chemistry, including both nontransition and transition elements; organic chemistry of nonmetallic elements; and organic chemistry as such.

His first publication in 1929 on organometallic chemistry described a new "double diazonium salt" (that is, diazo) method for preparation of organomercury compounds, such as ArHgHAl and Ar_2Hg. (In this article Ar = aromatic, M = metal, X = halogen.) On the one hand, he applied this method for preparation of other organometallic compounds, such as Ar_2TlX, Ar_2SnX_2, Ar_2PbX_2, $ArSbX_2$, Ar_2SbX, Ar_3Sb, and Ar_3Bi,

on the other hand, he utilized the readily available organomercury compounds for synthesis of organometallic compounds of some other metals (Zn, Cd, Al, and Sn) by interchange reactions, as shown in Eqs. (1), (2), and (3). Reverse

$$M^nX_n + HgAr_2 \longrightarrow Ar_mM^nX_{n-m} + ArHgX \quad (1)$$

$$M^n + HgAr_2 \longrightarrow M^nAr_n + Hg \quad (2)$$

$$SnX_2 + HgAr_2 \longrightarrow Ar_2SnX_2 + Hg \quad (3)$$

reactions of transfer of the radical bonded with B, Sn, Pb, Sb, As, and others, to mercury under the action of $HgCl_2$ were also investigated. The method for synthesis of compounds such as ArHgAr' was found in this way.

As to the structure of the adducts of mercury salts to the olefins and acetylenes, a question arose whether these are π-complexes or addition compounds formed via disruption of the π-bond. The study of these adducts showed that they are "quasi complexes," no longer having a double (or triple) bond and resembling π-complexes only in the ease of β-elimination of the olefin (or acetylene). Along with the strictly chemical arguments, one of a categoric basis for this conclusion was the discovery of the cis-trans isomerism of the quasi-complex adducts of $HgCl_2$ to acetylene—the β-chlorovinylmercuric chlorides (and a number of their derivatives)—and of the cis-trans isomerism of adducts of $SbCl_5$ to acetylene.

As a result of research on the interchange between the metal in mercury and antimony compounds of this type and other metals in electrophilic (Eq. 1) and homolytic substitution reactions (Eqs. 2 and 3), a rule of the retention of the configuration in electrophilic and homolytic substitution on the olefinic carbon atom was published in 1948. This rule was then confirmed for many olefin metal derivatives, such as stereo-isomers of propenyl lithium in reactions with metal salts and organic molecules. The rule of

the retention of the configuration was extended to the tetrahedric carbon atom in S_E2 reactions, as the next stage of this research.

The same method that was applied for determining the structure of quasi complexes, that is, establishing the existence of cis-trans isomers, was also used for solution of the problem of the structure and dual reactivity (at the C and O atoms) of magnesium and alkali metal enolates. The conventional hypothesis of a mesomeric enolate anion capable of reacting at the C and O terminal atoms was found to be unsatisfactory, as metal enolates exist in cis and trans forms and keep these forms in O alkylation, and yet are capable of C alkylation. A contrary phenomenon was discovered in the same way for mercury compounds. The monomercury derivatives of aldehydes and ketones, prepared for the first time, appeared to be compounds with a C-Hg bond that are incapable of tautomeric interconversions and yet show dual reactivity, for instance, tritylation and acylation at both the C and O atoms. Such "pseudomeric" behavior was explained by a shift of the reaction center of the molecule along a system of conjugated (or hyperconjugated) bonds. This phenomenon was differentiated from tautomeric phenomena as reversible interconversions between isomeric forms.

A classification of the conjugation phenomena ($\pi\pi$, $p\pi$, pp, $\sigma\pi$, and σp), of the reaction center shift, and of the differentiation of tautomerism from these phenomena was given in a plenary session of the International Union for Pure and Applied Chemistry meeting in Zurich in 1954 and in a paper with M. I. Kabachnik (1955). Later research revealed the unique phenomenon of metallotropic tautomerism for heavy metals (Hg, Pb, Sn) but not for alkali metals. In this field of Nesmeyanov's investigations, organometallic chemistry was interlaced with organic chemistry, and the former gave theoretical grounds for the latter. Monometallic and bimetallic olefin derivatives were extensively studied later.

In the field of transition metal chemistry, a method for preparing Group VI metal carbonyls by the action of carbon monoxide on higher halides of these metals in the presence of a reducing agent was reported as far back as 1940. From 1952 onward intensive investigations were carried out of sandwich compounds, especially ferrocene, for which certain aromatic substitution reactions were observed: Friedel-Crafts alkylation, metalation to form lithium and sodium derivatives, sulfonation, arylation, condensation with aldehydes and ketones, and particularly the "ricochet" reaction—direct cyanation. Boron and halide derivatives, amines, hydroxy compounds and their derivatives, and diazo and azo derivatives of ferrocene were prepared and investigated for the first time. Substitution of a benzene ring for one of the cyclopentadienyls was found, and a number of isomeric derivatives with chloro, hydroxy, and amino substituents in the phenyl and cyclopentadienyl ligands, as well as photodecomposition of the substituted ferrocenes to the ylides, were studied. The effect of substituents in the ring on the redox potential, on the acidity of carboxy derivatives, and so forth was described quantitatively and related to the Hammet-Taft equation. The inability of substituted ferrocene to undergo the usual rearrangement in the aromatic ring was established. Similar research was carried out for ruthenocene and cyclopentadienyltricarbonyl-manganese and -rhenium. The regular effect of acyl, halo, and alkoxy ligands on NMR shifts for titanium sandwich compounds was established, and monocyclopentadienyltitanium derivatives were investigated in detail.

A number of dimetallic carbonyls with $M(I)$-$M(II)$ bonds were described and studied. A method for preparation of diaryliodonium salts by arylation of ICl_3 was reported. It was shown in 1928 that diphenyliodonium salts are formed by decomposition of double diazonium salts with HgI_2. Later on diphenylbromonium salts were prepared by the same method. Triphenyloxonium, diphenylbromonium, and diphenylchloronium salts were prepared for the first time by the action of phenyldiazonium tetrafluoroborate on diphenyl oxide and phenyl halides. The reactions of these unexpectedly stable compounds were studied extensively.

Interchange reactions involving the halogen in chlorovinylketones (and their mechanism) were studied by kinetic and stereochemical methods. A method for synthesis of certain five- and six-membered heterocyclic compounds from chlorovinylketones was reported. The telomerization reactions of ethylene with CCl_4 and their products were investigated in some detail, and some syntheses were developed on this basis (the "enant" fiber); tetrachloroalkanes, such as $Cl(CH_2CH_2)_nCCl_3$, as well as hydroxy- and amino-trichloroalkanes, and hydroxy and amino acids prepared from these compounds were investigated extensively.

In recent years Nesmeyanov studied the problem of synthetic food—synthetic caviar being the first result obtained.

All this research was carried out by Nesmeyanov with numerous colleagues, among whom were O. A. Reutov, R. K. Freydlina, and N. K. Kochetkov.

Nesmeyanov graduated from the physico-mathematical faculty at Moscow State University in 1922 and completed a postgraduate course there in 1924. He was awarded a doctorate in chemical science in 1934. He was appointed professor in Moscow State University's department of chemistry in 1934 and from 1948 to 1951 was rector of this university. He took an active part in organizing the new Moscow State University on Leninskie Gory. Nesmeyanov became a corresponding member of the Academy of Sciences of the U.S.S.R. in 1939, a member in 1943, a member of its presidium in 1946, and was president of the Academy from 1951 to 1961. He was director of the Academy's Institute of Organic Chemistry from 1939 to 1954, when he became director of the Institute of Hetero-organic Compounds, organized by him. His memberships in foreign scientific societies and academies included the Indian National Institute of Sciences (1955), the American Academy of Arts and Sciences (1960), and the Royal Society of London (1961), as well as the Royal Society of Edinburgh and the academies of Berlin, Poland, Hungary, Rumania, Czechoslovakia, and Bulgaria. He was an honorary member of the Society of Chemical Industry. He received honorary degrees from the universities of Calcutta (1957), Jena (1958), Paris (1964), and Bordeaux (1966). Nesmeyanov was awarded a State Prize in 1942, the Lomonosov Gold Medal in 1961, a Lenin Prize in 1965, five Lenin Orders, and the Red Banner Order.

More than 500 papers by Nesmeyanov were published. His *Selected Works in Organic Chemistry* (4 vols., 1959) was condensed to one volume and published in England (1964). Nesmeyanov edited the series *Methods of Elementoorganic Chemistry*, with R. A. Sokolik (4 vols., 1967). He wrote *A Handbook of Magnesium-Organic Compounds*, with S. T. Yoffe (3 vols., 1956).

For background information *see* ISOMERISM, MOLECULAR; ORGANIC CHEMISTRY; ORGANOMETALLIC COMPOUND; TRANSITION ELEMENTS in the McGraw-Hill Encyclopedia of Science and Technology.   □

★ NEURATH, Hans

American biochemist
Born Oct. 29, 1909, Vienna, Austria

NEURATH DEVOTED 30 years of his research to an understanding of the relation between the chemical structure and biological function of proteins. He approached this fundamental problem with a wide variety of chemical, physical, and biological procedures, some of which he himself developed. His most important contributions dealt with the chemical properties and enzymatic functions of protein-digesting enzymes, notably pancreatic trypsin, chymotrypsin, and carboxypeptidase. His studies de-

lineated major features of the specificity of these enzymes, the nature of the active site, and the formation of these enzymes from inactive precursors, a process commonly known as zymogen activation. With G. W. Schwert, Neurath discovered the ability of these enzymes to split ester bonds and, with K. A. Walsh, he determined for the first time the amino acid sequence of bovine trypsin.

Neurath's work on proteins began at a time when the protein molecule was considered to be a colloid of ill-defined composition and structure. His early studies were therefore concerned with the characterization of the contour of protein molecules in terms of size and shape as determined by hydrodynamic procedures, such as diffusion and viscosity measurements. A significant period of his research was concerned with the changes in these properties that occur during denaturation of proteins by heating or by certain organic reagents (for example, urea), processes which lead to the loss of biological function. In order to correlate such changes with quantitative biological measurements, he turned his attention to a study of antibodies and to the effects of denaturation on the interaction of antibodies with native and denatured antigens. Neurath's pure academic research was interrupted by World War II, and he was asked to head a research team to study the occurrence of false-positive reactions in the serological diagnosis for syphilis. After approximately 4 years Neurath and co-workers turned their attention once again to the problem of structure and function relationship of proteins. This was the beginning of 20 years' uninterrupted effort to elucidate the mechanism of action of proteolytic enzymes.

The pancreatic enzymes carboxypeptidase, chymotrypsin, and trypsin were selected for this purpose because J. H. Northrop, M. Kunitz, and M. Anson of the Rockefeller Institute had previously described procedures for the isolation of these enzymes and their inactive precursors (zymogens) from bovine pancreatic tissues. Carboxypeptidase in particular proved to be an important enzyme for further study, since its molecular properties and substrate specificity were largely unknown. In the course of a search for synthetic substrates for these enzymes, Neurath and co-workers discovered that all three enzymes were capable of splitting ester (carbon-oxygen) bonds in compounds that otherwise resemble peptide substrates in structure and wherein carbon-nitrogen bonds are normally cleaved by these enzymes. The mechanism of formation of these enzymes from inactive precursors was elucidated first for chymotrypsin and trypsin and later for carboxypeptidase, and a common pattern of activation was clearly established. Together with B. L. Vallee, he discovered that carboxypeptidase was a metalloenzyme containing one atom of zinc per molecule, this metal atom being essential for catalytic function. In later work, with Walsh, the chemical structure (amino acid sequence) of bovine trypsinogen was determined. Comparison with the amino acid sequence of chymotrypsinogen indicated sufficient detailed resemblance, particularly in those regions of the molecule which had been previously implicated as being components of the active site, to suggest that both enzymes originated from a common primordial form. In further pursuit of this idea, pancreatic enzymes from other species were isolated and characterized, notably from the dogfish, a species which developed early in biological evolution. Sufficient similarity in chemical structure and enzymatic function was found to sustain the idea of a common molecular pattern in the evolution of these pancreatic enzymes.

Neurath, whose father was professor of pediatrics at the University of Vienna, received his education at that university, where he received a Ph.D. in physical chemistry in 1933. His dissertation was carried out in the laboratories of the colloid chemist Wolfgang Pauli, father of the theoretical physicist of the same name. After postdoctoral studies at the University of London under F. G. Donnan and the University of Minnesota, Neurath held a position at Cornell University during 1936–38. From 1938 to 1950 he rose through the academic ranks at Duke University to professor of physical biochemistry. In 1950 he became the first chairman and professor of biochemistry at the University of Washington. He was elected to the American Academy of Arts and Sciences in 1960 and to the National Academy of Sciences in 1961.

Neurath coedited *The Proteins* (4 vols., 1953–54) and edited the second edition (4 vols., 1963–66). He also served as editor of the journal *Biochemistry* of the American Chemical Society.

For background information *see* ENZYME;

PROTEIN; PROTEIN METABOLISM in the McGraw-Hill Encyclopedia of Science and Technology. ☐

★ NEWELL, Norman Dennis

American paleontologist and geologist
Born Jan. 27, 1909, Chicago, Ill., U.S.A.

NEWELL BECAME interested in the geological history of life through the influence of his teachers Raymond Cecil Moore and Carl Owen Dunbar, both leading Earth historians. This interest was further stimulated by association with William H. Twenhofel, sedimentologist, and George Gaylord Simpson, paleontologist and architect of the synthetic theory of organic evolution. Newell contributed evidence that the evolutionary history of life has been profoundly episodic, marked by sweeping concurrent extinctions through diverse habitats and "sudden" introduction of new biotas at rates far above the average evolutionary rates of the component organisms. Nineteenth-century polemics between catastrophists and uniformitarians confronted by alternatives of mysticism versus the scientific method are no longer an issue. Newell was concerned with evaluation of the adequacy of the fossil record of life for historical interpretations. He found that the empirical evidence from biostratigraphy demonstrates successive episodes of waxing and waning in diversity and abundance of well-defined organism communities. The communities themselves have evolved, and some of the worldwide changes have not been gradual. It is these episodic revolutions in life that serve as the basis for defining and recognizing fundamental building blocks of international classification and dating of fossiliferous rock strata, the stratigraphic *stages* and *series*. These are not uniform or equivalent to particular time spans in the ordinary sense, but they mark chapters in the development of the modern biota. Newell attributed marked fluctuations of

diversity, abundance, and changes in geographic distribution of organisms of the past to changes in the nonbiotic environment, as yet not generally identifiable. One such factor, favored by Newell, which undoubtedly has produced myriads of correlated environmental changes, is fluctuations in absolute sea level, which rose and fell in response to diastrophism and glaciation, an idea expressed in 1898 by T. C. Chamberlin.

Newell's research in historical geology and paleontology stressed the sound principle of James Hutton and Charles Lyell that present-day geological and biological configurations and processes provide a scientific basis for understanding the past. He made numerous regional geological and paleontological investigations throughout the United States, in South and Central America, the Southern Alps, the Middle East, the Urals, West Pakistan, India, Japan, Australia, and the West and South Pacific. He investigated living and fossil bivalve mollusks from 1935 on for the light they shed on evolutionary principles, and his classification of this large group of organisms was adopted by the international Treatise on Invertebrate Paleontology.

From 1942 to 1945, during World War II, on the recommendation of the U.S. State Department, Newell worked as a geologist for the Departamento de Petróleo of Peru in a nationwide survey of petroleum resources of that geologically varied country. He discovered and recommended a favorable petroleum site near the village of Contamana, State of Loreto, in the tropical eastern rainforest. Some years after the war this was successfully exploited by a German oil company. During this period he undertook an arduous survey of the Lake Titicaca basin, which lies at a minimum altitude of $2\frac{1}{2}$ mi above sea level, and subsequently he published a technical report and map of this area of rough terrain approximately equivalent in size to one-half the state of Pennsylvania. An outcome of this study was a new theory of Andean structure, which specifies an episode of compression and thrust faulting from both east and west toward the present Lake Titicaca, followed by arching of the Andean system and rift faulting along the central axis of the arch.

From about 1951 to 1960 Newell engaged in extensive field surveys with his graduate students of Columbia University on the ecology of the Great Bahama Bank and simultaneously made parallel studies of one of the outstanding fossil reef complexes of the world, the Guadalupe Mountains of western Texas. This area has since been designated as a national park for its geological and biological interest.

A related team study of the ecology of a Pacific atoll, Raroia, of Kon Tiki fame, was organized and completed by Newell under auspices of the National Research Council. In this work he confirmed Charles Darwin's subsidence theory to explain the history and evolution of coral atolls, and likewise he presented evidence that the Great Bahama Bank and adjacent islands represent remnants of a barrier reef, which during early Tertiary times was far more extensive than the present Great Barrier Reef of Australia. For these and related studies he was cited for distinguished service by the University of Kansas (1960) and was awarded the Mary Thompson Clark Medal of the National Academy of Sciences (1962), the Medal of the University of Hiroshima (1964), the Hayden Award in geology and paleontology from the Philadelphia Academy of Sciences (1965), and the Verrill Medal of Peabody Museum, Yale University (1966).

In 1965 Newell discovered fossil corals in unequivocal geological setting in the Berry Islands, Bahamas, indicating a level of the sea some 3 m above present level at a time some 80,000 years ago. Since Quaternary fluctuations of absolute sea level have been dependent on climatic changes and consequent waxing and waning of continental glaciers, he interpreted the high level to represent an important but generally overlooked warm interlude within the Wisconsin stage of the Pleistocene continental glaciation.

Newell's father, a dental surgeon, was an amateur student of nature with leanings toward geology. After childhood in central Kansas, Newell studied for 5 years at the University of Kansas, where he earned the B.S. in 1929 and A.M. in 1931. During this period he served apprenticeship working for the Kansas Geological Survey. To supplement a meager income, during his undergraduate days he played in his own and other jazz bands. He earned the Ph.D. at Yale University in 1933, and his studies were extended an additional year while he was a Sterling fellow at that institution. Greatly influenced while at Yale Peabody Museum by the personality and counsel of the eminent paleomalacologist James Brookes Knight, he turned to the bivalve mollusks as a fruitful field for taxonomic and phylogenetic research. In subsequent years he taught both undergraduate and graduate students at the universities of Kansas (1934–37) and Wisconsin (1937–42). At the age of 28 he was a State Department delegate to the 17th International Geological Congress in Moscow. In 1945 he joined the staffs of Columbia University, as professor of geology, and the American Museum of Natural History, as curator of historical geology and fossil invertebrates. He also served the museum as dean of the council of the scientific staff.

For background information *see* CORAL REEF; GLACIAL EPOCH; PALEONTOLOGY; PETROLEUM GEOLOGY in the McGraw-Hill Encyclopedia of Science and Technology.   □

★ NEWITT, Dudley Maurice

British chemist and chemical engineer
Born Apr. 28, 1894, London, England

NEWITT'S SCIENTIFIC work fell within two fields. In 1921 he joined W. A. Bone and D. T. A. Townsend in an investigation into gaseous combustion at high pressures and later extended the work to include the influence of pressure on the oxidation of a range of hydrocarbons. During these investigations evidence was obtained of the activation of nitrogen in the explosive combustion of carbon monoxide–air mixtures, the formation of methyl alcohol in the combustion of methane at high pressures, and the two-stage oxidation of a number of higher hydrocarbons.

In the field of chemical engineering he carried out extensive research into the mechanism of drying and of granulation and showed the role of surface tension and capillary forces in the movement of liquid in moist granular masses. He also studied the pressure-temperature relationships of a number of single and multicomponent systems and, in collaboration with S. Angus, measured the enthalpy of steam up to pressures of 800 atm and temperatures up to 750°C.

Newitt graduated in chemistry at the Imperial College of Science, London, in 1921, and was later awarded the degrees of Ph.D. and D.Sc. He was elected a fellow of the Royal Society of London in 1942 and was awarded the Rumford Medal of the Society in 1962. He was Courtauld Professor of Chemical Engineering from 1945 until his retirement in 1962. He was a founding member of the Institution of Chemical Engineers and its president from 1949 to 1951.

For background information *see* COMBUSTION; STEAM; SURFACE TENSION in the McGraw-Hill Encyclopedia of Science and Technology.   □

★ NIER, Alfred Otto Carl

American physicist
Born May 28, 1911, Saint Paul, Minn., U.S.A.

WHILE AN undergraduate student in electrical engineering, Nier became interested in physics. He began his graduate career in the early 1930s, at a time when nuclear physics was becoming the exciting frontier of science. The University of Minnesota physics laboratory was well known for its work on ionization and dissociation of gases by electron impact, and Nier saw the opportunity to apply his background and interest in engineering methods to nuclear physics investigations that relied on electron impact phenomena. He became interested in the improvement of mass spectrometers and in their application to the study of the relative abundances of isotopes and the detection of rare, naturally occurring isotopes.

While still a graduate student, he discovered K^{40}, the rare isotope of potassium, suspected and later proved to be responsible for the radioactivity of potassium. As a postdoctoral fellow at Harvard University, Nier constructed a mass spectrometer having considerably more resolution and sensitivity than any hitherto in use, and was able to start a systematic study of the istopic composition of elements throughout the entire atomic table. In addition to making the first accurate isotope abundance measurements for many elements, he discovered the rare isotopes S^{36}, Ca^{46}, Ca^{48}, and Os^{186}. With Earl Gulbransen, he showed that in naturally occurring carbon the C^{13}/C^{12} abundance ratio varies significantly, depending on the source of the carbon.

Uranium, as it occurs in nature, consists of the radioactive isotopes U^{238}, U^{235}, and U^{234}. U^{238} decays with a half-life of 4.5×10^9 years, ultimately forming Pb^{206}. U^{235} likewise decays and forms Pb^{207}, the half-life for this process being 7.1×10^8 years. U^{234} is merely an intermediate-stage product in the decay of U^{238} to Pb^{206}. A knowledge of the decay rates, together with a determination of the relative amounts of uranium and lead in a mineral, makes possible a calculation of the age of the mineral. The problem is complicated since common lead, having isotopes Pb^{204}, Pb^{206}, Pb^{207}, and Pb^{208}, may be present as an impurity in the mineral. In early work the approximate amount of impurity was determined by a chemical measurement of the atomic weight of the lead, making use of the knowledge that common lead has an atomic weight of approximately 207.21, whereas the atomic weight of uranium lead is near 206.

With his high-resolution mass spectrometer Nier was able to make a systematic study of the isotopic composition of many samples of both common and uranium lead, and also of uranium, establishing that the abundance ratio U^{238}/U^{235} lies within 1% of 139 rather than being two or three times as large, as had been previously believed. Relative abundance measurements of the lead isotopes found in nearly pure uranium minerals, together with isotopic measurements on uranium, led to the first accurate determination of the decay constant for U^{235}, and a demonstration that the isotope abundance ratio Pb^{207}/Pb^{206} in a mineral, when corrected for possible common lead impurity present, gives an accurate measure of the age of the mineral, t, as follows:

$$Pb^{207}/Pb^{206} = [e^{\lambda_{235}t} - 1]/139[e^{\lambda_{238}t} - 1]$$

Here λ_{235} and λ_{238} are the decay constants of U^{235} and U^{238}, respectively. It is generally agreed that this is the most accurate method for determining the age of a uranium mineral, since in most cases ages computed from this formula are less influenced by possible alteration of the mineral.

In a study of a large group of common lead samples, Nier showed that the isotopic composition of common lead varies rather widely and that the variations are consistent with the assumption that common lead consists of "primordial" lead—that is, lead which existed when the Earth was formed—to which has been added lead generated by the radioactive decay of uranium and thorium between the time of formation of the Earth and the extraction of the lead from the Earth's mantle. This discovery provided Arthur Holmes with the data needed to show that the Earth is considerably older than 2×10^9 years, as had been generally assumed. Extension of the work by others led to calculations giving the age of the Earth to be around 4.5×10^9 years, a value close to that found by Claire Patterson for meteorites, using the same method. This value is now generally accepted as the age of the solar system.

In 1940, after the discovery of nuclear fission, there was uncertainty as to which isotope of uranium is responsible. By operating one of his instruments at a relatively high pressure so that an arc struck in the ion source, and much larger ion currents could be obtained than when it was used as a measuring instrument, Nier employed it as an isotope separator. He was able to separate measurable amounts of U^{234}, U^{235}, and U^{238}, and with J. R. Dunning, E. T. Booth, and A. V. Grosse of Columbia University, he demonstrated that U^{235} is responsible for the slow neutron fission of uranium. The instrument was the prototype for the much larger and more elaborate calutrons subsequently constructed for the large-scale separation of U^{235} during World War II.

Following the invention of the thermal diffusion column by K. Clusius and G. Dickel in 1938, Nier became interested in the problem of separating isotopes by thermal diffusion and produced some of the first enriched carbon-13 available for experimentation. Because of his interest in interdisciplinary efforts and his having one of the few existing mass spectrometers capable of measuring isotope abundance ratios accurately, it was only natural that he collaborated with colleagues in biology in studies in which C^{13} was used as a tracer. In 1941 he assisted H. G. Wood and C. H. Werkman of Iowa State College in their work showing that heterotrophic bacteria have the ability to assimilate carbon dioxide.

Prior to 1940 mass spectrometers used for gas or isotope analyses employed 180° deflection magnets. Nier showed that with a sector magnet as small as 60° one could obtain comparable performance. This resulted in a very large reduction in weight and provided flexibility in application not otherwise possible. It was an important step in making the mass spectrometer a routine tool, available to a variety of disciplines.

During World War II Nier was active in designing and developing mass spectrometers for the Manhattan District Project, particularly the Oak Ridge gaseous diffusion plant for the separation of U^{235}. The helium leak detector, the uranium isotope abundance ratio instrument, and the first on-line, analytical mass spectrometer were all products of his laboratory during this period.

Following the war he resumed his interest in geophysical and geochemical problems, and with L. T. Aldrich, he demonstrated that the He^3/He^4 ratio varies widely in nature and that A^{40} is a decay product of K^{40}. This latter discovery set the stage for the potassium-argon method of measuring geological age. For these discoveries, together with the early work on uranium and lead, the American Geological Society in 1956 awarded him the Arthur L. Day Medal.

During this same period he and his students produced enriched He^3 by thermal diffusion and collaborated with C. T. Lane and H. D. Fairbank of Yale University on some of the first experiments performed with He^3 in liquid helium. Together with students and colleagues, he also started a systematic program of investigating the rare gases formed in meteorites as a result of cosmic-ray bombardment or other sources. His laboratory made many useful contributions in this area. As an offshoot of the work, he developed a portable mass spectrometer for medical applications, which was used successfully in surgical experiments and surgery.

Prior to 1950 precise measurements of atomic masses were made with mass spectrographs—instruments in which ions are allowed to impinge on a photographic plate and the mass of the particles is correlated with position along the photograph plate. Nier saw the opportunity of applying the electronic techniques developed for the measurement of isotope abundances to this problem and developed the first double-focusing mass spectrometer. He and his students made many accurate determinations of atomic masses with this type of instrument. Because of its convenience and high resolution, the instrument has also been valuable to chemists for molecular structure studies of heavy organic compounds.

In 1959 a program of developing miniature mass spectrometers which could be rocket-borne was initiated, and in 1963, with colleagues, he began a study of the composition and temperature of the lower thermosphere.

Son of German immigrants, Nier attended the University of Minnesota, receiving a B.S. (1931), an M.S. in electrical engineering (1933), and a Ph.D. in physics (1936). After 2 years at Harvard University as a National Research Council fellow, he returned to the University of Minnesota physics department. World War II was spent on the Manhattan Project, first on various projects at Minnesota, later in charge of a special laboratory for the Kellex Corp. in New York. Nier served as chairman of the Minnesota physics department from 1953 to 1965, and was named Regents' Professor in 1966. He was elected to the National Academy of Sciences in 1950 and to the American Philosophical Society in 1953.

For background information *see* BETA RAYS; ISOTOPE; ISOTOPE DILUTION TECHNIQUES; ISOTOPE SEPARATION (STABLE ISOTOPES); LEAD ISOTOPES, GEOCHEMISTRY OF in the McGraw-Hill Encyclopedia of Science and Technology. □

☆ **NIRENBERG, Marshall Warren**

American biochemist
Born Apr. 10, 1927, New York, N.Y., U.S.A.

IN EXPERIMENTS that began in 1960, Nirenberg pioneered in the decipherment of the genetic "code," by means of which the genetic material of the living cell directs the synthesis of the cell proteins which are all-important in determining the structure and activities of the cell. Nirenberg's findings represented an important advance in understanding both genetics and cell biochemistry.

In 1953 the biologists James D. Watson and Francis H. C. Crick proposed the "double-helix" model of the structure of deoxyribonucleic acid (DNA), the complex giant molecule making up the genetically active material of most cells. The Watson-Crick model gave DNA the shape of a very long spiral ladder: The "runners" were composed of alternate molecules of a phosphate and a 5-carbon sugar, deoxyribose; the "rungs" were made up of nitrogen-base compounds, four in number, arranged in pairs connecting the two sugar-phosphate chains at regular intervals. In DNA the four bases were adenine, guanine, cytosine, and thymine, symbolized respectively by the letters A, G, C, and T. A was always found paired with T, C always with G. Watson and Crick established that the simple linear arrangement of these pairs of "letters" along the DNA molecule very probably constituted the genetic "code." Then in 1954 the theoretical physicist George Gamow pointed out that such a four-letter "alphabet," if the letters were taken three at a time, could provide 64 different "messages," which would be more than enough to specify the 20-odd different amino acids, the subunits from which protein molecules were assembled under the direction of DNA.

Nirenberg and his colleagues from the National Institutes of Health began in 1960 to seek experimental evidence bearing on the questions: What was the ratio of the four nitrogen-bases A, C, G, and T in each triplet that specified a particular amino acid? Which triplet specified which amino acid? What was the exact sequence of letters within each triplet?

The experiments fell broadly into two groups. The first group to be performed involved the interaction of ribosomes (the intracellular bodies where protein synthesis occurred) and "messenger ribonucleic acid" (mRNA). The ribosomes were obtained by breaking up the cells of the common bacteria *Escherichia coli* to produce a cellfree system, containing ribosomes, tRNA, enzymes, and other cell components. RNA was used because it was strongly suspected that DNA did not act directly on the protein synthesis mechanism in the ribosomes. Instead, the genetic message was "copied" onto a molecule of mRNA, very similar to DNA except for the presence of the sugar ribose in place of deoxyribose and the substitution of the nitrogen-base uracil (U) for the thymine of DNA. The mRNA was manufactured on DNA templates, eventually reaching a ribosome, where the actual protein assembly took place. Because RNA was investigated first, the genetic code came to be specified in terms of the triplets ("codons") found in mRNA, instead of those of DNA. However, a "translation" from one code to the other was very simple. By adding to this cellfree system the various amino acids, an energy source [usually in the form of the energy-rich compound adenosinetriphosphate (ATP), normally found in all cells], and different kinds of RNA, Nirenberg and Matthaei were able to promote the incorporation of amino acids into proteins. This process was followed with the aid of the radioactive isotope carbon-14, with which different amino acids were "labeled."

At first the RNA was obtained from viruses and other natural sources, and it was discovered that these "foreign" RNAs could cause the cellfree *E. coli* system to manufacture proteins. Nirenberg and his colleagues then thought to use in place of these RNAs a simple, synthetic RNA polymer, thus hoping to simplify the task of identifying the RNA triplet responsible for each amino acid. For example, if a synthetic RNA polymer made up only of molecules of uracil were introduced into the system, it might reasonably be expected that the resulting protein would be made up entirely of molecules of some one amino acid. Such RNA polymers had been synthesized, and the substance polyuridylic acid, consisting of uracil only, was then tried. The experimentalists were able to show that the resulting amino acid was phenylalanine, whose code triplet was therefore UUU. (At this point it had not yet been fully established that the code was indeed a triplet one, but there were strong suggestions that this was the case.) The experimentalists proceeded to repeat this experiment, substituting a polymer containing only cytosine (C). They found that the resulting amino acid was proline.

This start having been made, Nirenberg and his group went on to perform experiments with different synthetic RNA polymers containing the different possible combinations of A, C, G, and U. They were able to establish a tentative "dictionary" of the code on this basis. Statistical tests were used to determine the specificity of, for example, an RNA polymer containing U and C, by measuring the relative proportions of the resulting proteins. It was found that the code was "redundant": A particular amino acid could be specified by more than one codon. Thus the amino acid proline could be produced by any of the combinations CCU, CCC, CCA, or CCG. It was also found that certain triplets did not seem to specify any amino acid; and it was suggested that these so-called "nonsense" codons were the "punctuation" in the genetic code, signifying the beginning and end of a "message." Nirenberg assigned values to 50 different code triplets. Of these, about 45 were subsequently found to be correct.

Up to this point very little evidence had been obtained regarding the order of the bases within each triplet; only the letters were known with certainty, not their arrangement. Another series of experiments was directed toward this problem. Again, the experimental mechanism was a cellfree system. Instead of stimulating protein synthesis, however, Nirenberg and his colleagues studied a system containing ribosomes, amino acids, the different kinds of "transfer RNA" (tRNA), and synthetic nucleoside triplets. For each of the 20 amino acids it was known that there existed specific molecules of tRNA. Amino acids could not reach the ribosome by themselves; tRNA functioned as a carrier, attaching itself to its specific amino acid and bringing it to the ribosome, where it was incorporated into protein. These synthetic nucleoside triplets were in effect single codons, such as GGU or UAC, small fragments of the normally very long chains of mRNA. The order of bases in each triplet could be specified precisely. The experimentalists considered that if a triplet of known composition were introduced into the system, its presence would induce the formation of a protein from one amino acid, and one only. There was strong evidence that in this process the molecule of tRNA, bearing its specific amino acid, attached itself to the ribosome, where the amino acid would be detached and incorporated in the growing protein chain; the tRNA molecule would then drift away. The purpose of the experiment was to discover which particular amino acid was found attached to the ribosome in the presence of a given code triplet. This object was accomplished with the aid of a technique devised by Nirenberg and Philip Leder. By labeling one amino acid at a time with carbon-14, passing the experimental material through a filter which retained only the ribosomes (with tRNA and amino acids attached), and then measuring the amount of radioactivity present in the filter, it was possible to determine exactly which code triplet specified which amino acid. Nirenberg and his colleagues synthesized all 64 of the possible codons and obtained unambiguous results for about 60 of them. By this method and by several quite different techniques developed independently, almost all of the 64 triplets could be assigned definite values.

Following these experiments, work continued in Nirenberg's laboratory on the role of "synonym" codons, the mechanism of codon recognition by RNA, and the mechanisms controlling the rate of protein synthesis during viral infection and embryonic differentiation.

Nirenberg took a B.S. in 1948 and an M.S. in biology in 1952 at the University of Florida. He then went to the University of Michigan's department of biological chemistry, where he received a Ph.D. in 1957. That same year, he joined the National Institutes of Health (NIH) as a postdoctoral fellow of the American Cancer Society, remaining at the NIH National Institute of Arthritis and Metabolic Diseases until 1962. He then went to the NIH National Heart Institute as chief of the Laboratory of Biochemical Genetics. Nirenberg's achievements earned him the National Medal of Science in 1965, the Research Corporation Award for 1966, and other awards. He was elected to the American Academy of Arts and Sciences in 1965, and to the National Academy of Sciences in 1967.

For background information *see* DEOXYRIBONUCLEIC ACID; NUCLEIC ACID; RIBONUCLEIC ACID in the McGraw-Hill Encyclopedia of Science and Technology.   □

★ NØRLUND, Niels Erik

Danish mathematician and geodesist
Born Oct. 26, 1885, Slagelse, Denmark

NØRLUND CONCENTRATED mainly on the calculus of finite differences, an increasingly important field for the treatment of discontinuous processes. In his Ph.D. dissertation in 1910 particular attention was given to the linear difference equation with rational coefficients. He considered a fundamental system of meromorphic solutions having properties similar to those of the well-known gamma function. The expansion most used in the theory of functions is the power series, but in this case it is applicable only in a very limited range. The power series is

inadequate for the difficulties encountered in the case of the solutions of difference equations. But the factorial series yields itself readily to summation and performing of finite differences. It is well adapted to represent the above mentioned important class of new functions. Nørlund therefore studied the factorial series extensively, especially transformations of these series. He proved that the factorial series converges uniformly over a half-plane interior to its half-plane of convergence and it is thus able to represent a function in a certain neighborhood of a singular point. He investigated the possibility of obtaining the analytical extension of functions defined by such series. He further showed that linear difference equations whose coefficients can be developed into factorial series possess a fundamental system of solutions which can be expressed in terms of factorial series.

Nørlund also investigated the solutions of the equation $f(x+1) - f(x) = \phi(x)$, where $\phi(x)$ is a given function; he thus in a fairly general case defined an operation inverse to the difference operation.

Considerable further work on difference equations was done by G. D. Birkhoff and other investigators. To G. F. B. Riemann is due the characterization of a function in simple descriptive terms which are independent of the equations of definition of the function. Nørlund gave a formulation and explicit solution of the Riemann problem for the hypergeometric difference equation, and at about the same time Birkhoff solved the generalized problem of Riemann for linear differential equations with irregular singular points and the analogous problem for linear difference equations.

The Gregory-Newton formula of interpolation permits expression of a function in terms of the factorials x, $x(x-1), \ldots, x(x-1) \ldots (x-n)$ when a difference table of the function is given. In a similar way the Stirling formula of interpo-

lation gives an expression in terms of the factorials x, x^2, $x^2(x^2-1^2), \ldots, x^2(x^2-1^2) \ldots (x^2-n^2)$. Nørlund investigated the possibility of representing a function by one of the expansions obtained when n tends to infinity. He showed that the conditions for the representation of a function by one of these series can be given in a very remarkable way.

Two classes of polynomials play a most important part in analysis, namely, the polynomials of J. Bernoulli and the polynomials of Leonhard Euler. These were the object of much research and were generalized in an elegant manner by Nørlund. Special attention was devoted to the asymptotic behavior of these functions for large values of the parameters.

He also considered the complete logarithmic solutions of the hypergeometric differential equation satisfied by the Gauss function $F(a, b, c; z)$, that is, those solutions which arise when one or more of the quantities $a-b$, c, $c-a-b$ are integers. He gave complete tables of the linear and quadratic relations which hold between the various solutions in every possible case.

Nørlund further investigated the generalized hypergeometric function ${}_nF_{n-1}(z)$ where $n > 2$. It satisfies a linear differential equation of the order n with three singularities. He studied the behavior of the solutions in the neighborhood of the singular point $z = 1$. Several expansions were given, with interesting relations satisfied by the coefficients. The solutions belonging to the exponents $0, 1, \ldots, n-2$ were represented by infinite series of hypergeometric polynomials.

Divergent series can in some cases be used with advantage. Several methods of summation have been invented. One of them is called the Nørlund method; its properties have been investigated by many authors.

In 1905 Nørlund published a new orbit of the double star Xi Ursae Majoris, and he pointed out that the micrometer measurements showed a very small perturbation of the orbit with a period of 1.8 years. He concluded that this is a triple star with an invisible satellite. This hypothesis has been verified at the Lick Observatory by W. H. Wright through measurements of the radial velocity and at Potsdam by E. Hertzsprung. The disturbing satellite was found to have the predicted time of revolution.

From 1923 onward Nørlund directed the geodetic surveys in Denmark. He initiated a new triangulation covering the whole country, as well as a great number of gravity measurements and astronomical determinations of longitude and azimuth. In Greenland under his direction a first-order triangulation was carried out from 60 to 76° N latitude.

Nørlund was educated at Sorø High School, there receiving the first glimpse of the world of mathematical sciences to which he was to devote his life. In 1903 he entered the University of Copenhagen and graduated in 1910 with a Ph.D. He was professor of mathematics at the University of Lund during 1912–22 and at the University of Copenhagen during 1923–56. From 1923 to 1955 he was also director of the Royal Geodetic Institute in Denmark. From 1928 to 1948 he was president of the International Time Commission and from 1934 to 1937 president of the International Council of Scientific Unions. He was elected a foreign member of the Royal Society of London in 1938.

Nørlund wrote *Differenzenrechnung* (1924), *Leçons sur les séries d'interpolation* (1926), *Sur la somme d'une fonction* (1927), and *Sur les équations aux différences finies* (1929).

For background information *see* DIFFERENTIAL EQUATION; GAMMA FUNCTION; INTERPOLATION in the McGraw-Hill Encyclopedia of Science and Technology.   □

NORRISH, Ronald George Wreyford

British physical chemist

Norrish shared the 1967 Nobel Prize in chemistry with Manfred Eigen and George Porter. See *McGraw-Hill Modern Men of Science*, Volume I.

★ **O'BRIEN, Brian**

American physicist
Born Jan. 2, 1898, Denver, Colo., U.S.A.

THE CLASSICAL work of Fabry and Buisson had produced photographs of the solar spectrum below 3000 A in the ultraviolet but no quantitative measurements of the distribution of energy in this spectral region. O'Brien combined his rotating spiral aperture disk technique with a double-dispersion optical system to eliminate stray light and measured by photographic means the solar energy distribution at the Earth's surface to wavelengths less than 2900 A. To determine the solar energy outside the Earth's atmosphere, he determined the atmospheric absorption, due largely to ozone, by applying the same technique at known solar elevations.

To extend these measurements with balloon-borne instruments, he developed a method for evaporating metallic optical wedges, which eliminated the need for a rotating disk. Instruments carried on manned balloon flights to elevations of 72,000 ft and on unmanned balloons to 101,000 ft yielded the first precise measurements with laboratory-size spectrographs of the vertical distribution of ozone in the atmosphere. Collaborators with O'Brien in these investigations were F. L. Mohler, H. S. Stewart, M. P. Givens, F. W. Paul, and L. J. Krolak.

It had long been known that the quantitative response of photographic emulsions to light depart from a simple reciprocal relation between intensity and time, and also that an intermittent exposure is not equivalent to a continuous one of the same total light energy. O'Brien devised a refined method for measuring the reciprocity failure and the intermittency effect, and he found that they are precisely equivalent if the frequency of interruption of the intermittent exposure is sufficiently high. This result provided further support for the Guerney-Mott

theory of the photographic process as extended by J. H. Webb.

In 1940 O'Brien, then director of the Institute of Optics, undertook development of optical and infrared devices for the armed forces in collaboration with the Institute staff and continued this through 1945. From this effort of some 50 people there resulted a number of successful instruments used extensively in combat by all three services. These included the night-attack sight for night-fighter aircraft, the series of infrared telescopes known as Metascopes for night amphibious and paratroop operations, and the optical volume limiter known as Icaroscope for defense against bombing attacks from the direction of the Sun. For this work he received from the President the Medal for Merit in 1948.

By devising cameras to use photographic photometry with time resolution of less than 0.0000001 sec, the early (1946) nuclear test explosions were recorded (with G. G. Milne and B. O'Brien, Jr.) and the early time-temperature history of the air shock and fireball was determined.

In 1933 Stiles and Crawford had observed a pronounced directional effect in the response of the central retina of the human eye, and no satisfactory explanation had been proposed. In 1946 O'Brien proposed a theory based on the physical optics of the cone cells of the retina. By a macroscopic optical experiment which neglected diffraction, he showed that the theory must be at least approximately correct. Later, with J. H. Jean, using microwaves, he constructed a macroscopic model which took full account of diffraction and gave experimental results in very close agreement with the Stiles and Crawford effect in the eye as measured by a number of experimenters. This theory, now generally accepted, also explains why, because of light concentration, much less photosensitive pigment is needed for the cone cells of the retina than a simple calculation based on retinal area would predict. This interest in the human retina led to a detailed study of the retinal receptor cells and the physical optics of retinal illumination. For this and other work in optics O'Brien received the Frederick Ives Medal of the Optical Society of America in 1951.

In addition to scientific work, O'Brien was responsible for a number of practical developments. These included motion-picture cameras (with G. G. Milne) operating in excess of 10,000,000 frames per second with which several of the Pacific nuclear tests were photographed, a successful process and devices for irradiation of food liquids to convert sterols to vitamin D, and an electrostatic mineral separation process now in large-scale operation. He directed the group which developed the Todd-AO wide-angle motion-picture system, and was the first to recognize the necessity for, and to apply, a low-refractive-index coating on optical fibers; this coating has made fiber optics successful.

O'Brien, son of a geologist, received his Ph.B in electrical engineering in 1918 and his Ph.D. in physics in 1922 from Yale University. He was employed in the Westinghouse research laboratory in 1922–23 and in a biophysics research laboratory at Perrysburg, N.Y., from 1923 to 1930, when he went to the University of Rochester as professor of physiological optics. In 1938 he became director of the Institute of Optics at that university and in 1946 also research professor of physics and optics. In 1953 he joined the American Optical Co. as vice-president and director of research, remaining there until his retirement. From 1951 to 1953 he was president of the Optical Society of America, and from 1953 to 1961 he was chairman of the Division of Physical Sciences of the National Research Council. He was elected to the American Academy of Arts and Sciences and to the American Philosophical Society, both in 1953, and to the National Academy of Sciences in 1954.

For background information *see* ASTRONOMICAL SPECTROSCOPY; CINEMATOGRAPHY; SPECTROSCOPY; VISION in the McGraw-Hill Encyclopedia of Science and Technology.   □

OPPENHEIMER, J. Robert

American physicist
Born Apr. 22, 1904, New York, N.Y., U.S.A.
Died Feb. 18, 1967, Princeton, N.J., U.S.A.

OPPENHEIMER FROM 1943 to 1945 was director of the Los Alamos Scientific Laboratory in New Mexico, where the world's first atomic bomb was developed. This huge and highly secret operation, for which many scientific disciplines were pooled to meet problems of novel complexity, was carried out under his direct supervision. Besides his scientific and administrative involvement with the United States

nuclear effort, he made a number of original contributions to theoretical physics and also pursued a distinguished career as a scientific educator. In 1963 he received the Atomic Energy Commission's Fermi Award.

As a teacher and organizer of broad experience who had also done important theoretical work, Oppenheimer was involved in the bomb project almost from the beginning of World War II. By 1942 he was in charge of the work on the bomb itself, which was going on in laboratories scattered throughout the United States. In that year it was decided that this program could be accelerated by concentrating it in one place. He helped select the site of the future laboratory at Los Alamos, and early in 1943 he was made its director.

Oppenheimer began by facing difficulties of construction and supply, working at first against wartime priorities and the geographical isolation of the place. Concurrently, there was the problem of assembling a group of scientists, ultimately to number around 4500, specializing in a vast range of fields. He played a key part in selecting this group, persuading them to work at Los Alamos and maintaining order among a large, brilliant, and heterogeneous group of specialists. He was intimate with all areas of the laboratory's work and his achievements were both administrative and technical.

It was Oppenheimer's task as director to produce an atomic weapon as quickly as possible. His was the final responsibility for planning the overall program of research, dividing up the task, and organizing the laboratory. One of his most important administrative actions was the selection from several competing designs of the actual method of assembling the bomb. Under Oppenheimer the laboratory developed a deliverable nuclear weapon in less than 3 years.

Atomic fission reactions come about as the result of neutron emission by certain radioactive materials. If enough of the pure material is assembled in one place (critical mass), spontaneous neutron emission affects a sufficient number of nuclei to initiate a self-sustaining reaction. (Enrico Fermi and his group at the University of Chicago had achieved the world's first self-sustaining nuclear chain reaction in late 1942.) Moreover, it was realized that, if a "supercritical" amount of the radioactive substance was assembled quickly enough, the reaction could become explosive. Much of the engineering work at Los Alamos was concerned with the device for bringing about supercritical mass very quickly. The bomb developed in 1945 employed uranium-235, the only naturally occurring radioactive material suitable for use as a nuclear fuel. In the final design the reaction was set off when two subcritical masses of U-235 were brought together by firing a small explosive charge. Each of the two spheres weighed about a pound.

The uranium metal received from the Oak Ridge and Hanford processing plants underwent precision machining at Los Alamos, a matter made more complex by the dangerous radio-activity of the material, its high melting point, and other difficult characteristics. The Los Alamos group also had to calculate the effec-tiveness of shielding and safety procedures, then design and build the necessary equipment. Finally, it was necessary to design and perform the testing procedure for the bomb.

In 1945, shortly after the first bomb test, Oppenheimer resigned his directorship at Los Alamos. Before the war, from 1929 onward, he had been a teacher of growing reputation and had gained international recognition for the qual-ity and originality of his instruction at the Cali-fornia Institute of Technology and the Univer-sity of California at Berkeley. In 1947 he became director of the Institute for Advanced Study at Princeton, N.J., the unique establishment where many postwar advances in theoretical physics were made. Here Oppenheimer continued his involvement with the work of the international group of scientists, permanent and transient, who worked at the Institute.

Oppenheimer made many original contribu-tions to theoretical physics. Among his papers were: A 1930 paper concerning the interaction of particles and fields showed that the theories of Werner Heisenberg and P. A. M. Dirac were inapplicable to nuclear structure. Another 1930 paper contributed to the interpretation of the celebrated doctrine of "holes" attendant on Dirac's electron theory of 1929. Dirac proposed that, if these "unoccupied" states actually oc-curred, they would represent new subatomic particles of unknown properties. (These later came to be called collectively "antiparticles.") Oppenheimer's paper helped invalidate an earlier mistaken identification of "holes" as pro-tons. Another paper, with W. H. Furry in 1934, developed the modified Dirac electron-positron theory (positrons had meanwhile been detected experimentally) and gave it a concrete physical interpretation, and also suggested independent tests for the theory. A 1931 paper, with Paul Ehrenfest, presented strong evidence against the then current theory that electrons made up part of the atomic nucleus. A year later Sir James Chadwick's discovery of the neutron made feasible the modern proton-neutron hypothesis of

nuclear structure. A 1935 paper, with Philips, considering neutron capture, showed that other forces were involved in this process besides the very short-range "nuclear" force. A series of papers with J. F. Carlson, beginning in 1937, offered a theory of pair production and shower effects at cosmic-ray energies. It showed how a single very energetic particle striking the atmos-phere could initiate a "cascade" of secondary and tertiary particles. A paper, with H. A. Bethe in 1946 predicted the breakdown of "classical" quantum electrodynamics at very long and very short wavelengths. Another paper explained the "soft" component of cosmic radiation as being made up of electron-photon pairs produced in the upper atmosphere by a "cascade" process. Oppenheimer distinguished this process from that yielding the meson-nucleon "hard" or "penetrating" component. A 1948 paper, with H. W. Lewis and S. A. Wouthuysen, proposed an influential theory of multiple meson production in nucleon-nucleon interactions at very high energy.

The son of a New York textile importer, Oppenheimer received an A.B. in chemistry at Harvard University in 1925. He did graduate work, first under Lord Rutherford at Cambridge University, then under Max Born at the Univer-sity of Göttingen, where he received a Ph.D. in physics in 1927. After further study in the United States and Europe, in 1929 Oppenheimer went to California to accept concurrent appointments as assistant professor (and later professor) of physics at the University of Cali-fornia, Berkeley, and at the California Institute of Technology. He undertook the atomic bomb project in 1941. In 1947 he was appointed to the directorship of the Institute for Advanced Study, Princeton, N.J. He resigned this position in 1966 but remained at the Institute as senior professor of physics. From 1947 to 1952 Oppenheimer served as chairman of the General Advisory Committee to the Atomic Energy Commission; he was also on President Eisenhower's Scientific Advisory Committee and served as an adviser to the Departments of State and Defense and the National Security Council. He was elected to the National Academy of Sciences in 1941.

Oppenheimer wrote *Scientific Foundations* for *World Order* (1947) and *The Open Mind* (1955; paper 1960).

For background information *see* ATOMIC BOMB; THEORETICAL PHYSICS in the McGraw-Hill Encyclopedia of Science and Technology.   □

★ PAPPENHEIMER, John Richard

American physiologist
Born Oct. 25, 1915, New York, N.Y., U.S.A.

PAPPENHEIMER CONTRIBUTED to several different fields in general physiology, but is perhaps best known for his studies of capillary permeability. Beginning in 1946 he and his colleagues developed methods for the measurement of capillary pressure, in vivo protein osmotic pressure, and rates of transcapillary ultrafiltration in skeletal muscle. These methods were later extended to the measurement of transcapillary diffusional exchange, and provided the first quantitative data on capillary permeability to small lipid-insoluble molecules. The results formed the basis of a general theory of permeation in which the coefficients of osmotic flow and restricted diffusion were related to the number and dimensions of ultramicroscopic pathways for molecular exchange. The theory (1951) has been widely used in defining the permeability characteristics of biological and artificial porous membranes. As applied to the capillary membranes of skeletal muscle, the theory accounted for observed permeabilities to molecules ranging in size from water to hemoglobin in terms of aqueous channels penetrating through or between endothelial cells. The width of these channels was calculated to be about 60 angstroms and their total cross-sectional area about 0.1% of the capillary surface. The ultrastructural basis for these pathways is still a matter of dispute among electron microscopists; recent studies suggest that junctional clefts between endothelial cells may have the requisite dimensions.

In recent years Pappenheimer and his colleagues studied the formation, composition, and function of cerebral extracellular fluids. A unique feature of this work was the development of techniques for perfusion of the cerebral ventricular system in chronically prepared, unanesthetized goats. Perhaps the best known of these studies concerns the control of breathing. It was found that pulmonary ventilation could be simply related to the hydrogen ion concentration of cerebral interstitial fluid, both at rest and during a wide variety of disturbances in acid-base balance. Respiratory compensation for chronic metabolic acidosis or alkalosis was accounted for quantitatively by observed changes in transport of bicarbonate ions between cerebral blood and interstitial fluid surrounding respiratory neurones. This work was reviewed by Pappenheimer in a Harvey Lecture entitled "The ionic composition of cerebral interstitial fluid and its relation to control of breathing" in 1967.

Pappenheimer was brought up in an academic environment. His father, Alwin M. Pappenheimer, Sr., was professor of pathology at Columbia University; his brother, A. M. Pappenheimer, Jr., became professor of biology and master of Dunster House at Harvard. Pappenheimer himself graduated from Harvard College with a B.S. in 1936. As an undergraduate, he worked on the physical chemistry of amino acids with Jeffries Wyman, Jr. From 1936 to 1939 Pappenheimer worked as a research student at the University of Cambridge and at University College, London. He gained a Ph.D. at Cambridge in 1940. With F. R. Winton, he published a series of papers on urine formation and renal metabolism; in this period also he described the action of sympathetic vasoconstrictor nerves in diverting blood from nutrient to nonnutrient channels in the microcirculation of skeletal muscle (1941). This latter work was perhaps the earliest functional study of what is now termed the dual circulation in muscle. From 1939 to 1945 Pappenheimer worked on the development of oxygen equipment for military aircraft, this work being carried out for the Office of Scientific Research and Development in D. W. Bronk's laboratory at the University of Pennsylvania. After the war he moved to the Harvard Medical School. In 1953 Pappenheimer was appointed career investigator of the American Heart Association and visiting professor of physiology at Harvard. He served as president of the American Physiological Society in 1964–65. He was elected to the American Academy of Arts and Sciences in 1954 and to the National Academy of Sciences in 1965.

For background information *see* CAPILLARY (ANATOMICAL); LYMPHATIC SYSTEM in the McGraw-Hill Encyclopedia of Science and Technology. ☐

★ PARDEE, Arthur Beck

American biochemist
Born July 13, 1921, Chicago, Ill., U.S.A.

BIOCHEMISTS ATTEMPT to explain as much of life as possible in terms of chemistry. Their work has emphasized three sorts of information: the kinds of molecules found in living things, the chemical reactions that make and use these molecules, and most recently the control and coordination of these reactions into organized life processes. Pardee contributed fundamental ideas and discoveries to this last area.

In living cells chemical changes are always catalyzed by enzymes. The rate of each chemical reaction is determined in two ways: by the quantity of its enzyme, and by the conditions under which the enzyme acts as a catalyst.

The quantity of an enzyme is determined by its rate of production and its rate of disappearance. For many years it has been known that cells produce some enzymes at different rates when they are exposed to different environments, for example, when different sources of food are available. Enzymes are often made only when they are needed. Pardee made several contributions to this area, including discovery of some of these enzyme inductions and repressions. With J. Monod and F. Jacob, he provided a mechanism by which the environment can control specific enzyme formation. Regulatory proteins (repressors), whose function is solely to control structural genes, are made by special regulatory genes. Nutrients or other molecules interact with repressors and modify their function. Aside from transferring concepts of enzyme regulation from the nutritional to the genetic level, these studies also provided one of the major clues in the discovery of messenger ribonucleic acid (mRNA), the immediate gene product.

Rates of reactions also can be controlled by regulating the catalytic activity of enzymes already present. Their activity can be inhibited or

stimulated specifically by chemicals in the environment. When these chemicals are themselves intermediates of metabolism, they create interactions whereby one part of metabolism affects another. Probably the best-known case is "end-product" inhibition, in which a compound at the end of a long metabolic pathway inhibits an initial reaction of the same pathway. This produces a feedback loop, with the result that the end product is not overproduced since it limits its own synthesis. Pardee and his colleagues provided one of the earliest examples of this end-product control. They also discovered fundamental ideas of the mechanism of the inhibition. The end product inhibits because the enzyme is constructed with a special part designed to receive it, distinct from the sites which receive molecules that undergo chemical change. Also, these enzymes are constructed from protein subunits whose interaction is modified by activators or inhibitors, with catalytic activity changes resulting.

Pardee's group made more than 100 original contributions over a wide area of biochemistry, including identification of ribosomes and bacterial photosynthetic particles, mutagenesis by chemicals structurally similar to the genetic material, enzyme changes after virus infection, regulatory links between synthesis of proteins and nucleic acids, periodic events in the cell cycle of bacteria, and effects of numerous agents, including ultraviolet light, on gene actions and enzyme formation. Later Pardee studied mechanisms for transport of materials through cell surface barriers. This work resulted in isolation of a pure protein component of a transport system for the first time, thus opening the way to studies of transport in terms of molecules rather than whole cells.

Pardee received a B.S. from the University of California, Berkeley, in 1942, and a Ph.D. in chemistry under L. Pauling from the California Institute of Technology in 1947. Several years of war work on gases and radioactive substances intervened. He spent 2 years as a Merck postdoctoral fellow with V. Potter at the University of Wisconsin (1947–49). He was on the staff of the University of California, Berkeley, during 1949–61 with a year (1957–58) at the Pasteur Institut with J. Monod. He became professor of biology and chairman of biochemical sciences at Princeton University in 1961. In 1966 he was made Donner Professor of Science. Recipient of the Paul-Lewis Award in Enzyme Chemistry from the American Chemical Society in 1960, he was elected to the American Academy of Arts and Sciences in 1963.

Pardee wrote *Experiments in Biochemical Research Techniques,* with R. Cowgill (1957), and contributed numerous articles to books on biochemistry and microbiology.

For background information *see* ENZYME;

METABOLIC DISORDERS in the McGraw-Hill Encyclopedia of Science and Technology.   □

★ PAUL, John Rodman

American physician and epidemiologist
Born Apr. 18, 1893, Philadelphia, Pa., U.S.A.

STARTING HIS professional life as a pathologist and then shifting to medicine, Paul was naturally oriented toward the idea that disease was the main focal point in efforts by the physician to cope with many problems of the sick patient. Gradually this led to the idea that, if one was to deal with disease adequately from the physician's standpoint, one should not only consider it from the individual's point of view but from that of the community as well. This approach epitomized the concept of social pathology, a term coined by John Ryle of Oxford University, who also started out life as a physician. This idea was the one which Paul tried to impress upon his students at the Yale University School of Medicine during his 33 years as teacher at that institution—21 of them spent as professor of preventive medicine.

A by-product of this concept was an attempt to bring the ideology of the physician and the public health worker together instead of the two being far apart. Prior to 1930 it had been pointed out that there were profound differences in the manner which these two "specialists" approached their respective subjects, amounting almost to a difference in religions. The physician's primary interest is in his patient as a sick individual in which disease is apt to play a positive role, whereas for the public health worker disease has negative values and health plays a positive role—so-called "positive health," not only in the individual but in the community. Furthermore, the physician is on a very different professional basis from the public health official, who by his authority as an officer with legal rights is empowered to enforce certain rulings, whereas the physician has no such authority. It

is said that another fundamental difference is that the discriminating physician treats nearly all of his patients differently, recognizing their individual traits, whereas the public health officer must of necessity treat all his patients of the same age group in the same manner. However, there is at least one discipline which has a common usefulness between the two professions, the science of epidemiology, and so in the Yale Medical School the discipline of preventive medicine has been taught as applied epidemiology, or to make it more palatable to embryo physicians, as clinical epidemiology. This subject of epidemiology may require an explanation. Paradoxically its meaning is not the study of epidemics, but—in part, at least—of the circumstances under which disease occurs. Such circumstances may be microbiological, toxicological, geographic, climatic, sociological, even political—making it an immense and all-embracing subject indeed.

During World War II there was formed an important semimilitary body known as the Armed Forces Epidemiological Board through which many prominent physicians loaned their services to the United States government for the solution of certain epidemiological problems which were bound to arise and did arise. For a fair number of these physicians this was the first time that they had been asked to consider these problems; some of them took to these newly imposed tasks as ducks to water. This prompted the view that physicians in the mid-20th century did indeed have a common interest with the public health profession, and it proved to be an added boost to the idea that the teaching of epidemiology be admitted into the medical student's curriculum, which was an innovation, at least in the 1940s. Another boost was the establishment by the U.S. Public Health Service of its Epidemiological Intelligence Service, which gave in-training service to many young physicians just out of medical school. Such services were to be extended by many state health departments and departments of preventive medicine in many universities.

But this idea of introducing the concept of clinical epidemiology into the already overcrowded curriculum of the medical school has not been without its labor pains. To offset some of these difficulties in recent years, Paul sought the aid of the World Health Organization (WHO). In assuming the directorship of one of the WHO serum banks he greatly increased the scope of the Yale's epidemiological operations, particularly in the field of serological epidemiology.

Paul graduated from Princeton University with an A.B. in 1915 and from the Johns Hopkins University School of Medicine with an M.D. in 1919. For 6 years he was associated with the Pennsylvania Hospital in Philadelphia as director of laboratories and also with the University of Pennsylvania. Going to the Yale University School of Medicine in 1928, first as an assistant-associate professor of medicine, he became professor of preventive medicine in 1940, which position he held until he became professor emeritus in 1961. During World War II he served as director of the Commission of Viral Infections (Armed Forces Epidemiological Board) and also as consultant to the Secretary of War. He was elected to the National Academy of Sciences in 1945 and to the American Academy of Arts and Sciences in 1951.

Books which Paul wrote include *The Epidemiology of Rheumatic Fever* (1930; 3d ed. 1957), *Rheumatic Fever in New Haven* (1941), and *Clinical Epidemiology* (1958; 2d ed. 1966).

For background information *see* EPIDEMIOLOGY; PUBLIC HEALTH in the McGraw-Hill Encyclopedia of Science and Technology. □

★ PECORA, William Thomas

American geologist
Born Feb. 1, 1913, Belleville, N.J., U.S.A.

THE BASIC concerns of a research-oriented field geologist are to investigate how and why different rocks and minerals reached their present position and composition and to identify and explain the abnormal relations observed at any given locality on the Earth. Out of these studies emerges an orderly body of earth science that involves chemistry, physics, biology, engineering, and three-dimensional geometry—all in the framework of total time or rate of process that extends over many millions of years.

In his investigations of nickel silicate deposits in the Western Hemisphere, Pecora was the first to recognize a dual control of specific rock type and weathering history over several million years in formation of the garnieritic laterites. His principles, published in the 1940s, became the definitive references in search and exploration for new deposits throughout the world wherever

peridotite formed upland physiographic surfaces.

During World War II he directed the investigation of mica-bearing pegmatites in southeastern Brazil and synthesized a great complexity of occurrences into an orderly assortment of natural structural controls. His conclusions led to discovery of important mica deposits needed at a time of national emergency and earned him a reputation in Brazil that later led to his honorary election as a foreign member of the Brazilian Academy of Sciences.

His most spectacular research, however, evolved from his several years' effort on the alkalic igneous rocks of north-central Montana. Selecting the Bearpaw Mountains as the most complex geologic problem among alkali-rich, silica-poor volcanic provinces in North America, he personally directed a thorough mapping program with the aid of younger associates, mostly students, in order to derive the sequence and correlation of events in a rugged mountainous area of more than 1600 sq mi. Laboratory studies of selected suites of specimens led to a deep understanding of the geologic history, variations of magma movements with time, and geochemical affinities of each segment of the evolutionary development. He was able to trace the mineral facies changes of the mafic, potassium-rich magma to the felsic end members of the magma series and to demonstrate and predict characteristic concentrations of rare constituents such as zirconium, rare earths, columbium, barium, and strontium. His concept of ion complex transport explained metal concentrations.

Most peculiar to this province was the enrichment of carbonate in the nepheline syenite facies that resembled the silicate-carbonatites from Norway and Sweden. A detailed search of the literature, much of which was in foreign languages, led him to publish a critical world review of the carbonatite problem that received international recognition and stimulated laboratory experiments and papers by many others. This research demonstrated the validity of his view of carbonatites as a magmatic derivative, instead of ingested limestone inclusions. He followed this general paper by a specific one dealing with the silicate-carbonate sulfide volcanic neck in the Bearpaw Mountains. This pair of papers won him election to the National Academy of Sciences in 1965.

During his field investigations he collected many suites of minerals that puzzled him by their appearance and associations. Subsequent laboratory study with colleagues led to discovery of nine mineral species hitherto unknown to science. Their descriptions carried not only the customary physical and chemical characteristics but also detailed accounts of the natural rock and genetic associations to complete the full understanding of their formation.

Through his early researches Pecora became

known as a pioneer in the joint-discipline approach of geology, mineralogy, and geochemistry, equally at home with a field team or a laboratory group. Because of this capability he was selected in 1957 as chief of the Branch of Geochemistry and Petrology of the U.S. Geological Survey. By selective recruitment in subsequent years, he strengthened the research capability of the Geological Survey in these joint disciplines, with the result that an outstanding community of creative young research scientists was established. In 1964 he was appointed chief geologist of a division composed of some 1000 scientists, and in 1965 he was appointed director by President Johnson.

Pecora's field and laboratory investigations led to more than 40 scientific publications. Several of these deal with regional geologic problems in Alaska, the United States, and South America; others deal with specific problems in mineral occurrences or geologic theory. Some of his papers are: "Nepheline syenite pegmatites" (1942), in which he emphasizes the regrouping of elements to form a continuous sequence of minerals during the rock formation process; "Lazulite-scorzalite isomorphous series" (1950), in which he identifies a complete magnesium-iron substitution in an alumina phosphate mineral structure; "Geology of the Warrick Quadrangle, Montana" (1957), in which he displays the rock formations and structural habit of about 200 sq mi; and "Carbonatites: a review" (1956).

Born to parents of Italian ancestry, Pecora was the ninth of 10 children. He attended Barringer High School in Newark, N.J., and Princeton University, where he obtained his B.S. in geology in 1933. He received his Ph.D. in geology in 1940 from Harvard University. In 1939 he joined the U.S. Geological Survey as junior geologist and remained with that organization throughout his career. In 1965 he rose to its highest post, director. In that year he was elected to both the American Academy of Arts and Sciences and the National Academy of Sciences.

For background information *see* IGNEOUS ROCKS; MAGMA; MINERAL in the McGraw-Hill Encyclopedia of Science and Technology.   □

★ PEIERLS, Rudolf Ernst

British theoretical physicist
Born June 5, 1907, Berlin, Germany

WHEN PEIERLS began research in 1928, the laws of quantum mechanics had been formulated consistently, and it was possible to apply them to the many unexplained phenomena in atomic, molecular, and solid-state physics. His first work was in the theory of solids. He sug-

gested that the anomalous (positive) sign of the Hall effect in certain metals is due to the fact that the carriers of electricity are "holes" in an almost full band. Later (1930) he showed that the properties of the electron bands, which he had to assume to describe the positive sign of the Hall effect, followed even for a very weak periodic potential from the Bragg reflection of electron waves. In 1929 he developed the theory of heat conduction in nonmetalic crystals. P. J. W. Debye had shown that the mobility of lattice waves (phonons) in perfect crystals is limited by the mutual interaction of phonons because of anharmonic forces. Peierls showed that Debye's treatment was oversimplified and that the correct picture is very sensitive to details of the vibration spectrum of the lattice, so that in a one-dimensional model the phonon mean-free path would be infinite in spite of anharmonicities. He also showed the importance of "Umklapp" processes, which are essentially phonon interactions accompanied by Bragg reflection. These are rare at low temperatures, and he concluded that the thermal conductivity of a large perfect crystal should grow exponentially at low temperatures, a conclusion verified experimentally only in 1951.

Peierls also proposed a general theory of the diamagnetism of metals and the explanation of the oscillatory behavior of the susceptibility discovered by de Haas and van Alphen in bismuth in terms of L. D. Landau's theory of the quantization of electron orbits in the magnetic field. In 1940 Peierls solved a simple model, suggested by E. Orowan, for the forces opposing the motion of a dislocation in a crystal.

In nuclear physics Peierls contributed, jointly with H. A. Bethe, to the early theory of the neutron-proton system. He gave, with P. L.

Kapur (1938), the first complete treatment of resonances in nuclear collisions. Further work with Niels Bohr and G. Placzek on the general features of nuclear reactions was interrupted by the war and never finally written up. When analytic methods became important tools for studying scattering, Peierls was the first to point out (1954) that resonances and decaying states correspond to poles on the unphysical sheets of the Riemann surface for the relevant scattering amplitudes. In 1959 he gave a general formalism for scattering theory using these ideas. He developed with J. Yoccoz a way of connecting the rotational states of certain nuclei with the basic many-body problem (1957), and this method was improved in work with D. J. Thouless (1962).

When it became clear in the 1930s that the infinities arising in classical field theory from the assumption of point particles were still present in quantum theory, Peierls became interested in the possibility of particles of a small but finite size, as envisaged by H. A. Lorentz. Working with H. McManus (1949), Peierls showed how to reconcile a finite size with the requirements of relativity, and in later work with M. Chrétien (1954) he attempted to formulate a quantum theory of such "nonlocal" interactions. The conclusions were negative, but they provided some clarification of the problem.

During World War II, Peierls was mainly concerned with atomic energy. After uranium fission and the emission of secondary neutrons had been discovered, the possibility of releasing nuclear energy became of wide interest. Most work was then concentrated on the use of natural uranium, since large-scale isotope separation appeared unrealistic. Natural uranium could sustain a chain reaction only with thermal neutrons, and thus might open up the possibility of nuclear power (or, as was later seen, of producing plutonium), but had no direct military significance. In 1940 O. R. Frisch and Peierls noticed that one could make a plausible guess about the nuclear properties of uranium-235 on the basis of the ideas of Bohr and J. A. Wheeler, and that on this basis the critical size of a body of pure uranium-235 would be surprisingly small. A simple estimate of the energy released in a chain reaction in such a body showed that this would be a weapon of such formidable power that it would be well worth making the effort required to achieve large-scale isotope separation. Frisch and Peierls drew the attention of the British authorities to this early in 1940, and a committee was set up to examine the possibility of separating isotopes. The committee reported in 1941 that the production of an atomic weapon appeared feasible and recommended that greater efforts be made to develop the separation process. At this time Peierls was directing a small theoretical group concerned with the theory of isotope separation and with more precise methods for evaluating the chain reaction and its efficiency. In 1943 it was decided that it would not be economical to continue work

on nuclear energy in England in wartime, and Peierls was included in a number of scientists who were moved to the United States to help in the work of the Manhattan District. He first worked in New York, in consultation with the designers of the isotope separation plant, and later at Los Alamos.

Peierls studied at the University of Berlin, then under Arnold Sommerfeld at Munich, under Werner Heisenberg at Leipzig, and under Wolfgang Pauli at Zurich. He remained at Zurich from 1929 to 1932 as Pauli's research assistant. He held a Rockefeller fellowship at Rome and Cambridge (England) in 1932–33, a fellowship at the University of Manchester in 1933–35, and a research fellowship at the Royal Society Mond Laboratory, Cambridge, from 1935 until his appointment to a chair in the University of Birmingham in 1937, which he held until 1963. He then became Wykeham Professor of Theoretical Physics at Oxford and a fellow of New College. He was awarded the Order of the British Empire for his work on atomic energy in 1946, the Royal Medal of the Royal Society in 1959, the Lorentz Medal of the Netherlands Academy in 1962, and the Max Planck Medal of the German Physical Societies in 1963. He was elected a fellow of the Royal Society of London in 1945 and a foreign member of the American Academy of Arts and Sciences in 1963.

Peierls wrote *The Quantum Theory of Solids* (1955) and *The Laws of Nature* (1955).

For background information *see* BAND THEORY OF SOLIDS; CRYSTAL STRUCTURE; NUCLEAR EXPLOSION; NUCLEAR REACTION in the McGraw-Hill Encyclopedia of Science and Technology.   □

★ PETTIJOHN, Francis John

American geologist
Born June 20, 1904, Waterford, Wis., U.S.A.

BEGINNING AS a field assistant in 1924 to Frank Grout of the University of Minnesota, Pettijohn devoted a large part of his professional career to the study of Precambrian geology. Grout was then working on the problem of the Coutchiching, a formation of sedimentary origin thought to be the oldest rock in North America. Pettijohn's interest in the problems of the oldest rocks was aroused, and he spent the next decade in field study of these rocks. Heretofore the study of Precambrian sediments had been largely neglected; most work on the Precambrian centered about mining districts and was done largely by mining geologists and those more interested in the ores or in the problems of the igneous and metamorphic rocks.

While on a canoe trip in northwestern Ontario in 1927, Pettijohn encountered some Archean

conglomerates on Abram Lake, which became the subject of his doctoral dissertation. Pettijohn's work on the Archean rock culminated in his "Archean sedimentation" (1943)—a paper synthesizing what was then known about these ancient deposits. They were recognized by Pettijohn as belonging to a eugeosynclinal facies, that is, an assemblage of submarine lavas (greenstones) and dark sandstones, known as graywackes, comparable in all respects to younger formations of the same type such as the Franciscan (Jurassic-Cretaceous) of California and the late Paleozoic formations of the Harz Mountains in Germany. The rhythmically interbedded graywackes and slates were an enigmatic assemblage previously interpreted as fluvial or deltaic in origin; they were interpreted by Pettijohn (1950) as turbidite and pelagic sediments, respectively.

The contrast in structure and petrology of these graywackes and the cleaner quartzites of the much later Precambrian led to an interest in the petrology of sandstones in general and their geologic significance. This interest found expression in Pettijohn's papers on sandstone classification (1948, 1954) and on their chemical composition (1963). The graywackes were shown not to be indicative of any particular epoch or climatic regimen, but rather to be the product of turbidite sedimentation in a markedly unstable tectonic belt. They are the characteristic sandstone of folded mountain chains, arising from a eugeosyncline, and are not known to occur elsewhere.

Pettijohn's later work on the Precambrian centered about strata of younger age. This work, begun in earnest in 1943, was done largely under the auspices of the U.S. Geological Survey. Although the work led mainly to the unraveling of the stratigraphy and structure of the iron-bearing districts in Iron and Dickinson counties in Michigan and to the discovery of the Precambrian Fern Creek glacial beds, it brought Pettijohn's attention to the cross-bedding in the quartzites and to the utility of this structure in determining direction of current flow and sediment transport—the paleocurrent problem. Work by Pettijohn and his students in the Great Lakes region showed that there was a regionally consistent transport off the core area of the continent (the inner Canadian shield), a pattern of transport found to persist not only during late Precambrian, but also during the whole of the Paleozoic. Similar paleocurrent analyses were made in the central Appalachian region, where the Paleozoic sandstones were found to have been deposited by currents derived from the east and southeast, an observation which supported the somewhat discredited concept of "Appalachia"—a source land southeast of the present Appalachians. The stability and persistence of paleocurrent systems through time sheds an important light on continental evolution.

The work on cross-bedding led to an interest in other primary structures of sediments and their utility as paleocurrent indicators. This interest found expression in two books, written in collaboration with P. E. Potter: *Paleocurrents and Basin Analysis* (1963) and *Atlas and Glossary of Primary Sedimentary Structures* (1964). These were the first works of their kind. Pettijohn's work on Precambrian sediments, together with his teaching at the University of Chicago, led to a general review and synthesis of the field of sedimentary petrology—a review which first appeared in book form as *Sedimentary Rocks* (1949; 2d ed. rev. 1957), a work that was destined to be the standard reference on the subject for several decades.

Pettijohn was the oldest of six children of school teacher parents. He was educated wholly in public schools, receiving his B.A. in 1924, his M.A. in 1925, and his Ph.D. in 1930 from the University of Minnesota. He taught geology at Oberlin College from 1925 to 1927, joined the faculty of the University of Chicago in 1929, and advanced to professor of geology in 1945. In 1952 he left Chicago to go to Johns Hopkins University, where he became chairman of the department of geology in 1963. While at Chicago he was editor of the *Journal of Geology* from 1947 to 1952. He was geologist on the U.S. Geological Survey from 1943 to 1952 and consultant for Shell Development Co. from 1952 to 1963. Pettijohn was elected a fellow of the American Academy of Arts and Sciences in 1960, an honorary member of the Society of Economic Paleontologists and Mineralogists in 1964, corresponding member of the Geological Society of Finland in 1965, and member of the National Academy of Sciences in 1966.

Pettijohn also wrote *Manual of Sedimentary Petrography*, with W. C. Krumbein (1938).

For background information *see* PETROLOGY;

PRECAMBRIAN; SEDIMENTATION (GEOLOGY) in the McGraw-Hill Encyclopedia of Science and Technology.   □

★ PFAFFMANN, Carl

American physiological psychologist
Born May 27, 1913, New York, N.Y., U.S.A.

PFAFFMANN'S INTEREST in physiological psychology was focused early on the sense of taste, as well as smell. He pioneered the application of electrophysiological methods to the study of single nerve fibers arising from taste buds in different mammals. Although other workers at this time began to study taste by this method, his was the first extensive single-unit analysis of taste-receptor specificity. This early work of 1939 has since been confirmed and extended by other investigators to show that the mammalian taste receptors are selectively sensitive to salt-, sour-, bitter-, or sweet-eliciting stimuli, but they are not exclusively so. Many receptors respond to a combination of stimuli arousing these qualities. Chemical sensitivity in animals is differential, not sharp. Thus there are some receptor-fiber units that respond to salt plus sugar, others to acid plus salt and sugar, others to acid plus quinine, and so forth; receptors that react to only one of the basic taste stimuli are in the minority. These findings contrast with the recently revived classical view that there are four primary types of specific receptors in man, each responsible for salty, sour, bitter, and sweet sensations. As yet, however, no unit electrophysiology has been possible on humans. Since the original studies, Pfaffmann extended the observations to other species such as the cat, rat, hamster, and monkey, and along with other investigators he gave objective demonstration of species differences in taste sensitivity. In addition, he and his students (R. M. Benjamin, R. P. Erickson, J. P. Frommer, B. P. Halpern, S. G. Nord, and B. Oakley) explored the central neural pathways of taste by electrophysio-

logical recording in the medulla, thalamus, and cortex. Benjamin especially made an extensive study of the central nervous system taste pathways in his own laboratory. With M. M. Mozell and D. F. Mathews, Pfaffmann carried out electrophysiological studies of sensory coding in olfaction.

Using electrophysiological methods, Pfaffmann and his students carried out correlated studies of behavior. During adrenal insufficiency or deprivation of sodium ions, animals and often man show a sodium hunger and apparently greater sensitivity to sodium salts. Observations with J. K. Bare and M. Nachman showed that the taste receptors themselves are not modified in sensitivity. These results, along with work by other investigators, pointed to a change in central neural state rather than in the peripheral sense organ in specific hunger behavior. For these and other related studies Pfaffmann was awarded the Warren Medal of the Society of Experimental Psychologists in 1960 and the Distinguished Scientific Contribution Award of the American Psychological Association in 1963.

Adaptation of taste was studied with L. M. Bartoshuk and D. H. McBurney. That saliva affects taste sensitivity has long been known. By adapting the human tongue to pure water or different concentrations of sodium chloride lower than or greater than the salt concentrations of saliva, it was shown that the thresholds for salt taste can be raised or lowered in direct proportion to the concentration of the adapting solution. When the tongue is adapted to salt or other stimuli, the sensation of taste for the adapting solution disappears; but more interestingly, pure water and all solution below the adapting concentration have a complementary taste quality. Weak saline after adaptation to saline (NaCl) tastes bitter, water after such adaptation having the strongest bitter taste. These observations suggest that not only does adaptation change receptor sensitivity, but it may also activate or arouse a complementary taste system in a manner analogous to the arousal of complementary colors in the visual sense.

Studies on the motivating properties of taste have emphasized that, in lower animals at least, taste preferences have an innate basis for acceptance and rejection which can be modified to varying degrees by learning. The patterns of rejection-acceptance may be modified by the state of need or deprivation, taste stimulation interacting with metabolic and nutritional needs, so effectively in some cases that the animal can modify his dietary preferences to compensate for varying nutritional states. The extent to which these effects are seen in man is yet to be subjected to systematic analysis. But taste may not be an infallible guide in dietary self-selection. C. P. Richter's extension of the concept of homeostasis to include behavior as part of this basic principle is generally correct, although detailed studies show failures of homeostasis because the conditions may exceed the working limits of such mechanisms. Diseases, genetically determined deviations of sensitivity or metabolism, or unusual environmental or experimental conditions may lead to homeostatic shortcomings.

In addition to their role in appetite and eating, certain naturally palatable taste stimuli, like sugar, act as rewards for learning a variety of instrumental responses. Many organisms will learn to press a bar of a device which delivers a drop of sweetened solution. The rate of response, for example, number of bar presses, is proportional to concentration of the taste solution. The effectiveness of saccharin or other artificial sweetnesses as reinforcers for learning shows that the nutritive value of the solution is not essential. The "sweet tooth" appears to have a biological basis from taste stimulation alone. Interference with taste sensitivity not only reduces the organism's ability to select among different solutions but markedly reduces the effectiveness of taste as a reward for learning. Further neurophysiological study of taste should provide insight into the biological basis of reward and sensory pleasure.

Pfaffmann received a Ph.B. in 1933 and an M.A. in 1935 from Brown University. Appointed Rhodes scholar, he attended Oxford University, obtaining a B.A. in animal physiology and biochemistry in 1937. He worked under E. D. Adrian at Cambridge University as a research student and received a Ph.D. there in 1939. Returning to the United States in 1939, he spent 1 year with Detlev W. Bronk at the Johnson Foundation and then joined the faculty of Brown University in 1941. He remained there until 1965 except for a 4-year period in the U.S. Navy as an aviation psychologist during World War II. In 1965 he joined the Rockefeller University as vice-president and professor. He was elected to the American Academy of Arts and Sciences in 1957 and to the National Academy of Sciences in 1959.

For background information *see* CHEMO-RECEPTION; HOMEOSTASIS; TASTE in the McGraw-Hill Encyclopedia of Science and Technology. ◻

★ PIAGET, Jean

Swiss psychologist
Born Aug. 9, 1896, Neuchâtel, Switzerland

PIAGET'S HIGHER education focused on the fields of biology and philosophy, and between 1911 and 1925 he published about 25 studies on terrestrial and aquatic mollusks. This training was extremely useful for his subsequent psycho-

logical investigations and formed in him the habit of thinking simultaneously in terms of adaptation to environment and of an interiorly regulated development on the part of the subject.

While he wanted to devote himself to biology, he had an equal interest in the problems of objective knowledge and in epistemology. His decision to study the development of cognitive functions in the child was related to his wish to satisfy the two interests in one activity. By considering development as a kind of mental embryogenesis, one could construct a biological theory of knowledge. Various investigations on children's thinking were published by him from 1921 onward. At the same time he did not entirely abandon biological studies and published research in zoology (1929, 1965), as well as in botany (1966). A synthesis of these various interests is found in his *Biologie et connaissance* (1967), including his biological theory of knowledge.

Initially in his studies on the formation of intelligence and thinking in children he used predominantly verbal methods. These investigations concerned the relations of language and thinking, reasoning in the child, the child's representation of the physical world, his moral judgment, and his ideas on physical causality. These five investigations were restricted to verbal questions and answers, with no provision for concrete objects that the children could manipulate. Consequently, the results of the first works were limited and simply served to pose problems that were new at the time.

However, about 1936, having critically observed day by day the development of his own three children, Piaget was in a position to publish *The Origin of Intelligence in Children* (2d ed. 1953), *Play, Dreams, and Imitation in*

Childhood (1952), and *The Construction of Reality in the Child* (1954). In these works he studied for the first time the formation of intelligence and of thinking on the basis of sensory-motor actions. Particularly in the first and third volumes he was able to consider the psychological problems of thinking formation in an epistemological perspective. By an analysis of the manner in which the notions of the permanent object (until the child is 8–9 months old, objects hidden behind a screen are not considered to maintain their existence), of space, of time, and of causal relations are established, Piaget could demonstrate that they are not simply the result of perception or experience in the sense in which empiricists use the term. On the contrary, he discovered that a continual organizing activity on the part of the subject is necessary to lead to the formation of these fundamental structures.

Subsequently, as he studied and published, with A. Szeminska, *The Child's Conception of Number* (1952; paper 1965) and, with B. Inhelder, *Développement des quantités physiques*, Piaget reached an understanding of the development of intelligence different from that attained in his first books. He considered that the central mechanism of intelligence is found in the construction of operations that derive from the general coordinations of actions. The fundamental operations, such as uniting (related to inclusion and classification), serializing (related to order, chaining, and asymmetrical relations), equalizing, and interrelating, are actions that are interiorized (in part with the help of language but not deriving from it), reversible (through inversion and reciprocity), and coordinated in wholistic structures. At that time he started to study these structures formally, publishing *Classes, relations et nombres* (1942) and *Traité de logique* (1949), and he especially emphasized studies in an experimental manner. From these investigations stemmed the above-mentioned books on number and quantity, as well as the two books *Le développement de la notion de temps chez l'enfant* and *Les notions de mouvement et de vitesse chez l'enfant*. Then there followed a series of studies, undertaken with Inhelder, on space, chance, elementary logical structures, and the work published as *The Growth of Logical Thinking from Childhood to Adolescence* (1958). These numerous works, not all of which have appeared in English translations, demonstrate clearly that operational structures are characterized by the forming of notions of conservation (conservation of a whole, of continuous quantity in concrete material, of length, of surfaces, and so on). The beginnings of such notions can even be observed between 4 and 6 years of age at the preoperational stage of thinking.

Over a long period of time Piaget studied the development of perception in children, resulting in the book *Les mécanismes perceptifs* (1961). With Inhelder, he published *L'image mentale chez l'enfant* and completed a study of memory as it develops between 3–4 and 11–12 years of age. All these investigations were carried out by constantly relating the particular phenomenon to the formation of intellectual operations.

Another major interest of Piaget's career was epistemology. Philosophical epistemology asks about the nature of knowledge in general. However, because all knowledge is continually evolving and in no branch can be said to be closed, it appeared to him more scientific to reformulate the problem thus: How does knowledge come about? This question implies an attempt to explain knowledge through its formation and its development. *Introduction à l'épistémologie génétique* (3 vols., 1950) enlarged upon these notions. Based on these ideas an International Center of Genetic Epistemology was created at Geneva by Piaget and numerous collaborators, and it has already published some 22 volumes. Quite recently appeared *Logique et connaissance scientifique* as a volume in the *Encyclopédie de la pléiade*, in which present and former members of the center collaborated in a new presentation of epistemological questions. He considered epistemology as a science distinct from philosophy and upheld this proposition more directly in a small book that caused lively discussion in Europe. In this book, *Uses and Abuses of Philosophy*, he suggested that philosophy does not attain a "knowledge" but rather a "wisdom," as long as its investigation does not become dissociated as a specialized science, precisely as is the case with genetic epistemology.

After studying at the universities of Neuchâtel, Zurich, and Paris, Piaget became a privatdozent in 1921. In 1926 he was appointed professor of philosophy at Neuchâtel and in 1929 professor of child psychology and of history of scientific thought at Geneva. He also became director of the International Bureau of Education in 1929. From 1937 to 1954 he was professor of general psychology at Lausanne University and from 1952 to 1963 at the Sorbonne. He was elected a foreign member of the U.S. National Academy of Sciences in 1966.

For background information *see* LEARNING THEORIES; PSYCHOLOGY, PHYSIOLOGICAL AND EXPERIMENTAL; SENSORY LEARNING; VERBAL LEARNING in the McGraw-Hill Encyclopedia of Science and Technology.   □

★ PICKERING, Sir George (White)

British physician
Born June 26, 1904, Whalton, Northumberland, England

Pickering's work was chiefly concerned with vascular disease in man, and in particular with high blood pressure and diseases that afflict the coronary and cerebral vessels. He was trained in the Cambridge School of Physiology under J. Barcroft, E. D. Adrian, and F. G. Hopkins.

After qualifying as a doctor at St. Thomas's Hospital, he went to work with Sir Thomas Lewis, the pioneer of clinical science, at University College Hospital. Pickering saw clearly that the problem of raised arterial pressure in man should be capable of simple physiological analysis.

It was known that arterial hypertension in man sometimes followed kidney disease and in other cases existed as a disease in its own right (essential hypertension). Pickering showed that many of the theories about the diseases were based on inadequate evidence; for example, that the raised blood pressure was not due to sensitivity to adrenalin, to overaction of the vasomotor center, or to overaction of the sympathetic nerves. He was unable to demonstrate a pressor substance circulating in the blood. His thoughts turned to the possibility of a chemical agent fixed by the receptors in the arterial walls. Here the obvious claimant was renin, discovered in 1898 by the Finnish physiologist Tigerstedt but afterward lost. Early experiments were a failure until, in desperation kidney extracts were tested on an unanesthetized rabbit.

Pickering and M. Prinzmetal described the existence and properties of renin to the Physiological Society in 1937. In 1934 Harry Goldblatt of Cleveland had shown that constricting the renal arteries would produce in the dog a sustained hypertension resembling that in man. Pickering and his colleagues showed that prolonged intravenous infusion of renin would produce a sustained hypertension but that the pressure could never be driven so high as after renal artery constriction. They showed that there were differences between the hypertension developing soon after renal artery constriction and that continuing later: The first was compatible with renin release, the latter was not. Pickering and Prinzmetal also found that renin had a profound effect on the renal tubular reabsorption of sodium and chloride. Renin was subsequently shown by Braun-Menendez and his colleagues in Buenos Aires and by Page and his colleagues in Indianapolis to be an enzyme splitting off a vasoactive polypeptide from a plasma protein. This polypeptide angiotensin was first isolated by S. Peart, a member of Pickering's staff, and its amino acid sequence determined by Elliott and Peart. Skeggs and his colleagues at Cleveland did the same, while Schwyzer quickly synthesized the vasoactive octa- and decapeptides. The renin angiotensin system is now a subject for worldwide investigation. Unfortunately, this promising contender for the hypertension stakes is now out of favor. One function alone can be attributed to it, that of regulating sodium balance through aldosterone secretion by the adrenal gland. It may be an intrarenal hormone. It is almost certainly not the agent responsible for the common form of hypertension in man.

Pickering's failure to identify a single specific mechanism for high blood pressure in man led him to wonder if indeed there was one. One alleged fact stood out, that essential hypertension was inherited as a mendelian dominant. However, close inspection showed that the evidence was as full of holes as a sieve. It seemed important to try and establish the point one way or another, so M. Hamilton, Pickering, E. S. G. Sowry, and J. A. Fraser Roberts made a survey of arterial pressure in (1) a sample of the population at large, (2) first-degree relatives of patients with essential hypertension, and (3) first-degree relatives of patients of similar age and sex but without essential hypertension. This survey established that the so-called dividing line between normal blood pressure and hypertension is nothing more nor less than an artifact; that arterial pressure tends to rise with age, and more in some subjects than others; and that the first-degree relatives of patients with essential hypertension have higher pressure at all ages. Analysis provided evidence of graded or polygenic inheritance, as in the classical case of stature. This hypothesis of the inheritance of arterial pressure has now been firmly established for the population at large by the careful work of W. E. Miall and P. D. Oldham in southern Wales.

It then became apparent that essential hypertension represented a type of disease new to medical thought, a disease characterized by a quantitative deviation from the norm. Pickering originally enunciated this concept in 1942 to explain the supervention of the so-called malignant phase of hypertension. The genetic data pointed in the same direction, and so did common sense, for arterial pressure is a quantity and can only be treated as a quality artifactually. This new approach to essential hypertension proved extremely fruitful in explaining the variable course and symptomatology of essential hypertension, but it is still looked at askance by the majority of physicians.

Through his experience with patients Pickering became extremely interested in transient attacks of blindness and paralysis. These were attributed to vascular spasm, a hypothesis which Pickering could not accept. One evening a patient was admitted to his service with a stroke. The patient had had several brief ones before, also a blindness attack. He again developed an attack of blindness, and Pickering's resident, R. W. Ross Russell, observed a white body emerging from the central artery of the retina and passing distally. The patient was operated on at once. He had an atheromatous plaque in the carotid artery on which were layers of thrombus of different ages. The newest was quite fresh, had occluded the artery, and was composed mostly of platelets. A fragment of this thrombus had passed through the arteries of the eye, giving transient blindness. It was evident from the layering on the plaque that there had been several episodes of thrombosis.

This chance observation was the beginning of an intensive period of observation and experiment by J. A. Honour, J. R. A. Mitchell, Ross Russell, and others of Pickering's staff. They concluded that the cerebral vascular disease responsible for stroke consists of two utterly different components. One, specifically associated with high arterial pressure, is represented by aneurysms of the small cerebral arteries, which tend to rupture and produce cerebral hemorrhage. This disease, discovered by Charcot and Bouchard in 1868 and rediscovered by Ross Russell in 1963, is a weakening of the middle coat of small arteries. The second disease is atheroma, a thickening of the inner coat of big arteries. This disease is a general one, maiming or killing because thrombi tend to form on the plaques projecting from the inner coat into the arterial lumen. These thrombi stop the blood flow to the tissues supplied by the artery, producing gangrene, infarction of the heart (coronary thrombosis), or stroke. Pickering's group collected much evidence from man to suggest that the whole disease is thrombotic. Platelet thrombi form on the arterial wall, age and lose their structure, and become organized as fibrous or fibro-fatty plaques. The thrombus that occludes is the decisive event in a series that in a smaller way has been progressing for some time. This hypothesis has begun to stimulate a spate of new work, which it is hoped may serve to identify the factors leading to thrombosis and thus to the prevention of coronary heart disease and stroke.

Pickering took first class honors in the Natural Science Tripos at Cambridge University in 1925–26 and an M.B. in 1930 at St. Thomas's Hospital, London University, in 1930. He was appointed to the Regius Chair of Medicine at Oxford University in 1956. He was president of the British Medical Association in 1963–64. Elected a foreign member of the American Academy of Arts and Sciences in 1959, he became a fellow of the Royal Society of London in 1960. He was knighted in 1957.

For background information *see* CIRCULATION DISORDERS; HYPERTENSION in the McGraw-Hill Encyclopedia of Science and Technology.   □

★ PINCUS, Gregory

American biologist
Born Apr. 9, 1903, Woodbine, N.J., U.S.A.
Died Aug. 22, 1967, Boston, Mass., U.S.A.

PINCUS'S SCIENTIFIC career was launched at Harvard University under the joint influence of William E. Castle, geneticist, and William J. Crozier, general physiologist. The overall aim of his early research was the study of the inheritance of physiological traits. With Crozier, he discovered quantifiable tropistic behavior in rats and analyzed the mode of transmission of proprioceptive function. Concomitant studies of temperature-responsive reactions in newborn mice led to investigation of the transmission of reaction mechanisms governing respiratory movements and heartbeat in inbred mouse strains. The opportunity to analyze the extensive data of the Joslin Clinic resulted in publications on the inheritance of diabetes mellitus as an age-conditioned genetic disease.

A curiosity about the developmental sequences leading to the manifestation of certain genetic traits in mammals led to a study of the early stages of rat and rabbit ova, the nature of their fertilization, and the means of studying their development in vitro. The observation of spontaneous parthenogenetic activation of rabbit ova in culture initiated a long series of studies concerned with the artificial activation of mammalian eggs and the behavior and development of normally fertilized and artificially activated eggs in vivo and in vitro. In collaboration with his students and his colleagues E. V. Enzmann and N. T. Werthessen, Pincus achieved long-term development of rabbit ova in culture and demonstrated on transplantation to foster mothers the feasibility of following into fetal life the subsequent development of cultured ova. After establishing exposure to low temperature as a ready means of inducing rabbit ovum parthenogenesis, Pincus and H. Shapiro developed a method of cooling rabbit ova in the Fallopian tubes and even obtained a rare parthenogont. Studies of human ova revealed also a capacity for parthenogenetic activation.

Pincus found almost at once that certain phases of ovum development in vivo were regulated by ovarian hormone secretion. Therefore, he launched a series of studies on female sex hormone biogenesis and metabolism along with investigations of the action of ovarian hormones on ovum travel, uterine function, and blastocyst and embryo maintenance. The extreme dependence of the uterine blastocyst upon progestational hormone and studies of factors affecting blastocyst growth in vitro suggested modes of action of gestogen upon the uterus as a mediator in the proper nutrition of the growing ova.

With W. H. Pearlman, Pincus extended the work on steroid hormone metabolism to the human and soon observed defects in steroid metabolism in the cancerous state. Work with sex steroids was extended to adrenocortical steroids, and preceding and during World War II Pincus, H. Hoagland, and their colleagues concerned themselves with aviation and war-work fatigue, adrenocortical function, and means of effecting useful hormonal equilibria. These investigations led to a series of studies of adrenocortical and sex hormone function in mental and physical stress conditions. At the same time, with L. P. Romanoff, Pincus initiated studies of variations of steroid excretion in aging. These studies were continued in a series of investigations of steroid production rates in young and elderly subjects, of the effects of various trophic hormones, and of age-conditioned decrements in steroid production. Replacement therapy in aging persons was attempted by steroid medication.

Studies of steroid production and transformation by adrenals and ovaries perfused in vitro, with a team of investigators guided by O. Hechter, led to the formulation of the first experimentally substantiated scheme of steroid hormone biogenesis. These studies were extended to other in vitro systems by R. I. Dorfman and colleagues with a thorough examination of the enzymatic mechanisms involved.

Responding to the need for an oral contraceptive described by Margaret Sanger early in the 1950s, Pincus and M. C. Chang initiated a series of animal studies which led to the development of oral contraception. They decided to concentrate on the natural periods of anovulation, for example, pregnancy and pseudopregnancy, and the hormonal influences determining anovulation. Using the rabbit as an experimental animal, they soon found that progestins were excellent ovulation inhibitors and that the 19-norsteroids included orally effective progestins. The extension of their findings to the human was first made in collaboration with J. Rock and C. R. Garcia. Millions of women now use the cyclic estrogen-progestin regime of Pincus, Rock, and Garcia for contraception and menstrual-cycle regulation. In recent years Pincus, J. Jacques, and U. K. Banik developed ovum implantation in animals, and their studies are being extended to the human.

Pincus did his undergraduate work at Cornell University (B.S., 1924). He received his M.S. and D.Sc. from Harvard University in 1927. As a National Research Council fellow, he conducted his postdoctoral research at Harvard, Cambridge University, and the Kaiser Wilhelm Institute. Returning from Europe to Harvard, Pincus became an assistant professor of general physiology. He went to Cambridge in 1937 and then to Clark University in 1938 as professor of experimental zoology. In 1944 he founded, with H. Hoagland, the Worcester Foundation for Experimental Biology, where he was first director of laboratories and then research director. Among the awards for his work in reproductive physiology, Pincus received the Albert D. Lasker Prize and the Cameron Prize in Practical Therapeutics. He was elected to the American Academy of Arts and Sciences in 1939 and to the National Academy of Sciences in 1965.

Pincus edited the 20-odd volumes of *Recent Progress in Hormone Research*, resulting from the Laurentian Hormone Conference, which he founded. With K. V. Thimann he edited *Hormones: Physiology, Chemistry and Applications* (5 vols., 1948–64). He wrote *The Control of Fertility* (1965) and *Steroid Dynamics*, with others (1966).

For background information *see* EMBRYOLOGY, EXPERIMENTAL; ESTROGEN; OVUM; STEROID in the McGraw-Hill Encyclopedia of Science and Technology.   □

★ PIPPARD, Alfred Brian

British physicist
Born Sept. 7, 1920, London, England

PIPPARD BELONGED to that considerable group of scientists whose careers were largely determined by World War II. As a boy, he had been attracted by the curiosities of low-temperature physics, but he was discouraged by his lack of outstanding mathematical ability from making this his principal interest. He intended to be a chemist until the war deflected him to physics

and thence, on graduation in 1941, to the design of radar aerials. After the war he returned to Cambridge and to low-temperature physics. He concentrated on the task of applying microwaves to the study of superconductors, a field of research Heinz London had pioneered in the 1930s, which was ripe for the new techniques developed for radar. Pippard's studies in the following 10 years yielded information about superconductors more precise than any available earlier, especially concerning the way in which electric currents flow without resistance in a thin layer at the surface of the metal. By measuring the thickness (about 1000 A) of this penetration layer and its variation with temperature and especially purity, he was led to conclude that the electrons in superconductors possess a property he called "coherence"—any attempt to change the properties at one point by applying a suitable disturbance influences the metal over a distance which in pure metals is usually greater than the penetration layer. From this starting point he elaborated an equation relating current and magnetic field which was a nonlocal extension of the earlier equation of Fritz and Heinz London. At the same time in the Soviet Union, V. L. Ginsburg and L. D. Landau were developing a deeper theory which contained many of Pippard's crude ideas in quantitative form but ignored nonlocal effects. In 1957, when the definitive theory of superconductivity was developed by John Bardeen, L. N. Cooper, and J. R. Schrieffer, it was found to provide a consistent explanation for both sets of ideas. Shortly afterward Pippard's guess that impurities in the metal could shorten the coherence length were confirmed in the theory and put to practical use in the production of dirty superconductors having the important technological property of carrying currents and generating extremely strong magnetic fields without reappearance of their resistance.

Meanwhile, Pippard's investigation of microwave conduction in normal (nonsuperconduct-ing) metals resulted in the elucidation of another nonlocal phenomenon, the anomalous skin effect, in collaboration with G. E. H. Reuter, E. H. Sondheimer, and R. G. Chambers. It was discovered that the absorption of microwaves at the surface of a given metal at low temperatures is governed by one particular characteristic of the conduction electrons (the shape of the Fermi surface). This started a sequence of experiment and theory in many laboratories which transformed understanding of the dynamical laws governing the motion of electrons in metals and of the way in which one metal differs from another in the details of this motion. Pippard's contribution was the application of the anomalous skin effect to the first determination of a Fermi surface, that of copper, which he carried out as a visiting professor in Chicago in 1956; this had the effect of encouraging others, notably David Shoenberg, to apply their already sophisticated experimental techniques to similar ends, using such phenomena as the de Haas–Van Alphen effect, which has proved extremely powerful for this work. In this way the earlier ideas of William Shockley and Lars Onsager have come to fruition in the concentration of attention on the Fermi surface as a geometrical shape defining the properties of the electrons. This new approach to metals is developed systematically in Pippard's *Dynamics of Conduction Electrons* (1964), the aim of which is to demonstrate how well most problems in metallic conduction can be understood in terms of an almost classical, deterministic description of particle motion. One exception is the phenomenon of magnetic breakdown, in which partial Bragg reflection of electrons, when they execute orbits in a magnetic field, may lead to specifically quantal effects, revealed experimentally as vigorous oscillations of resistance as a function of magnetic field. In developing a successful network model, Pippard gave a further example of the power of geometrical ideas in this field of physics.

Son of an eminent professor of engineering, Pippard was educated at Cambridge University (B.A., 1941; M.A., 1945), where he spent most of his scientific life. He was elected to the Plummer Chair of Physics in 1960, and in 1965 he was appointed the first president of a new graduate college, Clare Hall. He was elected a fellow of the Royal Society of London in 1956 and was awarded its Hughes Medal in 1959. The British and French Physical Societies awarded him the Holweck Prize in 1961.

Besides the work cited, Pippard wrote *Elements of Classical Thermodynamics* (1957) and *Cavendish Problems in Classical Physics* (1962).

For background information *see* BAND THEORY OF SOLIDS; MICROWAVE; RADAR; SUPERCONDUCTIVITY in the McGraw-Hill Encyclopedia of Science and Technology.   □

★ PITTS, Robert Franklin

American physiologist and medical scientist
Born Oct. 24, 1908, Indianapolis, Ind., U.S.A.

For most of Pitts's scientific career the study of the function of the kidney provided both investigative charm and challenge. The charm derived from the circumstance that this organ is ideally suited for precise physiological study: one artery, one vein, one ureter. Arterial input, venous output, and product may all be sampled without significant interference with function. The challenge derived from the circumstance that the kidney is primarily a regulatory organ, charged with the maintenance of composition and volume of the body fluids. The investigative questions which may be asked are, therefore, legion; the significance of the questions and the clarity with which they are posed need be limited only by the imagination and ingenuity of the questioner.

For more than two decades the renal mechanisms which regulate the acid-base balance of the body have been major concerns of Pitts, to which he has returned repeatedly as new techniques and concepts have made further advances possible. In 1945, in association with Robert S. Alexander, he provided the first definitive evidence that the hydrogen ions which are excreted in the urine as titratable buffer acid are secreted by the renal tubules in exchange for sodium ions. Because sulfanilamide, a known inhibitor of carbonic anhydrase, greatly reduced the excretion of titratable acid, he postulated that the hydrogen ions secreted by the renal tubules are derived from cellular carbonic acid. Subsequent studies by Pitts and William D. Lotspeich demonstrated that bicarbonate is reabsorbed indirectly by this same mechanism of ion exchange. Thus the exchange of cellular hydrogen ions for sodium ions converts the filtered bicarbonate within the tubular lumen to carbonic acid. This acid dehydrates to carbon dioxide and diffuses into tubular cells where it is reconverted to carbonic acid. The hydrogen ions, dissociated from this cellular carbonic acid, are fed into the secretory machinery and cycled into the tubular urine. Their bicarbonate counter ions, in association with equivalent numbers of sodium ions, are restored to the renal venous blood. Bicarbonate reabsorption, like titratable acid excretion, is reduced by inhibitors of carbonic anhydrase. Accordingly, a single ion-exchange mechanism accomplishes two ends: the secretion of titratable acid and the conservation of circulating stores of bicarbonate. Within limits, they vary reciprocally in such a way as to maintain constancy of bicarbonate concentration of extracellular fluid.

A third important aspect of renal regulation of acid-base balance is the tubular secretion of ammonia. Quite early in his studies Pitts postulated that the secretion of ammonia is passive and dependent on the diffusion of the lipid soluble free base, NH_3, from tubular cells, where it is generated, into acid tubular urine, where it buffers hydrogen ions to form nondiffusible ammonium ions. Buffering of hydrogen ions by ammonia at their site of secretion permits their continued transport into the urine against a low gradient of concentration. Buffering greatly reduces the energy cost of secretion. This concept has been firmly established by recent kinetic studies which have demonstrated that the free base ammonia reaches diffusion equilibrium throughout all phases of the kidney (intracellular, extracellular, and intratubular) in less than transit time of blood through the kidney. Diffusion of ammonia is therefore extremely rapid and not a factor which limits rate of excretion. Production rather than diffusion is rate limiting.

For the past 5 years most of Pitts's investigative effort was directed toward an assessment of the contribution of various circulating plasma precursors to the renal production of ammonia and toward an elucidation of the biochemical pathways of ammonia production in vivo. New techniques of study involving the controlled infusion of compounds labeled with isotopic nitrogen-15 into one renal artery showed that about 60% of the ammonia produced by the kidney is derived from the amide nitrogen of glutamine, 30% from the amino nitrogen of glutamine, and about 10% from a variety of amino acids, including alanine, glycine, and glutamic acid.

The renal metabolism of glutamine by pathways involving both glutaminase and glutamine amino transferase plus omega amidase, as well as the production of ammonia from other sources by transamination and oxidative deamination of glutamate, was demonstrated in vivo. Alanine and serine are produced by the kidney and added to renal venous blood in highly significant amounts. They are formed by transamination of pyruvate and hydroxypyruvate, and rates of formation are determined by the concentrations of the several reactants in renal tissue. Such studies presage the recent interests of Pitts in the metabolism of organic acids by the intact functioning kidney, an investigative field potentially rich, yet little exploited to the present. Past studies of the buffering capacities of blood and tissues and of the renal and respiratory compensations for excesses of acid or alkali contributed to an overall understanding of the means by which the reaction of body fluids is stabilized within narrow limits of normal.

In addition to his work on acid-base balance, Pitts studied a number of regulatory functions of the kidney and a variety of discrete transport mechanisms involved in these activities. These latter include renal transport mechanisms for sodium, potassium, phosphate, chloride, sulfate, calcium, creatine, phenol red, para-aminohippurate, urea, α-ketoglutarate, and a number of amino acids. Control of phosphate and calcium transport by parathyroid hormone and of sodium, chloride, and potassium by adrenal steroids briefly occupied his attention. The interaction of renal hemodynamics and the reabsorption and excretion of salt and water led into an extensive series of studies on the mode of action of diuretics, including organic mercurial compounds, xanthines, sulfonamides, thiazides, and the cardiac glycosides. Certain structure activity relationships for mercurial diuretics were defined, including the necessity for a terminal mercury atom and a hydrophilic group not less than three carbon atoms distant from the mercury. A two-point attachment was postulated to be necessary for diuretic activity. The early papers of Pitts on acid excretion, bicarbonate reabsorption, and the sensitivity of both processes to carbonic anhydrase inhibitors stimulated Arnold S. Relman and William B. Schwartz to investigate the diuretic activity of sulfanilamide in patients in congestive failure. The modest efficacy of the drug catalyzed the synthesis of new agents, including acetazoleamide, dichlorphenamide, and the presently used and highly effective thiazide diuretics. Finally, several purely hemodynamic studies were concerned with the distribution of blood flow between cortex and medulla, the action of acetylcholine and norepinephrine on distribution of flow, the autoregulation of renal blood flow and glomerular filtration rate, and the effects of dietary protein and amino acid metabolism on blood flow and filtration rate. Occasional excursions into comparative physiology contributed to knowledge of renal function in teleost and elasmobranch fishes, the chicken, and the rat.

For a period of some 4 years, between 1938 and 1942, Pitts forsook the kidney to engage in neurophysiological research. In association with Stephen W. Ranson and Horace W. Magoun, he described the respiratory centers of the cat, including their inspiratory and expiratory medullary divisions and a pontile pneumotaxic division. Two feedback systems, one peripheral and involving the vagi and one resident entirely within the brainstem, were described as contributing to the rhythm of breathing. In association with Detlev W. Bronk and Martin G. Larrabee, he studied the neural connections among hypothalamus, medulla, spinal cord, and sympathetic neuroeffectors in relation to control of heart rate and blood pressure.

Pitts received his B.S. with majors in zoology and chemistry from Butler University in 1929 and his Ph.D. in zoology from Johns Hopkins University in 1932. Teaching, research, and the study of medicine occupied the next 6 years at New York University College of Medicine, where he received his M.D. in 1938. It was under the tutelage of Homer W. Smith at the university that Pitts developed his interest in renal physiology. He became assistant professor of physiology at the N.Y.U. College of Medicine (1940), then at Cornell University Medical College (1942), associate professor at Cornell (1944), and professor and department head at Syracuse University Medical College (1946). In 1950 he became professor of physiology and chairman of the department of physiology and biophysics of Cornell Medical College. For his contributions to knowledge of renal function Pitts was awarded the Borden Prize of the Association of American Medical Colleges in 1960, the Homer W. Smith Award in Renal Physiology of the New York Heart Association in 1961, and the New York University Medical Alumni Award in 1962. Pitts was president of the American Physiological Society (1959) and of the Harvey Society (1960). He was elected to the National Academy of Sciences in 1956 and the American Academy of Arts and Sciences in 1957.

Pitts wrote *The Physiological Basis of Diuretic Therapy* (1959) and *Physiology of the Kidney and Body Fluids* (1963).

For background information *see* KIDNEY; URINARY SYSTEM in the McGraw-Hill Encyclopedia of Science and Technology.   □

★ PITZER, Kenneth Sanborn

American chemist
Born Jan. 6, 1914, Pomona, Calif., U.S.A.

WITH THE development in the first third of the 20th century of nonrelativistic quantum mechanics and quantum statistical mechanics, it became apparent both that a sound basic theory of chemistry had been found and that this theory was so complex as to be useless in the direct

solution of most chemical problems. Pitzer pioneered in the development of useful approximations, which made possible the calculation of chemical thermodynamic properties of broad classes of chemical substances. These results not only provided predictions as to the direction in which chemical reactions would occur and gave the location of their equilibrium points as a function of temperature, but also provided a basis for the interpretation of the rates of reactions with statistical rate theory. In addition to theoretical contributions, Pitzer made thermodynamic and spectroscopic measurements of key properties in order to check theoretical approximations or to provide empirical parameters.

The simplest series of organic compounds is that of the paraffin hydrocarbons. All members except the first comprise molecules which have internal rotational motions in addition to the simple vibrations, translation, and overall rotation. The quantum theory for the latter motions was relatively simple, but that for an internal rotation restricted by a potential barrier was quite complex. By providing general tables of the contributions of an internal rotation to the various thermodynamic properties, Pitzer made it possible to deal with the entire paraffin series and, later, with other hydrocarbon series.

It was found by J. D. Kemp and Pitzer that a potential barrier near 3 kcal per mole restricted the internal rotation in ethane. This result, with extensions to related paraffins, removed a series of contradictions which had arisen from earlier work which assumed a zero barrier to rotation about single bonds.

Subsequent theoretical work dealt with more complex types of molecular motion, such as the internal rotation of unsymmetrical groups, the pseudo rotation of the puckering of cyclopentane and similar ring molecules, and the inversion of molecules such as ammonia and cyclohexane which exist in forms distorted in either of two equivalent directions from a more symmetrical structure. In the case of most substituted cyclohexanes the two distortions are no longer equivalent. A theory of dimethylcyclohexanes demonstrated the distinction between axial and equatorial methyl groups, and satisfactorily fitted the entropies and enthalpies of all seven isomers, provided the cis- and trans-1,3-dimethylcyclohexanes were interchanged from the assignment then current. This reversal of the cis and trans assignment was confirmed by other evidence. A general theory of conformational analysis of six-membered rings was developed especially by D. H. R. Barton, from the foundations provided by this research on methylcyclohexanes.

The theory for individual molecules yields thermodynamic properties for substances in the ideal gas state. In order to extend these results to nonideal gases, liquids, and solids, appropriate approximations were developed for the statistical theories for many-molecule systems. The theoretical criteria for conformity to the principle of corresponding states were identified, but this principle does not provide a satisfactory approximation. It was found, however, that an extension of corresponding states theory by inclusion of a third parameter, called the acentric factor, did provide a good approximation to the properties of normal fluids. A qualitative theoretical picture was developed for the acentric factor, which was, however, defined precisely in terms of the relation of vapor pressure to temperature. General tables were prepared on the basis of the acentric factor theory for volumetric and thermodynamic properties throughout the liquid, gas, and supercritical regions for fluids. This work has been extended by others, especially J. M. Prausnitz.

In addition to the sequence of investigations already described, Pitzer contributed to such diverse topics as the synthesis of aluminum alkyls, the heat of ionization of weak acids and bases and of water, the nature of C_3 and higher species in carbon vapor, and the hydrogen bond in KHF_2, which was the first example with the proton symmetrically located.

Pitzer received his B.S. in 1935 from the California Institute of Technology and his Ph.D. in 1937 from the University of California. He joined the faculty of the University of California at Berkeley in 1937 as an instructor, and he was promoted through the ranks, becoming professor of chemistry in 1945. He served as assistant dean of letters and science in 1947–48 and as dean of the College of Chemistry from 1951 to 1960. While on leave from the University of California he served as technical director of the Maryland Research Laboratories (for war research) in 1943–44 and again as director of the Division of Research of the Atomic Energy Commission from 1949 to 1951. He was a member of the General Advisory Committee of the Atomic

Energy Commision from 1958 to 1965, and in 1964 was appointed to the President's Science Advisory Committee. In 1961 Pitzer became president and professor of chemistry at Rice University. Besides several honorary degrees and other science awards, Pitzer in 1965 received the Gilbert Newton Lewis Medal of the American Chemical Society. He was elected to the National Academy of Sciences in 1949 and to the American Philosophical Society in 1954.

In addition to nearly 200 articles in chemical journals, Pitzer wrote *Quantum Chemistry* (1953) and *Thermodynamics*, with L. Brewer (rev. 2d ed. 1961), a major revision of the classic text on that subject by G. N. Lewis and M. Randall. He also collaborated with F. D. Rossini and others in *Selected Values of Physical and Thermodynamic Properties of Hydrocarbons and Related Compounds* (1947; 2d ed. 1953).

For background information *see* QUANTUM MECHANICS; STATISTICAL MECHANICS; THERMODYNAMICS (CHEMICAL) in the McGraw-Hill Encyclopedia of Science and Technology.   □

★ PONTECORVO, Guido

British geneticist
Born Nov. 29, 1907, Pisa, Italy

FOR THE first 9 years after graduation Pontecorvo was engaged in organizing a selective breeding program, centered in Florence, for the beef and draft cattle of Tuscany. Toward the end of 1938 on his way from Italy—which he left because of political circumstances—to similar work in Peru, he was invited to work on animal breeding at the Institute of Animal Genetics in Edinburgh. There the geneticist H. J. Muller, later to become a Nobel Laureate, happened to be a research visitor on his way from Moscow to his native United States. This happy accident immediately shifted Pontecorvo's interests from animal breeding to pure genetics. He was intro-

duced to genetics by one of its foremost founders, and under Muller's guidance he attacked the following problem.

Two very similar species of *Drosophila* (*melanogaster* and *simulans*) can be crossed, but the hybrids are completely sterile. There was, therefore, at that time no possibility of carrying through further generations the analysis of how the genetic makeup of the two species diverged in evolution. By rearing hybrids from eggs of triploid *melanogaster* fertilized by heavily irradiated sperms of *simulans* it was possible to obtain in the first generation hybrids with some of the combinations of chromosomes of the two species which would have arisen in later generations if it had been possible to breed the hybrids. This work was expanded later when Pontecorvo worked in the department of zoology at the University of Glasgow in 1941. The main conclusion was that the two species diverged mainly by pairs, or higher combinations, of complementary changes in their genetic constitution. In this early work the challenge was that of a biological situation apparently impervious to further probe. This sort of challenge repeatedly influenced the directions of Pontecorvo's later research, for instance, in his approach to the genetics of fungi lacking a sexual stage, or in his attempts to carry out genetic analysis in man, bypassing sexual reproduction by means of somatic cell cultures.

In Glasgow, where he moved in 1941, at the suggestion of the parasitologist E. Hindle, Pontecorvo investigated the puzzle of the erratic sex ratios in the progeny of single pairs of the human body louse. At that time research on lice could only be carried out by rearing them on oneself, and for this work many hundreds had to be reared at one time. Though this research did not solve the puzzle of the sex ratios, it led to the discovery that proceeding differently from the usual situation in most animals and flowering plants, meiosis in the male of the body louse is followed by six divisions before spermatogenesis. It also showed that during these six divisions the haploid nuclei of the germ cells play little or no part in the activities of the cells themselves: Enormous doses of x-rays, which shatter the chromosomes, do not interfere with the normal sequences of these six divisions, or with the complex process of differentiation into spermatozoa which follows them.

In 1943 Pontecorvo's interest was diverted toward the genetics of fungi. The initial motivation was the conviction that genetics could contribute substantially to the production of strains of *Penicillium* with higher yields of penicillin, at that time desperately needed. There was also the intellectual stimulus from the first successes of microbial genetics. Ø. Winge had shown that yeasts were amenable to genetic analysis; C. C.

Lindegren, and G. W. Beadle and E. L. Tatum had done their pioneer works on genetic mapping and on genetic control of nutritional requirements, respectively, in the mold *Neurospora*; Max Delbrück, S. E. Luria, and Milislav Demerec were beginning to grapple with the genetics of bacteria and bacteriophage; and foremost, O. T. Avery, C. M. Macleod, and Maclyn McCarty had identified the "transforming principle" of pneumococcus as deoxyribonucleic acid (DNA). Pontecorvo started thinking in which areas the genetics of microorganisms was likely to contribute most decisively; his conclusion, which led him after exploratory work with a number of microorganisms to choose in 1945 the homothallic ascomycete *Aspergillus nidulans*, was that one such area was that of gene structure and function.

The work with *Penicillium* did not proceed for long because the official policy in war-battered Britain was to leave research on penicillin production to the United States. However, this first confrontation with a fungus lacking sexual reproduction, but in which multinucleate cells with genetically different nuclei ("heterokaryotic") occur, focused Pontecorvo's interest toward the problems of what J. B. S. Haldane later epitomized as "alternatives to sex." These are genetic systems in which recombination, that is, the reassortment of genes from different ancestral lines, takes place by processes other than by sexual reproduction. One of these processes, widespread in filamentous fungi, either side by side with sexual reproduction as in *A. nidulans*, or replacing it as in *A. niger* and *P. chrysogenum*, was discovered by Pontecorvo and J. A. Roper about 1950 and called the "parasexual cycle." It consists of a series of steps individually similar to those occurring in sexual reproduction, but not following each other in the exact sequence which characterizes it. The final outcome is the same: Nuclei arise which recombine genes from different lines of descent. Since recombination is the main tool for genetic analysis, any process leading to recombination can be used. This is why the parasexual cycle opened to genetic analysis asexual species of fungi, the first among them *A. niger*, and provided an additional powerful tool for analysis in those species in which sexual reproduction occurs.

By about 1953 the parasexual cycle was understood in its essentials, and the techniques for harnessing it for genetic analysis in *A. nidulans* were taking shape. This, however, was only one—though the most generally known—outcome of the work on this species started by Pontecorvo in 1945 and in which he was joined by a number of able students, among them E. C. Forbes in 1946, Roper in 1948, and R. H. Pritchard in 1953. The discovery of the para-

sexual cycle was in a sense an accidental by-product of the main purpose of the work on which Pontecorvo embarked in 1945, first by making *A. nidulans* into a powerful tool for genetic research. By 1952, mainly on the basis of the fine genetic analysis carried out by Roper with *Aspergillus*, Pontecorvo was able to propose the picture of the gene as a unit of function based on hundreds of linearly arranged sites of mutation exchangeable by recombination.

Only a few years later this picture was completely vindicated. On the one hand, the structure of DNA proposed by J. D. Watson and F. H. C. Crick in 1953 made it possible to identify in chemical terms the mutational sites of the gene as the nucleotide pairs of DNA. On the other hand, the classic work of Seymour Benzer with bacteriophage in 1955 left no doubt that the gene is in fact based on a large number of interchangeable mutational sites. The ease with which genetic analysis could be carried out outside sexual reproduction in filamentous fungi led Pontecorvo to consider the possibility of something similar for man and other slow-breeding organisms, using cultures of somatic cells. About 1958 he embarked on this program with the awareness of the enormous technical difficulties to be surmounted. In principle this program is feasible; in practice it is formidable.

Pontecorvo graduated in agricultural sciences from the University of Pisa in 1928; he obtained his Ph.D. in the Institute of Animal Genetics, Edinburgh, in 1941. He was elected a fellow of the Royal Society of Edinburgh in 1946, of the Royal Society of London in 1955, an honorary foreign member of the American Academy of Arts and Sciences in 1958, and of the Danish Royal Society of Science and Arts in 1965. In 1961 he was awarded the Hansen Foundation Prize for Microbiology. He became president of the British Genetical Society in 1964. He was appointed head of the newly created department of genetics in the University of Glasgow in 1945, and was holder of the first chair of genetics in that university in 1955.

For background information *see* CHROMOSOME; EUMYCETES; GENE ACTION in the McGraw-Hill Encyclopedia of Science and Technology.   ☐

☆ PORTER, George

British chemist
Born Dec. 6, 1920, Stainforth, Yorkshire, England

I N THE years following World War II, Porter, together with the British chemist Ronald G. W. Norrish, developed the new technique of flash photolysis to initiate and record very fast chemical reactions. This method employed very brief,

intense bursts of light to produce and study excited, transient, and "unstable" chemical states which had been inaccessible to earlier methods of observation. For this achievement Porter shared the 1967 Nobel Prize in chemistry with Norrish and the German chemist Manfred Eigen.

The original flash photolysis apparatus was built at Cambridge in 1947 for the detection and study of short-lived gaseous free radicals. The materials for the desired reaction were assembled in a cylindrical vessel of glass or quartz, which was flanked by one or more electronic flash tubes, the whole assembly being enclosed in a reflector. A pulse of visible or ultraviolet light from the flash tubes brought the reactants within milliseconds to a highly excited state (naturally, the substances in question had to be photoreactive). The resulting transient absorption spectra were recorded by two methods.

In the first method, called flash spectroscopy, at some time after the initial pulse an additional flash tube is caused to discharge. The light from this source, passing through the reaction vessel, reaches the slit of a spectrograph, where it is photographed. In the second recording method, called kinetic spectrophotometry, the additional flash tube is replaced by a continuous light source, whose light, after traversing the reaction vessel, is passed through a monochromator and monitored continuously, providing a complete record of the reaction as observed at a single wavelength. These two methods proved complementary: The first yields more accurate single spectra, while the second is more valuable for kinetic studies.

The technique of flash photolysis was soon taken up enthusiastically, both by its originators and others, and began at once to give important results. Its unique value lay in its ability to produce chemical situations which are not only very short lived, but which do not exist at all except far from any equilibrium state. In this respect it differs from the technique developed by Eigen, in which the system under consideration is commonly rather close to some equilibrium point.

One of the most important applications of flash photolysis was in the investigation of unstable free radicals—the use for which it was originally devised. Since 1949 the technique has yielded to many investigators the detailed spectra of well over a hundred free radicals, in both gaseous state and solution, as well as much information about the kinetic behavior of these compounds.

In the study of short-lived, excited-state absorption spectra—another important application of flash photolysis—Porter in 1953 was the first to obtain spectra of the upper triplet states of aromatic molecules in fluid solvents, with lifetimes on the order of 1 msec. The technique also proved valuable in studying longer-lived excited states of fluid solutions.

In 1952 Porter, Norrish, and others used flash photolysis to follow the recombination of iodine atoms—the first study of gas kinetics to employ this technique. From further work in this field it became clear that the flash spectroscopic method of recording could be used, at least in theory, to observe each successive rotational and vibrational level of a reaction, a great improvement in detail over the statistical methods and results of conventional kinetic studies.

Finally, flash photolysis was of importance in the investigation of complex organic molecules and reactions. The approach elucidated, for example, transient stages in the hemoglobin-oxygen reaction; and, of course, it was extensively used to observe the behavior of chlorophyll.

Porter's later work involved, among other things, the development of microscopic flash photolysis techniques for in situ investigation of complex molecules in the biological context of the cell. He also extended the applications of the technique by initiating the use of laser and spark sources and other improvements.

In 1941 Porter received his B.Sc. at the University of Leeds. After wartime service with the British navy, he returned to his studies at the University of Cambridge, obtaining a doctorate in chemistry in 1949. Porter then became assistant director of research in the department of physical chemistry at Cambridge, spent a year (1954–55) as assistant director of the British Rayon Research Association, and next moved to the University of Sheffield as professor of physical chemistry (1955–63) and subsequently Firth Professor of Chemistry (1963–66). From 1963 to 1966 Porter was also professor of chemistry at the Royal Institution, London. In 1966 he was named director of the Royal Institution and Fullerian Professor of Chemistry there.

Porter wrote *Chemistry for the Modern World* (1962).

For background information *see* PHOTOLY-

SIS (PHOTOCHEMISTRY); SPECTROPHOTOMETRIC ANALYSIS; SPECTROSCOPY in the McGraw-Hill Encyclopedia of Science and Technology.   □

★ **POTTER, Van Rensselaer**

American biochemist and oncologist
Born Aug. 27, 1911, Day County, S.Dak., U.S.A.

BIOCHEMICAL TECHNIQUES and their application to the fundamental nature of the cancer problem were Potter's primary concern. The homogenate technique and the Potter-Elvehjem homogenizer (1937), used throughout the world, were the main basis for his Paul-Lewis Award in Enzyme Chemistry, received from the American Chemical Society in 1947. The homogenizer consisted of a motor-driven glass pestle mounted on a glass rod and made to fit closely in an ordinary test tube. Fresh pieces of animal tissue, such as liver or brain, could be suspended in a chilled medium with carefully controlled composition, and within a few moments all cells could be disrupted and dispersed without the disruption of many subcellular components—cell nuclei, mitochondria, and submicroscopic particles such as ribosomes. From the earliest experiments with homogenates, Potter was concerned with the microdissection of cells by means of the homogenizer, a technique which most cytologists at the time regarded as a hopelessly brutal attack on the cellular structure. With the help of a talented graduate student, Walter C. Schneider, Potter applied the newly developed centrifugation techniques of Albert Claude to homogenates, and the resulting cell fractions were examined in the light microscope and also analyzed for enzymatic function and nucleic acid content. Cell nuclei were isolated at low speeds, whereas the small, rodlike mitochondria were isolated at much higher gravitational forces and were shown to be the main sites of the oxidative machinery of the cell. Subsequent electron microscopic studies by others, especially George Palade at the Rockefeller Institute, showed that the supernatant fraction obtained after sedimentation of the mitochondria contains the ribosomes and membranes which together make the so-called microsome fraction of the cell, now known to be the major locus of protein synthesis. Thus, the homogenate, separated by centrifugal fractionation into various-sized components, became a major tool for studying subcellular biochemical events.

Following World War II, Waldo Cohn at Oak Ridge showed that ion-exchange resins could be used to separate the hydrolysis products of the nucleic acids. Potter decided to follow the steps in the synthesis of the nucleic acids by using resin columns to examine the acid-soluble intermediates. In collaboration with a graduate student, Robert B. Hurlbert, he modified the Cohn technique to provide an automatically increasing concentration or gradient of the solution used to move the unknown acid-soluble materials off the column. In this way Potter and Hurlbert were able to discover that all the building blocks for ribonucleic acid occurred as the mono-, di-, and triphosphates in mononucleotide form. They demonstrated that the same nucleotides which coordinate fuel consumption with functional load are essential building blocks for ribonucleic acids; this was one of Potter's contributions cited as a basis for his Bertner Foundation Award in 1961 from the University of Texas M. D. Anderson Hospital and Tumor Institute "for outstanding achievement in the field of cancer research."

While maintaining an interest in the methods of biochemistry, Potter continued to compare normal and cancer tissues and to develop his original interest in the theoretical aspects of cancer biochemistry. Starting from the basic contributions of Otto Warburg which dated from 1930, Potter developed the concept of multiple alternative metabolic pathways and emphasized that for many intermediary metabolites there is no predetermined pathway but rather a shifting balance among several competing pathways. Cancer was at first regarded as a simple imbalance between synthetic and degradative pathways, and this concept was referred to as the catabolic deletion theory of cancer. When it was found that the normal process of liver regeneration was brought about by an increase in the number of enzymes needed for nucleic acid synthesis, the concept of feedback deletion or derepression was elaborated to explain the release of cancer cells from normal controls, and catabolic deletion was explained as a progressive development affecting growth rate. Potter's continued attempt to achieve an overall view resulted in his being recognized as a generalist, and he was called upon frequently to present views on such broad topics as the biochemistry of cancer—for example, when he received the Clowes Medal from the American Association for Cancer Research in 1964.

Potter was continually dissatisfied with the experimental cancers that were available for investigation, and as his basic concepts began to crystallize, it became increasingly necessary to find improved experimental material. On the basis of considerable data supporting the catabolic deletion theory, he decided to examine as large a variety of experimental liver cancers as possible and either to establish the generalization or to disprove it. One of the new hepatomas which was furnished by Harold Morris of the National Cancer Institute was found to be an exception to the catabolic deletion generalization. The next step was to determine whether the new cancer strain was unique or whether other examples could also be found. With the cooperation of H. C. Pitot and Morris, Potter found many other examples, and the question now became whether the new hepatoma strains were alike or different. It soon became evident that each hepatoma strain was different from all the rest, and each was unique in its biochemical balance of pathways, despite the fact that all were cancerous. The problem then called for sorting out the more essential from the less essential changes in terms of cancer formation, and this led to the concept of the minimal deviation hepatomas as a class of operational experimental hepatomas which approach a hypothetical "minimum deviation" from normal liver that is nevertheless malignant. There is, of course, the additional question of whether a single minimum actually exists.

Potter graduated from South Dakota State College with a B.S. in 1933 and continued in the South Dakota Agricultural Experiment Station, where he had worked as an undergraduate, to study the mechanism of trace selenium poisoning. In 1935 he began graduate work in biochemistry under C. A. Elvehjem at the University of Wisconsin. He received his M.S. in 1936 and his Ph.D. in 1938 at Wisconsin and then studied with H. von Euler in Stockholm, H. A. Krebs in Sheffield, and T. R. Hogness in Chicago. In 1940 he returned to the University of Wisconsin, where he began research on the biochemistry of cancer with Harold P. Rusch in the McArdle Laboratory, becoming a professor in 1947 and assistant director in 1959. His interests in control mechanisms were largely expressed in cancer research, but were also called upon when he was a principal investigator on the biochemistry of traumatic shock in World War II and on studies on adaptation to high altitude in Peru in 1952–53. He was elected to the American Academy of Arts and Sciences in 1959.

Potter edited *Methods in Medical Research* (Vol. 1, 1948) and wrote *Enzymes, Growth and Cancer* (1950) and *Nucleic Acid Outlines* (Vol. 1, 1960). He also published several articles on science and philosophy, in addition to some 200 research articles.

For background information *see* CENTRIFUGATION (BIOLOGY); NUCLEIC ACID; ONCOLOGY in the McGraw-Hill Encyclopedia of Science and Technology.   □

☆ POUND, Robert Vivian

American physicist
Born May 16, 1919, Ridgeway, Ontario, Canada

SOON AFTER the discovery of the Mössbauer effect, Pound realized that it offered possibilities for conducting research relating to the general theory of relativity within the confines of the laboratory. With his co-workers at Harvard University, he was able to utilize the new tool to demonstrate unambiguously the red shift of photons caused by gravity and thus to verify a prediction of the principle of equivalence. The principle, which holds that there is no observable difference between an acceleration produced by gravity and an acceleration produced by another force, is a basic premise of the general theory of relativity, proposed by Albert Einstein in 1911. This led Einstein to predict that gravity distorts light (or other electromagnetic radiation) by shifting its wavelength. A number of attempts were made to verify this by using astronomical bodies and light moving across astronomical distances, but distortions and uncertainties in shifts, from other causes, rendered results inconclusive.

In 1958 the German physicist R. L. Mössbauer published his discovery of the phenomenon of recoilless emission of low-energy gamma rays by excited nuclei that are tightly bound in the crystal lattice. The remarkable precision of the frequency of such gamma rays means that an atomic nucleus like that which emits the gamma ray can absorb only another gamma ray of frequency in a very minute fractional range determined by the excited-level lifetime. In this phenomenon broadening due to thermal vibrations is eliminated.

In November, 1959, working at Harvard University with the assistance of Glen A. Rebka, Jr., Pound suggested that the effect of gravitational potential on the apparent frequency of electromagnetic radiation could be measured if an example of recoilless resonant gamma rays of suitable precision were found. He proposed to do this by aiming the gamma rays from an emitting source at an appropriate absorber, since in this way an extremely small frequency change could be detected. The first step was to demonstrate that iron-57, as an emitter and absorber with a large recoil-free fraction even at room temperature, provided a suitably precise system, with a sensitivity a thousand or so greater than in the original iridium system discovered by Mössbauer. The gamma-ray source was prepared by diffusing a small amount of 270-day cobalt-57 as an impurity into a piece of iron; the cobalt-57 atoms then decayed into excited iron-57, and finally emitted the 14.4-kilovolt (wavelength about 1 angstrom) gamma ray in the last step to stable iron-57. As the required stable vertical base line, he used an enclosed, isolated tower in the Jefferson Physical Laboratory; the net operating base line was thus 74 ft. To reduce the absorption of the 14.4 kiloelectron-volt gamma rays by air, the emitter and absorber were placed at opposite ends of a 16-in.-diameter cylindrical plastic bag filled with helium.

The emitter was moved sinusoidally by either a ferroelectric or a moving-coil magnetic transducer. During the quarter of the modulation cycle centered about the time of maximum velocity, the pulses from a scintillation spectrometer—placed behind the absorber and adjusted to select the 14.4-kev gamma-ray line—were fed into one scaler; during the opposite quarter cycle, they were fed into another. The difference in counts recorded was then a measure of the asymmetry in, or frequency shift between, the emission and absorption lines. The shift caused by gravity was separated from other contributions by comparing results, with radiation going from top to bottom, to results with the system inverted.

In March, 1960, Pound and Rebka announced their results, which matched the theoretical expectations by a factor of $+1.05 \pm 0.10$ (the plus sign indicating that the frequency increases in falling, as expected). Four years later Pound and J. L. Snider published the result of a redesigned experiment, as $+0.9990 \pm 0.0076$, with an estimated additional systematic uncertainty of ± 0.006. This removed all doubts concerning the existence and extent of the gravitational red shift. H. J. Hay, J. P. Schiffer, and A. B. Whitehead—working independently of Pound at the Atomic Energy Research Establish-

ment, Harwell, England—had performed a similar experiment and had published their results almost 2 months earlier. These were based on much less data than those of Pound and Rebka and had a statistical error, therefore, of 43%. In addition, many fewer precautions were taken to eliminate systematic errors and, in particular, an inversion of the system was not carried out. In analyzing the data from their own experiment, Pound and Rebka had discovered that a very important source of instability and of systematic error was a temperature difference between source and absorber. The thermal motion produced a relativistic time dilation of such size that a difference of 1°C between source and absorber resulted in a frequency shift about equal to that predicted by the principle of equivalence. By discovering the variation with temperature of the energy of recoilless gamma rays, Pound was able to extend the accuracy of the predictions of the Mössbauer effect and to establish the validity of his experimental results—and thus of the apparent weight of photons as predicted by the principle of equivalence.

While a fellow of Harvard University in 1946, Pound collaborated with Edward M. Purcell in simplifying Isidor I. Rabi's method of detecting the nuclear magnetic moment. They developed resonance methods in which the Larmor precessional frequency is determined from the energy absorption from an oscillating magnetic field by nuclei subject to a fixed magnetic field. This work led to Purcell's sharing the 1952 Nobel Prize in physics with Felix Bloch, who had independently developed this method of nuclear resonance absorption.

In 1947 Pound joined with Purcell and Nicolaas Bloembergen to carry out experiments on nuclear magnetic relaxation, which pioneered many fruitful ideas in nuclear resonance. Pound first used nuclear magnetic resonance to observe effects due to nuclear electric quadrupole interactions and called attention to the importance of electric quadrupole interactions in solids. In 1950 he published results including the first double resonance experiment in which the effect on one line of driving another one was observed. Pound performed research in the area of microwaves and radar during World War II.

Pound went to the United States in 1923 and his parents were naturalized 9 years later. He attended the University of Buffalo, receiving his B.A. in 1941. After spending the following year as a research physicist at the Submarine Signal Company, Pound became a staff member of the Radiation Laboratory at the Massachusetts Institute of Technology, a position he retained until 1946. He began his association with Harvard University in 1945 as a junior fellow of the Society of Fellows. Three years later Pound was appointed an assistant professor of physics. In 1950 he was made an associate professor and in 1956 professor. Among his honors were the B. J. Thompson Memorial Award of the Institute of Radio Engineers (1948) and the Eddington Medal of the Royal Astronomical Society (1965). He was elected to the National Academy of Sciences in 1961.

Pound was the editor of, and principal contributor to, *Microwave Mixers* (1948).

For background information *see* MOSSBAUER EFFECT; RELATIVITY in the McGraw-Hill Encyclopedia of Science and Technology.   □

★ PRELOG, Vladimir

Swiss organic chemist
Born July 23, 1906, Sarajevo, Yugoslavia

FROM HIS student days Prelog was fascinated by the spatial forms of organic molecules and by the chemistry of natural products with their stereochemical complexities. Apart from some research influenced by external circumstances—for example, cooperation with the pharmaceutical industry—most of his work was concerned with these aspects of organic chemistry. In the field of natural compounds his interests turned first to alkaloids, then to polyketides (steroids and terpenes including ionone derivatives), and in recent years particularly to metabolites of microorganisms (antibiotics and growth factors). For each of these classes of compounds Prelog made important contributions to the methods of isolation and to the establishment of constitution and configuration.

His early investigations of the important antimalarial *Cinchona* alkaloids led to the complete elucidation of the configurations. In 1945 Prelog showed that the formulas proposed by Robert Robinson for the *Strychnos* alkaloids required revision; Robinson's subsequent formulas were shown to be correct. The definitive structures of the steroid alkaloids of solanidin from *Solanum* and of the alkaloids from *Veratrum* species (the latter together with Barton, Jeger, and Wood-

ward) were derived on the basis of results from various laboratories, thus opening a way into this important group of natural products. The unusual structures of the aromatic *Erythrina* alkaloids were likewise established. Together with Janot and Goutarel, the *Yohimbe* and *Pseudocinchona* alkaloids were taken up, leading to important early results on the determination of the constitution and configuration of the indole alkaloids. These investigations were carried out mainly by the classical methods of organic chemistry. They have been confirmed by more modern techniques, especially by x-ray crystallographic structure determinations, and provide the basis for numerous researches in the alkaloid field.

In 1941, when Prelog went to Zurich to work with L. Ružička, he found there large quantities of lipoid extracts from animal organs. The investigation of these extracts led to the discovery of the steroids with musklike odor from testicles of boars and to the isolation from the urine of pregnant mares of a series of compounds derived from the violetlike-smelling ionones. The structures of these compounds, whose biological significance still remains unclear, were elucidated and confirmed by synthesis.

Together with W. Keller-Schierlein, Prelog carried out investigations of metabolic products of microorganisms in cooperation with a number of research groups (H. Bickel, E. Vischer, and A. Wettstein, CIBA Co., Basel; P Sensi, Lepetit Co., Milan; E. Gäumann, L. Ettlinger, and H. Zähner, Institute for Special Botany, Federal Institute of Technology, Zurich). These studies led to the isolation of a number of complex, novel natural products with interesting biological properties. The constitutions of these compounds, some of which have been synthesized, were established. These compounds include macrotetrolides (antibiotics inhibiting oxidative phosphorylation), ferrioxamines (naturally occurring iron trihydroxamates that act as bacterial growth factors), ferrimycins (naturally occurring iron trihydroxamates that possess antibiotic activity), and rifamycins (antibiotics of therapeutic value). A common feature of all these classes of metabolites is that their molecules contain large rings; these posed special structural problems, which could speedily be solved with the help of modern methods.

Among the stereochemical problems with little connection with the structure of natural products, the relationships between topography and chemistry of the many-membered rings (8 and more ring members) were intensively studied. The medium rings (8–11 ring members), which have become easily available by the acyloin synthesis, were investigated most intensively. It was recognized in 1946 that their anomalous properties represent conformational effects, that is, effects due to restricted rotations around single bonds. The recent x-ray studies by J. D. Dunitz and his co-workers in Zurich provided more exact information on the conformations of medium rings and made it possible to rationalize anomalous medium-size ring effects. In the course of this work nonclassical transannular reactions of the medium rings were discovered and investigated.

Other works were devoted to studying the steric course of asymmetric synthesis. Many examples were found where the asymmetric course of an asymmetric synthesis was established as resulting from conformational effects due to differences in the sizes of the substituents. The regularities that were recognized here made it possible to determine the then unknown absolute configurations of important classes of compounds, such as steroids and terpenes. Asymmetric synthesis was also applied as a sensitive tool in studying the details of reaction mechanisms, for example, in the asymmetric cyanhydrin synthesis.

After this it seemed tempting to try to interpret microbiological and enzymatic asymmetric syntheses in a similar fashion. The first step in this direction was the experimental demonstration that certain microorganisms are capable of reducing the carbonyl group of certain alicyclic substrates with high stereospecificity. In such cases, too, the specificity could be correlated in terms of the size of the group attached to reacting carbonyl. The pyridine-nucleotide–dependent enzymes, which could be isolated from the microorganisms, showed the same specificity as the microorganisms themselves. By confronting the isolated enzymes with a series of substrates, it was possible to arrive at interesting conclusions about the interactions between enzyme, coenzyme, and substrate.

Together with Cahn and Ingold, Prelog developed a widely used system for the specification of molecular chirality ("handedness") and of stereoisomerism in general; his interest in this problem led him to a more comprehensive chemical topology in place of classical stereochemistry. Experimental studies on elements of chirality, psueudoasymmetry, and cycloenantiomery were taken up to show the usefulness of these extensions.

Prelog passed his early years in Zagreb. He studied chemistry at the Prague Institute of Technology, where he carried out his doctoral work under Votoček. After some years in Prague, spent in a laboratory for the preparation of fine chemicals, he returned to Yugoslavia in 1935, first as a lecturer and subsequently as an associate professor of organic chemistry at the Technical Faculty of Zagreb University. In 1941, after the German occupation of Yugoslavia, he moved to Zurich. He served first as a lecturer, then as an associate professor, and finally as a full professor of organic chemistry at the Fed-

eral Institute of Technology. In 1957 he was appointed successor to L. Ružička. A foreign member of the Royal Society of London, the U.S. National Academy of Sciences, the American Academy of Arts and Sciences, the Soviet Academy of Sciences, and the Italian Accademia dei Lincei, Prelog received honorary degrees from the universities of Zagreb, Paris, and Liverpool. He was awarded the Marcel Benoist Prize, the highest scientific recognition of Switzerland.

For background information *see* ALKALOID; BACTERIAL ENZYME; STEREOCHEMISTRY in the McGraw-Hill Encyclopedia of Science and Technology. ☐

☆ PRESS, Frank

American geophysicist
Born Dec. 4, 1924, New York, N.Y., U.S.A.

Press in 1959 was a member of a team of geophysicists at the California Institute of Technology who first experimentally identified "free oscillations" of the Earth. These vibrations, which may persist for weeks or months, arise from the fact that earthquakes and other geological events disturb the entire globe and set it "ringing" like a bell. Detection and analysis of such oscillations yielded new and valuable information about the Earth's structure.

The possibility of free oscillations of very low frequency was worked out mathematically and applied to the planet Earth at the end of the 19th century; early in the 20th the English geophysicist A. E. H. Love calculated that the $_0S_2$ mode, the lowest possible frequency of the Earth's free oscillation, should have a period of about 1 hr. Until the 1950s, however, conventional seismometers were unable to detect with accuracy any waves with a frequency longer than about 100 sec. Then, in the middle 1950s, Press and Maurice W. Ewing, working at the Lamont Geological Observatory of Columbia University, devised a seismological detector combining an inertial seismometer with a galva-nometer. This instrument was able to detect waves down to about 400 sec in frequency. (At about the same time Hugo Benioff and his colleagues at the California Institute of Technology developed the "strain seismometer," of comparable or even superior sensitivity but operating on an entirely different principle.)

With the advent of digital computers for the analysis of seismological data and the dispersion of the new, more sensitive instruments to various world localities, the remaining requirement for advances in the study of free oscillations was a major seismological disturbance to furnish the necessary information. This came in the form of the great Chilean earthquake of 1960. Teams of geophysicists from the California Institute of Technology, Columbia University, and the University of California at Los Angeles were able within weeks of the disturbance to distinguish about 40 fundamental "spheroidal" modes and some 25 "torsional" modes of vibration. Among the spheroidal modes was the $_0S_2$ mode, the period of which had been set by Love at 1 hr. The observed mean frequency was 53.95 min, a very good agreement.

The measurement of free oscillations provided information on the vibrational behavior of the Earth as a whole; and, because the longer a wave is, the deeper it penetrates the Earth's interior, new evidence was gained from the free oscillation data about the structure of deeper layers of the Earth's mantle. The data indicated that the elastic quality Q of the mantle increases with depth and also that there seems to be a low-Q zone in the upper mantle.

Correlation of records of the Chilean earthquake with those taken during the Alaskan earthquake of 1964 provided new information for the testing of theoretical models of free oscillation, surface-wave propagation, and other geological phenomena. Free oscillation data were particularly valuable because the measurements were independent of the type or location of the original disturbance. Working from measurements of the Alaskan earthquake recorded in Hawaii, Press was able to demonstrate the occurrence of a very small permanent deformation of the Earth as a result of that disturbance. The investigation of such "zero frequency" effects, he suggested, might yield valuable information about the actual mechanism of earthquakes and about the relation of earthquakes to mountain-building and continental drift.

In addition to his work on free oscillations, Press played an important part in measuring the thickness of the Earth's crust and mantle, beneath both the oceans and the continents. During the International Geophysical Year (IGY), on the basis of seismic data from an earthquake in Samoa, he helped show that the portion of the Earth's crust occupied by the North American continent is between 23 and 30 mi thick.

Also during the IGY Press helped analyze seismic data that showed Antarctica to be a true continent and not simply an island of ice and debris floating on the Earth's crust. A mountain discovered in the course of the IGY Antarctic explorations was named Mount Press in honor of his contributions to the IGY effort.

As consultant to the Arms Control and Disarmament Agency, Press was active in developing seismic techniques for the detection and measurement of nuclear weapons tests. Following the Alaskan earthquake of 1964, Press was appointed chairman of a special panel of the Office of Science and Technology in the Executive Office of the President, which in 1965 recommended a 10-year study program to develop an earthquake detection and warning system.

Press received the B.S. from the City College of New York in 1944. At Columbia University he was granted an M.A. and a Ph.D. in geology in 1946 and 1949. In 1948 he was made a university fellow at Columbia and was appointed instructor there in 1949, assistant professor in 1951, and associate professor in 1952. Press went to the California Institute of Technology in 1955 as professor of geology; in 1957 he became director of the Institute's Seismological Laboratory. In 1965 he assumed the position of professor and head of the department of geology and geophysics at the Massachusetts Institute of Technology. Press's service as consultant to various government and professional bodies included membership from 1961 to 1964 in the President's Science Advisory Committee and from 1955 to 1959 on the IGY Glaciology and Seismology Panel. He was elected to the National Academy of Sciences in 1958.

Press wrote *Propagation of Elastic Waves in Layered Media*, with M. W. Ewing and W. S. Jardetzky (1956). He was associate editor of the *Journal of Geophysical Research* and the *Transactions of the American Geophysical Union*.

For background information *see* SEISMOGRAPH; SEISMOLOGY in the McGraw-Hill Encyclopedia of Science and Technology.   □

★ PRUVOST, Pierre

French geologist
Born Aug. 1, 1890, Raismes, Nord, France

BORN OF a medical family in northern France, Pruvost would have followed the family profession. However, while studying medicine at the University of Lille, he was attracted to geology by Charles Barrois, professor of this science at the university, and by Jules Gosselet,

Barrois's predecessor, who took Pruvost as an assistant on field trips. In the 1900s Barrois devoted himself to the study of the old formations of Brittany, as well as those of coalfields in the north of France. He brought his young pupil on these studies, and Pruvost specialized in the geology of coal-bearing deposits and in formations attributed to Hercynian orogenesis, publishing in 1909 his first in a series of more than 200 papers.

Beginning with a study of the continental fauna of the coal measures, which were nearly neglected at that time, Pruvost proved that they can be used with the flora for establishing the stratigraphical subdivisions of the nonmarine Carboniferous series in western Europe (France, Netherlands, Belgium, Saarland). The knowledge he had acquired in studying these coalfields induced him to write an article, "Sédimentation et Subsidence" (1930), in which he insisted that accumulations of several thousand meters of sediments had been laid down in areas where the water level had always remained low, the ground progressively collapsing in the course of accumulation. The present depth of such basins is due to the amount of sinking and to the alternation of short periods of high water levels (subsidence being faster than sedimentation) with those of low water levels (sedimentation being faster than subsidence), with the latter predominating. He thus pointed out the part played by such vertical movements in the production of rhythmic structure in the sediments (cyclothems), and did not exclude this mechanism from application to marine "geosynclines" and deep-sea deposits.

Since such a lasting descending motion, apparently spasmodic, entails deformation of the strata already deposited, it is implied that it is partly responsible for the final structure of the basin. These earliest deformations are the frame orienting the future general outlines of the tectonics. As soon as the process begins, the subsidence not only keeps up with the accumulation but also controls the orogenesis. Instead of being clearly separated in time as well as by their causes (man's tendency to simplify things proposes to him that he conceive contrasting periods of glyptogenesis and orogenesis), such apparently different phenomena as sedimentation, subsidence, and folding are connected and penecontemporaneous, all being imputable to vertical movements of the lithosphere. What appears to be an orogenic paroxysm may simply correspond to the instant when a long and continuous process of deformation has been stopped.

The "theory of subsidence" was favorably received by geologists at mid-century. It instigated various researches on the analysis and precision of its mechanism, particularly the study of sedimentary cycles. It also modified overformal ideas concerning the contemporaneousness and instantaneousness of the Earth's orogenic phases. As Pruvost wrote in the article "Les Jeux Propres du Socle" (1960), the first deformations of sediments during their deposition "have not ceased orchestrating on the same theme," and are the forces that led to the edifice being investigated.

Working with mining engineers on the application of geological methods to the exploration of subterranean fields, Pruvost often forewarned the geologists and coal miners against the dangers of extrapolations (and even of interpolations) from obvious structures that they know by direct approach.

In his public lectures on historical geology at the Sorbonne and during the last sessions of the Congrès internationaux de Géologie du Carbonifère, Pruvost proposed to incorporate into the Carboniferous System the Autunian stage, which French geologists used to place at the base of the Permian. It restored the value of the old limit of A. G. Werner—between his "Uebergangsgebirge" and his "Flötzgebirge." In 1964 geologists in China and the U.S.S.R. came to an agreement adopting a common inferior limit of the Permian System that left the series corresponding to the French Autunian at the top of the Carboniferous. This implied a deduction on which Pruvost had insisted: The Gondwana flora is not a facies of the Carboniferous flora, exactly contemporaneous with it, but has succeeded it both in the Northern and Southern hemispheres.

Pruvost studied at Lille University (Licence ès sciences in 1910 and Doctorat ès sciences in 1918). In 1927 he became chairman of the department of geology of that university and in 1943 dean of the Faculty of Sciences. In 1950 he was appointed to the chair of geology at the Sorbonne. He retired from teaching in 1961, but remained president of the Comité National de Géologie. He was elected to the French

Académie des Sciences in 1954. He was made a foreign member of the Lisbon Academy of Sciences (1915), the Geological Society of London (1926), the Royal Academy of Belgium (1949), the Geological Society of America (1959), and the Royal Society of Edinburgh (1963). His honors included the Wollaston Medal (Geological Society of London, 1959), the Steinmann Medal (Geologische Vereinigung, 1959), the André Dumont Medal (Geological Society of Belgium, 1955), and the Van Waterschott Medal (Royal Society of Mines and Geology, Netherlands). He received honorary degrees from the universities of Louvain and Mainz.

For background information *see* GEOLOGICAL TIME SCALE; OROGENY; SEDIMENTATION (GEOLOGY) in the McGraw-Hill Encyclopedia of Science and Technology.   □

★ **PUCK, Theodore Thomas**

American biophysicist
Born Sept. 24, 1916, Chicago, Ill., U.S.A.

BEGINNING ABOUT 1940, microbial genetics was developing into the field known as molecular biology, and provided a revolutionary new understanding of the dynamics of biochemical and genetic processes in cells. In large part these developments were made possible by the single-cell plating techniques, whereby populations of single cells could be simply and quantitatively grown into large, discrete colonies. This made possible measurement of the growth response of cells to various physical, chemical, and biological agents; identification and measurement of mutational processes; and establishment of mutant cell stocks which could then be used in systematic genetic and biochemical investigations.

Experience with mammalian cells gained in the course of investigations on the mechanism of virus invasion suggested to Puck a new departure in the study of mammalian biochemical genetics. Reasoning that the procedures of single-cell plating could be adapted to mammalian cells grown in culture on a quantitative basis, Puck and his students in the department of biophysics at the University of Colorado Medical Center launched such an experimental program. Participating in these studies were J. Christiansen, Philip Marcus, Steven Cieciura, and Harold Fisher.

A simple, rapid, and precise method was devised whereby single mammalian cells from tissue culture could be added to petri dishes so that each one would grow in isolation to produce a discrete, recognizable colony. These colonies could be counted so that measurement of the number of cells capable of long-term reproduction in the original population could be scored. Single colonies with mutant characteristics could be selected and developed into new mutant cell strains. The actions of a number of agents which affect mammalian cell reproduction were quantitatively determined, and the first mammalian cell survival curves for x-irradiation were measured. The latter studies demonstrated that the mean lethal dose for mammalian cell killing is only 100 rads, a value more than 50 times smaller than that which had been widely accepted as the mean lethal dose of mammalian cells. The x-ray studies also demonstrated that the principal target for irradiation death is in the chromosomes and that virtually all mammalian cells have very similar radiation sensitivities. These studies made possible reinterpretation of the basic phenomena of the mammalian radiation syndrome and provided a much more effective theoretical basis than was previously available for understanding mammalian radiation injury and the use of radiation in cancer therapy.

The molecular requirement for single-cell growth into large colonies was determined for several cell strains (with Fisher, Gordon Sato, and Richard Ham). It was established that a glycoprotein, found in the fetuin fraction of serum, is necessary for mammalian cell reproduction. This protein occurs in large concentrations in fetal serum but is also present in smaller amounts in all mammalian sera tested. The single-cell plating method made possible accurate measurement of the biological action of fetuin, as well as that of cell antibodies and other agents.

A method was developed with J. Steffen, a postdoctoral fellow, which permits precise analysis of the biochemical events in the reproductive life cycle of mammalian cells in culture. This method permitted identification of the point in the life cycle at which various macromolecules are synthesized and precise localization of the points at which drugs and other agents exercise their effects on mammalian cells. It has been applied to determine the action of a variety of agents on the life cycle of dividing mammalian cells.

Methods were also developed for routine sampling of the cells of any individual and setting these up for stable, long-term growth in culture. With J. H. Tjio, Puck used these methods to establish the first means for determining the chromosomal constitution of large numbers of persons, and helped to demonstrate that the only normal chromosomal number in man is 46, in accordance with the original observation of Tjio and Levan, rather than values such as 47 and 48, which had variously been claimed by other workers. The first complete analysis of human chromosomes was made in Puck's laboratory. The study of human chromosomes in health and disease has since become one of the newest branches of medicine, and has elucidated the basis of many classical diseases and birth defects.

Recently, the work of Puck's laboratory turned toward a study of the biochemistry of mammalian cells and of differentiation processes. Cell turnover numbers in different tissues were measured, and biochemical and genetic factors underlying specific differentiation phenomena were sought. These studies involved many of the techniques developed for studying cells in vitro, as well as transplantation of cells into specific sites in experimental animals.

New methods were devised with Arthur Robinson and Helene Hill for measurement of specific reaction rate constants for enzyme chains in mammalian cells. These have been applied to the detection of heterozygous gene defects in human populations and to study of the biochemistry of mammalian cells under a variety of conditions.

Puck received a B.S. in chemistry (1937) and a Ph.D. in physical chemistry (1940) at the University of Chicago. His Ph.D. work was directed by James Franck and involved study of the fluorescence of chlorophyll and its implications for the mechanism of photosynthesis. Thereafter he successively became a research associate in the department of medicine and assistant professor in the departments of medicine and biochemistry at the University of Chicago, working in the laboratory of O. H. Robertson. Puck undertook studies on aerosol dynamics with particular reference to the prevention of infection by airborne bacteria and viruses. He analyzed the mechanism by which certain aerosols were supposed to kill airborne microorganisms, and demonstrated that the lethal action involved condensation of vapor molecules onto air-suspended bacteria and virus particles to produce a sterilizing concentration in the particle within a small fraction of a second. New methods for accurate measurement of vapor pressures of involatile liquids and for analysis of multicomponent vapor-liquid systems were developed. During World War II Puck became a member of the commission on airborne infections of the Office of the Surgeon General of the Army. Practical application of methodologies to assist in prevention of airborne infection in hospitals and other installations and study of the epidemiology of airborne infective processes were undertaken.

In 1947 Puck left Chicago to accept a senior fellowship at the California Institute of Technology under the sponsorship of the Committee on Growth of the National Research Council. There he joined Max Delbruck's laboratory and began study of the attachment and invasion of host bacterial cells by bacteriophages. In 1948 he was invited to become professor and chairman of a new department of biophysics at the University of Colorado Medical Center in Denver. This department became a department of the medical school and of the graduate school.

In Colorado Puck continued his investigations on the mechanism of virus invasion, working with a graduate student, Alan Garen. Individual steps in the process were isolated, including an initial reversible attachment which is a diffusion-limited reaction; a subsequent enzymatic reaction which produces irreversible cell attachment and a limited lysis of the cell wall, presumably for injection of the viral DNA; and finally a resealing of the hole which was made by the virus. The kinetics of these various reactions were studied, and synthetic molecules were found which can mimic the behavior of the virus and the host cell in particular steps of this sequence. Puck also turned his attention to mammalian viruses during this period and initiated study on the interaction of these viruses with their host cells.

In 1962 he was appointed director of the Eleanor Roosevelt Institute for Cancer Research. In 1966 he was awarded a Lifetime Research Professorship in Biophysics by the American Cancer Society. Puck received the Lasker Award of the American Public Health Association in 1958, the Borden Award in 1959, and the General Rose Award in 1960. He was elected to the National Academy of Sciences in 1960.

For background information see AEROSOL; CHROMOSOME; CULTURE, TISSUE; MOLECULAR BIOPHYSICS; VIRUS in the McGraw-Hill Encyclopedia of Science and Technology.   □

★ **RACKER, Efraim**

American biochemist
Born June 28, 1913, Neusandez, Poland

IN STUDIES that begin in 1941, Racker found a defect in glucose utilization in the brain of mice infected with poliomyelitis. The analysis of this phenomenon led him into numerous problems in the field of enzymology. In the course of attempts to localize the lesion in infected brain homogenates, he used for the first time an artificial ATP-regenerating system by addition of phosphocreatine and creatine kinase. He developed sensitive spectrophotometric assays for several glycolytic enzymes, devised a micromethod for the quantitative determination of glutathione, and elucidated the mode of action of glyoxalases. In collaboration with I. Krimsky, he localized the lesion in the infected brain at the site of glyceraldehyde-3-phosphate dehydrogenase, the key enzyme of energy production during glycolysis. Racker and Krimsky proceeded to study the mechanism of action of this enzyme and in 1952 presented the first evidence for the participation of a thiolester in the course of the reaction. A few years later they crystallized the thiolester produced by the interaction of the substrate and the enzyme and demonstrated that it is indeed the intermediate in the process of oxidative phosphorylation at the substrate level of glyceraldehyde-3-phosphate. Later these studies served as a model system for the analysis of phosphorylation coupled to electron transport in mitochondria.

Following these studies Racker discovered the enzyme transketolase and elucidated its role in the oxidative and reductive pentose phosphate cycle. In 1955 he reconstructed the multienzyme pathway which catalyzes the synthesis of sugar by CO_2 fixation in photosynthesizing plant tissues. Substrate-enzyme intermediates of both transketolase and transaldolase were discovered, and the findings shed light on the mode of action of these enzymes.

After completing these investigations, Racker returned to his major field of interest: the mechanism and control of energy metabolism. Earlier efforts in 1951, in collaboration with G. Pinchot, had shown that the system of oxidative phosphorylation in bacteria can be resolved into a soluble and a particulate fraction, both required for the process. In collaboration with M. E. Pullman and H. S. Penefsky in 1958, Racker reported the successful resolution of beef heart mitochondria into a particulate fraction that catalyzed electron transport and a soluble component. The latter was called coupling factor 1 since it was the first factor shown to be required for the coupling of the phosphorylation of ADP to ATP during electron transport. Coupling factor 1 was isolated as a homogeneous protein with a molecular weight of 285,000 and was shown to catalyze the cleavage of ATP to ADP and inorganic phosphate.

During studies of the combination of the soluble coupling factor 1 with particulate fractions from mitochondria, Racker observed several alterations in the properties of coupling factor 1 following adsorption to insoluble fragments. He proceeded to purify the components responsible for these changes in properties such as the induced sensitivity to the antibiotic oligomycin. In collaboration with D. F. Parsons and B. Chance, Racker described the morphological and biochemical properties of the reconstituted system of particles and coupling factor. Characteristic spheres of the inner membrane of mitochondria which had been discovered by H. Fernandez-Moran were shown to be identical with coupling factor 1. Aided by such morphological and biochemical studies, Racker and Y. Kagawa succeeded in the purification, resolution, and reconstitution of the inner membrane of mitochondria. The role of phospholipid in the formation of vesicles was clearly demonstrated.

Racker studied for a short period at the Academy of Arts in Vienna. He then switched to the Medical School, where he obtained his M.D. in 1938. After the occupation of Austria by the Nazis, he left for England. His early interest in psychiatry led him to seek out J. H. Quastel, in Cardiff, Wales, who had written articles on the relation between biochemistry and mental disorders. Racker's first biochemical research was carried out in Quastel's laboratory. In 1941 he left England for the United States. After a short period in Minnesota, where the first observations on a defect of metabolism in poliomyelitis were made, Racker went to New York. He completed his internship and residence at Harlem Hospital and taught part-time at New York University. In 1944 he joined the staff of the department of microbiology of New York University, where he was promoted to assistant professor in 1947. In 1952 he went to Yale University as associate professor of biochemistry. In 1954 he returned to New York as chairman of the Department of Biochemistry at the Public Health Research Institute of the City of New York. In 1966 he became Albert Einstein Professor and chairman of the department of biochemistry and molecular biology at Cornell University. Racker was elected to the American Academy of Arts and Sciences in 1962 and to the National Academy of Sciences in 1966.

For background information *see* ENERGY METABOLISM; ENZYME; MITOCHONDRIA in the McGraw-Hill Encyclopedia of Science and Technology.   ☐

★ RAMAN, Sir (Chandrasekhara) Venkata

Indian physicist
Born Nov. 7, 1888, Trichinopoly, India

THE STUDY of color always had a great attraction for Raman. During a sea voyage to Europe in 1921, he observed with admiration the brilliant blue color of the Mediterranean, and later also noticed the blue color of ice in the Swiss glaciers. After returning to India, he experimented on the diffusion of sunlight in its passage through clear water, transparent blocks of ice, and other materials. From observations it emerged that the diffusion of light is a phenomenon exhibited by all transparent bodies, but the intensity and state of polarization of diffused light vary greatly between different materials. It also became evident that, while the phenomenon has a molecular origin, it is strongly influenced by the grouping of the molecules in the material. Systematically pursuing his investigations in this field, Raman was led to the discovery in 1928 of the effect now known by his name. He used, instead of sunlight, the monochromatic radiations emitted by the mercury-arc lamp and applied the spectroscope

to the study of the diffused radiations emerging from the material under examination.

A. Einstein's concept of the corpuscular nature of light leads to a simple explanation of the effect discovered by Raman. The energy of the individual light corpuscle may be either added to, or diminished by, the energy of rotation or vibration (in any particular mode) of the individual molecule that it encounters. The result is the appearance in the spectrum of the scattered light, besides the lines present in the incident light, and also of other sharp lines displaced with respect to them toward the violet or the red. The difference of frequency between the excited and the exciting radiations may therefore be identified with a characteristic frequency of the molecule, located in the infrared range of the spectrum.

As Raman pointed out in his first published report of the discovery, explaining the effect as above, the method affords a technique of great simplicity by which the modes of vibration of molecules may be enumerated and their frequencies accurately measured. Additional information is also furnished by the observed intensity and state of polarization of the excited radiations. Thus, the effect becomes a powerful tool for the exploration of the structure of the molecules. The spectroscopic examination of light diffused by liquids and in crystals also reveals other features that may be identified as arising from the movements of molecular groups in liquids, or from the modes of vibration characteristic of the three-dimensionally periodic structure of crystals. Thus, the Raman effect proves also to be an invaluable aid to the understanding of the physical behavior of the liquid and crystalline states of matter.

Especially in the field of the physical applications, Raman and his collaborators were very active. They examined by spectroscopic methods the nature of thermal agitation in liquids and in crystalline solids. Raman showed that the thermal energy of crystals can be completely evaluated on the basis of spectroscopically determined frequencies of lattice vibration. In addition, the optical effects arising from the passage of a beam of light through a liquid or a solid traversed by acoustic wave trains were considered in detail. The Raman-Nath theory of these effects is well known and succeeds in explaining every detail of the observed phenomena.

It is noteworthy that the ideas and results emerging from the light diffusion studies have found fruitful application in the domain of x-ray studies. Three such cases may be mentioned here. The first is the explanation of the x-ray diffraction halos exhibited by liquids. Raman showed that their main features follow as a natural consequence of molecular grouping in liquids, indicated by their observed behavior in light scattering. The second case is furnished by the Compton effect in x-ray scattering. In a paper published in 1927, Raman showed that the existence of two types of x-ray scattering follows from the theory of wave optics as applied to the scattering of the incident x-radiations by the electrons in atoms. The formulas derived by him quantitatively explain the observed angular distribution and the relative intensities of the two types of x-ray scattering as a function of the atomic number of the scattering substance. The third case is that of the supernumerary or non-Laue x-ray reflections exhibited by crystals. It was shown by Raman that these arise as necessary consequences of the specific modes of vibration of the lattice structure of crystals, exhibited in the spectra of scattered radiation.

Raman was educated in India, taking his B.A. in 1904 and M.A. in 1907 at Presidency College, Madras. His first published paper appeared in 1906, while he was still a student. In 1907 he became an officer in the civil service. This position was resigned in 1917, when he accepted a research professorship at Calcutta. In 1933 he moved to Bangalore, where he remained. In 1934 he sponsored the foundation of the Indian Academy of Sciences, of which he became president. The Raman Research Institute, built, endowed, and later directed by him, commenced functioning in 1949. He became a fellow of the Royal Society of London in 1924, and was knighted in 1929. For his work on the scattering of light, Raman received the Nobel Prize for physics in 1930.

Raman wrote *New Physics: Talks on Aspects of Science* (1951).

For background information *see* RAMAN EFFECT; SCATTERING (ELECTROMAGNETIC RADIATION) in the McGraw-Hill Encyclopedia of Science and Technology.   ☐

★ RAMMELKAMP, Charles Henry, Jr.

American internist and epidemiologist
Born May 24, 1911, Jacksonville, Ill., U.S.A.

RAMMELKAMP'S INTEREST in treatment of infectious diseases and in the streptococcus and staphylococcus originated while working with Chester S. Keefer, first at Harvard and then at Boston University. His early studies included the use of tyrothricin in the treatment of experimental infections in animals and localized infections in man. At the same time he began studies of the group A streptococcus, employing the agglutination technique for the typing of these organisms.

When penicillin first became available for study, little was known concerning its use in human infections. It was first necessary to de-

velop a method for the measurement of penicillin in various body fluids and excretions. The rate of excretion and factors influencing excretion in the urine were determined, as well as the diffusion of penicillin into various body fluids and cells. From these and other data, dosage regimens were planned and tested in various infections in man.

In 1943 Rammelkamp was appointed to the Commission on Acute Respiratory Diseases at Fort Bragg, N.C., under the direction of John Dingle. There he developed a broad interest in various respiratory infections. His major efforts were directed toward the study of exudative tonsillitis and pharyngitis, both from the clinical and laboratory aspects. Nonstreptococcal exudative tonsillitis was defined, and from the data it became apparent that it was caused by a virus. Laboratory studies conducted with Melvin Kaplan involved primarily the investigation of streptokinase. Other major studies included transmission of atypical pneumonia in volunteers and a study of Q fever in military personnel.

In 1946 Rammelkamp joined the staff at the Western Reserve University School of Medicine in the department of preventive medicine, working with J. Dingle. During the next few years he participated in the study of a group of Cleveland families, defining the various diseases encountered in the family group. He began studies on the staphylococcus, which included definition of three separate coagulases that proved to be antigenically distinct. During this period the theory was developed and subsequently proved that acute glomerulonephritis is caused by a limited number of types of group A streptococci, thus explaining many of the epidemiological differences between nephritis and acute rheumatic fever.

In 1949 Rammelkamp became director of the Streptococcal Disease Laboratory at Warren Air Force Base, Wyo. The staff made many major contributions to the epidemiology of streptococcal infections and rheumatic fever. Perhaps of most importance were the studies on the prevention of streptococcal infections, rheumatic fever, and acute glomerulonephritis. Many present treatment and prevention programs are based on these studies. In 1954 the staff members received a Lasker Award of the American Public Health Association for their contributions in this area.

From 1956 Rammelkamp's investigative interests were devoted to study of the mode of transmission of staphylococcal infections. With E. Wolinsky and E. Mortimer, he demonstrated that these infections are spread primarily by the hands of personnel in the hospital. With P. Hall, R. Griggs, and J. Gaon, he instituted in 1961 an intensive study of Balkan nephropathy in Yugoslavia. This apparently new disease involving thousands is limited to villages along various tributaries of the Danube River, and the cause has not been elucidated as yet. Finally, Rammelkamp became interested in medical education and in the problems of delivering good medical care within a county hospital complex.

Rammelkamp graduated from Illinois College (A.B., 1933) and the University of Chicago (M.D., 1937). Graduate training in medicine and research included periods at Chicago, Washington, Harvard, and Boston universities. In 1946 he joined the staff of the Western Reserve University, where in 1950 he became professor of medicine and professor of preventive medicine. He was also director of medicine and research at the Cleveland Metropolitan General Hospital and visiting lecturer at the Harvard School of Public Health. Besides the Lasker Award, his honors include an honorary degree from Illinois College, the Alvarenga Prize of Philadelphia, the first Research Achievement Award of the American Heart Association, and the Bruce Medal in Preventive Medicine of the American College of Physicians.

For background information *see* BACTERIOLOGY, MEDICAL; EPIDEMIOLOGY in the McGraw-Hill Encyclopedia of Science and Technology. □

☆ RAMO, Simon

American engineer
Born May 7, 1913, Salt Lake City, Utah, U.S.A.

RAMO'S SCIENTIFIC and engineering work was in two main areas: microwaves and electron optics, and guided missiles and systems engineering. His first published work, based on researches at the California Institute of Technology, involved highly accurate measurement of voltages in the neighborhood of 1,000,000 volts. Upon joining the General Electric Co. in 1936, Ramo further advanced the high-voltage measurement art by perfecting the first cathode-ray oscillograph technique for high-voltage, simulated lightning transients. This was the begin-

ning of Ramo's work with electron beams, the core of the problem being to control the beam with unusual precision for recording of transient phenomena with a resolution in time comparable with the transit time of the electrons in the stream. Prior to Ramo's work with sealed tubes, the recording film for the obtaining of a permanent record had to be introduced into the vacuum chamber. With the sealed oscillographic technique, of course, the film recording was taken from an optical trace on the fluorescent screen by the single, high-intensity sweep of the beam.

This early work led in two directions. One was in the electron optical field, particularly with regard to the electron microscope. Ramo worked out and published basic formulas for aberrations in electrostatic electron lenses, which were used in the General Electric microscope that he developed. He also became interested in traveling waves in electron streams and published some of the pioneer articles in the quantitative analysis of electromagnetic wave travel in electron streams, taking account for the first time of many of the complex interactions between the electromagnetic fields and the density variations within the space charge of the stream itself. His work in rectilinear streams convinced him that for the generation of larger amounts of microwave power it would be necessary to use higher velocities and hence higher voltages, so as to obtain the proper relationship between the electron velocity and the frequency of oscillation. Furthermore, his work led to early realization that strength and efficiency in the generation of frequencies in thousands of megacycles per second would be best obtained by using a rotating space charge, allowing the same stream to pass the resonators many times. His was the first pub-

lished work in the United States on traveling waves in rotating space charges.

Also, he began the pulsing of the magnetron type of tube, which represented the application of a relatively high voltage of short duration to a rotating space charge. Some of his early designs of such rotating space charge within resonant cavities led to patents on microwave generation with cavity magnetrons, constituting the earliest work in this field in the United States. By the pulsing technique, which combined his background in high-voltage pulse generators and in electron streams, Ramo was able to reach the level of tens of kilowatts, which was the highest power generated in the United States at that time. (Classified work in Great Britain, it was learned later, had anticipated this technique.) Ramo also gave attention during World War II to the development of the "lighthouse" electron tubes, which involved exceedingly close spacing diodes, triodes, and tetrodes in which the electrodes were further arranged so as to become integral with enclosing resonant cavities. These devices, on which Ramo worked out some of the fundamental theory and on which he did some of the initial experiments, were used as generators and amplifiers and elements of receiving apparatus in advanced lightweight radar systems.

Ramo's publications on the basic microwave art were widely published in books and articles and used for the education of a considerable fraction of the generation of engineers and scientists who came into radar and other aspects of microwaves during, and just after, the war. Some of these works on basic electricity and magnetism applied to higher-frequency electronics have, through later editions revised by coauthors, continued to be widely used in colleges and universities as a text, and they have been published in several foreign language editions.

After the war Ramo moved to California, where he organized the technological operations now known as the Hughes Aircraft Co. This was a broad organizational effort, creating teams for systems engineering of guided missiles and related apparatus such as airborne radar. Ramo's innovation in organization and in breakdown of the complex systems engineering problems represented by guided missiles and radar brought those operations to high prominence in meeting the air defense requirements of the nation for a decade. His writings on guided missile engineering and systems engineering were widely utilized both as individual articles and in textbooks. Among other projects, Ramo acted as chief scientist for the research, development, and ultimately the production of the Falcon guided missile, this being actually a family of airborne missiles, which more than any other such missile has been the mainstay of the air defense of the United States since about 1950.

Ramo went on to organize the Ramo-Wooldridge Corp. and Space Technology Laboratories (now all merged into TRW, Inc.), and he also was given responsibility for technical direction of the nation's intercontinental ballistic missile program (Atlas, Titan, and Minuteman). He served as chief scientist on this program. In this capacity Ramo was involved mainly in executive and policy decisions. However, he also was a very active participant in the technical decisions and the development of systems engineering as a technological discipline, including broad extensions in the use of the large-scale computer as an analytical tool for these purposes, the application of statistical analyses, and the simulation of complex multiparameter problems containing many critical instability and nonlinear aspects. The use of mathematical modeling and of trade-off analyses to ensure the selection of an optimum ensemble among the many factors making up the typical large system was particularly pioneered and directed by Ramo.

In recent years Ramo became interested in the relationships of science to society and wrote very widely on this subject, with original analyses and creative elucidations of the problems and possibilities of improving the utilization of science for the benefit of society.

Ramo received a B.S. at the University of Utah in 1933 and a Ph.D. in electrical engineering and physics at the California Institute of Technology in 1936. He was a research engineer with the General Electric Co. in Schenectady, N.Y., during 1936–46. With the Hughes Aircraft Co. he was director of research in electronics (1946–1948) and then directed guided missiles research and development (1948–51); he became director of operations in 1951 and a vice-president in 1952. He was executive vice-president of the Ramo-Wooldridge Corp. during 1953–58 and, following a company merger, executive vice-president and director of Thompson Ramo Wooldridge, Inc., from 1958 to 1961, when he became vice-chairman of the board. He was also science director of the U.S. Air Force ballistic missile program in 1954–58 and president of Space Technology Laboratories in 1957–58. Ramo was elected to the American Academy of Arts and Sciences in 1964.

For background information *see* CATHODE-RAY TUBE; ELECTROOPTICS; GUIDED MISSILE; MICROWAVE in the McGraw-Hill Encyclopedia of Science and Technology.   □

★ RAPER, John Robert

American botanist
Born Oct. 3, 1911, Welcome, N.C., U.S.A.

THE LOWER plants—myxomycetes, algae, and particularly fungi—display a range of variation in basic biological characteristics that is perhaps unparalleled elsewhere in the realm of living organisms. This is most strikingly true of sexuality and other aspects of sexual reproduc-

tion. The variety and complexity of sexual processes in the fungi early aroused Raper's interest, and his work, except during the war years 1943–46, was devoted to a better understanding of the physiological aspects and genetical bases of fungal sexuality. In connection with the interest in the broad problems of sexuality, Raper did extensive experimental work on hormonal coordination of sexual interaction in the water mold *Achlya*, and on the bifactorial incompatibility mating system in the higher fungi, typified by *Schizophyllum*.

Individual plants of most species of *Achlya* and other biflagellate water molds produce both ♂ and ♀ sexual organs and are self-fertile. There are a few species, such as *A. bisexualis* and *A. ambisexualis*, in which sexual reproduction requires the interaction of two strains, one reacting as ♂, and the other as ♀. Such species, however, were found to comprise numerous strains of varying ♂ and ♀ potentialities, and all strains, save the strongest ♂s and ♀s, can react either as ♂ or as ♀ depending upon the relative sexual affinity of the mate. Strong ♂ and ♀ strains in isolation produce no sexual organs, but when they are brought together ♂ and ♀ organs are produced and interact within a day. In matings of ♂ and ♀ strains on semisolid media, sexual organs of both signs were sometimes formed prior to any contact of the interacting plants, a reaction that clearly indicated the activity of diffusible inducing substances. (The induction of sexual organs at a distance was first described by Burgeff in 1924 in *Mucor*, a "black bread mold," and a preliminary study of the effect was made by H. Bishop in 1936 with *Sapromyces*, a water mold related to *Achlya*.) Raper demonstrated the initiation of the sexual interaction, the induction of ♂ organs, to be dependent upon a secretion of the ♀ plant (hormone A), and the induction of ♀ organs to be dependent upon a secretion from the sexually activated ♂ plant (hormone B). By interposing semipermeable membranes between reacting plants and by de-

termining the hormonal activities of filtrates of vegetative and sexually activated ♂ and ♀ plants, Raper delineated a complex hormonal system that coordinates and quantitatively controls the several stages of the sexual interaction to the time of full differentiation of ♂ and ♀ sexual organs and fertilization.

In collaboration with A. J. Haagen-Smit of the California Institute of Technology, an effort was made in 1940–41 to isolate and identify hormone A. Although this effort was unsuccessful, enormous enrichment of the hormone was achieved (37% of the hormone in 1440 liters of filtrate from ♀ plants was recovered in 2 mg of material). Raper discontinued this work shortly thereafter, largely because of the lack of the highly specialized facilities required—the sexual hormones of *Achlya* were at that time of little interest to any supporting agency. The work was resumed a few years later by Alma W. Barksdale, who, in collaboration with a team of chemists, isolated hormone A and established its probable structural formula.

Raper's more recent work dealt with the most complex pattern of sexuality found among the fungi, bifactorial incompatibility or tetrapolarity, the predominant mating system of the higher Basidiomycetes. Progeny from each fruiting body, such as *Schizophyllum commune*, are of four distinct mating types, each of which will interact with only one other mating type to complete the sexual cycle. Yet the progeny of one fruiting body are completely interfertile with the progeny of other fruiting bodies of different origins. Mating competence was early recognized (1920) to depend upon two genetic factors, *A* and *B*, which occur in extensive series of alternate states and which segregate and assort independently. When two mated strains carry different *A*s and different *B*s, there is a reciprocal exchange of nuclei between the two mates and the establishment in each of a specialized, balanced heterokaryon, the dikaryon, which is capable of indefinite growth and which eventually produces the fruiting body to complete the sexual cycle. From the early 1950s, the more complete dissection of this system was the major objective of the work of Raper and numerous associates and students. The more important aspects of the system as now understood may be summarized as follows:

When any two haploid (homokaryotic) strains grow together, fusions between cells of the two strains establish binucleate fusion cells. Further developments depend upon the relationships of the incompatibility factors of the two mates. Any of four types of interactions may ensue, and each leads to the establishment of a specific type of heterokaryon (a vegetative system containing nuclei of different genotypes). When *A*s and *B*s are different ($A{\neq}B{\neq}$), a dikaryon is formed, and the life cycle is completed; when the two mates share either factor ($A=B\neq$ or $A\neq B=$) or both factors ($A=B=$), three distinct and infertile heterokaryons are formed. The four types of heterokaryons differ in the distribution of the two types of nuclei, in nuclear ratios, in certain physiological characteristics, and in gross and microscopic morphology.

The A and B factors are each composed of two distinct loci, α and β, separable by crossing over. Each of the four basic incompatibility loci is multiple-allelic and 9 $A\alpha$s, 26 $A\beta$s, 7 $B\alpha$s, and 7 $B\beta$s have been identified. Estimates of the number of alleles at each locus in the worldwide population are 9 $A\alpha$s, 50 $A\beta$s, 7 or 8 $B\alpha$s, and 7 $B\beta$s. Two factors of either A or B series are compatible when they have different alleles at either or both of the two loci: $A\ \alpha 1 - \beta 1$ is thus equally compatible with $A\ \alpha 1 - \beta 2$, $A\ \alpha 2 - \beta 1$, and $A\ \alpha 2 - \beta 2$. All A factors seem to be similarly constituted, but the B factors belong to three classes that differ in interlocus distance and in minor details of their interactions.

Primary mutations in the basic incompatibility loci lead to the loss of factor discrimination (self-compatibility) and a functional equivalence of the mutated factor to two different, normal factors of the same series. A mutant-B homokaryon is thus a mimic of the $A=B\neq$ heterokaryon; a mutant-A homokaryon, a mimic of the $A\neq B=$ heterokaryon; and a mutant-A–mutant-B homokaryon, a mimic of the $A\neq B\neq$ heterokaryon, the dikaryon. Secondary mutations in the incompatibility loci restore the normal morphology and self-incompatibility and endow the secondary mutant allele with a new specificity, different from that of the wild-type progenitor allele.

Each incompatibility factor, A and B, appears to operate as a dual-regulator gene that turns on or off one of two partial but interlocking morphogenetic sequences which together constitute the process of dikaryosis. Numerous modifier mutations, located in genes other than the incompatibility factors, disrupt the orderly progression of events comprising the morphogenetic sequence. As the modifier mutations have expression only when the sequences controlled by the A and B factors are operating, the wild-type alleles of the genes are thought to be the structural genes responsible for the specific stages of the morphogenetic progression.

The youngest in a family of eight children, Raper attended the University of North Carolina, from which he received the A.B. in 1933 and the A.M. under J. N. Couch in 1936. He transferred to Harvard University, where he worked with W. H. Weston for his Ph.D. in 1939. Two years were spent at the California Institute of Technology as a National Research Council fellow prior to his appointment as instructor in botany at Indiana University. During 1943–46 he was research biologist in the Plutonium Division

of the Manhattan Project at Chicago and Oak Ridge, Tenn. His work there was concerned primarily with the biological effects of external irradiation with beta rays. Appointed assistant professor of botany at the University of Chicago in 1946, he was promoted to associate professor in 1949 and to professor in 1953. In 1954 he became professor of botany at Harvard University. He was elected to the American Academy of Arts and Sciences in 1955 and to the National Academy of Sciences in 1964.

For background information *see* EUMYCETES; GENE ACTION; PLANT HORMONES in the McGraw-Hill Encyclopedia of Science and Technology. ☐

★ RASMUSSEN, John Oscar, Jr.

American nuclear scientist
Born Aug. 8, 1926, Saint Petersburg, Fla., U.S.A.

THE HEAVIEST isotopes existing in large amounts in nature are uranium-238, uranium-235, and thorium-232, and nuclear power and nuclear explosives are based on these as raw materials. That these isotopes exist, while elements of higher atomic number apparently do not, is a consequence of the relatively slow rate of radioactive decay of the three isotopes. They and many of their neighbors decay by the alpha decay process, whereby an energetic helium ion is ejected to form an isotope of a lighter element. The alpha decay half-lives of U^{235}, U^{238}, and Th^{232} are at least comparable to the time since the elements on Earth were formed.

Rasmussen concentrated especially on study of the alpha decay process and other properties of nuclei of a type similar to thorium and uranium. Nuclei of these and heavier elements, as well as most nuclei of mass number between 150 and 190, are believed to be egg-shaped, not spherical like other nuclei. In 1953, on a 7-month research visit to Stockholm, he began the development of an improved alpha decay rate theory to apply to the deformed (egg-shaped) nuclei. The deformed alpha emitters that had been carefully studied did not emit the alpha particle (helium ion) with a single energy, but rather in complex spectra with alpha "lines" at several slightly differing energies. Rasmussen recognized that these complex patterns could be simplified by grouping many lines into a few families (rotational bands). According to theories advanced by Aage Bohr of Copenhagen the previous year, deformed nuclei should always have their energy levels grouped into rotational band families, where levels of the same family differ only in the speed of rotation.

The next problem was to try to understand the intensities of transitions to the main family, called the favored band, wherein the structure changes were very small during the alpha emission process. Rasmussen suggested that the intensity patterns to a rotational band really measured the zones on the egg-shaped nucleus from which the alphas were emitted. He began in 1954 a collaboration with Ben Segall, a postdoctoral physicist at the Lawrence Radiation Laboratory in Berkeley, in which they performed numerical calculations showing the meaning of the intensity patterns. That is, in element 90, thorium, the alphas are mainly emitted from the ends of the egg-shaped nucleus, but as one goes to higher elements the emitting zones shift from poles toward the equator, with the main emission coming at 60° north and south latitude for element 96, curium. They recognized that these zones of greatest alpha emission are the zones from which neutrons and protons can theoretically be removed with the least energy. However, it was not until others had developed theories in which nucleon-pair behavior in nuclei was likened to electron-pair behavior in superconductors that it was possible to go further with a theory of alpha decay intensities of deformed nuclei based on motion of individual neutrons and protons (a "microscopic" model).

The rapid improvement of computer facilities for scientific research provided an essential condition for the next advance. In 1960 Rasmussen and Hans-Jörg Mang, a German physicist, began work on a completely microscopic theory of alpha decay, wherein alpha intensities were to be calculated on the basis of the orbital motion of individual neutrons and protons in the nucleus. By 1962 they had completed calculations explaining the intensity patterns to favored bands, and by 1965, with the help of a graduate student, J. K. Poggenburg, extended calculations were complete on several hundred alpha groups, including the weaker unfavored bands, where the internal motion of nucleons is altered substantially during alpha decay.

Paralleling the theoretical work on alpha decay and related topics, such as superfluid, pairing-force effects in nuclei, Jack M. Hollander and Rasmussen, aided by graduate students, experimentally studied energy level systems of many deformed nuclei, measuring the energy spectra of gamma rays and electrons ejected following radioactive decay. They attempted to relate their results in detail to the theoretical models advanced by A. Bohr, B. R. Mottelson, S. G. Nilsson, and others.

Son of a Danish immigrant who eventually retired from the U.S. Army as a colonel, Rasmussen received his B.S. in chemistry in 1948 from the California Institute of Technology, his undergraduate years having been interrupted by a 2-year period in the Navy. He received his Ph.D. in chemistry from the University of California at Berkeley in 1952, following thesis research on new alpha-emitting nuclei in the rare-earth region. This research was guided by G. T. Seaborg and S. G. Thompson. In 1952 Rasmussen became a member of the faculty of the University of California in Berkeley and of the staff of the Lawrence Radiation Laboratory in Berkeley. He received an E. O. Lawrence Memorial Award from the Atomic Energy Commission in 1967.

For background information *see* ATOMIC STRUCTURE AND SPECTRA; ELEMENTS (CHEMICAL); ISOTOPE; RADIOACTIVITY in the McGraw-Hill Encyclopedia of Science and Technology.   □

★ RATCLIFFE, John Ashworth

English physicist
Born Dec. 12, 1902, Bacup, Lancashire, England

R ATCLIFFE'S SCIENTIFIC work was concerned with the investigation of the ionosphere by means of radio waves. Immediately after taking his degree in physics at Cambridge in 1924, he started at the Cavendish Laboratory as a research student under E. V. Appleton, who was then making his first experimental investigations of radio waves reflected from the upper atmosphere. Although Appleton almost immediately moved to become a professor in London, while Ratcliffe remained in Cambridge, they continued to work together at a distant field station. They published a series of papers, with Ratcliffe as the junior collaborator, describing investigations made by Appleton's wavelength-change method. The radiated wavelength was changed continuously over a small range, so that the superposition of the ground wave and the sky wave produced a series of maxima and minima or "fringes." They paid particular attention to the state of polarization of the reflected waves.

As the demands of the collaborative work at the field station became less, Ratcliffe established his own Ionospheric Research Group in the Cavendish Laboratory and, with the help of research students, started to use the Breit and Tuve method of working by means of pulses reflected from the ionosphere. When he found that the strength of a single pulse reflected from the ionosphere fluctuated in the phenomenon known as "fading," he began to develop a detailed diffraction theory to show how this fading came about. After World War II he elaborated this theory to show the close relation between the random fading of an ionosphere echo and the random noiselike fluctuations of current in a circuit.

In another investigation, which was started before the war and continued afterward, very long radio waves (18 km) emitted by a commercial sender were used to investigate the structure of the lowest part of the ionosphere, the D region. Two different kinds of experiment were carried out. In one the stationary interference pattern produced on the ground by the superposition of a ground wave and a sky wave was delineated by measurements made in a traveling laboratory—at first in a van drawn by a motor car and later in an airplane. In the other experiment the sky wave was isolated by a special antenna system, and the variations of its amplitude and phase were studied at a fixed observing point. It was found that the behavior of these very long waves is remarkably regular, except that during sudden ionosphere disturbances (SIDs), or ionosphere storms, the behavior changed in a characteristic way. A long run of observations, extending over the 11 years of a sunspot cycle, provided a very complete account of these changes. Theory to explain them came later, as outlined below.

During World War II Ratcliffe served with the British research and development organization known as the Telecommunications Research Establishment (TRE), responsible for the development of radar in the Royal Air Force. When the war was over, he returned to Cambridge and was in charge of the radio research work at the Cavendish Laboratory until 1960. The strength of this radio group varied from time to time, usually containing about 20 re-

search workers. Many of these had come from universities overseas and later returned to them to continue their research. The group continued the prewar investigations mentioned previously and started some new ones. Researches on "whistlers," ionospheric cross modulation, and ionosphere theory were the most important.

A "whistler" is a particular type of naturally occurring audio-frequency atmospheric, which can be heard if a long wire is connected to an audio amplifier. It originates in the impulsive radiation from a lightning flash; it is guided in its travel through the ionosphere along a geomagnetic line of force, and during its travel it is dispersed, so that when it reaches Earth at the other end of the line it sounds like a whistle of changing frequency. Study of the frequency variation in this whistle led to an estimate of the electron concentration at the outermost point reached by the line of force, and this provided at the time the only estimate of this quantity at distances from the center of the Earth equal to about 3 earth radii.

In the 1930s the phenomenon of the Luxembourg effect had been discovered, in which the modulation of one radio transmission can be transferred to another as the waves pass through the ionosphere. The Cavendish group made detailed investigations of this ionospheric cross modulation and showed how, by studying the amplitude and the phase of the transferred modulation, it was possible to deduce the collision frequency of the ionospheric electrons at a known height.

Ratcliffe was deeply interested in theory and liked to see in a simple and physical way how nature works. His theories were usually expressed in quite simple mathematical terms and, if those proved inadequate, he hoped that some mathematicians would pursue the investigations when he had reached his limit. He was fortunate in having able mathematicians associated with him and in having available the university's digital computer, which had been designed and built by one of them.

Among the theoretical advances, one was concerned with problems of diffraction, particularly from irregular and "random" media. Another was concerned with the results of Appleton's magneto-ionic theory, which were expressed in a complicated equation. From this theory it was not at all easy to see how waves behave when the frequency is changed or when they travel in different directions relative to the Earth's magnetic field. Ratcliffe developed some simple ways of visualizing this behavior, which have proved useful over a long period of time.

Appleton had pointed out in the mid-1920s that in principle it should be possible to deduce the height distribution of ionospheric electrons from the "ionograms," which are made regularly at ionospheric observatories in several places all over the world. Because of certain difficulties in the calculations, this suggestion had never been followed up. Ratcliffe initiated computation of these electronic distributions, at first making the computations by hand. Later the radio group devised methods for use on the digital computer and published a number of typical distributions. By examining these, they showed clearly that the electrons in the upper part of the ionosphere (the F layer above about 150 km) were lost by a process which had previously been suggested by H. S. W. Massey and others, and they explained why this layer is sometimes split into two.

A continuing objective of the Cambridge group was to deduce the electron concentration in the lowest ionosphere (the D region below about 95 km) from the long series of observations which had been made on very long waves. This involved mathematical techniques of considerable complexity, and was carried out not by Ratcliffe but by others in the group. The research involved a long series of papers and did not yield a final result until 1966, when it proved possible to deduce the required electron distributions and to show how they change with the time of day and the season and during the changes of the solar cycle, a solar storm, and a solar eclipse.

In 1960 Ratcliffe left Cambridge to become director of the Radio Research Station at Slough, a post he held until his retirement in 1966. He joined the Research Station at a time when its interests were expanding to include space science in addition to radio-wave propagation. His 6 years there saw the completion of this transition and a change of name to the Radio and Space Research Station. It was while he was at Slough that the analysis of the very long wave measurements, mentioned above, was finally made.

Ratcliffe went to Sidney Sussex College, Cambridge (M.A., 1924). He was a fellow of that college from 1927 to 1960 and was made an honorary fellow in 1963. During 1939–45 he was with the Telecommunications Research Establishment. At Cambridge his teaching activities were as important as his research. He made a long but unsuccessful attempt to persuade the university to teach some science to those reading the humanities. Elected to the Royal Society of London in 1951, he was awarded its Royal Medal in 1966; in the same year he received the Faraday Medal of the Institution of Electrical Engineers, and was president of the Institution in 1966–67. He was awarded the Holweck Medal of the Physical Society in 1953.

Ratcliffe wrote *Magneto-Ionic Theory and Its Applications to the Ionosphere* (1959) and edited *Physics of the Upper Atmosphere* (1960). Beginning in 1965, he served as editor in chief of the *Journal of Atmospheric and Terrestrial Physics*.

For background information *see* IONOSPHERE; RADIO-WAVE PROPAGATION in the McGraw-Hill Encyclopedia of Science and Technology.   □

★ REGGE, Tullio

Italian physicist
Born July 11, 1931, Turin, Italy

FOR HIS role in introducing the idea of complex angular momenta into elementary-particle physics, Regge received the American Physical Society's Dannie Heineman Prize in 1964. Regge's work started at the University of Turin about 1956, when he became interested in obtaining a complete understanding of potential scattering theory. In its simplest form this theory is concerned with the problem of investigating the nonrelativistic scattering of two spinless particles interacting through an isotropic local potential. Because of its simplicity, this problem lends itself to a rigorous mathematical treatment. Until 1958 potential scattering had been discussed in line with the ideas of Jost, Pais, Bargmann, and others who exploited the well-known partial wave expansion of the scattering amplitude. A second independent approach had been developed by Khuri, who derived dispersion relations similar to those found in field theory. At this time the feeling was that these two approaches had to remain foreign to each other and that, in fact, the standard partial wave expansion simply could not cope with the typical formalism of dispersion theory.

At the beginning of 1959 Regge was working on the problem of reconstructing the potential from the phase shifts at a given energy along the methods of Gelfand and Levitan. While at the Max Planck Institute in Munich he became aware that his techniques, involving the definition of phase shifts for complex angular momenta, could be applied to a variety of less academic problems, including the question of the validity of the Mandelstam double-dispersion relations. The standard tool for this kind of investigation was the Watson-Sommerfeld transform, originally devised by J. H. Poincaré, in which the standard Rayleigh-Faxen partial wave expansion is converted into an integral over complex angular momenta. This kind of approach provided a unified treatment of potential scattering, yielding at the same time the interesting result that the asymptotic behavior of the scattering amplitude for large momentum transfers is determined by the resonance poles of the partial scattering amplitude in the complex angular momentum plane. Many leading physicists, among them G. F. Chew, M. L. Goldberger, and Murray Gell-Mann, quickly realized that, if Regge's results were valid for a relativistic theory, the crossing symmetry would yield an extremely interesting conjecture for the high-energy behavior of scattering amplitudes. In the years following the 1962 Geneva Conference, this conjecture was extensively investigated; and it is now generally agreed that, although things are not quite as simple as originally assumed, the experiments show that the theory is here to stay.

Regge also worked in group theory, where he discovered some intriguing new symmetries of the Clebsch-Gordan coefficients and of the Racah coefficients. He was interested in general relativity, and in 1960 he proposed a method of approximating Riemannian manifolds with higher-dimensional analogs of polyhedrons with the aim of obtaining solutions to the Einstein equations in those cases where current approaches fail because of lack of symmetry. His recent interests included the analytic properties of Feynman relativistic amplitudes and the investigation of the semiclassical limit of group representations.

Regge obtained a doctorate at the University of Turin in 1952; he received a Ph.D. from Rochester University in 1956. He was appointed a full professor at the University of Turin in 1962. In 1965 he became a member of the Institute for Advanced Studies at Princeton.

For background information *see* GROUP THEORY; RELATIVITY; SCATTERING EXPERIMENTS, NUCLEAR; SCATTERING MATRIX in the McGraw-Hill Encyclopedia of Science and Technology.   □

★ REICHELDERFER, Francis Wylton

American meteorologist and science director
Born Aug. 6, 1895, Harlan, Ind., U.S.A.

SOME BASIC concepts of the broad-scale circulation of the atmosphere were described in mathematical terms by V. Bjerknes in the 19th century and by a few earlier scientists. The greater impetus toward analytical and quantitative meteorology came with the work of

J. Bjerknes and the Bergen "school" about 1915 and with L. F. Richardson's book on weather prediction by numerical process in 1922. Since World War I the international system for observations and reports of the state of the atmosphere at a particular moment has increased very greatly through air soundings by aircraft, balloons, rockets, space satellites, and other new technological devices. Prior to 1915 data of the atmosphere were fragmentary and usually delayed. Occasional balloon soundings and kite ascents gave little evidence of the complex motions and variations of the air at higher altitudes and over the wide expanse of oceans and remote lands. Since the late 1950s the modern devices for probing the atmosphere have given literally millions of bits of data daily for thousands of different localities spread over perhaps one-fifth of the globe. Although measurements are not yet sufficient to enable meteorologists to develop the desired exact science, the phenomenal increase in atmospheric data and the invention of high-speed electronic computers have transformed meteorology from the minor, descriptive subject it was in the 1920s to a fairly sophisticated science.

Reichelderfer's career spanned this eventful and often tempestuous period of evolution from 1917 to the present, and he was fortunate to have been among the very few meteorologists in the 1920s and 1930s to take part in many eventful "firsts" in aeronautics, meteorology, and related sciences. He decided early in his schooling to seek a career in science and chose research in chemistry as his primary interest. The determining factors that led him into meteorology in 1917 and kept him largely in this field were World War I, the new and almost unlimited opportuni-

ties in aeronautics and meteorology, and the acute shortage of young "aerologists." These circumstances led to his being "drafted" for important assignments, which in turn led to new and challenging opportunities for research and development in aeronautical meteorology and its rapidly expanding applications. The epochal expansion of the atmospheric sciences resulted from many pressing circumstances. World War II created an urgent demand. Technological advances in aircraft, radio, radar, computer machines, space satellites, and other devices provided the means for manyfold increases in data gathering in the atmosphere and, moreover, added to the importance of these data for their roles in further advancement of aircraft design and operations. Another influence that contributed to meteorological developments in the United States was the expansion of graduate courses in universities. The competitive milieu, the urge provided by the military meteorological organizations and the American Meteorological Society with its emphasis on the private practice of applied meteorology, and the functions and programs of the U.S. Weather Bureau all favored rapid change and growth in meteorology.

The acute scarcity of meteorologists in the early stages of this growth gave greater opportunities to those who were available. Reichelderfer was called to take primary roles in many of the new concepts and programs in research, service applications, and education. In the spread and strengthening of graduate studies in meteorology and in promoting research and development, he was initially one of the prime movers.

The first full graduate course in meteorology was organized by C.-G. Rossby at MIT in 1928. The students consisted mainly of Naval officers recruited by Reichelderfer with the support of Captain W. D. Puleston, then head of the Navy Department's office of graduate programs. In 1922, when attrition had reduced the number of Naval officer meteorologists to a total of two, Reichelderfer had sought the cooperation of the Signal Corps, the agency responsible for Army meteorology, and the U.S. Weather Bureau in establishing a graduate course at a leading university where civilians and officers could study to become meteorologists. However, the Signal Corps and the Bureau preferred to continue the then existing practice of recruiting teachers or 4-year college graduates in physics or mathematics and relying on in-service training to qualify them as meteorologists after they entered government employ. Not until 1926 could Puleston and Reichelderfer persuade Harvard climatologist R. DeC. Ward to accept a class of eight Naval officers, graduates of the U.S. Naval Academy, as graduate students in meteorology with courses in climatology, synoptic meteorology, and hydrodynamics, the latter given at MIT. The following year at Ward's request the course was reestablished at MIT. Reichelderfer had enlisted the interest and support of Assistant Secretary of the Navy for Air E. P. Warner and had

proposed that Rossby, then in California, be offered the opportunity at MIT. From this beginning Rossby went on to academic and research programs that made him world renowned as a leader in modern meteorology.

Reichelderfer established new programs which led to the first regular APOBs (upper-air observations by airplane) for weather map use in the Weather Bureau at Washington, D.C.; the first radiosonde network in the Western Hemisphere; and other technical developments. His report in 1932 of synoptic analysis as practiced in Bergen, Norway, led to adoption of the "Norwegian methods" in the U.S. Weather Bureau and the U.S. Navy, where he had first introduced these concepts from Norway in 1920, and helped to open opportunities for several young meteorologists from abroad to find careers of distinction in the United States. He placed the first radiogoniometers in the United States for location of thunderstorms by cross bearings of "static" discharges; he emphasized storm detection radar, tornado and hurricane alert procedures for the public, and space satellites for meteorology. His support made possible the Physical Research Laboratory headed by Ross Gunn in 1950; the General Circulation (atmospheric) Research Laboratory by J. Smagorinsky in 1960; and Project Stormfury in 1962, designed to test possibilities of modification of hurricanes. Reichelderfer consistently advocated development of experimental meteorology after enthusiastic endorsement of the beginnings of cloud seeding by Irving Langmuir and V. J. Schaefer in 1946. He strongly opposed the premature commercial exploitation of rainmaking and stated that advertising of unverified claims of successful results from cloud seeding would delay and obscure the real possibilities of experimental meteorology for 10 years and waste millions of dollars in fruitless wildcatting in field testing, a view confirmed by subsequent events.

The international nature of meteorology offers unique opportunities for cooperation among nations. As United States representative to the International Meteorological Organization (1939–51) and first president (1951–55) and United States permanent representative (1951–63) of the World Meteorological Organization, Reichelderfer played a major part in WMO plans and programs. He proposed for adoption Harry Wexler's concept of an expanded World Weather Watch in the WMO Congress of 1963. Reichelderfer's international work in meteorology was recognized by awards from many countries, among them the Japan Order of the Sacred Treasure in 1960, the French LeVerrier Medal in 1963, and the WMO's International Meteorological Organization Prize in 1964. For his national and interdepartmental work he received citations from the Air Force, the Navy, and the Department of Commerce. Although his own research career was limited to early studies of wind structure and electrical phenomena in the atmosphere as related to airship navigation, his action as a scientist-director created numerous opportunities and research facilities for meteorologists whose accomplishments have become well known. His frequently stated purpose was to encourage and support the Weather Bureau's basic and applied research institutes with as much flexibility, vision, and freedom from administrative impediments as a university might provide.

Reichelderfer, son of a Methodist minister, graduated from Northwestern University (A.B., 1917). He studied meteorology at Harvard University (1918), the Geophysics Institute, Bergen, Norway (1931), and in federal government graduate schools. With aeronautics as his door into meteorology, he asked for flight training and eventually qualified both as an airplane pilot (1919) and as an aeronaut (1929)—balloons and zeppelin-type airships. In several other research and development positions in meteorology and other technical programs, and with growing executive responsibilities such as those as head of the Naval meteorological organization, Reichelderfer acquired the experience and recognition that led to appointment by President Roosevelt as the director of the U.S. Weather Bureau in 1938. He resigned in 1963 to continue as consultant for national and international meteorological organizations. He was awarded an honorary D.Sc. by Northwestern in 1939 and was elected a member of the National Academy of Sciences in 1945.

For background information *see* ATMOSPHERE; METEOROLOGY; WEATHER (FORECASTING AND PREDICTION) in the McGraw-Hill Encyclopedia of Science and Technology.   □

★ RENSCH, Bernhard

German biologist
Born Jan. 21, 1900, Thale, Germany

A NEW principle of zoological systematics was developed between 1900 and 1920. The growing material in the museums suggested that many species could be looked upon as geographical representatives of one another, and were normally connected by intermediate forms on the borderlines of their geographical areas. Therefore, they were combined in large polytypic species, the extreme geographical races of which were often morphologically more different than "good species" in the older sense.

In 1929 Rensch showed that this geographical principle of taxonomy, first mainly used in birds

and butterflies, can be applied to most classes of animals. He proved that a high percentage of borderline cases between true species and geographical races exist and that these can be looked upon as normal prestages of new species. As the polytypic species, which he called "Rassenkreise," were true natural units, they provided a much sounder basis for zoogeographical studies than the former "species." He could use them to work out the faunal history of the chain of Sunda Islands from Sumatra to the Moluccas, after his expedition to Java and the Lesser Sunda Islands in 1927.

Rensch further pointed out that these large polytypic species enable the zoologist to work out several rules of climatic parallelism of characters. He especially analyzed the rule of Bergmann (larger size of races of homoiothermic animals in colder regions) by calculating the percentage of exceptions, formulated and named Allen's and Gloger's rule (smaller size of legs, tails, ears, and bills and lighter colors in colder regions), and established rules concerning the wing shape of birds, the number of eggs, and the body size of poikilothermic animals.

The research on geographical speciation made it necessary to estimate the relative frequency of other types of speciation coming about by historical, ecological, physiological, sexual, and genetical isolation and by hybridization. It could be shown that there exist many ways of speciation, although the geographical type seems to prevail.

Rensch then tackled the question of whether the well-analyzed factors of speciation are sufficient to explain also the transspecific evolution—the origin of higher taxonomic categories, new organs, and new types of anatomical con-

struction. He found that this is the case and that all rules of phylogenetic branching, or cladogenesis, do not need the assumption of unknown autonomous forces driving the evolution in certain directions. This interpretation of cladogenesis is especially applicable to the "explosive" radiation of new species, genera, and families after the evolution of a new favorable type of construction, Cope's rule of increase of body size in the lines of descent, "orthogenetic" trends, and "overspecialization." Moreover, the evolutionary progress toward higher levels, or anagenesis, can be explained by undirected mutation and natural selection. After the book which treated these problems appeared in 1947, Rensch discovered that during the war the general biologist J. S. Huxley, the geneticist Theodosius Dobzhansky, the paleontologist G. G. Simpson, and the systematist Ernst Mayr also had drawn the same conclusions. This consensus of leading scientists of different fields of biology formed the basis of the present synthetic theory of evolution.

In the course of his evolutionary studies Rensch and his co-workers mainly investigated the correlations between the body size and different morphological and physiological characters of animals. They showed that certain growth ratios of cytological, histological, and anatomical structures remain more or less constant during phylogeny (cases of allomorphosis) and that several corresponding phylogenetic rules can be established. The following examples may indicate the form these rules take. In larger species of insects the brains have more neurons (nerve cells) and relatively larger mushroom bodies (main associative centers), and in some families they also have more complicated instincts than smaller related species. In mammals the isocortex, the most complicated five- to seven-layered part of the forebrain, is relatively larger in larger species compared with related small species (for instance, in rats compared with mice). Corresponding to this rule, larger species have a greater learning capacity and a longer duration of memory. In larger species of insects the epithelium of the intestine consists of cylindric cells, whereas in related small species it has cubic or flat cells. The retina of larger vertebrate species is relatively thinner, and the sense cells and ganglionic cells are not as crowded as in related smaller species. All these rules come about because the embryological and juvenile growth tendency of those parts which grow relatively quicker than the others (positively allometric) remains more or less equal during phylogeny.

The elaboration of such rules led Rensch and his co-workers to study also the highest brain achievements of birds and mammals, that is, the ability of abstracting, generalizing, and acting according to plan. Inspired by H. F. Harlow's successful experiments with monkeys on the oddity problem, but using another method, they showed that a civet cat can learn to act as if she has formed a limited concept of odd and equal.

Later they were also concerned with other questions of "animal thinking." They worked, for instance, with apes to find out how far these animals can transfer their knowledge of manipulations with human instruments such as keys, scissors, and screwdrivers when they are presented with new tasks and get altered instruments. Together with J. Döhl, Rensch also succeeded in training a chimpanzee to master rather difficult labyrinth tasks. The ape had to choose between two complicated white alleys on a board, one leading to a goal and the other ending in several blind alleys. The chimp had to conduct a little plate of iron with the help of a magnet along the right alley and to avoid all blind alleys. Such brain achievements showing some "reflecting" about the right way up to 1–2 min come near to human thinking.

Rensch received his Ph.D. at the University of Halle in 1922. From 1925 to 1937 he was leader of the Mollusk Department of the Zoological Museum of Berlin. In 1937 he became director of the Museum of Natural History in Münster and lecturer in zoology at the University of Münster. In 1947 he became full professor and director of the Zoological Institute of the university. He was awarded an honorary doctorate by Uppsala University, the Leibniz Medal by the former Prussian Academy of Sciences, the Darwin-Wallace Medal by the Linnean Society of London, and the Darwin Plaque by the German Academy of Naturalists "Leopoldina."

Rensch wrote *Evolution Above the Species Level* (1959; 2d ed., paper 1966).

For background information *see* ANIMAL SYSTEMATICS; SPECIATION; SPECIES CONCEPT in the McGraw-Hill Encyclopedia of Science and Technology.   □

★ REVELLE, Roger

American oceanographer
Born Mar. 7, 1909, Seattle, Wash., U.S.A.

P RIMARILY AN explorer rather than an experimenter or a theoretician, Revelle was fortunate in coming to scientific maturity at the close of World War II, when newly developed techniques made it possible to study the deep ocean floor in new ways and with greater precision than before. It was difficult to go to sea on a scientific vessel in those days without making unexpected and often important discoveries.

In 1946–47, while still on active duty in the Navy, Revelle organized the environmental surveys that were undertaken before and after the atom bomb tests at Bikini Atoll. Among the geologists and geophysicists who took part were Beauregard Perkins, Kenneth Emery, Harry Ladd, and Joshua I. Tracey, Jr. Seismic studies

showed that the material under the atoll had a low sound velocity down to about 1300 m. Below this depth the velocity abruptly increased. Dredgings from a flat-topped seamount on the northern flank of the atoll consisted of manganese-encrusted basalt. It seemed likely the high velocity material under the atoll was also basalt, overlain by porous limestone. This suggested that Charles Darwin had been right when he proposed, a hundred years earlier, that coral atolls are sunken volcanic islands on which great piles of skeletons of corals and other shallow-water, reef-building animals and plants accumulated as the volcanoes slowly became submerged. In the 1947 resurvey of Bikini, the atoll was drilled and cored down to 800 m. All the samples consisted of reef limestones and limey sediments laid down in shallow water. At the bottom of the hole the sediments were about 30,000,000 years old, and they became progressively younger as the surface was approached.

In the early 1950s Ladd and his associates drilled deeper into Eniwetok Atoll, 200 mi west of Bikini. They found basalt at 1300 m, underlying shallow-water calcareous sediments of Eocene age, close to 50,000,000 years old; as in Bikini, progressively younger limestones, all of which had been laid down in shallow waters, occurred all the way to the surface. The Darwinian hypothesis, a subject of controversy for 100 years, was clearly correct. But perhaps more important for understanding the history of the oceans was the evidence for intermittent submergence of the central Pacific floor throughout the last epoch of geologic time. The average rate of sinking was 2.5 mm per century.

Revelle became acting director of the Scripps Institution of Oceanography in 1950, and during the summer of that year he led the joint Mid-Pacific Expedition of the Scripps Institution and the Navy Electronics Laboratory, the first of many voyages of deep-sea exploration he sent out from Scripps during the next 15 years. These were carried out on several small ships, the most famous of which became the seagoing tugs *Horizon, Spencer F. Baird,* and *Argo* and the converted yachts *Stranger* and *E. W. Scripps.* The total distance covered was close to a million miles; the ship tracks extended into all the oceans, including the Arctic and the Antarctic, and many bordering seas.

One of the objectives of the Mid-Pacific Expedition was to study the flat-topped seamounts (guyots) discovered by Harry Hess when he was captain of a Navy cargo ship during World War II. Echo soundings from the *Horizon* showed that some of these seamounts are the flat summits of a great underwater mountain range, the Mid-Pacific Mountains, extending from Necker Island in the middle of the Hawaiian chain toward Wake Island in the western Pacific and rising nearly 3000 m above the deep-sea floor. Two of the members of the expedition, Robert Dietz and Edwin Hamilton, took many rock dredgings from these summits nearly 2000 m below the ocean surface. Most of the material in the dredge hauls was manganese-encrusted basalt, but some of the crusts enclosed fossils—fragments of reef coral and shells of marine snails. Later study by Hamilton showed these were remains of animals that had lived in shallow water during the Middle Cretaceous Period, 80,000,000 years ago. They were almost the oldest fossils ever found in the deep sea and, together with the topography revealed by the echo soundings, demonstrated that the seamounts once had been volcanic islands in an ocean at least 3000 m deep. The islands were planed off by the waves 80,000,000 years ago and partly covered with coral reefs. Subsequently, they had become submerged under 2000 m of water without acquiring the coral cap that covers the atolls. Perhaps the initial sinking to a few tens of meters had been too rapid for the reef animals.

Two other major findings of the Mid-Pacific Expedition came from seismic measurements by Russell Raitt. He found that the blanket of sediments on the sea floor is extremely thin, usually less than 200 m. This strongly suggested that the sediments laid down prior to 100,000,000 years ago have been removed or otherwise lost. Raitt also was able to determine the depth to the Moho, the boundary between the Earth's crust and mantle. He found this to be surprisingly shallow, only about 7 km beneath the sea floor.

The English geophysicist Edward Bullard spent the summer of 1949 in La Jolla. He had thought of a way to measure what was then one of the most important unknown quantities of geophysics, the flow of heat from the Earth's interior out through the deep-sea floor. Several determinations of heat flow on land had been made in deep mines and wells. It was thought that some of the outflowing energy came from the cooling of the primordial Earth, which was supposed to have been very hot, but most of the heat was believed to originate in the radioactive decay of uranium, thorium, and potassium in the granitic rocks of the thick continental crusts. Since the crust under the ocean was supposed to be thin and to consist of basaltic rocks with low radioactivity, the conventional wisdom was that the heat flow through the deep-sea floor should be much lower than that from the continents and should approximately correspond to the rate of cooling of the Earth.

Bullard's idea was to plunge a steel spear, fitted with two thermometers a measured distance apart and attached to a temperature recorder in a pressureproof chamber, into the bottom muds. He proposed to record the temperature difference against time over a period of half an hour or more as the thermometers approached equilibrium in the sediments. This record, combined with a measurement of the thermal conductivity of the sediments, would give the heat flow. Such a method could not succeed on land because of the marked seasonal temperature fluctuations near the surface, but the virtually constant temperature of the deep-ocean bottom waters should provide ideal conditions. Revelle assigned a young graduate student, Arthur Maxwell, to work with Bullard.

The development problems were formidable and remained unsolved when Bullard had to return to England at the end of the summer. James Snodgrass and John Isaacs of Scripps worked with Maxwell throughout the next year to solve the problems; the instrument was ready for use by the time of the Mid-Pacific Expedition in the summer of 1950. Maxwell and Revelle made six measurements during the course of the expedition. All gave roughly the same value. The average, instead of being one-fifth of the land value as expected from the prevailing theory, was about equal to the average of previous measurements on land.

An analytical search for all possible sources of the heat proved that it could not originate in the sediments and must come from the underlying rocks, where most of it could be accounted for only by radioactive decay. But samples of ocean bottom rocks show a very low concentration of radioactive materials, and from known processes of chemical differentiation in rocks the concentration of these substances in the underlying mantle must be lower still. Revelle and Maxwell concluded that the heat must come from the decay of small concentrations of radioactive materials throughout a column of rock at least several hundred kilometers thick. They calculated that, if the heat were being carried outward by ordinary thermal conduction, the temperature at depth must be so high that the

mantle rocks would be molten. Yet seismology showed the mantle to be solid down to more than 2000 km.

Maxwell and Revelle concluded that the heat must be carried outward by another process, a slow convective churning of the rocks of the Earth's mantle, with a time constant for a complete convective overturn of about 300,000,000 years. If this were so, then the Earth could not be cooling from an initial hot state. It must have been in a state of approximate thermal equilibrium for a long time, because an essential feature of the convection process was that it could transport heat up to the surface about as fast as it was generated at depth.

One of the virtues of this hypothesis was that it appeared possible to test it experimentally. The oceanic heat flow should be high over the upward moving limbs of the mantle convection cells and low over the areas of downward moving rocks. Studies by Robert Fisher on a series of Scripps Institution expeditions of the deep, long, narrow trenches which ring the Pacific basin strongly indicated that the trenches are areas of active downward rock movement. Indeed, the finding of negative gravity anomalies over the trenches prior to World War II had caused the Dutch geophysicist F. A. Vening Meinesz and the American geophysicist David Griggs to propose the hypothesis of convection as a trench-forming mechanism. If the diameter of the largest convection cells was about equal to the thickness of the mantle, it seemed likely that the upward-moving limbs would lie beneath the midocean ridges, such as the Mid-Atlantic Ridge and the East Pacific Rise.

Revelle and Maxwell predicted that high heat-flow values would be found near the Rise and low values in the neighborhood of the trenches off the Central and South American coasts. A series of measurements by Maxwell along sections extending several thousand miles westward from northern South America showed that this was so. The heat flows in the neighborhood of the East Pacific Rise were higher than those on either side and several times higher than those near the South American Trench. Bullard obtained similar high values from the Mid-Atlantic Ridge. The convection hypothesis, though not proven, was strongly reinforced. It explained not only the heat flow and the characteristics of the trenches but also, at least in part, the existence of the midocean ridges. Moreover, the short geologic history of the Pacific basin and the thinness of sediments could be accounted for by the relatively short times predicted for a complete overturn of the convection cells in the mantle, and the consequently even shorter times required for the horizontally moving upper limbs of the mantle convection cells to drag the overlying crustal materials across the sea floor from the midocean ridges to the trenches and other regions of crustal submergence.

About 2000 measurements of heat flow through the deep-sea floor were made during the next 15 years, many of them by Richard Von Herzen, then of the Scripps Institution. As might have been expected, the pattern of high and low values turned out to be much more complicated than that indicated by the relatively small number of measurements carried out in the early 1950s by Bullard, Maxwell, and Revelle. Evidently, there are multiple heat sources and modes of heat transport in the earth beneath the sea, and parts of the mantle are much closer to the melting point than Revelle and Maxwell supposed.

During the late 1950s Scripps scientists found new evidence of an entirely different kind for the convection hypothesis. Magnetic surveys by Ronald Mason, Arthur Raff, and Victor Vacquier demonstrated that the deep-sea floor in the eastern North Pacific is striped magnetically, with long, narrow highs and lows of magnetic permeability in the rocks under the thin blanket of sediments. These stripes are broken and displaced by east-west–trending "fracture zones" several thousand miles long. Vacquier's studies showed that the stripes are offset by many hundreds of miles along the fracture zones, clear evidence of relative horizontal movement of the crustal rocks. It is hard to see how such a motion could have occurred unless the crust was dragged along by the horizontally moving limb of a mantle convection cell.

That horizontal motion of the ocean crust is widespread is shown by the fact, first demonstrated by William Menard of Scripps, that fracture zones cut across and displace the mid-ocean ridges at intervals of a few hundred miles throughout their lengths. Convincing new magnetic and paleoclimatic evidence for continental drift also strongly supports the convection hypothesis.

The National Academy of Sciences gave Revelle its Agassiz Medal in 1963 for "outstanding achievement in oceanography." He was cited for "significant contributions to the understanding of oceanic processes and the geology of the sea floor, and for the stimulus he has given, through his research and special efforts, to the advance of scientific oceanography throughout the world."

Revelle became science advisor to the Secretary of the Interior in 1961, and, as a result, began a new career. In his newly created post, one of his principal tasks turned out to be a study of the problems of salt accumulation and resulting soil deterioration in the Punjab and Sind regions of West Pakistan. Here the Indus River and its five tributaries of the Punjab flow through a vast, flat plain, covered by a network of great irrigation canals, which forms the largest single irrigated area on Earth and provides a livelihood for 25,000,000 human beings. In 1961 the people of the plain were in serious difficulty. Their farms were not yielding enough food to feed even the rural population. One obvious problem was the rising water table and the increasing saltiness of the soil. Over large areas this had become so serious that farms and even villages had been abandoned. At the direction of President John F. Kennedy and his science advisor, Jerome Wiesner, Revelle organized and led a panel of specialists from many disciplines to investigate the problem. Their conclusion was that waterlogging and salinity were symptoms of a more serious disease: poor agricultural practices. What was needed in the irrigated area was more water, not less. They recommended that a network of large "tube wells" be drilled. The water pumped out of the wells would be used for irrigation, at the same time lowering the water table, and the percolation back into the ground would wash the salt out of the soil. In addition to more irrigation water, it was necessary to introduce fertilizers, high-yielding seeds, pest control, and better farming methods if the great potentialities of the region were to be realized. Revelle and his colleagues estimated that, if these things were done, agricultural production could be increased fourfold within a generation. Following the report of the panel, the government of Pakistan took vigorous action, drilling government wells and supporting the farmers in drilling their own wells. In consequence, agricultural production during the last few years has increased at about 5% per year, with a doubling time of about 14 years.

In recognition of this work Revelle was decorated in 1964 with the order of "Sitara-i-Imtiaz" by the President of Pakistan "for conspicuously distinguished work in science." During the same year he was appointed by the Indian Parliament as one of five foreign members of the Education Commission of the Government of India. This commission was charged to study and make recommendations concerning the entire Indian education system from preschool to university. The report of the commission, published in 1966, contains a comprehensive plan for educational reform in India.

Revelle received his A.B. in 1929 at Pomona College and his Ph.D. in 1936 at the University of California. He was a teaching assistant at Pomona College in 1929–30, held a similar position at the University of California the following year, and joined the Scripps Institution of Oceanography as a research assistant in 1931. During World War II he served as a commander in the U.S. Navy. In 1946–47 he headed the Geophysics Branch of the Office of Naval Research, and he organized the oceanographic investigations for Operation Crossroads, the 1946 atomic bomb tests at Bikini Atoll. Returning to the Scripps Institution, he became professor of oceanography in 1948, and was director of the Institution from 1951 to 1964. From 1958 to 1961 he was director of the La Jolla campus of the University of California and dean of the school of science and engineering there. During 1961–63 he occupied the newly created post of science advisor to the Secretary of the Interior. Revelle returned to the University of California in 1963 as university dean of research for all campuses, resigning in 1964 to accept directorship of the Center for Population Studies at Harvard University. Revelle College, the first of the new colleges established in the University of California, San Diego, was named in his honor in 1965. Revelle was elected to the National Academy of Sciences in 1957, to the American Academy of Arts and Sciences in 1958, and the American Philosophical Society in 1960. He was vice-chairman of the U.S. National Commission for UNESCO in 1961–64.

For background information *see* ATOLL; EARTH (HEAT FLOW); OCEANOGRAPHY; SUBMARINE TOPOGRAPHY in the McGraw-Hill Encyclopedia of Science and Technology. □

★ RICHTER, Curt Paul

American psychologist
Born Feb. 20, 1894, Denver, Colo., U.S.A.

RICHTER'S EARLIEST recollections were of times spent in his father's iron and steel factory, where he learned to do things with his hands. In his youth he learned to use all kinds of tools and particularly to work with iron, experiencing the joy of being able to hammer glowing iron into various shapes. He also learned to operate machinery and spent many hours taking locks and clocks apart and putting them together again. At the age of 8 he ran his first experiment to find out whether the strength of a magnet could be increased by gradually enlarging its load over a period of several months. He did this by adding a nail a day to a bag suspended from an armature on a small toy magnet, having first determined how many nails the magnet could support at the start. During six summers he worked on a farm.

After graduation from high school in Denver in 1912 he went to Dresden, Germany, to study engineering at the Technische Hochschule. This lovely city opened an entire new world to him, with its fine opera and theaters, its many other cultural opportunities, and exciting student life. For the first time he developed an interest in reading and went through much of English, German, and particularly Russian literature. At the same time he became much impressed with the thoroughness of German science. World War I brought this stimulating 3-year epoch to a close. He had passed his Vorprüfung—an examination given at the end of 2½ years—but he decided to give up engineering and return home.

He entered Harvard as a junior in 1915 and began a bewildering search for a new career. He thought of entering the diplomatic service but relinquished the idea fairly quickly; he then switched to economics but also gave that up at the strong urging of F. W. Taussig, head of the department. From a course on the "Philosophy of Nature" given by E. B. Holt, he first learned about Sigmund Freud and psychoanalysis and proceeded to read practically everything that had been written about psychoanalysis up to that time—by Freud, C. G. Jung, S. Ferenzi, O. Rank, and A. A. Brill. This stirred up a new interest. An experimental course on animal behavior by Robert M. Yerkes, many talks with biochemist Lawrence J. Henderson, and a book on animal behavior by John B. Watson showed Richter a way in which he could combine what was emerging as his greatest interest—the experimental study of animal and human behavior—with an opportunity to work with his hands.

After 2 years in the Army he started graduate work with Watson at Johns Hopkins University. At the invitation of Adolf Meyer, head of the Phipps Psychiatric Clinic at the Johns Hopkins Hospital, Watson had just moved his laboratory from the university campus at Homewood to the Phipps Clinic. Watson told Richter that the only thing required by Hopkins for the Ph.D. was a good piece of research—the number of courses taken was not important. Watson introduced him to the Norway rat, destined later to become Richter's favorite experimental animal. In observing rats Richter became impressed with the great amount of activity that seemed to occur without any external stimuli, and decided to study this gross, spontaneous bodily activity in an effort to find out what lay behind it. By means of a simple cage and recording device that he constructed, Richter found almost at once that the activity is not irregular, but occurs in cycles of 1½ to 2 hr. This discovery was the start of an enduring interest in periodic phenomena in animals and also in man—both in normal subjects and in psychiatric patients. Some results of these studies were summarized in *Biological Clocks in Medicine and Psychiatry* (1965).

Up to this point in his graduate training Richter had not had any firsthand experience in biology—he had not even pithed a frog. To satisfy a suddenly aroused interest in anatomy and physiology, he dissected a body in the anatomy laboratory on his own and likewise worked his way through many experiments in the physiology laboratory.

Watson left Hopkins within 18 months after Richter started working there, and it was then that Richter began to know Meyer. This contact turned out to be a major influence on Richter's career. After Richter graduated, Meyer put him in charge of Watson's laboratory with an appointment as psychobiologist, gave him complete freedom in his research, and influenced his development in countless other ways. Richter was not burdened with any great desire for book learning, so most of his knowledge from that time on came from results of firsthand experiments. His investigations ranged widely through the fields of behavior, physiology, neurology, and nutrition.

Study of spontaneous running activity of rats in revolving drums became a main and lasting interest, not only because of the cyclic nature of such activity but also because it turned out to be one of the best tools for the study of interrelationships between various internal needs and behavior. He used it in the study of endocrine glands, nutritive needs, and functioning of the central nervous system. He became impressed very early with the rat's ability to take care of its internal needs.

He found, for instance, that adrenalectomized rats (which lose their physiological regulators of salt metabolism and so die within 10–15 days) will, when given access to salt solution, drink enough to maintain their normal salt balance and so keep themselves alive. He showed that rats will make beneficial selections not only from electrolytes but also from fats, proteins, carbohydrates, and also some vitamins. He also demonstrated the ability of rats to avoid many kinds of poisons. He showed that the rat maintains homeostasis by behavioral as well as physiological regulators (Harvey Lecture, 1943).

Because of this knowledge of the reaction of rats to foods and poisons, Richter was appointed by the Office of Scientific Research and Development during World War II to work out a program for quick city-wide extermination of

rats in case of rat-borne germ warfare. Thousands of wild rats were trapped and brought into the laboratory for study. In this way Richter made the acquaintance of wild Norway rats. Comparison of behavior, functions of the endocrine glands and central nervous system, and gross anatomy revealed great differences between ordinary laboratory rats and their wild ancestors. Richter became aware of the wonderful opportunity offered for the study of effects produced by domestication on this animal, specimens of both the domesticated forms and their wild ancestors being available in large numbers. This resulted in the discovery of a rat poison— ANTU, a thiourea compound—and also in an extensive study of the physiology of the thioureas in general. Comparison between effect of domestication of the rat and civilization of man were discussed in the paper "Rats, Man and the Welfare State." Studies of wild rats led also to chance observations on the phenomenon of "sudden death" in animals and man.

Richter received his B.S. at Harvard University in 1917 and his Ph.D. at Johns Hopkins University in 1921. From 1922 he was director of the psychobiological laboratory of the Phipps Psychiatric Clinic; later he became professor emeritus of psychobiology. He was elected a member of the National Academy of Sciences, the American Philosophical Society, and the American Academy of Arts and Sciences, and an honorary member of Phi Beta Kappa (Harvard), the Harvey Society, and the Baltimore Medical Society. He received the Warren Medal of the Society of Experimental Psychologists, the scientific award of the American Psychological Association, and the Hamilton Award of the American Psychopathological Society.

For background information *see* PERIODICITY IN ORGANISMS; RAT; RODENTIA in the McGraw-Hill Encyclopedia of Science and Technology. □

★ ROBERTS, John D.

American chemist
Born June 8, 1918, Los Angeles, Calif., U.S.A.

MODERN SCIENCE progresses somewhat like the growth of a coral reef—the new being constructed on the old, with growth occurring most rapidly where nourishment is provided by new ideas and new techniques. In his scientific work Roberts endeavored to assist this kind of growth process by showing how new, or even old, techniques can be applied to outstanding theoretical and experimental problems in organic chemistry. In this his role was more one of a teacher than an explorer of the unknown. His work was typified by showing through example with

simple organic compounds what might be done with complex compounds. His achievements in this vein were recognized by his selection in 1967 as the fifth recipient of the American Chemical Society's Roger Adams Medal.

Roberts began his career in research as a junior at the University of California at Los Angeles and published seven papers as a result of undergraduate work on such varied topics as mechanisms of reactions of osmium compounds (with W. R. Crowell), thermodynamics of dithionite ion (with C. D. Coryell), dipole moments of acetylenic ethers (with T. L. Jacobs), and displacement reactions of allylic halides (with W. G. Young and S. Winstein). His experiences in undergraduate research during this period (1938–41) had a strong influence on his later activities in teaching and research.

His doctoral research (with Young) was concerned with a favorite substance of undergraduate organic chemistry courses—the Grignard reagent. Specifically the butenyl Grignard reagent, derived either from magnesium and 1-bromo-2-butene or magnesium and 3-bromo-1-butene, was found to behave in an almost capricious manner: sometimes as though it were 1-but-2-enylmagnesium bromide, sometimes as 3-but-1-enylmagnesium bromide, or even as a mixture of these substances. At the time Roberts's work was done, no very powerful physical methods for determining the structures of substances present in Grignard solutions were available, and the nature of the butenyl Grignard reagent had to be deduced from the character of its products with various reagents. After considerable difficulties resulting from discoveries relating to the extraordinary reactivity and reactions of the butenyl Grignard reagent, it was concluded that the substance could only be 1-but-2-enylmagnesium bromide, a conclusion that was not popular and less than universally accepted at the time. Confirmation of the correctness of this conclusion came almost 20 years

later by Roberts's own investigation of the proton magnetic resonance of the butenyl Grignard reagent, which showed that it is in fact very predominantly the 1-but-2-enyl isomer, even though in extraordinarily rapid equilibrium with a small amount of the 2-but-1-enyl form.

As a National Research Council fellow at Harvard University (1945–46, with P. D. Bartlett), Roberts began his investigations of the utility of small-ring compounds for providing critical tests of current theories of organic reactions. In continuation of this at the Massachusetts Institute of Technology (MIT) in 1946–53, he (with R. H. Mazur) discovered the fantastic reactions and reactivity of cyclopropylcarbinyl derivatives. Roberts early appreciated the value of C^{14} as a tracer for mechanism work and illustrated the use of this powerful new technique in studies of carbonium-ion rearrangements of alkyl, cyclopropylcarbinyl, and norbornyl derivatives, as well as in a proof that the amination of chlorobenzene occurs by an almost unprecedented elimination-addition mechanism involving a stripped-down aromatic intermediate benzyne (C_6H_4).

While at MIT Roberts showed the value of Hammett σ-constants and 4-substituted bicyclo[2.2.2]octane-1-carboxylic acids in investigating the properties of substituent groups, for which he received the American Chemical Society Award in Pure Chemistry (1954). He also helped to kindle the interest of organic chemists in molecular orbital theory, being the first to predict the unusual properties of cyclopropenyl cation and many other small unsaturated molecules (1952).

Roberts moved to the California Institute of Technology as professor of organic chemistry in 1953, and there he developed two lines of research that provided stimulation for much work elsewhere. The first of these was on the use of cycloaddition reactions for the formation of unusual cyclobutane derivatives, and the second, nuclear magnetic resonance (NMR) spectroscopy, where he did much pioneering work in applications to problems in organic chemistry. In the latter area Roberts was the first to demonstrate the nature and value of the so-called nonequivalence due to molecular asymmetry, slow inversion in imines and amines, slow inversion in cycloheptanes, cis-decalins and cis-decalones, as well as slow rotation around single bonds in substituted ethanes. He and his research students developed the first practical computer programs for calculations of line shapes in NMR processes for systems involving spin-spin splitting and realistic calculations of energy barriers for rotation in substituted ethanes.

Roberts received his B.A. (1941) and Ph.D. in chemistry (1944) from the University of California at Los Angeles, where he was an instructor in chemistry in 1944–45. He was a National Research Council fellow at Harvard University in 1945–46. At the Massachusetts Institute of Technology he was assistant professor from 1947 to 1950 and associate professor from 1950 to 1953, when he became professor of organic chemistry at the California Institute of Technology. He received honorary degrees from the University of Munich and Temple University. He was elected to the American Academy of Arts and Sciences in 1952 and to the National Academy of Sciences in 1956.

Roberts wrote more than 200 technical articles in the chemical journals and five books: *Nuclear Magnetic Resonance* (1959) ; *An Introduction to the Analysis of Spin-Spin Splitting in High-Resolution Nuclear Magnetic Resonance Spectra* (1961) ; *Notes on Molecular Orbital Calculations* (1961) ; *Basic Principles of Organic Chemistry*, with M. C. Caserio (1964) ; and *Modern Organic Chemistry*, with M. C. Caserio (1967).

For background information *see* COORDINATION CHEMISTRY; GRIGNARD REACTION; MAGNETIC RESONANCE in the McGraw-Hill Encyclopedia of Science and Technology.   ☐

★ ROBERTSON, Rutherford Ness

Australian botanist
Born Sept. 29, 1913, Melbourne, Australia

ROBERTSON WORKED in several fields of plant physiology, each dependent directly or indirectly on research on plant respiration. As a research student at Cambridge University, he was introduced to the problems of ion absorption by plant cells while working with G. E. Briggs, professor of botany. F. C. Steward had shown that active transport in plant cells depends on adequate oxygen supply, and H. Lundegårdh and H. Burström had shown that inhibitors of the oxidative stages of respiration will also inhibit salt uptake. Simultaneously, the distin-

guished school of plant nutrition under D. R. Hoagland at the University of California, Berkeley, had become interested in the mechanisms of absorption. Robertson's work at the University of Sydney established the relation between the salt absorbed by active transport and the stimulated respiration due to salt—the salt respiration. For this purpose cells of carrot tissue were used, but later, with Joan Milthorpe, the work was extended to barley roots and, with J. S. Turner, to beet tissue. The dependence of the active transport on the cytochrome-mediated salt respiration was clearly indicated by the light-reversible CO inhibition of both salt respiration and active transport. In 1945 Lundegårdh suggested that the H ions liberated in the respiratory process when the electrons pass through the cytochrome system might be the basis of active transport, so that the entry of a cation is in exchange for the H ion and the entry of an anion is in exchange for the unit negative charge associated with the electron transfer. In 1948 Robertson and Marjorie Wilkins showed that the maximum rate of ion transport is approximately that expected if the mechanism were dependent on this separation of H ions and electrons.

In 1946 Robertson left the University of Sydney to take charge of the plant physiological and fruit storage work in the Division of Food Preservation, Commonwealth Scientific and Industrial Research Organization (CSIRO). He had responsibility for the fruit storage program but also developed research in fruit ripening and postharvest physiology. With Joan Bain, he showed the relative importance of cell division and cell enlargement in apples and simultaneously, with J. F. Turner, followed the chemical and biochemical changes accompanying cell enlargement. This work led to an investigation of the causes of the climacteric rise in fruit respiration and later to evidence that this rise is associated with loss of control in respiration rate because of increase in adenosinediphosphate with aging of the tissue. Further studies of fruit development carried out with the pea pod and the enlarging seeds defined the changes in respiration associated with the decrease in sugar and increase in starch as the seeds pass to the dormant state. These changes also became the basis of collaborative work between Robertson and his team and the members of the phytotron team under F. W. Went at the California Institute of Technology, a transpacific collaboration with plants grown in Pasadena and analyzed in Sydney. The overwhelming importance of temperature on the chemical composition of the pea seed was established.

Both the fruit work and the ion absorption work led inevitably to investigations of plant mitochondria, the sites of oxidative respiration. Mitochondria were studied from several physiological and morphological aspects: in fruit, to see the changes associated with the climacteric rise; in beet tissue, to investigate changes in ionic composition and, with J. Farrant, to make the first estimates of thickness of the mitochondrial membrane and to obtain some of the first electron microscope pictures of plant mitochondria in section. In recent years mitochondrial investigations in collaboration with J. T. Wiskich and D. Millard were on the relation between the separation of H ions and electrons in respiration, oxidative phosphorylation, and ion uptake.

During 1939–45, when a large surplus of wheat had to be stored in Australia because of restrictions in shipping, heating of the stacks occurred. This led Robertson to measure the very low respiration rates of dry wheat grain and to measure the heat-transfer properties of a stack of wheat. The problem of heat production turned out to be due to the infestation of insects.

Robertson took his bachelor's degree at the University of Sydney in 1933 and worked there as a graduate student for several years. In 1936 he proceeded to the University of Cambridge and in 1939 obtained his Ph.D. in plant physiology. Until 1946 he was on the staff of the botany department, University of Sydney, and then he joined the CSIRO. In 1952 he established the joint Plant Physiology Unit of the Division of Food Preservation, CSIRO, and of the botany department, University of Sydney. In 1959 he became a member of the executive branch of CSIRO, concerned mainly with scientific administration, but he returned to academic work in 1962 as professor of botany at the University of Adelaide. He was elected to the Royal Society of London in 1961 and, as a foreign associate, to the U.S. National Academy of Sciences in 1962.

Robertson wrote *Electrolytes and Plant Cells*, with G. E. Briggs and A. B. Hope (1961).

For background information *see* MITOCHONDRIA; PLANT, MINERAL NUTRITION OF; PLANT RESPIRATION in the McGraw-Hill Encyclopedia of Science and Technology. ☐

★ ROEDER, Kenneth David

American zoologist
Born Mar. 9, 1908, Richmond, England

THE BEHAVIOR of an animal under natural conditions gives the impression of smoothly unified action. Whether its response is to a predator, a mate, or nourishment, all of its organs seem to be bent toward a single end at a given moment. Neurophysiology takes this unified system apart and shows that the nervous system is made up of assemblies and subassemblies of sense cells, nerve cells, muscle cells, and gland cells. Both the assemblies and the cells composing them have specific properties that can be studied in isolation and apart from the animal from which they came. How can the unified behavior of the intact animal be accounted for in terms of the properties of these neural mechanisms? Roeder was absorbed by this and related questions since he took a course in physiology at the Marine Biological Laboratory, Woods Hole, in 1932.

Insects interested Roeder since his childhood. Later he realized that the small size of insects and the peculiar organization of their sense organs and central nervous systems made them suitable subjects for attempting to resolve the above questions. Roeder's early work concerned the neural organization mediating sexual activity and locomotion in the praying mantis. He examined the normal pattern of these activities and compared them after removal of various parts of the mantis's nervous system. He showed that lower nerve centers are the sources of excitation of many behavior patterns, and that the absence of a certain pattern in biologically inappropriate circumstances may be due to inhibition of the corresponding nerve center by the brain. These experiments required the removal of whole ganglia, each in itself a large collection of nerve cells. Roeder saw that it was necessary also to become acquainted with the behavior of individual nerve cells and to attempt to relate these nerve cell activities to the behavior of the intact animal. In 1939 he began examining the activity of single units within insect nervous systems. This work included study of the action of salts, drugs, and DDT and other insecticides

on nerve cells of cockroaches, grasshoppers, and crayfish; the mechanisms of synaptic excitation of one nerve cell by another; neural organization of the startle response in the cockroach; and the neuromuscular mechanisms of insect flight.

These "fine-grained" physiological studies of nerve activity seemed to carry Roeder away from his general objective—to understand how nerve activity is concerned in insect behavior. However, they led back to this objective from two directions. Isolated insect ganglia continue to discharge nerve impulses for days after they have been deprived of input from the sense organs. Working with Elizabeth A. Weiant and Nancy S. Milburn, Roeder was able to show that spontaneous nerve activity in one of the abdominal ganglia is responsible for sexual movements in male cockroaches and mantises, and that this activity is normally checked by inhibition originating in the subesophageal ganglion.

The second direction occupied Roeder after 1955, when, in collaboration with Asher E. Treat, he recorded and analyzed the pattern of nerve impulses generated by a moth's ear when it is exposed to ultrasonic pulses. They showed that the ear is sensitive to the echo-locating cries made by bats. Donald R. Griffin demonstrated that nocturnal insect-eating bats find their aerial prey in darkness by means of sonar, that is, by emitting a series of ultrasonic cries and determining the distance and direction of objects from the returning echoes. Therefore, the ears of many common moths appear to serve as bat detectors or counter-sonar warning systems.

The ultrasonic ear of moths interested Roeder not only because of its obvious survival value but also because of its extreme simplicity compared with most sense organs. There are just two sense cells in each ear, only one of which is sensitive to faint sounds as those made by distant bats. It is easy to read out the information contained in the impulse pattern generated by one or two sense cells; yet this information must form the basis of an adaptive behavior pattern. Roeder observed and photographed the flight paths of moths in the field when they were exposed to attack by bats and to artificial ultrasonic pulses coming from a loudspeaker. He found that, if the sounds were intense, the moths dived and swerved in an unpredictable manner. If the sounds were faint, that is, equivalent to those coming from a distant bat, the moths turned and steered a course away from the source. He also showed that a moth can hear a bat's cries at a range of 130 ft. It is estimated that the range of a bat's sonar for a flying moth is no greater than 10 ft. In the light of these figures a moth's behavior makes sense, for it would be unable to outfly a bat that had detected its presence, but it could survive by making quick and unpredictable turns.

Roeder's object was to understand the organization of nerve cells in a moth's central nervous system that accepts the nerve impulse pattern generated by the right and left sense cells and transforms it into a nerve signal that steers the moth's flight path. Probing the central nervous system with microelectrodes, he examined a number of impulse patterns in central neurons caused by impulses arriving from the acoustic receptor cells and identified the muscles responsible for steering the moth in its flight away from an ultrasonic source.

Born in England of German and Australian parents Roeder was educated at the Bembridge School, Isle of Wight, and St. Johns College, Cambridge University, where he received his B.A. (1929) and M.A. (1933). After doing graduate work at Cambridge and the University of Toronto, he joined the department of biology at Tufts University in 1931. He became professor of physiology in 1947 and chairman of the department in 1959. Recipient of the Research Career Award from the National Institutes of Health in 1964, he was elected to the American Academy of Arts and Sciences in 1946 and to the National Academy of Sciences in 1964.

Roeder edited and contributed to *Insect Physiology* (1953) and wrote *Nerve Cells and Insect Behavior* (1963), as well as about 70 technical papers.

For background information *see* INSECT PHYSIOLOGY; PHONORECEPTION in the McGraw-Hill Encyclopedia of Science and Technology.   □

★ ROSE, William Cumming

American biochemist
Born Apr. 4, 1887, Greenville, S.C., U.S.A.

R OSE'S RESEARCH interests centered mainly on the dietary role and biosynthesis of amino acids. In 1914 T. B. Osborne and L. B. Mendel demonstrated that tryptophan and lysine are indispensable components of food, at least for the growing rat. Several years later, independent investigations by H. Ackroyd and F. G. Hopkins, by Rose and G. J. Cox proved that histidine also must be included in the food of animals. Thus, unequivocal proof was offered that certain amino acids cannot be synthesized by living cells out of materials ordinarily present and consequently must be supplied preformed.

Following these findings, investigations were undertaken in several laboratories for the purpose of demonstrating the dietary role of the other amino acids. Usually, such efforts were unsuccessful. Progress was impeded by the want of delicate tests for the individual amino acids and by the fact that available methods for their separation were not strictly quantitative. Thus, by 1930, when Rose's investigations began, not one of the remaining 16 amino acids then known had been classified with respect to its nutritive importance.

Obviously, if further progress was to be made, it would be necessary to resort to the use of diets in which proteins were replaced by mixtures of highly purified amino acids. However, at the time a venture of this character appeared to offer little promise of success. Biochemical literature contained the results of several such experiments, in which the animals declined in weight and rejected the food. In endeavoring to explain this behavior, the investigators usually assumed that the loss of appetite was due to the taste of the amino acids.

Despite these discouraging results, Rose decided to undertake studies of this kind and to include all known amino acids in the food. The first amino acid mixture was formulated to imitate as closely as possible the composition of casein of milk. The results of the feeding trials were quite similar to those reported from other laboratories. The young rats lost weight very rapidly at first and thereafter declined slowly until death resulted. To account for these effects, Rose postulated that proteins contain at least one indispensable component other than the amino acids then recognized. Proceeding on this hypothesis, Rose hydrolyzed the proteins and fractionated the resulting mixture of amino acids by a variety of chemical techniques. Each fraction was bioassayed for the unknown compound by testing its growth effect when added to a diet containing the 19 recognized amino acids. Eventually, a new amino acid, now known as threonine, was isolated and identified, and its spatial configuration was established. Its addition to an otherwise adequate ration containing the previously known amino acids was found to induce excellent growth.

The discovery of threonine added a fourth amino acid to the group of indispensable dietary constituents. Furthermore, it provided a technique for establishing the nutritive significance of the other amino acids by omitting them from the food one at a time. Making use of this device, Rose promptly classified the remaining components of proteins. As is now generally known, the results demonstrated that for the

young rat 10 of the amino acids ordinarily found in proteins are necessary for maximal gains in weight. The others can be synthesized in vivo out of simpler compounds and consequently need not be included in the food. The essentials for this species are valine, leucine, isoleucine, threonine, methionine, phenylalanine, tryptophan, lysine, histidine, and arginine. The exclusion of any one of these, with the exception of arginine, leads to a profound nutritive failure, diminished appetite, and eventual death. In contrast to such spectacular effects, depriving a growing rat of arginine merely decreases the rate of gain. This is attributable to the fact that arginine can be synthesized by the rat, but not at a speed in keeping with the requirements of the organism for optimal growth.

The classification of arginine as essential or nonessential is purely a matter of definition. Rose defined an essential dietary component as one which cannot be synthesized by the species in question out of materials ordinarily available to the cells at a speed which is commensurate with the needs for optimal growth. Under this definition, arginine must be classified as an essential, although it alone of its group may be excluded from the food without occasioning a loss of weight. Subsequent investigations demonstrated that the adult rat and the adult dog can be maintained in body weight and nitrogen equilibrium without arginine. Thus, the in vivo synthesis of this amino acid keeps pace with the needs for maintenance.

Throughout the course of the animal experiments, it was hoped that eventually nitrogen balance studies might be conducted in human subjects as a means of discovering their qualitative and quantitative amino acid requirements. Such investigations were actually initiated in 1942. Healthy male graduate students served as the subjects. In formulating the diets, only those articles of food were used which are virtually devoid of nitrogen of an unknown nature. These comprised amino acids, corn starch, sucrose, butterfat (which had been melted and centrifuged to remove particles of protein), corn oil, inorganic salts, and an appropriate mixture of vitamins. The amino acid mixtures, composed initially of the 10 acids previously found to be necessary for the growing rat, were consumed in aqueous solution flavored to taste with sucrose and filtered lemon juice. The vitamins were taken each day in the form of pills. The other components listed above and a baking powder made in the laboratory were mixed with water, rolled into thin layers, and baked into wafers.

Upon diets of this character, the young men came into nitrogen equilibrium, and could be so maintained indefinitely. This fact provides convincing proof that the 10 amino acids which are dispensable for the rat and the dog are dispensable also for adult man. Following this observation, the amino acids present in the food were excluded one at a time, and the effects noted. The findings were explicit and unmistakable in showing that eight amino acids are essential for the attainment and preservation of nitrogen equilibrium in adult man. These are valine, leucine, isoleucine, threonine, methionine, phenylalanine, tryptophan, and lysine. The removal of any one of these from the diet was followed by a strongly negative nitrogen balance, a profound failure in appetite, a sensation of extreme fatigue, and a marked increase in nervous irritability. With the return of the missing compound to the ration, nitrogen equilibrium was reestablished promptly, and the subjective symptoms disappeared. On the contrary, the removal of arginine or histidine was devoid of demonstrable influence. The observation with respect to histidine was quite unexpected, since this amino acid is required by all other species of mammals thus far tested.

After completing the qualitative experiments in man, attention was focused on the more difficult problem of establishing the *quantitative* needs of human subjects. The objective in these studies was to ascertain for each essential amino acid the mimimal intake which would permit nitrogen equilibrium when the diets contained excess amounts of the other seven. For this purpose the composition of the diet was kept constant with respect to every component except the amino acid being investigated, which was progressively lowered. When the diminished intake induced a negative balance of moderate intensity, the quantity of this substance was raised until a slight, but distinct, positive balance ensued. The latter amount represented the minimal requirement of the subject.

The findings in a given individual can be duplicated with astonishing regularity, even when the measurements are repeated at intervals of many months. On the other hand, considerable variation is frequently encountered in the minimal requirements of different individuals for a given amino acid. These variations cannot be correlated with differences in body weights or body surfaces. When they are observed, the highest figure must be taken as the minimum. It should be noted that the problem of variability is not unique for amino acids, but is observed in many other physiological measurements.

The table summarizes the data obtained in the quantitative tests. The figures reveal the range of requirements observed and the values which have been proposed as the minima. It can be demonstrated statistically that the odds are overwhelmingly against the possibility of an amino acid deficiency in a subject who is consuming twice the highest observed minimal requirement. Because of this fact, Rose chose to designate these double minimal values as *safe* intakes. They are listed in the fourth column of the table. As shown in the footnotes to the table, tyrosine and cystine are capable of exerting pronounced sparing effects upon the minimal needs of human subjects for phenylalanine and methionine, respectively. The cystine effect is particularly important, since methionine appears to be the limiting amino acid in the diets consumed in many areas of the world.

Numerous experiments were conducted in animals by Rose and his associates to ascertain whether the indispensable amino acids may be replaced in the diet by compounds more or less closely related to them in chemical structure. In such experiments the growth of a young mammal becomes an "indicator" of a chemical reaction in just as real a sense as a color change may denote the complexion of the neutralization of an acid by an alkali. Space does not permit a detailed consideration of the findings obtained in these experiments, but this technique affords a method whereby one may determine the extent

Amino acid requirements of man

Amino acid	Range of requirements observed, g/day	Value proposed as minimum, g/day	Value which is definitely a safe intake, g/day	Number of subjects maintained in N balance on safe intakes or less
Tryptophan	0.15–0.25	0.25	0.50	42
Phenylalanine	0.80–1.10*	1.10	2.20	32
Lysine	0.40–0.80	0.80	1.60	37
Threonine	0.30–0.50	0.50	1.00	29
Methionine	0.80–1.10†	1.10	2.20	23
Leucine	0.50–1.10	1.10	2.20	18
Isoleucine	0.65–0.70	0.70	1.40	17
Valine	0.40–0.80	0.80	1.60	33

* These values were obtained with diets which were devoid of tyrosine. In two experiments the presence of tyrosine in the food spared the phenylalanine requirement to the extent of 70–75%.

† These values were determined with cystine-free diets. In three experiments the presence of cystine was found to exert a sparing effect of 80–89% upon the minimal methionine needs of the subjects.

to which certain types of reactions may be accomplished by living organisms.

Rose graduated with a B.S. from Davidson College in 1907. He received the Ph.D. from Yale University in 1911, where he worked under the direction of Lafayette B. Mendel. During 1913 he studied under Franz Knoop at Freiburg, Germany. Rose then taught at the universities of Pennsylvania and Texas and in 1922 went to the University of Illinois, where he served as professor of biochemistry and head of the biochemistry division of the chemistry department until 1953, and research professor of biochemistry from 1953 until his retirement in 1955. He was elected to the National Academy of Sciences in 1936 and was awarded a 1966 National Medal of Science.

For background information *see* AMINO ACIDS; BIOASSAY; FOOD in the McGraw-Hill Encyclopedia of Science and Technology.   □

★ ROSSINI, Frederick Dominic

American chemist
Born July 18, 1899, Monongahela, Pa., U.S.A.

Rossini's contributions to science were in three areas: thermodynamics and thermochemistry, physical chemistry of petroleum and its components, and critically evaluated numerical data for science and technology. As a result of his doctoral thesis work on heat capacities in aqueous salt solutions, completed in 1928 at the University of California, Berkeley, Rossini became interested in making accurate thermochemical measurements. He saw the need to create reliable data on the heats of formation of selected chemical compounds—such data being sorely needed for the proper development of the chemical and petroleum industries. In 1928, through the efforts of W. C. Blasdale, professor of analytical chemistry at Berkeley, and F. G. Cottrell, director of the Fixed Nitrogen Research Laboratory in Washington, Rossini was put in

touch with Edward W. Washburn, chief of the Division of Chemistry at the National Bureau of Standards (NBS). He joined the NBS staff and began the development of the Thermochemical Laboratory.

In his first year at the NBS, Rossini completed work on SO_2 started by J. R. Eckman, who had left the laboratory because of illness. Working alone during 1929–35, Rossini began a renaissance in experimental thermochemistry by completing investigations leading to new values for the heats of formation of H_2O, CO, CH_4, C_2H_6, C_3H_8, n-C_4H_{10}, iso-C_4H_{10}, n-C_5H_{12}, CH_3OH, C_2H_5OH, and HCl. At the NBS with J. W. Knowlton, E. J. Prosen, W. H. Johnson, R. Gilmont, and F. W. Maron during 1935–50, and at the Carnegie Institute of Technology with C. C. Browne, Sr., M. C. Loeffler, H. F. Bartolo, D. M. Speros, J. D. Rockenfeller, A. Labbauf, and J. Chao during 1950–60, Rossini reported new values for the heats of formation of many important "key" hydrocarbons and other compounds. These included D_2O; CO_2; benzoic acid; the 10 normal l-alkanols, C_1 to C_{10}; 9 branched alkanols, C_3, C_4, C_5; 7 normal paraffin hydrocarbons, alkanes, C_6 to C_{10}, C_{12}, C_{16}; 9 normal l-alkenes, C_2 to C_8, C_{10}, C_{16}; 5 normal alkylcyclopentanes, C_5 to C_8, C_{16}; 6 normal alkylcyclohexanes, C_6 to C_{10}, C_{16}; the 4 branched hexanes; the 8 branched heptanes; the 17 branched octanes; tetraethylmethane and the 4 tetramethylpentanes; the 3 isomeric butenes; the 16 isomeric hexenes; 9 isomeric heptenes; 5 isomeric octenes; the 5 dimethylcyclopentanes; the 7 dimethylcyclohexanes; the 2 butadienes; the 2 butynes; the normal alkylbenzenes, C_6 to C_9, C_{16}; the 3 dimethylbenzenes; isopropylbenzene; the 3 dimethylethylbenzenes; and the 3 trimethylbenzenes; styrene; 1,3,5,7-cyclooctatetraene; *cis*- and *trans*-hexahydroindan; *cis*- and *trans*-9-methyldecahydronaphthalene; *cis*- and *trans*-decahydronaphthalene; naphthalene and the 2 methylnaphthalenes.

The data obtained in these thermochemical investigations threw new light on the atomic linkages in the simple paraffin hydrocarbons and the simple alcohols and for the first time gave definitive figures for the differences in energy among the many isomeric hydrocarbons measured. The data showed that the energy of a C-C bond is affected not only by the nature and size of the substituents of these two bonded C atoms, but also by the substituents on the C atoms once removed. In general, the more compact the molecule, the lower its energy, up to the point where steric hindrance or molecular constraint occurs, at which point the energy of the molecule begins to increase. The thermochemical data reported by Rossini and his co-workers formed the basis for a large number of theoretical papers on the relation between the energy and structure of hydrocarbon molecules. Included among these papers are one by W. J. Taylor and J. M. Pignocco and one by J. B. Greenshields, both with Rossini. The experimental data and the correlations resulting therefrom made it possible to calculate, without measurement, values for the heats of formation of an almost unlimited number of hydrocarbons of the several classes.

In 1938, with R. S. Jessup, Rossini published thermodynamic calculations on the transition of carbon (graphite) into carbon (diamond), giving reliable direction as to the temperatures and pressures that would be required to perform this transition. Less than 20 years later one of the big industrial research laboratories made this an accomplished fact on a large scale.

Rossini's work on the physical chemistry of petroleum and its components began in 1934 after the death of Washburn, whom Rossini succeeded as director of the American Petroleum Institute Research Project 6 on hydrocarbons in petroleum. He continued as director of this project at the NBS until 1950 and at the Carnegie Institute of Technology from 1950 to 1960. Under his direction the project isolated about 150 new hydrocarbons from petroleum and purified about 280 hydrocarbons for use as reference standards through investigations carried on principally with B. J. Mair, C. B. Willingham, A. J. Streiff, A. R. Glasgow, Jr., A. F. Forziati, N. C. Krouskop, and D. L. Camin. To accomplish these tasks, the project developed and operated fractionating processes of high separating power, including distillation, adsorption, extraction, and crystallization, in various forms. The work completed on the composition of the gasoline fraction showed that all petroleums contain the same hydrocarbons, that different petroleums differ only in the relative amounts of the several classes of hydrocarbons present, and that within certain groups of hydrocarbons the individual compounds are present in the same relative amounts in different petroleums (even though these petroleums differ widely in overall composition). One important aspect of the project was the accurate measurement of the physical properties of the highly purified hydrocarbons prepared as reference standards. Another very important aspect was the development and operation of apparatus for the determination of the purity of hydrocarbons by the precise and accurate measurement of freezing points. The method developed made it possible to determine the amount of impurity in the purest samples available. The work published by the project by the beginning of World War II, as well as later, served to provide the petroleum industry of the United States with information and data on the components, properties, and means of separating and processing desired components for the production of specialty products and petrochemicals. Much of this work is summarized in *Hydrocarbons from Petroleum* (1953) by Rossini, Mair, and Streiff. Rossini's connection with petroleum science and technology was capped in 1967, when he was elected president of the World Petroleum Congress for a 4-year term.

Rossini's work in the field of critically evaluated numerical data for science and technology developed naturally from his association with Washburn, who was editor in chief of the famed *International Critical Tables* (7 vols. and index, 1926–33). *Thermochemistry of the Chemical Substances* (1936), by F. R. Bichowsky and Rossini, served as a standard self-consistent tabulation of the heats of formation of all inorganic compounds and all organic compounds having one or two carbon atoms per molecule. This tabulation was revised and extended by Rossini, with D. D. Wagman, W. H. Evans, S. Levine, and I. Jaffe, in *Selected Values of Chemical Thermodynamic Properties* (1952), which appeared as NBS Circular 500.

Meanwhile, in 1942, the American Petroleum Institute Research Project 44 on the properties of hydrocarbons had been set up under Rossini's direction at the NBS, where it continued until 1950, when it was moved to the Carnegie Institute of Technology. With W. J. Taylor, J. P. Ebert, K. S. Pitzer, J. E. Kilpatrick, C. W. Beckett, R. L. Arnett, R. M. Braun, G. C. Pimentel, K. Li, B. J. Zwolinski, and others, Project 44 issued thousands of loose-leaf data sheets containing critically evaluated numerical data on the physical, thermodynamic, and spectral properties of hydrocarbons and related compounds. In addition, the project published two bound volumes, *Selected Values of Properties of Hydrocarbons* (1947) and *Selected Values of Physical and Thermodynamic Properties of Hydrocarbons and Related Compounds* (1953). These volumes and data sheets provided the petroleum and chemical industries throughout the world with reliable data.

During 1955–60 Rossini also served as director of the Manufacturing Chemists Association Research Project on the properties of chemical compounds. Although no bound volume was issued, this project, with J. C. M. Li, H. Li, B. J. Zwolinski, L. P. Bitler, and others, released almost 1000 pages of critically evaluated numerical data on compounds important to the chemical industry. With P. A. Cowie, F. O. Ellison, and C. C. Browne, Rossini published *Properties of Titanium Compounds and Related Substances* (1956) for the U.S. Office of Naval Research.

Rossini's work on numerical data for science and technology continued after his transfer to the University of Notre Dame in 1960. In 1963 he became chairman of the executive committee of the Office of Critical Tables of the National Research Council, which coordinates work in this field on a national basis. In 1966 he became president of the Committee on Data for Science and Technology of the International Council of Scientific Unions, to coordinate similar work on an international basis.

Rossini received from the Carnegie Institute of Technology a B.S. in chemical engineering in 1925 and an M.S. in science in 1926. In 1928 he received his Ph.D. in physical chemistry from the University of California, Berkeley. He worked at the NBS from 1928 to 1950, becoming chief of the Section on Thermochemistry and Hydrocarbons in 1936. From 1950 to 1960 he was at the Carnegie Institute of Technology as professor and head of the department of chemistry and as director of the Chemical and Petroleum Research Laboratory. In 1960 he moved to the University of Notre Dame to be dean of the College of Science, until September, 1967, when he became vice-president for research. His awards included the Pittsburgh Award of the American Chemical Society in 1959, the John Price Wetherill Medal of the Franklin Institute in 1965, and the William H. Nichols Medal of the American Chemical Society in 1966. Rossini was elected to the National Academy of Sciences in 1951 and to the American Academy of Arts and Sciences in 1964.

In addition to the books mentioned, Rossini wrote the textbook *Chemical Thermodynamics* (1950).

For background information *see* DIAMOND; HYDROCARBON; PETROLEUM; THERMOCHEMISTRY in the McGraw-Hill Encyclopedia of Science and Technology. ☐

★ ROSSITER, Roger James

Canadian biochemist
Born July 24, 1913, Adelaide, Australia

As a Rhodes scholar from Western Australia in 1935 and later as a Carnegie scholar and Harmsworth senior scholar at Oxford University, Rossiter became associated with Rudolph Peters, then head of the department of biochemistry. Inspired by Peters, Rossiter developed an interest in the chemistry and metabolism of the nervous system that was to persist throughout his research career. Upon migrating to Canada to take up an appointment at the University of Western Ontario in 1947, he embarked upon a series of investigations, first on the chemistry and metabolism of normal degenerating and regenerating nerve and subsequently on the metabolism and biosynthesis of lipids in brain and nerve.

During 1947–57 Rossiter outlined the chemical and metabolic changes that occur in a peripheral nerve when it degenerates after section. Such a degeneration, first described by the English physiologist A. V. Waller in 1850 and later named for him, has been studied with the aid of the classic techniques of histology, histochemistry, physiology, and, later, electron microscopy. Until the time of Rossiter's studies, however, the techniques of chemistry were rarely used.

For convenience Wallerian degeneration was divided into three stages, somewhat arbitrarily, for its rate depends upon the species studied, the age of the animal, the type of nerve, the size of the fiber, the temperature, and many other factors. During stage I (collapse of axon and physical destruction of myelin), there is a loss of the ability of the nerve to conduct an impulse, accompanied by a loss in the activity of certain enzymes, such as true cholinesterase, choline acetylase, and alkaline phosphomonoesterase. The nerve is depleted of some essential constituents, notably acetylcholine, thiamine, and nicotimide-adenine dinucleotide. The resting oxygen consumption falls, and certain metabolic processes, such as the in vitro labeling of lipid from acetate-1-C^{14}, are decreased. Undoubtedly many of these changes are associated with destruction of the axon and loss of axoplasmic enzymes.

As the myelin sheath is destroyed during stage II (cellular proliferation and chemical degradation of myelin), cholesterol ester appears, and there is a loss of nonesterified cholesterol, sphingomyelin, cerebroside, ethanolamine plasmalogen, and polyphosphoinositide. These lipids are called the myelin lipids. Accompanying the cellular proliferation, there is an increase in the concentrations of DNA, RNA, and

total protein and an increase in the activity of enzymes, such as pseudocholinesterase, 5'-nucleotidase and β-glucuronidase. The resting oxygen consumption and the labeling of lipids from inorganic P^{32}-C^{14}-labeled precursors is increased. It is tempting to suggest that such an increase in the in vitro labeling of lipid is related to the coincident proliferation of Schwann cells and that sectioned nerves are more amply provided with the metabolic machinery necessary for the formation of myelin lipids. Such nerves have the ability to form myelin, and indeed they do form myelin when a suitable opportunity is presented, that is, when the degenerating nerve fiber receives a growing axon tip from the central stump.

During stage III (fibrosis), DNA, RNA, protein, and enzyme activity disappear from the nerve, but the concentration of collagen increases. If the degenerating distal stump becomes reinnervated, the nerve remyelinates, and myelin lipids and enzymes, such as true cholinesterase and alkaline phosphomonoesterase, reappear. Coincident with a loss in cellularity, there is a decrease in the concentration of DNA and RNA and in the activity of the enzymes acid phosphomonoesterase, 5'-nucleotidase, and β-glucuronidase.

From 1955 Rossiter became increasingly interested in the metabolism and biosynthesis of phospholipids in brain and nerve. It is apparent that in these tissues most of the phosphatides are synthesized in situ from appropriate precursors of low molecular weight. The characteristic phosphodiester grouping of the phosphatides is formed through the mediation of a series of cytosine-containing nucleotides (CDP-choline, CDP-diglyceride, and so on). One example of this method of phosphatide biosynthesis is the formation of phosphatidyl choline (lecithin) by the transfer of phosphorylcholine from CDP-choline to 1,2-diglyceride. Another is the formation of phosphatidyl inositol (monophosphoinositide) by the transfer of a phosphatidyl group from CDP-diglyceride to myoinositol, or alternatively glycerol-3-phosphate, with the formation of phosphatidyl glycerophosphate, which may then be dephosphorylated to yield phosphatidyl glycerol.

In addition, there are many known instances of one phosphatide being derived metabolically from another. Examples are the formation of phosphatidyl ethanolamine by the decarboxylation of phosphatidyl serine and the formation of polyphosphoinositide by the phosphorylation of phosphatidyl inositol. The phosphatide is formed as the result of lipid-to-lipid interconversion, the reaction presumably taking place while the lipid is oriented in a membranous structure. In brain and nerve, as in most tissues, lipids are in a dynamic state—that is, they are continually being built up and broken down, but by quite different metabolic routes. A notable exception is the myelin sheath of a nerve fiber, where many of the constituent lipids are extremely inert metabolically.

Rossiter obtained his B.Sc. (1934) from the University of Western Australia and his Ph.D. (1940) and his M.D. (1941) from Oxford University. After serving in the British army as a major during World War II, he became professor and head of the department of biochemistry at the University of Western Ontario in 1947. In 1965 he became dean of graduate studies at this university. In 1954 Rossiter was elected a fellow of the Royal Society of Canada, and in 1963 he was awarded its Flavelle Medal. He also was the recipient of the Radcliffe Prize of Oxford University and the Warner-Chilcott Award of the Canadian Society for Clinical Investigation. In 1959 he spent a sabbatical year studying the metabolism of phosphodiesters at the Institute for Advanced Studies, Australian National University, during which period he held a Royal Society and Nuffield Foundation Commonwealth bursary.

For background information see LIPID; LIPID METABOLISM; NERVOUS SYSTEM; NERVOUS SYSTEM DISORDERS in the McGraw-Hill Encyclopedia of Science and Technology.   □

★ RUSHTON, William Albert Hugh

British physiologist
Born Dec. 8, 1901, London, England

WHEN AT the age of 50 Rushton took up the study of vision, S. Hecht's photochemical theory was still generally accepted. The theory asserted that much of the performance of the human eye could be explained quantitatively in terms of the kinetics of the visual pigments in the rods and cones. But as it was impossible to measure even rhodopsin in man (in whom the performance was studied), it was impossible to judge whether the theory was right. Rushton hoped to measure rhodopsin in man by using the "eye shine," such as is seen when a cat's eye is caught in a car's headlights. Since the reflected light has passed twice through the cat's retina, he reasoned, it must have undergone absorption by the pigments there, and it seemed possible that analysis of the light would give information about the nature and amount of visual pigments. This method proved successful. The bleaching and regeneration of rod and cone pigments could be measured objectively. Results showed that the photochemical theory in its most successful domain was in error by a factor of 1,000,-000. Adaptation was not as the photochemical theory had represented it. The immense complexity of retinal nerves, entirely ignored by the followers of Hecht, is obviously concerned with the processing of information. Rushton, often with colleagues, studied this organization by subjective observations in man and by electrophysiology in animals.

In research on the rod pigments F. W. Campbell and Rushton built (1955) a densitometer that would measure rhodopsin in man rapidly and accurately. They showed quantitatively how the pigment is bleached in the light and regenerated in the dark. The well-known change of threshold with luminous background was shown to be accompanied by negligible bleaching and (contrary to the photochemical theory) to be unaffected by such bleaching. On the other hand, when bleaching is substantial, Rushton showed (1961) that log threshold is raised in proportion to the amount still bleached, confirming J. E. Dowling's electrical measurements on the rat (1960).

The cone pigments had never been successfully extracted from any mammal. Though they were known to underlie color vision, the density of these pigments was held to be immeasurably small, and the nature of the pigments themselves was as controversial as color vision theory. By restricting measurements to the rod-free fovea centralis, the cone pigments were measured uncontaminated by rhodopsin and found to be about as dense as rhodopsin itself. Blue light was reflected too poorly to give information about the blue-cone pigment, but the red-sensitive pigment erythrolabe and the green-sensitive pigment chlorolabe were measured in normal eyes.

In studying color blindness Rushton found at once (1955) that the red-blind defectives (protanopes) lacked erythrolabe, and somewhat later defectives of the other type (deuteranopes) were shown to lack chlorolabe. Thus, at last an objective analysis was given of these color defects, entirely independent of the subject's sensations. Protanopes cannot see red because they lack the pigment that catches red light. Deuteranopes likewise cannot tell red from green (suitably matched for brightness) because they also have only one pigment in the red-green range. One pigment can do only one thing, namely, assess brightness; a second pigment is required to go further and distinguish color. Each pigment was shown to catch the quanta with which humans see because lights, which are physically different but look the same, bleach the pigment equally. Moreover, the effect of bleaching by strong lights is to raise the log cone threshold in proportion to the pigment remaining bleached, just as with rods.

The kinetics of bleaching and regeneration of cone pigments was studied and embraced by a single equation that represents the facts that the bleaching rate is proportional to the quantum catch, the regeneration rate is proportional to the residual bleaching, and these two processes act simultaneously and independently.

So long as visual adaptation was believed to be due to the level of visual pigment in the rods and cones, it seemed obvious that adaptation was a change in sensitivity of the receptors themselves. Rushton was one of those who questioned this. He showed that the threshold of the rod mechanism may be raised three times by a background that has not been "seen" by 99% of the rods, in the sense that only 1% have caught as much as a single quantum from it. Since rods adapt to lights that they have not seen, there must be a pooling of light information and a lateral spread of the resulting adaptation. This holds for adaptation both to backgrounds and to bleaching. The rods themselves always send a signal to the pool for every quantum caught, whatever the state of adaptation, but that state alters greatly the number of signals required for vision.

In electrophysiology Rushton conducted experiments with Donner on frogs and with Naka on fish that confirmed the complexity of neural processing in the retina. Some exact relations in the neural coding were established, but it is not clear how these are related to what humans think they see.

Son of a London dentist, Rushton received his school education at Gresham's (the school of Nobel Laureate A. L. Hodgkin, poets W. H. Auden and Stephen Spender, and musician Benjamin Britten). At Cambridge University he studied medicine, in which he eventually qualified (but never practiced it). He studied for his Ph.D. (1927) under E. D. Adrian and, together with H. K. Hartline and R. Granit, became a fellow of the Johnson Foundation when D. W. Bronk started it in 1929. He returned to Cambridge in 1931, becoming research fellow of Emmanuel College, staff fellow of Trinity College, and lecturer, reader, and finally professor of visual physiology in Cambridge University. Up to the age of 50 his research was upon the theory of nerve excitation. Then he spent a year with Granit in Stockholm, and was deflected into the study of vision. Rushton was elected a fellow of the Royal Society of London in 1948 and a foreign member of the American Academy of Arts and Sciences in 1963.

For background information *see* Color vision; Eye; Photoreception; Vision in the McGraw-Hill Encyclopedia of Science and Technology. ☐

★ RUSSELL, Sir Frederick (Stratten)

British zoologist
Born Nov. 3, 1897, Bridport, Dorset, England

Russell started his academic career with the intention of studying medicine, but before going to Cambridge University he was caught up in World War I, when he flew with the Royal Naval Air Service (later Royal Air Force) in France. At Cambridge he was influenced by J. Stanley Gardiner to enter the field of biological research. Having lived all his life close to the sea, mainly on the north coast of Cornwall, his interests were somewhat naturally in marine science. After a year studying the eggs and larvae of marine fish for the Egyptian government at Alexandria in 1923, Russell joined the research staff of the Marine Biological Association of the United Kingdom at Plymouth. There, at the suggestion of the laboratory director, E. J. Allen, he continued to study fish eggs and larvae, directing his attention especially to their vertical distribution and migrations in the sea. As these investigations were carried on for several years, the material collected also provided an excellent opportunity for the study of the vertical distribution of other plankton organisms, and the scope of Russell's research was widened to include all the macroplanktonic animals. At that time W. R. G. Atkins was making his pioneer observations with H. H. Poole, using photoelectric cells to measure the conditions of light at different depths beneath the sea surface. An opportunity was thus afforded to compare the observations on light intensities, made with greater accuracy than was previously possible, with the distribution of plankton animals at different depths in the sea.

As a result of these studies, it became evident to Russell that the same species of animal might exhibit different types of behavior with respect to light intensity at different times of the year. This led him to study more closely the individual biology of the crustacean copepod *Calanus* and the chaetognath worm *Sagitta*. He found that these animals pass through a number of generations in the year and that some generations behave differently from others, as do the different stages of growth within a single generation.

In the process of examining collections of plankton over a number of years, the seasonal cycle of abundance of different species was evident, but it was also noticed that there are differences in the component species of the population in some years. It had long been known that plankton organisms can be used as indicators of movement of water masses. Alexander Meek, professor of zoology at Newcastle, had recently shown that off the coast of Northumberland in northeast England there were two species of *Sagitta*, *S. elegans* and *S. setosa*, and that these appeared to occupy different types of water. Having such a wealth of material available, Russell decided to analyze the *Sagitta* population off Plymouth. He found marked changes in the relative abundance of the two species in different years, and was able to point to other species of plankton animals which seemed to be specially associated with one or the other of the two *Sagitta* species. In this way he established in some detail the value of certain plankton animals as indicators of the movements of different types of water in the English Channel and North Sea. This also threw some light on the reasons for differences in the abundance of herring in different areas.

Among these indicator animals were certain species of medusae, whose bottom-living hydroid stage was not known, which might throw light on the place of origin of the medusae. The need thus to know more about the life histories of these cnidarians, together with a love of making drawings, diverted Russell to make a special study of this group of animals. One of the leading specialists in this subject at the time was E. T. Browne, who was also a benefactor of the Marine Biological Association. Browne encouraged Russell and made possible a collaboration between him and W. J. Rees, later keeper of cnidarians at the British Museum. This collaboration resulted in the elucidation of the life histories of a number of species of medusae by rearing the hydroids from the parent medusae. Russell at that time started on the preparation of a monograph on British medusae which Browne had had in mind for some years. But World War II intervened, and Russell returned to the Royal Air Force for 5 years.

At the end of the war, following the sudden death of Stanley W. Kemp, Russell was appointed director of the Plymouth laboratory, a post he held until 1965. The opportunities for research were much reduced, but he succeeded in completing the *Monograph on the Medusae of the British Isles* (1953). He then turned his attention to the larger jellyfish, the Scyphomedusae, and undertook a companion monograph, for which his retirement provided the necessary time.

In 1959 one of the Plymouth laboratory research vessels caught a large red jellyfish from deep water in the Bay of Biscay. This was named *Stygiomedusa fabulosa* by Russell, and he and Rees made a detailed description of the medusa, which was unique in that it brought forth fully formed baby jellyfish 8–9 cm in diameter.

In 1928 Russell was a member of the Great Barrier Reef Expedition under the leadership of C. M. Yonge, with whom he had written a popular book, *The Seas* (1928; 3d ed. 1963). The revised edition is much used by students in biology. In Australia he had the opportunity to make a comparison between the abundance of plankton in tropical coastal waters and that of northern temperate regions.

For his work on plankton and medusae Russell received the Gold Medal of the Linnean Society in 1961. He was elected to the Royal Society of London in 1938.

For background information *see* COELENTERATA; JELLYFISH; MARINE ECOSYSTEM in the McGraw-Hill Encyclopedia of Science and Technology.   □

★ **RUSSELL, Loris Shano**

Canadian paleontologist
Born Apr. 21, 1904, New York, N.Y., U.S.A.

WHEN RUSSELL was still a schoolboy in Calgary, Alberta, he determined to make natural science his life's work. However, he could not decide between geology and zoology, so he chose the study of fossils. Years later, as a visiting graduate student, he explained to Professor E. C. Case of Michigan that he wanted to be a stratigraphic vertebrate paleontologist. Case, then somewhat disillusioned with the Permian record, replied that there was no such thing. Russell tried thereafter to prove him wrong.

Calgary lies in a trough of fossiliferous Paleocene rocks, and is only about 100 mi from the rich Cretaceous dinosaur fields of the Red Deer valley. By the time Russell was ready to go to the University of Alberta in Edmonton, he had assembled a large collection of fossil mollusks and vertebrates, all carefully labeled as to locality and horizon and more or less correctly identified. These served as the basis of several papers published while he was still an undergraduate, in which he demonstrated the Paleocene age of the Paskapoo formation and its correlation with the Fort Union group of Montana. His Ph.D. thesis at Princeton University dealt with the Cretaceous-Tertiary transition in Alberta and attempted to synthesize the evidence of stratigraphy with that of vertebrate and invertebrate paleontology. The conclusions on the position of the Cretaceous-Tertiary boundary and the demonstration that the Cretaceous sea withdrew slowly from west to east were novel at the time. His most startling finding, however, was that the so-called Laramide mountain building, which was supposed to mark the end of the Cretaceous Period, actually occurred in post-Paleocene Tertiary time.

Detailed geologic mapping and stratigraphical and structural studies in Alberta during the 1930s enabled Russell to amplify his conclusions that the advances of the Cretaceous sea were relatively rapid and the withdrawals prolonged and oscillatory. An extension of this work into southwestern Saskatchewan revealed in detail the events during the last marine withdrawal. Here he found and described the youngest marine molluscan fauna known from the Canadian plains. His work on invertebrate fossils, however, was mostly with freshwater and land mollusks, and he added many new species and records to the faunas, as well as two entirely new assemblages from the Tertiary of British Columbia. He was the first to try to bring the classification of Cretaceous and Tertiary freshwater mussels into line with that based on living examples.

His early interest in dinosaurs and other Cretaceous reptiles revived from time to time in special studies, such as his interpretation of the musculature and movements in the horned dinosaurs, and detailed descriptions of skeletal anatomy. He wrote on the ecology of dinosaurs and proposed a hypothesis to explain their extinction, based on the conclusion that they were endothermic. Two expeditions to the Devonian of Gaspé led to the description of fossil fishes. Russell's main work, however, was in mammalian paleontology. He added to the knowledge of the Cretaceous and Paleocene mammals of Alberta and of the Oligocene and Miocene mammals of Saskatchewan and described new Eocene faunas from Saskatchewan and British Columbia. His demonstration that the plateau gravels of the Canadian plains date from Eocene, Oligocene, Miocene, and Pliocene time exploded the old idea that major Tertiary aggradation occurred here only once or possibly twice.

Some field work and numerous visits in the fossil-bearing Tertiary rocks of the western United States enabled him to extend his conclusions on the Eocene age of the Rocky Mountain uplift as far south as New Mexico. In recent years he engaged in systematic studies of the Tertiary mammals of Saskatchewan and in working out the Cretaceous-Paleocene fossil succession in northern Alberta. Russell believed that the Cretaceous and Tertiary formations of western Canada and the adjacent United States are an important field for the study of evolutionary paleontology, not only because of the abundance of fossils but also because the stratigraphic relationships, and even the potassium-argon ages, can be determined in many cases.

Russell was educated in the public schools of Alberta, and received his B.Sc. from the University of Alberta in 1927 and his M.A. from Princeton University in 1929. After receiving his Ph.D. at Princeton in 1930, Russell served for 7 years as a paleontologist with the Geological Survey of Canada, doing general geology as well as vertebrate and invertebrate paleontology. In 1937 he went to the University of Toronto as assistant professor of paleontology and as assistant director of the Royal Ontario Museum of Paleontology. While on the Toronto staff he was on leave for over 3 years in military service. He returned to Ottawa in 1950 as chief zoologist of the National Museum of Canada and continued his paleontological research. But a growing interest in museum work led him in 1956 to accept the position of director of the Museum's Natural History Branch. Not long afterward a shakeup in the Human History Branch forced him to take over direction of the whole National Museum of Canada. This enabled him to expand the fields of anthropological as well as biological research in the Museum. In anticipation of the Canadian centenary he built up a very large collection of objects illustrating the social and technological history of Canada, but this aroused the opposition of influential Canadian historians, who were able to have his project stopped. So he returned in 1963 to the University of Toronto as chief biologist of the Royal Ontario Museum and as a professor in the department of geology. He was elected a fellow of the Royal Society of Canada in 1936 and was awarded the Miller Medal of the Society in 1959. The University of Alberta conferred on him the degree of LL.D. in 1958.

Russell's findings were published in over 100 papers in scientific journals, in the *Transactions of the Royal Society of Canada*, and in the publications of the Royal Ontario Museum, the National Museum of Canada, and the Geological Survey of Canada.

For background information *see* GEOLOGICAL TIME SCALE; MAMMALIA FOSSILS; PALEONTOLOGY; STRATIGRAPHIC NOMENCLATURE in the McGraw-Hill Encyclopedia of Science and Technology.   □

★ **RUSSELL, Richard Joel**

American geomorphologist
Born Nov. 16, 1895, Hayward, Calif., U.S.A.

LOVE OF the outdoors attracted Russell into a career in the earth sciences emphasizing field work. His first professional publication described offset streams and alluvial fans along the Hayward fault (1926). His earliest comprehensive investigation was mapping 550 sq mi of igneous rock, resulting in deciphering of the structure and stratigraphy of the Warner Range, northeastern California (1928). Conclusions from both of these studies appeared many years later in the Geological Survey map of the geology of the Hayward Quadrangle (1956) and in the California Division of Mines Alturas sheet (1958).

With a "hard rock" background in California and Great Basin geology, Russell found little of interest during 2 years spent on the High Plains of Texas or on moving to Louisiana in 1928. His principal publications were in climatology, a hobby. Five years elapsed before he issued his first Louisiana paper (1933), in which he identified Larto Lake, although far removed, as being an old Mississippi River channel. The flood of 1927 prompted the Mississippi River Commission to issue the first detailed topographical maps of Louisiana flood plains in the early 1930s. Soon came T-sheets of the Coast and Geodetic Survey covering the coastal marshes. Under auspices of the newly reestablished Louisiana Geological Survey, Russell began flood plain, marsh, and delta investigations that continued as his main interest until 1956. The report attracting the most widespread attention was a monographic study of the Mississippi River Delta (1936). It emphasized the effect of sedimentary loading on landforms and drainage patterns and related subsidence to the development of the Gulf Coast geosyncline. This work resulted in the first W. W. Atwood Award of the Association of American Geographers, which made possible a detailed investigation of the Rhône delta, published in 1942.

In 1935 Harold N. Fisk moved to Louisiana and soon became Russell's closest scientific associate. Most of their field work was concentrated on Louisiana coastal and fluvial terraces, eventually to be extended north across Arkansas into southern Missouri. After finding proof of alluvial origin and learning that the terraces exhibit the same topographical and depositional facies that exist on the active flood plain, they related the terraces to glacioeustatic Quaternary changes of sea level. Five periods of low level were accompanied by widespread valley cutting, each followed by rising sea level, during which coastal valley systems were alluviated, resulting in four Pleistocene terraces and the Recent flood plains and deltas. Following Russell's papers on Quaternary surfaces in Louisiana (1938) and the Quaternary history of Louisiana (1940), Russell and Fisk published many flood plain and terrace studies. Cooperative and independent studies of terrace escarpments led both to discard the popular eolian theory of the origin of loess, which they regarded as a colluvial facies derived from Pleistocene terrace silt deposits. Russell's 1944 paper advanced ideas unacceptable to most geologists but endorsed by others, particularly in eastern Europe, where much loess exists. Cited in favor of colluvial origin were shapes of loess accumulations, emplacement without regard to compass directions, inclusion of lignite float only below lignite outcrops, absence of loess from slopes above the highest Pleistocene terrace, patterns of gravel distribution in loess, and other criteria. Although Russell conducted loess investigations in several European countries, he felt it unnecessary to publish papers that added no new concepts and merely duplicated his Lower Mississippi Valley findings. He believed that nothing would be gained by fanning the flames of controversy with American geologists, who held firmly to the eolian hypothesis. Russell felt certain that eventually the whole question would be approached with an open mind by investigators who would confirm his views. Fisk, who published papers asking some penetrating questions about how an eolian hypothesis might be supported, felt the same way.

For many years Russell was anxious to study the Great Meander River, but arrangements were not worked out until 1952, when he became a visiting professor at the University of Istanbul. He investigated the delta of the Sakarya River on the Black Sea, the combined deltas of the Seyhan and Ceyhan rivers on the Gulf of Alexandretta, the coast westward to Antalya, and the entire length of the Great Meander, resulting in a paper on the alluvial morphology of Anatolian rivers (1954). The Great Meander is an excellent "type locality" for meandering rivers. As with many others, its regular, sinuous bends give way to braided channels below tributaries carrying immense loads at time of extraordinary floods ("hydrologic monsters" of the French). The Great Meander's delta is the product of much channel shifting during an advance of some 10 mi in 25 centuries.

A trip along the Amazon below Manaus in 1956 resulted in Russell's recognizing a sharp contrast between ordinary flood plains and surfaces resulting from delta advance into the magnificent estuary that crossed Brazil when sea level had risen close to its present stand about 5000 years ago. Deltaic stream patterns result from underwater natural-levee building ahead of a delta and are characterized by branching and rejoining channels. Later, when the sides of submarine channels alluviate high enough to become land, their stream patterns persist. This is evident in the Lower Mississippi Delta, the Atchafalaya Basin of Louisiana, Mobile Bay of Alabama, and in many other places. Advancing alluviation dammed off tributaries of the Amazon, creating deep, wedge-shaped lakes, as is also true of Bafa Lake, near Miletus on the Great Meander. Toward Belem and Macapá, Marajó and other islands display Pleistocene terraces and exhibit uplift in isostatic compensation of the tremendous weight of Amazon sediment now being deposited offshore. A similar uplift occurs along the Louisiana-Mississippi boundary in response to the load imposed by Recent Mississippi River deposits. These conclusions were stated in Russell's presidential address to the Geological Society of America, published in 1958.

Believing that a scientist should not devote his entire career to one research field, Russell decided in 1956 to shift from flood plains, deltas, swamps, and marshes to sea coasts. His first objective was to find possible relationships between beach morphology and mineral composition in the West Indies. Some generalities were established, but other problems diverted his attention, the first being the origin of beach rock. Publications starting in 1959 advanced the idea that beach rock is only a species of a whole genus of cemented rocks that form in the vicinity of the water table, then exposed when beaches retreat or streams or excavations cut into them. Investigations involved not only the West Indies, but the shores of the Pacific and Indian oceans, including Oahu, Fiji, east and west coasts of Australia, Cocos-Keeling, Mauritius, most of the coast of South Africa, Greece, Rhodes, and Spain on the Mediterranean. The first Australian trip, with W. G. McIntire, concentrated on beach rock, but a second trip was concerned mainly with surfaces of low tidal flats in an area where the spring range goes up to over 50 ft (published in 1965). They were impressed by sand movement seaward, to depths whence it will not be returned, and advanced the idea that sand accumulated on oceanic shores during the time seas were making their Recent rise of some 450 ft, resulting in maximum beach and dune volume about 5000 years ago, as stillstand was approached. For the last 3000 years sand has been dissipating along most beaches, and little has been available for dune nourishment.

Familiarity with coasts in most parts of the world led to detailed studies, usually with McIntire, of eustatic changes of level and the conclusion that, if they consider the existing stand as 0, other high stands of Quaternary seas, in order, reached about 20, 30, and 0 ft, with the earliest one probably somewhat lower. These observations, chiefly from Indian Ocean shores and the West Indies, were taken, together with intervals between Quaternary levels on Crowley Ridge in Arkansas, as a basis for estimating the length of the Quaternary and its subdivisions (1964). The Quaternary was estimated as beginning at least 1,800,000 years ago, but subsequent measurements suggest about 2,000,000, a conclusion that appears to be confirmed by others. Russell and McIntire later investigated the reefs and depositional surfaces of Barbuda (1966) and the coral cap of Barbados (1966). Their most recent field work, in St. Vincent, was concerned with transport of volcanic ash from the vicinity of La Soufriére southward along the windward coast, where it forms immense sand waves that turn shoreward to nourish beaches and dunes near the southeastern corner of the island. Narrow, deep trenches across the windward shelf appear to be caused by density currents, created when the volcano was active in 1902.

Russell received his A.B. in 1920 with a major in vertebrate paleontology and his Ph.D. in structural geology in 1926, both from the University of California, Berkeley. In 1928 he joined the faculty of Louisiana State University, where he served 13 years as dean of the graduate school and became Boyd Professor of Geography. He received the Vega Medal from Queen Louise of Sweden (1961), the Cullum Medal of the American Geographical Society (1963), and the U.S. Navy Distinguished Public Service

Award (1967). He was elected to the National Academy of Sciences in 1959.

Russell wrote *Culture Worlds*, with F. B. Kniffen (1950; rev. ed. 1961, with E. L. Pruitt) and *River Plains and Sea Coasts* (1967) besides more than 100 journal articles and chapters contributed to a dozen books.

For background information *see* COASTAL LANDFORMS; ESCARPMENT; FLUVIAL EROSION CYCLE; GLACIAL EPOCH; PLAINS in the McGraw-Hill Encyclopedia of Science and Technology. □

★ RUŽIČKA, Leopold Stephen

Swiss chemist
Born Sept. 13, 1887, Vukovar, Croatia

FOR HIS work on many-membered rings and higher terpenes (including male sex hormones) Ružička shared with Adolf Butenandt the 1939 Nobel Prize for chemistry.

All Ružička's work fell into one of the four main divisions of organic chemistry: the alicyclic division, the aliphatic, the aromatic, and the heterocyclic. The isoprenoids, which include terpenes, steroids, and carotenoids, form the major part of alicyclic chemistry. The carotenoids are tetraterpenes or their biological degradation and transformation products, just as steroids are derived from certain triterpenes (squalene and lanosterol).

From 1916 onward Ružička's laboratory worked on natural odoriferous chemicals, mostly from the plant kingdom. Of greater importance was the work on the constitution of animal products with musk odor: civetone, $C_{17}H_{30}O$, from the civet cat and muskone, $C_{16}H_{30}O$, from the musk deer. Ružička found that civetone is a 17-membered and muskone a 15-membered ring ketone. Until then rings higher than 8-membered had neither been found in nature, nor could they be prepared synthetically. In addition, as A. von Baeyer's strain theory (1884) predicted that such rings would be very unstable, the prejudice arose that rings composed of more than 8 members did not exist. The discovery of the great stability of the many-membered musk ketones annihilated this prejudice. Indeed, a simple method was found which permitted the synthesis of the unknown series of many-membered ring ketones and hydrocarbons from the 9-membered to the 30-membered and above. Ružička and his co-workers also synthesized many-membered heterocyclic rings, especially in the form of lactones and imines. Thus a new and interesting chapter of organic chemistry was opened that today occupies a considerable region.

The terpenes, alicyclic compounds containing 10, 15, 20, 30, and 40 carbon atoms in the molecule and therefore called mono-, sesqui-, di-, tri-, and tetraterpenes, are widespread in the plant and animal kingdoms. Caoutchouc and gutta-percha are macromolecular aliphatic polyterpenes, analogous to macromolecular polysaccharides and polypeptides.

Otto Wallach was awarded the 1910 Nobel Prize for his work on monoterpenes. In the domain of the higher terpenes only two structural formulas, both in the sesquiterpene group, had been determined by 1921, when Ružička started his work. The method of dehydrogenation of the higher terpenes, containing 6-membered rings, to aromatic hydrocarbons proved to be very convenient for a quick penetration into the broad fields of sesquiterpenes, diterpenes, and triterpenes. Thus, for example, from the products of dehydrogenation of pentacyclic triterpenes, it was possible to determine the arrangement of 27 carbon atoms in the carbon skeleton. The advantage of this technique is clearly shown by comparison with the work on structure determination of cholesterol and bile acids. Adolf Windaus and H. O. Wieland tried to elucidate the structure of these tetracyclic compounds by degradation methods only, without considering dehydrogenation at all. Consequently, in their Nobel lectures (1927–28), from correct degradation results they proposed wrong formulas. It would have been still more difficult to determine the structures of pentacyclic triterpenes in their way.

For the pentacyclic triterpenes whose carbon skeleton had been established by dehydrogenation, it was relatively easy to determine the further details by degradation and other reactions. A fortunate hypothesis of great service in this work was the assumption that all carbon skeletons of higher terpenes could formally be composed of isoprene units. This hypothesis, the "isoprene rule," soon gained general recognition and application, and until 1952 only one exception was known. In that year the second exception, lanosterol, found in the Zurich laboratory, was the stimulus for the proposal of an improved isoprene rule in 1953, called the "biogenetic isoprene rule," which explained not only the structure of the terpenes but also their biogenesis in nature. Moreover, the formula of lanosterol stimulated the rationalization of the biogenesis of cholesterol from squalene by K. E. Bloch and R. B. Woodward.

The measurements of the unit cells of steroids by Y. D. Bernal in 1932 provided the stimulus for the acceptance of the dehydrogenation results of sterols obtained by Otto Diels since 1925; these results were neglected by Windaus and Wieland. Diels's results, together with the degradation results of Windaus and Wieland, made it immediately possible to settle the correct formulas for cholesterol and bile acids. Moreover, starting from the structure of cholesterol and the empirical formulas of the sex hormones (isolated from 1929 to 1932, especially by Butenandt), researchers could now suggest plausible hypothetical structures for the sex hormones. Therefore Butenandt was able to confirm by degradation and dehydrogenation the suggested steroid structure for the female hormone estrone, $C_{18}H_{22}O_2$, although the stereochemistry remained completely unknown. The great importance of the stereochemistry for the sex hormone activity was shown in 1934. Four sterically different formulas were envisaged for the hormone androsterone, $C_{19}H_{30}O_2$, isolated by Butenandt from male urine in 1931. Of course, these formulas were completely hypothetical; when Ružička began his work, only an incorrect empirical formula of this hydroxy ketone was published. The four stereoisomerical hydroxy ketones were prepared by oxidative degradation of the acetates of the four related saturated sterols. Two of these hydroxy ketones, the 5β-derivatives (in contrast to the 5α-derivatives) showed no hormone activity at all; 3α-hydroxy-5α-androstanone-17 was identical with androsterone, and the 3β-hydroxy-5α-derivative had only one-seventh of the androsterone activity. Thus the complete stereochemical relationship of a sex hormone with a sterol of known configuration (epi-cholestanol) was demonstrated for the first time.

Ružička, often pondering the structure of the then unknown male hormone from the testes, reached early in June, 1935, a hypothetical formula. A few days later while traveling to the United States he received a cable telling of a publication that described the isolation of the testicular hormone (named testosterone) from bull testes in E. Laqueur's laboratory in Amsterdam. Although an incorrect empirical formula for testosterone was given in this publication, Ružička had previously applied for a patent (priority date June 18, 1935) for the preparation from cholesterol of the compound corresponding to his hypothetical formula. (In pursuit of his researches on bisexual hormones, Butenandt also prepared this compound by using the same obvious procedure.) This product was in every respect—chemically, physically, and physiologically—identical with testosterone, Δ^4-17β-hydroxy-androstene-3-one, the real male hormone. He prepared also the 17α-methyltestosterone, which found considerable use, particularly in oral therapy. The fortune which he earned with his happy guess was transformed into a collection of Dutch and Flemish pictures from the 16th and 17th centuries, which was presented to the Zurich Art Museum.

In his research Ružička was assisted by M. Stoll in the synthesis of many-membered rings, by M. W. Goldberg in the field of sex hormones, by O. Jeger in the clarification of the constitution of higher terpenes, and by A. Eschenmoser, who developed the mechanism of cyclization reactions involving the biogenetic isoprene rule. D. Arigoni is continuing in the Zurich laboratory with great success the work on the structure and biogenesis of complicated higher terpenes.

Ružička studied chemistry at the Institute of Technology in Karlsruhe (Germany) and graduated in 1910. As an assistant of Hermann Staudinger, he worked from 1911 to 1916 on the constitution of insecticides in pyrethrum. In 1912 he went with Staudinger to the Swiss Federal Institute of Technology (ETH) in Zurich where he became a Swiss citizen and privatdozent in 1917–18. In 1925–26 he was director of research for Naef and Cie. (later Firmenich and Cie.) in Geneva, manufacturers of odoriferous chemicals. He was professor of organic chemistry at the University of Utrecht (Holland) during 1926–29 and at ETH during 1929–57. Starting in 1916, Ružička worked on monoterpenes and compounds related to quinine. In 1921 he began work on sesquiterpenes and diterpenes, in 1922 on many-membered rings, in 1928 on triterpenes, and in 1932 on male sex hormones. His work on higher terpenes continued until 1957, when he retired.

For background information *see* HORMONE; STEREOCHEMISTRY; TERPENE in the McGraw-Hill Encyclopedia of Science and Technology.   □

★ SADRON, Charles Louis

French physicist and biophysicist
Born May 12, 1902, Cluis, Indre, France

S ADRON'S SCIENTIFIC activity developed in various, though logically connected, fields. Just after his doctorate in ferromagnetic alloys (1932) he went as a Rockefeller fellow to the California Institute of Technology, where he worked for 18 months under Theodor von Kármán in the field of fluid mechanics and aerodynamics. There he developed an optical method for measuring the distribution of velocities of a liquid flowing at the vicinity of a solid surface by using the phenomenon of streaming double refraction (Maxwell effect). The results of this original device were perhaps not very encouraging for practical use, but it was in this way that Sadron became interested in the phenomenon itself, which at that time was not very well known. Back in France he systematically studied relations between the molecular structure and the Maxwell constant in series of homologous liquids, and he was able to show that molecular theories of the streaming refraction—such as C. V. Raman's—were not built on sound theoretical bases and that they did not yield values of the right order of magnitude when compared with the correct experimental results. In fact, in this case and in many others for the liquid state a molecular theory is very difficult to derive and—as far as one may tell—no satisfying achievement has yet been obtained.

On the contrary, the situation is much easier when one considers, instead of pure liquids, solutions of large anisodiametric particles. In that case a strong Maxwell effect is easily detected, and its origin lies in the orientation of the particles in the flow. Satisfying though approximative theories had been given by different authors, such as A. Peterlin and W. Kuhn. Sadron achieved some improvements and in this

way became interested in what has been often called "microhydrodynamics," that is, the study of the effect of the forces exerted by a flowing viscous liquid on included particles small enough to exhibit a Brownian motion.

He published several papers on this subject, and his most important and significant contribution was to establish—as early as 1942, during the German occupation of France and shortly before he was arrested by the Nazis and sent to a concentration camp in Germany—a new and general method of determining the dimensions of submicroscopic particles of a simple shape from macroscopic properties of their suspensions (intrinsic viscosity, Brownian translatory and rotatory diffusion constants, and so on). This method, or at least one of its aspects, was rediscovered more than 10 years later by other authors and was widely used for the investigation of the morphology of large molecules in solution. Sadron published in 1953 a general paper on this quite important matter.

In addition, during this period not only did he consider the case of small, solid particles, which is a rather crude one, but he worked on the case of long, flexible macromolecular chains (that is, high polymers), which can take an infinity of configurations, and made some progress in the calculation of their statistics. Also he contributed, with his collaborators, to the application of the light-scattering method to the characterization of the macromolecules—rigid or flexible—contained in a solution.

By 1953 Sadron had developed a whole laboratory concentrated on the study of large molecules in solution, where it was possible to use simultaneously on the same material a great number of different techniques (viscometry, free translatory diffusion, Kerr effect, Maxwell effect, centrifugation, dielectric dispersion, ultrasonic wave dispersion, light scattering, x-ray low-angle diffraction, and so on). It was a powerful tool, perhaps the only one of this kind, for the investigation of macromolecules in solution. Consequently, and at the same time because of the rapidly growing importance of the physical chemistry of large molecules, the French Centre National de la Recherche Scientifique (CNRS) decided, following Sadron's proposition, to establish a large laboratory in Strasbourg: the Centre de Recherches sur les Macromolecules (CRM). This was to include not only the team of physicists already formed in Sadron's laboratory but groups of chemists and biologists who would prepare or extract large molecules of a known composition and also study problems of macromolecular chemistry and biology needing the use of all the devices, theories, and techniques established by the physicists. The CRM opened in 1954 and grew very rapidly. Ten years later it employed about 220 people, half of them research workers and half technicians and administrative agents. During this time more than 80 scientists from many countries came to work in the laboratories for periods over 3 months.

Sadron had many responsibilities as director of the institution. He intimately collaborated with a group of senior scientists, some of whom had been his students and many of whom had obtained international reputations. Among them were H. Benoit, R. Cerf, G. Scheibling, V. Luzzati, A. Skoulios, P. Rempp, A. Kovacs, M. Daune, and G. Bernardi. It is not possible to give here a thorough account of the work done at the CRM, but the more important research included: (1) extension and improvement of the methods and techniques of characterization of macromolecular (or of a mixture of macromolecular) species in a solution, with special reference to light and low-angle x-ray scattering, automatic viscometry, and the ultracentrifugation scanning system; (2) elucidation of some mechanisms of polymerization processes, study of new polymerization catalysts, and preparation of "tailor-made" macromolecules; (3) investigation of the transitions in the solid state; (4) investigations on the structure and physicochemical properties of deoxyribonucleic acid (DNA) and of some nucleases (DNase II).

The existence of mesomorphic structures in gels of block-copolymers was discovered at the CRM in 1961. This new type of solid material (the organized polymers) was constituted of a bulk of plastic material containing—according to the case—microfilaments of microspheres ranged in periodical array (hexagonal network for filaments, cubic network for spheres) and formed of polymer chains of a different nature from that of the polymer forming the matrix. The organized polymers have now attracted the attention of industry, which is investigating the quite interesting properties of this material. Also discovered at the CRM was the existence, on a DNA double-helix filament prepared from mammals, birds, or bacteria, of special sites where the filament can be a readily broken (by ultrasonic waves) or attacked by different reagents. This may have an important connection with molecular genetics.

A new turn in Sadron's scientific activity came about 1962 when he began to study the macromolecules—such as proteins and nucleic acids—that play a fundamental role in the processes of "life." Since the outstanding properties of these macromolecules (enzymic catalysis, template in replication processes) have been recently shown to exist not only in situ—that is, in the very complicated structure of the cell—but even when the macromolecules are simply dispersed in dilute aqueous solutions, it appears that their study could be hopefully considered as relevant to macromolecular physical chemistry. Sadron progressively abandoned the industrial aspects of the high polymers and focused his attention on the physicochemical aspects of molecular biology, persuaded as he was, together with many fellow physicists all over the world, that the end of the 20th century will bring in this new field essential discoveries that will bear strongly on the future of mankind.

In fact, the biological macromolecules, or biopolymers, have a very complicated and specific conformation, the determination of which implies not only the use of the classical means of characterization, as those previously cited, but also requires the application of very elaborate methods; for instance, spectrographic methods using the Hertzian to the ultraviolet frequencies, and the observation of emission as well as absorption waves. It is necessary, moreover, to extract the proper biopolymers, carefully chosen either for reasons of simplicity or of biological interest, and to have them in a state of high purity and integrity. Lastly, it is very important to be able to prepare simple models (polypeptides, polynucleotides), thus permitting the necessary preliminary approach to the natural macromolecules. Such a laboratory, consequently, must bring together molecular physicists thoroughly trained in wave mechanics, electrochemists and physical chemists trained in macromolecular mechanics, specialists of the organic chemistry of peptides and polynucleotides, and well-trained molecular biologists who are not afraid to tackle physicochemical notions.

The Centre National de la Recherche Scientifique commissioned Sadron to start the Centre de Biophysique Moléculaire (CBM), where such means as those listed above could be concentrated. The CBM was built on a new campus near Orléans, in the vicinity of Paris, and was expected to begin operating before mid-1967. Sadron was lucky enough—actually he would not have accepted without prior assurance—to count on teams of young but very distinguished scientists to start this adventure. It is, of course, too early to prognosticate its success.

Sadron attended the universities of Poitiers and Strasbourg, where he received his Licencié ès sciences, Agrégé de l'université, and Docteur ès sciences. He taught at Troyes (1927–28) and at Strasbourg (1928–31), then worked on aeronautical research before going to the California Institute of Technology as a Rockefeller fellow for 1932–33. At Strasbourg he was director of research at the Centre National de la Recherche Scientifique in 1934–37 and was a professor at the University of Strasbourg during 1937. Sadron became director of the Centre de Recherches sur les Macromolécules and scientific councillor to UNESCO in London in 1947. For more than 10 years he was chairman of the section of chemical physics of CNRS. From 1959 to 1961 he was one of 12 members on a government committee in charge of reforming the structures of scientific research in France. A member of the executive committee of the European Molecular Biology Organization, he was professor of macromolecular chemical physics at the University of Strasbourg in 1957–61, professor of biophysics at the Museum National d'Histoire Naturelle in Paris from 1962, and director of the Centre de Biophysique Moléculaire in Orléans from 1966. He was awarded the Holweck Prize of the Physical Society, London, in 1946.

For background information *see* BROWNIAN MOVEMENT; FLUID MECHANICS; NUCLEIC ACID; POLYMER; PROTEIN in the McGraw-Hill Encyclopedia of Science and Technology.   □

★ SARETT, Lewis Hastings

American chemist
Born Dec. 22, 1917, Champaign, Ill., U.S.A.

DURING THE late 1930s the hormones of the adrenal cortex were isolated and structurally identified in three laboratories: E. C. Kendall's in the Mayo Clinic, Oskar Wintersteiner's at Columbia University, and Tadeus Reichstein's at the University of Basel. One of these steroid molecules, now known as cortisone, became the subject of great speculative interest as a possible adjunct to military medicine in World War II. Because of the minute amounts available from beef adrenal glands, the Committee on Medical Research of the wartime National Defense Research Council established a cooperation program designed to discover a synthetic route to cortisone. Merck & Co., Inc., of Rahway, N.J., participated in the effort, and it was in their laboratories that the first synthetic cortisone was prepared by Sarett late in 1944. This work opened up a route to supplies of cortisone adequate for clinical testing. By 1948 the efficacy of this hormone against rheumatoid arthritis was demonstrated by Philip Hench at the Mayo Clinic. A second and independent synthesis was completed by Sarett and collaborators in 1952 and led to the first route which was independent of naturally occurring starting materials. For this work Sarett received the American Chemical Society Award for Creative Work in Synthetic Organic Chemistry in 1964.

The steroids are a family of chemicals which occur in nature and which have in common a four-ring structure called a cyclopentanopolyhydrophenanthrene nucleus (Fig. 1). Members of this family are present in small quantities as hormones in the ovary, testis, and adrenal gland as well as in the bile and in various plants. Comparison of the structure of cortisone with that of other naturally occurring steroids suggested that desoxycholic acid, a more abundant chemical relative found in cattle bile, might serve as a starting material. The process could be visualized as consisting of three major synthetic operations (Fig. 2).

By combining known chemical transformations with new ones where necessary, a 37-step synthesis of cortisone was achieved. The attrition in material resulting from a synthesis of this length meant that only 15 mg of final product

(a)

(b)

(c)

Fig. 1. Structure of (*a*) the steroid nucleus, (*b*) desoxycholic acid, and (*c*) cortisone.

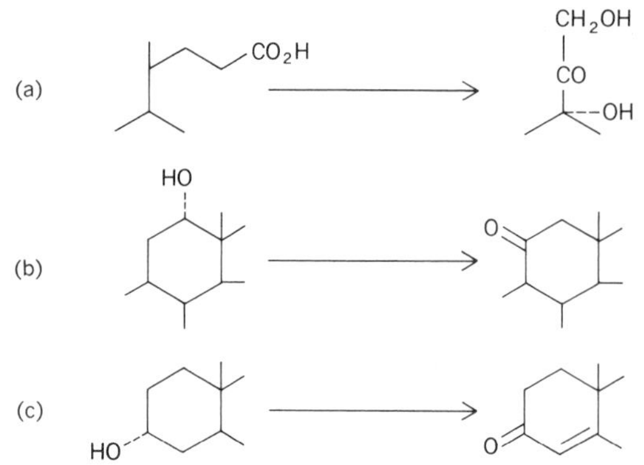

Fig. 2. Three synthetic operations in converting desoxycholic acid into cortisone. (a) Conversion of the bile acid side chain to the dihydroxyacetone side chain. (b) Shifting of a ring hydroxyl to the adjacent position with conversion to a ketone. (c) Conversion of the other ring hydroxyl to an unsaturated ketone.

was obtained the first time through. Improvements were necessary in order to make a practical route for reasonable clinical quantities, and between 1945 and 1948 these were forthcoming. Nevertheless, when introduced in 1949, the process was the longest ever to be carried out in a factory.

For this reason and also because the supply of cattle bile was limited, an alternative synthesis commencing with raw materials derivable from coal, air, lime, and water—available in unlimited quantities—was initiated in 1949 by Sarett in collaboration with G. E. Arth, R. E. Beyler, R. L. Lukes, G. I. Poos, and W. F. Johns. This work required only 18 steps and was completed in 1952 (Fig. 3).

Son of a professor of speech, poet, and woodsman, Sarett grew up in Wisconsin in the small lumbering town of Laona. He was influenced to take up chemistry at an early age through the gift of a beginner's chemistry set. He received

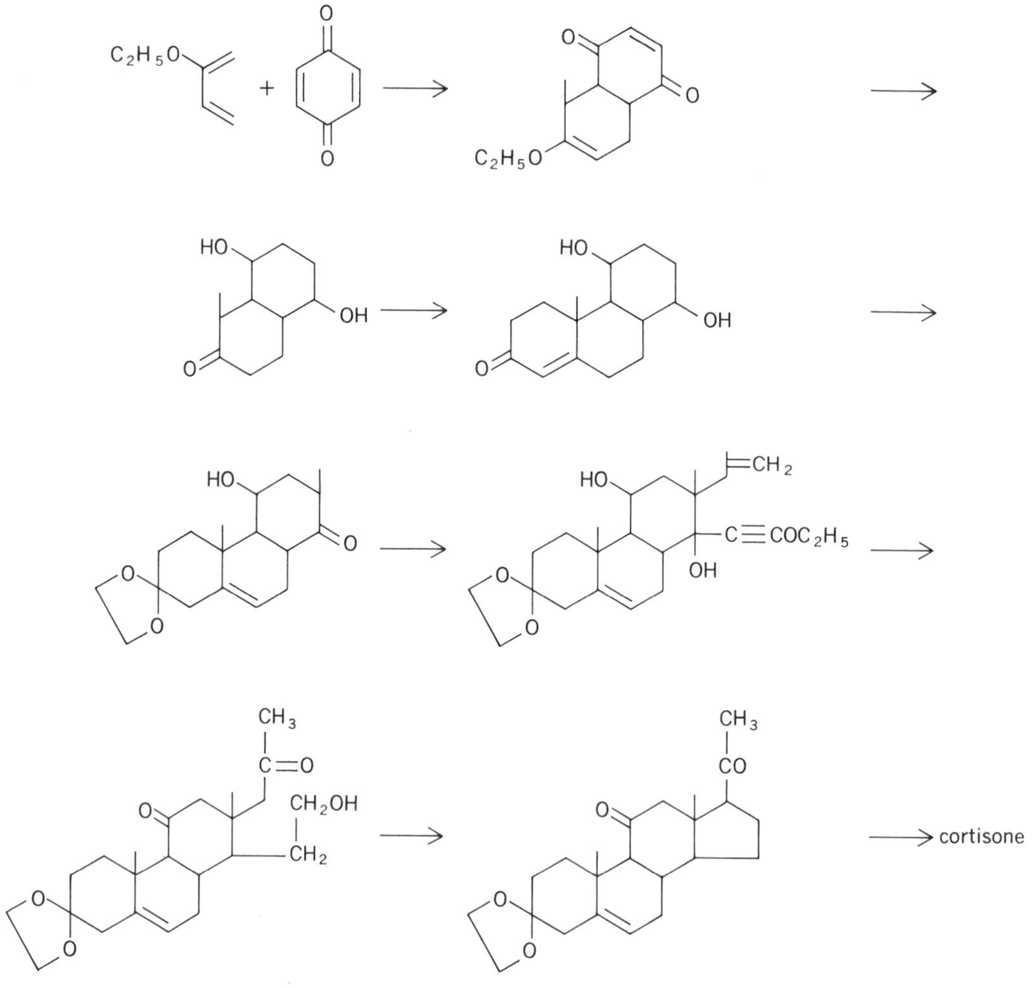

Fig. 3. Cortisone manufacturing process using raw materials derived from coal, air, lime, and water.

Each arrow represents several of the 18 chemical steps which are involved.

his B.S. in 1939 from Northwestern University and his Ph.D. from Princeton in 1942. His association with the Merck Research Laboratories began in 1942 as a research chemist and led to a succession of positions including: director, Department of Synthetic Chemistry (1953); executive director, Fundamental Research Division (1963); and vice-president, Basic Research Division (1966). He collaborated on approximately 100 technical papers and patents.

For background information *see* ADRENAL CORTEX STEROID; ORGANIC CHEMICAL SYNTHESIS; STEREOCHEMISTRY in the McGraw-Hill Encyclopedia of Science and Technology.   □

★ SCHMIDT-NIELSEN, Knut

American physiologist
Born Sept. 24, 1915, Trondheim, Norway

IN MANY respects Schmidt-Nielsen's approach to physiology was guided by considerations of the relation between an animal and its environment, and especially of the specific or unusual demands that extreme environmental conditions place on physiological mechanisms. This approach led to many investigations of animals that live in extreme or stressful environments where a certain physiological response is often particularly well developed, thereby giving a clear understanding of its adaptive importance.

In the late 1940s Schmidt-Nielsen started investigations of kangaroo rats and other desert rodents that were said to live on completely dry food and never to drink water. A careful study of all avenues of water loss (evaporation and urine and feces excretion) led to the conclusion that kangaroo rats can indeed meet all their water requirements with an extremely meager water supply, the major part of which comes from the oxidation of their food. Schmidt-Nielsen pointed out that this oxidation or metabolic water is formed in the same relative quantities in all animals and that only an extreme economy of water output enables an animal to live without an intake of free water.

The detailed account of the water balance of the kangaroo rat led to a number of related studies. The ability of the kangaroo rat to produce an extremely concentrated urine led to further studies in renal physiology. The finding that the water loss through respiration is lower than predicted led to the observation that the nasal passages of the kangaroo rat have a temperature considerably below that of the body. As a consequence, the expired air is cooler than expected and therefore contains less water vapor, thus reducing water loss. The mechanism responsible for the cool passageways is a countercurrent system. The common principles for countercurrent heat exchangers apply, but in the kangaroo rat the usual spatial separation of two streams is replaced by a temporal separation in a single passageway.

Schmidt-Nielsen's interest in desert rodents led to studies of other desert animals, including the camel. The camel's large body size drastically changes some of the relationships between it and its surroundings. For example, the camel cannot escape the heat of the desert day by burrowing. Thus evaporation of water must be used to prevent a fatal rise of body temperature. A main finding in these studies was that the camel does not store water but relies on the water resources of its body, which has a water content similar to that of other mammals. But the camel can tolerate a greater dehydration of its body than most other mammals, although it must eventually replenish this lost water by drinking. The two main mechanisms by which the camel can reduce water loss are by a limited rise in body temperature and by a relatively heavy fur which insulates it from the desert heat.

Another extreme environment which interested Schmidt-Nielsen and his collaborators was the sea which, because of its high salt content, imposes heavy restrictions on the drinking of seawater by marine animals. He demonstrated in studies of marine birds and reptiles that they can drink seawater with impunity although their kidneys are unable to excrete the large amounts of ingested salt. This led to his surprising discovery in 1957 that a gland, located in the head and known as the nasal gland, secretes an extremely concentrated solution of sodium chloride and by far surpasses the kidney in salt excretion.

Numerous other animals have been studied from the viewpoint of the physiological mechanisms which permit them to live in stressful environments. These researches led to expeditions to areas such as the Sahara desert and central Australia (studies of camels), the Near

East and South Africa (desert birds), and the North American deserts (desert rodents).

Schmidt-Nielsen was educated in Norway, where after a brief beginning in engineering (mining and metallurgy) he studied zoology and chemistry at the University of Oslo. He continued his advanced work in microchemistry at the Carlsberg Laboratory and in physiology at the Rockefeller Institute of the University of Copenhagen. He obtained his Mag.Scient. (1940) and Dr.Phil. (1946) from the University of Copenhagen. He moved to the United States in 1946, where he worked as research associate at Swarthmore College (1946–48) and Stanford University (1948–49) and as assistant professor at the University of Cincinnati (1949–52). In 1952 he went to Duke University, becoming in 1963 James B. Duke Professor of Physiology in the department of zoology. He was elected to both the National Academy of Sciences and the American Academy of Arts and Sciences in 1963.

Schmidt-Nielsen wrote *Animal Physiology* (1960; 2d ed. 1964), published in 10 languages, and *Desert Animals: Physiological Problems of Heat and Water* (1964).

For background information *see* ECOLOGY; ENVIRONMENT; MACROEVOLUTION; SALT GLAND in the McGraw-Hill Encyclopedia of Science and Technology.   □

★ SCHMITT, Francis Otto

American molecular biologist
Born Nov. 23, 1903, Saint Louis, Mo., U.S.A.

THE INVESTIGATION of the structure and the function of living systems at or near the molecular level was a career-long concern of Schmitt. His utilization of polarizational optics and x-ray diffraction in the 15-year period prior to World War II helped lay the basis for the modern development which came to be known as "molecular biology."

Called in 1941 from the chairmanship of the zoology department of Washington University, Saint Louis, to structure and head MIT's effort in molecular biology, Schmitt developed at Cambridge, Mass., the first center for electron microscopy in the United States. Many of the investigators trained in his MIT laboratories during and after the war later became international leaders in the study of ultrastructure.

Wartime studies of wound healing led to a deep and abiding interest by Schmitt and many of his group in the principal protein of the body, collagen. Discovery in 1942 of the 700-A axial repeat and intraperiod structure, by means of the electron microscope, initiated the finding in 1955 of the true molecular unit of collagen with length four times the axial repeat, or 2800 A; Schmitt called this molecular unit "tropocollagen" and, with his colleagues J. Gross, J. H. Highberger, and A. J. Hodge, showed how tropocollagen molecules are interbonded to form collagen. The role of interbonding of peptide chains ("telopeptides") at the ends and along the sides of tropocollagen was also demonstrated. Immunological studies, with A. L. Rubin and P. F. Davison, revealed antigenicity in the peptide appendages rather than in the collagen molecule proper; the role of such peptides in the "collagen and autoimmune diseases" was therefore opened up for study.

From his early college days Schmitt was interested in contractility as a fundamental property of living systems. His discovery of ciliary structure, published when he was an undergraduate, was confirmed by electron microscopy three decades later. Early postwar electron-microscope and x-ray studies of striated muscle were conducted in Schmitt's laboratory, where in 1953 H. Huxley and J. Hanson discovered the sliding-filament mechanism of muscle contraction. The determination by Schmitt, along with C. E. Hall and M. A. Jakus, of the structure of molluscan adductor muscle and the isolation and characterization of its protein, which he named "paromyosin," was facilitated by the use of "electron' stains" to reveal protein fine structure. Schmitt initiated extensive studies of heteropolar compounds of high electron density, such as phosphotungstic acid, phosphomolybdic acid, and uranyl phosphotungstate, for the positive staining of specific groups (acidic or basic) in proteins.

During his graduate training (1924–27) under Erlanger, Gasser, Bishop, and Ranson at Washington University Medical School, Schmitt developed an interest in neurological problems which was to be a determinative factor for his entire scientific career. Surmising that nerve action potentials result from processes occurring in their interfacial films, he made empirical studies of film models in the laboratory of G. N.

Lewis of the University of California. Limited success in producing propagation of an electrical wave in a rough film model caused Schmitt to make a detailed study of monomolecular films in the laboratories of J. C. Drummond, University College, London, in 1928 and of N. K. Adam, Sheffield University. After a year of study under Otto Warburg and O. F. Meyerhof in Berlin-Dahlem in 1928–29, Schmitt, then assistant professor of zoology at Washington University, began a series of biochemical studies of nerve, including redox mechanisms and substrate utilization related to excitability. Optical polarization and x-ray diffraction studies established the lipoprotein layered structure of nerve myelin, subsequently confirmed by electron microscopy. With J. Z. Young, Schmitt introduced the squid giant fiber to American neurophysiology, and he and his collaborators over the years characterized the chemical constituents of axoplasm, including the organic electrolytes (full acid-base constituents, established in 1959 by G. G. J. Deffner and R. E. Hafter) and the fibrous neurofilament protein. With P. F. Davison, Schmitt purified the latter, identified its amino acids, and prepared antibodies against it as a possible aid in clarifying the protein's function. With F. Huneeus-Cox, Schmitt conducted axonal perfusion studies, which led to the idea that excitability, mediated by ion gating, depends on fast conformational changes of a membrane protein.

Impressed by the need for improvement of interdisciplinary communication in the neurosciences, Schmitt in 1962 founded an interuniversity, international organization called the Neurosciences Research Program (NRP), in which mathematicians, physicists, chemists, and engineers join experts in various biomedical sciences dealing with nerve, brain, and behavior to investigate the physicochemical and biophysical bases of mental processes such as long-term memory and learning. With a "faculty" of 34 distinguished associates and a strong center staff, the NRP, sponsored by MIT, schedules work sessions on conceptual issues of central importance; their consensus is published in the *Neurosciences Research Program Bulletin*.

Schmitt received an A.B. in 1924 and a Ph.D. in 1927 at Washington University, where he was assistant professor of zoology in 1929–34, associate professor in 1934–38, professor in 1938–40, and department head in 1939–41. He was professor of biology and department head at MIT during 1942–55, institute professor from 1955, and organizer and chairman of NRP since its founding in 1962. Besides several honorary degrees, Schmitt received the Lasker Award of the American Public Health Association in 1956 and the T. Duckett Jones Memorial Award of the Helen Hay Whitney Foundation in 1963. He was elected to the American Academy of Arts and Sciences in 1941 and to the National Academy of Sciences in 1948.

Schmitt edited *Macromolecular Specificity and Biological Memory* (1962) and the first volume of *Neurosciences Research Symposium Summaries*, with Theodore Melnechuk (1966).

For background information *see* MICROSCOPE, ELECTRON; MOLECULAR BIOPHYSICS; NUCLEIC ACID; PROTEIN in the McGraw-Hill Encyclopedia of Science and Technology. □

★ SCHWARZENBACH, Gerold Karl

Swiss chemist
Born Mar. 15, 1904, Horgen, Switzerland

BECAUSE OF his discovery of the complexometric titration method, the name of Schwarzenbach is known to many analytical chemists. Almost every metal can be determined by this extremely simple method: To the solution containing the metal to be determined, a suitable indicator is added and then the titrant, containing a complexing agent, until the indicator changes color. The analogy with the process of neutralization of an acid with a base is striking and, indeed, the complexometric method was the result of Schwarzenbach's earlier studies revealing the similarity in nature of the formation of metal complexes on the one hand and conventional acid-base neutralization on the other.

In ancient times acids were detected by their action on the color of certain dyes, natural pigments of flowers and berries, and by their catalytic properties. During the 18th century it was believed that all acidic substances contained the same acidic principle, later identified with a certain element. Thus Lavoisier believed that all acids contained oxygen (from Greek *oxys*, acid). For almost a hundred years a certain form of hydrogen was thought to be responsible for the acidic phenomena: active hydrogen (J. V. Liebig,

1836), the hydrogen ion (S. Arrhenius, 1887), and the proton (J. N. Brönsted, 1928). In 1938 G. N. Lewis pointed out that certain substances not containing hydrogen, such as boron trichloride, tin tetrachloride, and silver perchlorate, dissolved in ether or benzene, also reacted with acid-base indicators, were sharply neutralized with amines or other bases, and had catalytic properties. According to Lewis, neutralization always consists in completing the stable number of electron pairs that is characteristic of the atom to which the acid properties are due; furthermore, this atom need not be hydrogen and as a matter of fact is boron, tin, and silver as in the compounds mentioned. Compounds which owe their acidity to an atom other than hydrogen are called Lewis acids today, as distinguished from proton acids.

Aqueous solutions of simple metal salts, such as chlorides, nitrates, or sulfates, contain the metal in the form of aquo ions, for example, $[Mg(H_2O)_6]^{2+}$, $[Hg(H_2O)_6]^{2+}$, $[Cu(H_2O)_4]^{2+}$, $[Al(H_2O)_6]^{3+}$, $[Fe(H_2O)_6]^{3+}$, $[Th(H_2O)_8]^{4+}$, and so forth. The question arises whether these species may be called Lewis acids like the silver perchlorate in benzene mentioned above. Their chemical properties indicate that indeed a reaction takes place with common bases, such as alkali hydroxides or ammonia. However, these processes have by no means the appearance of a neutralization. With alkali hydroxide sparingly soluble precipitates are obtained. The same happens by adding ammonia, and the reaction is different sometimes only because the precipitated metal hydroxide may again dissolve in an excess of the reagent, as is the case when ammonia is added to the aquo ions of mercury and copper. No indicators were known which could serve to follow these processes before Schwarzenbach's papers appeared during 1945–1955. The usual acid-base indicators respond only on the pH of the metal-containing solutions, which of course increases when a base is added. However, the pH rise is not abrupt but gradual, and therefore the process does not look like a neutralization and cannot be used as a basis for titration. Thus metal ions in aqueous solutions do not behave like the hydrogen ion, which can be titrated sharply with OH^- ions or with ammonia. By applying the theoretical definition given by G. N. Lewis, the answer to the posed question is not unequivocal. Within the ammonia complexes formed with mercury and copper, $[Hg(NH_3)_4]^{2+}$, $[Cu(NH_3)_4]^{2+}$, the molecules NH_3 probably are attached to the metal by electron pair bonds, and it may be maintained that the metal atoms have completed or stabilized their electron shells. This process is much less likely to have happened, however, during the precipitation of the hydroxides of magnesium, aluminum, iron, and thorium, which may be regarded as ionic compounds.

Schwarzenbach demonstrated that all metal ions in aqueous solution can show the typical phenomena of neutralization if suitable indicators and bases are used. It is by no means necessary that covalent bonds be formed during these processes, and whether a stable number of electron pairs is gained or not (a question which is usually very difficult to answer) is therefore irrelevant. What is known reliably is the fact that the oxygen atoms of coordinated H_2O of the aquo ions are replaced by atoms of other ligands during the reaction. According to Schwarzenbach, the aqueous hydrogen ions differ from aqueous metal cations not in principle, but in degree: The hydrogen ion has just one single coordination site, and the ligands bonded by it are usually held very firmly; the metal cations, on the other hand, have several coordination sites—the most frequent numbers being 4 and 6—and the ligands bound by these sites are held much less tightly. Ammonia, for instance, forms with a hydrogen ion the stable ammonium ion NH_4^+ and with the copper ion the series of complexes $[Cu(NH_3)_x(OH_2)_{4-x}]^{2+}$, which are species of much smaller stability in comparison to NH_4^+. This difference gives rise to reactions of different aspects.

As Schwarzenbach demonstrated, the reaction of metal ions can be simplified stoichiometrically by using a reagent which can satisfy several coordination sites simultaneously. Such reagents, called chelating agents, are organic molecules carrying several atoms capable of attachment to the metal. Instead of four individual ammonia molecules, for instance, the copper ion is offered a tetramine molecule which is endowed with four basic nitrogen atoms. The copper ion needs just one single molecule of such a quadridentate chelating agent. Not only is the stoichiometry simplified by chelation, but also a large stability increase is gained which renders the reaction with the typical aspect of a true neutralization.

Schwarzenbach demonstrated the important effects of chelation convincingly. In the complexometric titration procedures not only the titrants but also the indicators are chelating ligands. Chelating agents are also used in analytical chemistry for metal extraction, for metal masking, and as reagents for gravimetric and photometric determinations. Some chelating agents are used in industry, and metal chelation is important also in living cells.

Schwarzenbach graduated in 1928 in analytical chemistry from the Swiss Federal Institute of Technology (ETH), Zurich. He then went to Manchester and London for further studies in organic chemistry with Sir Robert Robinson. On his return from England in 1931, he became lecturer and in 1948 full professor of analytical chemistry at the University of Zurich. In 1955 he was elected to the chair of general and inorganic chemistry at ETH. He was elected a foreign member of the American Academy of Arts and Sciences in 1962.

Schwarzenbach wrote *Lehrbuch für Allgemeine und Anorganische Chemie* (1941; 4th ed. 1950) and *Die komplexometrische Titration* (1955; 5th ed. 1965). He was a coauthor of *Stability Constants of Metal-ion Complexes* (2 vols., 1957).

For background information *see* ACID AND BASE; ANALYTICAL CHEMISTRY; COORDINATION CHEMISTRY; STOICHIOMETRY; TITRATION in the McGraw-Hill Encyclopedia of Science and Technology. □

★ SEAMANS, Robert Channing, Jr.

American physicist
Born Oct. 30, 1918, Salem, Mass., U.S.A.

During World War II and up to 1955, Seamans worked out principles for automatic control equipment that engineers have been using ever since. He also made a series of guidance systems that were prototypes of much high-performance equipment built subsequently. This automatic equipment started the development leading to homing systems for airborne targets, control systems for ballistic missiles, and ultimately stabilization systems for space vehicles.

When he first arrived at the Massachusetts Institute of Technology as a first-year graduate student, Seamans was not even clear about the nature of the field of advanced instrumentation. His teacher C. Stark Draper brought the subject to life. It was in Draper's classes that Seamans first saw the relationship between his college work and a professional career in engineering. At the time of World War II, however, aerospace technology was far back along the road of development. There was, among other needs, an immediate and urgent requirement for advanced instrumentation for flight and fire control. Seamans, who had completed all but the thesis for his master's degree in two semesters, soon found

himself immersed in practical experimental work. In the summer of 1941 he became an instructor and research assistant, experimenting with equipment for testing aircraft engine vibrations.

Navy and Air Force contracts held by the MIT Instrumentation Laboratory provided Seamans with further experience. He worked with Draper on antiaircraft fire control for automatic firing of the Navy's 40-mm and 3- and 5-in. guns. Then he was given his own project of installing target director acquisition gear for the Mark 63 antiaircraft fire control director on the aircraft carrier *Bon Homme Richard*. The equipment was tied in with the vessel's central control and was designed to acquire targets automatically by other than visual means. He repeated the job on the destroyer *Purdy*.

Seamans chose the problems of high-performance aircraft—particularly control in combat maneuvers—for his doctorate. His approach to the problems stressed the human factor in the man-machine relationship. His view was that men must select and supervise the aircraft's mission and then make command decisions when new information becomes available. Seamans felt men can exercise judgment more effectively when they are relieved of routine operations, especially of actions involving fatigue and requiring manual dexterity. The basic problem in this field arose from insufficient knowledge of aircraft dynamics, of its control equipment, and of the pilot himself. With the trend then developing toward supersonic speeds, violent changes in aerodynamic loading were being injected into flight maneuvers. This caused significant changes in static stability as the center of pressure on the aircraft shifted with Mach number. There was not sufficient computer capability in the United States at that time to carry out complete mathematical simulation of an automatically controlled aircraft, even if the dynamic relationships had been quantified. This led Seamans to make a detailed analysis of aircraft dynamics and to work out control equipment problems.

His experiments involved dynamic testing of several aircraft, using elevators, ailerons, and rudder individually to induce motion. Similar tests were run on all other control equipment. Although the pilot himself was not subjected to dynamic tests, Seamans measured his responses in actual flight. This work showed that all elements of the aircraft, excluding the pilot, could be represented mathematically. The analysis and synthesis procedures of Seamans were directly applicable in developing automatic tracking interceptor aircraft, automatic flight control for commercial aircraft under maneuvering conditions, guided homing missiles, and intercontinental ballistic missile systems.

Immediately after the war Seamans became

actively engaged in Project Meteor, the Navy's guided missile work. The objective was to develop technology of importance to missile systems. To provide focus for this effort, a breadboard air-to-air homing missile was built that could be tested in flight. The dynamic problems in this project were directly related to those Seamans had analyzed for the earlier aircraft control effort. But there were many other areas of investigation: for example, the determination of suitable transonic and supersonic aerodynamic theory; the development of fast-acting, high-performance hydraulic actuators; the miniaturization of electronics; and the development of a guidance system that would have no moving parts and could continually track a moving target. His earlier work on aircraft control systems was applied directly to the missile control problem, with proper scaling for the difference between aircraft dynamics and missile dynamics.

A primary lesson learned from these two projects of aircraft and missile control involved a proper balance between theory and practice. In conducting advanced developments, it was necessary to have sufficient ground-based laboratory and flight test effort so that theory and practice could be continually cross-checked. Without suitable theory the design of complex equipment became merely trial and error that seldom converged on a solution. And without suitable testing of both the elements of the system and the total system, there was no assurance that the theory would, in fact, permit implementation.

Seamans earned a B.S. in engineering science at Harvard University in 1939. After beginning graduate work at Harvard, he transferred to the Massachusetts Institute of Technology in 1940. There he received an M.S. in aeronautical engineering in 1942 and an Sc.D. in instrumentation in 1951. He stayed at MIT as a teacher and project manager for 14 years, devoting most of his professional life to problems of aerospace. Seamans left MIT in 1955 to head the Airborne Systems Laboratory of the Radio Corporation of America (RCA) in the greater Boston area. He had assisted in setting up the new facility while teaching and heading MIT's Flight Control Laboratory. In 1958 RCA appointed Seamans chief engineer of its Missile Electronics and Control Division. In 1960 he joined the National Aeronautics and Space Administration (NASA) as associate administrator. Seamans received the Naval Ordnance Development Award (1945), the Lawrence Sperry Award of the American Institute for Aeronautics and Astronautics (1951), the NASA Distinguished Service Award (1965), and the Godfrey L. Cabot Aviation Award (1965). He was elected to the American Academy of Arts and Sciences in 1964.

For background information *see* AERODYNAMICS; GUIDED MISSILE; NAVIGATION SYSTEMS, ELECTRONIC in the McGraw-Hill Encyclopedia of Science and Technology.   □

★ SEARS, Ernest Robert

American geneticist
Born Oct. 15, 1910, Bethel, Ore., U.S.A.

BECAUSE COMMON wheat is a hexaploid, whose mostly triplicated genes tend to mask each other, geneticists made little progress with it during the 40 years following the rediscovery of Mendel's laws. Sears took advantage of the polyploidy of wheat to obtain aberrations not tolerated by diploids—aberrations that could then be used in genetic work. Starting in 1938, he had by 1954 obtained and described all the possible nullisomics (which have only 20 instead of the normal 21 chromosome pairs, that is, they are $2n-2$), monosomics ($2n-1$), trisomics ($2n+1$), and tetrasomics ($2n+2$).

These aneuploids made it possible to vary the dosage of each chromosome from 0 to 4 and thereby to obtain much useful information about the genes each carried. Genes in other varieties of wheat were easily located by observation of the second generation from crosses with the monosomics. Substitutions of individual chromosomes from one variety to another were made by means of crosses and backcrosses to nullisomics or monosomics, and this made possible the detailed analysis of one chromosome at a time on a standard background. Telocentric chromosomes were shown to be very useful for determination of distances of genes from centromeres. Thus wheat, the most important plant in the Western world, became at last a rewarding organism for genetic study.

It had long been known that the 21 chromosomes of common wheat belong to three groups, or "genomes," of seven chromosomes each. Each genome was assumed to have been contributed by a different diploid ancestor, one of which was diploid wheat, whose genome is designated A. The genome known as D was positively identified by E. S. McFadden and Sears in 1944. They crossed a tetraploid wheat (genomes A + B) with a wild relative, *Triticum tauschii* (formerly *Aegilops squarrosa*), and doubled the chromosome number. The resulting hexaploid was practically identical with existing types of hexaploid wheat.

From the fact that at least the A and D genomes had come from closely related species, whose chromosomes paired rather freely at the diploid level, it appeared that relationships might be found between at least some of the wheat chromosomes from different genomes. Additional support for this idea came from the finding that certain nullisomics, which differ strikingly from normal, resemble each other rather closely. By combining nullisomes with the appropriate tetrasomes, Sears was able to place the 21 chromosomes into seven groups of three, the members of each group being related, or homeologous. Some homeologs were found to be very closely related genetically and others less so, but every tetrasome compensated to some extent for the two homeologous nullisomes. Through crosses with diploid and tetraploid wheats, M. Okamoto and Sears determined which seven chromosomes come from each diploid ancestor.

The discovery of the close genetic relationship between corresponding chromosomes derived from different ancestral diploids gave new urgency to the question of why these chromosomes do not pair, even in haploids, where there are no homeologs to interfere. The answer was obtained independently by Okamoto in Sears's laboratory and by R. Riley in England. There is a gene (or genes) on one chromosome (5B) that suppresses pairing of homeologs, thereby causing wheat to behave cytologically like a diploid rather than the near autopolyploid it really is. Genetic suppression of homeologous pairing had long been suspected of being one means by which polyploids attain diploid-like chromosome behavior and the resultant fertility and stability needed for establishing themselves. Its discovery in wheat stimulated a search for similar regulation of pairing in other polyploids.

With homeologous pairing shown to be genetically suppressed in polyploid wheat, it was possible to accept the conclusion previously reached by P. Sarkar and G. L. Stebbins that the B genome had been derived from the very closely related *T. speltoides* (formerly *A. speltoides*) or one of its near relatives. Thus the source of all three genomes was finally established.

Another wild diploid species, *T. umbellulatum* (formerly *A. umbellulata*), was known to be highly resistant to leaf rust, one of the most destructive diseases of wheat; but no one had been able to cross *T. umbellulatum* with hexaploid wheat. Sears crossed it with tetraploid wheat and rendered it fertile by inducing chromosome doubling with the chemical colchicine. A cross and two backcrosses to hexaploid wheat gave rise to a resistant plant with a single added *umbellulatum* chromosome. Since the foreign chromosome did not pair with any of the wheat chromosomes, plants carrying it were x-rayed in order to break the extra chromosome and cause exchange of segments with wheat chromosomes. Following one such exchange, a mostly wheat chromosome was obtained that carried resistance but had little or no deleterious effect, even when homozygous. For this work, carried out during a period of 12 years and published in 1956, Sears received in 1958 the Hoblitzelle Award for research in sciences basic to agriculture. The method has since been used by several other investigators for transferring desirable characters to wheat from wild relatives.

Raised on a farm in western Oregon, Sears received a B.S. in agriculture from Oregon State College in 1932. His graduate work (A.M., 1934; Ph.D., 1936) was completed under E. M. East at the Bussey Institution of Harvard University. He then joined L. J. Stadler's genetics group at the University of Missouri as a research geneticist of the U.S. Department of Agriculture. Except for 6 months in Germany in 1958 on a Fulbright fellowship, he remained at Missouri. He was elected to the American Academy of Arts and Sciences in 1953 and to the National Academy of Sciences in 1964.

For background information *see* CHROMOSOME; GENE ACTION; POLYPLOIDY; WHEAT in the McGraw-Hill Encyclopedia of Science and Technology.   □

★ SEARS, Paul Bigelow

American ecologist
Born Dec. 17, 1891, Bucyrus, Ohio, U.S.A.

ALONG WITH early research on morphogenesis and pollen cytology, Sears became interested in the history of vegetation and its relation to man. His reconstruction of the vegetation of Ohio as it was at the time of white settlement led to a concern to explain the presence of prairie enclaves within that predominantly forested state. He began to apply the Swedish technique of fossil pollen statistics, publishing some of the earliest American reports in this field. These papers established the general sequence of late- and postglacial changes in vegetation and climate in the North Central States. They also showed the correspondence of these changes to

those in Europe and indicated their relation to American Indian cultures. Included in the sequence was a postglacial interval warmer and dryer than the present climate, as had been suggested by Gleason to explain the presence of western plants as relicts within the present area of forest climate.

Recognizing the importance of widely distributed studies of paleoecology, Sears also undertook, by means of conferences and the *Pollen and Spore Circular*, to encourage interest in pollen statistics. Meanwhile, his studies and those of his students expanded to include material, from the Far West to New England and from the Lake States to Mexico, showing the effects of glacial and postglacial climatic changes far beyond the limits of continental glaciation.

In Mexico he was invited by Pablo Martinez del Rio to seek an explanation of the shift of the Late Archaic culture, about 500 B.C., to higher ground at Teotihuacan and the return of activity to the lower part of the Basin of Mexico about A.D. 900. With the aid of Mexican colleagues, he was able to correlate archeological material with pollen profiles from the basin, showing that the basin lakes reached low level about 500 B.C., following a prolonged period of dry climate. Because the economy had been intimately associated with the basin lakes, an upward shift to other sources of water appears to have been necessary. With the recovery of lake levels during the early Christian era, the lower basin once more became the cultural center. Sears was assisted in the completion of this work by colleagues at Oberlin College.

Meanwhile, he had been engaged in field studies in the grassland province, with special attention to the effect of climatic fluctuations on vegetation, soil, and human cultural activity. In company with Warren Thornthwaite, whose early work on climates was then in progress, Sears explored the area of severe dust storms resulting from the prolonged drought and agricultural exploitation of the 1930s. Convinced at this point that there was a critical need for better public understanding of the extent and causes of environmental deterioration, he began the writing, lecturing, and consulting which subsequently occupied much of his time.

In his first book, *Deserts on the March* (1935; 3d ed. 1959), Sears reviewed the effects of exploitive land use in causing soil erosion, air and water pollution, and environmental depletion. He also emphasized the importance of applied ecology. In a second book, *This Is Our World* (1937), he called attention to the critical role of culture patterns in land use and management. Continuing this theme in subsequent books and journal articles, he insisted upon the importance of intangibles—values and sanctions —in determining treatment of the environment and establishing a rational population balance. Without deprecating the need for generously supported research of high quality, he was concerned over the failure to apply, in the light of historical experience, a great deal of the knowledge already gained.

Following undergraduate work in zoology (B.S., 1913) and economics (B.A., 1914) at Ohio Wesleyan University, Sears began the study of botany at the University of Nebraska under the ecologist Raymond J. Pool and Charles E. Bessey, a student of Asa Gray. A term as instructor at Ohio State, interrupted by military service, gave Sears the benefit of contact with John H. Schaffner and Edgar N. Transeau. He then moved to the University of Nebraska (A.M., 1915) and received a Ph.D. in botany (1922) at the University of Chicago, where Henry Cowles furthered Sears's interest in ecology. He also worked for a brief period in England with geneticist William Bateson. From Nebraska Sears was called to the University of Oklahoma as chairman of the botany department, then to Oberlin College in a similar capacity. In 1950 he was invited to Yale as chairman of a graduate program in conservation; he retired 10 years later but retained facilities for research and writing. Recipient of a Merit Award of the Botanical Society of America in 1956, he was elected to the American Academy of Arts and Sciences in 1954 and was president of the American Association for the Advancement of Science in 1956.

In addition to the books already mentioned, Sears wrote *Life and Environment* (1939), *Who Are These Americans?* (1939; paper 1940), *Charles Darwin* (1950), and *The Living Landscape* (1966).

For background information *see* CLIMATIC CHANGE; ECOLOGY; PALEOECOLOGY; PALYNOLOGY in the McGraw-Hill Encyclopedia of Science and Technology.   □

★ SEDOV, Leonid Ivanovich

Soviet physicist
Born Nov. 14, 1907, Rostov-on-Don, Russia

At the start of his scientific activity Sedov was engaged in two-dimensional problems of hydrodynamics and aerodynamics. His first works were a further development of the studies by N. E. Zhukovskii and S. A. Chaplygin and were related to new methods for the qualitative analysis and solution of two-dimensional problems of hydrodynamics with the aid of functions of a complex variable.

During the early 1930s Sedov published a number of papers on the development of a general hydrodynamic theory with rationally formulated statements and solutions to a number of problems. These problems were the impact of solid bodies on water, rapid submersion in water, gliding resistance with special reference to the weight of water, unsteady movement of the airfoils and other bodies in an incompressible liquid, the theory of stream movements during flow around many bodies in problems with doubly connected regions of the velocity field of a liquid, the theory of lattice profile, and other problems.

He developed effective methods for solving two-dimensional problems of hydrodynamics and presented effective formulas of aerohydrodynamic forces for unsteady movements of wings, gliding bodies, and for other cases. Different suggestions were established regarding the nature of the hydrodynamic forces for unsteady movements, and a quantitative evaluation was offered of the influence of the properties of the weight of water on the hydrodynamic resistance during gliding. Sedov formulated and solved the basic problem of gliding on the surface of a heavy liquid, with consideration of the formation of splashing streams at the forward edges of a wetted surface of a gliding profile. In a paper written jointly with M. V. Keldysh, he generalized the Mitchell and Hogner theory of wave resistance of ships for the case of the movement of a vessel in a canal of finite width and depth. Sedov described and analyzed problems of the optimal conditions of gliding, scalar effect during the modeling of the gliding phenomenon, and basic problems of the stability of gliding in water ricochets, and he identified the main parameters and the pertinent mechanisms of the phenomena. This work had significant applications.

The works on the theory of plane-parallel movements of a gas with large subsonic velocities contain studies on the approximate theory of Chaplygin, based on the approximation of the adiabatic curve with a straight line in the pressure-specific volume plane. Sedov refined this approximate formulation and offered a general theory of plane movements of compressible media with random thermodynamic properties. This theory points out the methods of an accurate, effective analytic description, which make it possible to solve the problems of steady movement of a gas and of the circulation flow by a gas around profiles with the aid of functions of a complex variable.

A considerable number of Sedov's works deal with the general theory of the dimension of physical magnitudes, the theory of physical similarity, modeling, and their applications to the theory of turbulence, problems of unidimensional unsteady gas movement, problems of astrophysics, the general theory of gas machines, and many other problems.

In his theory of isotropic turbulence, Sedov presents and analyzes in an accurate manner all possible cases of degeneration, when at different times the turbulent movements of an incompressible liquid are similar.

Sedov developed a general theory of automodel movements in hydrodynamics. In 1945 he published works on the general theory of automodel, unidimensional, unsteady gas movements, in which important types of automodel gas models were found; problems concerning the spherical cylinder, automodel and nonautomodel gas dispersion or focusing in one point, and many other problems were solved. The problem of a strong explosion with plane cylindrical and spherical waves was then solved in a complete and finite form. The laws of the propagation of explosive waves and perturbed fields of velocities, pressure, and density beyond the front of an explosive wave were found.

In succeeding works Sedov applied these theories to cases of the distributions with a variable along the radius of the initial density and with consideration of the detonation phenomena. He took specific problems into account for the simulation of outbursts of novae. In particular, for some initial distributions of the density in gas spheres, he established that there is a possibility of the formation during an explosion of a hollow space which expands from the center of symmetry. He found equilibrium states of gas spheres which are dynamically unstable and can be dispersed by an explosion without any outside cause or liberation of internal energy.

For automodel movements Sedov pointed out methods which are based on considerations of the theory of similitude and which make it possible to find the finite integrals for a complex nonlinear system of differential equations. It is precisely these methods that have made it possible to obtain the solution of the problem of a strong explosion in the finite form and to simplify considerably the solution of other problems in which it is necessary to use numerical methods of calculation.

Beginning in the 1940s a series of works by Sedov appeared dealing with the general theory and different individual problems of the mechanics of a continuous medium. The first works in this field dealt with the introduction of thermodynamic methods and consideration of electrodynamic effects in macroscopic mechanics of a continuous medium and, in particular, the substantiation of the need and methods of introducing into solid-state mechanics new physical-variable parameters for describing the internal degrees of freedom and internal physical mechanisms. It was pointed out that there is a need to identify such parameters in the theory of plasticity with strengthening. In his work of 1948 he developed the theory of the establishment of kinetic equations for nonequilibrium chemical reactions in gas mixtures.

In the field of the theory of symmetry of physical objects, Sedov showed, with V. V. Lokhin, that all finite-points crystal groups and groups of textures can be set, with the aid of tensors, with components that are invariant with respect to these groups. For all the indicated groups very simple systems of tensors were actually established, which set the corresponding groups and can be regarded as arguments in the functional relationships to which the corresponding properties of the symmetry are inherent. Sedov developed a general theory of nonlinear tensor functions from several tensor arguments. He pointed out systems of linearly independent tensors, the linear combination of which with scalar coefficients is any tensor which is a function of the given tensor arguments. He developed a general theory of differentiation of tensors with respect to the scalar argument and pointed out and analyzed the derivatives of the tensors of any rank with respect to the scalar argument.

Sedov substantiated and developed a tensor calculation in which the tensors of any orders are regarded as linear invariant objects in the form of the sum of polyadic products of the vectors of the base with components as coefficients. This point of view turned out to be very useful in applications to the theory of models of continuous media with internal degrees of freedom in the continual theory of dislocations in the nonlinear theory of elasticity with finite deformations and in other problems.

In the nonlinear theory of elasticity he developed a thermodynamic theory with consideration of the finiteness of the deformation and with the presence of internal reversible physicochemical processes.

Sedov developed, with M. E. Eglit, a theory of macroscopic physically nonholonomic models with internal physicochemical processes. A thermodynamic theory of hypoelastic bodies was suggested, and ways were indicated for establishing the connections of the theory of creep and the thermodynamic theories of solid, deformable bodies in the general case for irreversible processes.

In special works he took up various problems of different concepts of ponderomotive forces, ponderomotive moments, and tensor of the pulse energy in the electrodynamics of polarizing magnetizing bodies for models with complicated internal substances.

Within the framework of the general theory of relativity, he established equations of the state of the gravitation field and clarified the existence of two tensors of the pulse energy of the Einstein tensor and of a tensor that differs generally from it, which generalizes the ordinary three-dimensional tensor of internal stresses. He also showed that, in order to keep track of the internal reactions in the gravitation field, it is necessary to introduce tensors of the stresses of the third and fourth order.

In the general theory of models of continuous media, he advanced a new universal basic variation equation, which is founded on the basic physical concepts of energy, external sources of perturbations, and the mechanisms of dissipation. With the aid of this variation principle, he developed a new technique for obtaining invariant equations of movement—processes, equations of state, kinetic equations, and different types of additional conditions (boundary, initial conditions, conditions for discontinuities, and others). Recently Sedov began preparing a course on the mechanics of continuous media.

With the participation of Sedov and under his guidance, different studies have been going on for many years on gas dynamics in the field of hydrodynamic, unsteady movements of bodies with a high velocity in water, on cavitation, and on the general theory of the construction of new models in the mechanics of continuous media.

During recent years Sedov presented papers and participated in different international and national congresses, conferences, and symposiums. In particular, beginning in 1955, he participated actively in the work of the International Astronautic Federation (MAF). He was president of MAF in 1961 and 1962 and a member of the MAF Bureau since 1957.

Sedov received his Ph.D. in 1938 from Moscow State University, where he became a professor, assuming the chair of hydromechanics and direction of the department of mechanics-mathematics. He received several orders and medals from the Soviet Union, including the S. A. Chaplygin Prize for his work on the theory of explosions and the M. V. Lomonosov Prize, first class, for the application of gas dynamics to astrophysics. He was elected a corresponding member in 1947 and an active member in 1953 of the Academy of Sciences of the U.S.S.R. In 1959 he was elected an active member of the International Astronautic Academy. In 1960 he was made an honorary member of the American Academy of Arts and Sciences, in 1965 of the Serbian Academy of Sciences in Belgrade, and in 1966 of the Finnish Technical Academy of Sciences in Helsinki and of the American Institute of Astronautics and Aeronautics. In 1967 he was elected a corresponding member of the Academy of Science in Paris.

Sedov wrote *Two-dimensional Problems in Hydrodynamics and Aerodynamics* (3d ed. Eng. transl. 1965), *Introduction to the Mechanics of a Continuous Medium* (English transl. 1965), and *Similarity and Dimensional Methods in Mechanics* (English transl. 1959). He was editor in chief of the journal *Cosmic Studies* of the Academy of Sciences of the U.S.S.R. and deputy editor in chief of the *DAN SSSR*.

For background information *see* AERODYNAMICS; CALCULUS OF TENSORS; EXPLOSION; HYDRODYNAMICS; ISOTROPY in the McGraw-Hill Encyclopedia of Science and Technology.   □

★ SEITZ, Frederick

American physicist
Born July 4, 1911, San Francisco, Calif., U.S.A.

SEITZ STARTED his career in theoretical physics during the early 1930s. At that time classical wave mechanics had just been consolidated into a rationally consistent framework and was being applied to unraveling a host of perplexing problems related to the nature of matter and radiation. His undergraduate years were spent at Stanford University and the California Institute of Technology, where he was influenced by such men as David Webster, William Houston, and William Hansen, the inventor of the klystron.

As a graduate student at Princeton, under E. U. Condon and E. P. Wigner, Seitz became interested in the properties of the solid or crystalline state of matter and participated in research that helped to open this area for rich exploitation within the growing framework of quantum mechanics. With Condon, he formulated the principles of crystal symmetry in matrix form. Working with Wigner, he contributed one of the first quantitative treatments of the behavior of the electrons in a real metal—an analysis of the properties of the electrons in metallic sodium that has remained a classic in solid-state physics.

The years Seitz spent at Princeton (1932–35) were momentous ones for American science and for the development of science at Princeton. Because of Hitler, many brilliant scientists left Central Europe, and Princeton, with the university and the newly established Institute for Advanced Study, became a haven for such refugees. As a student, Seitz associated with such men as John von Neumann, Herman Weyl, Rudolph Ladenburg, and Albert Einstein.

Following graduate work, he went first to the University of Rochester, where L. A. DuBridge was building a department, and then to the General Electric Laboratory in Schenectady, where Seitz was involved in a variety of aspects of solid-state research, particularly crystal luminescence, which had become important for luninescent lamps and television screens. At that time the research laboratory at Schenectady was led by such scientists as W. D. Coolidge, Albert W. Hull, Irving Langmuir, and Saul Dushman, men who had had brilliant careers in the evolution of atomic and quantum physics and chemistry, as well as research in many applied problems.

During his years (1937–39) with the General Electric Co., Seitz and Kenneth Kingdon were interested in the potential applications of nuclear physics and urged the company to pursue

research in neutron physics—which was then in its ascendance—in the hope of finding practical applications. In fact, at that time, several years prior to the discovery of fission, Leo Szilard was attempting to persuade industry in the United

States, and the General Electric Co. in particular, to look into the practical possibilities of the field now known as controlled fusion. The depression years, however, were not good ones for such frontier endeavors. It took the discovery of fission in 1939 and the stimulation of World War II to unlock the potentialities of American industry. During this period Seitz wrote *The Modern Theory of Solids* (1940), which attempted to bring the knowledge of the field in the late 1930s into a single monograph. The book had a substantial influence on a generation of solid-state physicists, helping to stimulate the growth of the field.

During the war years, which he spent at the University of Pennsylvania and the Carnegie Institute of Technology, Seitz became deeply involved in military research. He spent the first part of the war on problems of ballistics and armor penetration, a second period on the development of radar components, particularly silicon diodes and radar screens, and a third on the development of fission reactors within the Manhattan District, particularly on problems associated with the behavior of materials in nuclear reactors. During 1945 he joined H. P. Robertson, the cosmologist at the California Institute of Technology, in Europe in the formation and operation of the Field Intelligence Agency, Technical, which undertook the coordination of the teams of technical intelligence groups that had moved forward into occupied Europe with the U.S. Army.

One of Seitz's most important contributions during the war was the stimulation of a program to produce chemically pure silicon for use in radar diodes in place of the technical grade used previously. In connection with studies associated with this work, he was the first to interpret the electrical conductivity of the various grades of silicon in terms of intrinsic and impurity components. These steps made it possible to place the use of both silicon and germanium as semiconductors on a relatively scientific basis.

In 1946 he joined Wigner at Oak Ridge in a program designed to accelerate the use of nuclear reactors for civilian purposes, organizing the first reactor school, the Oak Ridge Training Program. The class that year included 35 scientists and engineers from academic, governmental, and industrial organizations, as well as Admiral H. G. Rickover and his group of young technical officers, who were planning to design reactors for Naval purposes. A very large number of the participants are now leaders in reactor development in the United States.

In 1949 Seitz moved to the University of Illinois with the understanding that he might develop a substantial group in solid-state physics. He was soon joined by his graduate school classmate John Bardeen. In the following decade the university became one of the international centers for solid-state physics.

During the Korean War, Seitz joined with colleagues at the university to establish an applications laboratory that focused on problems related to radar and the use of electronic digital computers in control systems. The work of the laboratory on coherent radar provided the basis for many of the present applications of that phase of radar technology. The university had the first operative electronic digital computer on a campus, the ILLIAC, and helped open the road to many developments that are now commonplace.

In 1959 Seitz became science advisor to the North Atlantic Treaty Organization, succeeding Norman Ramsey, the first advisor, and spent 1½ years developing the NATO science program. One of the products of this period was the study "Increasing the Effectiveness of Western Science," carried out by a distinguished group of scientists and engineers from the NATO countries. This was one of the first studies to grapple with the problem of the "technological gap." It was Seitz's opinion, growing out of the NATO experience, that the principal problem facing the nations of western Europe stemmed from their difficulties in cooperating with one another rather than from any superior technical knowledge in the United States. He believed that the technological gap would vanish as soon as western Europe developed adequate institutions, such as the Common Market, to stimulate and foster cooperation among the European nations.

In 1962 Seitz was elected part-time president of the National Academy of Sciences, succeeding Detlev W. Bronk, who had done so much to develop the Academy after the war. Two years later a committee which had been reviewing the advisory role of the Academy reached the conclusion that the Academy would need a full-time president to do justice to the demands placed on it. Although he had recently accepted an appointment as dean of graduate studies and vice-president for research at the University of Illinois, Seitz yielded to the persuasion of members of the Academy who urged him to remain as full-time president for a 6-year term.

The National Academy of Sciences, in many ways unique as a national institution, is a private organization with a federal charter granted in 1863 for the purpose of fostering the orderly development of science and advising the federal government on matters relating to science and engineering. The pressures within the nation that brought about the creation of the Academy stemmed not only from immediate practical problems of the Civil War, but also from the fact that the United States was beginning to emerge as one of the technically advanced societies. An independent academy was needed to muster the best men to give objective guidance to the evolution of the nation's science and engineering.

The need for objective advice is no less important today. The strength of any great nation and the goals to which it aspires depend significantly on access to impartial value judgments which are made outside the structure of governmental authority and on which constructive programs can be based. The Academy, which selects and organizes its membership and thus enjoys an independent relationship to all aspects of science, plays a continuing role in this regard.

Initially the advisory groups were composed primarily of members of the Academy, first 50 and now about 730. In 1916, however, the Academy created the National Research Council as part of its structure in response to President Wilson's request for help in dealing with the scientific and technical problems of World War I. Since that time most of the Academy's advisory committees have been organized within the Research Council and are composed of scientists and engineers from outside as well as inside the elected membership of the Academy. At present about 5000 scientists and engineers, serving without compensation, are on the committees of the National Research Council.

One of the advantages of the chartered role of the Academy lies in the fact that the members, bearing a lifetime responsibility, tend to search continually for deeper understanding of the needs of the nation in their areas of competence. It was the farsighted concern of Academy members that enabled them to sense the need for a National Research Council in World War I, for the Science Advisory Board during the depression, and for the Office of Scientific Research and Development in World War II. The Academy also played a significant role in the discussions that led to the creation of the National Science Foundation in 1950 and the National Aeronautics and Space Administration in 1958.

In 1964 the officers of the National Academy of Sciences, in response to a request from the engineering profession, created a National Academy of Engineering as a counterpart institution. The new Academy is autonomous in the selection of its officers and members and in the conduct of its business. The expectation is that it will broaden and strengthen the participation of the engineering community in the activities of the National Research Council, as well as give added prestige to the fields of engineering.

One of the most active units of the Academy of Sciences is the Committee on Science and Public Policy, established so that the nongovernment scientific community may take a more active part in providing advice to the government on scientific and technological matters affecting society. The committee is frequently called upon by both the executive and legislative branches of the government.

Seitz received his A.B. from Stanford University in 1932 and his Ph.D. in physics from Princeton University in 1934. He became professor of physics at the University of Pennsylvania in 1939, professor and head of the physics department at the Carnegie Institute of Technology in 1942, professor at the University of Illinois in 1949 and head of the physics department there in 1957. In 1959 Seitz was appointed science advisor to NATO and in 1962 was elected president of the National Academy of Sciences. He received the Franklin Medal of the Franklin Institute of Pennsylvania in 1965. He was elected to the National Academy of Sciences in 1951.

For background information *see* CRYSTALLOGRAPHY; QUANTUM MECHANICS; SOLID-STATE PHYSICS in the McGraw-Hill Encyclopedia of Science and Technology.   □

★ SEKERA, Zdeněk

American atmospheric physicist and metereologist
Born Tabor, Czechoslovakia

SUCCESS IN the early phases of exploration of the neighboring planets will often depend on the ability of scientists to interpret the information that can be gathered from distant fly-by or orbiting space probes. An important source of information in this regard is contained in the radiation emerging from the atmosphere of the planet. This is essentially solar radiation reflected directly or diffusely by the planetary surface and by the atmosphere above it. The spectral distribution has a broad maximum in the visible region, where the energy is usually adequate enough for sophisticated measurements. While most of the directly reflected light comes from the planetary surface, the predominant physical process responsible for the diffuse reflection is the scattering of light by air molecules and by suspended particulate matter in the atmosphere.

The pioneer studies of light scattering in planetary atmospheres carried out by Sekera, beginning in 1933, are now sufficiently advanced for practical application to the problem of planetary exploration. Sekera was introduced to the study of atmospheric scattering by S. Hanzlik, whom he joined as an assistant at Charles University in Prague. In Sekera's attempts to understand the observed features of skylight, which is essentially sunlight scattered many times by air molecules, he realized that the polarization characteristics of the light have to be considered. As a first step, Sekera introduced photoelectric methods in the measurement of skylight polarization. He revealed the close relation between the dispersion of the skylight polarization (that is, its dependence on the wavelength of the measured light) and the so-called "polychroismus" of the polarization (that is, different coloring of the maximum and minimum intensity components), and he explained the observed increase of polychroismus with increasing dispersion. Since the polychroismus makes visual polarization measurements highly unreliable, Sekera stressed the necessity of polarization measurements in narrow spectral regions. However, such measurements of skylight polarization were impractical at that time because of the low sensitivity of available photodetectors and because of the lack of adequate amplification systems.

Sekera then returned to his research studies on atmospheric scattering in 1951, when he became interested in the problem of determining the dust and haze content in the atmosphere from a study of skylight polarization. Sekera's review article on skylight polarization appeared in *Compendium of Meteorology*, edited by T. F. Malone (1951). In this article he resolved the controversy about the sign of the difference of the degree of maximum polarization measured in the red (P_r) region of the spectrum minus that measured in the blue (P_b). He found that the difference is large and positive for large values of P_r, and this is the case when the atmosphere is fairly clear and not turbid. The difference disappears when considerable turbidity is concentrated near the ground, and it assumes large negative values when the turbidity is confined to the higher atmospheric layers. This finding has a clear theoretical foundation, and its quantitative proof was provided by M. Kano in 1964. Moreover, it offers a proper evaluation of the depolarization effects due to multiple scattering of air molecules and scattering by large particles of dust or haze. The observed deviation of the measured skylight polarization from the original Rayleigh theory of primary scattering, in which multiple

scattering and scattering by large particles were neglected, was attributed before World War II by one group of investigators (Ahlgrimm and Tichanowski) to multiple scattering only and by another group (Milch and Schirman) to the presence of large particles only. Sekera's analysis of the dispersion of polarization not only pointed out the existence of both effects, acting always simultaneously, but also indicated a way of assessing their respective magnitudes.

The successful quantitative evaluation of the effect of multiple scattering was by now possible mainly because of the ingenious solution by S. Chandrasekhar of the radiative transfer problem in a plane-parallel atmosphere scattering according to Rayleigh's law. Supported by generous extramural funds, Sekera gathered a group of graduate students in the department of meteorology at the University of California, Los Angeles, and returned to a concentrated and well-defined attack on atmospheric scattering problems. First, with the collaboration of G. Blanch, the intensity and polarization of light from a molecular atmosphere were computed for different wavelengths and other intrinsic parameters. Then a new photoelectric polarimeter was constructed that allowed an accurate measurement of the degree of polarization, as well as of the positions of the neutral points in narrow spectral regions. Numerous measurements conducted at different locations and elevations and under different turbidity conditions proved that for low turbidity the measured values of the skylight polarization and of the positions of neutral points were in accord with Chandrasekhar's theory, especially in the ultraviolet and the blue regions. For longer wavelengths deviations from this theory were observed which increased with increasing turbidity, that is, with increasing amounts of aerosol particles in the lower or upper part of the atmosphere. The measurements also confirmed the observed fact that maximum polarization depends on the reflectivity of the ground. In Chandrasekhar's theory it was assumed that the ground reflection is according to Lambert's law. The measurements proved that this assumption is not far from reality, provided that the ground reflectivity is considered to be wavelength dependent and increasing toward the red part of the spectrum. However, measurements near the sea indicated drastic deviations, especially in the positions of the neutral points, presumably because the reflection was specular in character in this case. Therefore, Sekera extended Chandrasekhar's theory for specular Fresnel reflection. The positions of neutral points as predicted by the indicated extension of the theory were found to agree remarkably well with measurements.

These initial successes led Sekera to embark on further extensions of Chandrasekhar's theory.

To evaluate the effect of multiple scattering in the "Umkehr" method of ozone determination, Sekera, in collaboration with I. V. Dave, computed the intensity and polarization of the emerging radiation from a Rayleigh atmosphere with an ozone layer situated at its top. This model was then generalized to derive the equation for radiative transfer in an atmosphere, where both absorption and scattering are present (that is, the case of the so-called imperfect scattering). This generalization, completed in 1962, opened up an unexplored avenue of theoretical research on scattering in planetary atmospheres. For the extension and application of Chandrasekhar's general theory of radiative transfer to atmospheric problems, Sekera was awarded the Carl-Gustav Rossby Research Medal of the American Meteorological Society in 1966.

One aspect of Sekera's work had great importance for space research. Scattering in a planetary atmosphere produces a radiation field in all directions. Therefore, if one knows how well the theory gives the radiation field in one direction, one can predict its behavior in other directions with some confidence. In fact, procedures for the computation of the radiation emerging from the top and the bottom of a planetary atmosphere are more or less identical. K. L. Coulson, Dave, and Sekera, with the use of a high-speed digital computer, calculated all the important parameters of the radiation emerging from the top and bottom of a Rayleigh atmosphere. The results of these calculations were published in *Tables Related to Radiation Emerging from a Planetary Atmosphere with Rayleigh Scattering* (1960), which shortly became an indispensable tool for all investigations relating to scattering in planetary atmospheres.

Until 1965 the usual practice was to calculate the characteristics of the radiation emerging from a planet for a particular atmospheric model —that is, various intrinsic parameters, such as optical thickness and ground reflectivity, were assumed known—and the radiation characteristics were computed for these special values of the parameters. In 1965, however, Sekera reversed this procedure by posing the inverse problem: Suppose all relevant characteristics of the radiation emerging from a planetary atmosphere are known from measurements. Is it possible to derive useful information about the nature of the planetary surface, the height distribution of scatterers in the atmosphere, and the like from such measurements? Sekera found that one can obtain four independent estimates for the optical thickness of a pure molecular atmosphere if it is bounded by a planetary surface completely absorbing all radiation falling on it. However, for a Lambert type of surface one obtains two independent estimates of the optical thickness and two estimates of the

ground reflectivity. The agreement between these independent estimates, as well as of other relationships among the measured parameters, can be used as criteria to judge whether the scattering atmosphere is purely molecular. Investigation now in progress is directed toward studying the feasibility of quantitative determination of the amount and size distribution of the non-Rayleigh scatterers, as well as of the effective level of their concentration from the deviations of the theoretical and measured values of the polarization parameters of the radiation. It is quite evident that the solution of this inversion problem is crucial to the exploration of planetary atmospheres.

In addition to his work on the polarization of skylight, Sekera also made significant contributions to problems in dynamic meteorology. He was at the University of Oslo in 1936–37 working on wave motions in a fluid with vertical wind shear. After his return to Prague in 1939, he started his teaching and research activities at Charles University. These activities were interrupted when the university closed in 1939. When it reopened in 1945, Sekera was an active participant in the reorganization of the meteorology curriculum at the Faculty of Natural Sciences and also in the modernization of the Czechoslovak Weather Services. In 1946 at the University of Chicago he started work with J. G. Charney on nonlinear solutions of dynamic equations. He extended his previous studies on wave motion with vertical wind shear to fluids with vertical temperature gradient and, by solving the nonlinear vorticity equation for special types of wind profile, discussed the energetics of jet streams. At the University of California, Los Angeles, Sekera continued his studies of nonlinear effects in atmospheric dynamics until 1950, when he once again returned to problems of atmospheric scattering and atmospheric radiative transfer.

Son of a hydrobiologist and professor of parasitology, Sekera studied at the Masaryk University in Brno, where he received his M.Sc. (1929) in mathematics and physics. He continued his studies at Charles University in Prague in mathematical statistics and theoretical physics, receiving the "doctorate in natural sciences" (R.N.Dr.) in theoretical physics in 1931 and "venia docendi" (Ph.D.) in meteorology in 1939. In 1946 Sekera was invited by C.-G. Rossby to the University of Chicago. In 1948 he joined the faculty of the department of meteorology of the University of California, Los Angeles, where in 1962 he became chairman of the department.

For background information *see* ATMOSPHERE; INSOLATION; METEOROLOGICAL OPTICS; POLARIZED LIGHT; SCATTERING (ELECTROMAGNETIC RADIATION) in the McGraw-Hill Encyclopedia of Science and Technology. □

★ **SHEEHAN, John Clark**

American chemist
Born Sept. 23, 1915, Battle Creek, Mich., U.S.A.

S HEEHAN'S LABORATORY at the Massachusetts Institute of Technology announced in 1957 the first rational total synthesis of a natural penicillin (penicillin V). In 1958 Sheehan reported, with research associate K. R. Henery-Logan, a general total synthesis of the penicillins, with details published in 1959 and 1962. Two routes were used: One formed the key "β-lactam" ring after attachment of the side chain; the other first formed the "penicillin nucleus," and then a variety of penicillins by attaching side chains by chemical acylation.

Both methods involve as the most important step the closure of the β-lactam (a four-membered amide ring) by a carbodiimide reagent, which previously had been introduced into peptide chemistry by Sheehan and Hess (1955). The second route constitutes the first, and to this date the only, total general synthesis of the penicillins. Together with subsequently developed biochemical methods of preparing the "penicillin nucleus" (chemically, 6-aminopenicillanic acid), the concept of synthesizing both "natural" (fermentation-produced) and side chain–modified penicillins through the "penicillin nucleus," as originally conceived and carried out in Sheehan's laboratory, has led to the medically important "semisynthetic penicillins." Several of the new penicillins are effective against the dread resistant strains of staphylococci, and another (ampicillin) is considered a "broad-spectrum" penicillin useful against a wider range of infections than can be controlled by penicillins produced directly by fermentation.

During World War II very extensive and intensive effort (more than 30 laboratories and 1000 scientists) unsuccessfully attempted to devise a meaningful chemical synthesis of the penicillin molecule. From 1948 to 1957 no laboratory other than Sheehan's even seriously attempted a penicillin synthesis, according to chemical literature sources.

In 1941 Sheehan and W. E. Bachmann of the University of Michigan devised a new and practical method of manufacturing the important military high explosive RDX (cyclonite, cyclotrimethylenetrinitramine). The method produces two molecules of RDX from one molecule of hexamethylenetetramine, and it is still used for the manufacture of the basic explosive for rocket, bomb, and torpedo warheads (displacing the less powerful TNT). Bachmann and Sheehan also discovered HMX, an explosive more effective for some uses than RDX.

Sheehan's carbodiimide method for peptide synthesis and amide bond formation (used at the key step of the penicillin synthesis) has been employed in recent years directly or indirectly (for example, via an "active" ester) for at least 60% of reported peptide syntheses. A remarkable feature of the reagent is its unique ability to abstract the elements of water from a carboxyl and an amine group to form an amide bond even in a fully aqueous system—that is, a chemical dehydration is effected in the presence of a huge excess of water as a solvent. This astonishing selectivity has been used for cross-linking and otherwise modifying gelatin, collagen, and other proteins, as formulated by Sheehan and Hlavka.

Sheehan and co-workers determined the structure of several antibiotics, including the first monocyclic peptide lactone antibiotic (Etamycin), Telomycin, and Terreic acid. His laboratory determined the structure of the last two "natural" amino acids (amino acids from animal protein sources) and sythesized them—namely, hydroxylysine (with W. Bolhofer) and 3-hydroxyproline (with J. Whitney). More recent work included the synthesis and reactions of α-lactams, an example of homogeneous asymmetric catalysis (the second in chemical history), and synthetic peptide models of enzyme active sites.

Sheehan received his M.S. (1938) and Ph.D. (1941) from the University of Michigan. From 1941 to 1946 he was senior research chemist at Merck and Co., Rahway, N.J. In 1946 he was appointed assistant professor of chemistry at MIT and full professor in 1952. He received the American Chemical Society's Award for Pure Chemistry in 1951 and the Society's Award for Creative Work in Synthetic Organic Chemistry in 1959. In 1964 he was the recipient of the John Scott Award and a medal from the city of Philadelphia for inventions "benefiting mankind." He was elected to the American Academy of Arts and Sciences in 1951 and to the National Academy of Sciences in 1957.

Sheehan wrote more than 100 papers for

scientific journals and obtained 20 patents, including the basic patent on the medically important synthetic penicillins.

For background information *see* Explosion and explosive; Penicillin; Thiazole in the McGraw-Hill Encyclopedia of Science and Technology.   ☐

★ SHEMIN, David

American biochemist
Born Mar. 18, 1911, New York, N.Y., U.S.A.

Shemin and David Rittenberg in 1945 initiated a study on the metabolism of amino acids in the human. Shemin drank a solution containing 66 grams of the amino acid glycine, which he had synthesized to contain 33% of the heavy isotope of nitrogen, N^{15}, to label or tag the nitrogeneous body constituents. A mass spectrographic analysis, performed by Rittenberg, on some compounds isolated from the subject's blood demonstrated that the nitrogen atom of glycine was specifically utilized by the red cell for the synthesis of the porphyrin of hemoglobin: porphyrin + iron = heme; heme + globin (a protein) = hemoglobin. This initial observation was followed by other experiments in which the source of all the carbon atoms of the heme molecule was elucidated. Furthermore, the specific utilization of glycine for heme synthesis permitted tagging or labeling the red cell of the human or of animals with isotopic nitrogen under physiological conditions and thus facilitated studying the life span of the red cell in both the normal individuals and those with blood dyscrasias. The average life span of the normal human red cell was determined to be about 120 days.

Porphyrins are tetrapyrrole compounds which are called hemes when chelated with iron. The porphyrin molecule and related structures are found in heme proteins, such as hemoglobin, myoglobin, cytochromes, and peroxidases, and in vitamin B_{12} and chlorophyll. They appear to be rather stable for they are found in fossilized excrements of crocodiles, and mineral hydrocarbon oils contain porphyrins of both plant and animal origin. They were recognized by the scientific community as organic entities as early as the 1840s, and their structures were established by the work of W. Küster, R. Willstätter, and H. Fischer. Functionally, in animal tissues the porphyrins are concerned with the reduction of oxygen to water, whereas in photosynthetic plants the chlorophyll is involved with the splitting of water into oxygen and hydrogen.

Shemin and his students soon found that eight carbon atoms of the porphyrin are derived from the α-carbon atom of glycine. In order to locate these carbon atoms and thereby gain some insight into the mechanism of porphyrin synthesis, Shemin and J. Wittenberg worked out chemical degradation procedures whereby each carbon atom of the C^{34} compound could be isolated from a particular and known position in the molecule. In order to study the intimate details of the synthesis of heme, a simpler biological system was sought, and Shemin found that red blood cells of birds, either intact or broken, are capable of synthesizing the complicated hemoglobin molecules in vitro from their small precursors. By carrying out experiments with this biological system with radioactive compounds, the heme synthesized during the experiment was degraded each time to obtain the labeling pattern in the molecule. In this manner the source of the remaining 26 carbon atoms was uncovered. These carbon atoms arise from succinyl coenzyme A, an intermediate in the Krebs citric acid cycle which is concerned with the oxidation of glucose and fatty acids. Since the carboxyl group of glycine was found not to be utilized for porphyrin synthesis, the mechanism of condensation of succinyl coenzyme A with glycine must include a mechanism permitting the decarboxylation of glycine. The suggested condensation of the activated succinate on the α-carbon atom of glycine would form a β-keto acid which can readily decarboxylate and yield an amino ketone, δ-aminolevulinic acid. To test this hypothesis, Shemin and C. Russell synthesized radiactively labeled δ-aminolevulinic acid and incubated red blood cells of a duck with this compound. It was found that δ-aminolevulinic acid replaces glycine and succinate and is indeed the source of all the atoms of the porphyrins; two molecules of δ-aminolevulinic acid condense to form a pyrrole, porphobilinogen, and four molecules of this pyrrole are linked together to form the porphyrins. The different porphyrins arise by modifications in the side chains on the β-positions. It is of interest to note that the intermediates, δ-aminolevulinic acid and porphobilinogen, are excreted in abnormal amounts in the urine of people with the hereditary disease of acute porphyria. Shemin, J. Corcoran, and R. Bray subsequently demonstrated that the porphyrin-like moiety of vitamin B_{12} is synthesized from the same precursors. Shemin recently investigated the mechanism of some of the early steps in porphyrin synthesis with enzymes isolated from photosynthetic bacteria in order to gain some insight in the control mechanisms operating in porphyrin and bacteriochlorophyll synthesis.

Shemin majored in chemistry and biology at the City College of New York, where he received his B.S. in 1932. He entered Columbia University and was awarded his M.A. in chemistry in 1933 and his Ph.D. in biochemistry in 1938. He worked in the field of immunology and on the chemistry of the Rous sarcoma virus in the department of pathology of Columbia until 1941, when he returned to the department of biochemistry; he became a professor in 1953. In 1947 he was a guest of E. Hammersten at the Karolinska Institute in Stockholm, and in 1958–59 he worked at the Pasteur Institute in Paris. He was elected to the National Academy of Sciences in 1958 and to the American Academy of Arts and Sciences in 1961.

Shemin edited *Biochemical Preparations*, Vol. 5 (1957).

For background information *see* AMINO ACIDS; HEMOGLOBIN; PORPHYRIN in the McGraw-Hill Encyclopedia of Science and Technology.   □

★ SHEMYAKIN, Mikhail Mikhailovich

Soviet chemist
Born July 26, 1908, Moscow, Russia

THE DEVELOPMENT of organic chemistry is intimately linked with the study of naturally occurring organic compounds. Interest in these compounds rose to a new level in the 1930s with the general upsurge in the biological sciences. Since that time organic chemists have increasingly studied compounds with an eye toward their physiological functions and biological importance. Thus there was gradually born a new branch of chemistry, bioorganic chemistry, whose main objective is the study of the various biopolymers (proteins, nucleic acids, lipids, carbohydrates) and the numerous natural and synthetic bioregulators, from vitamins and enzymes to antibiotics and synthetic pharmaceutical preparations. Present-day bioorganic chemistry advances hand in hand with biochemistry on the molecular, subcellular, and cellular levels, both disciplines having the same ultimate goal: comprehension of the physicochemical essence of the life processes and their regulation in the body.

It is in the chemistry of the naturally occurring compounds that Shemyakin found his life interest. In his first major series of studies he investigated the hydrolytic cleavage of carbon-carbon bonds: $R_2C(OH) - CR_3 \rightarrow R_2CO + HCR_3$. He showed (1941) that this reaction can occur in a wide range of compounds, providing the above grouping is present or can arise during the reaction and the environmental and structural factors are conducive to polarization of the bond. In an extension of these studies to the oxidative-hydrolytic transformations of organic compounds, it was established (1956) that in many cases an oxidant is incapable of splitting the carbon-carbon bond until, at a certain level of oxidation of the molecule, the bond is polarized by the incorporation of oxygen-containing substituents so that it becomes capable of hydrolytic fission. In this way the true nature was brought to light of the oxidative-hydrolytic transformations of a number of naturally occurring and synthetic compounds, in particular quinones and antibiotics, as well as of the enzymatic hydrolysis of the carbon-carbon bonds of some amino acids. As a logical sequel to the latter problem, Shemyakin and A. E. Braunstein evolved (1952) a theory for the processes of amino acid metabolism catalyzed by phosphopyridoxal enzymes, explaining from a single point of view the causes and mechanisms of numerous and, at first sight, seemingly highly differing conversions of the amino acids (transamination, racemization, α- and β-decarboxylation, exchange of β- and γ-substituents, fission of β- and γ-substituted amino acids, and so forth). All these transformations are due to the fact that the azomethines resulting from reaction of the amino acids with pyridoxal enzymes behave as α-keto, rather than α-amino, acids.

The second large series of studies undertaken by Shemyakin, beginning in 1947, concerned the structure, synthesis, and mode of action of various antibiotics. With regard to the tetracyclines, these studies culminated on the one hand in establishing the absolute configuration of these highly important compounds and on the other hand in the first total synthesis of the parent compound, tetracycline. Recently the structure and configuration of a large family of related antitumor antibiotics belonging to the group of olivomycins-chromomycins were also completely elucidated. Investigations of chloramphenicol that began with the elaboration of simple methods for synthesizing its optically active analogs resulted in the establishment of a number of structure-activity relationships. It was shown that the antibiotic action of chloramphenicol on the microbial cell depends upon the electrophilicity of both its aryl radical and acyl residue, whereas its inhibition of protein synthesis on ribosomes is independent of the nature of the acyl group, which is essential only for penetration of the antibiotic into the cell. The importance of these findings is enhanced by the fact that chloramphenicol and its analogs can be used as tools for studying the mode of s-RNA participation in protein biosynthesis. In the field of depsipeptide antibiotics (enniatins, valinomycin, serratamolide, and the like), it was first necessary to study the chemistry of the depsipeptides in general (a very little explored area at that time); then it was possible to establish the structure, carry out the synthesis, and investigate the structure-activity relations of these antibiotics. Research into the mode of action paved the way for a new approach to the study of biological membranes.

The third series of studies undertaken by Shemyakin was devoted to the chemistry of polypeptide systems. These studies began in 1955 with an investigation into a particular group of α-substituted α-amino acids and their peptides (constituent parts of ergot alkaloids); soon they spread over to depsipeptides and then to polypeptides in general. A study of the mass spectrometric behavior of depsipeptides made possible the use of this method for rapid determination of their structure, whereas for the synthesis of linear and cyclic depsipeptides, simple and reliable methods were developed for chain building and cyclization as well as for the incorporation of hydroxy acid residues into the cycle. Simultaneously, a number of generalities were established in the cyclization of linear depsipeptides and peptides and in the intramolecular interactions between amide and ester groups in cyclic depsipeptides and peptides of medium ring size. In line with this, studies were carried out on the intramolecular interaction of the hydroxy and amino groups with activated amide groupings, leading to the discovery of the hydroxy and amino acyl incorporation reaction in linear and cyclic peptides. It was shown experimentally that all such rearrangements in peptide systems occur via the corresponding oxa and aza cyclols, whose isolation in the individual

state was achieved for the first time, thereby providing the means for studying their formation, properties, and transformations. This group of studies clarified the cause, nature, and limitations of a number of rearrangements in peptide and protein systems.

The study of depsipeptides and peptides engendered still another field of study: the topochemical approach to their structure-activity relations. One of the fruits of such an approach was the discovery in a number of cases of the mutual exchangeability of the ester and amide groups without loss of biological specificity—as was confirmed on the examples of valinomycin, bradykinin, glutathione, and so forth—and of the possibility of retaining the biological activity of cyclodepsipeptides and cyclopeptides (for instance, enniatins and gramicidin S) in their enantio- and retroenantiomers. The problem of substrate-receptor interactions in peptide and protein systems, including the interaction of enzymes with substrates and inhibitors in the light of these results, could now be attacked from a new angle.

Finally, of considerable importance to polypeptide and protein chemistry were the laws, discovered by Shemyakin, governing the fragmentation of acylpeptide esters in mass spectrometry, leading to an express method for determining the amino acid sequence in oligopeptides from analysis of their mass spectra. The constancy of the principal (so-called amino acid) type of fragmentation and of a number of specificities in the behavior of different amino acids made possible facile interpretation of the mass spectra, thereby greatly simplifying the formerly highly cumbersome problem of determining the amino acid sequence (primary structure) of protein molecules.

A number of studies undertaken by Shemyakin were specifically aimed at the mechanistic aspects of several organic reactions. The reactions included pyrolysis of carboxylic acid salts, osazone formation, azoxy coupling, rearrangements in azoxy compounds, and sterically controlled carbonyl olefination.

Shemyakin attended the Moscow State University (1925–30) and received his D.Sc. there in 1941. He was dozent of analytical chemistry, Moscow Institute of Fine Chemical Technology (1930–37); senior scientist and then professor of organic chemistry, All-Union Institute of Experimental Medicine (1935–45); professor of organic chemistry, Institute of Biological and Medicinal Chemistry, U.S.S.R. Academy of Medical Sciences (1945–60); and deputy head, Division of Chemistry, U.S.S.R. Academy of Sciences (1957–63). He became the director of the Institute for Chemistry of Natural Products, U.S.S.R. Academy of Sciences, in 1959 and the head of the Division of Bioorganic Chemistry,

Biochemistry, and Biophysics, and a member of the presidium of the Academy in 1963. Shemyakin was elected to the U.S.S.R. Academy of Sciences in 1953.

In addition to some 300 papers in chemical and biochemical journals, Shemyakin wrote *Oxidative-Hydrolytic Splitting of Carbon-Carbon Bonds of Organic Molecules* (1956), *Chemistry of Antibiotics* (1949; 3d ed. 1961), *Chemistry of Depsipeptide Antibiotics* (1965), *Activation of the Amide Group by Acylation* (1965), and *Mass Spectrometric Determination of the Amino Acid Sequence of Peptides* (1966).

For background information *see* AMINO ACIDS; ANTIBIOTIC; CARBON; ORGANIC REACTION MECHANISM in the McGraw-Hill Encyclopedia of Science and Technology.   □

★ SHEPARD, Francis Parker

American marine geologist
Born May 10, 1897, Brookline, Mass., U.S.A.

S HEPARD STARTED his training in geology under R. A. Daly at Harvard but later differed widely from Daly in interpreting features of the sea floor. Despite these differences, Shepard in 1966 was the first American recipient after Daly of the Wollaston Medal of the Geological Society of London (Daly had received it in 1942).

Shepard obtained his Ph.D. in geology at the University of Chicago in 1922 with a thesis on the origin of the Rocky Mountain Trench in British Columbia, a locality where Daly had earlier 'done notable work. A few years later Shepard was diverted to a study of the sea floor. Having the opportunity on his father's small yacht to collect bottom samples along the Massachusetts coast, he found striking inconsistencies between the pattern of sediments on the continental shelf in this area from that commonly presented in geological textbooks. Shortly afterward, Shepard's investigation of published charts revealed many other inconsistencies be-

tween prevalent theory and fact in the interpretation of the origin and history of the sea floor. This finding was not surprising because at that time (the early 1920s) few people were investigating the field of marine geology. In contrast, today there are hundreds of scientists in the field in the United States alone, and marine geology sessions at scientific meetings are often the most crowded.

Starting his sea floor studies during vacations from his instructional duties at the University of Illinois, Shepard used every opportunity to further his knowledge by accompanying various cruises of the U.S. Coast and Geodetic Survey ships. Interest in the canyons of the sea floor came to him first from examination of charts, but was soon supplemented by his own field work. A year of study of the California canyons was accomplished during a sabbatical leave in 1933–34. This was followed in 1937 by what was then the largest grant of the Geological Society of America, allowing him to have 6 months' use of the *E. W. Scripps*, newly converted for the work of the Scripps Institution of Oceanography. A monograph resulted on the California canyons and sea floor. Shepard's student K. O. Emery was actively associated with this work and was started at this time on his career of studying the sea floor.

Work at the Scripps Institution soon prevailed over Shepard's teaching at the University of Illinois, and he joined the University of California in 1942 to work with their division of war research for the remainder of the war. In 1945 Shepard became a permanent member of the Scripps Institution and in 1948 a professor of submarine geology. After the war, Shepard wrote *Submarine Geology* (1948; 2d ed. 1963), the first textbook on the subject. For a few years he spent much of his time working on beach and near-shore sediment transportation problems. Studies of the changing depths of the La Jolla canyons were also undertaken. In 1951 the American Petroleum Institute chose Shepard to direct a large project for studying the shallow-water sediments of the northwest Gulf of Mexico. With the help of several young geologists, including T. H. van Andel, R. J. Curray, P. C. Scruton, and D. G. Moore, this study was terminated with the publication of *Recent Sediments, Northwest Gulf of Mexico* (1960). Various criteria helpful in identifying the environment of deposition of ancient sedimentary rocks were developed from this project; another outcome was Shepard's popular book on marine geology, *The Earth Beneath the Sea* (1959; paper 1964; 2d ed. 1967).

In 1959 Shepard returned to his study of submarine canyons and other types of sea floor valleys. This occupied most of his time until the publication of results in *Submarine Canyons and*

Other Sea Valleys (1966), coauthored by his former student Robert F. Dill. This work included cruises, mostly on Scripps Institution ships, to various parts of the world, but particular attention was paid to the California and Baja California canyons. Beginning in 1964, Shepard made many deep dives into the canyons by using J. Y. Cousteau's diving saucer and other deep-diving vehicles.

A study of the history of sea-level changes from the late Ice Age to the present interested Shepard, and his extensive travels gave him an opportunity to obtain many samples both above and just below sea level, which could be dated by carbon-14 techniques to help establish the sea-level trend. During the winter of 1966–67 Shepard was senior scientist of an expedition to the Caroline and Marshall Islands on a Scripps Institution ship to check the conflicting evidence of sea-level changes believed to exist in the area.

Shepard received his A.B. at Harvard University in 1919 and his Ph.D. at the University of Chicago in 1922. He advanced from instructor to professor of physiography and structural geology at the University of Illinois during 1922–42. At the Scripps Institution of Oceanography he was research associate in 1942–45, principal geologist in 1945–48, and professor of submarine geology beginning in 1948. He was elected a fellow of numerous scientific societies. An award in marine geology was established in his name.

In addition to writing the books cited, Shepard served as associate editor of *Sedimentology* and *Marine Geology*. His former students compiled a Shepard commemorative volume, *Papers in Marine Geology*, edited by R. L. Miller (1964).

For background information *see* CONTINENTAL SHELF AND SLOPE; MARINE SEDIMENTS; SUBMARINE CANYON; SUBMARINE TOPOGRAPHY in the McGraw-Hill Encyclopedia of Science and Technology.   □

★ SHOENBERG, David

British physicist
Born Jan. 4, 1911, Saint Petersburg, Russia

SHOENBERG BEGAN research in 1932 at Cambridge University in the Royal Society Mond Laboratory, which had just been built for Peter Kapitza's pioneering work on high magnetic fields and very low temperatures. Most of Shoenberg's scientific work made use of these two techniques to study the properties of normal and superconducting metals. For this work he received the Fritz London Award for low-temperature physics from the Institute of Physics and Physical Society in 1964.

His early work was concerned with the some-

what anomalous magnetic behavior of bismuth and in particular the oscillating field dependence of its magnetic susceptibility, which had been recently discovered by W. J. de Haas and P. M. Van Alphen in Leiden and was beginning to be explained theoretically by R. E. Peierls and L. D. Landau. Shoenberg spent 1937 in the Institute for Physical Problems in Moscow, which Kapitza had recently set up after his return to the Soviet Union in 1934. Here, following a suggestion which arose from a visit of Indian physicist K. S. Krishnan to Cambridge, Shoenberg developed a simple torsion method of studying the de Haas–Van Alphen effect. By a fortunate coincidence Landau, who was the Institute's chief theoretician, had just worked out a more explicit formulation of the theory, enabling Shoenberg to make a detailed interpretation of his results in terms of a three-ellipsoid model of the Fermi surface of bismuth. This was the first experimental determination of the Fermi surface of any metal.

Another of Shoenberg's early research interests had been the magnetic behavior of superconductors, and while in Moscow he wrote a monograph on superconductivity and benefited considerably from discussions with Landau and others in his understanding of the subject. On his return to Cambridge he made the first determination of the temperature variation of the penetration depth of a magnetic field into a superconductor by studying the magnetic susceptibility of small mercury spheres (in colloids). This work was interrupted by World War II, during which he was concerned with development of an antiaircraft device.

In 1945 he resumed research on superconductivity and was particularly stimulated by A. B.

Pippard, whose early work on the high-frequency behavior of superconductors proved very suggestive in the later development of a fundamental theory by John Bardeen, L. N. Cooper, and J. R. Schrieffer. Shoenberg's own work continued to be concerned with the penetration depth; he made the first absolute determination of it in tin and mercury, using a method suggested by Casimir. He also studied the intermediate state in which normal and superconducting regions coexist, and on the basis of a theory developed by Landau and E. M. Lifshitz he made the first realistic estimate of the surface energy between the two phases.

In 1949, following the discovery by J. A. Marcus at Yale of the de Haas–Van Alphen effect in zinc, it became clear that this effect is not limited, as was tacitly but mistakenly assumed, in practical conditions only to bismuth but may be easily observed in other metals and particularly polyvalent metals. Using the torsion method, Shoenberg soon showed that the effect does indeed occur in many metals and that probably it is only because of practical limitations that it cannot be observed in others. In 1951 Lars Onsager, during a visit to Cambridge, pointed out a very general and simple connection between the periodicity of the de Haas–Van Alphen oscillations and the detailed shape and size of the Fermi surface. This idea, also independently proposed by I. M. Lifshitz at about the same time, provided an important advance on the Landau theory, which had been limited to ellipsoidal Fermi surfaces and so could not deal with the wealth of new data beginning to accumulate.

Thus, Onsager's idea can be said to have transformed the de Haas–Van Alphen effect from a scientific curiosity to a powerful tool in the study of metals, and this stimulated Shoenberg to develop a new method of measuring the effect in the very high fields produced by discharging a condenser through a coil. Such fields, 5 or 10 times higher than those of conventional magnets, enabled him to observe oscillations of much shorter periods, corresponding to the major pieces of Fermi surface which had earlier eluded observation and, in collaboration with D. J. Roaf, he was able to determine in some detail the Fermi surfaces of the noble metals. In 1964, in collaboration with P. J. Stiles, Shoenberg took advantage of the recent availability of high-field superconducting magnets to develop a new and more sensitive technique of studying the de Haas–Van Alphen effect and made the first detailed study of the Fermi surface of an alkali metal.

The various techniques developed by Shoenberg have been very actively taken up elsewhere, particularly in the United States and the Soviet Union. The detailed understanding of the Fermi surfaces of many metals obtained in this way has proved a valuable guide to the development of the theory of metals.

Shoenberg's father was one of the pioneers of radio in Russia before 1914 and later, as research director at Electrical and Musical Industries Ltd., he was responsible for developing the system of television still in use in England. His influence guided Shoenberg to studying mathematics and physics. Shoenberg took his Ph.D. in 1935 at Cambridge University. Apart from visits to Moscow in 1937–38, to the National Physical Laboratory of India at New Delhi in 1953–54 as UNESCO expert in low-temperature physics, and to the University of Pittsburgh as Andrew W. Mellon Visiting Professor in 1962, Shoenberg remained at Cambridge from 1932. He was in charge of the Royal Society Mond Laboratory and a fellow of Gonville and Caius College beginning in 1947 and reader in physics in the university beginning in 1952. He was elected a fellow of the Royal Society of London in 1953.

Shoenberg wrote *Magnetism* (1949) and *Superconductivity* (1939; 2d ed., 1952; paper 1965).

For background information *see* CRYOGENIC ENGINEERING; LOW-TEMPERATURE PHYSICS; SUPERCONDUCTIVITY in the McGraw-Hill Encyclopedia of Science and Technology.   □

★ SIEGBAHN, Manne

Swedish physicist
Born Dec. 3, 1886, Örebro, Sweden

SIEGBAHN'S EARLIEST research work at the University of Lund was devoted to problems of electromagnetism. In 1913–14 he began studies on x-rays in the new field opened up by the discovery of M. von Laue and W. Friedrich on the diffraction of x-rays in crystals. From this discovery followed two different lines of development: the study of crystal structures, where W. H. and W. L. Bragg did the first pioneer work, and the investigation of atomic structure. In the latter case the x-radiation emitted from the different elements placed in the anticathode in an x-ray tube were analyzed with suitable crystals, mostly calcite, rock salt, or mica. According to Bragg's formula, $n\lambda = 2d \sin\alpha$, the wavelengths λ of the x-radiation could be determined through measuring the angle of reflection α against an atomic plane of the selected crystal, n being the order of reflection. Some preliminary experiments had shown that the "characteristic" x-radiation that C. G. Barkla earlier had found with an absorption method consisted of several well-defined spectral lines when analyzed with the crystal-grating method.

Siegbahn's main work was the development of new methods and the necessary technical equipment to obtain a high resolution of the x-ray spectra, as well as a highly increased precision in the determination of the wavelengths. In cooperation with several graduate students, he made a thorough investigation of the x-ray spectra of practically all elements from sodium up to uranium. It included the two groups of characteristic radiation, the K and L series of Barkla, as well as new series, such as the M series. By these investigations a great number of spectral lines constituting the different series were found. At the same time absorption spectra, obtained by letting a continuous x-ray spectrum pass through thin foils of the different elements, were registered on the spectral plate. The absorption appeared on the plate as a sudden drop of the blackening at fixed wavelengths—the "absorption edges."

It was found that the K series corresponds to one absorption edge, the L series to three, the M series to five, and so on. As soon as a complete measurement of all the x-ray spectral lines and their corresponding absorption discontinuities had been achieved, it was possible to give a full account of the electron structure of the atoms. The results showed that the electrons in the atoms are arranged in shells with different energies, the innermost being the K shell with 2 electrons, the next the L shell with 8 electrons in 3 groups, the M shell with 18 electrons in 5 groups, and so on.

As seen from graphical representation of the energy values (proportional to the inverse values of the wavelengths), these are quite similar for all the elements, with mainly a stepwise displacement with changing electric charge of the atomic nucleus.

A very interesting general result from the measurement of the emission lines and the absorption levels showed that not all of the transitions of electrons that would be expected did appear in the observation of the emission lines. It was obvious that special selection rules exist, as had earlier been found in the multiplets at ordinary optical spectra. The quantum theory of Planck and Einstein and its later developments gave a clue to formulate this fact in the advanced theories.

Another experimental result due to the increased exactitude in the measurements was the discovery by Siegbahn's co-worker W. Stenström that the Bragg equation had to be slightly corrected to give consistent values for the wavelengths measured in different orders. This was to be expected from the more elaborate theory of crystal diffraction by P. P. Ewald and by C. G. Darwin. Even if the x-ray spectra regularly do not show a dependence of the chemical state of the elements, it seemed probable that such an influence could be expected in cases where one of the outer electronic levels of the atom was involved. Also in this case the development of spectroscopic methods gave interesting results in the absorption spectra of chlorine, sulfur, and phosphorus. In Siegbahn's laboratory this was studied by A. E. Lindh and most thoroughly by the chemist H. Stelling.

Before the discovery of the diffraction of x-rays in crystals many experiments had been tried to decide if these rays were of corpuscular nature or were electromagnetic waves, but no decisive results to settle this question had been obtained. After the insight that the x-rays had wave character, an experiment to show both reflection and refraction of monochromatic x-rays in noncrystals was carried out by A. Larsson, Siegbahn, and J. Waller (1924). They used a prism of glass with a well-defined 90° angle in which a narrow beam of an x-ray hit the prismatic edge under a very small angle against the glass surface. On a photographic plate behind the prism could then be seen one strong line formed of the x-rays passing directly through the prism edge and further lines of refracted rays from the anticathode (Cu + Fe), as well as directly reflected rays. It may be mentioned that Roentgen himself had made unsuccessful trials to observe a refraction of x-rays with the primitive means available at that time.

Siegbahn was awarded the Nobel Prize in physics in 1924 "for his discoveries and research in the field of x-ray spectroscopy" and the Rumford Medal of the Royal Society of London in 1940.

X-ray spectroscopy with crystals as dispersing element had, as seen from the Bragg equation, its natural limits set by the double distance d between the reflecting atomic planes. For the crystals mostly used, the value of $2d$ varied from 5 or 6 Å in rock salt to 20 Å in mica. Some experiments using organic crystals with larger d values were tried to register x-rays with longer wavelengths, but even with these the limit was soon reached. To widen the field of x-ray spectroscopy, the next stage was to use ruled gratings as complement to the natural crystal gratings. This problem was attacked by Siegbahn after he had taken over the chair of physics at the University of Uppsala in 1923 (the same chair that A. J. Ångström held in

1858–74). The first experiments were carried out with a glass grating having 220 lines/mm, ruled by Norbert and used by Ångström in his famous investigations of the solar spectrum. Of special interest in these experiments, published in a thesis by E. Bäcklin, was the very surprising result that the value of the important elementary charge e, as calculated from the measurements, showed a remarkable discrepancy from the then generally accepted value of R. A. Millikan obtained with his oil-drop method. Following up this disagreement, it was finally found that the value on the inner friction in air, which Millikan had used in his calculating and which value was taken from measurements of E. L. Harrington, was about 0.7% too low compared with new measurements of this constant carried out at Uppsala. After considering this adjustment the two quite different methods gave consistent values for e.

By further development of the experiments with ruled gratings it was possible to bridge the gap between the x-ray spectra and the optical spectra. To achieve this extension, Siegbahn designed a ruling engine to produce gratings suitable for diffraction of x-rays as well as optical radiation under a very small angle of incidence, 2–5°, between the incoming rays and the surface of the grating. (Gratings ruled on this engine were recently used in the American orbiting solar observatory, or OSO, to register the extreme ultraviolet radiation from the Sun.)

The gap to be covered by the new methods of registration with concave gratings included a wavelength region from, say, 20 to about 500 A, that is, nearly five octaves. The extension of the soft x-rays included wavelengths up to 250 A. The L series was followed from potassium to magnesium with wavelengths around 48–250 A, the M series from silver to bromine with wavelengths 40–192 A, and the N series from the rare-earth group with wavelengths 40–190 A. The optical spectra emitted by condensed high-tension sparks were registered down to about 40 A. For instance, the optical spectra of the highly ionized atoms Li(III), Be(IV), and B(V), with λ-values 108, 49, and 39 A, were first found by Edlén and Ericson (1930). This last work was extended in a masterly thesis by Edlén (1934), and later led to his rather complete analysis of most of the spectra emitted by the lower elements up to the iron group, where spectra lines from 16- to 18-fold ionization were registered and analyzed.

In 1937 the Royal Swedish Academy of Sciences created a Nobel Institute of Physics with Siegbahn as director. The program of this institute was devoted to researches in nuclear physics. To this end the necessary equipment, consisting of an 80-cm cyclotron giving α-particles with energies up to 14 Mev and a Cockcroft-Walton high-tension generator with a maximum voltage 1200 kv, was designed and accomplished at the institute. An isotope separator and several β-γ-spectrometers of new types were developed, as well as a larger cyclotron with a diameter of 225 cm giving α-particles of energy 44 Mev. The specific problems studied were the energy levels of the atomic nuclei. Investigations of the distribution of different angles and their correlation at nuclear reactions were carried out to gain insight into the mechanism of the reactions. The results of these researches were published in more than 600 papers, among them about 40 theses presented for the D.Sc., mostly at the University of Stockholm and the Royal Institute of Technology.

Siegbahn received his M.S. and D.Sc. (1911) at the University of Lund, where he was lecturer in physics in 1911–20 and professor of physics in 1920–23. After serving as professor at the University of Uppsala during 1924–37, he was director of the Nobel Institute of Physics from 1937 to 1964. In addition to the honors already cited, Siegbahn was awarded the Hughes Medal of the Royal Society of London (1934) and the Duddel Medal of the Physical Society of London (1948).

For background information *see* ATOMIC STRUCTURE AND SPECTRA; X-RAY DIFFRACTION; X-RAY FLUORESCENCE ANALYSIS; X-RAY(S), PHYSICAL NATURE OF in the McGraw-Hill Encyclopedia of Science and Technology.   □

★ SIMPSON, George Gaylord

American biologist, geologist, and paleontologist
Born June 16, 1902, Chicago, Ill., U.S.A.

SIMPSON'S EARLY life was spent in Colorado. Influenced by an inspiring teacher, Arthur Tieje, who was briefly at the University of Colorado, Simpson transferred to Yale University and there completed his formal training under Richard Swann Lull. He received his Ph.B. in

1923 and his Ph.D (geology) in 1926 from Yale University. As a graduate student, he began research on early mammals. Mammals existed for at least 100,000,000 years before they became really abundant in the Age of Mammals. That long and crucial basic history is represented by comparatively few and fragmentary fossils, and those known in the 1920s had not been adequately described or well understood. Simpson's study of all the available American specimens was essentially completed in 1926, and in the following year he similarly studied all known specimens, mainly in the British Museum but also in other European collections. Publication of two large monographs and many shorter papers essentially finished what could be done on that subject at that time.

In 1927 Simpson joined the staff of the American Museum of Natural History in New York, where he was successively assistant curator, associate curator, and curator of fossil mammals and chairman of geology and paleontology. His interest in early mammals was continued with the intensive collection and study of fossil mammals of the Paleocene and Eocene (the first two of the seven epochs of the Cenozoic, or Age of Mammals) in North and South America. In the late 1920s and through the 1930s he collected North American Paleocene mammals in New Mexico and Montana. Research on those and allied forms included fundamental studies on the Multituberculata, a strange, extinct group of early mammals that was abundant in the Age of Reptiles and survived well into the Age of Mammals; revision of the only Asiatic Cretaceous and Paleocene mammals then known; discovery of some, and detailed study of all, of a long sequence of Paleocene faunas in Montana; revision of other Paleocene faunas from Colorado and Wyoming; and studies of Paleocene primates, the oldest-known members of the mammalian order to which man belongs. In the 1940s and early 1950s his field collecting was mainly devoted to the Eocene of the San Juan Basin of New Mexico, and he published on the stratigraphy of the San José Formation, which he named, and wrote a few further notes on fossils from that area. This work was terminated when he left the American Museum in 1959.

Interest in the evolution of mammals and especially of early mammals in South America was fanned by the peculiarity of those faunas, which long evolved in isolation from the rest of the world. Early work by Argentine paleontologists, especially the Ameghino brothers, had revealed the existence of those peculiarities but had not explained them and had raised more problems than were solved. Simpson began his special studies in that field in 1930. Expeditions to Patagonia in 1930–31 and 1933–34 produced large new collections of Paleocene and Eocene mammals. Simpson also studied the older, classic collections in Buenos Aires and La Plata. The results included dozens of technical papers on South American geology and paleontology, two large monographs (the second one completed in 1966), and a popular book on exploration in Patagonia.

Besides these major campaigns on early mammals, Simpson made many special studies of other fossil vertebrates, including later fossil mammals from Florida; fossil sea cows and evolution of their order, the Sirenia; fossil penguins and evolution of that group of birds; some North and South American crocodilians and turtles and the history of turtles in South America; the classification, evolution, and biology of early saber-toothed tigers; late fossil and living tapirs; and mastodonts of South America. In 1945 a classification of all then known mammals, with data on their distribution in space and time and extensive notes on taxonomy, was published.

His many basic studies of fossil and recent animals and faunas led Simpson to consider their theoretical interpretation and implications in several related fields. Methods in taxonomic work and the principles underlying classification were studied at levels from the most technical to the most theoretical. Simpson was among the first to use statistics extensively in this field. Among a number of special methods devised, that of ratio diagrams for studying proportions in related animals has been most widely adopted. Historical zoogeography, the study of geographic distributions of animals and their changes and underlying causes, first became important for Simpson in connection with his South American work and later also involved special research on North American, Australian, and West Indian mammals and on the general principles of the science. Here, too, some special concepts and techniques were developed, such as "Simpson's coefficient" for measuring the resemblance of faunas of different areas. Simpson also took an interest in the history of vertebrate paleontology, and a long essay on that subject was awarded the Lewis Prize by the American Philosophical Society in 1942.

In 1938–39 Simpson collected fossil mammals in Venezuela and also visited the then little-known southeastern part of that country with a Venezuelan expedition. The fossil collections, although of some interest, were disappointing, but the expedition provided material for a detailed monograph on a tribe of then uncivilized Indians, the Kamarakotos. Although not a specialist in anthropology, Simpson took part in a number of anthropological conferences and contributed to anthropological symposiums, especially on the application of evolutionary and taxonomic principles to this subject. Another extensive interdisciplinary effort arose from his interests in common with his wife, the psychologist Anne Roe. They organized two conferences on behavior and evolution and edited and contributed to a published symposium on that subject.

Simpson became perhaps most widely known for his studies of the principles of evolution, of their involvement and application in general biology, and of their philosophical import. In the 1930s the confused field of evolutionary theory was being organized into a new synthesis. In a sequence of theoretical papers and books Simpson undertook to show that the facts of paleontology are consistent with the synthesis and, further, that they can serve as a testing ground for it and can notably amplify it. He held that evolution is a completely natural process, proceeding without contemporaneous guidance or future goal in accordance with the material nature of the universe, and that man can understand his own nature and assure his own future only in the light of these facts.

Simpson was professor of zoology at Columbia University during 1945–59. In 1959 he left the American Museum and Columbia to become Alexander Agassiz Professor of Vertebrate Paleontology at Harvard University. In 1942–44 he was with the American, British, and Free French armies in the Mediterranean theater as a major in military intelligence. Scientific travels and expeditions took him to all the continents except Antarctica. He was elected to the National Academy of Sciences in 1941 and to the American Academy of Arts and Sciences in 1948. He also became a member of the national academies of Venezuela, Brazil, and Argentina, of the Royal Society of London, of the Accademia Nazionale dei Lincei, and of the American Philosophical Society. He was the first president of the Society of Vertebrate Paleontology and of the Society for the Study of Evolution, both of which he helped found, and was also president of the Society of Systematic Zoology and the American Society of Zoologists. He received 11 honorary degrees from universities in the United States, Canada, England, Scotland, and France. He was awarded 12 medals in the United States, England, France, Belgium, and Germany, including three from the National Academy of Sciences and the National Medal of Science.

Simpson wrote *Attending Marvels: A Patagonian Journal* (1934); *Quantitative Zoology*, with Anne Roe (1939; rev. ed. 1960); *Tempo and Mode in Evolution* (1944); *The Meaning of Evolution* (1949; paper 1965); *Horses* (1951; paper 1961); *Life of the Past* (1953; paper 1961); *The Major Features of Evolution* (1953); *Behavior and Evolution*, with Anne Roe (1958); *Principles of Animal Taxonomy* (1961); *This View of Life* (1964; paper 1966);

Life: An Introduction to Biology, with W. S. Beck (2d ed. 1965); and *The Geography of Evolution* (1965).

For background information *see* EVOLUTION, ORGANIC; MAMMALIA; MAMMALIA FOSSILS; PALEONTOLOGY in the McGraw-Hill Encyclopedia of Science and Technology.   □

SINNOTT, Edmund Ware

American botanist

Sinnott died on Jan. 6, 1968, in New Haven, Conn., U.S.A. See *McGraw-Hill Modern Men of Science*, Volume I.

★ SLICHTER, Louis Byrne

American geophysicist
Born May 19, 1896, Madison, Wis., U.S.A.

SLICHTER'S FIELD was the geophysics of the solid Earth. As a pioneer in the development of geophysical methods for prospecting for ore bodies, he was concerned with small- and large-scale interpretation problems and was engaged in both experimental and theoretical studies of the Earth. He also contributed studies of the probabilistic aspects of the search for minerals. He showed (1932) that the classical Herglotz-Wiechert method of interpreting seismic travel-time curves is also valid for discontinuous layered structures and for the associated cases in which rapid change of the velocity with depth produces triple-valued travel-time curves. Interpretation problems in which the observations ideally possess a unique interpretation are rare in geophysics, but Slichter (with R. E. Langer) found that other methods, in particular the dc, or resistivity, method and the electromagnetic method, also theoretically yield unique solutions when the pertinent physical properties vary only with depth. His study of the seismic interpretation problem for the sphere showed ideally, but not practicably, that the variation with depth of the two elastic parameters and the density may be deduced from observations of the complete seismic record at all distances from a known local source. Slichter and his students at the Massachusetts Institute of Technology made (1933) resistivity studies using as source a 30-mi power line grounded at each end. Refraction seismic studies of the crust and of the depth to the Mohorovičić discontinuity using large quarry blasts were made in Massachusetts and Wisconsin prior to World War II.

About this time extensive studies by Robley Evans and Clark Goodman indicated that the radioactivity of crust and mantle rocks is only one-third of that previously assigned to the corresponding rock types. Slichter reexamined the topic of the Earth's cooling, using the revised values of radioactivity, and illustrated the effects of the distribution of radioactivity and conductivity at depth with many models. The importance of heat transfer by convection, even for convection velocities as low as 0.002 cm per year, was emphasized, and the concept that the Earth could be heating rather than cooling at depth was given support.

Shortly after the war Slichter became director of the new Institute of Geophysics of the University of California. There he initiated early model studies of seismology and with his students continued model studies begun in 1928 concerning electromagnetic prospecting problems. He began (1949) gravity studies, which have continued since, of earth tides with LaCoste-Romberg gravimeters. He traced the major effects of the tidal losses in the dynamics of the Earth-Moon system (as had H. Gerstenkorn in Germany in a paper unfortunately then little known in the United States). Even today's minor loss rates imply an almost explosive change in the Earth's rotation rate and in the distance to the Moon in the early history of the system. Temporary earth-tide stations have been distributed over the world at 16 locations; the latest is a dual station recently established at the South Pole by C. L. Hager for long-term studies of monthly tides and for study of the Earth's natural vibrations. The high sensitivity of these gravimeters provides, in addition to the tidal variations, records of the free vibrations of the Earth excited by great earthquakes, first observed during the Chilean earthquake of 1960. On the axis of rotation these vibrations are expected to be unusually simple and sharply defined, since they should be free of the fine structure caused by rotation. (Since the zinc structure of the few low-degree modes which can be resolved has been found to be unsymmetrically excited, the center of an unresolved spectral band may be displaced slightly by an unknown amount and thus may lead to slightly erroneous frequency readings.) The vibrations of low degree which characterize the Earth as a whole, and in particular the purely dilatational $_0S_0$ mode, have been received with unusually high energy by LaCoste gravimeters. The studies by Slichter and his associates provide frequency values of high precision for the three dozen or so important spheroidal modes of low degree.

Both Slichter's parents were teachers. Slichter took his B.A. (1917) and Ph.D. in physics (1922) at the University of Wisconsin. Choosing an engineering career in steam turbines, he began as a student engineer at the General Electric Co., Schenectady. The change to the search for ore and thence to the more general aspects of geophysics occurred by the accident of his association with Max Mason's submarine detection work in World War I. After the war Mason's experience in this detection problem led to an invitation from a large mining company to study the applicability of electrical and other physical methods in the search for ore, and Slichter again became one of Mason's group. After a year (1930–31) as a research associate at the California Institute of Technology, Slichter joined the faculty of the Massachusetts Institute of Technology. He taught there from 1931 to 1945 and at the University of Wisconsin during 1946–47. In 1940 he was a member of the NAS committee to evaluate antisubmarine techniques for the U.S. Navy, and during World War II he was engaged in antisubmarine work. From 1947 to 1962 he was director of the Institute of Geophysics at the University of California, Los Angeles, and then became professor of geophysics there. Slichter was elected to the National Academy of Sciences in 1944 and to the American Academy of Arts and Sciences in 1957. In 1960 he received the Jackling Award of the American Society of Mining Engineers, in 1966 he was the recipient of the William Bowie Medal of the American Geophysical Union, and in 1967 he was awarded an honorary Sc.D. by the University of Wisconsin.

For background information *see* EARTH INTERIOR; EARTH TIDES; SEISMOLOGY in the McGraw-Hill Encyclopedia of Science and Technology. □

★ **SMALE, Stephen**

American mathematician
Born July 15, 1930, Flint, Mich., U.S.A.

THE GREATEST single influence on Smale's mathematics was the work in differential topology and global analysis of H. Poincaré. The work of M. Morse, H. Whitney, and R. Thom was also strongly influential.

Smale's first main work involved immersing spheres in euclidean space. Immersions are differentiable maps of manifolds (for example, surfaces and spheres) which have no corners or creases; in other words, the derivative does not collapse any tangent vectors, but the image may intersect itself. In 1956–57 Smale showed that any immersion of the 2-sphere in euclidean 3-space is deformable through immersions to the usual sphere in 3-space. The deformation is a continuous 1-parameter family of immersions with the derivative of the immersion also moving continuously with the parameter; for example, the map of the sphere which takes a point into its antipodal, that is, a reflection through the origin is deformable to the map which keeps every point fixed. In popular language this has been called "turning the sphere inside out."

Smale extended the 2-dimensional result to find the deformation classes of an arbitrary dimensional sphere into euclidean space of any dimension, and this became the basis of M. Hirsch's work classifying immersions of manifolds in general.

The next main phase was Smale's work on the structure of manifolds and the solution of "Poincaré's conjecture" in higher dimensions. Manifolds (spaces which are locally equivalent to euclidean space) classically have been central in topology; this discussion will assume that manifolds are compact (or closed, bounded subsets of euclidean space). Two manifolds are considered the same from the point of view of topology (or differential topology) if they are related by a homeomorphism or diffeomorphism. A homeomorphism is a continuous map with a continuous inverse, and a diffeomorphism is a differentiable map which has a differentiable inverse. Riemann had essentially solved the problem of classifying 2-dimensional manifolds, but little progress had been made for dimensions higher than 2.

The next simplest case seemed to be finding a solution to Poincaré's conjecture, which says that a manifold having the same homotopy groups (an algebraic invariant of a manifold) as the 3-dimensional sphere must be homeomorphic to a 3-sphere. This problem, still unsolved, seemed to be a barrier to understanding the structure of manifolds in general.

What Smale did, with his "handlebody theory," was to give an affirmative answer to the higher-dimensional problem. In fact, he showed that an n-dimensional (differentiable) manifold whose homotopy groups were the same as the n-sphere was homeomorphic to the n-sphere whenever n was larger than 4. At the same time he proved the "h-cobordism theorem," which says that two manifolds (of dimension greater than 4 and simply connected) are diffeomorphic if they are h-cobordant. Since h-cobordism is a relation between manifolds that is based on well-studied phenomena, namely, homotopy theory and cobordism theory, for the first time a practical criterion was established for telling when two manifolds are the same. This applied immediately to give algebraic criterion for a manifold to be an n-dimensional ball for n larger than 4. Furthermore, using the work of Milnor and Kervaire on h-cobordism classes of homotopy spheres (manifolds whose homotopy groups are the same as a sphere), Smale then obtained the diffeomorphism classification of homotopy spheres and showed that the number of unequivalent differential structures on the n-sphere is finite if n is larger than 4. In most respects the 3- and 4-dimensional problems were successfully bypassed in differential topology. In these dimensions the main problems are still unsolved.

In 1961 Smale left topology to study differential equations. He examined both partial and ordinary differential equations (mostly the latter, however) from the point of view of a topologist. This approach, called global analysis, implies that one considers the differential equation in terms of manifolds and vector space bundles and is ready to use the body of knowledge of topology as a tool in attempting to understand the differential equation. This approach allows one to consider the set of all solutions in a more natural setting. Smale studied nonlinear elliptic differential equations, in one case giving existence theorems using Morse calculus of variations theory abstracted to infinite dimensional manifolds. In a second case he found the nature of nearby solutions using a generalization of Sard's theorem to infinite dimensional manifolds. He considered an ordinary differential equation as a differentiable dynamical system or a 1-parameter group acting on a manifold. Around the idea of structural stability, he developed some picture of the nature of all solutions of a large class of such differential equations.

Smale was brought up and went to school in

Michigan, receiving his Ph.D. at the University of Michigan in 1956. His next years were spent at the University of Chicago; the Princeton Institute for Advanced Study; IMPA, Rio de Janeiro; and the University of California, Berkeley. He accepted a professorship at Columbia in 1961 but returned to Berkeley in 1964. In 1966 he received the Veblen Prize of the American Mathematical Society (shared with B. Mazur and M. Brown) and the Fields Medal of the International Union of Mathematicians.

For background information *see* DIFFERENTIAL EQUATION; TOPOLOGY in the McGraw-Hill Encyclopedia of Science and Technology.   □

★ SMIRNOV, Vladimir Ivanovich

Soviet geologist
Born Jan. 31, 1910, Moscow, Russia

THE PLANET Earth is about 4,000,000,000 years old, but the most essential part of its mineral deposits originated in its interior during the past 1,000,000,000 years, during the Neogea. In the course of this time the upper shells of the Earth's crust developed, including the bulk of the ores, as well as coal, petroleum, and combustible gas. The mineral deposits of the Earth are characterized to an extraordinary degree by the nonuniformity of their distribution on the territory of the planet. Smirnov demonstrated that such nonuniformity is determined by special features of the geological history of the development of the Earth's crust—its discrete, cyclic, and stage character and tectonic differentiation.

The discrete state is related to the separation of the Earth's surface into platforms (its most stable parts) and a geosyncline (its mobile zone), in which there has been a concentration of intensive tectonic movement, magmatism, and endogenic ore formation. Very complex is the geological history of endogenic ore deposits which originated in the interior of the Earth's crust from magma melts, as well as the gases and vapors which separated from it and condensed into the hot mineral sources.

The cyclic state determined the recurrence of the main geological events and the formation of endogenic deposits in the Neogea. Five cycles are separated: Baikal (1000–600 million years), Caledonian (600–400 million years), Hercynian (400–250 million years), Cimmerian (250–100 million years), and Alpine (100 million years to present time). Corresponding to these cycles are the metallogenic epochs with inherent collections of ore deposits.

The stage process is inherent to the development of the geosynclines, independently of their classification in one or another geological cycle. For geosynclines of any cycle three stages of development are indicated. In the early stage there is an accumulation of depositions, which is accompanied by the intrusion of basalt magma from the subcrustal depths. The origin of deposits of chromium, titanium, copper, iron, and platinum is related to the solidification of this magma. In the middle stage the rocks are compressed in folds, and there is the intrusion of granite magma, whose mineralized vapors and gases form the deposits of beryllium, lithium, tin, tungsten, molybdenum, and other rare elements. In the late stage mountain chains with volcanoes originate in the place of the geosyncline. These give rise to deposits of lead, zinc, gold, uranium, and certain other elements. The degree of manifestation of the magmatism and ore formation in successive stages of geological development is different for different types of geosynclines. In those cases in which there were intensive processes in the early stage, the magmatism and ore formation in the late stage turned out to be reduced. On the other hand, with a weak ore formation in the early stage, there was observed an abundance of deposits in the later stage. This phenomenon led to the separation of metallogenic provinces with characteristic ore deposits.

The tectonic differentiation led to a situation in which the intrusion of magmas of a definite composition and the origin of ore deposits associated with them during succeeding stages of the geosyncline cycle took place not over the entire bed of the geosyncline but in its strictly defined sections indicated by tectonic differentiation of its transverse cross section. Thus, the products of the basalt magma became localized in the deepest tectonic troughs while the granite magmas became localized in the interthrough space. This phenomenon led to ordering in the belt distribution of the endogenic ore deposits in the transverse cross section of the geosyncline and the mountain chains that form in their place, and it is the origin of the regional zonality in the distribution of the deposits on the territory of the metallogenic provinces.

By utilizing the enumerated natural correlations in the formation and regional distribution of the ore deposits, Smirnov prepared in 1958 the first metallogenic map of the Soviet Union. This map shows the areas of the distribution of the deposits of five metallogenic epochs which delimit the metallogenic provinces of the country. The map served as a document in directing the prospecting and discovery of new ore deposits. For this work Smirnov was awarded the Order of Lenin, the highest order of the Soviet Union. The regional analysis of the metallogeny of the territory of the Soviet Union was facilitated by the personal field geological studies of Smirnov in a number of large ore provinces of the country. For many years he studied the geology and ore deposits of ancient geological structures of Central Asia and young geological formations of the Caucasus and also worked in the Far East and in Siberia.

The study of the metallogeny of the territory of the Soviet Union made it possible for Smirnov to refine substantially the concept of the genesis of endogenic ore deposits. This refinement reflected particularly clearly during the determination of the conditions of the formation of copper-zinc deposits, related to the volcanic processes of the early stage of the neosyncline cycles in the geological history. To study these Smirnov divided the ore deposits into two large groups: magmatogenic ones, which form from magmas, and sedimentary ones, which form in the depositions of ancient seas. The copper-zinc deposits serving as an example, it was shown that it is possible to separate a third group of complex magmatogenic-sedimentary formations. Their genesis is determined by the deposition of a part of the substance at a depth from mineralized gases infiltrating through the porous rocks; the other part was deposited on the bottom of ancient seas, where there was penetration of such gases, which carried off the metallic compounds from the interior of the Earth.

Smirnov received his higher education at the Moscow Geological School in the Moscow Geologic-Prospecting Institute, finishing in 1934. There in 1938 he defended his candidate of science dissertation on ore deposits of Northern Tien-Shan. Prior to World War II he worked in the Institute as an associate professor. During the war he headed the geological service at the mercury pits in Central Asia. The data on the geology of the mercury deposits formed the basis of his dissertation for the degree of doctor of science, which he defended in 1945. From 1946 to 1951 Smirnov was deputy minister of geology of the Soviet Union and at the same time professor of applied geology in the Moscow Geologic-Prospecting Institute. From 1951 he held the chair of geology of minerals in the geology department of Moscow State University.

In 1958 he was elected a corresponding member of the Academy of Sciences of the U.S.S.R. and in 1962 an active member.

Smirnov wrote 320 scientific publications, including 11 books.

For background information *see* Geosyncline; Magma; Ore and mineral deposits; Tectonophysics; Zoogeographic region in the McGraw-Hill Encyclopedia of Science and Technology.   □

★ SMITH, Cyril Stanley

American metallurgist
Born Oct. 4, 1903, Birmingham, England

As a research metallurgist with the American Brass Company in Waterbury, Conn., from 1927 to 1942, Smith determined the constitution diagrams for several copper alloy systems; did the first work on internal oxidation of alloys (in which finely divided oxide particles on a minor alloying element are formed within a matrix of the principal one); made studies of magnetic brass, of copper-iron alloys and copper steels, and of free-machining copper alloys; determined various physical properties of alloys, including thermal conductivity, elasticity, and fatigue; and worked on the mechanisms of grain growth, precipitation hardening, and transformation in alloys. He spent many hours at the microscope in the study of alloy microstructure at a time when most research metallurgists were abandoning the "old-fashioned" microscope for the exciting new tool of x-ray diffraction.

In World War II, after a year in Washington, Smith joined the Los Alamos Laboratory at its inception in 1943, and was put in charge of metallurgy. The properties and technology of the new metal plutonium had to be learned on the basis of experiments with extremely limited quantities of material. Smith and his group discovered it to be quite unique, for it has five different allotropic forms with huge density differences between them. His group also learned to fabricate uranium metal, tungsten carbide, boron, and many other exotic materials in far larger pieces than any commercial company had ever done.

After the war Smith went to the University of Chicago, where he organized and directed the Institute for the Study of Metals, the first "interdisciplinary" materials research laboratory in the United States. For his personal research he returned to the microstructure of metals and established the fundamental relationship between the three-dimensional reality of a structure and what can be seen on a two-dimensional section. He also showed that the grains of different constituents in an alloy take their shape from their interfaces, not their bulk crystallinity. In a typical polycrystalline material these interfaces (grain boundaries) have the mobility of fluids and join at angles determined by surface tension, just as in a froth of soap bubbles. Simple topological relations show that the pentagon is the most frequent grain face, as it is in soap bubbles. The equilibrium angles vary with the specific interfaces involved. In alloys minor amounts of a liquid sometimes completely surround and prevent contact between the grains of the major crystalline phase—a fact that is responsible, for example, for the extreme brittleness of hot steel containing a little sulfur without manganese. These very simple concepts have proved useful in alloy development, and geologists are beginning to see their application to problems of ore formation. Another field of research was the study of the microstructure of metals after explosive shock, which contributed to understanding the double shock wave in steel and high-pressure phase changes generally.

Shortly after his marriage in 1931 to a historian, and encouraged by the proximity of the Yale library, Smith became interested in the historical literature on metallurgy. Because there was very little in the standard histories of science and technology, he had to seek and study the original sources themselves and eventually accumulated a library of his own. In collaboration with others expert in various languages, he published English translations of the metallurgical classics—Theophilus (ca. 1125), Biringuccio (1540), Ercker (1574), Réaumur (1722), Bergman (1781), and others. The impact of science on metallurgy, together with the converse influence of the craftsman's practical knowledge upon science was the topic of his book *A History of Metallography* (1960) and several papers. The search for texture in metals led him to the Japanese sword, which embodies perhaps the most skillful metalwork ever done, and he published the only detailed study of the metallography of these weapons outside of Japan. In recent years Smith used metallurgical laboratory techniques to "read" the record in archeological artifacts for information on the beginnings of metallurgy and, finding that most ingenious techniques usually appear first in decorative objects, he explored the historical use of metals in art.

Smith studied metallurgy at the University of Birmingham (B.Sc., 1924) and the Massachusetts Institute of Technology (Sc.D., 1926). He was elected to the American Academy of Arts and Sciences in 1950 and to the National Academy of Sciences in 1957.

For background information *see* COPPER ALLOYS; CRYSTAL STRUCTURE; METAL, MECHANICAL PROPERTIES OF; PLUTONIUM in the McGraw-Hill Encyclopedia of Science and Technology. □

★ SMYTH, Charles Phelps

American chemist
Born Feb. 10, 1895, Clinton, N.Y., U.S.A.

SMYTH'S PRINCIPAL research used electric dipoles in molecules as a means of studying the structure of matter. An electric dipole is a pair of electric charges equal in size, opposite in sign, and close together. Its size is measured by its moment ,a vector quantity which is the product of one of the two charges by the distance between them. P. J. W. Debye had provided a means of obtaining dipole moments by relating dielectric constant and absorption or loss to the dipole moments of molecules. Smyth used a modified version of the Debye equation to calculate approximate dipole moments for many molecules, and in 1924 he compared them with the moments estimated for the currently hypothecated electronic arrangements of the molecules. The moment thus obtained for the water molecule showed the incorrectness of the symmetrical structure which had been proposed for it. Many of the dipole moments found showed the necessity of the then controversial concept of directed covalence. Optical refractions, which arise from induced dipole moments, were used in 1925 to calculate group refractions and to show relations between polarizabilities and bonding forces. Many measurements of the dielectric constants of gases and of solutions were then carried out and used to calculate dipole moments for molecular structure studies. In 1927 the planarity of the hexagonal benzene ring was thus proved at a time when x-ray analysis was thought to indicate a puckered structure. Dipole moment values showed the incorrectness of some of the electronic theories of organic chemistry at that time. Measurements and calculations on molecules containing internally rotatable dipoles gave expressions for their resultant moments and for the internal potential energies hindering the dipole rotation. In 1935 evidence was obtained of the coexistence of molecules in different potential energy minima with different dipole moments, a phenomenon later extensively studied elsewhere and called "rotational isomerism." A different attack upon the problem of intermolecular forces had been employed in 1929 when the partial vapor pressures of binary mixtures were measured and used to show the inadequacy of an ingenious theory of intermolecular surface energies which had been proposed by Irving Langmuir.

From the determination of molecular geometry Smyth and his co-workers extended their dipole moment investigations to the polarities of chemical bonds and the electronegativities of the bonded atoms. The polarities of different types of bonds were established and some improvement was effected in the electronegativity scale of the elements. Moment measurements of aromatic molecules and molecules containing conjugated systems showed that electron shifts predicted in terms of resonance and mesomerism actually occurred, but to a much smaller extent than had been predicted. Moments found for many dye molecules containing conjugated systems showed a close relation between charge shift and color.

The relation between dielectric constant and dipole moment is dependent upon the ability of the dipolar molecules to orient in the alternating electric field used in measuring the dielectric constant. Therefore Smyth and his co-workers began in 1933 to use dielectric constant measurements to show that many nearly spherical or cylindrical molecules could rotate in crystalline solids even down to low temperatures where the disappearance of rotation accompanied a phase transition. In the cases of a few nearly spherical molecules, the internal friction hindering rotation was found to be even less in the crystal than in the liquid state. In many respects this crystalline rotator phase differed less from the liquid phase than it did from the normal crystalline phase, and years later it was termed by J. Timmermans a new mesomorphic state of matter. Dielectric constant and loss measurements showed proton transfer or jump from molecule to molecule in the rotator states of long-chain, hydrogen-bonded alcohols.

A dielectric investigation of polypeptides by Smyth and his co-workers in 1941 gave some information about their structure, but also made clear how little was known about the dielectric behavior of molecules in very high frequency electric fields. In 1946 a long-continuing investigation was begun of the dielectric relaxation of dipolar molecules at microwave frequencies. The consequent establishment of the relations of dielectric relaxation time to molecular structure, size, and shape, as well as the internal field in a liquid, and the intermolecular forces causing friction made dielectric relaxation time a tool for the study of the structure of matter. The development of accurate apparatus for measurement with millimeter waves led to more accurate molecular relaxation times and greatly facilitated the investigation of intramolecular motion. Resonance effects, steric hindrance, hydrogen bonding, and intermolecular action in liquids were thus investigated. The measurements of the dielectric absorption of liquids at 2.2-mm wavelength narrowed such gaps as may have remained between millimeter waves and the far-infrared.

Smyth received an A.B. with highest honors in chemistry from Princeton University in 1916 and an A.M. in 1917. In 1919–20 he studied at Harvard University with T. W. Richards, the first American Nobel laureate in chemistry, and obtained his Ph.D. in chemistry from Harvard in 1921. From 1920, when he returned to Princeton as an instructor, until his retirement in 1963 as David B. Jones Professor of Chemistry, he was a member of the faculty of Princeton University. After retirement he continued research at Princeton, but devoted a considerable part of his time to work as a consultant for the Office of Naval Research. During World War II he worked on the atom bomb as a chemist for the Manhattan District Project, and served on a special mission with the Army in the combat area. In 1947 he received the Medal of Freedom from the U.S. Army and in 1954 the Nichols Medal from the New York Section of the American Chemical Society. He was elected to the National Academy of Sciences in 1955.

Smyth published more than 275 scientific papers and two books, *Dielectric Constant and Molecular Structure* (1931) and *Dielectric Behavior and Structure* (1955).

For background information *see* DIELECTRIC CONSTANT; DIELECTRICS; DIPOLE MOMENT; INTERMOLECULAR FORCES; MOLECULAR STRUCTURE AND SPECTRA in the McGraw-Hill Encyclopedia of Science and Technology.   □

★ SNELL, Esmond Emerson

American biochemist
Born Sept. 22, 1914, Salt Lake City, Utah, U.S.A.

A T A time when little was known concerning the identity of the water-soluble vitamins or of substances required for the growth of bacteria, Snell undertook an analysis of the requirements for growth of the nutritionally complex lactic acid bacteria. He first confirmed the observations (S. Orla-Jensen) that the vitamin riboflavin was required by some of these organisms, and he introduced in 1939 the first successful microbiological assay method for the quantitative determination of a vitamin in food materials. This procedure was later extended to the quantitative determination of many different vitamins and amino acids. Such methods are based on the observation that cell growth, as measured by optical methods or by the formation of by-products of growth, such as lactic acid, is within limits proportional to the amount of an essential vitamin, amino acid, or trace element present in an otherwise complete growth medium. Such methods did much to stimulate the interest of biochemists in microorganisms as tools for biochemical investigations, a development of enormous importance in the history of biochemistry and nutrition.

Snell's investigations of the nutrition of lactic acid bacteria led to the initial or independent discovery of folic acid, pantothenic acid, and the "acetate-replacing factor" (lipoic acid) and provided methods used extensively in their subsequent isolation and characterization. They also led to the initial discovery and synthesis of two new forms of vitamin B_6, pyridoxal and pyridoxamine, and of pantethine and pantetheine, the latter being the bound form of pantothenic acid which forms the functional portion of coenzyme A (F. A. Lipmann) and acyl carrier protein (P. R. Vagelos). His observations that D-alanine replaces vitamin B_6 for growth of lactic acid bacteria under certain restrictive conditions led to his initial demonstration that this "unnatural" form of the amino acid is a structural component of the cell wall of bacteria. For growth with D-alanine replacing vitamin B_6, some bacteria require peptides. Identification of these as peptides of L-alanine led to the hypothesis, later confirmed, that D-alanine inhibits uptake of L-alanine and that peptides containing L-alanine promote growth because their uptake is mediated by a different stereospecific uptake system than that required for uptake of L-alanine. A number of other conditions under which peptides are required for growth in lieu of their component amino acids were discovered and explained in terms of independent uptake systems.

In work with organisms other than lactic acid bacteria, Snell purified the natural vitamin antagonist avidin and studied its interaction with biotin. He also demonstrated the essential metabolic role (still not fully explained) of spermidine and spermine by showing that these compounds were essential for growth of *Hemophilus parainfluenzae.*

Following clarification of the nutritional requirements of lactic acid bacteria, Snell turned to a detailed investigation of the mode of action of vitamin B_6. Pyridoxal was found to catalyze a series of nonenzymatic reactions of amino acids that simulated closely the corresponding enzymatic reactions catalyzed in living organisms by pyridoxal phosphate-dependent enzymes. Detailed study of these reactions and the structural features necessary for their catalysis, with D. E. Metzler, M. Ikawa, and other students and associates, led to the proposal in 1954 of a general mechanism for the action of vitamin B_6–dependent enzymes. This mechanism (also proposed independently by A. E. Braunstein) had predictive as well as correlative value in explaining the multiple roles played by vitamin B_6–containing enzymes in living organisms and forms the basis for currently accepted views of the action of these enzymes. Snell and his collaborators then studied several pure pyridoxal phosphate enzymes and also identified several metabolic intermediates which arise during the breakdown of vitamin B_6 by bacteria, which proceeds via succinic and acetic acids to carbon dioxide and water. Similar studies of metabolism of pantothenic acid revealed its breakdown via dimethylmalic acid and α-ketoisovaleric acid to carbon dioxide and water. Snell's recent interests revolved around the biosynthesis, function, and detailed mechanism of action of vitamin B_6 and its derivatives.

Snell received his B.A. (1935) in chemistry from Brigham Young University and his M.A. (1936) and Ph.D. (1938) in biochemistry from the University of Wisconsin, where his major professor was W. H. Peterson. In 1939 he went to the University of Texas as a postdoctoral research associate with R. J. Williams. He became assistant professor in 1941. Subsequently, he held professorial positions at the universities of Texas and Wisconsin. In 1953 he served as Walker-Ames Professor of Biochemistry at the University of Washington, and in 1954 and 1962 he was a Guggenheim fellow at Cambridge, Copenhagen, Zurich, and Munich. In 1956 he joined the University of California, Berkeley, as professor of biochemistry and served as chairman of the department of biochemistry from 1956 to 1962. Snell received the Eli Lilly Award in Bacteriology and Immunology from the Society of American Bacteriologists in 1945; and the Mead-Johnson Vitamin B Complex Award in 1946 and the Osborne-Mendel Award in 1951, both from the American Institute of Nutrition. He was elected to the National Academy of Sciences in 1954 and to the American Academy of Arts and Sciences in 1962.

For background information *see* BIOASSAY; PANTOTHENIC ACID; VITAMIN; VITAMIN B$_6$ in the McGraw-Hill Encyclopedia of Science and Technology. ☐

★ **SOBOLEV, Vladimir Stepanovich**

Soviet petrologist and mineralogist
Born May 30, 1908, Lugansk, Russia

THE MAIN volcanic rocks of Permian-Triassic age—the so-called Siberian traps—are distributed on the Siberian platform between the Yenisei and Lena rivers over an area of more than 1,000,000 km². These formed during the outflow of lava onto the Earth's surface as well as during intrusion of magma at a shallow depth. Sobolev studied these rocks in 1931–36 and showed that their differentiation varies substantially from the Bowen system. During the successive evolution of the melt there, no ordi-

nary interchange of the iron-magnesia minerals occurred, but there was a rapid rise in the FeO/MgO ratio; in particular, the content of the fayalite component in the olivines varied in the series of rocks from 20 to 80%. Later, using as an example the igneous rocks of the Ukrainian Shield and by comparisons with other areas, Sobolev showed that this feature is general for magmatic complexes of platforms; this was dealt with in a paper presented at the seventeenth session of the International Geologic Congress in Moscow in 1937.

While studying the Siberian traps, Sobolev observed the great similarity of the volcanism of the Siberian platform with other such areas and, in particular, with the entire geology and volcanism of South Africa. Later he described a specific alkali basaltoid which is close to the rocks that accompany the kimberlites and probably related genetically to the latter. This brought the history of the volcanism of the Siberian platform still closer to that of South Africa and made it possible in 1938–41 to hypothesize about the probability of the discovery in the northern part of the Siberian platform of a kimberlite formation and related diamond deposits. This hypothesis was later confirmed by discovery of the large-scale diamond deposits in northern Siberia.

During 1943–49 Sobolev studied general problems of mineralogy and, in particular, the mineralogy of silicates. At that time the basic problems of the structure of silicates were solved (W. L. Bragg, E. Shiebold, and others), and it was established that the different role of aluminum in the crystal lattice is related to its coordination number, that is, to the number of oxygen atoms surrounding it, which can be equal to 6 (for example, garnets) or 4 (feldspars). However, the great significance of these data was not yet fully recognized by all mineralogists, and some considered it possible to utilize old formulas and classifications. Sobolev showed that all properties of minerals (with increasing coordination number of aluminum, the hardness, specific gravity, index of refraction, and acid resistance increase) depend on the specific features of the structure, while the structure itself is related to the conditions of formation: Drop in temperature, rise in pressure, and drop in concentrations of strong bases favor a rise in the coordination number of aluminum and of cations in general. These data made it possible to predict the specific structural features of a number of silicates which had not yet been studied: epidote, prehnite, lawsonite, and tourmaline. The Grimm-Goldschmidt concept was also developed, and a direct relationship was shown to exist between the crystallochemical laws of isomorphism and the melting diagrams of solid solutions: With increasing r_1–r_2 of mutually interchangeable ions, the melting diagram changes from the first to the third and then to the fifth type (Roozeboom). For his book *Introduction to the Mineralogy of Silicates* (1949), Sobolev was awarded a State Prize of the U.S.S.R. and honorable mention by the All-Union Mineralogical Society. He also examined the general problem of mineral classification and proposed changes.

From 1950 Sobolev and his co-workers concentrated on the study of physicochemical conditions of mineral formation. He examined the role of pressure in the formation of jadeite, pyrope, and other minerals with a hexad coordination of aluminum, defending the need for high pressures of the order of 10–20 kilobars. At the same time it was assumed that the pressures in the Earth's crust could exceed considerably (up to 10 kilobars) those calculated from the hydrostatic system, considering the weight of above-lying rocks.

Sobolev studied xenolites of eclogites (partly diamond-bearing), and peridotites from kimberlite pipes of Yakutiya, supposedly eroded from the mantle of the Earth. He reached a conclusion about the considerable differentiation of the mantle by composition from ultrabasites to basites and about two types of the Moho discontinuity: The chemical boundary was related to a change in the composition from basites to ultrabasites in some areas, and to the physicochemical boundary of the transition of plagioclase-containing basic rocks into eclogites in other areas. The phenomenon of the transition of hypersthene crystalline slates of the Earth's crust into eclogites was shown.

He described a new type of the Earth's mantle rock, called grospydite, which formed under high pressures like disthene eclogite but differed in the grossularite composition of garnet.

Sobolev opposed the tendency in recent decades to reduce greatly the temperatures of formation of magmatic and metamorphic rocks. He indicated that indirect considerations, as well as the homogenization of vitreous and gas-liquid inclusions in minerals, show that the temperatures of formation of porphyritic phenocrysts of volcanic rocks are 1200–1300°C and of nepheline syenites and granites 800–1100° (and not 500–700°), and that the lower temperature boundary of metamorphism of green schists is 400°. In connection with this, he showed that the partial pressures of water in high-temperature metamorphism are small (about 20–40% of the total pressure) and rise for low-temperature processes (up to 70–80%). He established by direct methods that the partial pressure of carbonic acid in metamorphic minerals of noncarbonate rocks (inclusions in disthene) is high. These data were partly summarized in the *Map of Metamorphic Facies in the U.S.S.R.* (1966), which was the first map of its kind for such an extensive terri-

tory; its coauthors with Sobolev were N. L. Dobretsov, V. V. Reverdatto, N. V. Sobolev, E. N. Ushakova, and V. V. Khlestov.

Sobolev graduated from the Leningrad Mining Institute in 1930. He started to work in the Central Geological Research Institute in Leningrad while teaching at the Mining Institute. From 1945 to 1958 he was a professor at Lvov University. In 1951 he was elected a corresponding member of the Academy of Sciences of the Ukrainian S.S.R. and in 1958 an active member of the Academy of Sciences of the U.S.S.R. From 1958 he was deputy director of the Institute of Geology and Geophysics of the Siberian Branch of the Academy of Sciences of the U.S.S.R. and a professor at Novosibirsk University.

For background information *see* METAMORPHISM; MINERAL; PETROLOGY; SILICATE MINERALS in the McGraw-Hill Encyclopedia of Science and Technology.   □

★ SPEDDING, Frank Harold

American chemist
Born Oct. 22, 1902, Hamilton, Ontario, Canada

DURING THE 1940s and early 1950s, in collaboration with his graduate students and colleagues, Spedding succeeded in developing processes for separating the individual rare earths in exceptionally high purity and at reasonable cost. He also developed processes for reducing them to the pure metallic state in massive form. These processes have been adopted by a number of industrial companies and, as a result, the individual rare-earth compounds and metals changed from laboratory curiosities, which only a few scientists had seen, to readily available items of commerce at reasonable prices.

All the rare earths exist in the trivalent state in compounds and in solutions. The highly charged rare-earth ions strongly attract water dipoles so that each rare-earth ion is encased in a water envelope. Therefore, the rare-earth ions behave very much alike in aqueous solutions and in hydrated salts. They readily form precipitates composed of mixed salts or solid solutions of one rare earth in another. Accordingly, any chemical reaction carried out in aqueous solutions results only in a slight enrichment of one rare earth over another. As a result, literally thousands of fractionations had to be performed before reasonably pure rare-earth compounds could be obtained. Until the late 1940s most individual rare-earth compounds were isolated by fractional processes, and one of the tough problems of inorganic chemistry was how to separate the rare earths rapidly and cheaply.

Spedding and his associates developed separation processes using chelate ions which complex with the rare-earth ions and result in better separation factors. The chelates are organic molecules which wrap themselves around the rare-earth ions, replacing most of the adjacent water molecules, and the separations make use of ion exchange columns where the repeated operations are carried out automatically.

While working for his Ph.D. and studying thermodynamics and theoretical chemistry under G. N. Lewis, Spedding became interested in the mathematical relations which relate one property of a substance with another property of that substance. Noting that the properties of the rare-earth compounds change gradually and in a definite direction over several members of the rare-earth series, he became convinced that the rare earths are the ideal group of elements upon which to check these mathematical relationships. They also possess the very desirable property of having sharp line absorption spectra at low temperatures so that the techniques of spectroscopy can be applied. Spedding and his associates demonstrated that the structure of the multiplets reflected the crystal environment about the rare-earth ions and compounds.

During 1932–34 he also collaborated with Lewis in developing methods for concentrating heavy water. He did the spectrographic work which determined the degree of concentrations Lewis was achieving. As a by-product of this work, he teamed up with C. D. Shane and N. S. Grace in determining a more precise value of e/m and the fine structure constant.

At Cornell University in 1935–37 Spedding collaborated with H. A. Bethe in showing that the sharp absorption lines of the rare earths arise from inner transitions of the $4f^n$ electrons of the ions. At Iowa State University in 1937–41 he started research programs on methods of separating individual rare earths and of separating isotopes. He also continued his program on the study of the energy levels of the rare-earth ions.

Early in 1942 the United States government decided to form a laboratory at the University of Chicago for an all-out effort to see whether a self-sustaining nuclear chain reaction was possible. A. H. Compton was appointed director, and because of Spedding's wide knowledge of the rare elements, Compton asked him to organize the chemistry division of the laboratory. Since chemical and metallurgical research needed to be started immediately, it was agreed that Spedding would spend half of each week at Chicago, recruiting staff and obtaining space in which to do the work necessary to get the laboratory started, and he would spend the remaining half of each week at Ames, where some space was available for immediate research. The groups at Ames were to be pulled into Chicago when that laboratory got under way. However, the research groups Spedding was directing at Ames were so successful that by the end of the year the government decided to maintain a laboratory there, and Spedding was asked to be its full-time director.

The physicists at Chicago needed materials of high purity if they were to get a self-sustaining chain reaction going. While they started building their exponential piles with pressed uranium oxide and graphite, they urgently wanted very pure metal for the inner core. At the start of the project uranium metal was hard to get, not very pure, and very expensive, so an extensive program was started with a number of industries and government laboratories to develop processes for producing pure uranium ingots. During 1942, Spedding, H. A. Wilhelm, and C. F. Gray developed processes for casting uranium in graphite instead of beryllium oxide and found that pure uranium melted at around 1100°C instead of 1800°C as previously reported. Also during this period Spedding, Wilhelm, and W. H. Keller developed processes for producing high-purity uranium using first calcium and later magnesium to reduce UF_4 to uranium metal. These processes were so successful that during November, 1942, the Ames Laboratory produced about 2 tons, one-third of the metal available for the first self-sustaining nuclear chain reaction experiment, which took place on Dec. 2, 1942, at Stagg Field, Chicago.

Spedding was asked to turn the Ames uranium process over to industry and to produce as much metal as possible in the meantime, while industries were scaling up these processes. The Ames Laboratory produced over 2,000,000 lb, and for its achievement was awarded the Army-Navy E Flag with four stars. (These same basic processes are still used by industry.) As soon as these industries started large-scale production of the metal, the group at Ames devoted itself to the production of pure thorium and cerium.

Spedding, Wilhelm, and Keller developed a successful process for producing highly pure metallic thorium and also turned this process over to industry. During the industrial build-up they produced several hundred thousand pounds of thorium metal. They also developed a process for producing metallic cerium and produced a ton of this material for use in making high-purity cerium sulfide crucibles. For the wartime work at Ames, Iowa State University was granted the Chemical Engineering Achievement Award, and Spedding was awarded an honorary L.L.D. at Drake University.

At the end of the war the Manhattan District decided that it did not want to see the fine group of scientists Spedding had assembled—who were experts in pure materials, high-temperature metallurgy, and the chemistry and metallurgy of the rare elements—dispersed, so it asked Iowa State University to operate a national laboratory. When the Atomic Energy Commission took over the Manhattan District, it was decided to continue this laboratory as one of the broad-based integrated laboratories under university contract, with Spedding as director.

During the next several years, in additon to his administrative work, Spedding devoted his major research effort to finding methods of purifying individual rare earths, making pure metals, and determining the physical and chemical properties of the rare-earth metals, alloys, and compounds. During this period his group worked out in detail the theory of the separation of rare earths on ion-exchange columns and, in collaboration with Jack A. Powell, applied these methods to the separation of nitrogen isotopes. They succeeded in separating to 99.8% purity 200 grams of N^{15}. During the late 1950s, when yttrium metal was needed by the AEC for atomic research, Ames Laboratory again developed processses for large-scale production of the metal, turned this process over to industry, and produced 9 tons in the interim.

Son of a professional photographer, Spedding received a B.S. in chemical engineering with a major in metallurgy at the University of Michigan in 1925. He received an M.S. in analytical chemistry there under H. H. Willard in 1926. His Ph.D. in physical chemistry was earned under G. N. Lewis at the University of California, Berkeley, in 1929. He was a National Research Council fellow at California in 1930–32 and an instructor in chemistry in 1932–34. On a Guggenheim fellowship he spent 1934–35 studying theoretical chemistry and physics under J. E. Lennard-Jones and R. W. Fowler at Cambridge University. He taught at Cornell from 1935 to 1937, then moved to Iowa State University, where he became professor of physical chemistry (1941), professor of physics (1950), and professor of metallurgy (1962). From 1945 he was also director of the Institute for Atomic Research. In addition to several honorary degrees, he received

the Nichols Medal of the New York Section of the American Chemical Society in 1952 for his research in the chemistry of rare earths, and the James Douglas Medal of the American Institute of Mining, Metallurgical, and Petroleum Engineers in 1961 for his work in the metallurgy of the rare-earth metals and uranium. He was elected to the National Academy of Sciences in 1952.

Spedding wrote *The Rare Earths*, with A. H. Daane (1961).

For background information *see* CHELATION; METAL AND MINERAL PROCESSING; RARE-EARTH ELEMENTS; REACTOR PHYSICS in the McGraw-Hill Encyclopedia of Science and Technology.   ☐

★ SPERRY, Roger Wolcott

American neurobiologist
Born Aug. 20, 1913, Hartford, Conn., U.S.A.

FOLLOWING SOME early graduate work on the neural basis of memory and the cerebral control of motor coordination, Sperry was attracted by numerous reports that motor coordination remains undisturbed after surgical disarrangements of nerve-muscle and other end-organ connections. There seemed to be no functional limitation on the kinds of nerve, muscle, and sense organ substitutions that might be employed in clinical surgery to restore lost function. The implications for brain function were far-reaching and had become incorporated in various antiswitchboard interpretations of cerebral organization. When he tried to investigate the central mechanism of these reeducative readjustments in the laboratory, the anticipated readaptations failed to occur. His nerve and muscle transplants in rats and monkeys led instead to severe motor and sensory disturbances that persisted indefinitely with little or no correction by reeducation.

These experimental contradictions of the earlier claims of functional readaptation led to the publication in 1945 of an extensive critique and refutation of the whole doctrine of central nervous plasticity prevailing at that time. Instead of the loose, universal functional plasticity formerly inferred in brain connections, the new evidence pointed to a rather strict functional specificity in the basic wiring diagram of the vertebrate brain. This revised interpretation was subsequently confirmed in many nerve regeneration and related studies. Aspects of cerebral organization that formerly had seemed mysteriously dynamic and unapproachable were thereby tied to brain circuit patterns and accordingly brought within range of experimentation.

The only exception to the new interpretation was its failure to account for a series of experimental findings in lower vertebrates—frogs, toads, and salamanders, in which orderly functional recoveries were consistently obtained despite extreme surgical scrambling and radical disarrangements in the normal pattern of nerve connections. In an effort to resolve the foregoing, Sperry embarked on a series of experiments on the selective growth of nerve connections in development and regeneration. It was in his early studies on transplantation of the eye at Harvard University in 1941 that he first demonstrated the strict correlation between visual perception and the anatomical patterning of the optic nerve connections. Upside-down vision, vision inverted front-to-back, and various combinations of the two were found to persist in machinelike fashion and to correspond closely with the surgical orientation of the eye and with the nerve fiber patterns connecting eye and brain. The demonstrated correlation between perceptual functions and brain circuitry overrode prevailing theories to the contrary and provided an important new foothold in efforts to understand mind-brain relations.

During the mid-1940s Sperry turned to more general studies on the developmental patterning of behavioral nerve nets. These became focused largely on the role of cytochemical specificity in the guidance of nerve fiber outgrowth and synaptic formation. His findings indicated the presence of an extreme order of refinement in the biochemical differentiation of nerve cells. The inherent genetic organization of the basic wiring diagram of the brain was demonstrated, and the findings provided a developmental basis for understanding the inheritance and evolution of instinctive components in behavior. This series of experiments brought important changes in many of the basic concepts that had prevailed on nerve growth through the 1920s and 1930s. Older views favoring diffuse, nonselective growth pressures behind the advance and termination of nerve fibers gave way to the present doctrine of high selectivity. Where chemical guidance had formerly been rejected along with chemo-

tropism, chemotaxis, and neurotropism, Sperry's experiments pointed up the paramount importance of chemical factors. Earlier contentions that specific fiber connections are unimportant for orderly function were directly contradicted. A much better understanding emerged of how it is possible for more complex, delicately adjusted, and highly adaptive brain circuits to be prepatterned in development prior to, and without the aid of, function.

Sperry's main interest shifted after 1945 to experiments on the electric field theory of perception and the nature of integration in the mammalian cerebral cortex. Delicate microsurgical techniques, like those previously used on amphibian larvae, were applied to the cerebral cortex of cats and monkeys. Crisscross slicing of the cortex and cortical implants of dielectric and conductor elements were used to rule out horizontal interaction and electric field concepts in favor of vertically organized fiber circuit principles.

These studies on cortical organization were directed in the early 1950s to the problem of the corpus callosum posed in prior reports that complete surgical section of this largest of all the fiber bundles of the brain produces no detectable dysfunction either in man or in monkeys. Such observations seemed to refute the role of specific functional connections supported in the above experiments and posed an obstacle to almost any but radical field theories of cerebral integration. At this point Sperry was joined by Ronald Myers, a dedicated graduate student, who took up this callosal problem. Applying the microsurgical and behavioral techniques of the laboratory, they succeeded in demonstrating in cats a distinct dissociation of visual functions in the disconnected hemispheres.

During the next 10 years, from about 1954 to 1964, Sperry's laboratory along with others continued to attack, on an expanded scale, this problem of the corpus callosum and its many ramifications. As a result, the function of this structure became one of the best understood of all the fiber association systems in the brain. Once it had been shown that the surgically disconnected hemispheres function independently, it became possible to use the split-brain preparation to advantage to attack many other aspects of cerebral organization. The split-brain studies, like the earlier projects on nerve regeneration, have been dependent on the use of highly delicate microsurgical techniques.

Sperry's work on the split-brain syndrome was later extended and elaborated in human patients in whom surgical disconnection of the hemispheres had been carried out for control of advanced epilepsy. From the latter studies, in collaboration with Vogel and Bogen, neurosurgeons, and Michael Gazzaniga and other graduate students, it became possible to delineate more exactly the separate functions of right and left hemispheres of the human brain and to narrow somewhat the possible correlates of consciousness. Each of the disconnected hemispheres was shown to have its own separate conscious awareness, with "mind right" and "mind left" each being independent and out of contact, even though the brain remained undivided at its lower levels.

In theoretical papers on the mind-brain problem Sperry proposed a theory of consciousness in which he conceived mental forces to be emergent properties that possess causal potency and largely control the brain process. His scheme offers a monistic mentalism intermediate between dialectic materialism and older idealist philosophies.

Sperry took his M.A. in psychology under R. H. Stetson at Oberlin College in 1937 and his Ph.D. in zoology in 1941 under Paul Weiss at the University of Chicago. He then went on to postdoctoral work with Karl S. Lashley, first at Harvard and later at the Yerkes Primate Center in Florida. From 1946 to 1952 he taught at the University of Chicago. After 2 years with the National Institutes of Health, he moved in 1954 to the California Institute of Technology as Hixon Professor of Psychobiology. He was elected to the National Academy of Sciences in 1960 and to the American Academy of Arts and Sciences in 1963.

For background information *see* MOTOR SYSTEMS; NERVOUS SYSTEM in the McGraw-Hill Encyclopedia of Science and Technology.   □

only in response to specific stimuli from the environment. Detailed studies on the regulation of these enzyme syntheses, conducted by Stanier in recent years with G. D. Hegeman, L. N. Ornston, and J. L. Cánovas, showed that the systems of control are very complex. Enzymes may be induced singly or in coordinate blocks by certain of the metabolites in the specific metabolic pathway. It was found, furthermore, that different kinds of bacteria which employ the same metabolic pathway for the oxidation of a particular aromatic compound may regulate the synthesis of the operative enzymes in entirely different ways. The mapping of control systems thus promises to provide an additional approach to the exploration of biochemical evolution.

The purple bacteria perform a special type of photosynthesis, mechanistically simpler than plant photosynthesis. It is an anaerobic process, since it does not involve the specific photochemical reaction which, in plants, results in the formation of oxygen from water. Purple bacteria do not contain chloroplasts, and the intracellular site of the photosynthetic pigment system was obscure until 1952. With H. K. Schachman and A. B. Pardee, Stanier then showed that in cell-free bacterial extracts the pigment system is localized in submicroscopic particles, known as chromatophores. A year or so later, A. Frenkel demonstrated that isolated chromatophores can perform photophosphorylation, thus opening up in vitro study of the mechanism of bacterial photosynthesis. Later ultrastructural work by G. Cohen-Bazire showed that chromatophores are fragments of internal intrusions of the cell

★ STANIER, Roger Yate

Canadian biologist
Born Oct. 22, 1916, Victoria, British Columbia, Canada

S OME AEROBIC bacteria are nutritionally highly versatile and can use more than 100 different organic compounds, belonging to many different chemical classes, as sole sources of carbon and energy for growth. Early in his career Stanier began to study the metabolic basis of this nutritional versatility by examining the mode of attack of such bacteria on a variety of aromatic compounds. He showed that complex and catalytically specific enzyme sequences convert primary aromatic substrates to intermediates that lie on the central pathways of cellular respiratory metabolism. Furthermore, the enzymes concerned are specifically induced, being present at very low levels in cells that have not been exposed to the specific primary substrate. In aerobic bacteria, accordingly, many metabolic sequences are latent ones, coming into operation

membrane, which is the site in these bacteria of an important part of the photosynthetic machinery.

All photosynthetic organisms contain carotenoid pigments as well as chlorophylls in the photosynthetic apparatus. By studies on purple bacteria, in collaboration with M. Griffiths, W. R. Sistrom, and Cohen-Bazire, Stanier demonstrated that a major function of carotenoid pigments is to protect the cell from chlorophyll-catalyzed photooxidations. Purple bacteria without carotenoid pigments (as a result of mutation or physiological suppression of synthesis) can still grow photosynthetically under anaerobic conditions, but are rapidly killed by simultaneous exposure to light and air. Later work by others revealed that this photoprotective function of carotenoids is general, occurring in other photosynthetic organisms and even in some nonphotosynthetic ones.

Until recently no satisfactory formal definition of the bacteria as a biological group had been developed. Together with C. B. van Niel, Stanier proposed that the bacteria and the blue-green algae can be collectively defined by virtue of the possession of procaryotic cells, which differ with respect to many specific features of their organization from the more familiar eucaryotic cells, characteristic of other protists, plants, and animals. Shortly before this proposition was made by Stanier, A. Lwoff made clear for the first time the basic organizational differences between viruses and cellular organisms, so that the biological distinctiveness of the bacteria both from viruses and from eucaryotic groups of protists can now be stated in formal terms.

Stanier received his B.A. in 1936 from the University of British Columbia, his M.A. in 1940 from the University of California at Los Angeles, and his Ph.D. in 1942 from Stanford University, where he received his training in general microbiology from van Niel at the Hopkins Marine Station. Most of his scientific career was spent at the University of California at Berkeley, where he became a member of the department of bacteriology in 1947 and of the department of molecular biology in 1965. He received the Eli Lilly Award of the American Society for Microbiology in 1950, and in 1957 was elected to the American Academy of Arts and Sciences.

Stanier wrote *The Microbial World*, with M. Doudoroff and E. A. Adelberg (2d ed. 1963).

For background information *see* BACTERIA, TAXONOMY OF; BACTERIAL METABOLISM; MICROORGANISMS; PHOTOSYNTHESIS in the McGraw-Hill Encyclopedia of Science and Technology. □

★ STARR, Victor Paul

American meteorologist
Born Mar. 23, 1909, Dover, Del., U.S.A.

STARR ACQUIRED his interest in research concerning the general circulation of the terrestrial atmosphere from his colleague and onetime teacher, Carl-Gustav Rossby, the Swedish-American meteorologist and oceanographer. Encouraged by the later work of Rossby and the suggestions of the geophysicist Harold Jeffreys, Starr entered upon an extensive and protracted program of deriving from massive amounts of data the actual dynamics of the large-scale processes of the atmosphere. This program was initiated shortly after the close of World War II, when an adequate network of free air–observing stations covering the Northern Hemisphere was first organized. Through this means it was learned that the turbulent viscosity in the atmosphere, due to the large eddy motions, is negative, transforming the associated turbulent kinetic energy into zonal mean-flow kinetic energy. In collaboration with R. M. White, E. N. Lorenz, and H. L. Kuo, Starr showed that this effect is of primary importance in maintaining the general circulation of the atmosphere. Furthermore, the lack of this mechanism rendered the classical schemes of the general circulation incorrect and mainly of historical interest. On the other hand, the new numerical solutions of the general circulation now available in sufficiently elaborate form, due largely to the efforts of J. Smagorinsky, do show negative viscous effects in close agreement with observed evidence in all respects.

Using the International Geophysical Year data sources, Starr extended the program to include the Southern Hemisphere for the calendar year 1958. From this portion of the compilations G. O. P. Obasi, a member of the MIT project from the Nigerian Weather Service, showed the presence of marked negative viscous processes in the half of the atmosphere south of the Equator, as was anticipated.

The results of the program also revealed that the lower stratosphere acts not in the manner of

a heat engine, as does the troposphere below it, but is mechanically and thermodynamically driven by the troposphere in the manner of a refrigerating machine. Actually, the action is to cool the tropical zones to extremely low temperatures and to warm the polar regions, in spite of radiation processes tending contrariwise. This portion of the studies was accomplished through the cooperation of White, R. E. Newell, C. E. Jensen, A. C. Molla, C. J. Loisel, and J. H. Oort. More recently, Starr, with J. P. Peixoto and J. M. Wallace, showed evidence of other smaller portions of the atmosphere having forced eddy motions in the midtroposphere at tropical and subtropical latitudes.

From the start of the program much study has been devoted to the transport and redistribution of water vapor over the Northern Hemisphere, partly because of the energetic implications of its latent heat content and also because of its importance for climatology and hydrology. No previous analyses on so large a scale had been made by direct measurement methods. In these studies Starr received the invaluable cooperation of White and Peixoto. Recently, E. Rasmusson rendered service in this subject through his detailed analyses over the North American region during his sojourn at MIT.

The occurrence of negative eddy viscous effects was explored by Starr and his associates in a number of fluid and quasi-fluid systems other than the Earth's atmosphere. With the collaboration of R. R. Long, Starr studied the phenomenon in model laboratory experiments simulating the general circulation of the atmosphere. In these experiments, popularized by D. Fultz and R. Hide, the relative motion is produced by differential heating of a rotating fluid. Starr and Long found that the resulting flow has, among other similarities to the atmospheric motions when properly arranged, the property of exhibiting a negative viscous action which is an integral part of the hydrodynamic mechanism involved.

It was shown by Starr's associate F. Ward that, if one uses sunspots as tracers for large-scale motions in the solar photosphere, it turns out that the equatorial acceleration of the mean rotation is supported by an equatorward flux of momentum into the velocity maximum from each hemisphere. This manifestation of an anomalous viscous effect, due to large eddy motions, was studied jointly by Starr and P. A. Gilman from an energetic standpoint. It appears that this accelerative action on the mean equatorial velocity maximum is subjected to a systematic braking action through hydromagnetic forces which drain its kinetic energy into large magnetic disturbances. These latter disturbances correspond closely in form and distribution to those discovered observationally by R. Howard and V. Bumba at the Mount Wilson Observatory as components of the Sun's general magnetic field. The magnetic braking action is similar to that envisioned by H. W. Babcock, except that it is

many times larger because of the bunching effect on the lines of force by the turbulent eddies not included in Babcock's symmetrical theory.

In collaboration with Peixoto and Newell, Starr studied the radial outward transport of angular momentum in spiral galaxies, brought about by gravitational torques, an effect akin to tidal torques studied classically within the solar system. It is probable, as was suggested by Starr, Wallace, and J. Copeland, that this outward flux is at least partially offset by an inward momentum transfer due once more to a negative turbulent viscous effect.

Starr also undertook, with the aid of several associates, a current investigation of the mode of maintenance of the differential rotation of the atmosphere of Jupiter, using observational evidence. Likewise, he pursued studies to see whether the concepts already discussed can throw light upon the evolution of the solar nebula in the early stages of the formation of the planetary system, this subject being related to the theory of Oort concerning the existence of a large number of comets at great distances from the Sun, composed of materials from the original disk formation.

All of the previous topics represent an evolving and progressive personal plan of research, more or less tightly united as to purpose and general approach, with individual items exhibiting essentially similar turbulent and other phenomena. Apart from this extended plan of work, Starr engaged for many years in the theoretical study of ideal gravity waves of finite height in inviscid fluids. The procedures followed in the tradition of one of the lines of attack used by T. Levi-Civita. Portions of this work were performed in collaboration with G. W. Platzman. An expression was developed for the dynamic definition of the energy velocity, analogous to the classic one of Osborne Reynolds, but generalized so as to apply, without approximation under conditions assumed, to waves of arbitrary height. Similarly, it was found possible to define a new quantity, the momentum velocity, by using the same approach. It turns out that these two velocities are not equal but differ by an exceedingly small amount. A plausible expectation resulting from this difference is that an isolated wave group would suffer very slow secular changes in its spectral energy distribution, not possible in linear systems, as was shown by Rossby.

Starr received his education at New York State University, the Massachusetts Institute of Technology (M.S., 1938), and the University of Chicago (Ph.D., 1946). After a period of employment at the U.S. Weather Bureau, he taught meteorology at the University of Chicago during

World War II. From 1947 he taught at the Massachusetts Institute of Technology. Elected to the American Academy of Arts and Sciences in 1956, he received the Rossby Award of the American Meteorological Society in 1961.

For background information *see* ATMOSPHERE; CLIMATOLOGY; SUN in the McGraw-Hill Encyclopedia of Science and Technology.   □

★ STEBBINS, George Ledyard

American botanist
Born Jan. 6, 1906, Lawrence, N.Y., U.S.A.

STEBBINS HAS been linked with Theodosius Dobzhansky, Ernst Mayr, George Gaylord Simpson, and Julian Huxley as one of the biologists responsible for formulating and applying to all kinds of higher organisms the modern, synthetic theory of evolution. His book *Variation and Evolution in Plants* (1950) was the first to apply this theory to plant evolution. In addition, he was the first biologist to synthesize artificially a new, distinct species and establish it successfully under natural conditions.

During the period 1908–30 a number of botanists, particularly Otto Rosenberg and Arne Müntzing in Sweden, Øjwind Winge in Denmark, Hitoshi Kihara in Japan, G. D. Karpechenko in the Soviet Union, and Karl Sax, Roy E. Clausen, and T. H. Goodspeed in the United States, accumulated evidence which showed that new species of plants can arise from preexisting species by spontaneous doubling of the chromosome number. Furthermore, the same process of doubling can give rise to fertile, true-breeding progeny from sterile interspecific hybrids. Species which have originated by means of chromosome doubling are known as polyploids. Clausen and Goodspeed, through morphological and cytological comparisons, obtained strong circumstantial evidence to indicate that cultivated tobacco, *Nicotiana tabacum*, evolved as a polyploid from a hybrid between two South

American species of *Nicotiana*, a hypothesis verified by the experimental synthesis of *N. tabacum*. Müntzing, in 1930, was the first to synthesize a Linnean species, *Galeopsis tetrathit*, by means of artificial hybridization between two other species, followed by spontaneous doubling of the chromosome number of their sterile F (filial) hybrid.

Stebbins analyzed the variation patterns in three genera of flowering plants, *Antennaria*, *Paeonia*, and *Crepis*, combining information from comparative morphology and geographic distribution with that from the cytogenetics of diploid and related polyploid species. The work on *Crepis* was done with Ernest B. Babcock, who in 1935 brought Stebbins to the genetics department of the University of California, Berkeley, as a collaborator in research on the evolution of *Crepis* and related genera. As a result of these investigations, Babcock and Stebbins developed the concept of the polyploid complex. This is based upon the fact that, in the three genera mentioned and in several others studied later, natural polyploids combine to a large extent the morphological and ecological characteristics of their ancestral diploids and possess few if any distinctive characteristics of their own, except for the increased size of some of their parts. Polyploid complexes consist of a group of diploid ancestral species, which represent typically the morphological and ecological extremes of the complex, plus a large and taxonomically confusing assemblage of polyploid derivatives, which combine in numerous ways the characteristics of various diploids. In some instances, such as *Antennaria* and the American species of *Crepis*, the polyploids reproduce largely or entirely by parthenogenesis or some similar asexual means. The combination of polyploidy and asexual reproduction of otherwise sterile genotypes of hybrid origin is responsible for the extreme difficulty botanists have experienced in classifying the species of such genera as dandelions (*Taraxacum*), brambles (*Rubus*), and hawkweeds (*Hieracium*). By applying the concept of the polyploid complex, a reasonable systematic order was established in the American species of *Crepis*, which resemble the dandelions (*Taraxacum*) in their variation pattern. In addition, Stebbins used the relationships between the members of contemporary patterns of distribution to establish the probable age of various species in a number of plant genera.

When the colchicine technique was developed for doubling chromosome numbers artificially, Stebbins used it to produce polyploids from several species of wild grasses. One of these (from *Ehrharta erecta*) was established in a natural environment in 1944, and since then it has spread outward from its original site of establishment to occupy a distinctive ecological niche, adjacent to, but different from, that occupied by the diploid species from which it was derived. By means of the same method Stebbins produced a fertile polyploid from the sterile hybrid between two other species of grasses belonging to a different genus and established it as a persistent, spreading population in a different area.

From his studies of segregation for fertility in progeny of a partly sterile hybrid between two subspecies of the grass genus *Bromus*, Stebbins predicted that fertile, relatively true-breeding populations could be derived from partly sterile interspecific hybrids by recombination of chromosomal differences without change in chromosome number. Such populations would be likely to form partly sterile hybrids with both of the parental species, and because of this reproductive isolation these populations could evolve into new species. Stebbins verified this prediction by producing a fertile, reproductively isolated strain from the almost completely sterile hybrid between two grass species, *Elymus glaucus* and *Sitanion jubatum*. Further verification of this prediction has come from similar experiments in *Nicotiana* by Kevin Daly, in *Delphinium* by Harlan Lewis and Carl Epling, and in *Gilia* by Verne Grant.

Recently Stebbins turned to analysis of the development of the action of genes which affect external morphology in higher plants. Mutations of such genes are responsible for most of the observable changes in plant evolution. Experiments conducted in this laboratory led to the hypothesis that the genes responsible for differences of this kind in higher plants produce their effects largely through regulating the frequency of mitoses in certain restricted regions of the developing plant. This regulation may be accomplished by controlling the length of the interval (G_1 period) between mitotic telophase and the initiation of DNA synthesis prior to the subsequent mitotic division.

The son of a New York businessman, Stebbins spent much of his childhood and youth on Mount Desert Island, Maine, where he developed an early interest in natural history. He received his A.B. (1928), A.M. (1929), and Ph.D. in biology (1931) from Harvard. After 4 years as an instructor in biology at Colgate University, followed by 4 years as a junior geneticist at the University of California, he became assistant professor of genetics at Berkeley in 1939. He was promoted to professor of genetics there in 1947, and in 1950 moved to the Davis campus of the University of California, where he founded its department of genetics, of which he was vice-chairman and then chairman until 1963. Elected to both the National Academy of Sciences and the American Academy of Arts and Sciences in 1952, he received the Merit

Award of the Botanical Society of America in 1956.

Stebbins wrote the textbook *The Human Organism and the World of Life*, with Clarence Young (1938), and *Processes of Organic Evolution* (1966), as well as the work mentioned earlier.

For background information *see* GENE ACTION; PLANT EVOLUTION; POLYPLOIDY in the McGraw-Hill Encyclopedia of Science and Technology. ☐

★ STEWARD, Frederick Campion

American botanist
Born June 16, 1904, London, England

STEWARD'S EARLY interests stemmed from the application of chemistry to problems of botany. He first studied the preservation of semipermeability in slices of storage tissue (beet, potato, and so forth) under aseptic conditions. This early work directed attention to the importance of aeration and oxygen supply when investigating the behavior of submerged tissue slices and to the need to work under aseptic conditions. A study of the rates of diffusion of ions and molecules through membranes of isolated tissue emphasized how slowly they penetrate living membranes in physiologically quiescent tissue, for the solutes can pass through such membranes without reaching equality of concentration in the cells. This posed an obvious problem, since ions (K, Cl, and so forth) are normally accumulated by plant cells.

A study of the conditions that induce the accumulation of ions in cut slices of storage organs emphasized the role of respiration, as regulated by oxygen supply, of temperature, and of such variables as the thinness of the tissue disk, all of which regulate the metabolic activity. All these studies led to the idea that the ion uptake against a concentration gradient is an active process deriving energy from aerobic respiration, even as Hoagland and his collaborators had traced it ultimately to light in the green cells of *Nitella*. However, the first study suggested that the cells which are able to harness their metabolic energy to osmotic work are also performing many other functions of growing cells. This essentially biological approach to active secretion, as it was later called, was further elaborated by research on ion uptake in tissue slices (with W. E. Berry), on segments of roots to study gradients along the axis (with P. Prevot), and on entry of bromide into growing leaves of *Cucurbita* (with A. G. Steward). The result was the general idea, summarized in 1935, that actively metabolizing cells do osmotic work as they respire, synthesize protein, grow, and divide. An interlude to study the large vesicles of *Valonia* (with J. C. Martin) produced results not in conformity with then current hypotheses, but also aroused an interest in the biology of these organisms which was to persist and be applied to other problems.

Lacking present-day knowledge of the means by which respiratory energy is coupled to useful work, Steward (with C. Preston) set out to describe the general biological setting in which the energy of respiration can be linked to useful purposes. Just prior to World War II he had come to the view that the energy supplied by part of the respiration, more closely related to oxygen supply than to emerging carbon dioxide, can furnish the energy for protein synthesis while it also allows ions to be accumulated and nitrogen-rich compounds to be mobilized by cells for their protein synthesis.

On return to science study after the war Steward set up three objectives. First, he would seek means to fractionate the nonprotein nitrogen compounds of plants and to see how the accumulating cells, confined to endogenous sources of nitrogen, obtain their nitrogen for protein synthesis. Second, he would try to place the same cells and tissues reversibly under conditions of active growth and quiescent metabolism so that their behavior in salt intake and metabolism could be contrasted. Third, since all nutrition really begins with a fertilized egg, his ultimate hope was to study nutrition—organic and inorganic—with zygotes isolated from the ovule.

The first problem was greatly facilitated by the first application of two-directional paper chromatography to plant extracts (with Stepka and Dent). But this also opened doors which were to lead to the discovery of many new nitrogen compounds and to change ideas on nitrogen metabolism. In this phase Steward had a succession of collaborators (J. F. Thompson, R. M. Zacharius, J. K. Pollard, N. Grobbelaar, D. J. Durzan, and others).

The solution to the second problem was sought in the application of tissue culture techniques, appropriately modified for the purpose,

to such cells as those of carrot, potato, and artichoke. While this technique was later to shed light on the distinctive absorption of ions by dividing cells, it largely diverted attention from the original problem because of the dramatic effects disclosed on cell division due to the effects of coconut milk. In the work on the cell division growth factors in coconut milk and similar fluids, Steward had the collaboration of E. M. Shantz. This work triggered a whole study of metabolism in actively growing versus quiescent cells, and the study was extended to the free culture of plant cells, of morphogenesis, and of embryogeny. The work on aseptic culture of cells and tissues, leading to the study of morphogenesis and totipotency of adult plant cells, was carried out with many collaborators, notably K. Mears, J. Smith, L. M. Blakely, J. Mitra, M. O. Mapes, and A. E. Kent.

Meanwhile the studies of metabolism had become concerned with compartmentation in cells, and with the need to recognize that in growing cells the active turnover of protein furnishes carbon for respiration, but the nitrogen is reworked and stored in nitrogen-rich compounds to resynthesize more protein with exogenous sugar. Thus, to the familiar biochemical ideas of glycolysis and Krebs cycle, still other ideas were needed to show how the nitrogen metabolism of plant cells, which are highly compartmented, really works and how nitrogen metabolism is linked to concomitant physiological processes. Steward worked in this phase with J. K. Pollard. E. W. Yemm, R. G. S. Bidwell, and others.

The third problem was not approached directly. The free cell culture work showed that it was in fact easier, by various devices of chemical regulatory control, to make adult free cells behave like zygotes and grow into plants, recapitulating embryogeny as they do so, than to remove and culture the zygote directly.

Interest in growth, metabolism, and nutrition also prompted Steward to several comprehensive studies of such plants as *Mentha*, with F. Crane, K. Howe, and R. Rabson, and the banana (*Musa*), with S. R. Freiberg, W. G. Barker, H. Y. Mohan Ram, and others. The goal in this research was to study the interactions of nutrition, environment, growth, and metabolism and their impact on the growing regions.

Thus, while frequently immersed in the study of the behavior of molecules and metabolites in cells, Steward never lost sight of cell structure and development. His work encompassed studies of the early genesis of cell walls on *Valonia* sporelings (with K. Muhlethaler), of the effects on the organelles by the factors that induce growth (with H. W. Israel), and especially of the development of chloroplasts in cultured cells.

Steward received his B.Sc. (chemistry) in 1924 and his Ph.D. (botany) in 1926 from the

University of Leeds. As Rockefeller Foundation fellow in 1927–29, he studied and did research in Cornell University and the University of California, Berkeley. On his return to England Steward became assistant lecturer in botany at Leeds but returned to the United States for work at the University of California in 1933–34 and the Tortugas Laboratory of the Carnegie Institution of Washington. In 1934 he became reader in botany in Birkbeck College of the University of London; he received a D.Sc. from the University of London in 1938. During World War II he worked in the British Ministry of Aircraft Production. From 1946 to 1950 he was visiting professor and head of the botany department at the University of Rochester in New York. In 1950 he became professor of botany at Cornell University and subsequently Alexander Professor of Biology (1965) and director of the Laboratory of Cell Physiology, Growth and Development. He was elected to the American Academy of Arts and Sciences in 1956 and to the Royal Society of London in 1957. In 1961 he received a Merit Award of the Botanical Society of America and in 1964 the Stephen Hales Award of the American Society of Plant Physiologists.

Steward wrote *Plant Physiology: A Treatise* (6 vols., 1966). At a more elementary level he wrote *Plants at Work: A Summary of Plant Physiology*, with H. D. Krikorian (1964), and *About Plants: Topics in Plant Biology* (1966).

For background information *see* PLANT, MINERAL NUTRITION OF; PLANT GROWTH; PLANT METABOLISM; PLANT RESPIRATION in the McGraw-Hill Encyclopedia of Science and Technology. □

★ STEWART, Frederick Henry

British geologist
Born Jan. 16, 1916, Aberdeen, Scotland

S TEWART WORKED in two main fields of geology—igneous petrology and evaporite studies. He was trained in Aberdeen, in a region of complex igneous and metamorphic rocks. The work of H. H. Read had focused the attention of petrologists on the remarkable assimilation phenomena of a suite of basic and ultrabasic intrusions in Aberdeenshire, and after graduating in 1937, Stewart studied an undescribed member of this suite, the Belhelvie intrusion. At that time, as a result of N. L. Bowen's experimental work on the crystallization of silicate melts, the significance of igneous layering was a major interest in petrology, and Stewart suggested that the intrusion was a layered complex up to 2 mi thick which had been subjected to major deformation after crystallization. Later R. M. Shackleton suggested that the suite of intrusions comprised the exposed parts of a major igneous body which had been overfolded in places by the Caledonian

mountain-building movements, and Read and others showed that the Insch complex contains differentiates ranging from ultrabasic rocks through iron-rich gabbros to syenites.

It had become clear that the region was of exceptional interest in containing an extremely differentiated basic igneous suite with abnormal contaminated rocks, set in country rocks which had suffered a complex structural history and metamorphism of both Barrovian and Buchan types. In 1959 Stewart and M. R. W. Johnson began a series of studies, continued by other staff members and postgraduate students of Edinburgh University, to determine the relations of igneous activity, metamorphism, and structural deformation in this part of the Caledonian mountain chain. These workers brought to light a complex series of five fold episodes, metamorphism reaching a peak between the second and third of these, and intrusion and crystallization of a great volume of basic magma after the second, and its deformation during the third and later fold episodes. Chemical and mineralogical differentiation of the magmatic series was extreme, and certain factors, including the contamination and the scale of partial melting of the surrounding rocks, suggest an abnormally deep level of emplacement. These studies raise formidable problems connected with the development and uprise of a large quantity of basic material from the Earth's mantle in such a structural setting, and the relation of this large source of heat to the regional metamorphism. Other aspects of Stewart's studies in igneous and metamorphic petrology include the sulfatic-

cancrinite pegmatites of Loch Borolan; one of the first works on partition of magnesium and iron in coexisting minerals, in a Scottish hornfels; and (with L. R. Wager and others) a reinvestigation of the ring complexes of the Tertiary volcanoes of western Scotland.

The other major field of Stewart's work is quite a different one, in which he applied the methods of petrology to the study of marine evaporites—deposits of sodium, potassium, calcium and magnesium carbonates, sulfates, and chlorides which were formed by the desiccation of bodies of seawater. During World War II he left Cambridge for the Research Department of Imperial Chemical Industries (ICI) at Billingham. C. E. Tilley had just recorded the presence of polyhalite, $Ca_2Mg K_2(SO_4)_4 2H_2O$, in a specimen of Permian age from the Eskdale No. 2 borehole in Yorkshire (the first record of a potassium mineral in British evaporites), and on a weekend visit to the site of the borehole Stewart found a large number of pieces of this mineral.

He then began a study of the core samples and well cuttings which the D'Arcy Exploration Company had presented to ICI when the well was sunk in 1938, in which chemical analyses had proved the presence of potassium chloride. He found no less than 45 ft of polyhalite and some sylvinite (KCl + NaCl) at a higher horizon. His work on the Permian evaporites, published in 1949–51, after he had joined Durham University, was a comprehensive petrological account of a complex evaporite series, and its importance lay in the combination of a mineralogical-petrographical approach, like that of W. T. Schaller and E. P. Henderson's study of the Texas—New Mexico potash deposits, with a stratigraphical approach. He showed that complex replacement series can be deciphered by textural studies and gave evidence of major metasomatism at all levels in the evaporites. In fact, very few of the original precipitated minerals had escaped replacement or recrystallization. For these studies he received the Mineralogical Society of America Award for 1952.

Stewart continued his evaporite work at Durham and Edinburgh universities, using the British Permian as a model. After World War II further exploration disclosed very large potash reserves, potentially of considerable economic value, and supplied much more material for study. In a series of papers Stewart considered the gypsum-anhydrite problem and gave evidence of wholesale replacement of early gypsum by anhydrite, compared the European and American Permian evaporites, and discussed widespread and complex replacement series involving early carnallite and later sylvine in potash deposits. In 1963 he produced a general account of the mineralogy and geochemistry of marine evaporites, and in this and in two recent papers he discussed particularly the relative effects of primary precipitation, early and late diagenesis, geothermal metamorphism, and late near-surface processes in the origin of such deposits. He came to the conclusion that many of the wholesale mineral transformations are of early diagenetic origin. Since Stewart's original evaporite studies, many more petrologists have

entered the field, and rapid progress is being made by combining petrographic and geochemical approaches with the experimental approach.

Stewart obtained his B.Sc. in geology from Aberdeen University in 1937 and his Ph.D. from Cambridge in 1941. During World War II he worked in the physicochemical section of the Research Department of Imperial Chemical Industries at Billingham, before joining the geology department of Durham University as lecturer. He held the Regius Chair of Geology and Mineralogy at Edinburgh University from 1957 and was dean of the Faculty of Science from 1965. Recipient of the Mineralogical Society of America Award in 1952, he was elected a fellow of the Royal Society of London in 1964.

In addition to writing numerous scientific papers, Stewart edited *The British Caledonides*, with M. R. W. Johnson (1963), and contributed to *The Geology of Scotland*, edited by G. Y. Craig (1965).

For background information *see* EVAPORITE (SALINE); MAGMA; PETROGRAPHIC PROVINCE; PETROLOGY in the McGraw-Hill Encyclopedia of Science and Technology.   □

★ STEWART, Thomas Dale

American physical anthropologist
Born June 10, 1901, Delta, Pa., U.S.A.

DURING THE early part of his career Stewart concerned himself mainly with human skeletal remains from the New World. Being in the National Museum in Washington, where Aleš Hrdlička was still making one of the world's largest skeletal collections, Stewart had the advantage of seeing a steady flow of specimens from previously unrepresented areas and time periods. One of his first moves was to induce more archeologists to include in their site reports a description by a physical anthropologist of the skeletons recovered. In contributing his share of these reports Stewart was able to call attention to (1) the importance of cranial deformity as a variable cultural trait registered in bone, (2) the significant regional distribution of low cranial height, and (3) the chronological distribution of certain pathological afflictions.

It is only natural that in physical anthropology great interest centers around the oldest remains. Stewart thus soon became involved in the controversy over when man arrived in the New World, especially after his reexamination of the Melbourne (Fla.) skull showed that, contrary to Hrdlička's claim, it is unlike the recent Indian type of the region and therefore possibly contemporary with the associated extinct fauna. With this experience in mind Stewart traced the development of the concept of morphological dating which Hrdlička had long used to demolish all American claimants to considerable antiquity. Stewart also helped in assembling and presenting two new claimants for this honor, namely, Tepexpan man from Mexico and Midland man from Texas.

The human remains that are considered ancient in America date back only 10,000 to 20,000 years, which is well after Neanderthal man disappeared from Europe and southwestern Asia. To participate in the restoration and description of a Neanderthal has been a rare privilege for an American, so in 1957 Stewart promptly accepted an invitation from the director general of antiquities of Iraq to work on the skeletons of Shanidar I and II, newly discovered by Ralph Solecki, and eventually dated at 46,000 and 60,000(?) years ago, respectively. Stewart spent the last 3 months of 1957 in Baghdad restoring and studying the first of these specimens. He returned to Iraq for 3 months in the summer of 1960 to study Shanidar II and to help Solecki recover the remains of III, IV, V, and VI. Returning again to Iraq for 2 months in 1962, Stewart concentrated on studying the remains of Shanidar IV and VI. This work showed that the Shanidar Neanderthals are of the classic type and quite distinct from the somewhat later Skhul specimens from Mount Carmel, which can be considered essentially modern man.

Simultaneously with his evolutionary studies Stewart conducted closely related work in applied physical anthropology. Because of the proximity in Washington of the National Museum and the headquarters of the Federal Bureau of Investigation, he was called upon frequently to identify unknown human remains for medicolegal purposes. Finding that the criteria for estimating sex, age, stature, and so forth and the ranges of variation in these traits were poorly established, he promoted studies along these lines. His own principal contribution was a study of age changes in the American soldiers killed in North Korea, undertaken at the request of the quartermaster general and carried out at the Identification Laboratory of the Graves Registration Service in Kokura, Japan. This study is unique because there has been no other such opportunity to examine fully identified skeletons of men in the military age range. In addition to yielding more exact data for the events of skeletal maturation, the study showed that the range of variation for each event is greater than previously realized.

Throughout his skeletal studies Stewart called attention to the pathological changes encountered. His work on the spinal column in various racial groups led to a better understanding of defective neural arches in the lumbar vertebrae and to a better correlation of hypertrophic arthritis with age. The arm amputation which he discovered in the skeleton of Shanidar I perhaps will prove to be a very early example of true surgery.

Stewart received his A.B. from George Washington University in 1927 and immediately joined the staff of the U.S. National Museum, where he had been working on a temporary basis since 1924. Given leave of absence during the school year to go to medical school, he received his M.D. from Johns Hopkins University in 1931. Stewart was awarded the Wenner-Gren Foundation's Viking Medal in physical anthropology in 1953. He was elected to the National Academy of Sciences in 1962.

Author of 165 publications in scientific journals, Stewart edited Aleš Hrdlička's *Practical Anthropometry* (3d ed. 1947).

For background information *see* ANTHROPOLOGY, PHYSICAL; ANTHROPOMETRY; FOSSIL MAN; NEANDERTHAL MAN in the McGraw-Hill Encyclopedia of Science and Technology. □

★ STOKER, James Johnston

American mathematician
Born Mar. 2, 1905, Dunbar, Pa., U.S.A.

STOKER WAS trained as a coal mining engineer, but eventually received a Ph.D. in mathematics for a thesis in differential geometry. As a professional mathematician, he did the bulk of his work in applications of mathematics to a variety of problems in mathematical physics and engineering, in particular to problems in elasticity, linear vibrations, hydrodynamics, flow in rivers and channels, and the design of structures.

A typical example of Stoker's work concerns the calculation of flood waves, and flows generally, in rivers and large reservoirs. A mathematical formulation adequate to deal with the problem had been known since the 19th century as the result of work by such French mathematicians as St. Venant and Boussinesq. This

theory is expressed in terms of a pair of non-linear partial differential equations. These equations express two fundamental laws of mechanics, the laws of conservation of mass and of momentum, and serve as a basis for the calculation of the average velocity of the flow at each cross section of the river and of the so-called stage, or height H, of the surface of the river above sea level; in effect, H also measures the depth of the river. These two quantities are to be determined as functions of the position x along the river from some fixed station on it and of the time t. The differential equations for $v(x, t)$ and $H(x, t)$ are

$$B \frac{\partial H}{\partial t} + \frac{\partial}{\partial x}(Av) = q$$

$$\frac{\partial v}{\partial t} + v \frac{\partial v}{\partial x} + g \frac{\partial H}{\partial x} = -Gv|v|$$

In these equations $B = B(x,H)$ represents the breadth of the river, $A = A(x,H)$ its cross-section area, and $G = G(x,H)$ a resistance coefficient, all in their dependence on the position x along the river and of its stage H, or what is equivalent, its depth. The quantity $q = q(x,t)$ represents the flow into the main river channel from tributaries and the main valley. All these quantities must be known in advance or be estimated. One of the difficult tasks, in fact, is acquiring that information from the engineering records of past floods.

Unfortunately, these differential equations could not be solved, even by approximate numerical methods, until rather recently. What made a solution possible was the development of high-speed digital computers. Stoker realized that the differential equations are analogous to those for gas dynamics and that methods developed during World War II for solving such problems on computers could probably be modified and used to solve flood-wave problems in rivers. During 1953–56 the problem was attacked

with the cooperation of engineers from the U.S. Corps of Engineers in Cincinnati, Ohio. What was done first was to take one of the largest floods on record of the Ohio River and to verify whether the flows in the river could be calculated theoretically, with the aid of the differential equations, and with the accuracy desired. This calculation proved possible for flows in the 375 mi of the Ohio River between Wheeling, W.Va., and Cincinnati and for periods of time up to 3 weeks. The calculating machine used for this purpose was the best available at that time, the UNIVAC. This machine was located in the Institute of Mathematical Sciences of New York University. The sheer bulk of the numerical calculations that were required stretched the capacity of this machine to the limit, but the time required to compute such a flow was not too large from a practical point of view, since only 6½ hr of calculating time were needed.

Once the problem had been successfully attacked in one case, two additional cases were treated to test the method further. In both of these cases the methods of flood rating used by the engineers were not successful, whereas these same methods were reasonably successful for the case of the Ohio River. The first of the two further cases treated was the flow at the junction of the Ohio and Mississippi rivers, in which it was necessary to deal with the flows in each of the three river branches at the junction and put them together so that inflows and outflows balanced at all times. The second case was that of the 186-mi-long reservoir created by Kentucky Dam at the mouth of the Tennessee River, the last of the many dams in that river in the TVA system. In this latter case very accurate checks were obtained against observations of the flow during the largest flood on record (1950); at that time very large releases through Kentucky Dam were made in order to empty the dam partially because of the flood coming down through the next dam higher up (Pickwick Dam). Thus extreme conditions were involved. The observed stages as compared with calculated stages were the same within a few inches all along the reservoir and for a period stretching over 3 weeks.

These results showed that the theoretical method is entirely feasible. It cost very much less than another method used at the time, the building of large-scale models. The models cost, for each different river or reservoir, as much as a UNIVAC (about $1,000,000) and were only very large, very expensive computers of the type called analog computers. Even worse, such a computer could deal with only one case. The building of such models seems to have been abandoned in recent years.

Subsequently, two more cases were treated: flows in the Chattahootchie River in Alabama and the Columbia River in Washington. Computing equipment has improved enormously in the years since the UNIVAC was the only machine available. The computations on the Ohio River, as described previously, which required 6½ hr of computing time, would require something like 6½ min now on a CDC 6600 machine, for example, and could also be made in a more satisfactory, more accurate way because, in part, of the huge memory storage available in such a machine. Stoker believed that the river system of the entire Mississippi Valley can be coded successfully and stored on a few tapes, to be available readily to estimate the effect of floods and serial operation of dams, to cut down flood stages, or to attack large-scale problems under a variety of circumstances.

Stoker was the son of a coal mine inspector. He received his B.S. and M.S. from the Carnegie Institute of Technology in 1927 and 1931 and his Ph.D. from the Technische Hochschule in Zurich in 1935. He was assistant professor of mechanics at the Carnegie Institute from 1928 until 1937 and thereafter was professor of mathematics at New York University, becoming Distinguished Professor of Mathematics. From 1958 to 1966 he was director of the Institute of Mathematical Sciences of that university. He was elected to the National Academy of Sciences in 1962. In 1957 he was awarded the Heineman Prize for his book *Water Waves*.

Stoker also wrote *Nonlinear Vibrations in Mechanical and Electrical Systems* (1950).

For background information *see* GEOMETRY, DIFFERENTIAL; SURFACE WATER; VIBRATION; WAVE MOTION IN LIQUIDS in the McGraw-Hill Encyclopedia of Science and Technology.   □

cal physics, but are highlights in a general survey of a wide range of mathematical structures and theories.

Stone's early papers dealt with the Fourier analysis and spectral theory associated with linear ordinary differential equations of arbitrary order, thus growing out of the work of J. Fourier, J. C. F. Sturm, J. Liouville, and G. D. Birkhoff. He introduced Riesz summability methods into the theory and established general equiconvergence and equisummability results, some of which were parallel to results obtained earlier and independently by J. D. Tamarkin in Russia in 1917. It was an easy step to carry over techniques acquired in this field to the study of linear operators in abstract Hilbert space, as defined by F. Riesz and J. von Neumann. Stimulated by von Neumann's early unpublished work on operator theory, Stone and Erhard Schmidt independently introduced the concept of a self-adjoint operator, which immediately served to clarify some difficulties encountered by von Neumann and thereafter dominated the situation. Stone gave an independent proof of the spectral theorem for nonbounded self-adjoint operators and investigated many other aspects of their theory and applications. Many of his results were presented in his book *Linear Transformations in Hilbert Space and Their Applications to Analysis* (1932). One result which was announced and published separately was the representation theorem for one-parameter unitary groups in Hilbert space. The theorem was first formulated, but not proved, by H. Weyl because of its role in quantum theory. It has since played a fundamental part in theoretical physics and has been generalized by von Neu-

★ STONE, Marshall Harvey

American mathematician
Born Apr. 8, 1903, New York, N.Y., U.S.A.

S TONE'S MATHEMATICAL researches, beginning with concrete problems in the theory of differential equations, early took on an abstract character and became focused on the structural aspects of mathematical situations taking their origins in classic problems of analysis, geometry, and logic. Prominent among his results are four theorems to which Stone's name was attached by his mathematical contemporaries: Stone's representation theorem for one-parameter unitary groups, Stone's representation theorem for Boolean algebras, the Čech-Stone compactification theorem, and the Stone-Weierstrass approximation theorem. When viewed in context these theorems are not merely isolated results with numerous and important technical applications in modern analysis, logic, topology, and theoreti-

mann, W. Ambrose, and R. Godement. Stone noted that the theorem might be extended to semigroups, an observation confirmed by E. Hille's extensive researches on semigroups of operators in Banach spaces.

Because the spectral theory focused attention

on algebras of idempotent operators or projections, Stone was led to construct an abstract theory of Boolean rings (that is, rings in which every element a is idempotent, satisfying the identity $a^2 = a$) and Boolean algebras, arriving at the main representation theorem cited above. According to this theorem, every Boolean algebra is isomorphic to an algebra of sets which generates a specific and characteristic compact topology on the universal set. The algebraic part of this theorem was discovered and published independently by Birkhoff. The universal set needed for this representation was identified as the set of all prime or maximal ideals in the algebra to be represented. Stone noted that this theory could be applied with advantage to problems of logic and topology. The detailed applications to logic were the work of others, especially A. Tarski, A. Mostowski, and L. Henkin. Stone himself carried out extensive applications to topology, solving in general terms the problem of finding all spaces containing a given one as a dense subset. The Boolean algebra techniques used were equivalent to the techniques of filters invented independently by H. Cartan. In particular, Stone solved the problem of compactifying a given space (necessarily completely regular) independently of E. Čech and subsequently simplified both Čech's constructions and his own. The Čech-Stone compactification theorem has since found many applications. To explore adequately the case of completely regular and compact spaces, Stone found it necessary to study approximation properties of the continuous real functions defined on such a space, and was thus led to formulate and prove a generalization, cited above, of the classical Weierstrass approximation theorem. This Stone-Weierstrass approximation theorem has since occupied a fundamental place in modern functional analysis.

Stone sought a still deeper relationship between these results and the spectral theory which had led him to them. He looked for it in an abstract characterization of the ring of continuous real functions on a compact space. Stone found such a characterization in terms of ordered ring theory, independently of I. M. Gelfand's similar work on complex Banach algebras. Both Stone and Gelfand represented the abstract rings under consideration by using maximal ideals in the manner which had already yielded Stone's representation theorem for Boolean rings. Stone also gave a similar treatment of lattice-ordered Abelian groups independently of unpublished researches of von Neumann. He announced all these results in 1940–41 but did not publish them in full. Some of them appeared in detail in lecture notes given limited circulation by the Tata Institute of Fundamental Research (Bombay, 1950). Independent proofs of most of them have since been published by

R. Kadison, I. Fleischer, and D. Pappert. Stone continued studying general spectral theory and its ramifications, announcing or publishing a few secondary contributions, but did not secure any further definitive major results up to the end of 1966.

The development of mathematics and the extension of its applications in depth and in breadth had created a crisis in mathematical education which preoccupied Stone from 1945 on. After leading a modernization and upgrading of the undergraduate and graduate mathematics programs at the University of Chicago in 1946–50, he turned his attention to preuniversity mathematics instruction. Stone directed his efforts chiefly toward publicizing the need for fundamental reforms in the teaching of school mathematics and creating conditions favorable to their realization. He played leading parts in a long series of international conferences on mathematical education (Bombay, 1956; Royaumont, 1959; Bombay, 1960; Dubrovnik, 1960; Belgrade, 1960; Bologna, 1961; Bogotá, 1961; Budapest, 1962; Lima, 1966). These conferences eventually produced significant results in various parts of the world, especially in Europe and Latin America. In the United States Stone took part in the work of the School Mathematics Study Group, both as a member of its governing board and as a member of its panel on elementary school mathematics. Stone also devoted considerable time and effort to unpublished curricular studies prompted by his participation in the Dubrovnik Conference of OECD in 1960 and later in the Secondary School Mathematics Curriculum Improvement Project of Columbia Teachers College, directed by Howard Fehr. As president of the Inter-Union Commission on the Teaching of Science set up by the International Council of Scientific Unions in 1962, Stone temporarily (1962–65) broadened his educational activities to include the entire field of science teaching and took a leading part in organizing two conferences (Frascati, 1963; Dakar, 1965) called to inaugurate and orientate in promising directions the work of the commission.

Stone graduated from Harvard University (A.B., 1922; A.M., 1924; Ph.D., 1926) and held regular academic appointments at Columbia (1925–27), Yale (1931–33), Harvard (1927–31, 1933–46), and Chicago (from 1946). He also held numerous temporary lecturing appointments in the United States and abroad, and traveled widely in the course of his professional activities. He was elected to the National Academy of Sciences in 1938 and to the American Philosophical Society; he served as president of the American Mathematical Society (1944–45) and of the International Mathematical Union (1952–54). In 1967 Stone accepted appointment as honorary professor in the University of Madurai in South India.

For background information *see* BOOLEAN ALGEBRA; EQUATIONS, THEORY OF; LINEAR SYSTEMS OF EQUATIONS; TOPOLOGY in the McGraw-Hill Encyclopedia of Science and Technology. □

★ **STONER, Edmund Clifton**

British physicist
Born Oct. 2, 1899, East Molesey, Surrey, England

S TONER'S EARLIEST research work, from 1921 to 1924, was under the general direction of Ernest Rutherford at the Cavendish Laboratory, Cambridge. Stoner first joined G. Stead in investigating a peculiar type of glow discharge in gas-filled thermionic diodes and succeeded in explaining its main characteristics. Then he embarked on a detailed investigation of the variation with wavelength of the absorption of x-rays in different elements. This work, in which he was later joined by L. H. Martin, added significantly to quantitative knowledge of x-ray absorption, and was linked with work on the absorption of γ-rays by N. Ahmad, with some of which Stoner was associated.

During the course of his primarily experimental research Stoner familiarized himself with the various suggested quantum specifications of atomic energy levels and became interested in the topical question of how electrons in atoms are distributed among the various groups and subgroups. In a paper in 1924, "The distribution of electrons among atomic levels," he put forward a distribution scheme which was consistent with a wide diversity of experimental evidence, and which significantly differed from that suggested by Niels Bohr in 1922 and remedied its incompleteness and arbitrary features. In the new scheme the maximum numbers of electrons in the various levels and sublevels were shown to be simply related to the quantum numbers specifying those levels in such a way, as was

pointed out in the paper, that there was a maximum of "one electron in each possible equally probable state." Stoner regarded this as a very important conclusion, which had been reached inductively from the experimental findings. When stated in axiomatic form by Wolfgang Pauli in the following year, it became known as the Pauli exclusion principle, which could be used as a premise in a deductive treatment of distribution and other problems and which was later generalized in Fermi-Dirac statistics.

Among the matters briefly discussed by Stoner as having a bearing on the distribution question was the sequence of values of the magnetic moments of ions of elements of the various transition series as derived from the paramagnetic susceptibilities of the salts. The diverse magnetic properties of ordinary pieces of matter were very puzzling and almost unintelligible from a classical standpoint, and Stoner was attracted to investigating whether these properties could be better coordinated by a more thoroughgoing application of quantum ideas. Shortly after appointment in 1924 to the staff of the department of physics at the University of Leeds, he was surprised to find on looking through some of the older periodicals the extent of the work on magnetic properties which had been carried out in the early part of the century and before. In the standard books on electricity and magnetism little reference was made to any of this work, least of all to that on dia- and paramagnetism. Accordingly, Stoner began writing a book to include an account of some of the earlier as well as more recent work and of the newer attempts to interpret the experimental findings in the light of the quantum theory. The book was published in 1926 as *Magnetism and Atomic Structure*. It was written just before the effective introduction of the concept of electron spin, in itself of immense value in simplifying the correlating scheme relevant to the interpretation of magnetic properties, and, of more general importance, before the effective development of the initially unsatisfactory quantum theory into a consistent fundamental theoretical scheme of physics. A few years later it seemed to Stoner that the book could not be brought up to date in a new edition in a satisfactory way, and instead he wrote a substantially new book, *Magnetism and Matter* (1934). A smaller book, *Magnetism*, giving an introductory survey of the field of the larger books, was first published in 1930; this was kept up to date in many successive editions and was translated into several foreign languages.

Among Stoner's original contributions during 1924–34 to which he referred in *Magnetism and Matter* were papers dealing with the theoretical calculation of the diamagnetic susceptibility of ions; the explanation of the striking difference in the sequence of ionic moments in salts of the first transition series and the rare-earth series of elements, subsequently developed more quantitatively by J. H. Van Vleck and others in the crystalline field treatment; the relation between the temperature variation of the intrinsic magnetization of ferromagnetics below and of the susceptibility above the Curie point, showing that the magnetization is predominantly attributable to electron spin rather than to orbital moment; and, making use of Fermi-Dirac statistics, the explanation of the nonintegral atomic magnetic moments of ferromagnetic metals at low temperatures and of the changes on alloying. Stoner also contributed to the elucidation of a problem in astrophysics in showing, by the application of Fermi-Dirac statistics to highly ionized matter, that there is a limiting density related to mass in stars of the white dwarf type and in giving, with F. Tyler, a preliminary treatment of the course of change of stars toward the limiting state.

During the later interwar years Stoner reexamined the thermodynamics of magnetization and expressed the main relations in a form convenient for application to the interconnected magnetic and thermal properties of matter. These relations were later extensively applied. His main research work, however, was in the development, on the basis of Fermi-Dirac statistics, of a theory of the paramagnetism and ferromagnetism of metals, treated as arising predominantly from electrons shared collectively in unfilled electron energy bands. Widely different magnetic properties, ranging from the small and almost temperature-independent paramagnetism of many metals, through the larger temperature-decreasing paramagnetism of metals such as palladium, to the ferromagnetism characteristic of only very few elements, could be satisfactorily coordinated by the theoretical scheme using ideally only two parameters, one related to the band form and the other to the magnitude of the exchange interaction.

Unfortunately, even with the simplest realistic types of band form, accurate quantitative calculations were troublesome to make, for the series approximations hitherto used in applying Fermi-Dirac statistics were inappropriate for electrons in ferromagnetic and strongly paramagnetic metals over most of the relevant temperature range. Accordingly, Stoner collaborated with J. McDougall in making extensive computations of the basic Fermi-Dirac functions and drawing up a set of detailed tables applicable to electrons in bands of a standard form. These were published in 1938 and have since been widely used. Work in which Stoner made use of the tables includes detailed papers on the thermodynamic functions for a Fermi-Dirac gas and on collective electron

ferromagnetism, covering the thermal as well as the magnetic properties. These papers provide a basis for a more complete analysis and interpretation of the experimental results for particular materials, to which others, including some of his own associates, have since contributed.

Although Stoner in his research was almost exclusively concerned with the basic properties of ferromagnetics, he kept in touch with work on the magnetization curve characteristics. He was particularly interested in the development of the newer ternary alloys with coercivities which were many times greater than those of the previous standard permanent magnet materials and which certainly could not be accounted for by the current ideas. A possible explanation of how such high coercivities might arise occurred to him, but with the more urgent needs of wartime a proper exploration of the possibility had to be deferred. After the war he followed up his earlier idea that certain materials might contain ferromagnetic particles below the critical size for domain boundary formation in a less ferromagnetic matrix and that these—if anisotropic because of shape (having the form, say, of prolate ellipsoids) of magnetocrystalline effects or of longitudinal strain—could give rise to very high coercivities. Detailed calculations were made with the collaboration of E. P. Wohlfarth, and the results and a discussion of their bearings were presented in outline in 1947 and in full in a paper, "A mechanism of magnetic hysteresis in heterogeneous alloys," in 1948. This detailed theoretical treatment of a necessarily idealized model proved of great value in the understanding and further development of high-coercivity materials, and it was later elaborated and extended with reference to particular materials by Wohlfarth and many others.

The course of the small adiabatic temperature changes accompanying the step-by-step magnetization of ferromagnetics in low and moderate fields, which had been examined experimentally for many materials, notably by L. F. Bates, presented other puzzling problems. These were largely resolved by a thermodynamically based analysis, in which Stoner had the collaboration of P. Rhodes, of the various elementary processes by which change of magnetization occurs (1949). The complexity arises mainly from the superposition of heating and cooling effects, the first associated with increase in intrinsic magnetization and the second with rotation of the domain magnetization vectors in the anisotropic crystalline field toward the field direction. The relative as well as the absolute magnitudes of the two effects differ widely for different materials in a way which can be calculated from other magnetic data, and the resultant effect varies along the course of a magnetization curve. The treatment of irreversible effects presents great difficulties, but progress toward an experimental sorting out of reversible and irreversible changes has since been made by one of Stoner's associates, R. S. Tebble.

Stoner's later contributions included two long reports on the progress of research on ferromagnetism (1948, 1950); a general accout of the analysis of magnetization curves, that is, the determination of the character and extent of the various elementary changes occurring over any parts of the curves (1953); and a detailed survey and discussion of the magnetic susceptibility and electronic specific heat of transition metals in relation to their electronic structure (1954).

A member of the physics department of the University of Leeds from 1924, Stoner was appointed to the newly instituted chair of theoretical physics there in 1939; he was acting head of the department from 1940 to 1946; and he succeeded R. Whiddington as Cavendish Professor of Physics and head of the department in 1951. He retired in 1963. He was elected to the Royal Society of London in 1937; he gave the Kelvin Lecture to the Institution of Electrical Engineers in 1944 and the Guthrie Lecture to the Physical Society in 1955.

For background information *see* ELECTRON SPIN; FERMI-DIRAC STATISTICS; FERROMAGNETISM in the McGraw-Hill Encyclopedia of Science and Technology.   □

★ STRASSMANN, Fritz

German chemist
Born Feb. 22, 1902, Boppard, Rhine, Germany

STRASSMANN STUDIED chemistry at the Technological Institute (Technische Hochschule) in Hannover from 1920 to 1929. His undergraduate research was carried out in 1924 at the Institute of Industrial Chemistry, where he took the diploma examination, and his doctoral research from 1925 to 1929 at the Institute of Physical Chemistry. In 1929 he received certi-

fication for research in physical chemistry. Beginning in July, 1929, Strassmann worked in the field of radioactivity at the Kaiser Wilhelm Institute of Chemistry at Berlin-Dahlem on mixed crystal systems, diffusion of gases in crystals and glasses, determination of surface area in powdered substances, and reactions in the solid state. Beginning in 1934, there followed his determination, with Ernst Walling, of the age of minerals by the rubidium-strontium method and investigations of the transuranium region, with Otto Hahn and Lise Meitner. In 1938, with Hahn, he discovered nuclear fission, an accomplishment recognized in 1966 by the award of the Enrico Fermi Prize of the U.S. Atomic Energy Commission to Hahn, Meitner, and Strassmann.

After the destruction of the Kaiser Wilhelm Institute in 1944, the work on nuclear fission was continued in Tailfingen in South Württemberg. In 1946 the Institute was removed to Mainz. The University of Mainz was again opened, and Strassmann was named professor of inorganic chemistry. In the years which followed, he built the Institute of Inorganic Chemistry, later the Institute of Inorganic Chemistry and Nuclear Chemistry, which is numbered today among the most modern and efficient institutes of its kind. At the same time, as director of the Chemistry Division (1946) of the former Kaiser Wilhelm Institute, renamed the Max Planck Institute of Chemistry, he also had to construct the Max Planck Institute on the grounds of the university.

In 1952 he gave up his work in the Max Planck Society, which he had joined in 1945, since continuation of the research had become impossible for technical reasons. He dedicated himself exclusively to the development of chemistry at the Johannes Gutenberg University in Mainz. With the construction and installation of a TRIGA Mark II Reactor (General Atomics, San Diego), the first phase of the development was brought to its conclusion. Research at the Institute is concerned with problems of preparative inorganic chemistry, modern analytical chemistry, spectrochemistry, structural investigations, biochemistry and clinical chemistry, industrial chemistry, physical chemistry, and radiochemistry, especially with problems of nuclear fission.

The ninth child of a middle-ranking officer, Strassmann attended school in Düsseldorf and then went to the Technological Institute in Hannover in 1920. From 1929 to 1933 he held a fellowship of the provisional Association of German Scientists at the Kaiser Wilhelm Institute in Berlin-Dahlem under Hahn. Strassmann wrote no inaugural dissertation since he was opposed to National Socialism. Strassmann was a member of the Mainz Academy of Sciences and the Wilhelm Busch Society in Hannover.

For background information *see* FISSION, NUCLEAR; NUCLEAR CHEMISTRY; RADIOCHEMISTRY; SPECTROCHEMICAL ANALYSIS in the McGraw-Hill Encyclopedia of Science and Technology.   □

★ SWIFT, Ernest Haywood

American analytical chemist
Born July 2, 1897, Chase City, Va., U.S.A.

SWIFT BECAME interested in analytical and inorganic chemistry as a graduate student assisting Arthur A. Noyes in the experimental work preceding a revision of his well-known text of qualitative analysis. Similar work followed with Noyes and W. C. Bray in the final experiments leading to their qualitative analysis for the rare elements. In the course of the latter studies, Swift discovered that gallium was extracted from hydrochloric acid solutions by ethyl ether. This discovery led to subsequent studies of the factors affecting the distribution of ferric iron and other elements between hydrochloric acid solutions and various ethers and the identification of the species present in the ethereal and aqueous solutions.

After the work on the rare element system he developed a system of analysis for the so-called common elements which provided for their systematic qualitative detection and semiquantitative determination; this system was incorporated in a text—*A System of Chemical Analysis (Qualitative and Semi-quantitative) for the Common Elements* (1939)—which permitted teaching qualitative and quantitative analysis as an integrated course. The common element system led to measurements of what was designated as the formal half-cell potentials of various redox systems. These values differ from standard half-cell potentials in that they can be applied to systems of experimental interest where the total concentrations of the oxidant and reductant are known but the exact species present are unknown because of hydrolysis, polymerization, or complex-ion formation.

During World War II there was established at the California Institute of Technology, under the direction of Swift and Carl Niemann, a project aimed at developing a series of systematic analytical operations that could be used by the U.S. Chemical Warfare Service for the rapid identification and estimation under field conditions of unknown toxic agents or other munitions. One set of these operations was published by the Service as "A System for the Ultimate Analysis of Chemical Warfare Agents." After the war and the declassification of these procedures, they were simplified and adapted for use as a laboratory manual (Swift and W. P. Schaefer, *Qualitative Elemental Analysis* [1962]).

Another result of the work for the Chemical Warfare Service was the development of an improved method for the determination of vapor-phase concentrations of the toxic agent known as "mustard gas." In this procedure a difficult manual titration with dilute standard solutions of bromine water was replaced by the electrolytic generation of the bromine by a current controlled at a constant rate. The end point of the titration was determined by a dual-electrode amperometric method and the quantity of bromine produced, and therefore the mustard gas present was calculated from the value of the current and the time required for the titration. After the war a series of studies showed that this electrolytic generation of bromine can be used for the determination of substances other than mustard gas and that other oxidizing and reducing titrants can be produced electrolytically. Such methods have become known as constant current coulometry, and they have obvious advantages over manual titrations for the accurate determinations of very small quantities of substances and for cases where automation is desired.

In 1952 Swift became interested in the reactions involved when various metal sulfides are precipitated by thioacetamide. Shortly before that time this substance had been first used as a substitute for hydrogen sulfide in systems of qualitative analysis and also for the quantitative determination of various metals. In these procedures the assumption had been made that the thioacetamide rapidly hydrolyzes to give hydrogen sulfide, and published statements held that the reagent can be substituted for hydrogen sulfide without modification of conventional procedures. Swift and his associates found that in many cases this is not true. Reaction rate studies showed that the hydrolysis of the thioacetamide is much slower than was assumed and that, although under certain conditions the rate of sulfide precipitation can be predicted from the hydrolysis rate, under other conditions the rate of precipitation is much more rapid than would be predicted. In these cases the thioacetamide reacts directly with the metal.

Swift received his undergraduate training at Randolph-Macon College and the University of Virginia (B.S., 1918). He went to the California Institute of Technology (then Throop College of Technology) as a graduate student (M.S., 1920; Ph.D., 1924). In 1920 he was placed in charge of the sophomore courses in analytical chemistry, and he continued this responsibility until 1957, when he was granted a Guggenheim fellowship; the next year he became chairman of the Division of Chemistry and Chemical Engineering. His courses were characterized by his belief that analytical chemistry is a superb device for teaching descriptive inorganic chemistry and the principles of chemical reactions and that these objectives are more effectively attained if the introductory quantitative course precedes the qualitative. Because of the early influence of Noyes, he believed strongly in the value of undergraduate research as a source of student motivation, and a majority of his research publications involved the collaboration of undergraduate students. He received the American Chemical Society Fisher Award in Analytical Chemistry in 1955, an Honor Scroll from the American Institute of Chemists in 1961, the Tolman Award from the Southern California Section of the American Chemical Society in 1962, and a College Chemistry Teachers Award from the Manufacturing Chemists Association in 1963. He was elected to the American Academy of Arts and Sciences in 1962.

In addition to the two books mentioned above, Swift wrote *Introductory Quantitative Analysis* (1951) and revised Noyes's *Qualitative Chemical Analysis* (10th ed. 1942).

For background information *see* ANALYTICAL CHEMISTRY; CHEMICAL WARFARE; ELEMENTS (CHEMICAL) in the McGraw-Hill Encyclopedia of Science and Technology.   □

★ SWINGS, Pol

Belgian astrophysicist
Born Sept. 24, 1906, Ransart, Hainaut, Belgium

UNDERSTANDING OF the physics and chemistry of the astronomical bodies is based to a considerable extent on the spectrographic analysis of the radiations issuing from these bodies. Although his initial training was in celestial mechanics, Swings soon directed his major effort toward the applications of laboratory and theoretical spectroscopy to the study of all types of cosmic objects. Simultaneously, he carried out investigations in laboratory spectroscopy, especially in the field of the fluorescence of diatomic molecules, essentially those of sulfur, selenium, tellurium, arsenic, and antimony (1929–34). The experience gained in the field of laboratory molecular fluorescence was useful later in his investigations on comets. In collaboration with Bengt Edlén (1934), he identified the forbidden transitions of Ne V (four times ionized neon), A IV (three times ionized argon), and other elements in planetary nebulae, novae, and peculiar bright-line stars. Either alone or in collaboration with his students, he identified various emission or absorption lines of atomic or molecular origin in the Sun and in stars. Emphasis was placed on the molecular spectra of stars, a rather neglected field in the early 1930s. He carried out or directed investigations on the assignment of a number of molecular bands in the Sun, in late-type stars, and in cepheid variables, trying to interpret the observed intensities in terms of certain abundances which were poorly known. Simultaneously, he searched for atomic identifications, such as that of C IV in hot stars. From time to time (1951, 1960, 1967) he issued a report on the status of the identifications in astronomical spectra.

In 1936, together with Edlén, he realized the great astrophysical need for the laboratory study of the spectrum of Fe III (doubly ionized iron). This work took almost 3 years and necessitated the measurement and classification of almost 30,000 lines in the region λ 500–λ 6000 A. The results were gratifying. Many permitted Fe III lines were found in absorption or emission in hot stars, sometimes revealing dilution effects which could not have been ascertained otherwise. In several shell stars Fe III turned out to be the most outstanding feature of the spectrum. Moreover, the forbidden Fe III lines

gave the explanation of many unexplained emissions of novae and peculiar stars.

Swings applied his knowledge of atomic and molecular spectra to the nightglow, the polar auroras, the twilight flash, and the spectra of the solar disk and spots. He devoted many years of steady work to the comets. Either alone or in collaboration with several of his colleagues at the McDonald and Haute Provence observatories, he observed cometary spectra and discovered radicals, especially OH and NH (with C. T. Elvey and H. W. Babcock), CO_2^+ (with T. L. Page), NH_2 (with A. McKellar and R. Minkowski), CN (red system, with J. Dufay), and forbidden lines of oxygen (with J. L. Greenstein). He also found emissions of CH^+ and OH^+ and contributed to the assignment of the strong cometary emissions near λ 4050 to the tricarbon C_3 (a spectrum sometimes referred to as the Swings bands, following a suggestion of Otto Struve). On the basis of these new assignments Swings contributed to the physical understanding of the atmospheres of the cometary heads and tails. In collaboration with A. N. Delsemme, Swings envisaged the presence of solid hydrates in the icy nuclei. One of the most exciting results was his interpretation of the anomalous profiles of the CN bands, which had been the object of many controversies. Swings demonstrated in a most convincing way that these anomalous intensity distributions are due to the effects of the Fraunhofer lines of the exciting solar radiation, account being taken of the relative radial velocity of the Sun and comet—now known as the "Swings effect." It gave convincing evidence that the cometary emissions—at least those of CN—are excited by a pure fluorescence mechanism. Later the Swings effect was applied to OH, NH, CH, C_2, NH_2, and CO^+. Much remains to be done as the detailed investigations reveal information not only on the comets themselves but even on certain physical parameters of the radicals involved. The interpretation of the cometary profiles resulted essentially from Swings's earlier work on laboratory fluorescence spectra. The discovery of forbidden OI lines also inspired several investigations, but a great deal of work is still needed. The study of the continuum of the heads and tails led to its assignment to scattering by small solid particles. The *Atlas of Representative Cometary Spectra* (1956) by Swings and Leo Haser is widely used by astronomical and laboratory spectroscopists. The Darwin Lecture given by Swings in 1964 was devoted to the cometary spectra.

The C_3 radical, which plays an outstanding role in comets, is also present in the coolest carbon stars; indeed, the identification of C_3 in N stars (in collaboration with McKellar and K. N. Rao) was the first evidence for a polyatomic molecule in stars. Mainly in collaboration with Struve, Swings carried out many investigations on the emission lines of early-type stars. Indeed, the first detailed paper on the "rotational hypothesis" for the Be stars was published by Struve and Swings in 1932.

This was followed by many papers (some with O. Struve) on the axial rotation, dilution phenomena, and abundances (and their anomalies). During the period 1940–45 Swings published 35 papers jointly with Struve, mainly on peculiar bright-line stars. These investigations and those of Swings alone concerned the novae and postnovae, the stars of Of, Wolf-Rayet, P Cygni, Be, and Ae types. New identifications, including many new forbidden lines, were found. The excitation mechanisms and evolutionary aspects were discussed extensively.

The symbiotic objects were especially studied in detail; to a spectroscopist like Swings those monstrous stars were a source of bewilderment and surprise. A few normal early-type stars were examined for comparison. Other papers were concerned with variable stars, including β Canis Majoris and the rare-earth star α^2 Canum Venaticorum. A few objects, especially Wolf-Rayet stars, were observed in the photographic infrared region. The anomalies of the peculiar stars of the earliest types were discussed and related in the light of the fluorescence and dilution effects and of the departures from the blackbody distribution of the exciting or ionizing radiation. The physical mechanisms were particularly studied in various planetary nebulae and their nuclei. The new observations of these nuclei revealed exciting spectroscopic phenomena; the planetaries and their nuclei are sometimes strange associations which are far from fully understood. Similarly, the novae and postnovae exhibit queer spectroscopic behaviors, including nitrogen outbursts, coronal stages, and abundance anomalies which still require much work.

In collaboration with L. Rosenfeld, Swings identified (1937) a molecular interstellar line due to CH and discussed the low-temperature effect on the interstellar molecules. Swings continued to be interested in interstellar molecules and dust; he took part in the discussions which led to the identification of CH^+ in interstellar absorption (and found this ion in comets). He also compared extensively the behavior of molecules in the interstellar space and in cometary atmospheres (1942).

Although essentially an observer, Swings carried out several theoretical investigations, two jointly with S. Chandrasekhar (1936), on rotating stars and on the formation of blended absorption lines. He also did some work on the integration of the equation of radiative transfer (with L. Dor, 1938). Swings examined problems which should be studied from space vehicles. These concern cometary and auroral physics on the one hand and ultraviolet-infrared spectra of novae, novoids, symbiotic stars, and other peculiar stars on the other hand. He was active in the European Space Research Organization. Swings also carried out some research on industrial spectroscopy and occasionally found interesting analogies between the spectroscopic and optical problems presented by astrophysics and industry. He published the first textbook on applied spectroscopy in the French language (1935).

Swings obtained his Ph.D. in mathematics in 1927 at the University of Liège and then a special Ph.D. in physics in 1930. As a postdoctorate fellow, he spent several years abroad. He was appointed professor of spectroscopy and astrophysics in Liège in 1932. He was a visiting professor in Chicago, Berkeley, Pasadena, and other places. From 1952 to 1958 he was vice-president of the International Astronomical Union and was president from 1964 to 1967. He was elected correspondent of the Paris Academy of Sciences in 1956 and foreign associate in 1964. He was elected a foreign member of the American Academy of Arts and Sciences (1965), of the U.S. National Academy of Sciences (1966), and of the American Philosophical Society (1966). Besides three honorary degrees he received many prizes and medals in Belgium and abroad, including the two highest Belgian prizes, the Francqui Prize in 1947 and the Decennal Prize in Physics in 1958.

For background information *see* ASTRONOMICAL SPECTROSCOPY; MOLECULAR STRUCTURE AND SPECTRA; SPECTROSCOPY; STAR in the McGraw-Hill Encyclopedia of Science and Technology. □

★ SZENT-GYÖRGYI, Albert

American biochemist
Born Sept. 16, 1893, Budapest, Hungary

BEING, ON his mother's side, the fourth generation in a family of anatomists, Szent-Györgyi started his research in anatomy and histology. However, he soon turned to research on living material, embarking on physiology. Finding that the higher animals were much too

complex, he became a pharmacologist, hoping to find conditions simpler, since drugs are relatively simple substances. Pharmacology was too complex, also, so he became a bacteriologist. Szent-Györgyi soon discovered that a bacterium, though very small, is a universe in itself and thus is much too involved to give the expected, simple answers, so he descended to the level of molecules, becoming a chemist. After several decades he found even molecules too complex and started work on electrons in quantum mechanics. This frequent change of research subjects gave him a view of the whole range of biochemical sciences down to the electronic level, but it did not lead him to a better understanding of life because electrons have no life at all, nor indeed have molecules. In his later years his research ascended again to the cellular level.

Szent-Györgyi's first biochemical work related to biological oxidation. Life can be studied from two different points of view—that of the structure of the living machine and that of the energy which drives this machine. Oxidation, the source of all living energies, promised to give him an answer to the nature of life. First he studied oxidation in plants. He was interested in the brown color which develops in many plants when they are bruised; everybody knows this color from ripe bananas. Szent-Györgyi found that this brown color was due to the oxidation of a phenolic substance by an enzyme to a quinole. About half of the plants show such a brown coloration but the other half do not, so he turned to the plants which do not show brown coloration, such as lemons, oranges, and cabbages. He found that all these plants contain a substance which has a strong reducing agent that prevents the formation of colored material through the oxidation of aromatics. He isolated this substance, which turned out to be the long-sought vitamin C, and he called this substance "ascorbic acid."

Szent-Györgyi then turned his attention to animal tissues. During the early 1930s there was a violent discussion as to whether the foodstuff or oxygen is activated when oxidation takes place in the human body. He showed that both theories were correct and that the activated foodstuff, that is, activated hydrogen, is oxidized by activated oxygen. He also found that the enzymes, which oxidize substances that have two carboxylic and four carbon atoms or six carbon atoms and two carboxylic groups, have a universal catalytic role in animal metabolism. For this discovery and for the isolation of ascorbic acid Szent-Györgyi was awarded in 1937 the Nobel Prize for medicine or physiology. From oxidation studies he turned his attention to muscle. He soon discovered a new protein in muscle which he called "actin," and which was subsequently isolated by his pupil Straub. Actin and another protein which had been known for almost 100 years, called "myosin," formed the complex actomyosin. Szent-Györgyi made little artificial muscles of actomyosin and, when he added adenosinetriphosphate, the most important energy source of muscle contraction, these artificial muscles contracted. From muscle research he turned to the problem of cell division. According to his theory, the behavior of the cell depends on the equilibrium of two substances, one which tries to make the cell multiply and the other which inhibits this multiplication. He hoped to find a clue to the understanding of cancer by means of these substances.

Szent-Györgyi pursued his studies in different countries. He did his anatomical studies at the University of Budapest (M.D., 1917) and worked there in bacteriology. He continued his studies at the Institute of Tropical Hygiene in Hamburg, Germany. He went to Holland, where he worked in pharmacology and started in chemistry; he became a full-fledged biochemist at the University of Groningen in North Holland. He next went to England, where he got his Ph.D. in chemistry (1927) at Cambridge University. From Cambridge he went to the Mayo Clinic in the United States; he returned to his home country, Hungary, in 1930, and immigrated to the United States in 1947. He began working at the Marine Biological Laboratory, Woods Hole, where he headed the Institute for Muscle Research. He was elected to the National Academy of Sciences in 1956 and to the American Academy of Arts and Sciences in 1957.

Szent-Györgyi reported on his work in more than 200 scientific papers and wrote several books, the first being *On Oxidation, Fermentation, Vitamins, Health and Disease* (1940). His results on muscle were summed up in *Chemistry of Muscular Contraction* (1947; 2d ed. 1951), *Nature of Life: A Study on Muscle* (1948), and *Chemical Physiology of Contraction in Body and Heart Muscle* (1953). He wrote two books on quantum mechanics, *Bioenergetics* (1957) and *Introduction to a Submolecular Biology* (1960).

For background information *see* Ascorbic acid; Cell division; Enzyme; Motor systems in the McGraw-Hill Encyclopedia of Science and Technology.   □

★ SZWARC, Michael

American chemist
Born June 9, 1909, Bedzin, Poland

S ZWARC STARTED his academic research activities after World War II, when he had the good fortune to join Michael Polanyi's group in the University of Manchester. He was asked to investigate pyrolytic processes, with the ulti-

mate aim of determining bond dissociation energies of polyatomic molecules. Eventually he developed the "toluene carrier" technique, which allowed him to achieve this goal. In fact, within a few years his students and he were able to determine many bond dissociation energies of organic molecules, and early in 1950 more than half of the then available data was obtained by this method.

In the course of these studies, which started with the investigation of pyrolysis of toluene and its derivatives, he pyrolyzed *p*-xylene. His intention was to break the $CH_3 \cdot C_6H_4 \cdot CH_2$-H bond and to produce the *p*-xylyl radicals. He expected to isolate their dimer and was surprised to find instead a transparent polymeric film in the trap. The intended dissociation led to polymerization of a most unusual type. In a short time he solved the mystery. He proved that the *p*-xylyl radical decomposes, or disproportionates, and yields a quinonoid hydrocarbon

$$CH_2 = \bigcirc = CH_2$$

or its diradical

$$\cdot CH_2 - \bigcirc - CH_2 \cdot$$

This condenses on any surface and spontaneously and rapidly polymerizes, covering it with a tight and uniform film of *p*-xylelene.

This discovery aroused Szwarc's interest in polymer chemistry, and in 1952 he became professor of physical and polymer chemistry at the State University College of Forestry in Syracuse,

N.Y. There he started studies of addition of methyl radicals to aromatic hydrocarbons and other substrates, which led to the concept of methyl affinities. After publication of one of his first papers on this subject he met Sam Weissman, who told him how this work paralleled his own on the electron affinities of aromatic hydrocarbons.

In the course of their discussion Weissman explained how electrons may be transfered from one aromatic radical ion to another aromatic hydrocarbon and form a new radical ion. It occurred to Szwarc that an electron transfer to a vinyl monomer, such as styrene, could initiate a peculiar polymerization in which the growth occurs in both directions—one end of the chain would propagate by anionic mechanism, while the polymerization on the other end would proceed through a radical mechanism. Therefore, he asked whether Weissman had tried to investigate the electron-transfer process with styrene. Weissman replied that it was "no use" since it polymerizes. But Szwarc decided that this was what he would like to investigate and he started work in this field. It turned out to be most fascinating and rewarding. He and his coworkers found that termination could be prevented in anionic polymerization, and thus the concept of living polymers was created. This approach led to many corollaries—to synthesis of block polymers and other tailor-made polymers, to uniform-sized polymers, to the chemistry of radical ions and electron-transfer processes, and recently to studies of free ions and ion pairs in aprotic solvents. Living polymers provide excellent systems for kinetic studies, such as investigation of the relations between reactivity of ion pairs and their structure and clarification of the role of counterions and of solvent.

Szwarc received a degree in chemical engineering from Warsaw Polytechnic College in 1932. From 1933 to 1935 he was employed in a chemical factory in Warsaw. In 1935 he went to Jerusalem, where he taught and engaged in research at the Hebrew University, earning his Ph.D. in organic chemistry there in 1942. In 1945 Szwarc went to England to conduct research work in physical chemistry at the University of Manchester, where he gained another Ph.D. in 1947. In 1949 he was granted a D.Sc. at Manchester for his work on dissociation energies of the chemical bond. In that year Szwarc was appointed university fellow at Manchester, where he was later a lecturer in physical chemistry until 1952, when he was appointed to the State University College of Forestry at Syracuse University as professor of physical and polymer chemistry. In 1956 he was made research professor of physical and polymer chemistry, the first faculty member of the State University of New York to be awarded a research professorship; in 1964 he became Distinguished Professor of Chemistry. He was elected a fellow of the Royal Society of London in 1966.

For background information *see* ACID AND BASE; HYDROCARBON; PHOTOCHEMISTRY; POLYMERIZATION in the McGraw-Hill Encyclopedia of Science and Technology. □

★ **TAMIYA, Hiroshi**

Japanese biologist and biochemist
Born Jan. 5, 1903, Osaka, Japan

DURING THE first decade of his research career Tamiya worked on the growth physiology of the mold *Aspergillus oryzae*, which has been from ancient times a most important microorganism in the food industry of Japan and its neighboring countries. Being interested in its versatile utility—as fermenter of soybean protein, converter of rice starch into sugar in the process of wine brewing, and so on—he systematically investigated the capacity of the mold for attacking and utilizing various organic substances as carbon sources in its culture. The organism was found to be strikingly omnivorous, being capable of growing on a large variety of organic substances of widely different nature. Each of these substances was consumed partly as the energy source by being oxidized to carbon dioxide and water, and the rest was used as building blocks for the formation of cell materials. With more than 70 different substances he compared quantitatively their availability as energy source and as building blocks for the formation of the body of the mold. Considering the metabolic balance sheet thus formulated, Tamiya drew the general conclusion that during the culture of the mold heat will be produced in a quantity larger than that calculated from the rate of respiration. This prediction was confirmed by actually measuring the heat produced during the culture.

His studies then turned to the biochemical problem of cellular respiration; it was at the time when the heme-containing "respiratory enzyme" and cytochromes were discovered by O. Warburg in Germany and D. Keilin in England, respectively. The "respiratory enzyme" had been claimed to be present in all aerobic cells, and its hemoprotein nature was demonstrated in a most ingenious way by Warburg, using carbon monoxide as a photoreversible inhibitor of respiration.

Tamiya discovered, however, that in the case of *Aspergillus* carbon monoxide does not inhibit but rather stimulates the respiration, and he maintained that there are respiratory mechanisms that are different from that postulated by Warburg. In cooperation with some co-workers, he also found that different species of bacteria and different types of tumor cells show different cytochrome patterns, and that in some bacterial species there is a cytochrome different from those reported by Keilin.

Another remarkable discovery he made, in cooperation with a zoologist, was that a large amount of hemoglobin is contained in the cells of *Paramecium*, which is no doubt the lowest class of hemoglobin-containing animals. At that time the well-known dispute was still going on between Warburg and H. Wieland concerning the importance of "activation" of oxygen in air or hydrogen in the substrate in the process of respiration. Using a strain of *Acetobacter*, Tamiya compared the effects of various poisonous substances upon the aerobic and anaerobic processes of the acid formation from ethyl alcohol, and it was clearly demonstrated that Warburg's "respiratory enzyme" acts only in the aerobic process, while Wieland's dehydrogenase functions both in aerobic and anaerobic processes.

Having started his career as a plant physiologist, Tamiya always had an interest in the problems of photosynthesis. His first work in this field, performed in 1942 in cooperation with some physicochemists, was on the problem concerning the origin of oxygen produced in the process of photosynthesis. It was known that, when carbon dioxide and water are in isotopic equilibrium, the former contains a certain greater amount of heavy oxygen (oxygen-18) than the latter. Taking advantage of this fact and providing "equilibrated" carbon dioxide and water to the water plant *Elodea*, they compared the weight of the oxygen produced by photosynthesis with those of carbon dioxide and water. The result obtained was that the photosynthetic oxygen is a little heavier than the oxygen in water and lighter than that of carbon dioxide, suggesting that a part of photosynthetic oxygen is derived from carbon dioxide.

Among the series of photosynthesis studies that followed, the most extensive one was that measuring the photosynthesis of the unicellular green alga *Chlorella* under illumination with intermittent flashing light. The results of this experiment led Tamiya to the conclusion that the light-activated photosynthetic pigment undergoes a second-order deactivation when its energy is in surplus to the need for the occurrence of energy-requiring "dark reactions." Another series of investigations, designed to discriminate between light and dark steps of photosynthesis, was carried out by the use of the preillumination technique (using carbon-14 as a tracer) combined with the method of selective inhibition by specific poisons. Various modes of inhibition of photosynthetic carbon dioxide fixation were elucidated in this way.

Parallel with these studies Tamiya in 1951 started investigations on the feasibility of mass culture of *Chlorella*. This was at the suggestion of H. A. Spoehr of the Carnegie Institution of Washington, who brought forward the idea that an entirely new type of agriculture could be developed if some fast-growing microalgae, such as *Chlorella*, were cultured on a large scale by using modern engineering techniques. After many trials and errors Tamiya and his co-workers developed a unique culture method with a device for intermittent sweeping and called it the "open circulation method." An important by-product emerged unexpectedly from Tamiya's study on *Chlorella* culture. In a laboratory experiment *Chlorella* was grown under diurnal alternation of light and darkness (12 hours' light and 12 hours' darkness) simulating natural outdoor conditions. It was found that the algal cells grew and divided almost "synchronously," which meant that practically all the cells in the culture kept their pace in growth and cellular division. Growth occurred only during the light period, while cellular division took place during the dark period, so that almost all the cells were large at the end of the light period and small at the end of the dark period. Improvements of the culture technique made later by Tamiya and his co-workers made it possible to obtain a complete and very uniform synchronous culture of the alga. This technique (first reported in 1953) has opened a new avenue of approach to the elucidation of various cellular events occurring in the algal life cycle. Since then similar techniques have been widely used by algologists and cell physiologists in other countries, and a large body of information has accumulated about the physiology, biochemistry, and biophysics of algal cells that cannot be studied by conventional culture techniques.

Tamiya was the son of a medical doctor. He received a Sc.D. at the University of Tokyo in 1932, and a honorary Sc.D. at the University of Tübingen in 1963. He served as professor of botany at the University of Tokyo from 1939 to 1955 and then at the Institute of Applied Microbiology until 1963, when he retired and became professor emeritus at the university. In 1946 he became also director of the Tokugawa Institute for Biological Research, where he continued working actively with young scientists. In recognition of his work prizes were awarded to him by the Japanese Association of Science (1935), the Fujiwara Foundation (1963), and the Academy of Japan (1965). In 1963, on the occasion of his 60th birthday, he received from the Japanese Society of Plant Physiologists a Festschrift entitled *Studies on Microalgae and Photosynthetic Bacteria*, which contained valuable papers dedicated to him by many scientists at home and abroad. He was elected a member of Deutsche Akademie der Naturforscher in 1958 and a foreign associate of the U.S. National Academy of Sciences in 1966.

Tamiya wrote *Le bilan matériel et l'énergétique des synthèses biologiques* (1935) and *Mechanism of Photosynthesis* (in Japanese, 1943). He edited *Mechanism of Photosynthesis* (Proceedings of the 5th International Congress of Biochemistry, Moscow, 1963) and *Experimental Methods of Algology* (in Japanese, 1965).

For background information *see* ALGAE; BACTERIAL METABOLISM; EUMYCETES; PHOTOSYNTHESIS; PLANT RESPIRATION in the McGraw-Hill Encyclopedia of Science and Technology.   □

★ TARBELL, Dean Stanley

American chemist
Born Oct. 19, 1913, Hancock, N.H., U.S.A.

TARBELL's WORK illustrates two of the principal aspects of research in organic chemistry during recent decades: the determination of structure and synthesis of organic compounds, particularly of natural products, and the study of reaction mechanisms in an effort to establish the path of organic reactions.

His first independent work at Rochester, with J. F. Kincaid, showed that the Claisen rearrangement of allyl aryl ethers is a first-order reaction, and that the entropy of activation (probably the first application of this calculation to an organic reaction) indicates that the transition state for the rearrangement is a quasi-ring structure (Fig. 1). Other collaborators, J. W. Wilson, J. R. Vaughan, Jr., and V. P. Wystrach, investigated further aspects of the rearrangement.

Tarbell's war research, on methods of detecting toxic agents, in collaboration with J. F. Bunnett, established the mode of action of arsen-

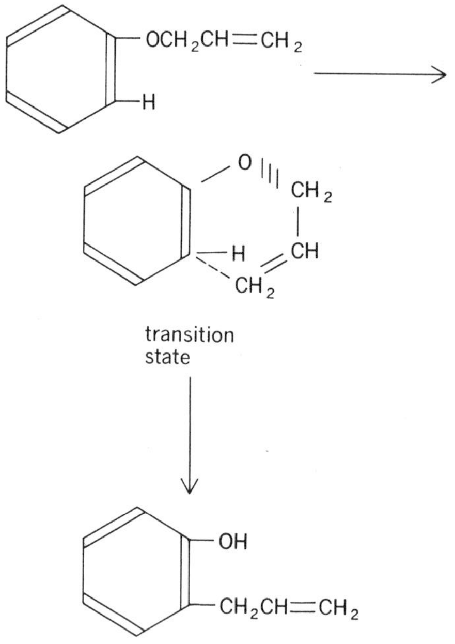

Fig. 1. Claisen rearrangement of allyl aryl ethers.

ical agents with dithizone. This and some synthetic studies directed his interest to a comparison of the reactivity of carbon-sulfur bonds as compared to carbon-oxygen bonds in analogous compounds. With D. P. Harnish, he wrote an extensive review of the cleavage of the carbon-sulfur bond, and with a number of collaborators, he carried out kinetic and synthetic studies defining the reactivities of sulfur and oxygen analogs. J. C. Petropoulos showed striking differences between the behavior of benzyl phenyl ether and the sulfide; P. M. Rylander and B. K. Morse compared rates of hydrolysis of esters and thiolesters; Stevens studied lactones and thiolactones; P. J. Hawkins and D. P. Cameron studied thiolesters related to coenzyme A; and I. Pascal determined the kinetics of oxidation of a thiol to a disulfide. M. A. McCall and W. E. Lovett discovered the isomerization by base of an allyl sulfide to a propenyl sulfide, a reaction later extended to the oxygen analogs by workers in other laboratories.

Some synthetic schemes required a knowledge of the reactions of mixed carbonic-carboxylic anhydrides, a class of compounds useful synthetically but never studied in any detail. J. A. Price and N. A. Leister showed that these compounds can be readily isolated, and E. J. Longosz, C. J. Michejda, and R. C. L. Chow worked out numerous features of their reactions, using kinetic, stereochemical, and tracer techniques. These studies were extended to sulfur and phosphorus anhydrides, with results that are useful synthetically and that increase the knowledge of carbonyl reactions in general. Photolysis of dithiocarbamic carboxylic anhydrides by

E. H. Hoffmeister led to novel types of sulfur-containing compounds.

Tarbell's inclination to the study of the structure of natural products was based on a lively interest in biochemistry. P. E. Fanta and H. R. Frank established features of the structure of colchicine, a natural product useful in treating gout, while H. R. V. Arnstein, G. P. Scott, and H. T. Huang showed that colchicine contains the novel tropolone ring system, first postulated by Dewar. Scott and A. D. Kemp synthesized the first benztropolone and reported the infrared spectrum of the tropolone ring. Syntheses of vitamin K analogs and of antimalarial drugs during World War II led to work on muscle relaxants, some of which had interesting pharmacological properties. A long standing interest in the cancer problem resulted in a study of metabolites of the carcinogenic hydrocarbon benzpyrene and to a study of free-radical substitution in benzpyrene. The benzpyrene work led to the development of several useful methods in paper chromatography.

The antibiotic fumagillin (Fig. 2), which showed several kinds of biological activity, formed the subject of a long series of structural studies over a 10-year period by many collaborators. The structure was elucidated completely, and experiments directed toward its total synthesis were undertaken. One reaction discovered in the structural work on fumagillin was unexpected enough to receive study from the mechanistic side by S. E. Cantor and E. R. Novak. It is worth pointing out as an example of the development and interconnection of a research program that synthetic approaches to the complex structure of fumagillin utilized the Claisen rearrangement, first studied from a mechanistic view nearly three decades earlier.

Other natural products investigated included actinospectacin, fenchone, and podophyllotoxin.

Tarbell received his A.B. (1934), M.A. (1935), and Ph.D. (1937) at Harvard University. After a year as a postdoctoral fellow at the University of Illinois, he joined the faculty of the University of Rochester in 1938, becoming professor of chemistry in 1942 and Charles Frederick Houghton Professor of Chemistry in

Fumagillin

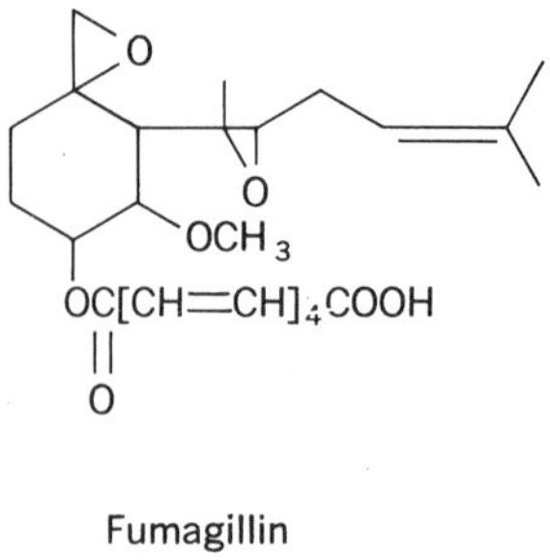

Fig. 2. Structural formula of fumagillin.

1960. In 1967 he became Distinguished Professor of Chemistry at Vanderbilt University. He was elected to the National Academy of Sciences in 1961.

For background information *see* CONDENSATION REACTION; FUMAGILLIN; ORGANIC REACTION MECHANISM in the McGraw-Hill Encyclopedia of Science and Technology.   □

★ TAYLOR, Sir Geoffrey (Ingram)

British mathematician
Born Mar. 7, 1886, London, England

TAYLOR's FIRST scientific work (1909) showed that diffraction patterns are unchanged when light intensity is so low that an exposure of 3 months is necessary to produce a faint image on a photographic plate. The official motivation for this work was Einstein's recently introduced idea that light is not continuous but occurs in discrete packets, so that if a long interval intervenes between the incidence of light packets on a sensitive grain, interference may not occur. The personal motivation was that Taylor had just bought a sailboat and wanted to live aboard, while the long exposure was being made, with conscience untroubled by the thought that he ought to be working in the laboratory.

He was not attracted to pure physics, and when the opportunity came to join a scientific expedition on the old sailing ship *Scotia*, he took it and spent most of 1913 flying kites that carried recording instruments over the cold water off Newfoundland. There he realized that the mechanism by which heat and momentum are transferred to the atmosphere is by means of irregular motions, now described as turbulence. He began to think how these motions could be represented mathematically, but World War I started and he had to turn to war work. In 1915, after joining the Royal Flying Corps, Taylor obtained his pilot's certificate on the 1913-model Maurice Farman airplane. In 1916 he made what were perhaps the first measurements of pressure

distribution over an airplane wing in flight. During this period he became interested in the strength of metals while trying to account for failures of engine crankshafts, and A. A. Griffith, who was working with him, developed his well-known theory of cracks to account for the much smaller strength of metals than had been predicted by using molecular theories. On Taylor's return to Cambridge in 1919 he developed the idea that turbulence could be described by means of correlation coefficients and published (1921) a theory of diffusion by continuous movements.

At that time theoretical hydrodynamics had little relationship to practical problems in aeronautics, and he started thinking about what kind of hydrodynamical situations could be discussed mathematically with some hope of verifying the calculations experimentally. He was fortunate to attract the friendship of Ernest Rutherford, who lent him a room in the Cavendish Laboratory. There (1921–22) Taylor found that theoretical predictions about the effect of rotation on fluid flow could be verified experimentally and later (1923) found the first case in which the instability of flow of a real fluid could be calculated. Experiments verified this calculation in all details. In 1923 A. V. Hill, O. W. Richardson, and Taylor were elected to Royal Society research professorships and later were joined by E. D. Adrian and Peter Kapitza.

During 1923–27 Taylor's interest in the strength of metals was revived on seeing a demonstration of the deformation of single crystals of aluminum. He worked out the geometry (1923) for determining the internal strain from surface measurements and, with Constance Elam, found how the strain is related to the crystal axes. This work brought home to him the fact that metals usually get stronger as they are strained, though the Griffith crack theory would lead one to expect an opposite effect. Taylor constructed a mathematical model (1934) in which crystallographic faults called dislocations can have the strengthening effect observed, and can by their migration produce the plastic strain observed in real metallic crystals. This was developed by others into the dislocation theory of metallic structures.

In 1935 he applied the idea of correlation to describe turbulence at a given instant of time and to show how energy dissipation due to viscosity is related to correlations. This led (1938) to finding the connection between the Eulerian correlations and the spectrum of turbulence.

In 1939 the outbreak of World War II diverted Taylor's attention to the mechanics of explosions, and in 1940 he was asked what mechanical effects might be expected from the sudden release at a point of a great deal of energy. This made him guess that someone had found a method for releasing nuclear energy, and he gave (1941) a mathematical solution representing the blast wave so produced. This work was put on the secret list and was not published till 1950, by which time L. I. Sedov in the Soviet Union and John von Neumann in the United States had found the same solution. The solution made it possible to estimate the yield of an atomic explosion from measurements of the blast pressure at distant points. The existence of Taylor's classified paper was the cause of his being asked to join the Manhattan Project, though he knew little of nuclear physics.

After World War II he published papers on the stability of the interface between two fluids (1949), the swimming of microscopic organisms (1951, 1952), standing waves in water (1952, 1963), dispersion of contaminants in flow through tubes (1953–54), dynamics of fluid sheets (1959–60), penetration of one fluid into another in a Hele-Shaw cell (1959, with P. G. Saffman), electrohydrodynamics (1963–66), and cavitation in narrow passages (1965, with A. D. MacEwan).

Taylor was brought up among artists (his father was a landscape painter) but perhaps inherited a taste for science from his mother, whose father was George Boole, the mathematician, and from his great uncle, George Everest, the geodesist after whom the mountain was named. He studied at Cambridge University (M.A., 1911), and in 1910 became a fellow of Trinity College, Cambridge. From 1923 until his retirement in 1951 he held a Royal Society research professorship at Cambridge. Among his many honors were the Royal Medal (1933) and the Copley Medal (1944) of the Royal Society of London. He was knighted in 1944. Taylor's scientific papers have been collected in three volumes; a fourth is in preparation.

For background information *see* CRYSTAL DEFECTS; HYDRODYNAMICS; TURBULENT FLOW in the McGraw-Hill Encyclopedia of Science and Technology.   □

★ TAYLOR, William Randolph

American botanist
Born Dec. 21, 1895, Philadelphia, Pa., U.S.A.

ALTHOUGH HE had a strong inclination for natural history studies from early youth, Taylor trained as an undergraduate to follow in his father's footsteps as a physician. The pull of biological research, particularly with plants, proved too strong, however, and he took his doctorate in botany. His first investigation dealt with the possibilities for artificially causing the development of cambia in plant tissues where they do not normally occur—cambia which in turn could produce vascular elements like those of the normal

conducting bundle systems. He followed this with a series of studies of the reproductive structures of flowering plants. First he studied the maples, genus *Acer*, investigating the meiotic process, chromosome numbers in several species including naturally occurring polyploids, and the development of the embryo sac and embryo. He made similar studies on other genera with special concern for chromosome form and the pattern of the chromosome complexes, which turned out to be very characteristic in many genera. Probably the culmination of this series was the study of the South African genus *Gasteria*, in which a low number of chromosomes of distinctive shapes favored critical work. Here again Taylor investigated the meiotic process, but more carefully, and elaborated a very precise technique which enabled him to see the spiral structure of meiotic chromosomes very clearly. He also studied the chromonemata of the developing chromosomes and located the period of their reduplication, making early observations on the seriation of distinctive chromomeres upon them.

The demanding techniques of critical cytological research and the strain of long hours at the microscope called for some counterbalance. Taylor undertook general botanical field studies, later concentrating on the algae. Although this field activity was in its early stage an avocation, Taylor felt that something worth recording would come of it. By 1930 the cytological phase of Taylor's researches had largely worked itself out. The growing demands of cytotaxonomy and cytogenetics for quick results could not be met efficiently by the meticulous techniques which appealed to him.

A natural desire to travel and see new parts of the world can hardly be satisfied in any large way during conscientious cytological study, but

for the algal student this can easily be done. Taylor felt that the need for botanical exploration was very great and that the algae in particular lacked adequate phytogeographic attention. This new phase in his research began to yield useful information some years before the chromosome studies ceased. Parts of four summers in the Selkirk Mountains of British Columbia netted a substantial study of the alpine algae from a particularly favorable area. It had an unanticipated result when materials collected by a Harvard-Pennsylvania expedition to Newfoundland were submitted to him for study. These materials yielded a most comprehensive account of the desmids of that province and resulted in Taylor's publishing what was at that time perhaps the most extensive paper on American desmids.

Even before the British Columbia study, Taylor had established an interest in marine algae by spending summers at the Marine Biological Laboratory, Woods Hole, Mass., but could hardly envisage then how few more freshwater algal studies he would carry out. Parts of summers at the Carnegie Institution of Washington station on the Dry Tortugas brought forth a study on the marine algae of Florida, the first substantial study of essentially tropical marine algal flora in United States waters. It required many years of further research, but eventually Taylor's descriptive books covered the eastern American marine flora from the Arctic to Brazil, excepting only the microscopic planktonic forms.

It is a familiar misfortune of field expeditions to find on returning that there is no one to report on some major parts of the collections. This was true on the algae collected on the cruises of the United States ships *Hassler* (1871–72) and *Albatross* (1887–88) around the end of South America. The algae lay at Harvard until they were combined by Taylor with Smithsonian Institution collections from the South Falkland Islands and the Straits of Magellan in a series of papers on South American seaweeds. This acceptance of responsibility for reporting on field studies of others is recurrent in Taylor's publications. Other major field expeditions in which he shared were also productive. Two with Captain Allan Hancock gave him another chance to study Caribbean and northern South American algae, as well as those of western Mexico and the Galapagos Islands. He wrote yet another volume from his studies in the Marshall Islands relative to the first atomic bomb expedition at Bikini. Later, Taylor was occupied in the field and the museum in extending the range records of New England and Caribbean algae, and in the museum those of the Philippines, Indonesia, and places visited by the International Indian Ocean Survey. All these studies made clear and amply confirmed Taylor's belief that the catalog of the world's plants, especially those of the sea, is far from complete, and that work in this field must be active for many years.

It is important to see to what degree research spreads from any particular center. Unfortunately, during most of Taylor's career academic posts for students of algae were rarely available. Some of his best students carried on distinguished work in mainland China, but in recent years little has been heard from them. One student is doing work on algae of streams in the United States, another is making exceptionally productive surveys in the Arctic, and still another on the structure and life histories of calcareous algae of potential geologic interest.

Taylor received his B.S. (1916), M.S. (1917), and Ph.D. in botany (1920) from the University of Pennsylvania. He joined the faculty of the university, becoming professor of botany in 1927. He moved to the University of Michigan in 1930. Awarded the Retzius Medal of the Royal Physiographic Society of Sweden in 1948, Taylor was a foreign member of the Royal Academy of Science and Letters of Belgium (1947), a foreign member of the Linnean Society of London (1955), and a corresponding member of the Academie des Sciences, Institute de France (1958). He was elected to the American Academy of Arts and Sciences in 1948, and received a Merit Award of the Botanical Society of America in 1961.

Taylor wrote *Plants of Bikini* (1950), *Marine Algae of the Northeastern Coast of North America* (2d ed. 1957), and *Marine Algae of the Eastern Tropical and Subtropical Coasts of the Americas* (1960).

For background information *see* ALGAE; FLOWER (BOTANY); REPRODUCTION, PLANT in the McGraw-Hill Encyclopedia of Science and Technology.   □

☆ TELLER, Edward

American physicist
Born Jan. 15, 1908, Budapest, Hungary

I N THE years 1949–51 Teller, working with a group of scientists, developed the principle that led to the successful construction of the first hydrogen bomb. This aspect of Teller's work, of great importance, remains classified. Teller's other work covered a great variety of topics, ranging from engineering and technology to abstract theoretical physics. Mainly on the technological side belong many ideas on thermonuclear devices which he originated while working on the Manhattan Project during World War II.

Even before the end of the war, Teller, Enrico Fermi, and others at the Los Alamos Scientific Laboratory had advanced the theoretical possibility of obtaining controlled fusion power through the confinement of hot plasma in a strong magnetic field. In the early 1950s, when after a lapse of several years large-scale experimentation with fusion power began in the United States, Teller was an active participant. He helped initiate the study of atomic explosions for peacetime uses. As first chairman of the Reactor Safeguards Committee of the Atomic Energy Commission, he was concerned in the establishment of procedures which were of great importance in setting the high standard of reactor safety in the United States.

Teller's theoretical work may be considered chronologically. Early in his career he was drawn to the fields of quantum mechanics and physical chemistry. His first paper, on the hydrogen molecular ion, was considered a major step in the development of the theory of molecular orbitals, which most successfully explains the phenomenon of the chemical bond. Another paper presented a theory of the conversion of *ortho-* to *para-*hydrogen. Also in this period Teller collaborated with S. P. Brunauer and P. Emmett in a paper that established the "BET" equation, expressing the relation (at constant temperature) between the volume of gas adsorbed on a surface and the pressure of the gas above the adsorbent. Other papers dealt with molecular vibration and sound distribution and the duration of the magnetic cooling process.

In the late 1930s Teller's interest turned increasingly to nuclear physics. His first paper in the field, written in collaboration with the physicist George Gamow, established new selection rules for the β-decay process and explained certain observed transitions that had been "forbidden" under earlier selection rules. A paper (1936) on the scattering of neutrons by *ortho-* and *para-*hydrogen contained suggestions for experiments to test the spin dependence of the neutron-proton force. This dependence was subsequently confirmed, and the experiments also yielded information on the spin of the neutron and the range of the nuclear forces.

In the postwar period Teller wrote his best-known paper with the physicist E. Fermi. A remarkable paper (with M. Goldhaber) explained the "giant resonances" as vibrations of protons against neutrons and furnished the basis for a new literature in nuclear physics.

After early studies in Germany Teller received his Ph.D. at the University of Leipzig in 1930. He was a research associate at the University of Göttingen from 1931 to 1933. After study and teaching at Copenhagen and London, Teller went to the United States in 1935 to become professor of physics at George Washington University. In 1941 he became a staff member of the Manhattan District, working first at Columbia University and later at the University of Chicago and the Los Alamos Scientific Laboratory. After the war he returned to the University of Chicago as professor of physics from 1946 to 1949 and again in 1951–52. From 1949 to 1951 he was assistant director at the Los Alamos Scientific Laboratory. From 1953 until 1960 he was professor of physics at the University of California. He became professor at large in 1960 and also assumed at that time the position of chairman of the department of applied science in the University of California at Davis and Livermore. While at the University of California Teller in 1954 became associate director of the Lawrence Radiation Laboratory, Berkeley; in 1967 he was appointed associate director in charge of physics and head of the physics department there. From 1958 to 1960 he was director of the Livermore Radiation Laboratory. From 1956 to 1958 Teller was a member of the AEC General Advisory Committee. Among other honors Teller received the AEC's Enrico Fermi Award in 1962. He was elected to the National Academy of Sciences in 1948 and to the American Academy of Arts and Sciences in 1954.

Teller wrote *The Structure of Matter*, with F. O. Rice (1949); *The Legacy of Hiroshima*, with Allen Brown (1962); and *The Reluctant Revolutionary* (1964).

For background information *see* COORDINATION CHEMISTRY; MOLECULAR STRUCTURE AND SPECTRA; SELECTION RULES (PHYSICS) in the McGraw-Hill Encyclopedia of Science and Technology.   □

★ THODE, Henry George

Canadian physical chemist
Born Sept. 10, 1910, Dundurn, Saskatchewan, Canada

THE MASS spectrometer and its application to a wide variety of chemical, physical, biological, and geochemical problems have been the theme of Thode's research. Although by 1940 the mass spectrometer had been used extensively for isotopic analysis, its potential as a tool for the study of chemical problems was only beginning to be explored. Thode, inspired by his work with Harold Urey on the concentration of isotopes by isotopic exchange reactions, recognized that sim-

ilar processes might result in variations in the relative abundances of isotopes in naturally occurring materials that would be indicative of their origin. He, therefore, initiated an extensive study of these variations, with particular reference to the isotopes of sulfur and carbon. The success of this work was made possible by the development of the simultaneous-collection mass spectrometer, which was capable of measuring differences in isotopic abundances of a few one-hundredths of 1%.

Soon after Thode had begun his study of the abundances of isotopes, Melvin Calvin reported that in the thermal decomposition of carboxyl-labeled malonic acid the ratio of the rates of rupture of C^{12}-C^{12} and C^{12}-C^{14} bonds had a surprisingly large value. This result was immediately questioned, and efforts were made in a number of laboratories to establish its validity. Thode recognized that the errors inherent in the measurement of isotopic fractionation using isotopically enriched compounds and counting techniques could be largely eliminated if he started with reactants having natural isotopic abundance. Thode first studied the decomposition of oxalic acid, and was able to measure both intermolecular and intramolecular carbon-13 isotope effects in this reaction and soon after in malonic acid decomposition as well. Although he found the effects were much smaller than had been indicated by Calvin's original results, Thode determined that they were capable of accurate measurement, and it soon became apparent that such measurements of kinetic isotope effects provide a powerful means for obtaining information on reaction mechanisms and in particular on the nature of the transition state. Many such studies subsequently were carried out in Thode's laboratory and elsewhere.

The recognition that measurable isotopic fractionation results from unidirectional as well as equilibrium processes gave added impetus to Thode's program of work on the natural varia-

tions of the sulfur isotopes. He showed that these variations are brought about by a variety of both biological and chemical processes. Thode showed that these natural isotopic fractionations result from both equilibrium and kinetic effects and are consistent with statistical thermodynamic calculations. These studies also determined that such natural sulfur deposits as those found in Texas were formed by bacterial reduction of sulfates that originated in seawater. Thode established this by making comparisons of the isotopic ratios of the elemental sulfur from in vitro experiments involving anaerobic bacteria with those found in the natural formations. He was able to demonstrate not only that the sulfur isotope ratios in the Texas deposits correspond to those in the free sulfur generated by the bacteria from similar source material, but also that the carbon isotope ratios in the carbonate associated with the sulfur deposits are similar to those of the CO_2 given off by the bacteria.

Thode was one of the first to realize the ability of the mass spectrometer to analyze minute samples. He applied its sensitivity to the study of isotopic abundance of fission products, and was able to show that the yields of the fission products do not have a smooth variation in yield with mass. This fine structure, which is primarily evidenced by an unusually high cumulative yield for Xe^{134}, has been important to a detailed understanding of the fission process. The use of the mass spectrometer has now largely replaced the radiochemical procedures for determining cumulative fission yields, and much of the knowledge of these yields was produced in Thode's laboratory.

Thode held many other interests related to isotopes. In particular, he played a significant role in the development of the use of radioiodine in the study of thyroid function. The United States Naval Hospital at Bethesda, Md., has reported that the saliva test which he and his collaborators developed is the most reliable method of evaluating hypothyroidism. He also contributed to the pioneering work on the fractionation of stable isotopes both by chemical exchange and by thermal diffusion. Using a countercurrent arrangement, he developed methods for the enrichment of both N^{15} and O^{18}.

Raised on a farm in the Canadian prairies, Thode received his early education in the schools of Saskatoon and attended the University of Saskatchewan, where he received the B.Sc. (1930) and M.Sc. (1932). Following his Ph.D. in chemistry (1934) at the University of Chicago under Simon Freed, he worked for several years in the laboratories of Urey at Columbia University and as a research chemist at the United States Rubber Co. Returning to Canada in 1939, he joined McMaster University, where he became professor of chemistry in 1944, chairman of the department of chemistry in 1948, principal of Hamilton College in 1949, vice-president of the university in 1957, and president and vice-chancellor in 1961. He was elected to the fellowship of the Royal Society of Canada in 1943, serving as its president in 1959–60, and he was made a fellow of the Royal Society of London in 1954. He received the Institute Medal of the Chemical Institute of Canada in 1957 and the Tory Medal of the Royal Society of Canada in 1959. He was one of the four scientists honored in Canada's Centennial Year (1967) by being made a Companion of the Order of Canada.

For background information *see* ISOTOPE; MASS SPECTROSCOPE; THYROID GLAND in the McGraw-Hill Encyclopedia of Science and Technology.   □

THOMAS, Hugh Hamshaw

British paleobotanist
Born May 29, 1885, Wrexham, Denbighshire, Wales
Died June 30, 1962, Cambridge, England

WHILE STUDYING the flora of the Jurassic, Thomas was led to believe that he had solved one of the prime puzzles of paleobotany—the origin of the flowering plants. In his 1925 paper on the Caytoniales, a new group of angiospermous plants he had discovered in Yorkshire, he presented his hypothesis, which was later shown to be based on tenuous and unproved relationships. However, the principles he presented led to the creation of a new morphological system that has evolved into the standard for paleobotanical studies.

Paleobotany can be said to have begun with the observations of some of the Greek philosophers: Xenophanes, for example, in the 6th century B.C. studied fossil laurel leaves in the rocks of Pharos. It was not until the latter part of the 16th century of the Christian Era, however, that opinions concerning fossils began to accumulate, and through the work of men such as Erasmus Darwin and William Smith paleobotany became a geological science by the beginning of the 19th century. The work of Adolphe Brongniart in organizing the Earth's history into four periods of vegetation and of H. R. Goeppert in describing fossils reintroduced a biological approach to paleobotany by 1885, and this in turn was in some instances taxonomical and in others morphological.

Working at the Botanical Museum at Cambridge University about 1910, Thomas engaged in field trips through the Gristhorpe Bed in Yorkshire, looking for coal ball petrifactions of Jurassic flora. By 1912 he had recognized the berrylike *Caytonia* fruit and published its name as a nomen nudum. He collected some hundred specimens, studied them, and sacrificed them in study. He went beyond preparing cuticles and took enormous pains to learn about the uncutinized interiors of the fruits and seeds. The established technique for isolating the cuticle of a fossil was first to oxidize the coaly substance and then dissolve it, leaving the cuticle as a flattened sac. However, this destroyed everything but the cuticle. Thomas devised a method to discriminate between a wall that had been cellulose, one that had been lignin, and middle lamella substance. He removed the little fruits, swelled them by boiling them for weeks in alcoholic potash, embedded them, and sectioned them—and found the sections homogeneous. He tried to etch his sections, using mitigated versions of the cuticle technique. Although he occasionally had a good result, he could seldom repeat it, for *Caytonia* seeds preserved side by side vary unpredictably in their preservation, and this complicated his procedure. However, his results, though falling short of what he hoped, were far in advance of what anyone else had achieved.

In 1925 Thomas published his paper on *Caytonia*. The flowering plants are distinguished by a dozen characteristics, of which the closed ovary is the most outstanding and gives them their name, angiosperms. Thomas's fossils were closed, berry-like ovaries. Although he had known this as early as 1912, by 1925 he had done much more, for he had recognized both the leaves and the pollen-producing organs of these plants. His fruits were new, but with the other organs he was hampered by previous work, for the leaves were classified with the ferns and the pollen organs as *Ginkgo* catkins.

Thomas based his synthesis first on careful collecting. In the Gristhorpe Bed plants are astonishingly local, and he noted the frequent association of these three kinds of organ at certain points and their joint absence at others. Then he looked for specific features of agreement. Since all three organs have petiole-like bases, he compared the epidermal cells of these three and found them remarkably similar. He also compared them with petioles of other plants in the Gristhorpe Bed and found them different. He was able to find pollen agreeing with that of the pollen organ on the stigma-like mouth of the fruit.

Although many authorities refused to accept his hypothesis that the Caytoniales link the Gymnospermae (seed-bearing plants) with the Angiospermae (flower-bearing plants), they did realize that his morphological treatment was sound. His new morphology, as expanded in later papers, is based on change by evolution. He took as his ancestral form the early fossil *Rhynia*, which also forms the basis of Zimmermann's telome theory. Thomas maintained that every organ of a higher plant is comparable with part of the *Rhynia* shoot system, for every organ is a telome or a group of telomes, at first plastic in organization but later stereotyped. Thus, a branched leaf of a fern and a branched inflorescence such as a poplar catkin are just differently organized telome systems and have no fundamental difference; for example, the seed-bearing organ *Umkomaasia* can be both a fertile leaf and a fertile branch system. With *Caytonia*, therefore, there was no confusion in the idea of a branched leaf (the fruiting megasporophyll) bearing fertile leaves, the berry-like organs he called carpels.

The second son of a Welsh men's outfitter, Thomas studied at Downing College, Cambridge, graduating in 1908 and receiving the Sc.D. in 1926. While there he studied botany, never taking any formal courses in geology. In 1909 Thomas was appointed curator of the Cambridge University Botanical Museum, a position he retained until 1923, and in 1914 he was elected a fellow of Downing College. Six years later he was made dean of Downing, an appointment he held until 1927, and steward of the college, a position he retained until 1937. Thomas was university lecturer in botany from 1923 to 1937, when he became a reader. He retained his position until 1950, when he also retired from his fellowship. Thomas served Great Britain in both world wars; from 1915 through 1919 he was first in the artillery and later the flying corps, where he was able to do original work in aerial photography—his maps from aerial photographs were the first ever made in that way; from 1939 through 1943 he served in the Royal Air Force Volunteer Reserve as an intelligence officer, taking part in the reorganization of the photographic intelligence service. Among the honors he received were the Darwin-Wallace Commemorative Medal of the Linnean Society in 1958 and the Linnean Gold Medal in 1960. He was elected to the Royal Society of London in 1934.

For background information *see* ANGIOSPERMAE; CAYTONIALES; FLOWER (BOTANY); PALEOBOTANY in the McGraw-Hill Encyclopedia of Science and Technology.   □

★ **THOMPSON, Harold Warris**

British chemist
Born Feb. 15, 1908, Wombwell, Yorkshire, England

THOMPSON BEGAN scientific research while he was still an undergraduate at Oxford University, working during the long vacations in C. N. Hinshelwood's laboratory on the kinetics of some gaseous reactions. His first work on a quasi-unimolecular reaction was followed by studies on the thermal chain reaction between hydrogen and oxygen, in which critical explosion limits were discovered and interpreted in terms of branching chain mechanisms. During 1929–30 he continued work in this general field in Haber's laboratory at the Kaiser Wilhelm Institute in Berlin. Here he became interested in photochemistry, and this led him to study the new interpretations of molecular spectra then being made in terms of quantum theory. The galaxy of distinguished scientific men in Berlin at that time made a deep impression upon him, especially since he lived in the house of Max Planck, and his interest in quantum theory and spectroscopy applied to chemical problems was greatly stimulated.

After returning to Oxford Thompson continued to work for a time on thermal and photochemical reactions. One general problem was the nature of the carriers in chain processes, active molecules or free radicals, and in one series of reactions he suggested the occurrence of the HNO radical, established much later by other methods. Thompson soon turned to measurements on ultraviolet absorption spectra, and as part of their interpretation it became necessary to know more about molecular vibrations. A few years later he was able to obtain some simple equipment for the measurement of infrared absorption spectra, and in the late 1930s he studied the vibrational spectra of a number of small molecules and assigned molecular vibration frequencies, calculated bond force constants, and other molecular properties.

Soon after the outbreak of World War II, Thompson became involved in the application of infrared and ultraviolet techniques for the analysis and identification of materials of importance to the war effort, such as hydrocarbon fuels. The essentially individualistic character of the vibrational spectrum of a molecule, together with the use of key absorption bands for the detection of particular atomic groupings, was used in the characterization of fuel samples and in the control of fuel production. Soon afterward Thompson and his co-workers made some of the earliest applications of this method to the study of structural features of the new synthetic polymers and plastics and of complex organic molecules such as penicillin. He used polarized infrared radiation in studying oriented polymers and crystals to establish stereochemical features. All this work stimulated a rapid development and improvement in the techniques, using new thermal detectors, better spectrometers, and automatically recording systems. There was a transition from the old visual point-by-point spectral recording using moving-magnet galvanometers to double-beam spectrometers with electronic amplifiers and potentiometric recorders.

After the war a broad new attack was made on the use of infrared and Raman spectroscopy in chemistry. Vibrational frequencies were determined for many small molecules, and compounds of biological and pharmaceutical interest were measured. Thompson built up some of the correlations between spectral and structural characteristics and contributed much toward laying the foundation for subsequent infrared structural diagnosis. He joined the reflecting microscope to an infrared spectrometer to measure small particles, crystals, and fibers, and devised equipment for measuring spectra down to very low temperatures.

Thompson was also among the first to use the newly discovered, highly sensitive photoconductive cells, such as lead sulfide, lead telluride, and indium antimonide, to obtain much higher spectral resolution with grating spectrometers and thus to analyze the rotational fine structure of vibrational bands of small molecules in the vapor state. This led to new information about molecular geometry and to other molecular constants bearing upon molecular dynamics. Some of the line positions measured in this way have served subsequently as secondary wavelength standards.

Thompson then turned from measurements of positions (frequencies) of lines and bands to the intensities of absorption bands, which are determined by other factors. He interpreted the intensities in terms of bond polar properties and electronic structural features. Also, he carried out extensive work using spectroscopic methods on weak intermolecular forces, which are revealed by shifts of frequency or changes in band intensity. Such measurements included solvent effects, pressure broadening studies, and equilibria and thermodynamics of hydrogen-bonding systems and of charge-transfer complexes.

More recently Thompson and his co-workers extended measurements into the far-infrared. They used conventional grating spectrometers and interferometers, where pure rotational spectra of polyatomic molecules and some of the lowest vibration frequencies can be determined.

Thompson obtained his M.A. at Oxford and his first doctorate in Berlin. He was appointed a fellow of St. John's College, Oxford, in 1930, subsequently reader in infrared spectroscopy, and later professor of chemistry. His scientific honors included the Davy Medal of the Royal Society, of which he was elected a fellow in 1946 and foreign secretary in 1966. He was Tilden Lecturer of the Chemical Society and John Tate Medallist of the American Institute of Physics.

Thompson wrote *A Course in Chemical Spectroscopy* (1938) and about 270 papers in scientific journals. He edited *Advances in Spectroscopy*, Vols. I and II (1958, 1962) and, from 1957, *Spectrochimica Acta*.

For background information *see* MOLECULAR STRUCTURE AND SPECTRA; PHOTOCHEMISTRY; SPECTROSCOPY in the McGraw-Hill Encyclopedia of Science and Technology.   ☐

★ THORN, George Widmer

American physician
Born Jan. 15, 1906, Buffalo, N.Y., U.S.A.

FOR HIS original studies demonstrating the life-saving effectiveness of adrenal cortical extract, in collaboration with Frank A. Hartman, Thorn was awarded the Gold Medal of the American Medical Association in 1932. Seven years later he received another AMA award for his studies on a synthetic adrenal hormone, 11-desoxycorticosterone. In part, this latter award recognized a new mode of human pharmacotherapy—namely, the subcutaneous implantation of hormone pellets to provide year-long, life-saving quantities of this vital substance.

Entering the University of Buffalo Medical School in 1925, Thorn was shortly attracted to the activities of Professor Hartman in the department of physiology. They carried out experiments on the newly discovered adrenal cortical extract. Thorn's initial contribution concerned the development of a suitable biological assay

which could be utilized in the further purification of the elusive hormone. Following graduation and internship, Thorn assumed responsibility for the clinical studies of the new extract, and it soon became evident that the effects of the life-saving hormone were mediated largely through the regulation of carbohydrate and mineral metabolism. Up to this point Addison's disease, a chronic, serious deficiency of adrenal gland secretion, had been uniformly fatal. Thus, the opportunity to provide a life-saving hormone for seriously afflicted patients represented an epoch in medical advance. Unfortunately supplies of the vital hormone were limited to the small amounts which could be extracted from large quantities of hog, sheep, or beef adrenal, and it was evident that the acute situation could not be remedied until the "active principal" could be identified and synthesized. In those days all of the extract was made in the physiology laboratory of the medical school by teams working day and night. Later, meat-packing houses and pharmaceutical concerns took over the large-scale production of the extract. Although Addison's disease is relatively rare, it became evident to Hartman and Thorn in the early 1930s that the widespread effect of adrenal cortical secretions on biological processes might make the hormone useful in conditions other than specific adrenal cortical insufficiency.

To further his training for a full-time career in teaching and investigative medicine, Thorn was awarded in 1934 a Rockefeller Foundation traveling fellowship. He spent 1934–35 with the outstanding endocrine-metabolic group of J. Howard Means, Joseph C. Aub, Fuller Albright, and Walter Bauer at the Harvard Medical School and the Massachusetts General Hospital in Boston, the second year as assistant professor of physiology at Ohio State University with Hartman (who had moved from Buffalo to chair this large department), and the third year with George Harrop at the Johns Hopkins Medical School and Hospital. During this period bio-

chemical and physiological techniques were developed, and the physiological effect of adrenal hormone in normal human subjects was demonstrated for the first time. A critical assay for the mineral-regulating effect of adrenal hormone was standardized in a colony of adrenalectomized Bassett hounds. This unique assay method permitted Thorn to screen new steroid compounds for "salt-retaining" capacity and resulted in the identification of the tremendously effective compound 11-desoxycorticosterone acetate, recently synthesized by Tadeus Reichstein. Also, it was possible for Thorn and his co-workers to translate directly their findings in adrenalectomized dogs to patients with Addison's disease. Thus, the rate of absorption of hormone pellets implanted in dogs was measured by removing the pellets from time to time, weighing them accurately, and then replacing them. The appropriate dose of hormone—or the necessary number of standardized pellets to be employed—was determined by carrying out careful balance studies with the dogs in metabolic cages. Subsequently, it proved possible to apply these formulas directly to the needs of patients with Addison's disease.

Although 11-desoxycorticosterone corrected abnormal mineral metabolism, it did not maintain the blood sugar nor correct the deep pigmentation which patients with advanced Addison's disease displayed, whereas the original extracts had done so. For these reasons, the search was continued for other essential compounds secreted by the adrenal. These investigations were carried out by such outstanding biochemists as Reichstein and Oskar Winterstein. In 1940 E. C. Kendall was able to supply Thorn with 85 mg of corticosterone and 33 mg of cortisone. With this limited quantity of material Thorn could demonstrate the qualitative effect of these hormones and the fact that they provided quite completely the "missing link." From this point on developments in the field were rapid and phenomenal, culminating in the commercial production of cortisone and cortisol and the preparation of adrenocorticotropin (ACTH), the pituitary hormone which stimulates the adrenal cortex. The availability of ACTH permitted Thorn to develop an accurate diagnostic test of early adrenal insufficiency by measuring cytological and clinical changes in the body following administration of a standardized quantity of ACTH. Up to this time identification of adrenal insufficiency was time consuming, hazardous, and uncertain. The fall in circulating eosinophils and the increased urinary excretion of adrenal steroids following ACTH administration became the classical method for identifying adrenal insufficiency, and also of separating adrenal insufficiency of primary adrenal origin from adrenal insufficiency due to pituitary failure or secondary insufficiency.

These latter studies were accomplished in Boston at the Peter Bent Brigham Hospital and the Harvard Medical School, where Thorn had been appointed physician in chief and Hersey Professor of the Theory and Practice of Physic. Physiological studies on the effect of cortisone and cortisol on the body processes also paved the way for an understanding of their widespread action. The discovery by P. S. Hench and his co-workers of the effectiveness of cortisone and ACTH in relieving the pain and disability of rheumatoid arthritis touched off an "atomic bomb" in medicine, with the subsequent widespread evaluation of these agents in such diverse disorders as skin diseases, granulomatous processes, hay fever and asthma, gout, hypoglycemia, and multiple sclerosis, as well as use of the agents in brain surgery. However, the careful metabolic studies of the effects of these substances on body tissues by Thorn and his co-workers indicated that these therapeutic agents in conditions other than adrenal insufficiency were "two-edged" swords which required expert scientific knowledge and discriminating application if therapeutic disasters were to be avoided.

Thorn attended the College of Wooster (Ohio) in 1923–25 and the University of Buffalo Medical School, from which he graduated with an M.D. in 1929. Appointments in the departments of physiology and medicine at Buffalo were followed by faculty appointments at the Johns Hopkins Medical School during 1936–42, then by appointment to professor and head of the Harvard department of medicine at the Peter Bent Brigham Hospital. Besides a number of honorary degrees, he received the Chancellor's Medal from the University of Buffalo and the Philips Award of the American College of Physicians.

Thorn was a senior editor of *Principles of Internal Medicine* (2 vols., 5th ed. 1966). His scientific publications exceeded 350.

For background information *see* ADRENAL CORTEX STEROID; ADRENAL GLAND; HORMONE in the McGraw-Hill Encyclopedia of Science and Technology. □

★ TILLETT, William Smith

American physician
Born July 10, 1892, Charlotte, N.C., U.S.A.

TILLETT MADE special clinical studies of pneumonia, along with research studies in the laboratory with pneumococci. He also studied beta-hemolytic streptococci with special reference to the original identification and characterization of two extracellular enzymes elaborated by this species of organism (streptokinase and streptodornase) and the practical use of these enzymes in relatively purified form as therapeutic reagents. During World War II Tillett and his associates published early and detailed reports on the highly successful clinical use of penicillin in pneumococcal pneumonia and empyema.

In laboratory research with pneumococci, while on the staff of the Hospital of the Rockefeller Institute, Tillett demonstrated that, using non–type-specific (rough) pneumococci for immunization purposes in rabbits, a broad immunity was established by which the animals resisted infection with different virulent types of pneumococci (types I, II, and III). The serums of the immunized rabbits possessed no demonstrable type-specific antibodies. It was concluded that the active immunity exhibited by the rabbits was the only method of demonstrating the broad pneumococcal immunity. In pursuing the basis for this immune response of rabbits, a strain of "rough" pneumococcus was subjected to chemical analysis, from which emerged the finding reported by Tillett, Goebel, and O. T. Avery that there is present in all strains of pneumococci a carbohydrate but it is unrelated to the type-specific capsular component. The serological reactivity of this "C fraction" was found by Tillett and Thomas Francis, Jr., to be unique in that it precipitated in the acute-phase serums of pneumonia patients but not in the serums of convalescent individuals. Subsequently this precipitin reaction was found to occur in the acute phase of a wide variety of diseases of diverse etiologies, and it is now widely used in clinical medicine to indicate active pathological changes.

Another finding that came from the pneumonia studies conducted at the Rockefeller hospital, with Francis and under Avery's direction, was that the purified type-specific polysaccharides of pneumococci give characteristic immediate wheal and erythematous cutaneous re-

actions when injected into patients convalescing from pneumonia due to comparable type. In pursuing the polysaccharide studies, Francis and · Tillett demonstrated that these sugars are antigenic in humans, and on repeated injections into the same individuals the sugars produce positive cutaneous reactions and also type-specific antibodies in the blood of the test subjects. These studies indicated for the first time that purified polysaccharides are antigenic, independent of any protein increment.

In 1933 in studies of streptococci Tillett and Garner reported that beta-hemolytic streptococci, as they grow, elaborate into the surrounding media a substance which mediates the rapid lysis of the fibrinous clot of normal human blood. The fibrinolytic reagent was subsequently designated streptokinase, which activates a blood increment identified as plasminogen into plasmin, which in turn causes fibrinolysis. During the succeeding years Tillett and his associates, as well as investigators in other laboratories, explored the fibrinolytic phenomenon from a variety of angles. Streptokinase was produced most regularly by group A streptococci. In exploring its occurrence in other bacterial species, streptokinase was found only in some strains of hemolytic staphylococci. Of special interest was the finding that a specific anti-fibrinolytic antibody appears in the blood of patients convalescing from acute hemolytic streptococcal infections. In addition to the specific antibody, studies with A. Johnson brought out the fact that a nonspecific, heat-labile inhibitor is present in varying degrees in different normal individuals. Its titer bears no relation to the presence or absence of specific antibody.

A second enzyme system was later found to be produced by beta-hemolytic streptococci, when Sol Sherry demonstrated that the thick, sticky quality characteristic of purulent exudates is due to the presence of deoxyribose nucleoprotein. Tillett, Sherry, and Christensen then demonstrated that beta-hemolytic streptococci produce a specific deoxyribose nuclease which rapidly reduces thick purulent exudates to limpid solutions.

The next step in the development of this streptococcal enzyme study was to explore the possibility of the use of these enzymes in patients having local fibrinous, purulent exudations, as in the pleural cavity with hemothorax or empyema. Christensen made the first step toward the purification of streptokinase derived from broth cultures of appropriate bacterial strains. Subsequently Lederle Laboratories supplied streptokinase of increased purification in larger quantities. Lederle also made available mixtures of streptokinase and streptodornase under the trade name of Varidase. Sherry and Tillett explored the possible therapeutic usefulness of these enzymes in patients. Therapeutic studies of individual disease groups were reported by Sherry and Tillett in separate articles. Johnson and Tillett explored the intravenous use of highly purified streptokinase in rabbits and in man for the purpose of liquefying artificially induced clots. When the infusion was started soon after the clot had been induced, the liquefaction was usually successful.

The use of streptokinase in the treatment of vascular disease characterized by thrombosis and embolization has become extensive in western Europe and Scandinavia, the preparations being manufactured there. In the United States the National Heart Institute of the U.S. Public Health Service has set up a Committee on Thrombolytic Agents to promote studies of thrombolysis. The plan involves using urokinase extensively because it is a normal product of humans and has properties like streptokinase. It can be isolated from normal human urine, a circumstance which reduces toxicity and eliminates antigenicity.

Tillett graduated from the University of North Carolina (A.B., 1913) and from the Johns Hopkins Medical School (M.D., 1917). After serving in the Medical Corps of the U.S. Army in World War I, he returned to the Johns Hopkins Hospital for a house officership. In 1922 he joined the resident staff of the Hospital of the Rockefeller Institute, being first associated with Thomas Rivers in the study of virus diseases; subsequently Tillett transferred to the pneumonia service directed by Rufus Cole and worked in the laboratory of O. T. Avery. In 1930 he became associate professor of medicine at the Johns Hopkins Medical School. In 1937 he transferred to the New York University School of Medicine to become professor of microbiology, and in 1938 he became professor and chairman of the department of medicine there and director of the Third Medical Division of Bellevue Hospital. He retired in 1958. In addition to several honorary degrees, he received with Christensen the Lasker Award of the U.S. Public Health Service in 1949, and was the single recipient of the Borden Award of the Association of American Medical Colleges in 1952. He was elected to the National Academy of Sciences in 1951.

For background information *see* BACTERIAL ENZYME; PNEUMOCOCCUS; PNEUMONIA; STREPTOCOCCUS; THROMBOSIS in the McGraw-Hill Encyclopedia of Science and Technology.   □

★ TILLEY, Cecil Edgar

British geologist
Born May 14, 1894, Adelaide, South Australia

TILLEY MADE minerals and mineral assemblages of metamorphism a major subject of his research. Throughout his work he stressed the application of the data and principles of physical chemistry and of integrated geologic knowledge to the interpretation of the phenomena of mineral associations and of rocks. In re-

gional petrology his earliest studies were on the Precambrian basement of Eyre Peninsula, South Australia, and later he elucidated some of the foundation rocks of Antarctica.

Moving to Cambridge from Sydney as a postgraduate student after World War I, he began a long series of investigations on the Dalradian rocks of Scotland, notably on the contact metamorphic aureole of the Comrie (Perthshire) diorite. This comprehensive study revealed novel mineral assemblages, interpreted and classified in the light of phase rule theory.

The mapping of metamorphic zones, originally begun by George Barrow in the southeast Scottish Highlands, was greatly extended by Tilley and G. L. Elles. In this research on progressive metamorphism the concept of isograd surfaces and isograds made a permanent contribution to metamorphic studies. He added to the ideas, understanding, and classification of metamorphic rocks in the light of the facies concept of Pentti Eskola. Beginning in 1924, a long series of publications dealt with specific examples of the variation of mineral assemblages, where on the one hand the range of physical conditions is similar or isogradic and the bulk composition varies, and on the other hand the bulk composition remains similar and the range of physical conditions varies. For the latter, particular chemical reactions could be formulated.

In his work on the contact zones of dolerite with limestone at Scawt Hill, County Antrim, and at Camas Mor, Muck, Tilley demonstrated that basic feldspathoidal (nepheline) rocks were formed by the reaction of basaltic magma with carbonate sediments, and he elucidated the chain of reaction products providing mineral associations which could be contrasted with the more common mafic alkali rocks in which syntexis was not involved. A product of this period was his experimental study at the Geophysical Laboratory, Washington, D.C., of the synthetic ternary alkali silicate system Na_2SiO_3-$Na_2Si_2O_5$-$NaAlSiO_4$.

Later in an exhaustive investigation of the zoned metasomatic skarns around a Tertiary granite of Skye, the formation of mildly alkaline assemblages, and even desilication, was demonstrated as a result of dolomite reacting with granite magma. In the course of these studies on the syntectic alkali rocks, seven new minerals —including larnite, bredigite, rankinite, and harkerite—were described from the associated contact zones.

Tilley investigated the relationship between the compositions of the nepheline and coexisting feldspar phases and the normative salic composition of their host rocks—volcanic, plutonic, and metamorphic. Thus, in subsolvus nepheline syenites and nepheline gneisses the nepheline phase was restricted in composition to the Morozewicz-Buerger convergence field, being then associated with low-temperature feldspars of the albite-microcline series. On the other hand, in hypersolvus nepheline syenites and volcanic phonolites, the composition of the nepheline was shown to vary more widely in response to the differing composition of the host rocks, and then to be associated with feldspars belonging to the high-temperature anorthoclase-sanidine series.

These studies in geothermometry had bearing on the field and laboratory studies he made of the Haliburton-Bancroft area of Ontario, a classic region of nepheline rocks originally interpreted as magmatic in crystallization. The metasomatic-metamorphic character of many of these gneissic rocks—arising from nephelinization of Grenville limestones—was demonstrated, and was attributed to alkali fluids emanating from truly magmatic feldspathoidal intrusives of hypersolvus character in neighboring areas.

More recently Tilley concentrated his attention largely on problems of basalt petrogenesis. By 1950 he recognized the role of tholeiitic basalt as a close approach to the primary magma of the Hawaiian Islands and of the ocean basins in general. Subsequently, with the cooperation of H. S. Yoder, Jr., and J. F. Schairer, he studied experimentally the anhydrous melting relations of basalts and their associated volcanic rock series, and in a major contribution with Yoder (1962) he made a systematic study of natural basalts and eclogites, both at low and high pressures and in the presence of water. The results were discussed in relation to petrological problems connected chiefly with the source and character of primary basalt magmas from the upper mantle, and with the nature of the equilibrium thermal divides both at high pressure and at the lower pressures where they influence the course of fractionation of derivative magmas.

Tilley graduated from the universities of Adelaide and Sydney and carried out his postgraduate studies at Cambridge University, where he received a Ph.D. There he was appointed a lecturer in 1928, becoming a professor of mineralogy and petrology in 1931 and also a fellow of Emmanuel College. Elected to the Royal Society of London in 1938, he received the Bigsby (1937) and Wollaston (1960) medals of the Geological Society of London and the Roebling Medal (1954) of the Mineralogical Society of America. He was elected a foreign associate of the U.S. National Academy of Sciences in 1967.

For background information *see* MAGMA; METAMORPHIC ROCKS; PETROLOGY in the Mc-Graw-Hill Encyclopedia of Science and Technology.   □

★ TINBERGEN, Nikolaas

British zoologist
Born Apr. 15, 1907, Netherlands

A COMBINATION of natural inclination and favorable circumstances enabled Tinbergen to play a part in the revival and development of a biological science of behavior. As a student, he nearly chose another field because academic zoology in Holland, preoccupied as it was with the dead animal, did not appeal to him. Sympathetic biology teachers had fostered his early interest in live animals, but it was the theoretical physicist P. Ehrenfest who first urged Tinbergen's parents to send him to J. Thienemann's Bird Observatory in East Prussia, and who later persuaded him to become a biologist.

The budding student of the natural behavior of animals found little guidance in the psychological literature of the period; studies of white rats running mazes seemed to have no relevance to, for instance, the social behavior of wild gulls.

The writings of Oskar Heinroth first introduced Tinbergen to the importance of comparative behavior descriptions, and Julian Huxley's early studies demonstrated the bearing of such descriptions on evolutionary problems. Karl von Frisch's work showed him how to do meaningful experiments in natural surroundings. A series of studies on the landmark orientation of homing wasps, his first mature research, gave him experience in outdooor experimentation. Tinbergen then worked with Konrad Lorenz, who showed him how to approach animal behavior along more comprehensive biological lines. His next research, on social interaction of fish, marked the beginning of a series of studies on stimulus response processes in social behavior. A stay at Yerkes's Primate Laboratories in Yale and Orange Park gave him an understanding of American psychology.

At a time when zoologists showed little interest in animal behavior, an invitation by C. J. van der Klaauw to found a school of animal behavior studies in Leiden University acted as a spur to widen Tinbergen's grasp of a subject which was still underdeveloped. It also gave him the chance to associate with generations of enthusiastic pupils who aided in his work.

Much of his early work centered on the analysis of complex stimulus situations, studies which led to demonstrations of the effectiveness of "sign stimuli" and their concomitant, the motivation-specific "filtering" or "gating" of sensory input. The switching of stimulus selection with changes in motivational state led to studies of motivation. For these the puzzling behavior patterns known as "displays" provided both a challenge and an inspiration, and one of Tinbergen's main contributions in this field was the demonstration that many displays that act as social signals are the result of dual motivation, which causes a state of conflict within the animal.

Under Lorenz's influence he returned to comparative behavior studies in which, following the work of Heinroth and C. O. Whitman, species-specific behavior patterns are treated as organs. The old, almost forgotten methods of comparative anatomy, now coupled with functional analysis, proved extremely valuable for a first analysis of adaptive radiation of animal behavior. A combination of this approach with studies of conflict behavior clarified the evolutionary origin of many social signals and their further "ritualization"—a process which was recognized as a special case of change of function in evolution.

While engaged in this work Tinbergen became increasingly aware of the need for experimental study of the effects of selection pressures and of the way animals respond to them in evolution. His recent work concentrated on such experiments and, as a result, the adaptive nature of many behavioral species characters was demonstrated. He paid particular attention to the mutual interaction between predator and prey, where behavior exerts and undergoes selection pressures at the same time. While acting as a scientific adviser to the newly founded Serengeti Research Institute in Tanzania, he took an active part in applying this approach to African plains game.

Tinbergen's main contributions were the demonstration of the fertility of a biological approach to behavior by prolonged, selective, and systematic observation as well as by experiment; the training of a considerable number of young behavior students; and the promotion of international and interdisciplinary collaboration.

Tinbergen obtained a Ph.D. at Leiden University in 1932. After a year in the Arctic he returned to Leiden as a lecturer. There he worked until World War II, a major part of which he spent in a German prison camp. In 1947 he became professor of experimental zoology and head of the department of zoology in Leiden. In 1949 he went to Oxford University to build up, as a professor, a school of animal behavior studies. He was named a fellow of the Royal Society in 1962 and a foreign fellow of the Netherlands Academy of Sciences in 1964.

Tinbergen wrote *The Study of Instinct* (1951), *Social Behaviour in Animals* (1953), *The Herring Gull's World* (1953; rev. ed. 1961), *Curious Naturalists* (1958), and *Animal Behaviour* (1965).

For background information *see* BEHAVIOR AND HEREDITY; POPULATION GENETICS; SOCIAL ANIMALS in the McGraw-Hill Encyclopedia of Science and Technology.   □

★ **TISHLER, Max**

American chemist
Born Oct. 30, 1906, Boston, Mass., U.S.A.

As A graduate student and teaching fellow at Harvard University, Tishler approached organic chemical problems of theoretical significance in a characteristically experimental fashion. In his first publications dealing with the Grignard reactions of α-haloketones, he contributed to attempts to understand the reactivity of ambient enolate anions in alkylations as well as the nucleophilic reactions of Grignard reagents. This problem is today still at the forefront of

mechanistic research; neither the course of alkylations nor the structure of the Grignard reagent is fully understood. This work was followed by the first resolution of an appropriately substituted allene, an accomplishment which settled in 1935 an important consequence of J. H. van't Hoff's tetrahedral carbon atom model, first proposed in 1875.

In 1936, shortly after Tishler was appointed instructor in the chemistry department at Harvard, George Merck persuaded him to join the research laboratories of the pharmaceutical firm he headed in Rahway, N.J. In collaboration with L. F. Fieser of Harvard, Tishler developed a rational synthesis of vitamin K_1 and published several papers on the relationship of biological activity to structural variations of this vitamin. This work is characteristic of his later efforts: development of sophisticated chemical reactions leading to complex organic molecules with therapeutic activity, coupled with attempts to establish correlations between chemical structure and biological activity. Similar investigations led to syntheses of other vitamins, such as pantothenic acid, biocytin, vitamin A, and pteroylglutamic acid, and contributions to the chemistry of vitamin C and nicotinic acid. One of the most interesting investigations dealt with the synthesis of riboflavin; here the key step involves interaction of an orthoaminoazobenzene with barbituric acid in an elegant example of what is now known as an alkylation by an eneamine.

Another fruitful segment of research was in the field of new sulfa drugs. Tishler took advantage of the knowledge of alloxazine chemistry growing out of his riboflavin work and developed practical syntheses of aminopyrazine and aminoquinoxaline and the corresponding sulfa drugs. Sulfaquinoxaline turned out to be the first of the long-acting sulfonamides, and over the years it has served as a useful and basic antiparasitic agent in fowl coccidiosis.

Tishler and his associates at the Merck laboratories developed practical syntheses of several important amino acids because of the need for large supplies of these substances for nutrition studies. New processes for the synthesis of racemic and optically active tryptophan were uncovered, based on the newly discovered reactivity of the N,N-dimethylamino group of gramine in what seemed to be a simple metathesis but is now known to involve an elimination-addition sequence. Two practical syntheses of racemic methionine were followed by synthesis of threonine. Here Tishler and his co-workers were able to isomerize the diastereoisomeric allothreonine and threonine through a cyclic oxazoline which was common to both diastereomers. An analogous sequence of reactions was proposed by Oskar Winstein in his classic work on neighboring group effects of monoacylated vicinal glycols.

Tishler was also involved in the chemistry of antibiotic metabolites of microorganisms. He worked with Selman Waksman on actinomycin and led the teams developing processes for the production of penicillin and streptomycin.

In the late 1940s the therapeutic activity of cortisone and hydrocortisone was discovered. Following L. H. Sarett's synthesis of cortisone, Tishler participated in the first synthesis of hydrocortisone. Under his leadership, the Sarett-Kendall synthesis of cortisone from desoxycholic acid was developed into a practical production process through alteration of the chemistry and simplification of the chemical operations. The production process involved chemistry of a degree of sophistication then unknown to the organic chemical or pharmaceutical industry.

In addition, Tishler and his associates published papers on other approaches to the cortical steroids starting with cholic acid, diosgenin, ergosterol, and stigmasterol. This work led to methods for the introduction of oxygen in position 11 of the steroid nucleus, an essential feature of the antiinflammatory cortical steroids. A new and practical method for the conversion of 20-ketopregnane to the dihydroxyacetone side chain of cortisone was also developed. It depended on the permanganate hydroxylation of the corresponding $\Delta^{17,20}$-cyanopregnene.

In 1956 Tishler became president of the Merck Sharp and Dohme Research Laboratories, with the responsibility for the planning and execution of research programs covering a broad spectrum of human and animal health problems. These efforts led to drug discoveries for the treatment of heart disease, hypertension, mental depression, and rheumatoid arthritis and other inflammatory diseases, as well as agents to control economically important diseases of poultry (coccidiosis) and livestock (helminthiasis).

Tishler received his B.S. (1928) from Tufts College and his M.A. (1933) and Ph.D. (1934) under E. P. Kohler at Harvard. He had contributed to his support in high school and college by working part time in a pharmacy. There he acquired his interest in pharmaceutical chemistry as a means to alleviate disease and pain, but at the time of his graduation his primary interest was in organic chemistry. At Harvard he was Austin teaching fellow (1930–34), research associate (1934–36), and instructor (1936–37). He joined Merck and Co. in 1937. His honors included the Lecture Award of the Royal Swedish Academy of Engineering Sciences, the Rennebohm Lecture Award at the School of Pharmacy of the University of Wisconsin, the Julius W. Sturmer Memorial Lecture Award of the Philadelphia College of Pharmacy, the Chemical Industry Award of the American Section of the Society of Chemical Industry, and the Medal of the Industrial Research Institute. In 1951 he was one of the first recipients of the Merck Board of Directors' Scientific Award. The funds accompanying this award were used to establish the Annual Max Tishler Visiting Lectureship at Harvard and the Max Tishler Annual Scholarship at Tufts. He was elected to the National Academy of Sciences in 1953 and to the American Academy of Arts and Sciences in 1965.

Tishler's research was reflected in more than 100 scientific publications and an equal number of United States patents.

For background information *see* GRIGNARD REACTION; STEREOCHEMISTRY; SULFA DRUGS; VITAMIN in the McGraw-Hill Encyclopedia of Science and Technology.   □

★ **TOBIAS, Cornelius Anthony**

American biophysicist
Born May 28, 1918, Budapest, Hungary

THE ROLE of radiation in the etiology and control of neoplastic diseases is not yet fully understood. In the course of investigations on cancer, Tobias and his associates helped in the development of a new field of investigation, heavy-ion radiobiology, and a new way of probing functions of some of the internal tissues of the body, sometimes called the "atomic knife." For contributions to the understanding of basic radiobiology of cells, Tobias was honored in 1963 by the U.S. Atomic Energy Commission with the Ernest O. Lawrence Memorial Award.

Shortly after the discovery of x-rays by Wilhelm Conrad Roentgen, it was realized that x-rays affect living tissues. Bergonié and Tribondot in 1906 proposed that the radiosensitivity of rapidly proliferating tissues is greater than that of tissues with slowly dividing cells. While the validity of this statement was reinterpreted in recent years, it nevertheless became a basis for a rationale of tumor radiation therapy. In the

1930s considerable successes were achieved with x-ray therapy in the management of skin cancer; one of the limitations of deep-tumor therapy seemed to be the fact that x-rays were rapidly absorbed with depth in tissue, and often one could not deliver sufficient therapeutic doses without causing serious radiation burns or ulcerations on the skin. Tobias, then a young nuclear physicist, began studying the depth-dose patterns caused by accelerated protons, following a suggestion made in 1946 by Robert Wilson to utilize an effect originally discovered by Sir Lawrence Bragg in 1913. Unlike x-rays, protons and other heavy ions ionize lightly at the point of entrance into the body; they transfer most of their energy in the form of ionization to tissue inside the body, just before they are slowed to a stop at the end of their range. It soon turned out that high-energy protons accelerated in large cyclotrons are indeed useful in producing deeply localized radio lesions, and many other applications besides radiotherapy were developed. For example, recently scientists and medical men had to resort to the use of the surgical knife or needle for internal studies on the central nervous system and brain. But when a knife is used, the accompanying profuse bleeding always makes this procedure hazardous; besides, millions of nerve fibers are cut by the advancing knife. Later, when the lesions attempt to heal, copious necrosis and scar tissue formation takes place, often producing a large permanent lesion. The heavy-ion lesions are bloodless, and can be made to resemble a clean cut with very little scar tissue formation. By means of such radiation lesions, studies were begun in animals not only at Berkeley but also at Harvard and Uppsala universities on the homeostatic role of the hypothalamus, on the role of the rhinencephalon in learning behavior, on the role of different lamina of the optic cortex in elaborating visual information, and on a host of other problems.

Chronologically, one of the first studies undertaken was proton radiation of the pituitary gland of animals. This gland lies at the base of the brain in a surgically almost inaccessible location. The pituitary is the "master gland" of the body. It produces hormones that are essential for many body functions. The feedback theory of cancer is based on the assumption that intricate relationships exist between peripheral tissues (target organs) and the pituitary-hypothalamic control centers—an idea developed over the past 80 years and based on many investigations. According to this model, the proliferating tumor cells in some instances still require pituitary hormones for their maintenance and proliferation. The theory is being tested that depression or elimination by radiation of hypophyseal hormonal synthesis may cause regressions of the primary tumor and of metastases. After it was

established (1954) that radiation hypophysectomy can be carried out safely, the first human with advancing metastatic mammary carcinoma was exposed to pituitary proton radiation therapy. This work was continued in cooperation with a team of specialists led by John H. Lawrence. Lasting remissions were demonstrated, and these studies led to better understanding of the role of hormones. Unfortunately, not all mammary cancer patients benefit from this procedure, since the cancer cells often become so undifferentiated that they appear to escape all hormonal control.

It was found that heavy-particle radiation of the pituitary is useful in therapeutic investigations in a number of diseases; in acromegaly most of the treated patients benefited. Long-term studies were undertaken to investigate the value of such therapy for advanced cases of diabetes mellitus with vascular disease, Cushing's disease, and malignant exophthalmos. The heavy-ion beams were also used in treatment of advanced cases of Parkinson's disease and for certain brain tumors. A team at the Uppsala cyclotron initiated proton treatments for Parkinson's disease.

In 1940 Tobias succeeded in a modest cyclotron acceleration of the nuclei of nitrogen, oxygen, and neon. One of his later inventions pointed the way to acceleration to higher energies of even heavier particles in the cyclotron. Using all available accelerated nuclei as projectiles, very much in the manner of nuclear physicists, the group set out to obtain quantitative relationships to help explain the basic mechanism of action at the nuclear level in single-celled organisms and later in mammalian cells. In 1953 Tobias, working with Zirkle, proposed the "migration model" to account for radiation effects on haploid and diploid yeast cells; they demonstrated that the critical ionizing events that lead to cell death or to mutation do not need to be initiated in the genetic material, but that in the end many permanent radiation effects are genetic. The group in Berkeley soon proposed two models for cell lethality—the "recessive" and "dominant lethal" models. Existence of these mechanisms was shown in yeast in genetically controlled experiments, and these models have since stimulated research on other organisms. It was also shown in 1953 that radiated yeast cells form microcolonies that have an inheritable modification in their radiosensitivity; such results were shown to be true in cultured mammalian cells 10 years later at the Argonne Laboratory.

The heavier particles produce much denser ionization in tissue than the lighter ones and are usually much more effective in causing lethality, chromosome breaks, or cancer. The Berkeley group proposed that there are two basically different actions of radiations: Light ionization causes effects that can be modified by oxygen, by chemical compounds, and sometimes by heat; the effects of heavy ionization are due to cooperative action of several ions and are much less modifiable by external agents. In the mid-1960s the exact molecular steps that lead to genetic alteration were under study.

In 1948 it was discovered in high-altitude balloon flights that primary cosmic rays consist of protons and energetic heavy ions impinging on the upper atmosphere. Nine years later the American *Pioneer I* satellite demonstrated the existence of a large radiation belt around the Earth, consisting of protons and electrons. It is known that solar flares contain many high-energy particles. All these findings produced intense interest in heavy-ion radiobiology, since these ions may prove to be a limiting factor in space flight. It is of fundamental interest to understand the role of space radiation on the origin and evolution of life.

Over the last few years it was shown at Berkeley that acceleration of all nuclei of the periodic table to very high velocities is entirely feasible. A proposed new accelerator—the Omnitron—would accomplish this acceleration, yielding new knowledge in physics and nuclear medicine through the use of heavy ions.

Tobias went to the University of California at Berkeley from the Technical University of Budapest as a graduate student in physics in 1939. At Berkeley he received his M.A. in 1940 and his Ph.D. in nuclear physics in 1942. During the war he worked in the field of aviation medicine. Later he spent some time at the Swedish Karolinska Institute as a Guggenheim fellow and at Harvard University as a visiting professor of biophysics. He was president of the Radiation Research Society and was a member of the Charter Council of the Biophysical Society. As professor of medical physics, he became head of one of the most active biophysical graduate educational programs in the United States. He was also vice-president of the International Commission of Radiation Biophysics of the International Union of Pure and Applied Biophysics.

For background information *see* BIOPHYSICS; ONCOLOGY; RADIATION BIOLOGY in the McGraw-Hill Encyclopedia of Science and Technology. □

★ TOLANSKY, Samuel

British physicist
Born Nov. 17, 1907, Newcastle-on-Tyne, England

T OLANSKY BEGAN research in 1929 as a spectroscopist, having been trained first in Newcastle-on-Tyne for 2 years, then for a year in Berlin under F. Paschen, and finally for 2 years in London under A. Fowler. His first appointment

was as assistant lecturer in physics at Manchester University under Sir Lawrence Bragg, who encouraged him to rebuild the spectroscopic department, which had been dormant for a quarter century following the retirement of A. Schuster.

Tolansky was an early worker in the new field of research that began to derive atomic nuclear data, such as spins, magnetic moments, quadrupole moments, and isotope displacement effects, from the analysis of hyperfine structures in line spectra. In a succession of papers he reported on such nuclear properties for iodine, bromine, chlorine, arsenic, antimony, tin, and platinum and made several other spectroscopic contributions. This work culminated in *High Resolution Spectroscopy* (1947), which was largely an original contribution to experimental techniques.

Early in World War II, while still teaching at Manchester University, Tolansky was asked by the Atomic Energy Organization to try to find the nuclear spin of uranium-235, and was promised enriched isotope material. However, the export of enriched uranium from the United States was suspended, and he was obliged to attempt the formidable objective of seeking the constant from normal uranium, in which the hyperfine structure components of 235 are almost swamped by the much stronger 238 isotope line. Despite grave difficulties he succeeded in arriving at a conjectural probable value for the nuclear spin of 235, which was later shown to be correct by others who had access to the almost pure, enriched 235 isotope. Tolansky could not arrive at the conjectured spin value from the faint isotope components until he had first developed optical devices to eliminate parasitic reflected ghost images in the Fabry-Perot interferometer that he used. He also had to study the

influence on definition of the deviations of the interferometer plates from true flatness. To examine the quality of the plate finish, he invented the method later known as multiple-beam interferometry, which is a simple, yet very powerful, interference technique capable, by simple methods, of revealing up-down surface microtopographical detail as small as 2.5 angstroms.

In 1946, in a paper in the proceedings of the Physical Society of London, the essential basic theory and practice of this technique were described (several new interferometric methods were to be described later). In late 1946 he was appointed professor of physics and departmental head at the Royal Holloway College, London University. He then largely dropped high-resolution spectroscopy and turned his attention to a vigorous exploitation of multiple-beam interferometry, for the development of which he was awarded the Boys Prize by the Physical Society of London in 1948. Soon afterward surface microtopographies were reported for a variety of natural and of cleaved crystal surfaces, especially minerals. Even some crystal lattice spacings were derived interferometrically by using only visible light waves. It was clear that the techniques had useful technological application. They were applied to the study of machined surface finish, examination of surface hardness indentations, percussion marks on crystals, etch pits, and especially crystal growth features, including screw dislocation spirals—the heights of which were first measured by multiple-beam interferometry. Tolansky became especially interested in diamond crystals and in the measurement of their hardness. He established an authoritative position among the many workers investigating the diamond, contributing usually several papers each year to international diamond physics conferences. His *Microstructures of Diamond Surfaces* (1955) was a summary of his findings in this field. In his *History and Use of Diamond* (1962), he included a number of his original contributions to the history of the diamond, both as a gem and as an industrial tool. For these contributions he was awarded the Silver Medal of the Royal Society of Arts in 1961.

One of his applications of multiple-beam interferometry was to the study of the vibration patterns of quartz crystal oscillators, and in 1951 he was invited to spend a month at a United States military establishment, where he installed a laboratory for this express purpose and trained personnel to secure the vibration interferograms. A widely used interferometric technique is his method for measuring accurately the thickness of a thin film. The output from his laboratory on applications of interferometry was summarized up to 1959 in his *Surface Microtopography* (1960), which included the content of 56 of his own papers and 26 Ph.D. thesis studies carried out by students under his direction.

A novel study was his investigation into the influence of geometrical optical illusions on the assessment of quantities. This work was summarized in *Optical Illusions* (1964) and aroused much interest.

Tolansky was educated at Rutherford College and King's College, Newcastle on Tyne, and Imperial College, London, receiving a D.Sc. and Ph.D. He was a fellow of Armstrong College in 1929 and an Earl Grey fellow in 1931. He became assistant lecturer in physics in 1934, lecturer in 1937, and senior lecturer in 1945 at Manchester University, and professor of physics, Royal Holloway College (London University) in 1947. He was a member of several British government science committees, including a meteorology committee, where his theory of the origin of symmetry of snow crystals aroused some discussion. Tolansky served on the governing boards of two schools of art and on the council of the Royal Society of Arts. He was a successful teacher, and one of his textbooks, *Introduction to Atomic Physics* (1942; 5th ed. 1963) has been widely used. For many years he was chairman of the board of examiners responsible for awarding B.Sc. degrees in physics at London University. The teaching of both undergraduate and postgraduate physics was one of his cherished interests. He was elected a fellow of the Royal Society of London in 1952.

For background information *see* ATOMIC STRUCTURE AND SPECTRA; CRYSTALLIZATION; INTERFEROMETRY; SPECTROSCOPY in the McGraw-Hill Encyclopedia of Science and Technology. □

★ TRÉFOUËL, Jacques

French chemist
Born Nov. 9, 1897, Raincy, Seine et Oise, France

TRÉFOUËL'S FIRST researches in chemotherapy at the Pasteur Institute in 1921 had as their objective the preparation of derivatives of pentavalent arsenic whose therapeutic activity could be demonstrated with experimental diseases easy to work with in the laboratory. There exist 10 different ways of attaching to a benzene ring simultaneously the three chemical groupings of arsonic acid, amine (or acetylated amine), and hydroxyl. Tréfouël was successful in preparing these 10 isomers and in demonstrating the remarkable specificity of action of two of them. One, Stovarsol, is very active against spirochetes, in particular against the agent of syphilis; the other, Orsanine, has a remarkable action against the trypanosome, the agent of sleeping sickness. The eight other derivatives are more or less active. It was Tréfouël's teacher Ernest Fourneau, founder of the Chemotherapy Laboratory at the Pasteur Institute, who had thought of resuming the study of pentavalent arsenicals (arsonic acids) abandoned by Paul Ehrlich for the sake of trivalent arsenicals (of the arsenobenzene type). From that time on, the studies of chemotherapy pursued in Germany and in France have overlapped.

The Bayer Co. introduced a new trypanocide, designated No. 205, which had extraordinary effectiveness. Tréfouël was able to discover the formula, a jealously guarded secret, and published it. This trypanocide is a complex molecule, with a molecular weight above 1400, possessing two differently substituted naphthalene rings connected via amide groups to four —methylated or not methylated—amino benzene rings. He established that the shift of only one of these methyl groups is sufficient to reduce or even cancel the therapeutic action of No. 205. Thanks to his work, the world was able to benefit from a remedy which still plays an effective role (Moranyl, in French; Suramine, in English). The research also served to reinforce Tréfouël's conviction that the least chemical modification in a substance can upset its therapeutic activity.

When Gerhard Domagk in 1935 published his paper on the efficacy of Prontosil in experimental bacterial diseases, the team of Tréfouël the chemist, F. Nitti the bacteriologist, and Bovet the pharmacologist attacked this new problem. Using their knowledge of the specificity of action of a given molecule, Tréfouël began to subject the Prontosil molecule to various chemical modifications. Prontosil consists of two benzene rings linked by an azo group, $-N=N-$. The first ring contains a sulfonamide group, $-SO_2NH_2$; the second ring contains two amine groups. Tréfouël was astonished to find that all the chemical modifications which he effected on the second ring left the therapeutic activity intact. He advanced the hypothesis that this ring plays no role in the antibacterial action and that the animal organism, which is a seat of oxidation-reduction reactions, can very well cleave Prontosil into two molecules containing amine groups.

One is inactive while the other, which contains the sulfonamide grouping, is alone the antibacterial. Tréfouël then prepared this latter molecule, p-aminophenylsulfonamide, or sulfanilamide, which had been obtained in 1903 by P. Gelmo but without any therapeutic objective. Using mice infected with streptococci, Nitti found in sulfanilamide all the properties of Prontosil. Evidence confirming this hypothesis was readily obtained. Prontosil is inactive in cultures since it cannot be cleaved, but sulfanilamide is itself active in vitro as well as in vivo. Moreover, in the urine of patients treated with Prontosil one can recover sulfanilamide and obtain it in a crystalline state. The sulfanilamide molecule became the focus of worldwide research.

At the Chemotherapy Laboratory Tréfouël continued his chemical work, and by successive oxidations he achieved the synthesis of a new chemical substance, di-p-aminophenyl sulfone, or sulfone-mère, which was still more active than sulfanilamide in infected mice. Through personal communication Tréfouël knew that his English friend G. A. Buttle, the first one to have experimented with sulfanilamide, had also found the activity of the sulfone, and by agreement the two published their results before their respective academies of science.

Sulfone-mère was found experimentally to be active against the Koch bacillus. Since the Hansen bacillus, which causes leprosy, is very closely related to it, the American G. H. Faget experimented on human leprosy with the sulfone and its derivatives substituted on the amine group. To this day sulfone-mère alone is still used against this disease, which had hitherto been deemed incurable but whose disappearance is now simply a matter of extending medical aid, the cost of treatment being minimal.

Some of Tréfouël's other researches dealt with malaria (the synthesis of Rodoquine), anesthetics, sympatholytics by synthesis (resolution), cardiac fibrillation, and avitaminosis K.

Tréfouël taught the course in chemotherapy at the Pasteur Institute. In 1940 it was necessary for Tréfouël to leave the Chemotherapy Laboratory, of which he was the head, to become the director of the Pasteur Institute; his term of office of 6 years was renewed four times. He was awarded the Medal of the Resistance in 1945. A Grand Officer of the Legion of Honor and doctor honoris causa of 10 countries, he was president of the French Academy of Sciences (1965), and president of the National Academy of Medicine (1967).

For background information *see* ANTIBACTERIAL AGENTS; CHEMOTHERAPY; PHARMACEUTICAL CHEMISTRY; SULFA DRUGS in the McGraw-Hill Encyclopedia of Science and Technology. □

★ TROFIMUK, Andrei Alekseyevich

Soviet petroleum geologist
Born Aug. 16, 1911, Khvetkovich, Brest Region,
Russia

THE FIRST oil deposits discovered on the western slope of the Urals in Chusovskiye Gorodki (1929) and Ishimbaevo (1932) were confined to buried limestone masses of Permian age. Some investigators thought that they were buried reefs, whereas others believed them to be either erosional outliers or dome-shaped folds. Trofimuk, in cooperation with A. N. Dubrovin, studied in detail the morphology and stratigraphy of the Ishimbaevo masses and proved their reef origin (1936). Within each mass biogenic microfacies were revealed, and it was found that hydroids composing reef cores were predominant in central parts of the reefs. Lithologic studies reconstructed conditions of dolomitization which took place in lagoons, enveloping reef protrusions and their slopes in younger sediments during the uplifting of reefs. These investigations laid the scientific foundation for the prospecting of other oil- and gas-bearing reef masses on the western slope of the Urals.

In 1944 Trofimuk received the title of Hero of Socialist Labor for his discovery of new deposits of oil. In cooperation with other investigators, he proved the necessity of prospecting for oil in Devonian beds, and prospecting carried out under his guidance led to the discovery of the first Devonian oil in Tuimazy in 1944. For this work Trofimuk received the State Prize of the First Degree (1946). Trofimuk substantiated the necessity of application of perimeter flooding in the Tuimazy region and took an active part in the development of this first Soviet experiment of perimeter flooding of a large oil deposit. For this work he received another State Prize of the First Degree (1950).

In 1949 Trofimuk became doctor of sciences (geology and mineralogy) for a monograph on oil content of Paleozoic beds of Bashkiria in which he summarized the results of geologic and geophysical investigations, the experiences of prospecting and exploring for oil, and his recommendation concerning further investigations and prospecting. Trofimuk studied (1955) the capacity of fractured reservoirs of several depleted deposits and showed that this capacity is approximately one order lower than that of porous reservoirs. He showed (1955) that the process of drilling an oil bed with the application of circulating mud is similar to the displacement of oil from the bed by water in conditions of water drive. Using this idea Trofimuk substantiated the possibility of determining the recovery factor of a bed on the basis of determining the residual saturation of core samples.

A series of Trofimuk's works explores the problem of the rational relation between oil reserves and yearly oil production and the problem of rate and methods of treatment of oil reserves in the rapid growth of the oil industry in the Soviet Union.

From 1957 Trofimuk dedicated his principal efforts to substantiating outlooks for oil and gas production of Siberia and the Far East. In this connection the problem of scientific substantiation of prognostic reserves of poorly studied sedimentation basins arose. To study such territories, stratigraphic drilling was carried out in the Soviet Union. The aims of this drilling were to find the composition of sedimentary cover and to determine general conditions of sedimentation and their relation to the processes of oil and gas formation and accumulation. However, sediments contain residual, often syngenetic bitumens, and in 1958 Trofimuk advanced the question of whether it was possible to judge by these residual bitumens the total amount of bitumens, part of which migrated from the sediments and took part in the formation of oil and gas deposits. Through the efforts of many investigators this problem was solved in 1962. The investigations of N. B. Vassoyevich and N. G. Neruchev showed that residual bitumens in sedimentary rocks from which some part of the bitumens had migrated are more oxidized, compared to those bitumens (on the same stage of metamorphism) completely preserved in the sediment; that is, they were not impoverished because of the migration of mobile bitumens. It became possible to determine the percent of migrated bitumens with the aid of the material balance equation, which balances the initial elementary composition of bitumens of the sediments which did not suffer migration with the sum of elementary composition of residual bitumen plus that of migrated bitumen.

Subsequent investigation by Trofimuk showed that, in comparatively thick beds of oil-source rocks underlain and overlain by reservoir rocks, residual bitumens are distributed according to the law of the chromatographic column. The central part of an oil-source bed is characterized by the highest state of reduction, and areas remote from the central part become more oxidized toward reservoirs due to the migration of mobile bitumen. These investigations allowed the creation of a scientific foundation of calculation of prognostic oil and gas reserves by the voluminar-genetic method, using thoroughly controlled studies of distribution and composition of bitumens in rocks which contain oil and gas.

The son of a laborer, Trofimuk graduated from Kazan State University in 1933. He received his candidate's degree in 1939 and his doctor's degree in 1949. From 1934 to 1950 he worked in scientific and industrial petroleum organizations in Bashkiria. From 1942 to 1950 he was a head geologist of Bashneft Trust, and from 1950 to 1953 he worked as a head geologist in the Main Department of Oil and Gas Prospecting of the Ministry of Oil Production of the U.S.S.R. From 1953 to 1955 Trofimuk was deputy director of the All-Union Scientific Research Institute of Exploration and Development of Oil Deposits, and from 1955 to 1957 he was the director of this institute. In 1957 Trofimuk became the director of the Institute of Geology and Geophysics of the Siberian Branch of the U.S.S.R. Academy of Sciences. In 1953 he was elected a corresponding member of the U.S.S.R. Academy of Sciences and in 1958 he became an academician.

Trofimuk authored numerous works in Russian, the most recent including *Oil- and Gas-bearing Basins of the U.S.S.R.*, with A. G. Vasiljev and S. P. Maksimov (1964); *Tectonics and Outlook for Oil and Gas Content of Platform Regions of Siberia*, with Y. A. Kosygin (1965); and *Some Problems of the Theory of Organic Origin of Oil and the Problem of Diagnostics of Oil-Source Beds* (1965).

For background information *see* MINERAL FUEL AREAS; OIL AND GAS FIELD EXPLOITATION; PETROLEUM GEOLOGY; TECTONOPHYSICS in the McGraw-Hill Encyclopedia of Science and Technology. ☐

★ TWITTY, Victor Chandler

American zoologist
Born Nov. 5, 1901, Martin County, Ind., U.S.A.
Died Mar. 22, 1967

TWITTY'S INTERESTS were concentrated on the biology of salamanders, including their development, growth, speciation, and behavior. He was a graduate student of Ross Granville Harrison, the famed experimental embryologist and inventor of tissue culture. Twitty's doctoral thesis was on the growth of eyes grafted between em-

bryos of a rapidly and of a slowly growing species of the salamander *Amblystoma*. He found that the growth rate of the transplanted organs was in accord with that of the donor control eyes, showing that genetic growth potential, not the dimensions of the host organism, controls the size of the eye. A fellow graduate student, Joseph Schwind, obtained similar results with grafted limbs. Twitty reasoned, however, that the grafted organs preserved their typical growth rate, not because they were actually independent of regulating influences exerted by the hosts, but because these influences were essentially identical in the two species and hence did not manifest themselves when eyes and limbs were exchanged between the two salamanders. This reasoning was confirmed by exchanging eyes in tadpole stages. When the eye of an old larva is replaced by an eye from a young one, there can be no question that the graft is truly "too small" for the host, and in the reciprocal transfer, from old donor to young host, the graft is unquestionably "too large." The results showed that there is indeed a mechanism that gears the growth of the part with that of the organism, since normal size relations between the eyes and their hosts were restored through accelerated or retarded growth of the transplants. Twitty postulated that the regulating mechanism involves a gradual decrease during the larval period in the rate at which the cells of the eye can assimilate foodstuffs, together with an increasing concentration of these foodstuffs in the bloodstream that nourishes the eye. Experimental tests, including determination of the concentration of amino acids in the blood of larvae of different ages, provided strong evidence that it is indeed an interlocking relationship between these two somewhat opposed sets of

changes that ensures harmonious size relationships between organ and organism.

At Stanford Universiy, where Twitty worked during most of his professional career, his research was importantly influenced by his discovery of new species of the western newt,

Taricha. Among other distinguishing characters, these species differ conspicuously in the patterns of larval pigmentation. In *Taricha torosa,* for example, virtually all of the skin melanophores (black pigment cells) are concentrated into a pair of compact longitudinal dorsal stripes, whereas in *T. rivularis* the melanophores are widely and uniformly dispersed over the flanks. As in his studies on the growth of the *Amblystoma* eye, Twitty tested the role of intrinsic and extrinsic factors in pigment pattern determination by exchanging the embryonic pigment cells between *torosa* and *rivularis.* Again he found that it is the genetic constitution of the chromatophores themselves, not the species of the host skin in which they develop, that determines whether they form a banded or dispersed pattern. Experiments on other aspects of pigment cell development followed, including a detailed analysis of the mechanism of stripe formation, the factors influencing pigment synthesis in the chromatophores, and especially the circumstances responsible for the scattering of the ameboid pigment cells from their original localized source as part of the embryonic spinal cord. Collectively, his studies and those of his students showed that the development of skin pigmentation is the product of an almost unprecedented array of cellular interactions, operating mutually between the pigment cells themselves, and between the pigment cells and other tissues of the embryo.

The studies on pigment cells led to the development of tissue culture techniques that later permitted Twitty and his student M. C. Niu to investigate one of the fundamental problems of development; the nature of the "induction" process by which one embryonic tissue or organ directs the differentiation of another. They showed for the first time that this induction action can be exerted in the absence of physical contact between the two tissues, through a diffusible substance emanating from the inductor tissue. Niu later investigated the phenomenon in detail and found evidence that the active substances may be nucleic acids.

Artificial hybridization of the species of *Taricha,* originally undertaken in conjunction with the study of pigmentary differentiation, raised questions that eventually led Twitty from embryology into the study of speciation and behavior. One question of evolutionary importance was the viability and fertility of *Taricha* hybrids in nature, and to test these aspects large numbers of hybrid embryos were released in a selected experimental stream at a field station established by Twitty in the coastal mountains of Sonoma County, Calif. Since it was not known whether these hybrids, assuming that they survived to maturity, would return to the stream where they had been released, experiments were undertaken to learn whether newts, like certain other animals, return for successive breedings to the area of birth. The local parental species was used to test this question, and large numbers of adult newts were marked to permit subsequent identification and then were displaced from their native segment of breeding stream to distant locations in the same or different creeks. The newts showed a remarkable homing ability, returning to the same segments of the stream from which they had been displaced. One series of displacement tests required a homing journey of about 5 mi across two mountain ridges and a stream that intervened between the home creek and the one to which they were displaced. The animals do not relocate the home area by random search, but find it instead by movements that are oriented in the proper direction from the beginning of the homeward migration. Successful homing of blinded newts showed that navigation is not by means of solar or other astronomical guidance. There are indications that odors associated with the home area help direct their movements, but evidence of this phenomenon is still inconclusive.

The hybrid newts that grew to maturity returned for successive breedings to the creek locations where they were released as embryos. Unlike most animal species hybrids, the newts are quite fertile, and this fertility factor made possible a hereditary analysis of the more conspicuous features distinguishing the parental forms. During the marked evolutionary diversification within the genus, the members remained genetically compatible. Although geographical, ecological, and behavioral factors serve to prevent interbreeding, no substantial genetic barriers such as hybrid inviability or infertility developed between the species.

Twitty received his B.S. from Butler College in 1925 and his Ph.D. from Yale University in 1929. He taught at Yale from 1929 to 1931 and studied the following year at the Kaiser Wilhelm Institute in Berlin. He joined the Stanford faculty in 1932, and was executive head of the department of biological sciences between 1949 and 1963, when he became Herzstein Professor of Biology. He was elected to the National Academy of Sciences in 1950 and to the American Academy of Arts and Sciences in 1962.

Twitty wrote *Of Scientists and Salamanders* (1966).

For background information *see* BEHAVIOR, ONTOGENY OF; CHROMATOPHORE; EMBRYOLOGY, EXPERIMENTAL; SALAMANDROIDEA in the McGraw-Hill Encyclopedia of Science and Technology.   □

★ ULAM, Stanislaw Marcin

American mathematician
Born Apr. 13, 1909, Lwów, Poland

WHILE WORKING at Los Alamos during World War II, Ulam devised the "Monte Carlo" method for finding approximate answers to problems where exact mathematical treatment is too complex or time-consuming. The initial formulation was made jointly with the mathematician John von Neumann. The procedure found immediate use in nuclear physics and later in a number of other fields.

With the Monte Carlo method one approaches a large, complicated problem by selecting for attention a relatively small number of typical events. For example, take the original problem for which the method was developed: How far would neutrons travel through different shielding materials? Most of the necessary basic information was known: a neutron's average distance of travel in a given substance before colliding with an atomic nucleus; its chances of being repelled or absorbed by the nucleus; and so forth. But it seemed impossible to devise a precise equation for predicting the result of a long sequence of such events, even though the individual probability of each event was easily calculable.

Ulam and von Neumann suggested that some idea of the answer could be obtained by selecting a large sample of neutrons and tracing the passage of each one through the shielding material. They proposed to do this not, of course, by actual measurement of single neutrons, but by the construction of artificial but accurate "life histories." A neutron's journey would be analyzed into a number of separate steps, such as collision with a nucleus in the shield, subsequent repulsion or absorption, another collision, and

so on, until the neutron either lost most of its energy or escaped through the shield. At each step the particular probability could be readily calculated. Suppose that the chance a neutron would be absorbed by a nucleus, rather than reflected, was 100 to 1. At this point Ulam proposed to determine the fate of a neutron under consideration by using a table of random numbers whose construction would reflect the actual probabilities involved. Each step would be decided from a separate table; each "life history" would be composed of a number of steps, and the entire sample would comprise perhaps millions of such histories—a number still very small compared to the total number of particles passing through the shield of a nuclear reactor.

Clearly, the Monte Carlo method was well adapted for use with electronic computers, and its popularity grew along with the efficiency and speed of the computers. One advantage was that an entire calculation could be checked simply by a rerun, since the computer left an exact record of its choices at each step. By the 1960s the method was in use in a wide range of subjects, including weapons design, mathematical economy, and operations research.

Ulam contributed to many fields of science. With Edward Teller, Enrico Fermi, and others, he performed work at Los Alamos leading to the construction of the first hydrogen bomb. In particular, he proved the inadequacy of the original plan and suggested the idea that eventually worked successfully. Another technological achievement was the "Orion" plan for nuclear propulsion of space vehicles, proposed jointly with Everett.

Ulam was the author of a series of papers on the use of electronic computers for problems in mathematics and mathematical physics. He also helped to increase the flexibility and usefulness of computers themselves.

In mathematics, Ulam's contributions include the following: (1) A paper published in 1929 establishes the existence of a measure that assumes only two values, 0 and 1, and that is defined for all subsets of an infinite set. The paper contains a construction of maximal prime ideas, a theorem with wide applications, elaborated later by Tarski and M. H. Stone. (2) A paper on problems of set theory proves the impossibility of a completely additive result for all subsets of noncountable sets and deals with other abstract measure problems. The constructions used still play a role in research on the foundations of set theory, particularly in connection with the problem of the continuum. (3) Several papers with K. Borsuk, beginning in 1931, treat problems of symmetric products (introduced by the authors here for the first time); present proof of the so-called antipodal theorem, an influential paper; and give proof of the invariance of some topological properties under rather continuous deformations. (4) A paper written jointly with J. C. Oxtoby proves that "most" transformations on a manifold which are continuous and which preserve measure (like Liouville flows) are argodic. The authors prove some fundamental properties of "almost every" such transformation. (5) A paper written jointly with Everett introduces the notion of projective algebras. This is a mathematical system which formalizes the "quantities" (for example, the "existence" and "for all" operations) besides the usual elementary (Boolean) operations of mathematical logic.

Ulam received his M.A. in 1932 and his D.Sc. in mathematics in 1933 from the Polytechnic Institute at Lwów. He lectured at various institutions in Europe before coming to the United States in 1936 as a visiting member of the Institute for Advanced Study, Princeton, N.J.

After teaching at Harvard University and the University of Wisconsin, in 1943 he joined the Manhattan Engineering District and went to Los Alamos, N.Mex., to work on the atomic bomb. In 1958 he became a research adviser to the Los Alamos Scientific Laboratory of the University of California. He later became professor of mathematics, and chairman of the department of mathematics, at the University of Colorado. He served on many committees concerned with science and government, and was a consultant to the President's Scientific Advisory Committee. He was elected to the American Academy of Arts and Sciences in 1957, to the National Academy of Sciences in 1966, and to the American Philosophical Society in 1967.

Ulam wrote *A Collection of Mathematical Problems* (1960).

For background information *see* MONTE CARLO METHOD; OPERATIONS RESEARCH; PROBABILITY in the McGraw-Hill Encyclopedia of Science and Technology. □

VAN DE GRAAFF, Robert Jemison

American physicist
Born Dec. 20, 1901, Tuscaloosa, Ala., U.S.A.
Died Jan. 16, 1967, Boston, Mass., U.S.A.

V AN DE GRAAFF profoundly advanced the experimental study of the atomic nucleus through his many creative contributions to the direct particle accelerators which bear his name. Most widely known for the electrostatic belt generator, he continued throughout his life to provide innovations directed toward the attainment of intense streams of high-energy nuclear particles with which to accomplish precision nuclear collisions.

While studying as a Rhodes scholar for his doctorate in physics at Oxford, Van de Graaff, deeply impressed with the importance of research on the atomic nucleus, conceived the constant-potential electrostatic generator, which was to revitalize the flagging field of high-voltage electrostatics. After his return to the United States as a National Research Council fellow in 1929 under physicist Karl Taylor Compton at Princeton, Van de Graaff showed his basically sound and simple generators, which developed direct current at a potential of more than 1,000,000 volts and captured the imagination of scientist and schoolboy alike. Van de Graaff went to MIT in 1931, where he designed the huge air-insulated electrostatic accelerator used for the next 20 years for a variety of fundamental nuclear and radiographic studies. During World War II he headed an Office of Scientific Research and Development project at MIT which developed 2-Mev x-ray sources and techniques for precision military radiography. In 1960 he resigned his associate professorship in physics at MIT to become chief scientist at the High Voltage Engineering Corp. (HVEC)—a company which he cofounded in 1946 and which

has supplied over 500 compressed-gas-insulated single-stage and tandem Van de Graaff accelerators for use in nuclear structure research, cancer therapy, and radiation processing.

For Van de Graaff the ultimate citadel to be assailed by energetic atomic particles was the nucleus of the heaviest atoms, particularly of the uranium atom. As early as 1931, while he and his associates at MIT were still engaged in building the first big accelerator, he had urged that it be used for the proton bombardment of uranium and thorium. "These nuclei," he wrote in a report to Compton, "are already unstable, and it would be interesting to see if an impacting proton of great speed would precipitate immediate disintegration. On the other hand it might be that the proton would be captured by the nucleus, thus opening up the possibility of creating new elements of atomic number greater than 92."

Van de Graaff never lost sight of this nuclear objective—the bombardment of uranium and even of transuranic nuclei. While nuclear structure physics remained occupied with the acceleration of the lightest group of atoms, Van de Graaff contributed in a determining way to the development of larger direct accelerators of highter voltage in which multiply charged ions are given multiple stages of acceleration. He selected uranium as the preferred nuclear projectile and vigorously advocated the bombardment of uranium by uranium as the most fruitful heavy particle experiment.

The opportunity to do this came in the fall of 1966, a few months before his death. The intense, often three-shift research program which Van de Graaff inspired and directed at HVEC was to be his greatest personal assault on the citadel of the uranium nucleus. With a team of scientists, engineers, and technicians from HVEC and MIT, Van de Graaff had planned with great care the tactics and instrumentation which would maximize the nuclear information attainable in the relatively short time allotted to this tremendous effort. He was confident that at the very minimum the crash research program would gain information invaluable for the next more powerful attempt. Using a two-stage Van de Graaff accelerator with a 10,000,000-volt terminal and injecting negatively charged uranium ions at the input end, the apparatus produced uranium atoms with energies well in excess of 200 Mev. It was found that as many as 50 electrons could be stripped from accelerated uranium atoms. Important data on the range and stripping coefficients of very heavy particles moving through matter were obtained, as well as valuable operational system experience.

Van de Graaff's vision of building and using a far more powerful experimental tandem is now an active program of HVEC. This accelerator, the XTU, will be placed in line with the present Emperor facility. This three-stage tandem combination, with multiple stripping, will have the potential of producing uranium atoms with energies approaching 1,000,000,000 electron volts. As this energy is achieved and exceeded, the prospect includes not only the fission but the fusion of two uranium nuclei. The inevitable disintegration of such an extraordinarily energetic compound nucleus could produce, as Van de Graaff had predicted in 1931, new combinations of matter, including possibly transuranic elements. This, as he wrote in August, 1966, would be a "new type of exothermic nuclear reaction greatly exceeding uranium fission in the energy release per fused nucleus."

Van de Graaff introduced other innovations based on fundamental principles and directed toward the more efficient electromagnetic generation of high-voltage power. One of these, a constant-potential source known as the Insulated-Core-Transformer, is now used for particle acceleration when much more current is needed than can be supplied by the electrostatic belt generator. These new techniques of managing electric and magnetic fields in the same space are again so direct and powerful that they may also be applied to the future energy conversion equipments of high-voltage electric power systems, particularly those involving the higher voltages and the larger units of power.

Van de Graaff was gentle and unassuming in his demeanor but vitally inspirational and encouraging to his associates at all levels. With extraordinary clarity and intuition he could extract the essence of a new physical approach and its consequences to nuclear science. Thereafter he would direct his planning and persuasion to bringing about a demonstration of this new approach to the very limit then attainable.

Van de Graaff received his B.S. (1922) and his M.S. in mechanical engineering (1923) from the University of Alabama. Following a short period of work for the Alabama Power Co., during which he became absorbed in the transformation of heat into mechanical and electrical energy, he studied at the Sorbonne in Paris (1924–25), then at Oxford, where he received another B.Sc. (1926) and a Ph.D. (1928). He was a research associate (1931–34) and associate professor (1934–60) at MIT. From 1946 he was a director of the High Voltage Engineering Corp., devoting his full time to the company from 1960. Besides several honorary degrees, he received the Elliott Cresson Medal of the Franklin Institute in 1937, the Naval Ordnance Development Award in 1947, the Duddell Medal of the Physical Society of Great Britain in 1947, the Charles B. Dudley Medal of the American So-

ciety for Testing Materials in 1948, and the Tom W. Bonner Prize of the American Physical Society in 1966 "for his contribution to and continued development of the electrostatic accelerator, a device that has immeasurably advanced nuclear physics." He was elected to the American Academy of Arts and Sciences in 1935.

For background information *see* ELECTROSTATICS; NUCLEAR STRUCTURE; PARTICLE ACCELERATOR; VAN DE GRAAFF GENERATOR in the McGraw-Hill Encyclopedia of Science and Technology.   □

★ VAN DE HULST, Hendrik Christoffel

Dutch astronomer
Born Nov. 19, 1918, Utrecht, Netherlands

R ADIO ASTRONOMY was nonexistent in 1940. In fact, the activities which are now hailed as the beginnings of radio astronomy were confined to some isolated pioneer experiments by K. G. Jansky and by Grote Reber and some theoretical speculations. This field blossomed after World War II. Van de Hulst was among the first astronomers acclaiming its potential as an important new branch of the old science of astronomy. His mimeographed *Course on Radio Astronomy* (1951) was the forerunner of the early textbooks in this field.

A significant personal contribution was the prediction Van de Hulst made as a student in 1944 of the atomic hydrogen line with a wavelength of 21 cm. Until that time only a continuous spectrum had been observed, and a theoretical search of possibilities for isolated wavelengths had led to the 21-cm line as the most likely opportunity. The detection by H. I. Ewen and E. M. Purcell came in 1951, and within a few years it proved possible to map the spiral arms of the galactic system from observations of this line. The key to this success is that the 21-cm line combines two advantages. Since it is in the radio region, it penetrates through the interstellar clouds, which otherwise make large parts of the galactic system invisible. By its sharp wavelength it permits the measurement of velocities in the line of sight. These velocities, by a plausible assumption about the galactic rotation, can be converted into distance estimates.

The 21-cm line research now constitutes only a minor part of all radio astronomy research. However, it has proved so fruitful that in many observatories throughout the world the 21-cm line is still the main part of the research program. Prominent among these is the radio observatory established in 1955 at Dwingeloo, Netherlands, under the direction of C. A. Muller.

In addition to developing radio astronomy as a way to overcome the problem of obstructing clouds in observing interstellar space, Van de Hulst made a direct study of these clouds. He studied, with J. H. Oort, the way in which grains of "dirty ice" condense and grow in the interstellar gas and the properties of scattering, absorption, and polarization attributed to their grains. The book *Light Scattering by Small Particles* (1957), in which Van de Hulst collected many studies on the optics of such grains, has become a standard reference for chemists, meteorologists, and astronomers. Van de Hulst also made important contributions to the light-scattering problems in other astronomical objects, notably in the solar corona, in the zodiacal light, and in planetary atmospheres.

Van de Hulst did not move from his native town until he had obtained his doctor's degree in 1946. Later he lectured and did research in several countries, keeping the Leiden Observatory as his home base. When the first artificial satellites had been launched, the International Council of Scientific Unions organized a Committee of Space Research (COSPAR), with the chief aim of establishing scientific cooperation in space matters between Americans, Soviets, and others. Van de Hulst acted as its first president for 3 years. He also served in various offices in the European Space Research Organization established several years later. Van de Hulst's work and that of his associates won him the Eddington Medal of the Royal Astronomical Society (1955), the Henry Draper Medal of the U.S. National Academy of Sciences (1955), and the Rumford Medal of the Royal Society of London (1964). A member of many professional societies, he was elected a foreign member of the American Academy of Arts and Sciences in 1960.

For background information *see* INTERSTELLAR MATTER; RADIO ASTRONOMY; SCATTERING (ELECTROMAGNETIC RADIATION) in the McGraw-Hill Encyclopedia of Science and Technology.   □

☆ **VAN NIEL, Cornelis Bernardus**

American microbiologist
Born Nov. 4, 1897, Haarlem, Netherlands

WHILE EXAMINING the reactions of photosynthesis in a variety of bacteria, Van Niel proved that the purple and green bacteria, which are unable to tolerate the presence of oxygen, carry out photosynthesis. He also discovered that in some bacteria photosynthesis liberates sulfur rather than oxygen, whereas in others it liberates more highly oxidized states of organic molecules or no by-product at all. These findings enabled him to formulate a general theory of photosynthesis.

In 1772 the British chemist Joseph Priestley announced his discovery that a sprig of mint placed in a closed jar in which candles had burned until they went out "restored" the air and the candles burned once again. Eight years later the Dutch physician Jan Ingen-Housz showed that light was necessary for the air restoration, and in 1782 Jean Senebier, a Swiss pastor, found that "fixed air" (carbon dioxide) was transformed by green plants into "pure air" (oxygen). In 1804 the Swiss biologist Nicolas Théodore de Saussure found that water also played a role in the photosynthetic process. About 1845 Julius Robert Mayer, a German doctor, recognized that the energy of sunlight was converted by "photosynthesis" into the chemical energy of the products of the process, and in 1897 Wilhelm Pfeffer coined the term "photosynthesis" for the energy conversion process, which until then had been known as carbon assimilation. The net result of this and other related work was a theory of photosynthesis which was erroneous because it held that the molecular oxygen liberated by the process was somehow derived from carbon dioxide, leaving the carbon to react with water to form carbohydrates.

Photochemical reaction	Dark Reactions	
	General	Special

$H_2O \xrightarrow[\text{pigment}]{\text{light}}$

$$H \begin{cases} E' \\ E'H \end{cases} \quad \begin{cases} BH_2 \\ B \end{cases} \quad \begin{cases} (CH_2O) \\ CO_2 \end{cases} \text{ or } \begin{cases} NH_3 \\ HNO_3 \end{cases}$$

$$HO \begin{cases} E'' \\ E''OH \end{cases} \quad \begin{cases} A \\ H_2A \end{cases} \quad O_2$$

Scheme of the photochemical reaction and the dark reactions in the photosynthetic process. (From A. J. Kluyver and C. B. Van Niel, The Microbe's Contribution to Biology, Harvard University Press, 1956)

About 1930, working at the Hopkins Marine Station of Stanford University at Pacific Grove, Calif., Van Niel investigated the metabolism of purple and green bacteria and found that they require light as well as hydrogen sulfide for growth; the former had been predicted by Theodor Wilhelm Englemann in 1883; the latter had been demonstrated by Winogradsky in 1887. Van Niel, however, went on to show that the green and purple sulfur bacteria can grow anaerobically in a medium containing an oxidizable inorganic sulfur compound and bicarbonate as the sole source of carbon—but only when the cultures are illuminated. The function of the chlorophyll in green plants was performed in the purple bacteria by a pigment called bacteriochlorophyll. Van Niel's interpretation of the process is shown in Eq. (1),

$$CO_2 + 2H_2S \xrightarrow{\text{light}} (CH_2O) + 2S + H_2O \quad (1)$$

where (CH_2O) represents a cell material. The essential step in the process is the reduction of carbon dioxide by a hydrogen donor, in this case hydrogen sulfide, of which two moles are required for the assimilation of one molecule of CO_2.

Van Niel reasoned that all types of photosynthetic reactions could thus be expressed by Eq. (2), where A is oxygen in the oxygen-evolving

$$CO_2 + 2H_2A \xrightarrow{\text{light}} (CH_2O) + 2A + H_2O \quad (2)$$

photosynthetic reactions of green plants and sulfur in the sulfur-producing photosynthetic reactions of purple bacteria. He then went on to propose that the reaction takes place in two stages known as the photochemical, or light, reaction and the dark reactions (see figure). The photochemical reaction proceeds under the influence of radiant energy that is absorbed by the pigment system of the organisms and leads to the splitting of H_2O with the help of two different enzyme systems, E' and E''. As a result, two entities are formed: a reducing one, E'H, and an oxidizing one, E''OH. In the dark, or nonphotochemical, stage a series of reactions takes place during which a substance B, normally CO_2, is reduced by E'H with the regeneration of E', and E'' is regenerated from E''OH either by oxidation of H_2A (as in bacterial photosynthesis) or by the evolution of O_2 (as in green-plant photosynthesis). Hence, Van Niel's theory maintains that the molecular oxygen liberated by photosynthesis in oxygen-evolving plants is derived from the water rather than from the carbon dioxide.

Using istopically labeled water, H_2O^{18}, or isotopically labeled carbon dioxide, CO_2^{18}, Samuel Ruben and Martin D. Kamen, working at the University of California at Berkeley, established that Van Niel's general equation is correct as it applies to photosynthesis in green plants. Other studies, by such investigators as Robert Hill, Melvin Calvin, and Hans Gaffron, led to a general understanding of the photosynthetic reaction that largely rests on Van Niel's work.

Van Niel received his Chem.E. in 1923 and his D.Sc. in 1928 from the Technological University, Delft, Netherlands. He became an assistant in microbiology in 1923 and conservator in 1925 at the university. Migrating to the United States in 1928, he joined the staff at Stanford University as an associate professor of microbiology in 1928, and 7 years later was appointed professor. He was named Herzstein Professor of Biology in 1946, becoming emeritus in 1963. Among his honors were the National Medal of Science in 1964 and the Rumford Premium of the American Academy of Arts and Sciences in 1967. He was elected to the National Academy of Sciences in 1945 and to the American Academy of Arts and Sciences in 1950.

Van Niel wrote The Microbe's Contribution to Biology, with A. J. Kluyver (1956).

For background information see CHLOROPHYLL; PHOTOSYNTHESIS; RHODOBACTERIINEAE in the McGraw-Hill Encyclopedia of Science and Technology.   □

☆ **VAN VLECK, John Hasbrouck**

American mathematical physicist
Born Mar. 13, 1899, Middletown, Conn., U.S.A.

A PIONEER in the field, Van Vleck developed to a great extent the modern quantum mechanical theory of magnetism.

About 1920 the Danish physicist Niels Bohr had pointed out that paramagnetism and ferromagnetism are found only in the transition elements—those elements in the middle of the long periods that differ from one another mainly in the completeness of an inner electron shell. Arnold Sommerfeld, working in Germany in 1923, then suggested that it should be possible to deduce the number of Bohr magnetons (units of magnetic moment) associated with paramagnetic atoms from their spectral terms. F. Hund, in 1925, showed how to do this for the various trivalent ions of the rare-earth elements (a major class of transition elements) by developing the so-called Hund rule for finding the quantum numbers appropriate to the deepest energy state of the ion. However, he failed to find the right paramagnetic susceptibility for the ions of samarium and europium. About 1930, working at the University of Wisconsin, Van Vleck showed that the discrepancy was caused by the fact that Hund did not include the contribution of the second-order Zeeman effect. If the energy of a quantum mechanical stationary state or energy level i is expanded as a power series in the magnetic field strength H so that $E_i = E^{(0)} + HE_i^{(1)} + H^2E_i^{(2)}$, then the proper expression for the molar paramagnetism is $X = N\Sigma_i[(E_i^{(1)}/kT)^2 - 2E_i^{(2)}]p_i/\Sigma p_i$ where $p_i = \exp(-E_i^{(0)}/kT)$. Here N is Avogadro's number, k is Boltzmann's constant, and T is the absolute temperature. Van Vleck showed that, when the previously overlooked $E^{(2)}$ terms were included,

agreement was achieved with experiment. He also used the above formula to explain the different magnetic behavior (different amounts of magnetic anisotropy and type of variation of paramagnetism with temperature) of the various paramagnetic salts of the iron group. He derived the conditions (energy intervals very large or small compared with kT) under which the above formula reduced, as regards temperature dependence, to an expression of the form $X = (C/T) + N\alpha$. The first and second terms arise respectively from the matrix elements of the magnetic moment associated with the small and large intervals. Curie's law is a special case in which the second term is unimportant.

Van Vleck was also active in studying the nature of the chemical bond, especially as related to magnetic properties. Drawing upon a general theory worked out by Hans Bethe about 1929, Van Vleck also helped to develop the ligand, or crystal, field theory of molecular bonding. This theory treats electrostatic systems as a series of point charges and dipoles. It then determines the potential energies of various types of interaction between atoms or groups of atoms by means of classical electrostatics. The ligand theory is usually applied in such a way as to permit the evaluation—from experimental data—of parameters representing the strength of the ligand field and the magnitudes of the d electrons. He showed that, if the ligand field is sufficiently strong, the spin of the paramagnetic ion—and hence its paramagnetism—is less than that given by the Hund rule. This distinction is of interest to inorganic chemists because it yields information on the strength of the chemical bond. Since World War II the ligand field theory has achieved a measure of prominence.

Van Vleck also contributed to the theory of the spectra of free molecules, and of ions in the solid state, and to the theory of the paramagnetic relaxation and resonance of solids containing rare-earth or transition ions.

The son of a professor of mathematics, Van Vleck received his A.B. (1920) from the University of Wisconsin and his A.M. (1921) and Ph.D. (1922) at Harvard University. After another year at Harvard as an instructor in the physics department, Van Vleck joined the faculty of the University of Minnesota as an assistant professor, becoming an associate professor in 1926 and a professor of physics in 1927. He left Minnesota in 1928 to accept a professorship at the University of Wisconsin, where he remained until 1934. Van Vleck then accepted a similar position at Harvard, where he was to remain for more than three decades. He served as head of the theory group in the radio research laboratory from 1943 to 1945 and then as chairman of the physics department until 1949. In 1951 Van Vleck was named Hollis Professor of Mathematics and Natural Philosophy, and from 1951 to 1957 was dean of engineering and applied physics. He was Lorentz Visiting Professor at Leiden in 1960 and George Eastman Professor at Oxford in 1961–62. Among his many honors were the Albert A. Michelson Award (1963), the Irving Langmuir Award (1965), and the National Medal of Science (1966). He was elected to the American Academy of Arts and Sciences in 1934, to the National Academy of Sciences in 1935, and to the American Philosophical Society in 1939.

Van Vleck wrote *The Theory of Electric and Magnetic Susceptibilities* (1932), the first comprehensive treatment of quantum magnetics.

For background information *see* CHEMICAL BINDING; MAGNETOCHEMISTRY in the McGraw-Hill Encyclopedia of Science and Technology.   □

VENING MEINESZ, Felix Andries

Dutch geophysicist and geodesist

Vening Meinesz died on Aug. 12, 1966, in Amersfoort, Netherlands. See *McGraw-Hill Modern Men of Science*, Volume I.

★ VERHOOGEN, John

American geophysicist
Born Feb. 1, 1912, Brussels, Belgium

THE EARTH is so impenetrable that it is very hard to discover by direct observation what goes on inside it and how it functions. What, precisely, is it made of? What causes earthquakes? What makes mountains, what forces move continents, what is the source of the lava that occasionally spills out on its surface? To answer such questions one must proceed in two directions: On the one hand, geologists attempt to read in rocks a record of what has happened; on the other hand, geophysicists, starting from known physical laws, attempt to discover what could happen. The two approaches are necessarily complementary.

Verhoogen tried to follow both approaches simultaneously, interpreting the geological evidence in terms of physical laws. His early work was mainly on volcanoes. He spent some time in the Congo observing a spectacular eruption of the volcano Nyamuragira in 1938–40. There he was able to make one of the first reliable estimates of the amount of gases, mainly water vapor, discharged during an eruption, and to show that contrary to an opinion widely held at the time these gases play only a minor role in the mechanics of the eruption; he also obtained the first spectrograms of volcanic flames. He was also engaged at that time in the application of thermodynamics to geologic processes, particularly to volcanic phenomena and to the genesis of rocks that form or recrystallize at elevated temperatures.

Turning to the physics of the Earth's interior, Verhoogen devoted some time to the hypothesis, suggested by Arthur Holmes, that mass motion (convection) may occur inside the Earth because of gravitational instability induced by internal heating and consequent temperature gradients. He first applied to the Earth a theorem of astrophysics, due to H. von Zeipel, which shows that a rotating body with internal heat sources cannot be in hydrostatic equilibrium. Noticing that the only parameter of the Earth's interior that is reasonably well known is the velocity of the seismic (elastic) waves, he made use of P. J. W. Debye's theory of specific heat to calculate the adiabatic gradient, which is the temperature gradient at which an inviscid fluid becomes unstable; this calculation showed that instability is indeed likely to occur in the Earth. In 1954 he formulated a mechanism for generating magma (molten rock) in the otherwise solid mantle of the Earth by convectional upwelling. He later showed that phase transitions which are believed to occur at depths between 300 and 1000 km are not likely to affect much the large-scale convective phenomena. A study of the effect of pressure and temperature on the thermal expansion of solids led in 1955 to an estimate of the actual temperature in the lower mantle (2900 km deep).

From 1952 Verhoogen was much interested in magnetic properties of rocks, particularly the "remanent" magnetization which they acquire when they form and which reflects the direction of the Earth's magnetic field at the time and place of their formation. Paleomagnetism, as this new science is called, led in recent years to a number of remarkable conclusions regarding both the past history of the Earth's magnetic field and geologic processes, such as continental drift. The peculiar thermoremanent magnetization that rocks acquire while cooling in the Earth's field has been particularly useful in paleomagnetism, although its origin is still not entirely clear. Verhoogen was the first to suggest that it is related by magnetostriction to the stress field of dislocations in the mineral grains that carry the remanence. The mineralogy of the magnetic carriers in igneous rocks, mainly iron-titanium oxides, is quite complicated and very important, as magnetic properties are very sensitive to slight changes in composition and structure. Verhoogen examined such mineralogical problems as the distribution of titanium between silicates and oxides in igneous rocks, and the effects of low-temperature oxidation, and suggested mechanisms that could lead to spontaneous "self-reversals" of the magnetization, that is, the acquisition of a magnetization opposed in direction to the field that produced it. Self-reversed rocks are occasionally found.

Verhoogen, whose father was a medical doctor and professor in the University at Brussels, acquired very early an interest in rocks that he never lost; he was also inclined toward physics and soon felt attracted to the then relatively new field of geophysics. He earned degrees in mining engineering at the University of Brussels (1933) and geological engineering at the University of Liège (1934) before obtaining his Ph.D. at Stanford University (1936). In 1946 he joined the faculty of the University of California, Berkeley, becoming professor in 1952. For his applications of physics and chemistry to geology, he received in 1958 the Day Medal of the Geological Society of America. He was elected to the National Academy of Sciences in 1956.

Verhoogen wrote *Igneous and Metamorphic Petrology*, with F. J. Turner (1951; 2d ed. 1960) and *Metamorphic Reactions and Metamorphic Facies*, with W. S. Fyfe and Turner (1958).

For background information *see* ASTROPHYSICS; PETROLOGY; ROCK MAGNETISM; VOLCANO in the McGraw-Hill Encyclopedia of Science and Technology.   □

★ VICKERY, Hubert Bradford

American biochemist
Born Feb. 28, 1893, Yarmouth, Nova Scotia, Canada

THERE HAS long been a vast amount of investigation of alkaloids, proteins, sugars, pigments, organic acids, and many other kinds of substances found in plants. Until recent years, however, very few chemically trained scientists have devoted their lives to plant biochemistry, that is, to the study of the transformations that

such substances undergo in the course of the development and growth of plants. Of these the first, and still from many points of view the greatest, was Ernst Schulze (1840–1912), who began his investigations at Zurich in 1872. With complete mastery of the analytical techniques of his period, he worked out the details of the transformations of the proteins of the lupine seed during sprouting into the soluble amino acids, especially asparagine, found in the young growing plant. He also discovered the amino acid phenylalanine and the amide of glutamic acid, glutamine.

The second great plant biochemist of the period was Heinrich Ritthausen (1826–1912) at Königsberg in East Prussia. Ritthausen devoted his life to the study of the proteins of plant seeds. In the course of this work he discovered glutamic acid, established aspartic acid as a component of proteins, and became the first to attempt to characterize proteins in terms of their amino acid composition, a matter that is today routine. He was also the first to classify plant proteins in a logical manner.

The third great plant biochemist was Thomas B. Osborne (1859–1929) at the Connecticut Agricultural Experiment Station in New Haven. He began his work in 1889, and with the aid of improved methods he greatly extended the scope of Ritthausen's investigations. At a time when protein chemistry was regarded by his scientific contemporaries as a distinctly profitless occupation, Osborne learned how to deal with these unattractive and difficult substances. By 1910 he had become an internationally known authority on the preparation and analysis of proteins.

Toward the end of his career, in association with Lafayette B. Mendel (1872–1935) of Yale University, he solved the problem of the differences in the nutritive properties of proteins by the demonstration that the amino acids lysine and tryptophan are essential in nutrition.

Vickery in 1921 had the unique good fortune

to be accepted as Osborne's only graduate student. Under Osborne's direction he prepared a dissertation submitted to Yale University on the rate of hydrolysis by acids and alkalies of the protein gliadin. The following year Vickery was invited to join Osborne's group, and in 1928 he succeeded him as head of the Biochemistry Department at the Connecticut Station.

Because of the current interest in the presence of vitamins in plant tissues, Vickery at first undertook an examination of the composition of the alfalfa plant. Fractionation of the nitrogenous substances in water extracts of the leaves, with use of the salts of heavy metals as precipitants, then the only technique available for such studies, resulted in the isolation of about 55% of the soluble nitrogen as pure crystalline compounds, notably asparagine, adenine, stachydrine, choline, arginine, lysine, and a number of other amino acids. It became clear, however, that the available methods were entirely inadequate to solve the problem in any satisfactory way. Much time was accordingly devoted to the improvement of the conventional methods for the determination of the basic amino acids of proteins and for the separation of the basic substances present in plant tissues. Vickery found that purines, histidine, arginine, and lysine could be separated by control of the pH after the addition of excess of a soluble silver salt to the acidified solution. Purines and cystine precipitate at acid reaction, histidine at neutral reaction, and arginine at strongly alkaline reaction, lysine together with methylated bases remaining in the filtrate. With the aid of flavianic acid for arginine and 3,4-dichlorobenzene sulfonic acid for histidine, new and greatly improved methods were developed for the determination of these bases in hydrolysates of proteins. Lysine, isolated from proteins as picrate, was crystallized for the first time as the free base, and shortly thereafter its lower homolog ornithine was also obtained in crystalline form. Preparations of arginine and of histidine as crystalline free bases were also described.

Although these early methods to determine the basic amino acids of proteins have been entirely superseded by modern chromatographic procedures, at the time they led to analyses of a number of proteins of greatly improved reliability. The data permitted the calculation of the acid-binding capacity of proteins, then a matter of importance in the study of the physical chemistry of these substances.

Parallel to the studies of the protein bases, Vickery's colleague George W. Pucher developed simple and accurate methods to determine the chief organic acids found in plant leaves. His method for citric acid, although since modified by others, is still widely used. Methods to determine the amides asparagine and glutamine in plants were also worked out, as were methods to prepare both of these substances in quantity. At that time glutamine was one of the rarest of the amino acids, and its importance in animal physiology was entirely unknown.

Armed with new and accurate analytical methods suitable for the study of the behavior of the nitrogenous substances, the organic acids, and the carbohydrates of leaf tissue, Vickery and Pucher undertook a program of study of the composition of the tobacco leaf and of the effect of culture of detached leaves under a wide variety of conditions of exposure to light and darkness and variation in the composition of the culture solution used. The remarkable enrichment of detached leaves in citric acid at the expense of malic acid during culture in darkness was observed, as well as the rapid disappearance of a large part of the protein and the accumulation of much of its nitrogen as asparagine and ammonia. Similar transformations were found to occur during the commercial process of curing the tobacco leaf. After Pucher's death in 1948, these studies were broadened to include an investigation of the effect of culture of tobacco leaves in darkness on solutions of many of the common organic acids. All members of the tricarboxylic acid cycle were found to contribute to the accumulation of citric acid, but tartaric acid and oxalic acid are not metabolized. A method depending on statistical principles for collecting samples of leaves of identical composition was developed by means of which the sampling error of such experiments was diminished to about 2%. It was thus possible to establish reliable quantitative relationships among the organic acids which underwent metabolic transformations.

In 1942 Pucher had discovered that isocitric acid is a major component of the leaves of several plants of the family Crassulaceae. This observation solved the problem of the identity of the so-called crassulacean malic acid, which had been a puzzle in the literature for more than 60 years. It led to a long-continued investigation of the phenomena of diurnal variation of acidity in the leaves of *Bryophyllum calycinum*. This study ultimately showed that malic acid and, to a smaller extent, citric acid, which accumulate in substantial amounts at night, are derived from starch and that these acids are reconverted to starch during the day. A few years ago Vickery returned to the study of isocitric acid and found that its monopotassium salt has excellent physical properties. A new and simple method to isolate isocitric acid was worked out, and specimens of this extremely rare and important member of the tricarboxylic acid cycle are now easily obtained. An improved method of synthesis was also described.

Vickery served for many years on various

committees concerned with biochemical nomenclature. He was chairman of the committee which brought about the revision of the nomenclature of the amino acids and the introduction of the small capital-letter prefixes to indicate configurational relationships. He wrote many of the rules now in universal use, and was instrumental in having them approved by international committees on nomenclature. He also served for many years on the editorial boards of several journals.

Vickery received his B.Sc. from Dalhousie University in Halifax with honors in chemistry in 1915 and obtained his M.Sc. in 1918. In 1920 he was awarded an 1851 Exhibition scholarship by Dalhousie, and did his graduate study at Yale University, receiving the Ph.D. in 1922 and then joining the staff of the Connecticut Agricultural Experiment Station. From 1925 until his retirement in 1963 he served as a lecturer in the Graduate School of Yale University, giving a short annual course of lectures on protein and amino acid chemistry. During the war he was associated with the Plasma Fractionation Laboratory at the Harvard University Medical School, and in 1946 was among the 22 scientists from the National Academy and from industry invited by the U.S. Navy to observe the atomic bomb experiments at Bikini. He received the Stephen Hales Award of the American Society of Plant Physiologists in 1932 and its Charles Reid Barnes Honorary Life Membership Award in 1956. He was elected to the National Academy of Sciences in 1943 and to the American Academy of Arts and Sciences in 1948.

Vickery wrote over 200 scientific papers on subjects concerned with amino acid chemistry and the metabolism of the organic acids of plants.

For background information *see* AMINO ACIDS; PLANT METABOLISM; PROTEIN in the McGraw-Hill Encyclopedia of Science and Technology. □

★ VISSCHER, Maurice Bolks

American physiologist
Born Aug. 25, 1901, Holland, Mich., U.S.A.

THE CHALLENGE of the application of the ripening field of physical chemistry and physics to the problems of the behavior of living systems was the impetus to Visscher's work. His doctoral dissertation dealt with the kinetics of the enzymatic breakdown of glycogen. As a postdoctoral fellow with Ernest Starling, he began a series of studies on the energetics of cardiac contraction which led to the generalization that in heart failure the mechanical efficiency of the heart declines and effective therapeutic drugs increase its efficiency.

Visscher did not confine his interests to a single field in physiology but contributed to several. He wrote many papers on intestinal absorption. His interest in this subject was engendered by a postdoctoral fellow who wanted to try to use the intestine as a dialysis mechanism in place of a damaged kidney. A long series of subsequent studies on basic transport processes across the intestinal epithelium led to the utilization of isotopic tracers in the study of unidirectional fluxes of various solutes across the epithelium and an elucidation of facts about the active transport of certain ions, particularly chloride and sodium. Visscher's work demonstrated that the greater absorptive capacity of the lower bowel as compared with the jejunum or duodenum is not a function of greater unidirectional flux rates but a function of a greater disparity between fluxes in the two directions under circumstances where the unidirectional rates are actually smaller.

Visscher always considered the science of physiology to have a twofold position, as a science in its own right and as a major underpinning of scientific clinical medicine. In addition to doing studies on basic problems, he collaborated in studies of such clinical physiological problems as pulmonary edema, pulmonary embolism, and pulmonary blood-flow characteristics, as well as toxic shock and other forms of circulatory shock, hypertension, and heart failure. He devoted himself largely to the explication of clinical disorders in terms of physicochemical factors. He and his students showed that several types of lung edema previously erroneously ascribed to "neurogenic" changes in lung capillary permeability are in reality due to changes in filtration pressure and that, contrary

to earlier ideas, hypoxia in degrees compatible with life does not increase capillary permeability to protein and does not therefore cause edema by that mechanism. In connection with the elucidation of bacterial toxic shock, he and his collaborators demonstrated that in various species of animal the primary shock organs are not the same. In one species, for example, the cat, vasoconstriction of pulmonary blood vessels predominates whereas in the dog the hepatic venous bed produces the primary hemodynamic disturbance. Visscher and his co-workers also devised new methods for studying vascular resistances in series, separating effects of drugs and other agents on the arterial and venous portions of the vascular bed in organs.

In addition to his scientific work, Visscher concerned himself seriously with the national and international aspects of cooperation in science and with the social values and position of science and scientists. He was a member of a National Research Council (NRC) committee concerned with medical science before the United States entered World War II and continued throughout the war. He was a member and for a time chairman of the NRC Committee on Science in UNESCO. He helped organize the International Union of Physiological Sciences, and was its secretary-general for the first 6 years of its operation. He assisted in the formation of the Council of International Organizations of Medical Sciences, and was the president of its Assembly. He was the chairman of the Special Committee on Civil Liberties for Scientists of the American Association for the Advancement of Science during the McCarthy era. He was the chairman of a committee of a Governor's Atomic Energy Commission in Minnesota which first detected the high levels of radioactivity in food grains in the United States, resulting in large public interest in the hazards of large-scale thermonuclear bomb testing. As an officer of the National Society for Medical Research, he devoted substantial effort to public education in connection with counteracting antivivisection propaganda in the United States.

Visscher received his primary and secondary school education in the public schools in Holland, Mich., and his bachelor's degree from Hope College in 1922. His decision to become a biologist was due primarily to the inspiration of his biology teacher in college, Frank N. Paterson. Visscher earned his Ph.D. at the University of Minnesota in 1925 and later received an M.D. from the same institution after spending several summers in clinical studies. He was a National Research Council fellow at University College, London, and at the University of Chicago in 1926 and 1927. He was professor of physiology and department head at the universities of Tennessee, Southern California, and Illinois before returning in those capacities to Minnesota in 1936. He was elected to the National Academy of Sciences in 1956 and the American Academy of Arts and Sciences in 1964.

For background information *see* CIRCULATION DISORDERS; DIGESTIVE SYSTEM; HEART DISORDERS in the McGraw-Hill Encyclopedia of Science and Technology. □

VON KÁRMÁN, Theodore

American aerodynamicist
Born May 11, 1881, Budapest, Hungary
Died May 6, 1963, Aachen, Germany

As a theoretician, Von Kármán made widely varied contributions to aerodynamics. In the field of engineering he made the Guggenheim Aeronautical Laboratory of the California Institute of Technology, under his directorship during 1930–49, the scene of pioneering aeronautical work, including the development of the first rockets designed and fired by the United States. As an administrator, Von Kármán played a large part in interesting the Air Force in long-range research and development programs after World War II.

Von Kármán's theory of vortex streets, propounded about 1910, was one of the first steps in the mathematical treatment of turbulent motion. Consider a two-dimensional flow of fluid (either gas or liquid) past a cylinder whose long axis is perpendicular to the direction of flow. A certain amount of turbulence will occur "downstream" of the cylinder. At relatively low velocities of flow the vortexes formed in this way will remain near the cylinder. At much higher flow velocities the turbulent motion will approach a random condition. At intermediate velocities, however, vortexes are formed, grow to a certain size, and then are "shed" and slip downstream. Von Kármán found that under certain conditions the vortexes are shed alternately, first from one side of the cylinder, then from the other. Surprisingly, he found that this phenomenon can occur even when the flow of fluid is perfectly regular. This periodic shedding of vortexes forms a regular train composed of two lines of vortexes, a phenomenon known as the Von Kármán vortex street. Von Kármán was able to show that for one value (h/a), involving the spacing of the vortexes and the distance of the two rows from each other, the "street" tends to be self-stabilizing with regard to relatively small external factors. He pointed out that in many naturally occurring situations (for example, winds blowing past bridges or exposed pipelines) this value is quite close to the one he had calculated from theory.

Among Von Kármán's other theoretical contributions is a theory of the specific heats of solids, advanced in 1912 in collaboration with the German physicist Max Born.

Von Kármán was an early pioneer in helicopter theory and design although he did not actually succeed in developing a machine that flew. After he came to the United States in 1930 to take up the directorship of the Guggenheim Aeronautical Laboratory at the California Institute of Technology, the laboratory improved its already notable reputation and began producing a great quantity of basic aerodynamic research, ranging from airfoil, propeller, and wind tunnel design to jet propulsion and rocketry. In the last field, Von Kármán's group played a major role in the development of the first space-sounding United States rocket, the WAC-Corporal, which first began to be fired in 1946. They developed the liquid-fueled, self-cooling engine design, employing fuming nitric acid and aniline, which powered the WAC-Corporal and the later Aerobee. Another product of the laboratory was a solid-fuel booster for the same rockets, using a slow-burning propellant which burned long enough to give the rocket a sizable push without reaching temperatures that would destroy the rather primitive throat linings then in use.

After World War II Von Kármán became chairman of the Army Air Force Scientific Ad-visory Group. Under his guidance this group had a great impact on Air Force thinking. Its recommendations, as embodied in some 30 volumes of reports, contributed to the establishment of agencies to promote long-term basic research and development, such as the Air Research and Development Command (later the Systems Command) and the Air Force Institute of Technology. Perhaps most importantly, in terms of immediate results, the Scientific Advisory Group's reports helped to convince the Air Force of the importance of a program for developing intercontinental ballistic missiles (ICBMs), a crucial element in later United States defenses.

The son of a professor of philosophy, Von Kármán received an M.E. from the Royal Technical University at Budapest in 1902 and a Ph.D. from the University of Göttingen in 1908. In 1912 he became the director of the Aeronautical Institute of the University of Aachen, remaining there until 1929. During World War I he served as a lieutenant-colonel in the Austro-Hungarian Aviation Corps. In 1930 he went to the United States to become director of the Guggenheim Aeronautical Laboratory of the California Institute of Technology, forerunner of the Jet Propulsion Laboratory. In 1942 he founded the Aerojet-General Corp. In 1944 he was made the first director of the Air Force Scientific Advisory Board; in 1951 he organized the Advisory Group for Aeronautical Research and Development to NATO, and was chairman until his death. Von Kármán received over 30 awards, including in 1963 the first National Medal of Science. The Air Force Association's Von Kármán Trophy is named after him.

Von Kármán wrote *Aerodynamics* (1954).

For background information *see* KARMAN VORTEX STREET; ROCKET ENGINE in the McGraw-Hill Encyclopedia of Science and Technology. ☐

★ WADDINGTON, Conrad Hal

British biologist
Born Nov. 8, 1905, Evesham, Worcestershire,
England

D URING HIS student years Waddington studied geology and did his graduate work on the evolution of a group of fossil ammonites. These ammonites are shells in which the whole life history of an individual is permanently recorded in the changing patterns of successive whorls so that one is presented simultaneously with development and evolution. Thereafter Waddington worked in the territory where embryology, genetics, and evolution overlap.

His first noteworthy research was on the role of tissue interactions in the early embryonic development of birds and mammals. A few years before, Hans Spemann in Germany had demonstrated the importance of such interactions (embryonic induction) in the newts and salamanders. By developing the first successful techniques for keeping warm-blooded embryos alive in artificial culture, Waddington was able to show that the basic principles of Spemann's results apply, with appropriate modifications, to other vertebrate embryos. In a series of papers from 1932 to 1937, he elucidated the main aspects of tissue interaction as it occurs in birds. For this work he was awarded the Albert Brachet Prize by the Royal Academy of Belgium in 1936.

Waddington found in 1933 that the inductive action of some regions of the chick embryo can be performed even after that tissue has been killed. This discovery disposed of the idea, which some people were tempted to hold, that induction involves some mysterious life-dependent process. There followed a few years of fruitful collaboration with Joseph Needham on the biochemical nature of the inducing factors. At first there was a period of some confusion, in which different groups of workers claimed to identify different active substances. Waddington and his co-workers showed in 1936 that induction can be carried out by substances, such as the dye methylene blue, which certainly do not occur naturally in embryos. They propounded the theory of the "masked inducer." According to this theory, the substances which are sufficiently specific to switch on one type of cellular differentiation rather than another are already present in the cells but require activating before they can operate, and it is this "unmasking" which is brought about by the inducing chemicals used in the experiments. This hypothesis is extremely similar to the well-known Jacob-Monod theory of the mechanism of induced enzyme synthesis in bacteria, developed a quarter of a century later.

Specific types of cellular differentiation are certainly under the control of genes. In the late 1930s Waddington began a long series of studies on the genetic control of the development of organs and tissues in *Drosophila*. He and his students continued these studies over the years. His book *Organisers and Genes* (1940) was the first serious attempt to work out in detail the relations between the basic ideas of genetics and the new results achieved in experimental embryology.

World War II interrupted Waddington's biological career. He became one of the group of British scientists, drawn from many different fields, who developed the idea of operations research and showed how it could be used to practical effect in military affairs. He finished the war as scientific advisor to the commander in chief, Coastal Command, Royal Air Force. Returning to genetics and embryology, he retained a sense of responsibility for seeing that scientific procedures and methods of thought are more widely utilized in public affairs. This concern led him to such activities as membership on the British Advisory Council on Science Policy, membership on the "Trend" Committee on the organization of civil science in Britain, and presidency of the International Union of Biological Sciences whan it took the lead in initiating the International Biological Program.

From 1946 Waddington was professor of animal genetics and director of the institute for that subject at the University of Edinburgh. This institute contained a large contingent of geneticists financed by the Agricultural Research Council to study the basic science underlying livestock breeding. By applying operational research methods in this new field, they made a considerable impact on commercial breeding, particularly of dairy cattle (by artificial insemination) and poultry, including turkeys.

Waddington's own main work after the war was partly a continuation of previous interests in embryology, in which he was one of the first to utilize new techniques (for example, isotopic tracers in 1950). He also made several important studies on evolutionary mechanisms. His most striking result was the demonstration that, when selection favors a character developed as a physiological adaptation to a particular environment, a process of "genetic assimilation" may take place which, after several or many generations, renders the character relatively independent of the originally necessary precipitating environmental stress. This process, in which selection changes a character from being mainly acquired to mainly inherited, provides a much more convincing, though still perfectly orthodox, Mendelian explanation for the apparently Lamarckian phenomena of evolution than do previous ideas, which could do no better than appeal to the omnipotence of chance. Genetic assimilation and the use of stressful environments to reveal hidden genetic variation are also potentially powerful tools in the field of applied breeding.

Waddington was educated at Cambridge University. He was lecturer in zoology and embryologist at Strangeways Research Laboratory, Cambridge, during 1933–45. During World War II he was engaged in operational research in the Coastal Command, Royal Air Force. In 1947 he became Buchanan Professor of Animal Genetics at the University of Edinburgh. He was elected a fellow of the Royal Society of London in 1947 and a foreign member of the American Academy of Arts and Sciences in 1960.

Waddington's books included *The Ethical Animal* (1960), *The Nature of Life* (1961), *New Patterns in Genetics and Development* (1962), *Biology for the Modern World* (1962), and *Principles of Development and Differentiation* (1966).

For background information *see* BREEDING (ANIMAL); EMBRYOLOGY, EXPERIMENTAL; EMBRYONIC ORGANIZER; EVOLUTION, ORGANIC; OPERATIONS RESEARCH in the McGraw-Hill Encyclopedia of Science and Technology.   □

WALD, George

American biologist and biochemist

Wald shared the 1967 Nobel Prize in medicine or physiology with Haldan Keffer Hartline and Ragnar Granit. See *McGraw-Hill Modern Men of Science*, Volume I.

★ WALKER, John Charles

American plant pathologist
Born July 6, 1893, Racine, Wis., U.S.A.

WHEN WALKER began his graduate studies at the University of Wisconsin in 1914, interest was growing steadily in the use of host resistance as a means of controlling plant disease. A few examples were on record as the result of selection. The first case of mendelian inheritance of resistance was that in wheat to yellow rust, reported 7 years earlier by Rowland Biffen at Cambridge University. Walker became interested in the striking resistance of onion varieties with colored scales to the smudge disease. In his doctoral thesis (1918) he showed that the dry, colored outer scales of maturing bulbs contain a water-soluble fungistatic agent which either prevents germination of smudge spores or, if they begin to germinate, the young germ tubes "burst" so as to become functionless. In water extracts from white (susceptible) scales, normal germination and growth occurs. Continuing research on this subject, Walker showed, with K. P. Link and H. R. Angell, that the fungistatic effect is due to water-soluble phenolic compounds, protocatechuic acid and catechol, which are colorless but intimately associated with the yellow-color compound in onion scales, the water-insoluble quercetin. Walker later cooperated with G. H. Rieman and with A. E. Clarke and H. A. Jones, who studied the genetics of scale color in onions and showed three gene pairs to be involved. One of these (I) suppressed color completely in the homozygous state (II), but only partially in the heterozygous (Ii) condition. Walker, with Jones, T. Little, and R. H. Larson, showed complete susceptibility in II plants, intermediate resistance in Ii plants, and complete resistance in ii plants. He went on to show that this mechanism of resistance is effective only when the outer scales in which the water-soluble substances can diffuse to the infection drops. If living scales are inoculated, colored and colorless are equally susceptible, either because the water-soluble phenols have not formed or because the mechanism of penetration in living scales prevents their protective function. This was the first case on record in which a genetic disease-resistant character in plants was tied to a specific compound produced in the host.

Other protective substances in onion, the allyl sulfides, were demonstrated. Although these are even more fungistatic than the phenols, they are not associated with color and are not effective in varietal resistance. Walker thus propounded the principle that the presence of a material demonstrated in a given host to be fungistatic or fungicidal to a given pathogen does not prove it to be a factor in resistance to that pathogen. The actual function of the material at the point of infection or during pathogenesis is necessary before it can be accepted as a resistant factor.

Walker continued a lifetime study of theoretical and applied aspects of disease resistance in plants. With M. A. Stahmann, he refuted the claim that resistance to clubroot in black mustard is due to the fungistatic allyl isothiocyanate present in the roots. It was shown that this substance which exists as a glucoside is not fungicidal in that form, but as soon as tissue containing it is macerated, an enzyme system breaks down the glucoside and releases the fungicidal material. A world collection of black mustard showed some strains very resistant and others very susceptible with no corresponding difference in isothiocyanate glucoside. With D. E. Pryor, Walker grew resistant plants supplied with sulfur-free nutrient. Although no isothiocyanate could be detected in such plants, their resistance was not altered.

The resistance in cabbage to yellows was next shown to have a monogenic dominant character. This was later shown to be the case in resistance in cucumber to mosaic, in bean to halo blight, and in several other diseases.

Later studies were directed toward the host-parasite interactions in resistant and susceptible plants. With D. N. Srivastava, Walker showed that the freshly cut surface of the sweet potato root is resistant to the soft rot fungus, *Rhizopus stolonifer*, which once established in the tissue rots it rapidly through the excretion of pectinolytic exoenzymes. With Gerhardt Menke, Walker showed that the ungerminated spores of *Rhizopus* on the freshly cut root surface stimulate the production by the host of a coumarin compound which is sufficiently fungistatic to prevent germination of the spores without killing them. If germinated spores are placed on the cut surface, either coumarin is not formed or the germ tubes are not sensitive to it. With Menke, Walker also showed that in cucumbers susceptible to mosaic the oxygen uptake and peroxidase activity rises rapidly in leaves 7 days after inoculation. In resistant plants rise is slight in both. Although the virus multiples in the resistant plants, the resistant mechanism restricts its detrimental effect so that growth and fruit production of the host assumes a rate close to that of the uninoculated, healthy susceptible plant. Walker also participated in the development and release of some 30 disease-resistant varieties of vegetable of great value to the vegetable-producing industry in Wisconsin and other states.

Walker received his B.S. (1914), M.S. (1915), and Ph.D. (1918) from the University of Wisconsin. He joined the staff of the department of plant pathology at the university in 1919, becoming a full professor in 1928 and emeritus professor in 1964. Elected to the National Academy of Sciences in 1945, he received a Merit Award of the Botanical Society of America in 1963.

For background information *see* PLANT DISEASE; PLANT GROWTH in the McGraw-Hall Encyclopedia of Science and Technology.   □

★ WALL, Frederick Theodore

American chemist
Born Dec. 14, 1912, Chisholm, Minn., U.S.A.

WALL'S MOST significant contributions to science were in theoretical physical chemistry. He was among the first physical chemists to make extensive use of high-speed digital computers to obtain solutions of statistical mechanical problems. He also worked on the statistical aspects of macromolecular configurations and on reaction kinetics from a fundamental atomic and molecular point of view.

Early in his scientific career, while still an assistant professor at the University of Illinois, Wall formulated a theory of rubberlike elasticity which provided the basis for numerous other developments and improvements. He also became interested in other aspects of macromolecules, such as the statistics of intramolecular polymeric reactions and copolymer composition. During World War II he worked on the government-sponsored synthetic rubber program. After the war he returned to more fundamental problems related to polymers; in particular, he devoted a substantial part of his research effort to inquiries about macromolecular configurations.

The problem of the size and shape of coiling-type polymer molecules, which more or less can be represented as flexible chains, is of considerable importance for understanding the behavior of polymers in solution and for understanding rubberlike elasticity. Approximate solutions to configuration statistics had been obtained by considering a chain polymer to resemble a random three-dimensional walk. This model is deficient, however, for it does not take into account the "excluded volume" effect; in simple terms, this requires that no two links in a randomly coiled chain can occupy the same space. Wall tackled the problem by a statistical method, using a high-speed digital computer. He simulated thousands of configurations by randomly selecting a succession of vectors to represent bonds in a polymer chain, all the time making sure that no two sites in space were multiply occupied. In this way he obtained "samples" of long-chain polymers and hence a practical answer to some significant aspects of the problem. In carrying out the process, he used the computer essentially as an experimental device, analyzing the results obtained therefrom just as one might analyze results from a laboratory experiment. His empirical results were subsequently verified in asymptotic form by other theoreticians using analytical methods.

Another important piece of his work dealt with the calculation of exchange probabilities attending the collisions of atoms with diatomic molecules. For example, when an atom A hits a molecule BC, the interaction may give rise to a new molecule AB and an atom C. Using classical mechanics, Wall made calculations on a high-speed computer to determine the factors influencing exchange of the type described. Following his pioneer work of this nature, numerous other investigators have carried out more extensive calculations of a related character.

Wall had also been actively concerned with the behavior of polymeric electrolytes, both from an experimental and a theoretical point of view. He and his co-workers performed some interesting and highly instructive experiments on the electrolytic transference properties of such materials. Among other things, they demonstrated that, when an ionizable salt of a polymeric acid, such as sodium polyacrylate, is electrolyzed, it is possible under certain conditions for more sodium to be transported to the anode than to the cathode. This fact was interpreted to mean that a large polymer ion tends to sequester substantial quantities of smaller ions of opposite charge. Hence, a substantial amount of sodium ions can well be carried along with the giant anion moving toward the anode during electrolysis. By carrying out calculations requiring numerical solutions of certain nonlinear differential equations, Wall analyzed theoretically the sequestering of small ions by polymeric ions and thereby answered some perplexing questions about orders of magnitude of the corresponding ionic interactions.

For some years Wall was dean of the Graduate College and chairman of the Research Board of the University of Illinois, meanwhile continuing his research as a professor of chemistry. In fulfilling this combination role, he maintained a close association with the faculty and demonstrated that university administrators and professors need not be regarded as working in separate realms, notwithstanding the fact that the Graduate College was a large and complex organization involving both graduate education and faculty research.

Wall received most of his formal education in the state of Minnesota, taking his B.Chem. (1933) and Ph.D. (1937) at the University of Minnesota. After completing his graduate studies, he went to the University of Illinois, where he remained for 27 years. In 1964 he moved to the University of California, Santa Barbara, as professor of chemistry and chairman of the department of chemistry. For a year he was also vice-chancellor for research at Santa Barbara. In 1966 he transferred to the University of California, San Diego, to become vice-chancellor for graduate studies and research and a professor of chemistry. In 1945 Wall received the American Chemical Society Award in Pure Chemistry. He was elected to the National Academy of Sciences in 1961 and the American Academy of Arts and Sciences in 1966.

Wall wrote *Chemical Thermodynamics* (1958; 2d ed. 1965) and numerous research articles. In 1965 he became editor of the *Journal of Physical Chemistry*.

For background information *see* KINETICS (CHEMICAL); POLYMER PROPERTIES; POLYMERIZATION; THERMODYNAMICS (CHEMICAL) in the McGraw-Hill Encyclopedia of Science and Technology.   □

★ **WALLING, Cheves Thomson**

American chemist
Born Feb. 28, 1916, Evanston, Ill., U.S.A.

Aʟᴛʜᴏᴜɢʜ ᴛʜᴇʀᴍᴏᴅʏɴᴀᴍɪᴄꜱ in principle permits unequivocal answers to the question of what chemical reactions are possible, the problems of how to bring them about, of when they will actually occur, and of what their rates will be are much more complicated and together make up the field of reaction mechanisms, or chemical dynamics. Great progress has been made in this field within the last 30 years, and it now seems clear that the most complex processes can be analyzed in terms of a relatively small number of types of elementary reactions. Often these involve transient intermediates, unstable molecules of very short life, present at such low concentrations that they may not be detectable by direct physical measurement. In organic chemistry an important group of such highly reactive intermediates are free radicals containing an odd number of electrons. Frequently the odd electron is associated with a carbon atom, and the radical may be thought of as a derivative of trivalent carbon, but radicals in which the odd electron is on another atom are also important.

In 1943 Walling joined a group headed by F. R. Mayo for studying the mechanism of vinyl polymerization, a field of great significance in connection with the wartime synthetic rubber industry. When two olefins are polymerized together, they often produce a mixed polymer, or copolymer, in which units derived from each olefin are strung along the polymer chain. Walling showed that copolymer compositions provide a valuable test for polymerization mechanism, since reactions involving carbonium ions, carbanions, and free radicals yield products of quite different compositions. Accordingly, the nature of the transient intermediate can be detected quite unequivocally from polymer analysis.

Copolymerization studies yielded the first really comprehensive body of data on the effect of structure on reactivity in free-radical reactions, demonstrating that three factors play important roles: overall reaction energetics, steric effects, and the polar properties of radicals and the molecules with which they react. The last factor, the "polar effect," was an unanticipated property of radical reactions, and Walling studied it by comparing reactivities of styrenes containing electron-withdrawing and electron-supplying groups; he related his results to those observed in ionic reactions via the well-known Hammett equation. In 1950 he and Mayo pointed out the broad application of these ideas to other radical reactions, a prediction which has been amply confirmed in a whole variety of systems.

Molecules with an odd electron on sulfur, for example, thiyl radicals, RS·, participate in many processes, are unusually reactive, and probably play an important role in some biochemical systems. Walling showed the importance of polar effects in the reactions of thiyl radicals and mercaptans as transfer agents in polymerization and, with W. Helmreich and R. B. Rabinowitz, the facile reversibility of many of their reactions. The work with Rabinowitz involved the formation of thiyl radicals by photolysis of disulfides and provided one of the first examples of radical formation by energy transfer from one excited molecule to another.

Phosphorus lies next to sulfur in the periodic table, and Walling and his students showed that it also possesses interesting radical chemistry, particularly via expansion of its valence shell to the tetravalent phosphoranyl radical, for example, $(RO)_4P$.

Organic derivatives of hydrogen peroxide, ROOR (where R = hydrogen, alkyl, or acyl groups), occupy a central place in free-radical chemistry since they are intermediates in many of the reactions of organic compounds with molecular oxygen, and since they provide a convenient source of alkoxy radicals or their derivatives by thermal or photochemical scission. See Eq. (1).

$$ROOR \longrightarrow 2 RO \cdot \qquad (1)$$

Much of Walling's work was with peroxide chemistry and the properties of alkoxy radicals. In 1954 he and Buckler showed that hydroperoxide salts are the primary products of the reaction of Grignard reagents and other organometallic compounds with oxygen. Subsequent work included studies of the effects of styrene and other solvents on the decomposition of hydroperoxides (Y. Chang and L. Heaton), the reactions of amines (N. Indictor) and phenols (R. Hodgdon) with peroxides, and the photosensitized decomposition of peroxides (M. Gibian). This last work showed that photosensitized and thermal decompositions of peroxides can yield quite different products.

In 1959 Walling and R. B. Jacknow showed that the halogenation of hydrocarbons by organic hypohalites involves a radical chain—such as the examples in Eqs. (2) and (3)—and provides a

$$t\text{-}C_4H_9O \cdot + RH \longrightarrow t\text{-}C_4H_9OH + R \cdot \quad (2)$$

$$R \cdot + t\text{-}C_4H_9OCl \longrightarrow RCl + t\text{-}C_4H_9O \cdot \quad (3)$$

versatile technique for generating alkoxy radicals and studying their properties, particularly their relative reactivities with C-H bonds in different types of molecules. The reaction has proved of considerable synthetic use and, with hypohalites with long side chains, permits intramolecular halogenation of high specificity (A. Padwa). Olefins undergo allylic substitution, and the reaction has been used to study the stereochemistry and other properties of allylic radicals (W. Thaler). It has also been possible to show large solvent effects in alkoxy radical reactions (P. J. Wagner), a rarity in free-radical chemistry.

An important technique used by Walling and his students in the study of radical and other reactions was the investigation of high pressures (up to 10,000 atm) on the rate of reaction. The method provides information on the size of transition states, since pressure accelerates or retards reactions, depending on whether transition states are smaller or larger than the reactants. Many radical reactions are accelerated, but retardation may accompany diffusion-controlled (very fast) reactions. Walling also applied the method to the study of "no mechanism" reactions, such as Diels-Alder reactions and intramolecular rearrangements, and also to aldehyde polymerizations, an interesting process in which the aldehydes polymerize under pressure but depolymerize when the pressure is released.

Walling received his A.B. (1937) from Harvard and his Ph.D. (1939) under Morris S. Kharasch from the University of Chicago. He was engaged in industrial research with the Du Pont Co. (1939–43), the U.S. Rubber Co. (1943–49), and Lever Brothers (1949–52). In 1952 he was appointed professor of chemistry at Columbia University, and served as department chairman from 1963 to 1966. He was elected to the National Academy of Sciences in 1964 and to the American Academy of Arts and Sciences in 1965.

Walling wrote *Free Radicals in Solution* (1957) and more than 120 scientific papers.

For background information *see* ESTER; ORGANIC CHEMISTRY; POLYMERIZATION; RUBBER in the McGraw-Hill Encyclopedia of Science and Technology.   ☐

☆ WARBURG, Otto Heinrich

German biochemist
Born Oct. 8, 1883, Freiburg, Baden, Germany

WARBURG MADE a number of significant contributions to biochemistry and physiology, among them the introduction of manometric methods for metabolic studies, the introduction of the optical methods of hydrogen transfer, the discovery of intracellular and yellow enzymes and their activity, investigations of the mechanisms of photosynthesis, and studies of the metabolism of tumors. In recognition of his efforts, in particular for his discovery of the nature and mode of action of the respiratory enzyme, Warburg was awarded the 1931 Nobel Prize for medicine or physiology.

The modern study of respiratory processes began with the discovery of oxygen by Antoine Laurent Lavoisier in 1777. Although Lavoisier believed that oxidation occurs in the lungs, it soon became evident that the oxygen is carried by the hemoglobin of the red blood corpuscles from the lungs to the cells, in which the oxidation actually occurs. However, the mechanism of the cellular oxidation reaction remained a mystery.

About 1914, while experimenting with crushed sea urchin eggs, Warburg noted that the absorption of oxygen was increased by the addition of small quantities of iron salts. This interested him in an investigation of the chemical composition of the oxygen-transporting enzyme. He decided that the best course of action would be to determine which substances specifically and reversibly stop the operation of the enzyme since this retardation would be the result of a chemical reaction. In this way Warburg discovered the first active group of enzymes.

Because he wanted to study the enzyme under natural conditions, that is, in the intact respiring cells, Warburg spent portions of the next several years developing a new method of biochemical manometry. In the Warburg manometer, sometimes known as the Barcroft-Warburg apparatus, the substrate and the living tissue or enzyme are contained in a flask, which is connected to one end of an otherwise open U tube filled with liquid. As the tissue respires, the uptake of oxygen can be measured by the decrease of pressure in the flask, as measured by the change in level of the liquid. In 1923, to facilitate the preparation of the cells, he devised a means— now known as the Warburg technique—for obtaining thin slices of living tissue.

When in 1924 Warburg discovered that iron is the oxygen-transferring constituent of the respiratory enzyme (which he then called iron-oxygenase), he decided to utilize an observation made by the British physiologists John Scott Haldane and J. L. Smith three decades earlier to the effect that light upsets the equilibrium of hemoglobin, carbon monoxide, and oxygen in favor of the oxygen compound. Working with Erwin Negelein, Warburg filled two conical manometric vessels with 2 cm^3 of a dilute yeast suspension; the gas space of one vessel was filled with a mixture of nitrogen and oxygen, and the other with a mixture of carbon monoxide and oxygen. A 75-watt metal-filament lamp was then switched on and off for periods of 20 min. While no change took place in the rate of respiration of the yeast cells in the nitrogen-oxygen environment, the rate of respiration of the cells in the carbon monoxide–oxygen environment decreased while the light was off. Hence, in 1926 Warburg was able to announce that the carbon monoxide compound of the oxygen-transporting enzyme is decomposed by light.

Warburg then proceeded to test the influence of wavelength on the reaction. He tested carbon monoxide–inhibited yeast cells with light from four regions of the spectrum. Warburg thus discovered that there is no action in the red part of the spectrum, weak action in the green and yellow, and strong action in the blue, and that optimum action results from light at 4360 A. Since this is a characteristic absorption wavelength of iron hemochromagen–containing porphyrins, Warburg was able to identify the respiratory enzyme as being similar to these compounds. He called this iron porphyrin compound the oxygen-transferring part (*Atmungsferment*).

During the 1930s Warburg studied the dehydrogenation reactions. In 1932, with W. Christian, he isolated the first of the yellow enzymes, or flavoproteins, that are essential to such a reaction in cells and discovered the active group of the yellow enzymes, flavin adenine dinucleotide. Three years later he discovered nicotinamide as the active group of the dehydrogenase enzymes. These discoveries led to Warburg being nominated for the Nobel Prize again in 1944, but the political situation at that time prohibited his receiving it.

In 1920–24 Warburg studied the quantum yield of photosynthesis; this involved measuring exactly the light energy absorbed and the volume of oxygen produced in *Chlorella*, which since 1920 has been the object of nearly all the important experiments on photosynthesis. In order to obtain the maximum yield, Warburg worked with very weak light to avoid saturation effects. He found an absorption of four quanta per molecule of oxygen, an efficiency of 70%. In 1949, working with Dean Burk, he returned to the study of photosynthesis and discovered the one-quantum reaction of the prototype of photosynthesis.

In 1923 Warburg began his study of the metabolism of tumors. He found that cancerous tissue requires noticeably less oxygen than does normal tissue. Furthermore, the cancer cells maintain themselves by a different sequence of reactions from normal cells and can dispense with free oxygen. Thus life without oxygen in cancer cells was discovered to be their fundamental difference from normal cells. In 1927, as a result of Warburg's findings, the Nobel Committee proposed that he share the award with the Danish pathologist Johannes A. G. Fibiger. The undivided award, however, was given to Fibiger.

Warburg also made several other notable contributions to biochemistry. In 1935 he discovered the nature of coenzyme action, and in the following year he found the mechanism of alcohol fermentation in nature: dihydronicotinamide + acetaldehyde = nicotinamide + ethyl alcohol. He investigated the fermentation enzymes in the blood of tumor-bearing animals in 1943, developed the manometric actinometer in 1948, and discovered the chemical constitution of the hemin of cytochrome oxidase in 1953.

The son of Emil Warburg, a noted physicist, Otto Warburg studied under Emil Fischer at the University of Berlin, receiving the degree of Dr.Chem. in 1906. He then attended the University of Heidelberg, from which he received the degree of M.D. in 1911. In 1913 he became a member of the Kaiser Wilhelm Society. With the exception of the period 1914–18, when he served in World War I with the Prussian Horse Guards, Warburg was associated with the Kaiser Wilhelm Institute for Cell Physiology (later renamed the Max Planck Institute for Cell Physiology) in Berlin-Dahlem, becoming director in 1931. In addition to the Nobel Prize, he received many awards, including the Order of Merit with Star and Shoulder Ribbon of the German Federal Republic in 1952 and the Paul Ehrlich Prize in 1962. He was elected a foreign member of the Royal Society of London in 1934.

Warburg's books included *Katalytische Wirkungen der lebendigen Substanz* (1928), *Hydrogen Transferring Enzymes* (1948), *Heavy Metal Prosthetic Groups and Enzyme Action* (English transl. 1949), and *New Methods of Cell Physiology* (English transl. 1962).

For background information *see* BACTERIAL METABOLISM; ENZYME; PHOTOSYNTHESIS; PHYSIOLOGICAL ACTION SPECTRA in the McGraw-Hill Encyclopedia of Science and Technology ☐

★ WARDLAW, Claude Wilson

British botanist
Born Feb. 4, 1901, Glasgow, Scotland

As a student of Glasgow University and as assistant to F. O. Bower, the most distinguished exponent of phylogeny based on comparative morphology of his day, Wardlaw was introduced to the wide range of plant materials, fossil and living, on which the theory of plant evolution in its sweeping, historical aspect necessarily rests. But Bower also introduced him to the fascinating problems of causation as approached through the study of size-and-form correlations, and this led to Wardlaw's earliest publications on pattern formation in vascular structures, illustrations from which have been reproduced in many standard texts. The causes underlying the development of form and structure in the embryonic and maturing regions of plants became the essential and sustained interest in his scientific work. He was fortunate in that his initial university studies, beginning in 1918, in chemistry, mathematics, and physics gave him the necessary foundation; and his first scrutiny of D'Arcy Thompson's great and unique book, *On Growth and Form* (2d ed. 1942; reprint 1952) was an enthralling experience. Wardlaw never forgot: "Cell and tissue, shell and bone, leaf and flower, are so many portions of matter, and it is in obedience to the laws of physics that the particles have to be moved, moulded and conformed." In brief, all organic forms must come into existence and eventually be interpreted in relation to the laws or principles of physics, chemistry, and mathematics.

After a period of 12 years of applied botany in the tropics—providing detachment from his earlier tuition in comparative morphology—Wardlaw was appointed in 1940 to the chair of cryptogamic botany at the University of Manchester. There, between intervals of military duties, he began his studies of shoot apical meristems and of experimental morphogenesis. In the manner of Hofmeister's *Allgemeine Morphologie* (1868), his central theme was simply: How, during the growth of plant embryos and of embryonic regions, does the observed form or structure with all its specific, harmonious development come to be as it is? What are the physiological and genetical factors and the organismal and mathematical relationships that are specially involved, yielding, on the one hand, the great diversity of species and, on the other, the numerous homologies of organization that pervade all development in plants? Wardlaw maintained that, if his thinking about the observed morphological facts was right, it should be possible to devise crucial, validating experiments, that is, experiments with predictable results. In elegant experiments calling for a precise knowledge of morphology and anatomy, imaginative ideas, and delicate surgical techniques, he showed that the large apices of ferns and even the smaller ones of flowering plants can indeed be used in crucial experiments. Some of his results and those of his co-workers and other exponents had shattering effects on long-held views based on comparative studies. To cite one example, he predicted and demonstrated, using a simple technique, that the large characteristic dictyostele of the *Dryopteris* rhizome could be induced to develop as a solenostele or even as a protostele. In these studies, undertaken by a growing number of his research students, he maintained the principle that every noteworthy new experimental demonstration should be illustrated by an impeccable photograph—one that spoke its own message. In other experiments Wardlaw showed that the shoot apical meristems of ferns and flowering plants, suitably provided with nutrients from below, are self-determining organogenic regions; that in ferns buds can be induced to form in leaf sites and the leaves in bud sites; that older leaf primordia regulate the development of younger ones, thus supporting a field concept of the regulated growth and harmonious morphogenetic activity of the shoot apex; and that the vascular system, normally continuous in the shoot, can be made discontinuous. These and other observations, based on surgical techniques, were confirmed and extended in a very interesting and satisfying complementary fashion by R. H. Wetmore, Ernest Ball, and others in the United States, using the methods of tissue culture—the whole effort resulting not only in a considerable advance in this basic aspect of botanical science but also in long-enduring transatlantic friendships.

Wardlaw's contributions to morphogenesis and indeed to botany were twofold: his extensive analytical and experimental studies and his scholarly attitude toward his science. Botany, he affirmed, should be a sustained, integrated scholarly discipline. This attitude is implicit and pervasive in his several books: *Phylogeny and Morphogenesis* (1952), *Morphogenesis in Plants* (1952), *Embryogenesis in Plants* (1955), and *Organization and Evolution in Plants* (1965). These books have enjoyed a wide distribution over the world and are regarded as having enabled plant morphogenesis—the ultimate, visual, physical reality or resultant of all the reacting factors in ontogenesis—to regain its essential place in any adequate study of the numerous and diverse entities that constitute the plant kingdom. In *Organization and Evolution in Plants* he not only broke much new ground in what may become the major scientific-philosophic theme for biologists of the coming decades, but he made a strong plea, in these days of specialization, never to diminish the scholarly dignity of botanical science. Rather, he urged constant work for its unification and integration, the topic of organization perhaps affording a central theme both for the practical experimenter in the bio-physico-chemical phenomena of living things and for the scholar-philosopher. According to Wardlaw's vision, it should become possible to deal with the great range of taxonomic materials—the result of the process of evolution—in terms of simplifying concepts and general truths; and, as part of general education, botanists should aim at presenting their subject as an essential, gracious, and distinguished science.

Opportunity, interest, and a thirst for travel took Wardlaw to the Imperial College of Tropical Agriculture, Trinidad, British West Indies (as it then was), from 1928 to 1940 to study banana diseases, together with storage and transport, and also those of other tropical fruits. After World War II consultative work introduced him to the West African oil palm and to abaca (or Manila hemp, *Musa textilis*) in different parts of the tropical belt. For him these excursions to the world's great tropical rainforests and to other distant places were matters of the greatest relish. Some of his adventurous enjoyment comes out in his book *Green Havoc*

(1935), but the solid substance of his tropical life is seen in his classical book *Diseases of the Banana* (1935), subsequently entirely rewritten as *Banana Diseases* (1961). Discoveries of special interest and importance included his reporting the first appearance of *Cercospora* leaf disease, an Old World epidemic malady, in the Caribbean region and of other banana diseases; his diagnosis of the vascular wilt disease of the oil palm (*Fusarium oxysporum*) in the Belgian Congo and in Nigeria; his observations (with colleagues) on the carrying temperatures for new varieties of bananas, mangoes, avocados, tomatoes, citrus fruits, and the like; and his observations on the changes of internal gas composition and pneumatic pressures in papayas and bananas during growth and ripening—this series of studies leading to a comprehensive investigation of the gas storage of bananas. Although at heart a true academic, Wardlaw never underestimated the importance of applied botany. On the contrary, in his view agriculture is primarily and ultimately the essential industry, the sine qua non of all the great urban civilizations on which mankind prides itself.

Wardlaw received a B.Sc. (1921), a Ph.D. (1925), and a D.Sc. (1928) at Glasgow University and a M.Sc. (1943) at the University of Manchester. He was an assistant and lecturer in botany at Glasgow from 1921 to 1928. During 1928–40 he was pathologist and officer in charge of the Low Temperature Research Station at the Imperial College of Tropical Agriculture, Trinidad. Joining the faculty of the University of Manchester in 1940, he was professor of cryptogamic botany there from 1940 to 1958 and professor of botany from 1958 to 1966. He also served as dean of the Faculty of Science and pro-vice-chancellor at Manchester. In 1951 he gave the Prather Lectures in biology at Harvard University and was elected a foreign member of the American Academy of Arts and Sciences. On his retirement in 1966 he was presented with a Festschrift, *Trends in Morphogenesis*, edited by E. G. Cutter.

For background information *see* PLANT DISEASE; PLANT EVOLUTION; PLANT GROWTH; PLANT MORPHOGENESIS in the McGraw-Hill Encyclopedia of Science and Technology.   □

★ WARNER, John Christian

American physical chemist
Born May 28, 1897, Goshen, Ind., U.S.A.

WARNER BEGAN his career in university teaching and research in the mid-1920s, a very exciting period for physical chemists because new hypotheses and theories were being formulated and new sophisticated experimental techniques were being developed in a host of impor-

tant fields. In a number of these fields—dipole moments of molecules, new theories of the thermodynamic properties and conductivity of electrolytes, generalized theories of acids and bases, the nature of intermolecular forces in solutions of nonelectrolytes, and rate and mechanism of homogeneous reactions, especially in solution, including salt and medium effects—Warner prepared critical reviews of the voluminous periodical and monograph literature which constituted well-organized but annually revised lectures for graduate students in chemistry over a quarter of a century. There was an unusually close relationship between this course of lectures and the research carried on by Warner and his students. In preparing his lectures the lack of explanations for observed phenomena or the lack of experimental evidence to test a hypothesis or theory always suggested important research problems, and the solution of these problems always brought about satisfying improvements in the lectures.

Although he published research during his career in diverse fields, his enduring interests and most important contributions were concerned with the kinetics of reactions in solution. With F. B. Stitt, E. L. Warrick, and W. J. Svirbely, he reported detailed studies on the influences of ionic strength and the dielectric constants of solvents upon the rate of the famous Wöhler reaction, the conversion of ammonium cyanate into urea. It was demonstrated that the experimental results were in excellent agreement with those calculated from theory if it was assumed that the mechanism was one involving collisions between monovalent ions of opposite sign. At about this time there were attempts by various scientists (for example, Moelwyn-Hughes and La Mer) to apply the kinetic equation of the collision theory of bimolecular gas reactions to bimolecular reactions in solution. Warner recognized that these attempts were marred by the practice of using an energy of activation obtained under the most diverse experimental conditions and then comparing the

resulting term representing the collision frequency with a frequency calculated by using the ordinary formulas for gases. He pointed out that under the circumstances it was not surprising that the summary by Moelwyn-Hughes revealed values for solution reactions of $k_{\mathrm{obs}}/k_{\mathrm{calc}}$, which ranged from 10^2 to 10^{-9}. Neither was it surprising that La Mer found activation energies obtained from

$$2.3\,RT^2\,\frac{d\log k}{dT} = \Delta E_{\mathrm{act}}$$

to be temperature dependent. Recognizing the strong dependence of rate constants in reactions involving ions on ionic strength and upon the dielectric constant of the solvent, the latter changing with temperature at constant composition, Warner saw little merit in comparing activation energies in solution reactions obtained from

$$\frac{d\log k}{dT}$$

Warner reasoned that in gaseous reactions there is no appreciable change in the environment of reacting molecules with temperature, and the energy of activation is obtained from what might be termed a dependence of rate constants upon temperature alone. Thus, for a reaction in solution to obtain an activation energy to be compared with that for gaseous reactions, it should be derived from

$$\left(\frac{\partial \log k}{\partial T}\right)_{x^i}$$

where the x^i's represent all variables other than the temperature which influence the rate. For reactions in solution between ions and between ions and unchanged (but polar) molecules there was an abundance of evidence that the principal variables influencing the rate at constant temperature were ionic strength and dielectric constant of the solvent. One could eliminate the influence of ionic strength by extrapolating rate constants to zero ionic strength to obtain k^0, leaving dielectric constant of solvent and temperature as the main variables. Thus, if

$$\log k^0 = f(D,T)$$

then

$$\frac{d\log k^0}{dT} = \left(\frac{\partial \log k^0}{\partial T}\right)_D + \left(\frac{\partial \log k^0}{\partial D}\right)_T \frac{dD}{dT}$$

and

$$(\Delta E^0)_C = (\Delta E^0)_D + 2.3RT^2\left(\frac{\partial \log k^0}{\partial D}\right)_T \frac{dD}{dT}$$

give the relation between activation energies at constant solvent composition and constant dielectric constant at zero ionic strength. The last term was designated as the electrostatic contribution to activation energy in solution reactions, and $(\Delta E^0)_D$, it was argued, was the quantity most nearly comparable to the ordinary activation energy in solution reactions. $(\Delta E^0)_D$ could be obtained from measurements of

$$\left(\frac{\partial \log k^0}{\partial T}\right)_D$$

by adjusting solvent compositions to maintain D independent of temperature. It also could be obtained by substracting the electrostatic term from $(\Delta E^0)_C$. The electrostatic term could be evaluated from theory or from experimental measurements of

$$\left(\frac{\partial \log k^0}{\partial D}\right)_T$$

In a series of researches with Svirbely, Sam Eagle, Leon Winstrom, and A. A. Colón, Warner verified all of the above relationships experimentally and by calculation from theory for various reactions between ions of like and unlike sign and a variety of reactions between ions and unchanged molecules.

In the reaction between ethylene chlorohydrin and hydroxy or ethoxy ions, Warner, with J. E. Stevens, K. H. Vogel, H. D. Cowan, and C. L. McCabe, found substantial differences in the rate of this reaction in different solvent mixtures of the same dielectric constant, increasing over the rate in water as 1,4-dioxane was added but decreasing over the rate in water as methanol was added. By assuming the Winstein mechanism for this type of reaction and that the effect of the acid-base level of the solvent mixture was superimposed on the dielectric constant effect, Warner and his students, in a series of experiments with the entire series of ethylene halohydrins and with measurements of the acid-base levels prevailing in the solvent mixtures used, were able to make satisfying quantitative explanations of all experimental results.

The son of a farmer, Warner graduated from Indiana University, where he majored in physical chemistry, receiving his A.B. in 1919, M.A. in 1921, and Ph.D. in 1923. He interrupted his formal education twice for periods of employment in the petroleum and chemical industries. He served as an instructor in chemistry at Indiana University during his last 2 years in graduate work and for 1 year following the receipt of his doctorate. Then, following 2 years in industry, he began his academic career at the Carnegie Institute of Technology in 1926. He became a professor and head of Carnegie's chemistry department in 1938, dean of graduate studies in 1945, president in 1950, and president emeritus in 1965. From 1943 to 1945 Warner was on leave to the Manhattan Project, where he supervised research on the chemistry and metallurgy of plutonium. He served as president of the Electro-Chemical Society in 1952, as president of the American Chemical Society in 1956, and as a member of the General Advisory Committee to the AEC from 1952 to 1964. He received the 1945 Award of the Pittsburgh Section, American Chemical Society, and the Gold Medal of the American Institute of Chemists in 1953. He was elected to the National Academy of Sciences in 1956.

For background information *see* ACID AND BASE; COORDINATION CHEMISTRY; KINETICS (CHEMICAL) in the McGraw-Hill Encyclopedia of Science and Technology.   □

★ WATERS, Aaron Clement

American geologist
Born May 6, 1905, Waterville, Wash., U.S.A.

WHILE STILL in college Waters had the good fortune to assist Richard E. Fuller during three summers of field research. The first summer was spent on an investigation of the Miocene Snoqualmie batholith in the Cascade Mountains of central Washington; the second, a reconnaissance of the deep canyons and coulees which contain thick and continuous sections of the Columbia River basalts; and the third, a field study of the high-alumina basalts on Steens Mountain and other large fault blocks of southeastern Oregon. These summers were decisive in selecting a career; thereafter, Waters never lost interest in the two major igneous rocks, granite and basalt.

Early field work during 1927–36 on granitic masses raised more problems than answers. German petrologists explained diaschistic dikes (mafic lamprophyres and felsic aplites) by *spaltung* of granitic magma during final consolidation. Waters's studies of the Chelan batholith, however, showed that lamprophyres are early and that gradations can be found to aplitic granophyres. Furthermore, these dikes occur along the periphery of the batholith, not deep in its interior where final residues should be expected. Also, many dikes have been reinvaded, boudined, and partly recrystallized by continued movement of the batholith's still molten core.

The associated migmatites, contact breccias, and areas of protoclastic granulation were also puzzling: Amphibolite xenoliths, engulfed by the granite, have been softened and reintruded into fissures within newly congealed granite, forming rocks indistinguishable from some lamprophyres; aplite-like rocks have formed by recrystallization and replacement of crush zones within the granite; other aplites are obviously filtration products from protoclastically deformed crystal mushes. In 1936–38 Waters demonstrated that in the Colville and Osoyoos batholiths protoclastic deformation, recrystallization, and squeezing out of interstitial residues from the partly crystallized batholiths, and from the complex migmatic gneisses surrounding them, were important processes.

In 1938 there was no experimental basis for predicting the nature of silicate reactions in such a complex environment. Therefore, Waters decided to leave the granite problem and work on basalts, his second compelling interest. Years later, after O. F. Tuttle's development of the hydrothermal bomb and brilliant experimental work on the granite problem unlocked the secrets of the "subsolidus," Waters did return briefly to the granite problem. He and coworkers T. L. Wright, C. A. Hopson, and R. S. Fiske were able to show that at Mount Rainier National Park the Tatoosh and Snoqualmie batholiths reached the surface and fed widespread volcanic rocks; also, they demonstrated that this history of shallow-level plutonic-volcanic associations could be predicted by the zoning, structural state, and subsolidus relations of the feldspars and by the characteristic autometamorphic alterations affecting the granitic rocks and their volcanic products.

Waters's investigation of Pacific Northwest basaltic rocks began in 1938, but was recessed during World War II by work on quicksilver and uranium deposits. Study of the basalts proceeded slowly for other reasons. The area is huge, and at the beginning even its basic stratigraphy was unknown. Waters recognized early that the high-magnesia basalts of the Snake River plain and the high-alumina basalts of the Cascade Mountains and southeast Oregon plateaus are different from the tholeiitic basalts of the Columbia River region. Moreover, on stratigraphic grounds, the Columbia River basalt was found to comprise two formations—an older Picture Gorge basalt and a younger Yakima basalt. Furthermore, the Yakima basalt contains three petrographic variants, or magma types: the Yakima, Late Yakima, and Pomona. The Picture Gorge basalt also has two unnamed but geographically distinct petrographic variants.

Once the general scale, time relations, and petrographic character of the major basaltic lava fields of the Pacific Northwest were ascertained, a basic generalization became self-evident: There are no transitional varieties between the various petrographic types. Each is distinct and has been generated in huge volumes. Moreover, as each type of magma arose from the mantle, it retained its uniformity unaffected by crystal settling or other differentiation processes, except where pools of magma were trapped in underground chambers high in the crust. In such chambers the high-alumina basalts, in particular, gave rise to andesites and rhyolites. The much drier Yakima basalts, on the other hand, produced almost no differentiates. The conclusion was that in the quest for unity among the igneous rocks the classical idea of a single uniform basalt parent should be abandoned; instead, a common genetic link is more likely perceived in uniform granite whose ancestors probably encompass a wide variety of both mantle and crustal rocks. Waters hoped that recent work with natural isotope tracers would clarify some of the complex genetic problems for the Pacific Northwest volcanic and plutonic suites.

Son of a wheat farmer, Waters was educated at the University of Washington (B.Sc., 1926; M.Sc., 1927) and at Yale (Ph.D., 1930). He taught at Yale (1928–30), Stanford (1930–51), Johns Hopkins (1952–63), and from 1963 in the University of California system, first at Santa Barbara and later at Santa Cruz. His professional honors included Guggenheim and National Science Foundation senior postdoctoral fellowships, the S. F. Emmons and the Thomas Condon lectureships, and election to the National Academy of Sciences in 1964 and the American Academy of Arts and Sciences in 1966.

Waters was a coauthor of the textbook *Principles of Geology* (1951; 3d ed. 1968).

For background information *see* BASALT; IGNEOUS ROCKS; PETROGRAPHIC PROVINCE; PETROLOGY in the McGraw-Hill Encyclopedia of Science and Technology.   □

★ WEBER, Hans Hermann

German physiologist
Born June 17, 1896, Berlin, Germany

WEBER'S SCIENTIFIC development was decisively influenced when he worked as a pupil of Otto Meyerhof in Kiel in 1922. He learned from this eminent biochemist how to differentiate between scientific problems of greater and lesser importance and how and under which conditions great problems can be solved. In addition, Meyerhof directed Weber's attention to the field of

bioenergetics, especially of molecular bioenergetics.

While working in the Physiological Institute of the University of Rostock (directed by H. Winterstein), Weber came into contact with American science when he received a grant from the Rockefeller Foundation. In 1925 Weber acquired the qualifications for an assistant professorship (privatdozent). In 1923–25 he was engaged in the physicochemistry of muscle proteins, believing that an intimate knowledge of muscle proteins is one of the prerequisites for understanding muscle contraction. From 1925 to 1938 he investigated (first at the University of Berlin) general problems of the physicochemistry of proteins. He concentrated particularly on the question of the hydration of proteins and on the binding of ions to proteins. He was the first to produce convincing evidence that isoelectric proteins are "zwitterions" (dipolar ions).

On the basis of these studies he received the chair for biochemistry at the University of Münster in 1933. There he found the pH ranges within which the different ionic groups of proteins dissociate (COOH, imidazole, amino, and guanidine groups). At the same time he analyzed the molecular structure of the contractile elements of the skeletal muscle by studying both intrinsic and form birefringence, as well as the x-ray diagrams of the contractile structures. For these studies he used muscles and artificial well-oriented threads obtained from the muscle proteins actin and myosin (actomyosin threads). By means of these actomyosin threads it was possible to observe the structure, and later on the physical (contraction) and chemical reactions (ATP splitting), of the contractile proteins in a pure condition.

In 1939 the National Socialist government brought pressure to bear on Weber to take over the chair for physiology and biochemistry at the University of Königsberg, the most easterly German university. From Königsberg Weber fled with his family before the Russians to western Germany, where in 1946 he assumed the chair for physiology at Tübingen. From Tübingen he went in 1954 to the Max Planck Institute for Physiology at Heidelberg.

About the time that Weber arrived in Königsberg, other laboratories were beginning to investigate the molecular structure of the contractile elements. A. V. Engelhardt in Moscow found physical and chemical interactions between ATP, the bioenergetic key substance, and Weber's actomyosin thread. In Albert Szent-Györgyi's laboratory in Szeged these interactions were defined exactly in such a way that all isolated contractile systems contract under ATP and these systems consist of the two different proteins, actin and myosin. Furthermore, it had been observed in Szeged that these two proteins dissociate under certain conditions and form a complex (actomyosin) under others. Stimulated by these discoveries Weber thereafter worked primarily in the field of molecular physiology of the muscle.

Szent-Györgyi's conception of muscle contraction, based on ATP and the splitting of ATP, found little approval, especially among the English research workers on muscle. The reason was that the contraction of isolated contractile structures (actomyosin structures) observed by Szent-Györgyi was very different from that of the living muscle as far as quantitative measurements were concerned (much smaller speed of contraction and less tension than in living muscle). Above all, it had been impossible for many years to reverse the contraction of the isolated structure. Thus, both the relaxation and the state of rest remained incomprehensible. By improving the experimental technique in Weber's laboratory, quantitative correspondence was obtained between the contraction phase of the isolated systems and that of the living muscle, and a complete relaxation following the contraction of the isolated systems was achieved. The results of these findings showed that contraction both in muscle and in the isolated systems occurs when ATP is present and split by the contractile proteins (but not by other enzymes); relaxation occurs when ATP is present but not split by the contractile proteins themselves. Under the conditions of relaxation, ATP causes the dissociation of the actomyosin complex. (Through the extraordinarily important findings of H. E. Huxley it soon became understandable why dissociation produces relaxation.) After the discovery by the Englishmen B. B. Marsh and J. R. Bendall that the living muscle contains a factor that inhibits ATP splitting by the contractile proteins, it was established in Weber's laboratory that this factor consists of particles (later recognized as sarcotubular vesicles) which during relaxation and rest keep the Ca^{++} level extraordinarily low

$(< 10^{-7} M)$, accumulating calcium by a Ca^{++} pump. This fact was complemented by Weber's daughter Annemarie Weber, who found that the contractile structures need a Ca^{++} level $> 10^{-7}$ M for their activity and for contraction. These Ca^{++}-storing vesicles made possible a pioneering analysis of the molecular mechanism which provides the biological concentration (osmotic) work. However, these analyses are the work of Wilhelm Hasselbach, a former pupil and recent successor of Weber.

After service in World War I, Weber studied medicine at the universities of Rostock and Heidelberg in 1919–21. He qualified as a privatdozent in 1925. He was professor of biochemistry at the universities of Münster (1933–39), Königsberg (1939–45), and Tübingen (1946–54). From 1954 to 1966 he was director of the Physiological Institute in the Max Planck Institute for Medical Research in Heidelberg. He was elected a foreign member of the American Academy of Arts and Sciences in 1958.

For background information *see* ADENOSINE-TRIPHOSPHATE (ATP); MUSCLE (BIOPHYSICS); PROTEIN in the McGraw-Hill Encyclopedia of Science and Technology.   □

★ WEISS, Paul Alfred

American biologist
Born Mar. 21, 1898, Vienna, Austria

EMERGING FROM 3 years' service as an officer in World War I, Weiss went to study engineering and biology. The combination turned out to have hybrid vigor, both in conceptual and technical regards. In his doctor's thesis, "Animal Behavior as System Reaction" (1922), he departed from antiquated mechanistic doctrine to introduce the more flexible "system" approach to the study of organisms, which has become a standard tool in both the physical and behavioral sciences. His concurrent experimental studies on organ regeneration then led him to a logical counterpart of system theory—a pragmatic "field" concept of development, contrasting sharply with the vitalistic "field" theory of Gurwitsch. In this search for the actual formative factors that give a regenerating amphibian limb its shape, Weiss succeeded for the first time in grafting fully developed limbs with full restoration of function. What attracted his attention was not so much the looked-for pattern of regeneration, but the mode of functioning, which was wholly unforeseen. Each muscle of an extra limb grafted near a native limb always contracted exactly together with its namesake muscle in the neighboring normal limb, regardless of whether the resultant movement of the graft was of any use to the animal. However wasteful or even obstructive, the duplicate movements remained for life. Thus, he accidentally discovered the explanation (first as a "resonance" principle and later as a principle of "matching specificities") of how individual nervous systems can manage to come through the developmental process with essentially the same standard inherited repertory of coordinated performances despite the enormous variability of their individual embryonic histories.

Even while pursuing this new track, Weiss continued to carry on his analytical studies on morphogenesis. Recognizing that organ formation is basically a cooperative product of cells and the matrix (ground substance) in which they are embedded, he went to the tissue culture laboratory of Albert Fischer in Berlin to try to impose form on formless cultured cell masses. By subjecting the colloidal medium to mechanical stresses, he found that he not only could orient cell movements and tissue growth at will, but could actually identify the underlying mechanism. The lessons thus learned later proved crucial for understanding the mechanics of wound healing in general and for the design of improved methods of peripheral nerve repair in particular. Moreover, in regard to developmental theory, the demonstrated integrative unity between the cells and their medium gave further support to the theory of the organism as a hierarchy of "field continua."

In 1930, after 3 years' work in various laboratories for acquisition of wider technical experience, Weiss decided to accept an earlier invitation by Ross Harrison, the great experimental embryologist, to move to his Yale University laboratory. Because Harrison had invented the method of tissue culture specifically for the study of nerve growth, Weiss immediately proceeded to test whether his own earlier results on enforced cell orientation would also hold for nerve fibers. They did. In consequence, a general rule of "contact guidance" for protoplasmic movement was established, soon supplemented by the demonstration of "selective contact affinities" between given nerve fibers and their specific pathways.

The focus of Weiss's work thus was back on nerve. Expanding his older evidence for self-matching linkages between the central nervous system and the receptor and effector organs, he found that remarkably high orderliness characterizes the functions of even completely isolated nerve centers and that even thoroughly deranged nerve cell pools exhibit intrinisic rhythmic automatism, thus contradicting a conventional notion that sensory input directly patterns motor output. However, World War II forced discontinuance of these fruitful investigations in favor of an intensified search for improved methods of surgical nerve repair. As indicated above, the basic knowledge gathered earlier on the guidance of cell and nerve growth in culture lent itself at once to such an application. Weiss designed and elaborated a technique of sutureless splicing of severed nerves by arterial (later tantalum) cuffs. This work earned a merit citation by the U.S. War and Navy departments for "outstanding contribution" to the war effort and also yielded the following two significant developments.

First, the urgent need for a steady supply of arteries for splicing led Weiss and his associate A. C. Taylor to test the feasibility of using frozen-dried and stored pieces. Having proved successful, the method was then refined and extended to include frozen-dried, vacuum-storable, nerve stumps, as well as corneas, for grafting. Thus originated the first "tissue bank" for surgical use.

Second, an outgrowth of the nerve-splicing technique was the discovery of "neuroplasmic flow"—an unsuspectedly intensive internal growth activity going on permanently in what had been supposed to be the "resting" nerve cell and nerve fiber. Nerves locally constricted by tight arterial cuffs developed chronical swellings at the cell—near proximal entrance to the narrows, concomitantly with commensurate shrinkage at the distal side. While part of the swelling could be traced (in one of the earliest applications of the high-powered isotopes from the Chicago atomic pile) to the throttling of a continuous fast centrifugal stream of interstitial fluid *between* the fibers of peripheral nerve trunks, the major force of the effect proved to be due to the existence of a perpetual, but slower, flow of the content *within* each individual nerve fiber away from its central cell of origin. The widenings upstream from bottlenecks are simply the results of damming. From continued research on the phenomenon, combining techniques of microsurgery, explantation, autoradiography, electron microscopy, cytochemistry, and cinemicrography, Weiss and his collaborators ascertained that the nerve cell body continuously reproduces its macromolecular mass, foremost protein, which

then is taken over by a conveyorlike action of the nerve fiber channel for shipment to sites of consumption and repair, as well as export to extranervous tissue. His double training in biology and engineering undoubtedly predisposed Weiss to recognize and correctly interpret this neuroplasmic flow and its role in the adaptive functioning of the nervous system.

With the end of World War II, Weiss resumed collateral work on more general cell-biological problems, establishing in greater detail the mechanisms of movement, orientation, shape, and lodging of cells, individually, in artificial groups, and in the organism. High differential specificity, marking cells of different tissue types, was recorded and most tellingly demonstrated by Weiss and Andres in the "homing" of cells of a given type in their precise tissue location after the cells had been injected into the bloodstream, through which they were then broadcast throughout the (embryonic) body. There followed a long series of studies on the type-specific sorting out of mixed cell populations in tissue culture (largely by Moscona in Weiss's laboratory) and, further, the cinemicrographic analysis by Weiss and Taylor of the manner in which cells establish contact, mutual recognition, and affinitive behavior. This series culminated in the demonstration by Weiss and Taylor that random-mixed and random-reassembled suspensions of cells from differentiated organs can reconstitute themselves into complete and typical miniature replicas of the donor organs.

With the advent of the electron microscope, Weiss carried his studies of morphogenesis down into the submicroscopic range. With Ferris, he investigated the ordered collagen fabric in the skin and the mode of the restoration of its pattern after wounding. The data pointed to the existence of a principle of "macrocrystallinity" in the collagen matrix, thus linking up, on the macromolecular scale, with Weiss's much earlier conclusions about the ordering role of ground substances in morphogenesis.

In general, Weiss tried to keep a balance between analytical experimentation and theoretical interpretation. His theoretical formulations of system behavior, of the field concept, of the molecular basis of cell specificity and cell differentiation, of growth control (including a rigorous mathematical treatment with Kavanau), of neuronal resonance, and so forth all grew out of firsthand observations and experiments and, in turn, engendered the design of further research. Similarly, no sharp boundary was made in his research between "basic" and "applied," and although most of it might be cataloged under the former label, Weiss also, for instance, obtained a metallurgical patent on how to render tantalum foil elastic.

Weiss received his Ph.D. at the University of

Vienna in 1922. From 1922 to 1929 he was assistant director of the Biological Research Institute of the Vienna Academy of Sciences. Going to the United States in 1931, he was a Sterling fellow at Yale University in 1931–33 and professor of zoology at the University of Chicago in 1933–54. In 1954 he joined the Rockefeller Institute as head of the laboratory of developmental biology. He went to the University of Texas in 1965. Weiss's interests were not only in laboratory work and teaching (he held visiting professorships at nine major universities) but also included broader problems, such as the role of science in education, the historical and philosophical foundations of science, the relations between science and art, the place of science in society, the husbanding of natural resources, and science in the international scene. These interests were reflected in the many administrative posts he held, including membership on the President's Science Advisory Committee, chairman of the Division of Biology and Agriculture of the National Research Council, member of the council of the National Academy of Sciences, special consultant to the U.S. State Department, chairman of several United States delegations to the International Council of Scientific Unions and the International Union of Biological Sciences, and chief science adviser to the Brussels World's Fair. His contributions to medical education and research placed him in the role of adviser to medical schools and major hospitals. He earned the rare award of two honorary degrees of doctor of medicine and doctor of medicine and surgery, as well as many honorary lectureships and awards in the medical sciences. He was elected to the National Academy of Sciences in 1947 and to the American Academy of Arts and Sciences in 1954.

For background information *see* ANIMAL MORPHOGENESIS; CELL (BIOLOGICAL); CULTURE, TISSUE; EMBRYOLOGY, EXPERIMENTAL; NERVOUS SYSTEM in the McGraw-Hill Encyclopedia of Science and Technology.   □

★ WEISSKOPF, Victor Frederick

American physicist
Born Sept. 19, 1908, Vienna, Austria

WEISSKOPF'S WORK covered three fields of theoretical physics: quantum electrodynamics, nuclear physics, and the physics of elementary particles. His first contributions were all in the field of quantum electrodynamics. In 1931, together with E. P. Wigner, he studied the process of light emission by atomic electrons. The frequency of light, emitted when the atom performs a transition from one quantum level to another, is equal to the energy difference of the levels divided by Planck's constant. This frequency, however, does not have a sharp value but exhibits a broader distribution about a mean value. The work of Weisskopf and Wigner dealt with this broadening, and they showed that the breadth in frequency of an emitted light quantum is equal to the sum of the breadths of the two levels. The breadth of a level, in turn, is related by the Heisenberg relation with the lifetime: The shorter the life of a level, the broader it is. Special methods had to be invented to tackle this problem, methods which are still in use for modern problems of similar character.

In 1934 and later Weisskopf investigated the problem of the electromagnetic self-energy of the electron. This is an old problem which refers to the energy of the electric field of the electron which, in classical electron theory, is inversely proportional to the electron radius. Weisskopf examined this problem in the light of quantum electrodynamics, and he found, with the help of W. Furry, that the existence of positrons plays an important role. The so-called virtual electron-pair creation near the electron reduces its electromagnetic energy such that there is a logarithmic dependence of the energy on the radius. The admissible radius of the electron turned out to be much smaller than in the classical theory.

Since quantum theory excludes a finite radius, the self-energy nevertheless is infinite. The difficulties of this infinity were analyzed by Weisskopf, and he found in 1936 that one can isolate these infinities, since they never appear, when one considers measurable phenomena different from mass and charge. This paper represents the first formulation of the so-called renormalization method, developed 12 years later by J. S. Schwinger and R. P. Feynman, which allows calculating electromagnetic phenomena unambiguously with any desired accuracy. Weisskopf

used his own method in 1947, with J. B. French, for one of the first calculations of the Lamb shift (a small displacement of the ground state of hydrogen caused by the radiation field).

In the field of particle physics Weisskopf and

Wolfgang Pauli published in 1934 the first consistent quantum theory of charged particles without spin (bosons). At that time no such particles were known, but 12 years later "mesons" were discovered, which exactly corresponded to the Pauli-Weisskopf theory. This theory showed for the first time that pair creation and annihilation occurs not only with electrons but also with bosons. More recent contributions to particle physics dealt with the theory of high-energy particle collisions and with the possible substructure of protons.

Weisskopf's work in nuclear physics started in 1937, when he introduced the concept of temperature and evaporation into nuclear physics. The question arose when one wanted to describe what happens when an energetic particle hits an atomic nucleus. This occurs, for example, when a beam of accelerated protons is directed at a target. After the nucleus is hit, the energy of the particle is distributed among all constituents, which can be regarded as a "heating up" of the nucleus. Subsequently, the nucleus ejects some of its constituents, and this ejection in turn can be considered an evaporation process. The quantitative evaluation of this picture involved an adaptation of thermodynamics to small systems and gave a good description of many observed nuclear reactions. Niels Bohr's fruitful idea of the division of a nuclear reaction into two parts—the formation of an energy-rich "compound nucleus" and its subsequent decay— was taken up by Weisskopf and put into a quantitative formalism, which stimulated many experiments.

In 1950, after the discovery of the shell structure of nuclei by Maria Goeppert Mayer and J. H. D. Jensen, Weisskopf and H. Feshbach revised and refined the theory of nuclear reactions by introducing the so-called optical model. Here, the nucleus is considered to act like a refracting and partially absorbing sphere (a "clouded crystal ball") when the de Broglie wave of the incident particle impinges upon it. Weisskopf and Feshbach predicted correctly the occurrence of resonances when the incident beam forms a standing wave in the interior of the nucleus. A study of the emission of γ-rays by nuclei led to the introduction of the so-called Weisskopf units for their predicted intensity.

Weisskopf received his Ph.D. at the University of Göttingen in 1934. He was a research associate at the University of Copenhagen in 1932–34 and at the Institute of Technology, Zurich, in 1934–37. Going to the United States in 1937, he was assistant professor of physics at the University of Rochester until 1943, when he joined the Manhattan project at Los Alamos, N. Mex. In 1946 he joined the faculty of the Massachusetts Institute of Technology. From 1961 to 1965 he was director general of CERN, an international organization operating large particle accelerators in Geneva; then he returned to MIT. Recipient of the Max Planck Medal in 1956, Weisskopf was elected to the National Academy of Sciences in 1952.

Weisskopf's publications included a number of articles giving an account of the concepts and trends in theoretical physics understandable to the broader community of physicists. He wrote *Theoretical Nuclear Physics*, with John M. Blatt (1952), and a book on science for the intelligent layman, *Knowledge and Wonder* (1962).

For background information *see* ELEMENTARY PARTICLE; QUANTUM ELECTRODYNAMICS; RADIOACTIVITY in the McGraw-Hill Encyclopedia of Science and Technology.   □

★ WESTHEIMER, Frank Henry

American chemist
Born Jan. 15, 1912, Baltimore, Md., U.S.A.

IN THE 1930s physical-organic chemistry developed from meager foundations to a full-fledged science that attempts to understand the enormous complexity of organic chemical structures and to permit rational predictions of chemical reactivity. Westheimer was among those who contributed substantially to the advance. In the 1950s he turned his attention to the problems involved in the mechanism of enzyme action and attempted to understand these processes in the same depth and detail as the reactions of simpler organic molecules.

A chemical reaction generally does not take place in a single, simple step but is the result of a sequence of separable, individual elementary processes. Studies of the mechanism of chemical and biochemical reactions are concerned both with the pathway for reaction (that is, the sequence of intermediates between reactants and products) and with the energy and intimate geometry of molecules at the moment of reaction. Thus, studies of reaction mechanism are necessarily concerned with detail; the grand design can only be seen as a composite of many special cases. Here, however, only one example of Westheimer's work will be discussed in depth: the investigation, carried out in collaboration with Birgit Vennesland of the University of Chicago, of the mechanism of action of the coenzyme diphosphopyridine nucleotide (DPN). This compound (together with a close relative) participates in many of the most important biochemical oxidation-reduction reactions and provides an essential link in metabolic pathways. Examples include the oxidation of alcohol to acetaldehyde, shown in the equation, as well as the oxidation of lactic acid, glucose, glyceraldehyde phosphate, β-hydroxysteroids, and so on.

In the equation the symbol R represents a complicated organic moiety, comprising adenine, ribose, and pyrophosphoric acid; although essential to the coenzyme, it does not enter into the chemistry shown. Each of the reactions in which DPN participates is catalyzed by a specific enzyme; these enzymes (such as alcohol dehydrogenase) are complicated organic molecules for which the detailed chemistry is just beginning to be worked out. By using deuterium as a tracer, Westheimer, Vennesland, and their co-workers showed that the transfer of hydrogen occurs "directly" and "stereospecifically" from substrate to coenzyme. The statement that the transfer occurs directly means that hydrogen atoms attached to the alcohol molecule are transferred directly to the coenzyme. (Prior to 1951 many chemists thought that the transfer took place from the solvent, through the influence of the enzyme.) "Stereospecificity" means that the transfer is controlled by the arrangement of the atoms in space. Although two hydrogen atoms are attached to the α-carbon atom of alcohol, these two atoms occupy different locations in three-dimensional space. Two different kinds of monodeutero alcohol, CH_3CHDOH, can be prepared that differ from one another as do an object and its noncongruent mirror image or as do right and left hands. Although this distinction may appear subtle, one type of monodeutero alcohol is oxidized by DPN in the presence of

alcohol dehydrogenase to transfer a hydrogen atom to the coenzyme, whereas the other is oxidized to transfer a deuterium atom. The techniques and ideas of this research have had widespread application in biochemistry. Not only the oxidation-reduction examples that involve the pyridine nucleotide coenzymes but many other biochemical processes that involve the transfer of hydrogen atoms were shown by similar techniques to be stereospecific.

Other examples of Westheimer's studies of mechanism include a detailed analysis of chemical oxidations by chromic acid. The mode of action of this reagent, one of the most widely used in preparative organic chemistry, was substantially unknown prior to Westheimer's demonstration that the reaction with alcohols begins with an intermediate (an ester) between chromic acid and the alcohol and proceeds by a series of chemical processes involving unstable tetravalent and pentavalent compounds of chromium. Another major contribution for both the chemical and biochemical area concerned the mechanism of decarboxylation of β-ketoacids. The chemical pathway for this reaction was suggested by J. Bredt in 1927 and confirmed by the work of K. J. Pedersen in Denmark and by that of Westheimer. Later Westheimer and his collaborators isolated and purified the enzyme from *Clostridium acetobutylicum* that catalyzes the decarboxylation of a β-ketoacid and found the enzymic pathway for the process. The essential intermediate (a chemical combination, called a Schiff-base, between an amino group on the enzyme and the keto group of the substrate) was deduced in 1958 from isotope-exchange reactions and confirmed by chemically "trapping" the intermediate so that it could be observed. This study is one of those in the forefront of the detailed elucidation of enzyme mechanism.

Westheimer's earlier work, with J. G. Kirkwood, supplied a mathematical model to account for electrostatic effects in organic chemistry, and he later derived the equations for estimating the magnitude of certain hydrogen-bonding effects on acid strength. With J. E. Mayer, he showed how to make a quantitative estimate of the magnitude of steric strain in compounds (for example, he calculated the barrier to rotation in optically active biphenyls) where both bond bending and atomic compressions are important. His studies of nitration laid the foundation for a new acidity function for strongly acid solutions.

In the 1950s and 1960s he and his collaborators investigated the solvolysis of phosphate esters (compounds important in intermediary metabolism) and helped to establish the various pathways available for phosphorylations. Each of these fields later became an area of active research for many investigators.

Westheimer attended Dartmouth College (B.S., 1932) and Harvard University (Ph.D., 1935), where he was introduced to physical-organic chemistry by James B. Conant. In 1935–36 Westheimer held a National Research Council postdoctoral fellowship at Columbia, and subsequently was appointed to the staff of the University of Chicago. He took temporary leave from Chicago to serve as a research supervisor at the National Defense Research Council's Explosive Research Laboratory, Bruceton, Pa., during World War II, and then he returned to Chicago until his appointment at Harvard as visiting professor in 1953–54 and professor of chemistry in 1954. Westheimer was elected to both the National Academy of Sciences and the American Academy of Arts and Sciences in 1954. He was appointed to the President's Science Advisory Committee in 1967.

In 1964 the National Academy of Sciences appointed a committee, with Westheimer as chairman, to survey basic research in chemistry. The committee's report, *Chemistry: Opportunities and Needs*, was published in 1965.

For background information *see* COENZYME; ENZYME; NITRATION; ORGANIC CHEMISTRY in the McGraw-Hill Encyclopedia of Science and Technology.   □

★ WHEELER, John Archibald

American physicist
Born July 9, 1911, Jacksonville, Fla., U.S.A.

WHEELER INTRODUCED the concepts of the scattering matrix and resonating group structure into nuclear physics. With Niels Bohr, he elucidated the mechanism of nuclear fission and predicted the fissility of the plutonium that 5 years later, synthesized in unprecedented amounts in the Hanford piles, was to become a vital ingredient in nuclear weapons. In collaboration with members of the Chicago Metallurgical Laboratory group and the du Pont TNX group, he helped to develop many of the methods of controlling a nuclear reactor and other devices and procedures which are now standard parts of nuclear engineering. He identified 9.2-hr Xe^{135}, the daughter of 6.7-hr I^{135}, as the poison responsible for the remarkable drop in reactivity observed when the first of the plutonium production reactors was started at Hanford in 1944. With Richard Feynman, he showed that the loss of

energy by an accelerated charge particle can be interpreted in terms of the reaction of the distant absorbing particles back on the source—with each elementary interaction between particle and particle symmetric between advanced and retarded effects, but with all the appearance of advanced effects (except for radiation damping itself) being canceled out by destructive interference in all cases in which the absorption by the distant matter is complete. He predicted the existence, since confirmed, of polyelectrons composed of three or more particles of electronic mass, some positive, others negative. Following the discovery of the μ-meson he and Tiomno analyzed the mechanism of capture of slow mesons and predicted a variety of processes and effects which have since been observed.

In 1937 Wheeler described the concept of resonating group structure in light nuclei and supplied the mathematical formalism to construct nuclear wave functions, taking this structure into account; he showed how this approach supplied among other results a means to evaluate an effective potential—which turned out to be velocity dependent—for the interaction between one a-particle and another. In connection with the application of this formalism to the scattering of a-particles by a-particles and problems of similar complexity, Wheeler was led in the same year to formulate the concept of the scattering matrix and to derive its principal properties—a concept which in subsequent years in the hands of W. K. Heisenberg and others found application to elementary particle physics.

With D. L. Hill, Wheeler put forward in 1953 the collective model of the atomic nucleus, in which a distinction is made between the nucleonic state of the many-particle system—as de-

fined by the states occupied by the individual nucleons—and the state of vibration and rotation of the nucleus as a whole. In this model the kinetic energy of the collective motion is interpreted in terms of the degrees of freedom of the individual particles. The vibration frequencies predicted by this model correspond in general terms to those predicted by the simple liquid drop model with, however, certain characteristic quantum mechanical differences. This model predicts not only nonvanishing asymmetries in the distribution of electric charge in the ground states of certain nuclei, as had been elucidated by L. J. Rainwater, but also altered electric quadrupole moments in excited states, asymmetries in the angular distribution of a-particles emitted from atomic nuclei, coupling between individual particle effects and collective motions in the capture of neutrons, and a variety of new effects to be expected in nuclear fission. The collective model, or as they termed it, the unified model, has since been developed by Åge Bohr and B. R. Mottelson in beautiful generality and in a much more detailed mathematical formulation; it has been applied by them and many other nuclear physicists to the elucidation of more than a hundred nuclear spectra and more than a thousand nuclear transition probabilities. In 1956 Wheeler applied these considerations to predict differences in the asymmetry of nuclear fission between one slow neutron resonance and another. In subsequent work in this area he elucidated the concepts of yield-effective number of channels and fluctuation-effective number of channels accessible in nuclear fission. He estimated the vibrational properties of the transition state nucleus in the lowest handful of transition states or channels for the fissile nuclei of greatest interest, tracing out the consequences of these states for the angular distribution of the fission process.

Wheeler and F. G. Werner and colleagues worked out the consequences of the liquid drop model, as summarized in the semiempirical mass formula for the existence and properties of superheavy nuclei (in the range of masses from $A = 250$ to $A = 600$) insofar as one is entitled to look apart, for purposes of such rough estimates, from the effects of shell structure upon nuclear stability. This investigation was a precursor to more recent experimental work in progress in the United States and in the Soviet Union dedicated to the search for the magic-number superheavy nucleus 126^{310}. Wheeler, collaborating with Hill and then with J. J. Griffin, developed the method of generator coordinates for constructing an approximate wave function to describe collective motions in atomic nuclei; it has since received extended application.

At the time of the 1949–50 thermonuclear weapons crisis, Wheeler joined with Edward Teller and others at Los Alamos to explore the possibilities of making an explosive device fueled by heavy hydrogen. Following Teller's invention in 1951 of the key idea in such a device, Wheeler—with the support of Los Alamos—set up at Princeton a classified project to work out the detailed conceptual design of devices working on this and other principles. With the active participation of J. S. Toll, L. Henyey, K. W. Ford, L. Wilets, W. Aron, and other important contributors, this Project Matterhorn worked out during 1951–53 the hydrodynamics and nuclear physics of a wide variety of devices, deriving their energy from more than one type of thermonuclear fuel. The test of these calculations in the great "Mike" explosion on Elugelab Island at Eniwetok Atoll in November, 1952, made it possible to use similar Matterhorn calculations to work out improved designs for deliverable devices, which were also tested subsequently. Many of the Matterhorn codes, refined by the work of Matterhorn, Los Alamos, and Livermore physicists, continue to be a foundation for the design of thermonuclear devices.

As soon as Project Matterhorn had completed its immediate mission in the summer of 1953 with the preparation of a comprehensive report on the design of thermonuclear devices, Wheeler turned to Einstein's general relativity or "geometrodynamics" for new insight on the relations between fields and particles. Einstein had long argued that particles cannot be places where the geometry of space is singular. He stood for the long-term vision that particles, rather than being foreign objects immersed in space, are themselves essentially geometrical in construction. This approach was the direct opposite of that which envisaged the particles as the primary objects of the physical world and fields as mere mathematical constructs designed to describe the interaction between particles. Wheeler's work with Feynman, carrying this point of view of action at a distance to its logical extreme, made it clear what fundamental difficulties any such approach presented within the context of quantum electrodynamics. The difficulty did not lie in the concept of the interaction but in the concept of the particles between which such interaction is supposed to take place. There is no such thing as a single particle. Thus it does not make sense to talk of the interaction of particles. In effect, the world line of what purports to be a single particle examined under a microscope looks like a lightning stroke full of small-scale zigzags. These zigzags describe in symbolic fashion the virtual pairs of positive and negative electrons being created and annihilated all the time in the vicinity of the "experimental electron." Moreover, according to quantum electrodynamics, similar virtual pairs are being created and annihilated all the time throughout all space. For this reason neither particles nor the concept of interaction between particles furnishes a really simple and natural starting point for the description of nature.

Despite these difficulties with the concept of

elementary charged particles and elementary interactions between them, if it should make sense to talk of direct interparticle interactions in lieu of fields, then not only electromagnetic interactions but also gravitational interactions should lend themselves to description without any reference to the field concept. But the gravitational field according to Einstein is mediated by curvature in the geometry of space-time itself. Therefore, to carry the concept of direct interparticle interaction to the limit meant sweeping out from between the elementary particles not only the electromagnetic field but also the space-time continuum itself. In exploration of this line of reasoning Wheeler in 1949 developed a formalism to describe interaction between particles free of any reference to any space-time continuum. To carry the concept of action at a distance to this logical extreme, however, only made complications worse when turning from the particles of classical physics to the real world of quantum physics, where at all places and at all times, according to the best available evidence, virtual pairs of particles are continually being created and annihilated. Two conclusions from this 1949 work had ripened into convictions when 4 years later work along these lines could be resumed: (1) Particles do not offer the natural simple starting point for the description of nature, and (2) new points of view were to be won by studying afresh the content and consequences of Einstein's geometrical theory of gravitation.

No problem turned out to be more interesting than gravitational collapse as a link between the world of particle physics and the world of gravitation physics and general relativity. It had long been known that a sufficiently large mass of cold, dense matter should be unable to sustain itself against gravitational collapse. However, doubts had been expressed from several sides that enough was known about the equation of state of matter at extremely high pressures to make this conclusion compelling. Closer consideration of the physics of matter under extreme conditions made it natural to contemplate not matter alone as the ingredient of a star, but a mixture of matter and radiation. From there it was natural to ask for the properties of a star composed of radiation alone. It turned out that such a purely gravitational-electromagnetic entity or "geon" (1954) is unexpectedly stable against loss of the constituent photons, if only these photons are traveling about the center of gravitational attraction (which they themselves provide through their own content of mass-energy) in circular or approximately circular orbits. Thus, one was confronted with an object which possesses energy and therefore mass and which acts on a test object as does any other mass. Yet nowhere in it is there any place to

which one can point and say, "Here is where 'real' mass is located." Moreover, the geon moves as an entity under not too violent accelerating forces and manifests inertia. Thus, the geon imparted to classical general relativity theory an undreamed-of comprehensiveness. Not only does it account for the fields produced by bodies and the motions of bodies, but it even explains why there are bodies—and why these bodies should be capable of breakup into smaller concentrations of energy under the influence of sufficiently inhomogeneous forces. However, geons have not the slightest direct connection with the world of elementary particle physics. According to the equations, in principle they can be created in a variety of sizes and masses ranging from solar values upward, but smaller geons cannot be analyzed without encountering unsolved issues of quantum electrodynamics.

Further investigations into the consequences of Einstein's standard 1915 geometrodynamics taught one to go beyond the distinction between the geon of classical theory and the particle of the real world of quantum physics and to make a further and similar distinction between "classical electrical charge" and the elementary electrical charges also encountered in the real world of quantum physics. It turned out in 1955 to be possible to account for classical electrical charge as electric lines of force trapped in the topology of a multiply connected space. Previously, electric charge was said to be a place where Maxwell's electromagnetic equations break down; alternatively, it was a place where there is located some mysterious and magical electrical jelly beyond further explanation. Closer examination revealed that this rests upon the tacit assumption that space in the small has the same euclidean topology seen in the everyday world of experimental physics. However, as long ago as 1854 Riemann had pointed out that space at very small distances could have a very much more complicated geometry without these complications ever coming to attention under normal circumstances—and Weyl and Einstein and Rosen had recurred to similar ideas at later periods.

In 1955 Wheeler put forward the concept of "wormholes" in space, with electric lines of force threading through these wormholes. The mouth of the wormhole out of which the lines of force emerge, if viewed with an instrument of insufficient resolving power, appears to be the seat of point positive charge. The other mouth, which may be far away in space, appears to be the seat of an equal and opposite negative charge. Purely as a consequence of the equations of Maxwell's electromagnetic theory and Einstein's geometrodynamics, these charges move in conformity with observation. Thus was discovered in field theory the natural machinery to describe electricity. In a certain sense it can be said that the observation of electricity in nature supplies a powerful argument that space is multiply connected in the small. Despite the interesting new physical consequences that can be read out of classical electromagnetism and geometrodynamics, neither the geons nor the classical model for charge have the slightest connection with the particles or charges of quantum physics. For example, the wormhole model of charge implies that a given positive charge has some very special kind of connection to, and relation with, a particular negative charge different from its relation to other negative charges, despite the most direct experimental evidence for the identity of all electrons.

When quantum theory is tied together with geometrodynamics, the conclusion is that space is not described by any single geometry; it resonates between one geometry and another. In other words, there is a certain probability to find it in one configuration with one geometrical structure and one set of wormhole configurations and a certain probability to find it in one or another of many alternative configurations. All estimates indicate that these violent small-scale fluctuations in the geometry have a characteristic dimension of the order of magnitude of the Planck length $(\hbar G/c^3)^{1/2} = 1.6 \times 10^{-33}$ cm. A similar dimension is given by order-of-magnitude calculations for the scale of any multiple connectivity or wormholes. In this sense all space is to be envisaged as having a foamlike character.

Superspace is the arena in which the fluctuations of space geometry take place. Each point of superspace stands for an entire space geometry—one as different from another as one carpet of foam differs in its microscopic details from another. Thus, space geometry despite appearances is not frozen in a euclidean cast. Instead, there is a probability amplitude for this, that, and the other geometry, each differing from the other at the 10^{-33}-cm scale of dimensions. Only at the everyday scale of observation does space geometry appear to be well defined.

Quantum considerations demand these fluctuations in geometry so far unobserved as inescapably as they demand the experimentally well-confirmed fluctuations in the electromagnetic field going on throughout all space or—to take a simpler example—the fluctuations in the separation between the two hydrogen atoms in a hydrogen molecule. An oscillator can never settle down to rest. If it were at rest, it would have a well-defined position and a well-defined momentum. In this event two conjugate quantities would be known simultaneously in contradiction to the uncertainty principle. This principle makes fluctuations a universal phenomenon.

If general relativity and the quantum concept are held to be the two organizing principles of the physical world, order-of-magnitude estimates lead not only to these conclusions but also to a "geometrodynamical interpretation of matter." On this view a particle is a manifestation of the violent small-scale fluctuations in geometry which are continually taking place throughout all space. It is not itself a wrinkle in the geometry, not a 10^{-33}-cm fluctuation nor a single wormhole charge. Instead, it is a fantastically weak alteration in the pattern of these fluctuations extending over a zone containing very many such 10^{-33}-cm wormhole-bearing regions. In other words, if quantum geometrodynamics supplies a reasonable way of understanding physics, then a particle is a localized disturbance in the geometry just as an exciton is a localized disturbance of the electronic configuration within a crystal. A particle is as unimportant in the geometry of space as an exciton is unimportant for the energy density of a crystal —or as a cloud is unimportant in the physics of the sky. Thus, the energy density characteristic of an elementary particle, roughly 10^{14} g/cm^3, is fantastically small compared to the energy density of the quantum fluctuations in the geometry, 10^{95} g/cm^3. The particle, like the cloud, has no sharp limits.

The wave equation for the propagation of the probability amplitude $\psi(^{(3)}G)$ in superspace satisfies a wave equation qualitatively of the form $(\nabla/\delta^{(3)}G)^2\psi + {}^{(3)}R\psi = 0$, where $^{(3)}R$ is the scalar curvature invariant of the three-dimensional geometry $^{(3)}G$. In the semiclassical limit $\psi \sim$ (slowly varying amplitude) exp $(iS/\hbar)$, the Hamilton-Jacobi function $S(^{(3)}G)$ satisfies the equation $(g_{ik}g_{jl} - \tfrac{1}{2}g_{ij}g_{kl})(\delta S/\delta g_{ij})(\delta S/\delta g_{kl}) + {}^{(3)}R = 0$.

In *Geometrodynamics* (1962) Wheeler noted that "the most evident shortcoming of the geometrodynamical model as it stands is this, that it fails to supply any completely natural place for spin $\tfrac{1}{2}$ in general and for the neutrino in particular." John Milnor's 1965–66 work of the differential geometer on the classification of geometries in general and orientable three-geometries in particular pointed out that one may assign to a space not only a topology and a differentiable structure and a metric, but also an integer, the index number, which can take on any one of 2^n distinct values for the case of a geometry endowed with n wormholes. This mathematical development makes attractive a much more detailed working out of the quantum geometrical concept of matter than previously seemed possible, a concept which in its origins goes straight back to the 1915 geometrodynamics of Einstein and the quantum concept of Planck, Bohr, Heisenberg, and Schrödinger.

Son of librarians, Wheeler received his Ph.D. in physics at Johns Hopkins University in 1933. After a year with Gregory Breit in New York and another with Niels Bohr in Copenhagen, he taught for 3 years at the University of North Carolina before moving in 1938 to Princeton University, where in 1947 he became professor of physics and in 1966 Joseph Henry Professor of Physics. He took two extended leaves of absence from Princeton for defense work: the first (1942–45) on the plutonium project at the Metallurgical Laboratory of the University of Chicago and at the du Pont Co. in Wilmington, Del., and at Richland, Wash.; the second (1950–53) on the hydrogen bomb project at Los Alamos and as director of Project Matterhorn, Princeton. In 1946 he received the Cressy-Morrison Prize of the New York Academy of Sciences for his work on electron-positron physics and in 1965 the Albert Einstein Award of the Lewis and Rosa Strauss Foundation for his contributions to the uses of nuclear energy. He was elected to the National Academy of Sciences in 1952 and to the American Academy of Arts and Sciences in 1954.

Apart from the book already cited, Wheeler was coauthor of *Gravitation Theory and Gravitational Collapse*, with B. K. Harrison and others (1965), and *Spacetime Physics*, with Edwin F. Taylor (1966).

For background information *see* ELEMENTARY PARTICLE; FISSION, NUCLEAR; REACTOR, NUCLEAR; RELATIVITY in the McGraw-Hill Encyclopedia of Science and Technology.   □

★ **WHINNERY, John Roy**

American engineer
Born July 26, 1916, Read, Colo., U.S.A.

WHINNERY'S RESEARCH was primarily in microwave circuit theory, antennas, microwave electron tubes, the noise theory of electron devices, and the use of lasers in communication problems.

Hollow-pipe metal tubes for the guiding of electromagnetic energy were known from the work of Lord Rayleigh in 1897. They first became important practically through the work of S. A. Schelkunoff, G. C. Southworth, and others in 1936 and were of essential importance in the development of microwave radar during World War II. Analysis of systems or networks of such wave-guide components at that time proceeded either through an intuitive extension of low-frequency circuit and transmission line theory or through formal solution of Maxwell's equations subject to boundary conditions. The latter approach is limited by the boundaries which are subject to formal solution and to the difficulties of treating interconnections of such solutions. W. C. Hahn in 1941 developed a method of approximating solutions to planar discontinuities in resonant cavities and parallel-plane transmission lines through ingenious operations on series solutions of orthogonal functions. He also demonstrated that exact equivalent circuits in terms of transmission lines and lumped elements result from such solutions. Whinnery and H. W. Jamieson in 1944 applied the method to a variety of parallel-plane transmission line discontinuities and conducted measurements to demonstrate the importance of the discontinuity admittances that result from such solutions. With T. E. Robbins they also extended the method to coaxial transmission systems, which required evaluation of the less tractable Bessel series. The calculations were accomplished by finding corrections to the asymptotic solutions, the latter utilizing functions calculated for the planar system. They also solved and tested capacitive discontinuities in rectangular wave guides. With D. C. Stinson, Whinnery later applied the technique to radial transmission systems and demonstrated the results experimentally.

Although the Hahn technique was applicable to a wide range of wave-guide junctions, it was not applicable to all, so S. Ramo and Whinnery in 1944 also sought to apply the important equivalent circuits of G. Kron to the solution of field problems with arbitrary boundaries. Analog computers of that date were severely limited in the number of available elements but were adequate to demonstrate the usefulness of Kron's circuits in principle. These general equivalent circuits were also used to supply a formal tie to classical network theory, to evaluate quasi-static and other intuitive solutions to microwave circuit problems.

From 1946 to 1952 Whinnery concentrated on antenna problems. In attacking the classical problem of the input impedance of dipole antennas driven by finite transmission lines, he applied a variety of techniques growing out of the wave-guide junction problems which he had studied earlier, including the Hahn series method of field expansion, analog techniques, and quasi-static approximations. The work also led to a novel second-order quasi-static approximation from graphical field maps and a perturbation equivalent circuit for slightly nonuniform transmission lines. His work with T. T. Taylor on linear antenna arrays in 1950 developed theorems parallel to the basic network theorems of S. Darlington and others and led to a special analog computer for rapid synthesis of large-scale arrays.

Whinnery's work on microwave electron tubes included the analysis of planar triodes under transit-time conditions and the application of results to the study of oscillators (with A. M. Gurewitsch), power amplifiers (with H. W. Jamieson), and low-noise amplifiers (with N. T. Lavoo). His work on tubes of the traveling-wave class included the basic work with C. K. Birdsall on space-charge waves on electron streams with general admittance walls where an analog was again used to help with the analytic solution, and the coinvention (with M. R. Currie) of the cascade backward-wave amplifier.

"Noise" resulting from the statistical fluctuation in electron flow limits the sensitivity of all amplifiers utilizing electron streams. Whinnery's work on the tube noise problem was directed at the low-velocity region near the cathode. He developed a phenomenological model for this region which gave useful physical pictures of the noise behavior as a function of frequency, and which also was capable of solution either by integral equation or computer techniques. With T. Van Duzer and with M. A. Pollack, he later extended this to the cathode region of crossed-field (magnetron type) amplifiers, demonstrating that such tubes are not inherently noisy, as they were previously thought to be. (Van Duzer and others have since demonstrated the very low noise figures attainable with such tubes.)

Whinnery's recent work was in the field of quantum and optical electronics, with special emphasis on the use of lasers in communications and in the study of materials. In 1964 he proposed and analyzed an alternating-gradient lens utilizing acoustic waves in gases for the focusing of light and, with J. P. Gordon and P. K. Tien, he provided a general analysis for thermal and acoustic gas lenses. With Gordon, S. P. S. Porto, R. C. C. Leite, and R. S. Moore, Whinnery also identified the thermal lens effect resulting from materials placed within laser cavities and demonstrated its usefulness for measuring absorption coefficients of nearly transparent materials. He was also concerned with optical modulation and deflection techniques.

Son of a farmer whose hobby was mechanics and electricity, Whinnery received his B.S. in electrical engineering from the University of California, Berkeley, in 1937. He worked at the General Electric Co., Schenectady, N.Y., from 1937 to 1946. Returning to Berkeley, he received his Ph.D. in 1948 and continued on the faculty of the electrical engineering department except for periods of leave. In 1952–53 he worked at the Hughes Aircraft Co. in Culver City, Calif.; in 1959 he held a Guggenheim fellowship at the Swiss Federal Technical Institute (ETH) in Zurich; in 1963–64 he was a visiting member of the technical staff at the Bell Telephone Laboratories, Murray Hill, N.J. At Berkeley he was director of the Electronics Research Laboratory from 1953 to 1956, chairman of his department from 1956 to 1959, and dean of his college from 1959 to 1963. A member of the National Academy of Engineering, he received the Education Medal of the Institute of Electrical and Electronic Engineers in 1967.

Whinnery coauthored *Fields and Waves in Modern Radio*, with S. Ramo (1944; 2d ed. 1953); *Fields and Waves in Communication Electronics*, with S. Ramo and T. Van Duzer (1965); and *Introduction to Electronic Systems, Circuits, and Devices*, with D. O. Pederson and J. J. Studer (1966). He edited *The World of Engineering* (1965).

For background information *see* CIRCUIT, ELECTRIC; COMMUNICATIONS, ELECTRICAL; MICROWAVE; NOISE, ELECTRICAL in the McGraw-Hill Encyclopedia of Science and Technology.   □

☆ WHIPPLE, George Hoyt

American pathologist
Born Aug. 28, 1878, Ashland, N.H., U.S.A.

As an extension of his studies of bile pigment metabolism, Whipple investigated the construction of blood hemoglobin in the body, since the hemoglobin is a most important precursor of the bile pigment. His studies of the influence of various food substances on blood regeneration led him to the conclusion that liver stimulates the bone marrow to the most vigorous manufacture of red blood corpuscles. This finding was the basis of later investigations by the American physicians George Richards Minot and William Parry Murphy of the dietary effect of liver on pernicious anemia in man. In recognition of their discoveries respecting liver therapy in anemia, Whipple, Minot, and Murphy shared the 1934 Nobel Prize for physiology or medicine.

Whipple began his study of bile pigments in 1908 while at the Johns Hopkins University. By 1913, working in collaboration with C. W. Hooper, Whipple was able to show that hemoglobin can be rapidly changed to bile pigment within the circulation of the head and thorax, bypassing the liver completely. Furthermore, he found that hemoglobin can be rapidly changed to bile pigment within the pleural or peritoneal cavities. Whipple and Hooper continued their bile pigment investigations after moving to the University of California in 1914. It became apparent to them that it would be impossible to understand bile pigment metabolism completely without more detailed knowledge of the construction of blood hemoglobin in the body. In 1917 Whipple and Hooper began to induce simple anemia in dogs by bleeding and to trace the curve of hemoglobin regeneration back to normal. These short-term experiments, in which they were later joined by Frieda Robscheit-Robbins, showed that diet, particularly liver, had a powerful effect upon hemoglobin regeneration.

Whipple then decided to modify his experiments to use anemias that were uniformly sustained and maintained for periods of several years. In 1923, after 2 years at the University of Rochester working with Robscheit-Robbins, Whipple reduced the hemoglobin level to about one-third normal by aspiration from the jugular vein and maintained this level for indefinite periods by suitable removal of newly formed red corpuscles. The dogs were sustained with a basal food ration that, while adequate for health and maintenance, permitted minimal new hemoglobin generation. He then was able to determine the potency of various diet factors in terms of the grams of hemoglobin removed to preserve the constant anemia level. Whipple believed that the stimulus of the diet factor would be both maximal and uniform, and this was borne out when after several repetitions the reaction of a given dog was shown to be uniform.

Whipple published his results in 1925. Liver was shown to be the most potent diet factor, with kidney a close second, in the manufacture of red corpuscles. Other meats, such as gizzard, spleen, and pancreas, were also shown to promote abundant new hemoglobin production, as were some fruits, such as apricot. Iron was shown to be the most potent inorganic factor.

Minot and Murphy based their award-winning liver diet for pernicious anemia patients on Whipple's work, and other workers began to search for the active substance in the liver that promotes the hemoglobin regeneration. By 1930 Edwin Joseph Cohn of the Harvard Medical School prepared a concentrate about a hundred times as potent as the liver itself. Further attempts resulted in the independent isolation in 1948 of vitamin B_{12}, or cyanocobalamine, by Karl August Folkers in the United States and Ernest Lester Smith in England.

In addition to his work on hemoglobin regeneration and bile pigments, Whipple performed extensive research in several other areas. He studied several diseases, among them tuberculosis and pancreatitis, the regeneration of plasma protein, and chloroform poisoning in animals. Whipple also investigated protein metabolism by means of carbon-14-labeled lysine, the distribution and functions in the body of vitamin B_{12} by means of the cobalt-60-labeled compound, and the stroma of red blood corpuscles.

The son of a physician, Whipple received his A.B. in 1900 from Yale University and his M.D. in 1905 from Johns Hopkins University. He became an assistant in pathology at Johns Hopkins in 1905 and an instructor in the following year. In 1907 he went to the Panama Canal Zone, where he served as a pathologist at the Ancon Hospital for a year. Whipple than returned to Johns Hopkins as an associate professor in pathology, and he also served as resident pathologist at Johns Hopkins Hospital. In 1914 he became professor of research medicine and director of the Hooper Foundation at the University of California. He was named dean of the Medical School in 1920, but left in the following year to become professor of pathology and dean of the School of Medicine and Dentistry at the University of Rochester. He became dean emeritus in 1953 and professor emeritus in 1955. He was a trustee of the Rockefeller Foundation during 1927–43, member of the Board of Scientific Directors of the Rockefeller Institute for Medical Research during 1936–53, member of the Board of Trustees during 1939–53, vice-chairman of the Board of Trustees in 1953–60, and trustee emeritus in 1960. Besides the Nobel Prize, his awards included the Kober Medal in 1939, the Gold-Headed Cane Award of the American Association of Pathologists and Bacteriologists in 1961, the Kovalenko Medal of the National Academy of Sciences in 1962, and the Distinguished Federal Civilian Service Award from President John F. Kennedy in 1963. He was elected to the National Academy of Sciences in 1929, the American Philosophical Society in 1938, and the American Academy of Arts and Sciences in 1941.

For background information *see* ANEMIA;
HEMATOPOIESIS; HEMOGLOBIN; PROTEIN METAB-
OLISM in the McGraw-Hill Encyclopedia of Sci-
ence and Technology.   □

★ WHITE, Michael James Denham

Australian cytogeneticist
Born Aug. 20, 1910, London, England

THE MODERN "synthetic" theory of evolution
stresses the part played by cytogenetic
events and processes in speciation and phyletic
change. Chromosomal rearrangements are one of
the main kinds of mutational events in the evolution of species. White's main work—using animal
and especially insect material—was the elucidation of the roles played by chromosomal rearrangements (especially inversions and translo-
cations of various kinds) in natural populations
and in speciation.

These aspects of evolution have to be studied
against the background of the knowledge of
chromosome behavior at mitosis and meiosis in
the various groups of organisms. Thus, many
important questions have to be answered differently for, say, *Drosophila*, grasshoppers, salamanders, and mammals (to mention only a few
groups on which intensive cytogenetic work has
been carried out). And even within such major
groups the pattern of cytogenetic evolution
shows considerable variation.

Problems such as these may be studied in
organisms with essentially "normal" genetic systems or in ones with aberrant chromosome
cycles. During 1946–50 (first at University College, London, then at the Genetics Department
of the Carnegie Institution of Washington, and
later at the University of Texas) White worked
out some of the unique and bizarre chromosome
cycles of the midges belonging to the family
Cecidomyiidae. In these insects there are always
a large number of so-called E chromosomes,
which are present in the cells of the germ line

but are absent from the somatic cells, having
been eliminated in the early embryonic divisions
(only a small number of S chromosomes are
retained in the soma). The meiotic mechanisms
of these cecidomyiid midges studied by White
are highly peculiar; in most species the sperm
transmits only a haploid set of S chromosomes,
the egg contributing the other haploid set and
all the E chromosomes. The significance of the
extraordinary chromosomal dualism of these insects has not yet been worked out in terms of
developmental mechanisms, and in many respects it remains an enigma, although it has
obviously been an evolutionary success, as shown
by the very large number of species in the group
and the great variety of ecological niches they
occupy.

White's later work was on more "normal"
types of genetic systems. At the University of
Texas in 1947–53 and at the University of Missouri in 1957–58, he studied the populations of
the trimerotropine grasshoppers of western
North America, some of which reach an extremely high level of polymorphism for peri-
centric inversions. The main conclusion from
this work was that the genetic equilibria could
not be explained by simple heterosis (adaptive
superiority of heterozygotes).

After going to Australia in 1953, White devoted himself mainly to the study of chromosomal rearrangements in the population genetics
and speciation processes of the wingless (and
hence extremely sedentary) grasshoppers of the
endemic subfamily Morabinae. Studies on the
wild populations of one species (*Keyacris
scurra*) were aimed at revealing the adaptive
role played by the naturally occurring chromosomal inversions. It was shown that there is a
complex interaction between the inversions located on two different chromosome pairs, as far
as the determination of viability is concerned. A
10-year study of some of these natural populations showed that they are indeed in genetic
equilibrium, temporal changes in the frequencies of the inversions being statistically
insignificant. A computer analysis (carried out
in collaboration with R. C. Lewontin) suggests
that the equilibrium is most easily explained on
the assumption that the selective values of the
various karyotypes in the polymorphic population are frequency dependent, those of at least
some of the genotypes decreasing if they become
more frequent in the population. An alternative
interpretation based on the supposition that the
natural populations might be inbreeding, to
some extent, was not supported by experimental
evidence.

One species of morabine grasshopper is of
particular interest because it is parthenogenetic,
males being unknown. An extra chromosomal
replication occurs before the maturation of the

oocyte; the latter then enters on meiosis with the tetraploid number of chromosomes, which is then reduced again to the diploid number (a feature of this process is that synapsis occurs only between sister chromosomes that are molecular copies of one another). The karyotype of this species is highly peculiar, there being 15 chromosomes (2*n*) heterozygous for various structural rearrangements. The species is also heterozygous for certain late-replicating chromosome arms, which were revealed by tritiated thymidine autoradiography. By analogy with other cases, these late-labeling chromosome segments are, in all probability, genetically inactivated to a considerable extent. White interpreted this species as a cytogenetically complex permanent heterozygote, ecologically restricted to a very small range of food plants and phenotypically very uniform.

There was much discussion in recent years as to whether the structural differences between the karyotypes of related species of animals are merely incidental results of evolutionary divergence (being derived from adaptive polymorphisms that existed in ancestral populations). The alternative view is that certain types of chromosomal rearrangements, at any rate, may sometimes, or even usually, play a direct causative role in initiating the speciation process. The answer is not necessarily the same for all groups of animals, but as far as the 200 or so species of morabine grasshoppers are concerned, White's cytogenetic analysis tends to show that chromosomal fusions and dissociations (that is, structural changes decreasing or increasing the chromosome number) in many instances have played a primary determining role in the initial stages of speciation.

Chromosomal rearrangements have played an important part in the evolution of the sex chromosome mechanisms of many groups of animals. White put forward in 1940 the first general classification of complex sex chromosome mechanisms (that is, ones involving more than one kind of X or Y chromosome), based on their various modes of origin. He then studied the evolution of complex sex chromosome mechanisms in numerous species of orthopteroid insects.

White was educated at University College, London, where he was assistant lecturer in 1933–35, lecturer in 1936–46, and reader in 1947. He was professor of zoology at the University of Texas from 1947 to 1953, when he went to Australia as senior research fellow with the Commonwealth Scientific and Industrial Research Organization at Canberra. He was professor of zoology at the University of Missouri in 1957–58 and at the University of Melbourne in 1958–64. In 1964 he became professor of genetics at Melbourne. White was elected to the Australian Academy of Science in 1955, to the Royal Society of London in 1961, and to the American Academy of Arts and Sciences as a foreign honorary member in 1963.

White wrote *The Chromosomes* (1937; 5th ed. 1961) and *Animal Cytology and Evolution* (1945; 2d ed. 1954).

For background information *see* CHROMOSOME; CHROMOSOME ABERRATION; CYTOLOGY; EVOLUTION in the McGraw-Hill Encyclopedia of Science and Technology.   ☐

WHITTAKER, Sir Edmund (Taylor)

British mathematician
Born Oct. 24, 1873, Southport, England
Died Mar. 24, 1956, Edinburgh, Scotland

WHITTAKER'S MOST important work is contained in a magnificent series of papers on the special functions of mathematical physics, the differential and integral equations they satisfy, their asymptotic expansions, their recurrence relations, and so forth. Included in this research is the discovery (1903) that many of the special functions introduced at different times by various authors could be expressed in terms of the solutions $W_{k,m}(z)$ to Eq. (1). The functions

$$\frac{d^2W}{dz^2} + \left\{ -\frac{1}{4} + \frac{k}{z} + \frac{\frac{1}{4}-m^2}{z^2} \right\} W = 0 \quad (1)$$

$W_{k,m}(z)$ were called confluent hypergeometric functions by Whittaker, who established many of their properties, and concerning which there is now a vast literature.

Many of the special functions of mathematical physics are connected with solutions of the potential, or Laplace's equation, shown as Eq. (2).

$$\frac{\partial^2 V}{\partial x^2} + \frac{\partial^2 V}{\partial y^2} + \frac{\partial^2 V}{\partial z^2} = 0 \quad (2)$$

Whittaker obtained his now well-known general solution of this equation in the form shown in Eq. (3). He showed that expansion of other

$$V = \int_0^{2\pi} f(x \cos a + y \sin a + iz, a) \, da \quad (3)$$

solutions in series of spherical, cylindrical, and such harmonics is equivalent to the expansion of the function f under the integral in power series, Fourier series, and so on with respect to each of its arguments.

In 1912 in what was essentially an application of this result he showed that the periodic solutions of Eq. (4), called Mathieu's equation by

$$\frac{d^2y}{dz^2} + (a + k^2 \cos^2 z)y = 0 \quad (4)$$

him, are the eigenfunctions of the integral kernel $\exp[k \cos (z) \cos (a)]$, that is, they satisfy the homogeneous integral equation shown as Eq. (5). Moreover, he showed later that such

$$y(z) = \lambda \int_0^{2\pi} \exp \left[k \cos (z) \cos (a) \right] y (a) \, da \quad (5)$$

integral equations play the same role in the theory of ordinary differential equations with four regular singularities that definite integrals play in the theory of equations with three regular singularities.

This work on Mathieu's equation led Whittaker to discover analogous integral equations for the Lamé functions and also to introduce a class of functions, together with the integral equation which they satisfy, which bear the same relation to the Mathieu functions that the associated Legendre functions $P_n^m(z)$ bear to the Bessel function $J_m(z)$.

In addition to his original research papers, Whittaker wrote, and later revised with the collaboration of G. N. Watson, *A Course of Modern Analysis* (1902; 4th ed. 1928; reprint 1952), containing many of Whittaker's results on special functions; it remains an indispensable reference for students, mathematicians, and scientists in this field.

A second area in which Whittaker made major contributions is analytical dynamics. In a series of classic researches beginning in 1902, he investigated the integration of Hamiltonian systems and obtained a solution of such systems in terms of trigonometric series, the first terms of which correspond to small oscillations about a position of stable equilibrium. The culmination of these investigations was reached in 1916 with the discovery of the "adelphic" integral of a Hamiltonian system which elucidated and overcame a difficulty indicated by a celebrated theorem of Poincaré that the series encountered in celestial mechanics, if they converge, cannot converge uniformly for all values of time and all values of the parameters involved. What Whittaker found was that in Hamiltonian systems which have two degrees of freedom and which possess an integral of energy, there exists an integral of the system (the adelphic integral) and an associated infinitesimal contact transformation which changes every trajectory of the system into an adjacent trajectory, so that periodic trajectories go to periodic trajectories with the same period and constant of energy. In addition, Whittaker discovered a method of finding the adelphic integral of the system and showed that the form of the solution is not given by a single analytic expression but depends upon whether a certain parameter is rational or not. This is the underlying reason for the non-uniformity of the convergence of the series solutions for all parameter values pointed out by Poincaré, since as the parameter varies the form of the adelphic integral varies abruptly, depending on whether the parameter is rational or not.

Perhaps the most influential work Whittaker produced in the field of analytical dynamics is his *Treatise on the Analytical Dynamics of Particles and Rigid Bodies* (4th ed. 1937; paper 1959). This book, like his text on analysis already mentioned, is a classic on theory and methods.

Whittaker also made contributions to the fields of quantum mechanics, relativity and electromagnetic theory, astronomy, automorphic functions, interpolation, and algebra.

Whittaker received his education at Trinity College, Cambridge, where he was bracketed second wrangler in the tripos of 1895. He was elected a fellow of Trinity in 1896, and went to Dublin in 1906 as professor of astronomy at the University of Dublin with the title of Royal Astronomer of Ireland. In 1912 he took the post of professor of mathematics at the University of Edinburgh, where he remained until his retirement in 1946. He held various lectureships at several universities during this period. He was elected a fellow of the Royal Society in 1905 and received the Sylvester Medal in 1931 and the Copley Medal in 1954.

In addition to the two books already mentioned, Whittaker wrote *The Calculus of Observations* (1924; 4th ed. 1944; paper 1966), *A History of the Theories of Aether and Electricity* (2 vols., 1910; 2d ed. 1951, 1953), *The Theory of Optical Instruments* (1907; 2d ed. 1915), and other books not specifically dealing with science.

For background information *see* DIFFERENTIAL EQUATION; HAMILTON'S PRINCIPLE; MATHEMATICAL PHYSICS; RIGID-BODY DYNAMICS in the McGraw-Hill Encyclopedia of Science and Technology.   □

★ WILHELM, Richard Herman

American chemical engineer
Born Jan. 10, 1909, New York, N.Y., U.S.A.

THE DESIGN of a chemical reactor for any large-scale chemical plant requires not only knowledge about the chemical changes taking place to produce new substances but also, because of the large sizes of such devices, knowledge about many physical transport processes intimately coupled with the primary chemical rate processes taking place in them. Whether reactors will work at all or whether they can be operated under optimal conditions to produce desired products depends on a designed ability to move chemical reactants, products, and heat energy from one local reaction site to another within the large structures by such transport processes as flow and diffusion in viscous and turbulent conditions. Wilhelm was responsible for basic data and design procedures for such physical-chemical rate processes by engineers in major classes of chemical reactors.

The general problem of maintaining the reaction environment in the face of continuous evolution of heat and mass in reactors caused Wilhelm to study basic phenomena. He applied them in such diverse fields as catalytic reactors to produce chemicals, biological fermenters to produce antibiotics and the like, and flames to produce heat and chemical intermediates.

In packed-bed catalytic reactors in which reactant gases or liquids flow between the catalytic particles, it was long known from industrial practice, for example, that a "hot spot" which is potentially destructive to catalytic activity may develop in the case of heat-evolving reactions.

Through general studies of the transport of heat and of mass in such a matrix of particles, Wilhelm established a quantitative model of transport behavior in this complex system in terms of statistical-dispersion processes. The model has served in the design prediction of the "hot spot" in catalytic reactors.

An interesting mode of making contact between reactant streams and solid catalyst particles is to flow the former upward through a bed of very finely divided particles of the latter. A violent bubbling action takes place, leading to its identification as the boiling bed or fluidized bed reactor. Fluidized beds are used in huge reactors in the cracking of petroleum and in the oxidation of naphthalene, for example. Early studies by Wilhelm led to understanding fluid mechanics and heat and mass transfer phenomena in such reactors. He described extremes of observable behavior as "particulate" and "aggregative," terms commonly employed today.

When an extremely rapid reaction, such as the oxidation of methane to form acetylene and ethylene, is performed by mixing two reactive streams and heating them, the manner of mixing and heating may have a consequence on the capacity of a reactor or on its selectivity for a desired product. The fluid mechanics of the physical, turbulent mixing process was studied by Wilhelm as background for a future, more basic design of this complex class of reactors for rapid reactions. An incidental output of a sequence of studies using light-scatter techniques and a laser source (for sensitivity) was the establishment of a three-dimensional turbulent mixing spectrum, thereby defining the mixing process in a detailed experimental way.

A powerful experimental technique for establishing mechanisms of transport processes occurring in compound situations such as in chemical reactors is the frequency-response technique, in which a system is subjected to a sine-wave variation in composition or temperature, and the change in output amplitude and phase angle relative to the input is measured; analysis of the results leads to quantitative conclusions about any proposed mathematical model for the process. Wilhelm brought this technique to bear on transport between particles and also in a substantially different, but analogous, problem, namely, diffusion-reaction in the pores of a catalyst pellet. In an extension of frequency-response techniques, Wilhelm proposed a dynamic adsorptive technique called parametric pumping for separating fluid mixtures.

Wilhelm received his B.S. (1931) and Ph.D. (1935) from Columbia University. He became an instructor in chemical engineering at Princeton University in 1934, a professor of chemical engineering in 1946, and the chairman of the department in 1954. During World War II he worked with the National Defense Research Committee and the Office of Scientific Research and Development. In 1966 Wilhelm received the American Chemical Society Award in Industrial and Engineering Chemistry. From the American Institute of Chemical Engineers he received the William H. Walker Award in 1951, the Professional Progress Award in Chemical Engineering in 1952, and the Warren K. Lewis Award in Chemical Engineering Education in 1966.

For background information *see* AMPLIFIER; FLUID MECHANICS; PARAMETRIC AMPLIFIER in the McGraw-Hill Encyclopedia of Science and Technology. □

★ WILKINS, Robert Wallace

American medical investigator and educator
Born Dec. 4, 1906, Chattanooga, Tenn., U.S.A.

WILKINS WAS influenced in his research on the circulation and particularly on high blood pressure by his teachers William MacNider and Soma Weiss, his colleagues Ludwig Eichna and Stanley Bradley, and his junior associates Edward Freis and William Hollander, among others. Each of them, like Wilkins, emphasized the physiology, pharmacology, and pathology of circulatory diseases, especially hypertension and atherosclerosis.

Physiologic studies of the human circulation, at first the circulation in the extremities and later in the central organs, taught Wilkins about the extraordinary adaptability of vascular reactions to different circumstances. Vascular reactivity was found to be partly intrinsic and partly under the influence of the autonomic nervous system. In order to study sympathetic nervous vasomotor responses, he spent a year in London working with E. A. Carmichael at Queen's Square Hospital. This brought him under the influence of the British physiologic tradition, certainly among the finest in the world. It also equipped him for studies on the

effects of removing sympathetic nervous activity in various disease states, particularly hypertension. With Eichna at Johns Hopkins, Wilkins showed that the intrinsic reactions of the vascular system to the dilating effects of ischemia (reactive hyperemia) are much stronger than those to neurogenic stimuli and are as fully operative in most hypertensive patients as in normotensive persons. This latter finding suggested that the circulation in hypertensive patients is not irreversibly constricted, but can be dilated, as in normal persons. Later, at Boston University, by physiologic studies on patients before and after surgical sympathectomy for hypertension, Wilkins demonstrated the role of the sympathetic nervous system in hypertension, in vasomotor responses such as the Valsalva "overshoot," and in blood pressure regulation, particularly in the orthostatic position.

The concept that hypertension is a reversible physiologic state (at least early in its course) is basic to the idea that it may be relieved by vasodilating drugs and procedures. On this hypothesis Wilkins began to treat hypertension with pharmacologic and physiologic procedures known or reported to have favorable hypotensive effects in hypertensive states. One of the first drugs he tried was veratrum (sp. *viride*), in which MacNider had taken a great interest and on which Freis and Wilkins then collaborated. Another was rauwolfia (sp. *serpentina*), reported in India to have hypotensive and relaxing qualities. Finally, after observing in patients the striking hypotensive effects of a massive diuretic response during treatment for congestive failure, Wilkins and Hollander began a search for diuretic drugs suitable for long-term oral administration. This led them to try the thiazides and the aldosterone antagonists and to demonstrate their usefulness in treating hypertension.

On finding that in many hypertensive patients no single one of the available pharmacologic agents was clinically adequate, Wilkins fell back on the ancient pharmacologic device of combining the use of two or more preparations. This approach was especially valuable when a diuretic was added to the treatment. Wilkins and Freis had shown that the effect of a single hypotensive agent, say veratrum, upon renal function was to reduce urine output greatly during the hypotensive response. Some drugs, for example, rauwolfia, actually caused clinical edema to develop. However, by using a diuretic in combination with a hypotensive drug, not only was the fluid retention avoided but also the blood pressure effect of the hypotensive drug was markedly potentiated. Today the combined use of diuretics and hypotensive drugs is accepted as a standard treatment of hypertension.

Noting that with modern drug therapy hypertensive patients were dying less and less of hypertension only to succumb later to coronary and other atherosclerotic disease, Wilkins and his associates, especially Hollander and A. V. Chobanian, turned to the pathogenesis of vascular disease. Again drugs were tried, this time aimed at hypercholesterolemia, and concomitantly Hollander and Chobanian studied the metabolism of atherosclerotic versus nonatherosclerotic blood vessels. Wilkins became chairman of the policy board of the National Heart Institute's Cooperative Study of Drugs and Coronary Disease, a long-term, double-blind trial of various hypolipemic agents in men who had sustained one myocardial infarction.

Wilkins graduated from the University of North Carolina (A.B., 1928) and from Harvard Medical School (M.D., 1933). He had his hospital training at Boston City Hospital's Thorndike Memorial Laboratories (Harvard) until 1937, when he went to England for a year. Returning to the United States in 1938, he went to Johns Hopkins Medical School to teach and do research on hypertension. During World War II, as secretary for the Subcommittee on Acceleration, he worked on devices in aviation medicine, especially suits to counteract gravity effect in acceleration and high altitude. In 1940 he became an assistant professor at Boston University Medical School and a member of the Evans Department of Clinical Research in charge of cardiovascular disease. Here he remained, becoming a professor of medicine in 1955 and the chairman of the department of medicine and director of the Evans in 1960. He became president of the American Heart Association in 1957 and received its Gold Heart Award in 1962. In 1958 Wilkins was given the American Public Health Association's Albert Lasker Award "for distinguished contributions to the control of heart and blood vessel diseases through outstanding investigations in the causes, diagnosis and treatment of hypertension." He was elected to the American Academy of Arts and Sciences in 1957.

For background information see CARDIO-VASCULAR SYSTEM; CIRCULATION; CIRCULATION DISORDERS; PHARMACOLOGY in the McGraw-Hill Encyclopedia of Science and Technology.   □

★ WILKINSON, Denys Haigh

British physicist
Born Sept. 5, 1922, Leeds, England

AN EXPERIMENTAL nuclear physicist, Wilkinson made major contributions to the instrumentation and theory of his science.

His instrumental contribution was the invention in 1947 of the principle of analog-to-digital

conversion. Most nuclear experiments deliver their information in the form of a series of electrical impulses whose amplitude distribution must be found. The early way to do this was by stacked discriminators with independently adjustable biases, a system prey to electronic drifts and giving no intrinsic equalization of channel widths. Wilkinson realized that it was possible, with great stability and linearity, to convert a pulse height into a proportional interval of time and then to code that interval digitally via an oscillator. This analog-to-digital conversion reduces the problem of pulse height analysis to the trivial one of counting and routing into a memory, now effected by computer methods. Today, pulse height analyzers permeate the whole of nuclear science and technology; almost all depend on Wilkinson's principle.

Wilkinson's contribution to nuclear theory is his elucidation, beginning in 1953, of the mechanism of the photonuclear giant resonance. All nuclei interact resonantly with gamma rays, the absorption cross section as a function of gamma-ray energy passing through a "giant resonance" of width a few million electron volts centered on an energy of 15 to 20 Mev. The magnitude of the cross section is such that the resonance essentially exhausts the whole of the electric dipole absorption strength, the dipole sum. M. Goldhaber and E. Teller had shown in 1948 how this resonance could be pictured as a collective nuclear vibration, all the protons swinging to and fro together, all the neutrons similarly swinging together but in antiphase with the protons. The very simplicity of this picture led to difficulties in establishing it on a quantitative basis; the model also seemed to founder on the point of the

yield, energy spectrum, and angular distribution of the reaction products, particularly the charged ones. Wilkinson realized that if the ground state of the absorbing nucleus could be well described by the simple configurations of the shell model, then the great strength of the absorption demanded that the giant resonance itself also should have a simple configurational description in shell model terms. He showed that, contrary to naïve expectation, the stronger shell model transitions indeed cluster together in energy and that this cluster practically exhausts the dipole sum. He also showed that the behavior of the reaction products is correctly described by the model. For some years the two models of collective vibration and shell model excitation stood opposed until D. M. Brink in 1957 demonstrated their essential equivalence. The models are brought more evidently together by the ingredient missing from Wilkinson's original description and necessary for getting the resonance at the right energy, namely, the interaction between the particle raised to a higher configuration by the absorption of the gamma ray and the hole left behind in the parent configuration. The missing ingredient was supplied in 1957 in the special case of O^{16} by J. P. Elliott and B. H. Flowers; G. E. Brown and his co-workers in the years following 1959 showed its general applicability. An apparent superiority of the Goldhaber-Teller model over the shell model was the splitting of the giant resonance observed in strongly deformed nuclei such as the rare earths; the collective model immediately understands this in terms of the different frequencies of vibration of the nucleus along its short and long axes. In 1958, however, Wilkinson showed that the splitting also finds a natural explanation within his model, which is now used to provide the microscopic description of photonuclear absorption in all nuclei; the Goldhaber-Teller vibration is its visualization.

Wilkinson's experimental work was chiefly among the nuclei lighter than sodium. Much of it was directed at critical tests of the detailed shell model calculations of Elliott and Flowers and of D. Kurath and others. This work, done largely in collaboration with D. E. Alburger and others at Brookhaven National Laboratory, contributed to the confidence that has been built up in the meaningfulness of the full-dress independent particle model with residual nucleon-nucleon interactions. Interwoven with this work on the structure of light nuclei was an extended study of the validity of the isotopic spin quantum number; from this work emerged an understanding of isotopic spin purity and of the conditions under which the isotopic spin selection rules can be expected to work.

More recently Wilkinson became interested in the use that may be made of elementary particles in the study of nuclear structure. For example, he pointed out that the simplest interpretation of the abundant emission of energetic hyperons, unaccompanied by pions, following the capture of stopped K^--mesons, is in terms of the frequent but fleeting existence of alpha particle–like clusters in the tenuous outer layers of the nucleus.

Wilkinson went to Jesus College, Cambridge (M.A., 1943), where he was later elected an honorary fellow. After graduation he went into atomic weapons work in England and later in Canada at Chalk River. In 1946 he returned to the Cavendish Laboratory, where he received a Ph.D. in 1947 and was a staff member until 1957; he then took a professorship at Oxford University, and became the first head of its Nuclear Physics Laboratory. Radiation sickness, a consequence of his war work, forced him out of nuclear physics in 1947; he worked for a year on problems of bird navigation and on writing the book *Ionization Chambers and Counters* (1950), which summarizes his early interest in gas-filled detectors, particularly the Geiger counter. For his contributions to physics Wilkinson was made a fellow of the Royal Society in 1956, a Holweck medallist of the British and French Physical Societies in 1957, Rutherford Memorial Lecturer of the British Physical Society in 1962, and Hughes medallist of the Royal Society in 1965.

For background information *see* ANALOG-TO-DIGITAL CONVERTER; ELEMENTARY PARTICLE; ISOTOPIC SPIN in the McGraw-Hill Encyclopedia of Science and Technology. □

★ WILLIAMS, Carroll Milton

American biologist
Born Dec. 2, 1916, Richmond, Va., U.S.A.

As an undergraduate at the University of Richmond, Williams was enchanted by the biology of insects and particularly by the amazing transformations these creatures undergo in their development from egg to larva to pupa to adult. His interest centered on a very beautiful insect, the Cecropia silkworm, which requires a full year to make its journey from egg to adult moth. This slow pace is due to 8 months of developmental standstill which always ensues just after the silkworm has spun its cocoon and transformed into the pupal stage. Then the pupa goes to sleep and continues to sleep even when the season is early summer and therefore propitious for the completion of metamorphosis.

In a series of simple experiments Williams discovered that the continuation of development could be provoked by refrigerating the cocoons for 2 months and then returning them to room temperature. But how could the insect's development be shut down so abruptly, and why did the exposure to low temperature get it going again?

Ten years elapsed before Williams (by then a student at Harvard Medical School) found a clue to these mysteries. He knew that previously chilled pupae wake up and develop when placed at room temperature, and unchilled pupae do not. What would happen if the two kinds of pupae were grafted together to share the same blood? When this experiment was performed, the chilled and unchilled pupae terminated diapause and promptly developed into adult moths! From this result it seemed clear that the formation of the adult moth requires a hormone which can be secreted only by pupae that have been exposed to low temperatures. But where does the hormone come from? To answer this question, Williams removed individual organs from previously chilled pupae and implanted them into unchilled pupae. Here again, the result was unambiguous. Only one organ was active when tested in this manner: the brain. In further experiments he tracked down the source of the hormone to 26 secretory nerve cells embedded in the tiny mass of the pupal brain.

The brain's endocrine function was affirmed by the discovery that pupae deprived of their brains are incapable of forming an adult moth even though they often live for one or more years in the brainless condition. Yet at any time during this period one could cause them to develop by reimplanting a brain obtained from a previously chilled pupa. Unchilled brains were inactive in this test—a finding that clarified the effects of low temperature in terminating the pupal diapause. In retrospect, it turns out that the low temperatures of winter are effective because they enable the brain to secrete its hormone which, in turn, is necessary for the completion of metamorphosis.

In the course of his studies Williams developed several novel techniques for performing surgery on insects. Chief among these was his discovery of a simple method for the continuous carbon dioxide anesthesia of insects during surgery—a technique that was soon adopted the world over. In one such surgical maneuver Williams subdivided unchilled pupae into front and rear halves which were sealed onto plastic slips. The front end remained fully sensitive to the implantation of a chilled brain and promptly developed into the anterior end of an adult moth. But the isolated posterior end failed to respond to the implantation of even a dozen chilled brains. This curious finding suggested that the brain hormone might not be the whole story—that still another endocrine gland might be present in the front end to collaborate with the brain.

To test this proposition, Williams implanted a chilled brain into an isolated pupal abdomen along with one or more other organs obtained from the head end. After scores of negative experiments the sought-for second endocrine organ was identified as the "prothoracic glands"—a tiny pair of cellular masses which the Japanese workers S. Fukuda and K. Hasegawa had meanwhile shown to possess endocrine activity.

This was the first indication that insects are equipped with a miniature endocrine *system*—the "brain hormone" acting on the prothoracic glands to provoke the secretion of a second hormone which then acts throughout the insect to cause the completion of metamorphosis.

In 1953 Williams collaborated with the German chemists A. Butenandt and P. Karlson in the isolation of 70 mg of the prothoracic gland hormone from a half ton of silkworms—the first hormone to be isolated in pure form from any invertebrate. The hormone was named "ecdysone." Much further work was necessary before the chemistry of ecdysone was clarified. Finally, in 1965, its structural formula, published by a team of German scientists, turned out to be a complicated sterol akin to the sex and adrenal hormones of human beings. In 1966 the chemical synthesis of ecdysone was simultaneously announced by groups of European and American scientists. In conjunction with the American team, Williams performed the first biological tests of the synthetic hormone and found it to show the same high activity as the authentic ecdysone extracted from silkworms 13 years previously.

The story now reverts some 30 years to the pioneering work of the British biologist V. B. Wigglesworth, who discovered that a tiny pair of head organs (the corpora allata) secrete still another hormone, which he named "juvenile hormone." In a series of ingenious experiments, Wigglesworth showed that the role of juvenile hormone is to prevent metamorphosis until the growth of the larval insect is complete. As a necessary prelude to metamorphosis, the corpora allata are turned off, and the secretion of juvenile hormone stops. Subsequently, for nearly 20 years the juvenile hormone remained something of a will-o'-the-wisp for the reason that every effort to extract it met with failure.

In 1954 Williams made the startling discovery that male Cecropia moths contain a rich depot of juvenile hormone. By extracting male abdomens with ether, he obtained the first active hormonal preparations. Juvenile hormone proved to be a neutral, water-insoluble lipid which blocks metamorphosis when injected into immature insects. Indeed, it was not necessary to inject it; the same effects were achieved merely by placing the oily extract on the unbroken skin, through which it promptly penetrated. Exposure to juvenile hormone had the net effect of preventing metamorphosis and causing death in all insects that came in contact with it. In 1956 Williams reported these findings and called attention to the promise of juvenile hormone as the first of a new generation of hormonally active insecticides—agents with selective lethal effects on insects but without any recognizable effects on other forms of plant and animal life.

For a number of years male Cecropia moths constituted the only source of juvenile hormone. A small but thriving industry developed for rearing the tens of thousands of Cecropia moths needed each year for further studies of the hormone. Finally, in 1967, the chemistry of the hormone was worked out by a team of scientists headed by H. Röller of the University of Wisconsin. Unlimited amounts of the synthetic hormone should soon be available for use as an insecticide.

The Cecropia hormone remains the only authentic juvenile hormone that has been characterized. However, certain other synthetic products have been shown to possess juvenile hormone activity. Of these, the most active is a crude mixture which Williams and J. Law prepared in a simple, one-step synthetic reaction from farnesenic acid; this material possesses extremely high and lethal juvenile hormone activity for all species of insects on which it was tested.

Meanwhile Williams and K. Sláma discovered that American paper products contain an extractable substance with selective juvenile hormone activity for only one kind of insect, the Pyrrhocoridae—a family of insects which includes some of the world's most troublesome pests of the cotton plant. This finding points the way to the preparation of juvenile hormone analogs with selective action on individual kinds of noxious insects.

In recent studies of juvenile hormone a discovery by Williams, Sláma, and L. Riddiford concerned the ability of all of these juvenile hormone materials to block the embryonic development of insect eggs. Therefore, in addition to its lethal interference with metamorphosis, it appears that materials with juvenile hormone activity constitute ovicides of extreme effectiveness.

Williams received his A.B. (1937) at the University of Richmond and his A.M. (1938), Ph.D. (1941), and M.D. (1946) at Harvard, where he remained as a member of the faculty. He was chairman of the department of biology from 1959 to 1962. In 1966 he became the first Benjamin Bussey Professor at Harvard. He was elected to the American Academy of Arts and Sciences in 1951 and to the National Academy of Sciences in 1960. In 1967 Harvard University awarded him the George Ledlie Prize, given every 2 years to the member of the faculty who has made "the most valuable contribution to science or in any way for the benefit of mankind."

For background information *see* ENDOCRINE MECHANISMS; INSECT PHYSIOLOGY; INSECTA in the McGraw-Hill Encyclopedia of Science and Technology. ☐

★ WILLIAMS, Frederic Calland

British electrical engineer
Born June 26, 1911, Stockport, England

WILLIAMS BECAME best known for his invention of the Williams tube storage system for electronic digital computers. Essentially an inventor, he is named in more than 100 patent applications.

Williams's early inventions were concerned with diode modulators and switched-beam multitrace oscilloscopes. In 1939 he joined the Bawdsey Research Station, where radar was in its infancy. Early work provided the first practical identification equipment to distinguish friendly aircraft from bandits. This was quickly followed by the Rebecca-Eureka system, a forerunner of modern identification systems operating on wavelengths different from the main radar frequency and having intricate coding systems.

During 1940–41 he developed the first fully automatic radar for operation in single-seat fighters. This was based on his invention of the automatic tracking range gate, which was capable of performing without human intervention the function of target acquisition, examination of target characteristics to permit rejection of ground echoes and echoes from aircraft carrying identification equipment, and indication of target range and direction. Various systems of blind bombing and radio navigation quickly followed.

To facilitate these developments, many electronic circuits were developed which were applied over a very wide field, for example, the Miller integrator, which is still the basis of most precision time bases in oscilloscopes. This was also applied to many analog computers used for flight simulation in the form of the "operational amplifier," as was its electromechanical equivalent, the Velodyne integrator. Both are still widely used in analog computers. Best known of the Miller integrator circuits were the Phantastron, so called because of its fantastic waveforms, and the Sanatron, so called because its waveforms were more sanitary. In lighter vein the Pugnatron was devised. This electromechanical system employs overall negative feedback but contains an amplifier with positive feedback. This provides a machine which is normally at rest, but which if pushed in any direction will move *against* the applied force. In a gravitational field it is an automatic hill climber.

It was against the background of circuit expertise that the "cathode-ray tube store" (or Williams tube) was invented in 1946. Shortly afterward, Williams returned to the University of Manchester as professor of electrical engineering, and it was there, in collaboration with T. Kilburn, that the store was developed and made the basis of one of the earliest electronic computers to solve real problems. The store was adopted on a worldwide basis, and enjoyed a period of glory before being superseded by J. W. Forrester's magnetic core store. However, it launched the first generation of electronic digital computers and thereby expedited their development. This first computer also contained a device then called the B tube. Under its new name of "index register" this device is still an integral part of most modern computers, and has been said to be the only major advance on Babbage's original conception.

Leaving the electronic field, Williams turned to the more traditional field of electrical machinery. With the advent of semiconducting devices much of the old expertise of the valve circuit found applications in the machines field.

Williams obtained his B.Sc. in electrical engineering in 1932 from Manchester, his M.Sc. in 1933 and his D.Phil. in 1936 from Oxford, and his D.Sc. in 1939 from Manchester. For his radar work he was made an Officer of the Order of the British Empire in 1945, and for his subsequent activities a Commander of the Order in 1961. In 1957 he became the first holder of the Benjamin Franklin Medal; in 1960 he received the John Scott Award from the City of Philadelphia City Trusts; and in 1963 he was awarded the Hughes Medal of the Royal Society. The recipient of several honorary degrees, he was elected to the Royal Society of London in 1950.

For background information *see* ANALOG COMPUTER; DIGITAL COMPUTER; RADAR; STORAGE TUBE in the McGraw-Hill Encyclopedia of Science and Technology.   □

★ WILLIAMS, John Warren

American physical chemist
Born Feb. 10, 1898, Woburn, Mass., U.S.A.

THE DEVELOPMENT of the theory and practice of sedimentation analysis which followed the invention of the ultracentrifuge constituted a major contribution of physical chemistry to the study of biological macromolecules and to a lesser extent to the characterization in solution of synthetic organic high polymers. Williams and his associates participated in such activities.

In 1936, with the help of a generous grant-in-aid from the Rockefeller Foundation, Williams established at the University of Wisconsin the first ultracentrifuge laboratory associated with a university or scientific institution in the United States. A dual program was maintained, one portion directed toward the use of the equipment in the solution of problems related to biology and medicine and the other toward the elucidation of the theory basic to the understanding of some of the more complicated sedimentation processes. Associated with the maturation of the individual projects was a number of talented graduate students and research associates whose aid by act, discussion, and advice was invaluable.

In the years just prior to World War II investigations were begun (A. M. Pappenheimer, Jr., and H. P. Lundgren) of the nature of the reaction between antigen and antibody in immune systems. Studies in the ultracentrifuge were made of diphtheria toxin, its antitoxin, and their reaction products. The average molecular composition was calculated for the specific floccules at certain reference points throughout the equivalence zone. In addition, the number of combining sites on the antibody was determined to be two—not one, as many then believed. Research of this general type was later extended to a number of other systems.

As a by-product of this research ultracentrifugal analysis was used to demonstrate that, when the antibody molecule is partially digested by an enzyme, a large portion of it may be split off without the loss of antibody activity. This observation provided the impetus for a very extensive series of experiments (W. B. Bridgman, Pappenheimer, and M. L. Petermann) involving the effect of enzymes such as pepsin, papain, and bromelin on equine, bovine, and human gamma globulin antibodies. The presence of discrete reaction products could be established and their molecular weights determined. However, without the availability of the chromatographic column, which came later, they could not be separated from one another for more detailed characterization and study; hence the program was terminated. It was later revived and greatly extended by others.

With interest along these paths it was natural that, when the war came, Williams became concerned about the health of the nation and especially about the provision of materials for the control of infectious diseases. Under Office of Scientific Research and Development contract for work at the University of Wisconsin, the research (R. A. Alberty, Bridgman, H. F. Deutsch, L. J. Gosting, and Petermann) led to a greatly simplified procedure for the removal of the gamma globulin antibodies in the large scale of fractionation of the human blood plasma proteins over that already in use. Furthermore, in this way the yield of the gamma globulin fraction was increased by a factor of between 2 and 3. This procedure, or slight modifications thereof, is even now in pharmaceutical house use in a number of countries over the world, including the United States, for the large-scale production of antibody-rich protein preparations.

Following the war the interests of the Wisconsin group turned in large measure to the development of the theory basic to ultracentrifugal

analysis. The experiment, so simple in a fundamental way, is full of complications, which are now recognized. The equations descriptive of the sedimentation velocity processes in multicomponent systems were written by using the general theoretical and practical flow equations of the thermodynamics of irreversible processes in combination with statements of the conservation of mass (R. L. Baldwin, H. Fujita, and G. J. Hooyman). Those for the corresponding sedimentation equilibrium experiment are founded upon classical thermodynamics (Fujita, R. J. Goldberg, K. E. Van Holde, and M. Wales). The relationships are such that it is no longer necessary to assume idealized behavior in a two-component system for the interpretation of experiments which of necessity must be conducted in multicomponent systems.

With the more general equations it has become possible to move ahead in several directions. Thus, the thermodynamic equations which describe the equilibrium condition in a polydisperse nonideal solution were put into a form such that a series of experiments at several low concentrations and at several low rotor speeds would provide the information necessary to compute such thermodynamic quantities as the solute weight average molecular weight, and the light-scattering second virial coefficient for the solution (E. T. Adams, Jr., D. A. Albright, Fujita, and H. W. Osterhoudt).

In aqueous solutions many proteins exhibit association-dissociation phenomena. A unique method was recently described by which quantitative information descriptive of these equilibria may be extracted by making use of combined independent sedimentation equilibrium and sedimentation velocity data (Adams, Fujita, N. Iso, and K. Kakiuchi). Further, the experimental data descriptive of the combined sedimentation and chemical equilibrium have been shown to be amenable to exact analysis, giving the equilibrium constant and activity coefficients.

Another problem of concern was the description of mobility distributions in protein and polysaccharide systems by using the typical transport behaviors. To correct the apparent distribution as actually observed during the performance of an experiment, more or less definitive corrections were provided for the distortions of the boundary or boundary gradient curves due to diffusion and to the effect of solute concentration and of pressure on the mobility (Alberty, Baldwin, Bridgman, and Fujita). Mathematical expressions were supplied for the "heterogeneity constants" in the electrophoresis and sedimentation velocity experiments. The distribution of sedimentation coefficients for a polydisperse sample, after these corrections, was expressed in terms of its normalized weight frequency function.

In some of his earliest research Williams and his students engaged in measurements of the polarity of some of the simpler organic molecules, in connection with the elucidation of their chemical structure. In some cases it was found that the resultant molecular dipole moment varies with temperature. It was deduced that in such instances a rotation of groups about single bonds within the molecule is taking place. The first mathematical treatment, given by Williams, provided an expression for the effective resultant moment of two equivalent doublets, rotating freely at a given distance apart and at a fixed inclination to an axis. The whole mathematical problem has been greatly extended by others.

The oldest of three children of a chemical engineer, Williams was educated at Trinity College, in Connecticut, and at the Worcester Polytechnic Institute, receiving from the latter a B.S. in 1921. Graduate studies at the University of Wisconsin followed, and a Ph.D. in chemistry was awarded to Williams in 1925. Except for several study periods in Europe—as National Research Council fellow under J. N. Brönsted in Copenhagen and P. J. W. Debye at Leipzig, as International Education Board fellow with T. Svedberg at Uppsala, and later as Guggenheim Memorial Foundation fellow at Copenhagen and Oxford for independent investigations—he remained at the University of Wisconsin, becoming a professor in 1938. He received the Kendall Company Award in Colloid Chemistry of the American Chemical Society in 1955. He was elected to the National Academy of Sciences in 1952.

Williams was a coauthor of the six editions of *Experimental Physical Chemistry*, with Farrington Daniels and, from time to time, others (6th ed. 1962).

For background information *see* GAMMA GLOBULIN; POLYMER; PROTEIN; ULTRACENTRIFUGE in the McGraw-Hill Encyclopedia of Science and Technology.   □

★ WILLIAMS, Robley Cook

American molecular biologist
Born Oct. 13, 1908, Santa Rosa, Calif., U.S.A.

WILLIAMS WORKED in physics, astronomy, and molecular biology. Running throughout his career, however, was an interest in examining properties of matter by some type of optical analysis. Even as a graduate student, he split his activities between the development of the vacuum aluminizing process and an investigation of the hydrogen atom by high-resolution interference spectroscopy. In his spectroscopic investigation he established a definitive value of the ratio of the charge to the mass of the electron and uncovered the first intimation that existing theories were not adequate to explain the fine structure of the spectral lines of hydrogen.

As an astronomer at the University of Michigan, Williams devoted his work largely to a quantitative investigation of stellar spectra, particularly the energy distribution in the continuous spectra of stars. Stars are spheres of hot gas and emit radiation which varies in energy from the red to the violet ends of the spectrum in accordance with their surface temperatures. By measuring this energy it is possible to calculate a star's surface temperature. Astrophysical theory allows predictions of such temperatures to be made; experimental determinations of the temperatures allow the correctness of the theory to be checked. Williams carried out detailed and precise comparisons between the energy distribution in stellar spectra and the energy distribution in the spectrum of a standard incandescent lamp whose temperature was known. His results, published in the 1930s, remain acceptable temperature standards in astronomy.

During the early years of World War II, Williams was engaged in military research, part of which was improving the characteristics of aluminum films and aluminized mirrors. With a senior colleague at the University of Michigan, Ralph W. G. Wyckoff, he began studying aluminum and other metal films in the electron microscope. Results soon showed that it was necessary to obtain three-dimensional information (hills and hollows) about the fine structure of the films instead of the two-dimensional projections heretofore found in electron micrographs. Thus, means had to be found to measure the thickness (or heights) of objects which could not be directly scaled, because they were too tiny, and which could be seen only in magnified photographs. It occurred to Williams that this was an

old problem in astronomy, long ago solved, wherein the heights of mountains on the Moon were calculated by measuring the lengths of their sunlight-cast shadows. Thus originated the technique of electron microscopy known as "shadowing," in which electron microscope specimens are obliquely coated with a film of dense metal, such as uranium, in a vacuum chamber; projecting objects thereby cast "shadows," regions devoid of the metal film, and measurement of the length of the shadows allows the height of the objects to be easily calculated. Further application of the shadowing technique by Williams and Wyckoff showed that it greatly enhances the contrast exhibited by all manner of electron microscope specimens. Its use soon became almost universal.

Since Wyckoff in 1944 was what would now be called a "molecular biologist," he readily convinced Williams that the shadowing technique should be exploited in the electron microscopic examination of viruses. At this point Williams's path irreversibly turned toward exploration of virus structure and the relation of structure to function. Viruses, at least the chemically simpler ones, are very small objects which may have a variety of shapes but which contain primarily only two constituents, protein and nucleic acid. Of structural interest are the questions of how these two constituents are bonded together, how the nucleic acid is packed within a virus, and how the protein molecules in the outer coat are arrayed. Questions of structure-function interest are the roles of the protein and the nucleic acid in a virus's sole mission—infectivity of a host cell. Working with several colleagues from time to time but always maintaining his interest in electron microscopy, Williams joined in answering these questions.

Williams's work with viruses, particularly with R. L. Steere, R. C. Backus, and D. Fraser as collaborators, yielded early intimations that the small, spherical viruses had a symmetry of form which might use an icosahedron as its structural scaffold. The Shope papilloma virus was found to have surface subunits in regular array. With K. M. Smith in Cambridge, England, Williams showed that an insect virus, *Tipula* Iridescent, has precisely the shape of an icosahedron. These findings, later elaborated and improved by A. Klug, S. Brenner, R. W. Horne, and others, led to the current concept that the protein portion of viruses consists of molecular units packed in an exquisitely precise array, with icosahedral symmetry, on the viral surface. It can be said that the geometry of virus building is now well understood, although no one knows the cause of such precise building arrangements.

H. Fraenkel-Conrat and Williams in 1955 accomplished the first reconstitution of a virus, the rod-shaped tobacco mosaic virus. They separated the virus into its constituent protein and nucleic acid molecules and then reassembled it to produce an intact and biologically active virus. Shortly afterward, simultaneously with the German scientist G. Schramm, they showed that infectivity of viruses can be achieved by their nucleic acid portion alone, after removal from the virus and purification. Obviously, these discoveries have enhanced understanding of how viruses are assembled in host cells and have stimulated reexamination of the manner by which viruses direct the synthesis of their progeny during the process of infection.

Son of a physician, Williams spent his early years in California. He received both his A.B. (1931) and Ph.D. (1935) from Cornell University, majoring in physics. In 1935 he joined the astronomy department at the University of Michigan, transferring to the physics department in 1945. During 1941–42 he served with the National Defense Research Committee in Washington. Williams accepted an appointment in the biochemistry department and in the Virus Laboratory at the University of California, Berkeley, in 1950. In 1964 a department of molecular biology was established at Berkeley, with Williams as its chairman. He was also associate director of the Virus Laboratory. He was elected to the National Academy of Sciences in 1955 and to the American Academy of Arts and Sciences in 1957.

For background information *see* MICROSCOPE, ELECTRON; SPECTROSCOPY; STAR; VIRUS in the McGraw-Hill Encyclopedia of Science and Technology.   □

★ **WILLIAMS, Roger John**

American biochemist
Born Aug. 14, 1893, Ootacumund, India

WHEN WILLIAMS first became a serious student of biochemistry about 1918, a basic lack in the field was an elementary acquaintance with many of the essential chemical substances that enter into living matter. He was intrigued by the observation that there were present in milk and many other materials of animal and plant origin unknown trace substances that greatly promoted the growth of yeast cells, observed microscopically in hanging droplets. It was with respect to these unknowns that he determined to contribute knowledge.

His research led to the discovery, isolation, and synthesis of pantothenic acid, essential for all living things, and to the conclusion that trace substances include not only pantothenic acid, but also thiamin, vitamin B_6, biotin, and other nutrilites. He also did pioneer work on folic acid and gave it its name. His investigations played an important role in shifting the interest of biochemists toward microorganisms—a development which has yielded an enormous harvest, including the appreciation of the biochemical unity of all living things. Enzymology would still be in its infancy if it were not for this development, and biochemical genetics and molecular biology might not yet be born.

Individual scientists exhibit vastly different ranges of interest. Some are happy to spend a maximum of their time and effort delving into a specialized area where they become highly proficient and are able to make findings of great importance and interest. Their activities may be likened to an investigation under a high-powered microscope. Other investigators occasionally also take a look under a low-powered microscope; they pay some attention to a larger area and thus see relationships which are invisible under high magnification. There are still other scientists who may investigate specialized segments or larger ones, but they may also concern themselves with a macroscopic view of a whole organism or a society. Because he was always severely limited in the use of his eyesight for detailed reading and also because of his cast of mind, Williams did not devote his whole life to a small, specialized area. Because he did not typically get his ideas from library reading, he was not overinfluenced by the current thinking of other scientists; this facilitated his branching out on his own.

While Williams is generally best known for his discovery of pantothenic acid, a more important contribution was his attention to, and investigation of, biochemical individuality and his elucidation of the genetotrophic principle. Most biochemists agree that the ultimate aim of biochemical investigations is to benefit mankind in one way or another. Williams took this aim seriously and in a down-to-earth manner. As soon as the existence of the various B vitamins was established and their probable roles in enzyme systems were known, he asked: How can this information be of benefit to the people in daily life?

After he began explorations in the area of biochemical individuality, he lost interest completely in hypothetical people. In doing so he had to combat the idea, widely and firmly held, that when biochemical individuality is neglected a small percentage of the human population is overlooked. To those who hold this view, it is not apparent that there are so many striking biochemical (and other) peculiarities and that they are so distributed that if they are not considered every member of the human family is inadequately considered. Anyone unacquainted with the vast array of facts of biochemical individuality cannot appreciate how serious the inadequacies are when this individuality is disregarded.

Particularly important is the area of nutrition, where fivefold or greater variations in specific nutritional needs of normal individuals are not uncommon. Very little attention is currently paid to the application of modern nutritional knowledge to human beings. In line with the genetotrophic principle it is probable that many, if not most, human ailments are being managed in a highly inadequate fashion because of lack of appreciation of the importance of individual nutrition. Elaboration of this point of view is given in Williams's books and in his pamphlet, "A Short History of the Clayton Foundation Biochemical Institute."

Although much consultation took place between Williams and his elder brother Robert R. Williams, who first synthesized vitamin B_1, they never collaborated in research. While in general they never disagreed on important scientific matters, their approaches were highly distinctive and different.

Williams received his M.S. (1918) and Ph.D. (1919) from the University of Chicago. After a year as a research chemist with the Fleischmann (yeast) Co., he taught at the University of Oregon (1920–32), Oregon State University (1932–39), and the University of Texas (from 1939). From 1940 to 1963 he was director of the Clayton Foundation Biochemical Institute of the University of Texas. Besides several honorary degrees, he received the Mead-Johnson Award of the American Institute of Nutrition in 1941 and the Chandler Medal of Columbia University in 1942. He was elected to the National Academy of Sciences in 1946.

Williams wrote several textbooks of organic chemistry and biochemistry and edited, with his colleagues, an American Chemical Society monograph, *Biochemistry of B Vitamins* (1950). With E. D. Lansford, he edited the *Encyclopedia of Biochemistry* (1967). Aside from textbooks, his more important writings include *The Human Frontier* (1946), *Free and Unequal* (1953), *Biochemical Individuality* (1956), *Alcoholism: The Nutritional Approach* (1959), *Nutrition in a Nutshell* (1962), and *You Are Extraordinary* (1967).

For background information *see* ENZYME; NUTRITION; PANTOTHENIC ACID; VITAMIN in the McGraw-Hill Encyclopedia of Science and Technology.   □

★ WILSON, Edgar Bright, Jr.

American chemist
Born Dec. 18, 1908, Gallatin, Tenn., U.S.A.

THE DISCOVERY of quantum mechanics in 1926 for the first time opened the possibility of a detailed theoretical understanding of the whole range of molecular phenomena such as chemical binding, chemical change, and molecular spectra. As an undergraduate at Princeton University and a graduate student at the California Institute of Technology, Wilson was exposed to the tremendous excitement and great optimism generated by these discoveries as observations which had previously been shrouded in mystery were rapidly analyzed and interpreted.

The infrared and Raman spectra of polyatomic molecules seemed a likely field for the application of quantum mechanics, and in the period before World War II Wilson investigated this problem both theoretically and experimentally. It had been fairly well established that these spectra could be roughly accounted for by applying quantum mechanics to a very simple molecular model, namely, atoms treated as point masses and held together by forces very much like mechanical springs. Such a mechanical model shows a whole set of characteristic frequencies of vibration and also can have rotational energy. Wilson pioneered in the utilization of symmetry for the simplification of the application of quantum mechanics to vibrations. Then, with J. B. Howard, he set up the first reasonably complete mathematical formulation of the problem of rotation-vibration and the interaction of rotation and vibration in polyatomic molecules. With H. Gershinowitz, he built at Harvard University an automatic infrared spectrometer, which was used by a number of collaborators for experimental studies of molecular vibrations. He also developed the so-called FG method, a more powerful mathematical machinery for calculating vibration frequencies, and with A. J. Wells, he published an experimental method for determining the intensities of gas-phase vibrational infrared spectra. All these studies showed that one could indeed account for these spectra in terms of the very simple molecular model if quantum mechanics was used. Furthermore, the formulas permitted the analysis of the experimental data so that information about molecular structure and the strength of the forces holding atoms in an equilibrium position could be determined. This information has many uses, one of which is to serve as input data for the application of statistical mechanics to simple gases from which the thermodynamic properties can be calculated.

World War II interrupted this pure scientific work, and Wilson set up and directed the Underwater Explosives Research Laboratory at Woods Hole, where electrical gages for measuring explosion pressures were developed and other studies were made on the physics of explosions and the relative power of various explosives. The work included a large amount of full-scale testing for the U.S. Navy. In 1944 Wilson became chief of Division 2 of the National Defense Research Committee.

After World War II Wilson turned to microwave spectroscopy, that is, the study of the absorption by polar gases of radiation with wavelength near 1 cm. With R. H. Hughes, he invented the Stark effect microwave spectrometer, a device with very much greater sensitivity than was previously available. This permitted thousands of molecules to be observed, and many have since been studied at Harvard and elsewhere. In order to analyze these spectra, theories of the energy levels of vibrating-rotating molecules had to be extended and made to include the effects of electric fields, centrifugal distortion, internal rotation, and so forth. These extensions were carried out largely in collaboration with a series of very able students. The net result of this activity was the capability of determining from microwave measurements highly detailed information about molecules. For example, since the quantized energy levels of rotation are determined by the mechanical moments of inertia of the molecular model, these can be experimentally obtained and used to calculate interatomic distances. The Stark effect gives dipole moments, and the centrifugal distortion measurements give information about force constants. Barriers to internal rotation about single bonds, a subject which interested Wilson for a long time, can be reliably extracted from microwave spectra in many cases. The microwave technique has also been used to study rotational isomers, that is, molecules which can exist in two or more conformations by rotating one part about a single bond. These interconvert so rapidly that they cannot be chemically separated and studied by ordinary means. Microwave spectroscopy has been employed to characterize, identify, and determine the structure of various small esoteric inorganic species, such as O_2F_2, S_2F_2, and $OXeF_4$. Recently Wilson and collaborators used the technique to examine the transfer of energy from one molecule to another by collision, a process which seems to have some sort of rough selection rules. Altogether the microwave method has yielded an enormous quantity of detailed information about molecules. In addition, it has provided one of the most powerful demonstrations of the validity of quantum mechanics.

Wilson recently became interested also in the fundamental application of quantum mechanics to the a priori prediction of molecular properties. A variety of techniques were explored, with special attention to those promising to yield internal evidence of the reliability of the approximations necessarily used.

Wilson received his B.S. (1930) and M.A. (1931) at Princeton and his Ph.D. (1933) at the California Institute of Technology, where he remained an additional year with Linus Pauling. In 1934–35 he was a junior fellow of the Society of Fellows, Harvard. Thereafter he was a member of the chemistry department at Harvard, successively as assistant professor (1936–39), associate professor (1939–46), and from 1947 as Theodore Williams Richards Professor. In 1962 he received the American Chemical Society's Peter Debye Award in Physical Chemistry. He was elected to the American Academy of Arts and Sciences in 1944 and to the National Academy of Sciences in 1947.

Wilson wrote *Introduction to Quantum Mechanics*, with Linus Pauling (1935); *Introduction to Scientific Research* (1952); and *Molecular Vibrations*, with J. C. Decius and P. C. Cross (1955). He also published about 100 scientific papers, and members of his research group published nearly 165.

For background information *see* INFRARED SPECTROSCOPY; MICROWAVE SPECTROSCOPY; MOLECULAR STRUCTURE AND SPECTRA; QUANTUM MECHANICS; RAMAN EFFECT in the McGraw-Hill Encyclopedia of Science and Technology.   □

★ WINTERSTEINER, Oskar Paul

American chemist
Born Nov. 15, 1898, Bruck an der Mur, Austria

THE TWO decades after World War I saw a remarkable expansion of research on the endocrine glands, which led to a better understanding of their role in regulating essential body functions and the processes of reproduction, as well as to a commensurate increase in chemical research aiming at the isolation and elucidation of the structure of their secretion products, the hormones. Since the isolation procedures then employed were, by modern standards, inefficient and wasteful—chromatography did not come into general use until about 1936—usually only milligram quantities of the pure products could be secured in the laboratory. Fortunately, analytical methods were already on hand which permitted the determination of the elementary composition of substances available only in such small quantities: the methods of organic quantitative analysis developed by Fritz Pregl, professor of medical chemistry at the University of Graz, who received for his contribution the Nobel Prize in chemistry in 1923. It was Wintersteiner's apprenticeship with Pregl and his later preoccupation with hormones which determined the early course of his career and development as a scientist.

At the end of World War I, during which he served as an artillery officer in the Austrian army, Wintersteiner entered the University of Graz to study chemistry and received his Ph.D. there in 1922. He obtained in the same year a staff position in Pregl's department, where he spent a good deal of his time teaching the Pregl techniques to the many foreign scientists who journeyed to Graz to acquire them. At the persuasion of American friends he went to the United States in 1926 on an International Education Board fellowship to work with P. A. Levine at the Rockefeller Institute and with J. J. Abel, professor of pharmacology at John Hopkins Medical School, and to introduce the Pregl methods in their laboratories. Abel had just obtained the pancreatic hormone insulin in crystalline form, and Wintersteiner supplied the anal-

yses of the crystals. After the fellowship year he joined Abel's staff as instructor and continued working on the chemistry of insulin there, and then for some years at the College of Physicians and Surgeons of Columbia University, where he moved in 1929 as assistant professor of bio-chemistry and remained, later as associate professor, for the next 12 years.

Wintersteiner's skill in the preparative manipulation of small amounts led him to team up in 1933 with Willard M. Allen of the University of Rochester for the isolation from sows' corpora lutea of the hormone later called progesterone, which is essential for the implantation of the fertilized ovum in the uterus and the normal growth of the fetus. They achieved this objective in 1934 and determined some of the structural features of the hormone. At that time Wintersteiner was already engaged with J. J. Pfiffner in the isolation of yet another hormone, the so-called life maintenance factor of the adrenal cortex, the lack of which was known to lead to severe disturbances in mineral, water, and carbohydrate metabolism and eventually to death. They accomplished the isolation of the principal hormone of this gland, cortisone, in 1936, simultaneously with E. C. Kendall of the Mayo Clinic and T. Reichstein in Basle.

With the experience gained on these two hormones, both of which are steroids, Wintersteiner turned next to another type of female sex hormone, the likewise steroidal estrogens, and in particular to the elucidation of the nature of the "δ-follicular hormone" from the urine of pregnant mares. With H. Hirschmann, he showed that this product was a molecular compound consisting of one mole each of 17α-estradiol and 17α-dihydroequilin, which are reduction products, respectively, of estrone and equilenin, the main (17-ketonic) hormones of pregnant mares' urine. This discovery led to a study aiming at the identification of a third estrogenic diol occurring in that source and to other studies in this field.

Wintersteiner then embarked on an examination of the sterol fraction of pregnant mares' serum, not so much with the view of isolating the minute amounts of steroid hormones known to be present but of looking for derivatives of cholesterol which might lie on the metabolic pathway to these and to the bile acids. The companion sterols isolated were 7-keto-cholesterol and the two epimeric 7-hydroxycholesterols. These compounds are intermediates in the chemical (and possibly biological) synthesis of the antirachitic vitamin D_2; however, consideration also had to be given to the possibility that the isolated products were not of biological origin but were artifacts formed from cholesterol by air oxidation during the isolation procedure. Indeed, subsequent work, with S. Bergström, showed that these products can be obtained in this manner in high yield from colloidal cholesterol, although evidence was later adduced elsewhere indicating that they nevertheless may represent true metabolites.

From 1941, when Wintersteiner assumed the directorship of a division of the Squibb Institute for Medical Research, his research, while still partly in the steroid field, was mostly concerned with products from higher plants and with antibiotics. Among his first accomplishments along these lines was the isolation of D-tubocurarine, the toxic principle of the tube curare used as an arrow poison by Peruvian Indians, from the vine *Chondodendron tomentosum*. This finding solved the century-old question as to the botanical source of this poison and also made practicable its use as a drug, mainly as an adjuvant in surgical anesthesia (with J. D. Dutcher, 1942).

This was also the time when penicillin, then already proved to be a potent antimicrobial agent but available only in minute amounts, became a concern of the United States and British governments in view of its potential usefulness in the treatment of wound infections at the war fronts. The Squibb group was one of the first in the United States to take up this problem, and in July, 1943, Wintersteiner and H. B. MacPhillamy reported to Washington success in their effort to obtain this elusive substance in pure crystalline form as the sodium salt. The practical significance of this advance was that the crystalline salt in the dry state is completely stable, while the impure amorphous preparations from which it was obtained invariably lost potency on storage. It also opened the way for the determination of the structure and, it was then hoped, synthesis of penicillin in a government-sponsored cooperative project in which the Squibb investigators, along with a number of American and British academic and industrial groups, made important contributions.

In the postwar years it was the antitubercular antibiotic streptomycin, discovered by S. Waksman in 1944, which posed a similar challenge to the chemists bent on its isolation and structure elucidation. Here again the structure problem was solved by the efforts of several groups, among them Wintersteiner and his associates, notably J. Fried. Among their contributions was the isolation in 1945 of streptomycin in the form of a crystalline Reinecke salt, and its conversion by reduction to the clinically equally effective, but in certain respects less toxic, dihydrostreptomycin.

The need felt by clinicians for a potent blood pressure–lowering drug prompted Wintersteiner and Fried to embark in 1949 on an investigation of the American species *Veratrum viride*, which was known to contain in its alkaloidal fraction a factor or factors having such activity. Two new highly active alkaloids, named germidine and germitrine, were isolated and identified as derivatives of a previously known but hypotensically inactive base, germine, in which two or three, respectively, of the latter's seven hydroxyl-

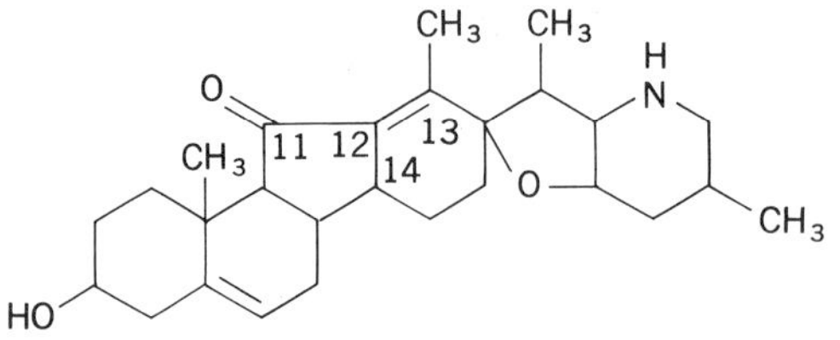

I

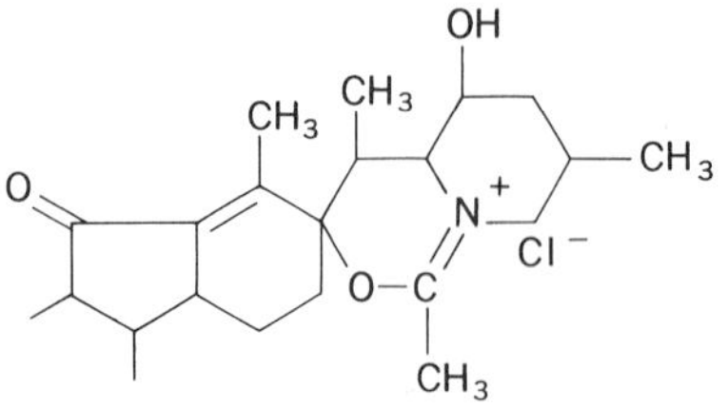

III

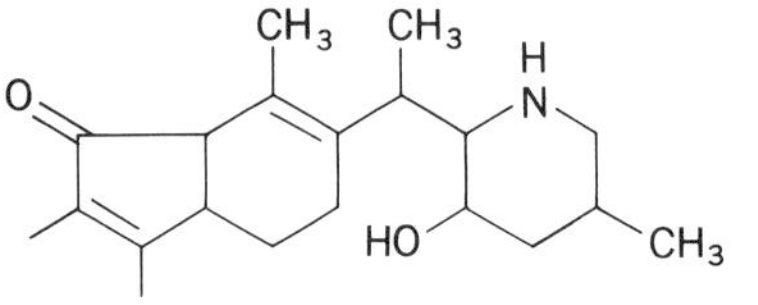

II

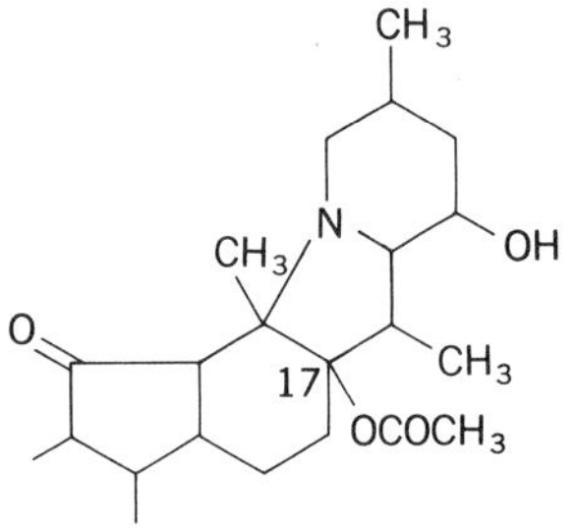

IV

groups are esterified with acetic acid, L-methy-butyric acid, and in the case of germitrine also with ethylmethylglycolic acid.

All veratrum alkaloids were at that time assumed to be regular steroids, mainly because it had been shown conclusively by W. A. Jacobs of the Rockefeller Institute that the carbon skeleton of two tertiary bases he had isolated from *V. viride*, rubijervine and isorubijervine, was identical with that of cholesterol. That this generalization was not tenable was first demonstrated by Wintersteiner and Fried in the case of the secondary base jervine, the main alkaloid of *V. viride*, and with C. Tamm for the related base veratramine.

Wintersteiner's reason for exploring the structure particularly of jervine was that this alkaloid had been tentatively formulated by Jacobs as a normal steroid carrying, like cortisone, a keto group in position 11, and hence deserved consideration as a starting material for the partial synthesis of this hormone. However, it soon became evident that the postulated structure had to be replaced by I, with a modified steroidal nucleus in which C^{14} was bonded to C^{12} instead of to C^{13} as in normal steroids. As Jacobs and others showed later, all veratrum alkaloids except rubijervine and isorubijervine have this rearranged skeleton.

Because of its unique structural features, jervine gives rise to a variety of isomerization and transformation products, the study of which occupied Wintersteiner until recently in what time he could spare from his directive and administrative responsibilities. Three of these products are portrayed in the partial formulas II-IV. Jervine is readily isomerized to isojervine (II) on short contact with strong acid, for instance, methanolic HCl. However, its *N*-acetyl derivative when

so treated gives as the main product the quaternary base chloride III, which with Na_2CO_3 in turn quantitatively rearranges to the tertiary base IV, jervisine-17-monoacetate. This base played an important role in the structure proof for isojervine, as the latter could be correlated with it through a series of unambiguous reactions.

In 1963 Wintersteiner retired from the position of scientific advisor, which he last held in the Squibb Institute, but remained associated with Squibb in a capacity which enabled him to continue laboratory research on problems of interest to him. In 1942 Wintersteiner was appointed an honorary professor of biochemistry of the graduate faculty of Rutgers University. In 1948 he was given the U.S. Presidential Certificate of Merit for his war work on penicillin. He was elected to the National Academy of Sciences in 1950 and in the same year he received the Nichols Medal of the American Chemical Society.

For background information *see* ENDOCRINE GLAND; ENDOCRINE MECHANISMS; HORMONE; PENICILLIN; STEROID in the McGraw-Hill Encyclopedia of Science and Technology.   □

★ WOLFROM, Melville Lawrence

American chemist
Born Apr. 2, 1900, Bellevue, Ohio, U.S.A.

WOLFROM WORKED mainly with problems of structure and reactivity in the carbohydrate field. The now well-established fact that acyclic structures exist as intermediates and are isolable in some carbohydrate reactions rests, to a considerable extent, upon his pioneering work.

Methods were devised for obtaining crystalline acetates of the sugars in which the carbonyl group, aldehydic or ketonic, is present in the free form, uncombined with any hydroxyl group of the sugar chain. New types of aldose derivatives from the hydrated carbonyl group, $R - CH(OH)_2$, were obtained, many of them in the predictable optically active forms. A higher carbon ketose synthesis was established and led to the preparation of acyclic *keto*-acetates, which on deacetylation gave ketoses of higher carbon content. It was shown that the *keto*-acetates could be used for the synthesis of branched chain structures. Pioneer work, in cooperation with T. M. Lowry of Cambridge University, was effected on the optical rotatory dispersions of these acyclic sugar acetates containing the accessible carbonyl band. Wolfrom demonstrated that many of the hydrazones and osazones of the sugars are either totally acyclic or contain such a structure as a significant tautomeric form. An early application of nuclear magnetic spectral measurements to carbohydrates was made when a sugar "anhydrophenyosazone" was shown to possess an unexpected unsaturated phenylazo structure.

The usefulness of the sugar dithioacetals (mercaptals) in the sugar field was demonstrated, and the first dithioacetal of a ketose (D-fructose) was obtained. The technique of mercaptolysis was established; in other hands this led to new results in polysaccharide structure, especially for the seaweed polysaccharides agar and carrageenan. The acetylated dithioacetals were shown to be useful in the identification of sugars, while the hydrogenolysis of the dithioacetals led to a new method for the reduction of carbonyl groups to the hydrocarbon stage. This general reaction was utilized later in the establishment of the nature of the streptose component of streptomycin and in a nonequivocal configurational correlation of D-glyceraldehyde with L-serine, the two configurational standards of the sugar and amino acid series, respectively. Further contributions were made to the elucida-

tion of the structure of the antitubercular antibiotic streptomycin, especially as regards its configurational centers. The configuration of the streptidine entity was established by its synthesis from 2-amino-2-deoxy-D-glucose (D-glucosamine).

The first pentosamine, 2-amino-2-deoxy-D-xylose, was synthesized, and a general method was developed for the synthesis of amino sugars by the hydrazinolysis of *p*-tolylsulfonyloxy groups and the subsequent reduction of the hydrazino group to the amino stage. The isomeric members of the pentosamine series were elaborated. Methods for blocking the amino group were established, and led to successful syntheses of nucleosides of the furanose forms of 2-amino sugars. Several gaps were filled in the systematic elaboration of the simple sugars established by Emil Fischer; these included the crystalline forms of racemic glucose, racemic glucitol (sorbitol), D-glucose dimethyl acetal, L-fructose, racemic talitol, L-talitol, and xylitol.

Color formation in sugar solutions was studied as well as the reaction of reducing sugars with amino acids in the technologically significant Maillard or browning reaction. Reactive intermediates were postulated and in part established. It was demonstrated that enolization down the chain occurs in the action of alkali on reducing sugars. The products obtained in the alkaline electroreduction of D-glucose were shown to involve carbonyl groups completely reduced to the hydrocarbon stage, with a 12-carbon atom aldol condensation product being formed as a side reaction. Pioneer work was instituted on the radiation damage of sugars, and interpretation was made on the basis of free radical chemistry; the oxidizing role of water was studied in this connection, and the paramagnetic resonance of the remarkably stable free radicals formed on irradiation in the solid state was studied. Extensive investigations were made for the armed services of the organic nature of the products formed from cellulose nitrate under controlled ignition conditions.

Incidental to the studies on cellulose nitrate, specifically labeled cotton celluloses were prepared biologically, and some insight into the biosyntheses in the cotton boll was obtained. β-D-Glucopyranose 1-phosphate, the anomer of the Cori ester, was synthesized; in other hands this was later shown to be of natural occurrence. A synthesis for L-iduronic acid was devised, and shortly thereafter this substance was found by others in nature.

New techniques were established in the carbohydrate field. These included the first application of extrusive column chromatography and ion-exchange resins; the first polymer-homologous series of oligosaccharides prepared by chromatographic methods; application of microcrystalline cellulose for thin-layer chromatography of the unsubstituted sugars; sodium borohydride as a reducing agent; phenylboronates and urethanes; as well as reliable analytical procedures for the determination of acetyl and methoxyl groups in carbohydrates.

After years of persistent effort the nature of the sugar units and their modes of linkage were firmly established on an isolative, crystalline basis for the very intractable polysaccharide heparin, the natural blood anticoagulant. The C-6 branch points in starch and glycogen were established on an unequivocal, isolative basis. The main branch point disaccharide, isomaltose, was put on a crystalline basis, and its synthesis, involving the difficultly accessible α-D-$(1 \rightarrow 6)$ linkage, was effected by a new method and extended to the synthesis of panose, one of the possible trisaccharides involved in the branch point. Structures were established for the galactan of beef lung and the mannan and arabinogalactan of the coffee bean.

In a series of investigations, not connected with carbohydrates, the chemical nature of two complex phenolic pigments found in the fruit of the Osage orange, *Maclura pomifera* Raf., was established on a chemical basis, and a synthesis of their skeletal components was effected. These compounds were the first to be developed possessing isoprenoid units condensed on the nucleus of a common plant pigment, in this case an isoflavone; other examples have since been found in plants. Three phenolic pigments containing isoprene units condensed on a xanthone nucleus were found in the root bark of the same plant, and their structures were elucidated almost solely by modern spectroscopic techniques; one was synthesized. Two of them contained an isoprenoid unit in the form of a 1,1-dimethylallyl group, and were the first natural phenolic compounds found to be so constituted.

Of German and Swiss ancestry, Wolfrom was the youngest child in a large family. He received his A.B. from Ohio State University in 1924 and his Ph.D. from Northwestern University in 1927. He was a National Research Council fellow at the National Bureau of Standards and the Rockefeller Institute and a Guggenheim fellow at the University of Zurich. In 1929 he joined the organic chemistry staff at Ohio State, becoming a professor in 1940, research professor in 1960, and Regents' Professor in 1965. From the American Chemical Society he was the recipient of the 1952 Honor Award in the Division of Carbohydrate Chemistry and of the 1967 Patterson Award of the Dayton Section. He was elected to the National Academy of Science in 1950 and to the American Academy of Arts and Sciences in 1951.

Wolfrom was coeditor and editor of *Advances in Carbohydrate Chemistry* from its inception in 1945 and also edited the carbohydrate section in *Chemical Abstracts*.

For background information *see* CARBOHYDRATE; CELLULOSE; MONOSACCHARIDE in the McGraw-Hill Encyclopedia of Science and Technology.   □

★ WOOD, Harland Goff

American biochemist
Born Sept. 2, 1907, Delavan, Minn., U.S.A.

IN COLLABORATION with C. H. Werkman, Wood demonstrated that CO_2 is utilized by heterotrophic organisms. Living forms may be classified on the basis of their growth requirements as either autotrophs, which require only inorganic compounds such as CO_2, ammonium sulfate, and metals as nutrients, or as heterotrophs, which require in addition some form of organic compounds such as amino acids, carbohydrates, or vitamins. There are two types of autotrophs, photosynthetic and chemosynthetic. The latter were discovered by the Russian microbiologist Winogradsky in 1890. Winogradsky found that organic compounds actually inhibit the growth of these bacteria and thus encouraged the view that autotrophs differ from all other forms of life. The difference was associated with a unique ability to utilize CO_2.

In 1935 Wood and Werkman showed that CO_2 is utilized by a typical heterotroph, the propionic acid bacteria, which requires amino acids, vitamins, carbohydrates, or other compounds for growth. They accomplished this by determining the products formed from the fermentation of glycerol and then calculated carbon and oxidation-reduction balances to see whether the carbon of the fermented substrate had been accounted for and also whether the oxidized products equaled the reduced products. The latter must balance since every oxidation requires a simultaneous reduction. Surprisingly, more carbon was found in the products than was supplied in the fermented glycerol, and furthermore there were apparently more oxidized than reduced products. They then found that the extra carbon was derived from CO_2 and that oxidation balanced reduction when the reduction of CO_2 was taken into account. The CO_2 was derived from the bicarbonate used to neutralize the acids produced in the fermentation. Thus, the dogma that CO_2 is utilized only by autotrophs was overthrown. Wood and Werkman proposed that CO_2 and pyruvate combine to form oxaloacetate; this became known as the Wood and Werkman reaction.

When carbon isotopes C^{11}, C^{13}, and C^{14} became available in the 1940s, it was readily shown with these as tracers that CO_2 is utilized by most forms of life, including man, although in practically all cases more CO_2 is produced than utilized. Wood and the physicist Alfred O. Nier did some of the first biological studies with C^{13}. At that time there was considerable controversy about the validity of H. A. Krebs's proposed mechanism for the terminal oxidation of foodstuffs to CO_2 by the tricarboxylic acid cycle. A critical part of the evidence for this cycle centered on the formation of succinate from fumarate by pigeon breast muscle when the inhibitor malonate is present. Malonate was known to inhibit the reductive formation of succinate from fumarate, and Krebs proposed that the cycle provides an oxidative pathway which can yield succinate even in the presence of malonate. The critics, on the other hand, suggested that in the presence of a high concentration of fumarate, malonate is not in fact an effective inhibitor. Wood saw the possibility of answering this controversy by use of $C^{13}O_2$. Oxaloacetate formed by CO_2 fixation from $C^{13}O_2$, and unlabeled pyruvate would be labeled only in a carboxyl position. Hence, the fumarate (and succinate formed from it by the reductive reaction) would also be labeled in the carboxyl groups. On the other hand, succinate formed via the oxidative route of the tricarboxylic acid cycle should contain no C^{13} because the carboxyl groups arising from fixed CO_2 are again lost as CO_2 during the oxidation of the citrate to succinate. Wood and his colleagues Werkman, A. Hemingway, and Nier found that the fumarate was labeled with C^{13} but the succinate was unlabeled. Therefore, the succinate did not arise from fumarate by reduction, but rather the malonate was effective and the succinate was arising by a nonreductive pathway. This experiment provided strong evidence for the Krebs cycle and indicated that CO_2 has an essential role in the metabolism of pyruvate via the cycle.

Wood's studies with labeled carbon then turned to in vivo applications. He wished to demonstrate that the mechanisms proposed from in vitro studies apply to the intact normal animal. A. B. Hastings and associates had shown in 1941 that C^{11} is incorporated into liver glycogen when $NaHC^{11}O_3$ is administered to rats. The problem was to isolate the glycogen after feeding labeled $C^{13}O_2$ and to degrade the glucose unit so as to obtain the 6 positions of the glucose as separate fractions. The distribution of the tracer in the 6-carbon chain could thus be determined and compared with predictions made from the proposed pathways. The predictions indicated that $C^{13}O_2$ should be fixed in carbons 3 and 4 of the glucose. In 1945 Wood, N. Lifson, and V. Lorber demonstrated that this is true. Subsequent studies with labeled acetate, propionate, butyrate, and lactate likewise proved that there is good conformity with predictions. These results, together with those of others, provided excellent evidence of the now generally accepted principle that in vitro studies with enzymes reflect the events which occur in vivo. Later Wood, in collaboration with P. Schambye and R. G. Hansen, studied the mechanisms of synthesis of lactose of milk. Using cows, they showed that free glucose rather than glucose-1-phosphate is the precursor of the glucose moiety of lactose. In collaborative studies with Joseph Katz and Bernard R. Landau, Wood estimated the proportion of carbohydrate metabolized via the pentose cycle and the Embden-Meyerhof pathway by studying C^{14} distributions in the glucose of glycogen.

Recently Wood's major efforts were the purification of enzymes and the study of reaction mechanisms. His studies led to the first demonstration that transcarboxylation is a biological process. Whereas CO_2 fixation leads to the formation of a carboxyl group, transcarboxylation permits the transfer of the carboxyl group from oxaloacetate to other acceptor compounds such as acetyl CoA or propionyl CoA. A combination of CO_2 fixation and transcarboxylation thus permits carboxylation of a wide variety of compounds. He collaborated with Lars Ljungdahl in a study of the role of B_{12} coenzymes in the total synthesis of the acetate from CO_2. This synthesis is remarkable since CO_2 combines with the cobalt of the B_{12} derivative, forming a methyl organometallic linkage like those in the Grignard reagent, alkyl lithium compounds, and others synthesized by organic chemists.

Wood majored in chemistry and mathematics at Macalester College and received his B.A. in 1931. He entered graduate school at Iowa State University, and was awarded a Ph.D. in bacteriology in 1935. He was a National Research Council fellow at the University of Wisconsin in 1936, where he and E. L. Tatum obtained the first proof that vitamin B_1 is required for bacterial growth. He returned to Iowa State University, and was a member of the department of bacteriology from 1936 to 1943. From 1943 to 1946 he was an associate professor in the department of physiology at the University of Minnesota, and in 1946 he joined Western Reserve University as department chairman and professor of biochemistry. He became dean of sciences at Case-Western Reserve University in 1967. He was elected to the National Academy of Sciences in 1953 and to the American Academy of Arts and Sciences in 1962.

For background information *see* AMINO ACIDS; BACTERIAL NUTRITION; KREBS CYCLE; MARINE MICROBIOLOGY in the McGraw-Hill Encyclopedia of Science and Technology.   □

★ WOOD, William Barry, Jr.

American physician and microbiologist
Born May 4, 1910, Milton, Mass., U.S.A.

WHILE STILL an undergraduate at Harvard, Wood became interested in white blood cells. Throughout his professional life, first as a teacher of internal medicine and later as a professor of microbiology, he continued to study leucocytes.

Following his medical residency at the Johns Hopkins Hospital, where he gained firsthand experience in the treatment of patients with acute bacterial pneumonia, he was awarded a National Research Council fellowship to work in the department of bacteriology and immunology of the Harvard Medical School. There, in 1940, under the guidance of John F. Enders, he began a long series of investigations on experimental bacterial pneumonia, summarized in a Harvey Lecture in 1951. In the course of these studies Wood and his colleagues described the phenomenon of surface phagocytosis, by which both polymorphonuclear leucocytes and monocytes phagocytize and destroy encapsulated bacteria in the absence of antibodies. This form of phagocytosis was shown to contribute to the defense of the host in the early (preantibody) phase of acute diseases caused by such pathogenic microbes as pneumococci, streptococci, and Friedlander's bacilli. The studies also led to a clarification of the pathogenesis of pneumococcal and Friedlander's bacillus pneumonias, the role of lymph nodes in antibacterial defense, the mechanisms of cellular destruction of encapsulated bacteria in the bloodstream, and the curative actions of bacteriostatic (sulfonamides) and bactericidal (penicillin) drugs.

In 1955 a new series of investigations on leucocytes was begun, dealing with the pathogenesis of fever. These resulted in the detection of an endogenous pyrogen in the blood of animals with experimental fever. The circulating pyrogen was shown to be indistinguishable from one that is released from polymorphonuclear leucocytes in acute inflammatory exudates. Chemical properties of the leucocytic pyrogen were defined, and mechanisms which trigger its release from the cells were identified. In addition, monocytes were found to generate endogenous pyrogen, thus apparently accounting for fevers in such conditions as agranulocytosis, tuberculosis, and viral diseases, where the inflammatory response of the host is predominantly monocytic.

After attending Milton Academy, Wood graduated with an A.B. from Harvard College in 1932 and with an M.D. from the Johns Hopkins School of Medicine in 1936. He served as professor and chairman of the department of medicine of the Washington University School of Medicine and as physician in chief of the Barnes Hospital in St. Louis from 1942 to 1955. In 1955 he was appointed vice-president of the Johns Hopkins University and Hospital, and in 1959 he became director of the department of microbiology of the Johns Hopkins University School of Medicine. In 1965 he received the Bristol Award of the Infectious Diseases Society of America. He was elected to the American Academy of Arts and Sciences in 1958 and to the National Academy of Sciences in 1959.

Wood wrote *From Miasmas to Molecules* (1961) and, with Bernard D. Davis, Renato Dulbecco, Herman N. Eisen, and Harold S. Ginsberg, published a textbook of microbiology in 1967.

For background information *see* BLOOD; PENICILLIN; PNEUMONIA; SULFA DRUGS in the McGraw-Hill Encyclopedia of Science and Technology.   □

★ WYCKOFF, Ralph Walter Graystone

American crystallographer and biophysicist
Born Aug. 9, 1897, Geneva, N.Y., U.S.A.

THE SCIENTIFIC career of Wyckoff was largely devoted to the study of the fine structure of solids. Present-day preoccupation with solids stems from the demonstration by W. H. and W. L. Bragg (1913) that x-ray diffraction, just discovered by M. von Laue, could be used to establish the positions of the atoms in crystals. As a

graduate student under Shoji Nishikawa, then a visitor at Cornell University, Wyckoff began x-ray investigations and presented the structures of cesium dichloroiodide and sodium nitrate as a doctoral thesis in 1919. Nishikawa had used the theory of space groups in his earlier work on spinel, and Wyckoff, recognizing that this theory offered a generally applicable basis for structure determination, published its first complete analytical description. After spending several years at the Geophysical Laboratory analyzing the structures of inorganic crystals, he went in 1927 to the Rockefeller Institute for Medical Research to begin investigation of organic crystals. There his growing interest in crystals of biological importance was fostered by intimate contact with P. Lecomte du Nouy, one of the pioneers of biophysics, and with Alexis Carrel, whose development of tissue culture made it one of the fundamental techniques of modern biology. Wyckoff and his collaborators were then engaged in early attempts to obtain x-ray diffraction patterns from crystalline proteins. Drawn by the possibility of using high-speed centrifugation as a means of preparing such crystals, he constructed air-driven ultracentrifuges and used them for the first ultracentrifugal purification of plant and animal viruses. In the midst of these developments, a change in administration of the Rockefeller Institute brought this program of research to an abrupt end.

The equine encephalomyelitis virus was one of those which had thus been purified; Wyckoff and J. W. Beard were attempting to make an effective formalin-killed vaccine from purified preparations. In view of the serious encephalomyelitis epidemics among the horses of the United States, Wyckoff was invited to go to the Lederle Laboratories to continue these vaccine attempts. There he developed and tested a practical vaccine, and his laboratory under the stimulus of a continuing epidemic produced several million doses with which a significant portion of the horse population was treated. Follow-

ing this massive use, the epidemic ceased, and there has been in the intervening years no major recurrence of the disease. After this first large-scale demonstration of the effectiveness of a killed virus vaccine, Wyckoff's laboratory turned to making a similar chicken embryo–propagated killed vaccine against epidemic typhus fever. With American entry into World War II, large quantities of typhus vaccine were produced for use by the U.S. Army. In response to the need for human blood plasma in the treatment of war wounds, Wyckoff's laboratory undertook the development of apparatus for the large-scale freeze-drying of plasma. During the succeeding years he built up and operated two plasma plants, each processing more than 1000 sterile plasma packages per day.

Returning to a life of fundamental research, Wyckoff worked and lectured at the University of Michigan in 1943–45 before going to the National Institutes of Health (NIH), from which he retired in 1959. In Michigan he sought to use an early electron microscope to examine directly the elementary virus and protein particles that he had studied with the ultracentrifuge several years before. There he and Robley C. Williams developed metal shadowing, which proved so unexpectedly fruitful in studying these particles that he spent the remaining years till retirement in their visualization in purified preparations and in the tissues in which they grow. A particularly satisfying result of this work was the direct demonstration of the ordered molecular arrangement within the crystals and paracrystals of many of these substances.

On retirement from the NIH Wyckoff became professor of physics and microbiology at the University of Arizona. He built up a laboratory devoted to continuing studies of the fine structure of biological solids and the development of x-ray techniques for their investigation. He extended his previous concern with collagen and other proteins to a search for them in fossils. Employing x-ray techniques as well as electron microscopy, he began studying the preservation of microscopic and submicroscopic structure in fossils of different ages. He demonstrated with the electron microscope that collagen can persist over geologically significant periods of time, and his laboratory began analyzing these ancient proteins to see how they differ from present-day collagen and whether or not these differences point to a chemical as well as a biological evolution in earlier life. With his students he also started to explore the use of very long x-rays, characteristic of the lightest chemical elements, for the further examination of the fine structure of living matter.

Educated at Hobart College (B.S., 1916) and Cornell University (Ph.D., 1919), Wyckoff received an honorary medical degree from the former Masaryk University in Czechoslovakia and an honorary doctorate from the University of Strasbourg. He was elected to the National Academy of Sciences (1949), the American Academy of Arts and Sciences (1950), and, as a foreign member, to the Royal Society of London, the Royal Netherlands Academy of Sciences and Letters, and the Indian Academy of Sciences and, as a corresponding member, to the Académie des Sciences (Paris).

One of Wyckoff's lifelong projects was the unified description of the results of crystal structure analysis; this resulted in *Crystal Structures* (4 sections, 5 supplements, 1948, 1960) and *Crystal Structures* (5 vols., 1963–67). He also wrote about 360 scientific articles.

For background information *see* CRYSTALLOGRAPHY; MICROSCOPE, ELECTRON; ULTRACENTRIFUGE in the McGraw-Hill Encyclopedia of Science and Technology. □

★ YANOFSKY, Charles

American biologist
Born Apr. 17, 1925, New York, N.Y., U.S.A.

YANOFSKY DEVELOPED an experimental system with which it was possible to demonstrate that the nucleotide sequences of genetic material correspond linearly with the amino acid sequences of proteins. Working with the bacterium *Escherichia coli*, he and his collaborators isolated several hundred mutants which had lost the ability to form tryptophan synthetase, the enzyme which catalyzes the terminal reaction in tryptophan biosynthesis. The mutants were divided into two distinct groups, A-gene mutants and B-gene mutants, each group lacking an active form of one of the two protein subunits of the enzyme. The A-gene mutants were subsequently shown to be of two types—one which produced an intact but enzymatically inactive A-protein subunit, and the other which appeared to be incapable of forming any protein resembling the A protein. Mutants of both types were employed in genetic crosses, and a genetic map was prepared in which their mutationally altered sites were arranged linearly. The wild-type or functional A protein and the inactive A proteins produced by the different A-gene mutants were then examined in protein structure studies in an effort to determine the nature of the changes in the mutant proteins that were responsible for enzymatic inactivity. It was shown that in each mutant the inactive A protein differs from the normal A protein by a change of only 1 of the 267 amino acid residues in the protein. The order of the positions at which these amino acid changes occur in different mutant proteins was determined, and this order was compared with —and found to be the same as—the order of the corresponding mutational alterations on the genetic map. In this manner direct evidence was provided showing that gene structure (the genetic map) and protein structure are colinear. It was also observed in these studies that distance on the gentic map is representative of distance in the protein chain. Colinearity of gene structure and protein structure was also established by S. Brenner and his co-workers in investigations with bacteriophage mutants.

Yanofsky and his collaborators employed this well-characterized gene-enzyme system to demonstrate that amino acid changes resulting from single mutational events are restricted to those changes that occur as a consequence of single nucleotide changes in deoxyribonucleic acid. Thus it was found when mutationally changed proteins were examined that a particular amino acid in the A protein is only replaced by members of a specific set of amino acids. It was also found that the inactivation resulting from an amino acid change at one position in the protein can be reversed by an amino acid change at a second position in the protein. Presumably the respective regions of the protein are near one another in the folded molecule, and a specific amino acid change in one region can compensate for the inactivating effects of a "mutant" amino acid in a different region.

Yanofsky and his co-workers also performed some of the pioneering investigations of the biochemical effects of suppressor mutations. Suppressor mutations are changes in one gene which reverse the visible effects of a mutation in a second gene. In studies with tryptophan synthetase mutants of the mold *Neurospora crassa*, suppression was shown to result in the restoration of the ability to form an active enzyme to a mutant which previously produced an inactive protein. In subsequent studies of suppression with the tryptophan synthetase A-gene–A-protein system of *E. coli*, it was found that the amino acid sequence of the restored, active enzyme differs from that of the inactive protein of the parental mutant. Suppression results in the replacement of arginine at one position in the A protein by the amino acid glycine. The protein with arginine at the critical position is enzymatically inactive while the protein with glycine at this position is fully active. These studies led to the suggestion that this type of suppression results from an alteration affecting the specificity of one of the components involved in the translation of genetic information.

Yanofsky was a graduate of the Bronx High School of Science in New York City. He was a student at the City College of New York in 1942–44, then served in the armed forces until 1946. He received his B.S. in chemistry at CCNY in 1948. He did his graduate work at Yale University under the guidance of David M. Bonner and received his M.S. (1950) and Ph.D. (1951) in the department of microbiology. As a graduate student, he studied the biosynthesis of the amino acid tryptophan and the vitamin niacin in the mold *N. crassa* and collaborated in the isolation of several biosynthetic intermediates. He remained at Yale as a member of Bonner's group until 1954. During this period he showed that suppressor mutations result in the reappearance of an enzyme that has been missing from a mutant organism. He also collaborated with S. Suskind in the first demonstration that mutants produce immunologically detectable inactive proteins. From 1954 to 1958 he was an assistant professor in the department of microbiology at Western Reserve University Medical School. He moved to the department of biological sciences at Stanford University in 1958 and initiated his studies on the relationship between gene structure and protein structure. He received the Eli Lilly Award in Bacteriology and Immunology in 1959, the United States Steel Award in Molecular Biology in 1964, and the Howard Taylor Ricketts Award in 1966. He was elected to the American Academy of Arts and Sciences in 1964 and to the National Academy of Sciences in 1966.

For background information *see* GENE AC-TION; MUTATION; PROTEIN in the McGraw-Hill Encyclopedia of Science and Technology. □

★ YODER, Hatten Schuyler, Jr.

American petrologist
Born Mar. 20, 1921, Cleveland, Ohio, U.S.A.

THE CONDITIONS of formation of some of the common igneous and metamorphic rocks were ascertained quantitatively by Yoder, who was one of the first to generate and utilize in the laboratory the requisite combination of temperatures and pressures believed to exist in the Earth's crust and upper mantle. He synthesized members of most of the common rock-forming mineral groups and outlined their pressure and temperature fields of stability. By combining these data on synthetic minerals, as well as on

the various mineral associations in simple synthetic systems, with similar studies on the natural mineral assemblages composing rocks themselves, he evolved new concepts pertaining to the modes of origin of these rocks. For his general contributions to experimental petrology and his success in outlining the quantitative parameters for the formation of common rocks and minerals, he was awarded the Mineralogical Society of America Award in 1954, the Columbia University Bicentennial Medal in 1954, and the Arthur L. Day Medal of the Geological Society of America in 1962.

The underlying philosophy of petrology is that rocks are mainly assemblages of silicate compounds which evolved in nature according to the laws of physical chemistry. Chemically, the principal rock types are composed of relatively few oxides, nine of which constitute over 99% of the Earth's crust. Physically, rocks collected on or near the surface of the Earth formed, according to field observation and deduction, at various depths down to about 50 mi, where the pressure is about 20,000 atm. The temperature at that great depth is, on the average, about 800°C and locally may reach 1400°C. In order to ascertain the conditions of formation of common rocks, therefore, it was necessary to study systematically in the laboratory combinations of the nine principal oxides which make up the common rock-forming minerals at temperatures up to 1400°C and at pressures up to 20,000 atm. By directly synthesizing the minerals and rocks and by subjecting natural rocks themselves to the same conditions, the depths and temperatures in the Earth requisite for the formation of specific rock types, both recent and ancient, could be outlined quantitatively. In 1948 Yoder developed apparatus for the extreme physical conditions of 1400°C and 10,000 atm. at the Geophysical Laboratory, Carnegie Institution of Washington. With the capability of reproducing conditions equivalent to those in the Earth's crust and upper mantle, it was then possible to study directly a vast array of petrological problems. Two main problems of special interest to Yoder were the origin of basaltic magmas and quantitative evaluation of the grades of metamorphism.

Basaltic magmas, the basic silicate liquids which form voluminous lava flows, are believed to give rise to most of the other igneous rocks by processes of crystal fractionation. Yoder, with his colleagues C. E. Tilley and J. F. Schairer, was able to represent these complex rocks as a series of critical, yet simple silicate systems. They showed that the course of fractionation of a basaltic liquid is greatly dependent on the pressure at which it is generated. The same liquids may produce one type of fractionation at high pressures and yet another at lower pressures. Recognition of the different rock suites which may be produced from a single magma at different depths in the Earth led to a new philosophy of rock formation and indicated the need for study of pertinent silicate systems at a series of elevated pressures, as well as at 1 atm.

Because water plays a vital role in the formation of igneous and metamorphic rocks, Yoder perfected techniques for studying many silicate systems under hydrous conditions. He found that the presence of water under pressure causes melting at greatly reduced temperatures, close to those believed to exist at the depths of magma generation deduced from seismic data. In addition, water produces compositional changes in liquids at the beginning of melting in accord with those observed in nature for some unusual rock types. Measurements on the variable water content of silicate liquids at different pressures led to a new theory of explosive volcanism. Practically all magmas of basaltic composition crystallize under high water pressures as amphibolite and under very low water pressures as basalt. It became clear, therefore, that some rock types containing hydrous minerals can form directly from a liquid as well as by the metamorphism of wet sediments.

The transformation of sedimentary and igneous rocks into metamorphic rocks of various grades usually involves reaction of the existing minerals into a new assemblage of minerals, with or without the addition or subtraction of material. These reactions, marked by diagnostic minerals and mineral assemblages, are difficult to deduce from field observations, and quantitative data on the pressures and temperatures involved were lacking. Yoder succeeded in synthesizing many of the diagnostic metamorphic minerals and mineral assemblages which mark the grades of metamorphism and in outlining their stability fields. Attempts to correlate the diagnostic mineral assemblages were begun in the belief that specific ranges of pressure and temperature, as well as other significant parameters such as water pressure, can be designated for critical rock types. In one set of illuminating experiments, Yoder demonstrated that water content and water pressure are independent variables and, as such, have great influence on the mineralogy of metamorphic rocks. It was anticipated that soon it will be possible to outline quantitatively the conditions of formation of most igneous and metamorphic rocks of the Earth's mantle by using newly available equipment of expanded capability.

Yoder's interest in geology began late in high school when his sister on holiday from college left behind an introductory volume on geology. Captivated by descriptions of the physical processes, he continued this interest at the University of Chicago, where he received his S.B. in 1941. During World War II he served in the U.S. Navy for 4 years as aerologist on aircraft carriers and at weather centrals around the world. Returning to the University of Chicago after the war, Yoder continued briefly his studies in petrology under N. L. Bowen and then transferred to MIT, where he received his Ph.D. in petrology in 1948. Immediately after graduation he was invited to work at the Geophysical Laboratory, Carnegie Institution of Washington, and remained there as research petrologist. He was elected to the National Academy of Sciences in 1958.

For background information *see* MAGMA; METAMORPHISM; PETROLOGY in the McGraw-Hill Encyclopedia of Science and Technology.   □

★ YOUNG, John Zachary

British physiologist
Born Mar. 18, 1907, Bristol, England

YOUNG WORKED mainly on the nervous system. In particular, he discovered the giant nerve fibers of the squid, which have provided the material for many of the studies of the way nerves conduct their messages. Later he transferred his attention to the memory system of the brain, particularly in the octopus.

The study of the impulses conducted in nerves developed rapidly in the 20th century, but was limited by the difficulty of inserting electrodes inside the fibers. The largest nerve fibers in man or any other mammal are about .01 millimeter in diameter and are surrounded by a thick, fatty sheath. In a squid there are fibers up to a millimeter across with a relatively thin sheath. These fibers have proved exceptionally suitable for all sorts of experiments. Not only can electrodes be pushed inside them, but nearly the entire contents can be emptied out leaving only the surface layers, which can still conduct the message. Moreover, the material squeezed out can be analyzed—the only way of studying the composition of intracellular material without contamination from the sheath and other cells.

Young came to the study of these nerve fibers from other work on squids and their relations, the octopuses. His studies of regeneration of their nerves led him during World War II to set up a unit for the study of nerve regeneration in mammals at Oxford. Injuries to nerves, which are common in war wounds, are relatively rare in peacetime. There was, therefore, a sudden demand for means of repairing them, and Young and his colleagues investigated various problems, such as how to join small nerves with a glue of plasma, a procedure which he devised with P. B. Medawar. Other studies were made of the rates of growth of nerve fibers and of the factors that control their size and other characteristics. It was suggested that a pressure from the nerve cell body maintains the fiber intact, one of the possible solutions to the still unresolved problem of how the outlying parts of the cell depend upon the operations of the nucleus. Transport of some sort must be involved, but exactly how this is accomplished remains to be discovered. There are also influences affecting the nerve from its contact with peripheral organs, and these also were investigated.

After World War II Young decided that problems of the central nervous system were more important than those of the peripheral nerves. He had noticed that the higher centers of the brain of the octopus seemed to present great possibilities for study. With Brian Boycott, Young was able to show that the animals are able to learn simple visual discriminations, for example, to attack a horizontal rectangle but avoid a vertical one. For a number of years they investigated the nerve centers involved in this learning. After some surgical operations the animals seemed to forget what they had learned. The systems proved to be complicated, involving mechanisms for what might be called "reading-in" to the memory and others for "reading-out." More recently Young postulated a model to explain the operations of the entire system, including units of memory, the mnemons. He was helped by numerous others, particularly N. S. Sutherland in working on the capacity of the animals for pattern discrimination and M. J. Wells on the animals' power of learning to recognize objects by touch. They showed that the visual and touch memories depend upon different nerve centers. This was the first time that the location of memory stores was definitely proved in an animal brain.

Many of the ideas in these various fields depended upon the belief that biological studies demand a knowledge of the structure and function of the whole animal. For this reason Young investigated various other animals and different parts of their structures. For example, at one time he was particularly interested in the nervous system controlling the color change of lampreys.

Young graduated from Magdalen College, Oxford, in 1928 and went immediately to Naples, where he began to study squids and octopuses. He returned to Oxford as a fellow of Magdalen College in 1931 and remained there until 1945, teaching in the zoology department. He became professor of anatomy at University College, London, in 1945. He became a fellow of the Royal Society in 1945.

Young wrote *Doubt and Certainty in Science* (1950), *The Life of Vertebrates* (1950), *The Life of Mammals* (1957), *A Model of the Brain* (1964), and *The Memory System of the Brain* (1966).

For background information *see* Cephalopoda; Memory; Nervous system in the McGraw-Hill Encyclopedia of Science and Technology.   □

★ ZANSTRA, Herman

Dutch astrophysicist
Born Nov. 3, 1894, Heerenveen, Netherlands

ZANSTRA'S CHIEF interest was the mechanisms which produce the bright line spectrum of a gaseous nebula. Diffuse nebulae, such as the great nebula of Orion, are irregular clouds of gas which emit a spectrum due to hydrogen, various other elements, and their ions. In extended research, E. P. Hubble of Mount Wilson Observatory showed that in nearly every case a star of high temperature is associated with a nebula and has to excite the nebula in some way to produce the observed ratio of brightness of the nebula to that of the star. At the instigation of W. Baade, Zanstra sought a theoretical explanation for this phenomenon when he went to do research at the California Institute of Technology.

Zanstra's explanation was the following: Hydrogen atoms are ionized by absorption of radiation of wavelengths smaller than 911 A (the head of the Lyman series), and thereby a photoelectron is produced for every quantum of radiation absorbed. The hydrogen atoms in the nebula are ionized by absorbing this ultraviolet radiation from the star and, assuming this absorption to be complete, the number of ultraviolet quanta in the star equals the number of ionizations in the nebula. Each ionization is then followed by a recombination of the photoelectron with a hydrogen ion, H^+, to produce a neutral hydrogen atom under emission of the hydrogen spectrum, including the Balmer series. Therefore, approximately, the number of ultraviolet quanta in the star = the number of ionizations = the number of recombinations = the number of such "Balmer quanta." Thus the brightness of the star is linked with the brightness of the nebula. Hubble's observed ratio of the two brightnesses requires that the tempera-

ture of the star be about 30,000°K. This is indeed the temperature of the stars in question, spectral type O, deduced from the theory of thermal ionization of stellar atmospheres. This result provided a quantitative check of the proposed theory. The explanation by ionization and recombination was conceived independently by D. H. Menzel.

Zanstra then turned his attention to the planetary nebulae, which are clouds of gas with a regular shape, such as disk or ring, and a very hot star at the center. At this time H. H. Plaskett at the Dominion Astrophysical Observatory in Victoria, British Columbia, had developed a photometric method to measure relative intensities in slit spectra of nebulae. Zanstra then developed a photometric method for dealing with a slitless spectrum of a nebula and its central star. During the summer of 1927 Zanstra secured slitless spectra of three planetary nebulae with their central stars, which in the subsequent winter were measured and further elaborated at Mount Wilson Observatory. I. S. Bowen had just succeeded in interpreting the origin of the so-called nebulium lines, which he found were due to forbidden transitions in ions of various elements, chiefly oxygen and nitrogen. He suggested that they might, in part at any rate, be excited by electron collision; the photoelectron from the hydrogen atom would do this before recombining. And so two methods could be used for determining the temperature of the central star, one based on the recombination of hydrogen as outlined above, and the other on the electron excitation of forbidden lines. The new method assumed that the photoelectrons would give up approximately all of their energy before they recombined. It was assumed, moreover, that the absorption of ultraviolet quanta from the stellar radiation was complete. The temperature of the star determined from the hydrogen recombination method was about the same as that from the forbidden lines method, thus providing a check of the theory. An indirect method based on the photographic magnitude of the star and the visual magnitude of the nebula was used for a temperature estimate in a large number of cases. The highest value found was about 100,000°K, which is more than twice the largest stellar temperature previously known. Later the method, slightly modified, was used by Berman at the Lick Observatory to study slitless spectra in a greater number of nebulae, and led to similar results.

Using more refined methods and slitless spectrograms taken by L. H. Aller in previous work, Zanstra in 1960 obtained results for 13 planetary nebulae. This was supplemented by a joint paper with Aller on the neutral helium spectrum (He^+ requires an extra mechanism of excitation). Zanstra's earlier conclusions were confirmed. In the first of these two papers, Zanstra pointed out that a planetary nebula works here as a quantum counter, counting the ultraviolet quanta emitted by the star. (This was also the subject of the George Darwin Lecture delivered in 1961.) It may be called "space research at low cost," and it could not be carried out by a space vehicle carrying man-made counters because the very quanta to be counted are destroyed by the nebula that absorbs them. Moreover, the quanta would be destroyed for all wavelengths between λ 911 and the x-ray region by the interstellar hydrogen (Aller). In this case the cheapest method is the best method.

After graduating as a chemical engineer in Delft in 1917, Zanstra was an assistant and teacher of physics. In 1921 he became instructor in the University of Minnesota, where he received his Ph.D. in theoretical physics in 1923. Then he was National Research Council fellow, assistant professor in the University of Washington and the Imperial College, London, assistant of physics in Amsterdam, Radcliffe traveling fellow in Oxford and Pretoria, and lecturer in Durban. During 1946–59 he was professor of astronomy in Amsterdam and in 1959–60 Netherlands Visiting Professor at the University of Michigan. In 1961 he received the Gold Medal of the Royal Astronomical Society of England.

For background information *see* NEBULA, GASEOUS; ORION NEBULA in the McGraw-Hill Encyclopedia of Science and Technology. □

★ **ZINDER, Norton David**

American microbiologist
Born Nov. 7, 1928, New York, N.Y., U.S.A.

A<small>N INTEREST</small> in biology, rejection by numerous medical schools, and a timely intervention by Francis Ryan led Zinder to graduate work with Joshua Lederberg at the University of Wisconsin. In 1948 the science of microbial gene-

tics was just in its infancy. Although some of the important phenomena were already discovered, they were scarcely understood and certainly needed generalization. Other basic phenomena were as yet unknown, and the technology was primitive.

To extend Lederberg's 1946 observation of mating in *Escherichia coli*, Zinder set out to obtain in the closely related species of *Salmonella* a large number of mutant strains with growth factor requirements. At that time mutants were obtained by random testing of the survivors of mutagen-treated bacteria, an extremely tedious procedure. Taking advantage of the fact that the antibiotic penicillin was known to kill only growing bacteria, a selective enrichment procedure for the isolation of mutants with nutritional requirements was developed. Mutant bacteria would not grow when in a medium lacking the nutritional requirement and hence would not be killed by the penicillin, whereas the nonmutant bacteria would be killed.

With the availability of large numbers of mutants, experiments seeking conjugation in *Salmonella* were set up. Instead of conjugation, another mechanism for genetic exchange in bacteria was discovered—genetic transduction. The analysis of this phenomenon showed that certain bacterial viruses can incorporate into their structure bacterial instead of phage genes. Upon infection of another bacterial host, these bacterial genes are deposited and become a part of the genome of the new host cells, thereby altering its properties. A phage particle is so small that it can contain only a small fraction of the genome of a bacterial cell. Thus, one is able to study in detail the genetic compositions of very small regions of bacterial genome. Using the technique of bacterial transduction, Milislav Demerec and his colleagues were able to show that bacterial genes affecting sequential biosynthetic steps are often clustered together in what are now called operons.

Zinder's interest in the genetics and physiology of bacteria led to the discovery by his student Loeb of a class of bacteriophage which is specific for *E. coli* male strains. These phage not only aided the analysis of the process of mating in bacteria, but proved to be unique in other ways. One of them, F1, is a long filamentous rod, 8000 × 50 A, and contains a single strand of deoxyribonucleic acid (DNA). The other, F2, is a small spherical virus, 200 A in diameter, the only known phage with ribonucleic acid (RNA) as its genetic material. Zinder and his colleagues studied in detail the chemical and genetic composition of the small F2 phage—so small that it is possible to encompass all of its elements and thereby to provide a model system for understanding the genetic control of structure and function. For the phage to grow, the proper functioning of three genes is necessary: a gene which specifies the phage RNA polymerase, a gene which specifies the viral shell protein, and a gene which is involved in the assembly of the RNA in the protein to make the particle. With the RNA from this phage, it was possible to demonstrate directly the synthesis in cell extracts of a known protein by a specific messenger RNA. This system also revealed the existence on RNA messages of specific punctuation signals for the initiation and termination of protein chains, in addition to the code words for specifying amino acids.

The coat protein of the small phage has been synthesized in vitro. In addition, the RNA of this phage has been synthesized in vitro by Spiegelman and his colleagues. Thus, it should be possible to effect the total biosynthesis of the small RNA-containing bacteriophage in extracts of bacteria, thereby providing a clue to the architectural principles used in nature.

Zinder received his B.A. from Columbia College in 1947. From 1948 to 1952 he studied with Lederberg at the University of Wisconsin, where he received his M.S. in 1949 and his Ph.D. in medical microbiology in 1952. In 1952 he joined the staff of the Rockefeller Institute for Medical Research, now the Rockefeller University, where he successively was an assistant, assistant professor, associate professor, and finally professor. In 1962 he received the Eli Lilly Award in Microbiology from the American Society of Microbiology and in 1966 the United States Steel Award in Molecular Biology from the National Academy of Sciences.

For background information *see* BACTERIAL GENETICS; ENTEROBACTERIACEAE; NUCLEIC ACID; SALMONELLA in the McGraw-Hill Encyclopedia of Science and Technology. □

★ ZYGMUND, Antoni

American mathematician
Born Dec. 26, 1900, Warsaw, Poland

ZYGMUND BELONGED initially to the Polish mathematical school that emerged in the years immediately following World War I and that achieved considerable success in the period between the two wars. His interest was classical analysis, especially harmonic analysis, real and complex variables, and applications of the calculus of probability to analysis. His teacher A. Rajchman and his older colleague S. Saks (both executed by the Nazis during the war) had considerable influence upon his early development. Saks was mainly interested in the metric theory of functions; Rajchman had done outstanding work in the theory of trigonometric series, that is, series of the form

$$a_0 + \sum_{n=1}^{\infty} (a_n \cos n x + b_n \sin n x)$$

Of Zygmund's early work the most significant achievements probably are (1) proof of the existence of sets of uniqueness of positive measure, (2) recognition of the importance of the class $L \log^+ L$ of functions in analysis, and (3) investigation of properties of lacunary trigonometric and power series. Following is an explanation of these notions.

A point set E situated in the interval $(0, 2\pi)$ is called a set of uniqueness, or set U, if every trigonometric series (as shown above) with coefficients a_n, b_n tending to 0 which converges to 0 at all points of the interval that are not in E must necessarily converge to 0 also in E. The problem of characterizing sets U by geometric properties is both important and difficult and is still open. It goes back to Georg Cantor, whose work almost a hundred years ago led him to the discovery of the theory of sets. It is not difficult to show that sets U must necessarily be of measure 0, though there are sets of measure 0 which are not U. Following some ideas of Rajchman, Zygmund showed that if, in the definition of sets U, instead of requiring that the coefficients a_n, b_n merely tend to 0, one imposes the condition that they tend to 0 with a prescribed rapidity (but no matter how slowly), then there exist sets U of positive measure—as a matter of fact, of measure arbitrarily close to 2π. Whether there exist sets U of measure equal to 2π is still an open problem.

Zygmund also showed that if a function $f(x)$ periodic and of period 2π is integrable and if the function $f(x) \log^+ |f(x)|$ is also integrable (one then says that f is in the class $L \log^+ L$ of functions), then the function

$$\widetilde{f}(x) = \int\limits_{0}^{\pi} \frac{f(x+t) - f(x-t)}{t} \, dt$$

called the Hilbert transform of f, is integrable. Moreover, he showed that no condition weaker than integrability of $f \log^+ |f|$ will guarantee the integrability of $\widetilde{f}$. This seems to have been the first case when the significance of the class $L \log^+ L$ was recognized, and in much of his subsequent work Zygmund systematically searched for this class—or its suitable generalizations—in various contexts. By now the importance of the class $L \log^+ L$ is generally recognized.

By a lacunary trigonometric series is meant a series (as shown in the first paragraph) where only "very sparse" terms are distinct from 0; more specifically, it is required that all a_n, b_n be 0 except possibly those with indices $n_1, n_2, \ldots, n_k, \ldots$ that tend to infinity at least as rapidly as a geometric progression (one may set, for example, $n_k = 2^k$). That such series have many remarkable properties had been known for a long time; Zygmund's contribution was to demonstrate that the global behavior of such series is, to a considerable degree, determined by their behavior on sets of positive measure, no matter how small. He also showed that in quite a number of ways the behavior of such series is similar to that of independent random variables appearing in the calculus of probability.

Methods developed by Zygmund at this time were used in subsequent work done with a young British mathematician, R. E. A. C. Paley (died 1933). The recurring theme of the work was as follows: Given a series of functions $\Sigma f_n(x)$, what can be said about the properties of the series $\Sigma \pm f_n(x)$ where the signs $\pm$ are inserted at random? The case when the series $\Sigma f_n(x)$ is a trigonometric or power series is particularly interesting. It turns out, in particular, that for almost all sequences $\{\pm\}$ the new series behaves in many ways like a series of random variables.

During the few years before 1940 Zygmund collaborated extensively with a former student at the University of Wilno, J. Marcinkiewicz (killed during the war) and wrote several papers with him. The work was mainly on the metric properties of functions. The most significant single result can be stated as follows: Suppose that the function $f(x)$ is defined in an interval and that each point x of a certain subset E of this interval has the nth derivative $d^n y / dx^n$ defined as the limit of $\Delta^n y / (\Delta x)^n$ for $\Delta x \rightarrow$ tending to 0, where $\Delta^n y$ means the nth difference of the function (this definition of the nth derivative goes back to the 17th century). Then at almost every point of the set E the function f has a Taylor development up to the nth terms; more precisely, for small h the value of $f(x + h)$ is represented by a polynomial of degree $\leq n$ in h plus an error term which is infinitesimal in comparison with h^n.

During the past 15 years Zygmund was mainly interested in the problem of singular integrals and wrote several papers on the subject with A. P. Calderón. Singular integrals are analogs of Hilbert transforms in the case of functions of several variables. They are defined as convolutions of functions with certain kernels which are not integrable but behave roughly like $1/x$ in the case of functions of one variable. Zygmund and Calderón developed a general theory that proved of importance in certain applications, in particular in the theory of partial differential equations. This theory is presently being actively developed by a number of mathematicians.

Zygmund attended high school in Warsaw and Poltava (Ukraine), entered the University of Warsaw in 1919, and obtained a Ph.D. from that university in 1923. During the war of 1920 he served in the Polish army. Between 1922 and 1929 he was an instructor at the Polytechnical School in Warsaw, and between 1926 and 1929 he was also a dozent at the University of Warsaw. He spent the academic year 1929–30 at Oxford and Cambridge on a Rockefeller fellowship. Between 1930 and 1939 he was professor at the University of Wilno. In 1939 he served in the Polish army, and in 1940 he went to the United States. He was successively a professor at Mount Holyoke College (1940–45), at the University of Pennsylvania (1945–47), and from 1947 at the University of Chicago, where in 1964 he was appointed Gustavus F. and Ann M. Swift Distinguished Service Professor. He was elected to the National Academy of Sciences (1961) as well as to the Polish (1961 and Argentine (1964) academies.

Zygmund wrote *Trigonometric Series* (1935; 2d ed., 2 vols. 1959) and *Analytic Functions*, with S. Saks (2d ed. 1966); the latter book was awarded the prize of the Polish Academy in 1939.

For background information *see* CALCULUS, DIFFERENTIAL AND INTEGRAL; COMPLEX NUMBERS AND COMPLEX VARIABLES; SET THEORY; TRIGONOMETRY, PLANE in the McGraw-Hill Encyclopedia of Science and Technology. □

Indexes

Preface to the Indexes

Two indexes, an analytical and a classified, are offered to facilitate use of this biographical volume.

The first, the analytical index, provides a guide to persons, concepts, and terms mentioned in the text. The general arrangement is alphabetical, word by word. For a main entry the spelled-out form rather than an abbreviation is used; that is, "Deoxyribonucleic acid" is to be consulted rather than "DNA." Hyphenated words are treated as single words.

As in most indexes, it is advisable to look first under the most specific heading. For example, the reader interested in penicillin should look first under "Penicillin," not "Antibiotic." Some topics are listed only on the specific level. Others are listed under more general headings as well,

but the information is more complete under the specific heading.

It should be remembered that this is an index to a volume of scientific biographies, not to a scientific encyclopedia. Scientific concepts can be looked up in order to connect them with particular scientists. If an *explanation* of the concept is desired, the reader should consult the index to the *McGraw-Hill Encyclopedia of Science and Technology*.

The second index, the classified, lists major scientific fields followed by the names of the biographees closely associated with them. It will serve the reader interested in making comparisons among the careers of scientists in the same discipline, or in selecting one or more scientists in a particular field for further study.

X

Y

Z

Classified Index

BOTANY—*cont.*
Robertson, R. N.
Sears, E. R.
Sears, P. B.
Stebbins, G. L.
Steward F. C.
Tamiya, H.
Taylor, W. R.
Vickery H. B.
Walker, J. C.
Wardlaw, C. W.

CHEMICAL ENGINEERING
Danckwerts P. V.
Newitt, D. M.
Wilhelm, R. H.

CHEMISTRY
Abelson, P. H.
Anfinsen, C. B.
Arnon, D. I.
Badger, R. M.
Baker, W. O.
Ball, E. G.
Barker, H. A.
Bartlett, N.
Belozersky, A. N.
Berg, P.
Brachet, J. L. A.
Braunstein, A. E.
Brode, W. R.
Burn, J. H.
Butenandt, A.
Chargaff, E.
Cohen, S. S.
Cohn, W. E.
Cotton, F. A.
Coulson, C. A.
Craig, L. C.
Cram, D. J.
Dale, H. H.
Danckwerts, P. V.
Dent, C. E.
Djerassi, C.
Domagk, G.
Drickamer, H. G.
Dubinin, M. M.
Edsall, J. T.
Eigen, M.
Emmett, P. H.
Engelhardt, W. A.
Fieser, L. F.
Freudenberg, K. J.
Friedlander, G.
Fruton, J. S.
Fuoss, R. M.
Fuson, R. C.
Goldsmith, J. R.
Green, D. E.
Hammond, G. S.
Haurowitz, F. M.
Heidelberger, M.
Hirschfelder, J. O.
Holley, R. W.
Horecker, B. L.
Hornig, D. F.
Huisgen, R.
Huizenga, J. R.

CHEMISTRY—*cont.*
Kargin, V. A.
Keilin, D.
Kennedy, E. P.
Kety, S. S.
King, C. G.
Kluyver, A. J.
Kondratiev, V. N.
Lardy, H. A.
Lehninger, A. L.
Leloir, L. F.
Leonard, N. J.
Lingane, J. J.
Lipscomb, W. N.
Long, F. A.
Longuet-Higgins, H. C.
Maynard, L. A.
McCarty, M.
McConnell, H. M.
Mehl, R. F.
Meister, A.
Meyer, K.
Nachmansohn, D.
Nesmeyanov, A. N.
Neurath, H.
Newitt, D. M.
Nirenberg, M. W.
Pardee, A. B.
Pitzer, K. S.
Porter, G.
Potter, V. R.
Racker, E.
Rasmussen, J. O.
Roberts, J. D.
Rose, W. C.
Rossini, F. D.
Rossiter, R. J.
Ružička, L. S.
Sarett, L. H.
Schwarzenbach, G. K.
Sheehan, J. C.
Shemin, D.
Shemyakin, M. M.
Smyth, C. P.
Snell, E. E.
Spedding, F. H.
Strassmann, F.
Swift, E. H.
Szent-Györgyi, A.
Szwarc, M.
Tamiya, H.
Tarbell, D. S.
Thode, H. G.
Thompson, H. W.
Tishler, M.
Tréfouël, J.
Vickery, H. B.
Wall, F. T.
Walling, C. T.
Warburg, O. H.
Warner, J. C.
Weber, H. H.
Westheimer, F. H.
Wilhelm, R. H.
Williams, J. W.
Williams, R. J.
Wilson, E. B.
Wintersteiner, O. P.

CHEMISTRY—*cont.*
Wolfrom, M. L.
Wood, H. G.

CIVIL ENGINEERING
Kavanagh, T. C.

CRYSTALLOGRAPHY
Bernal, J. D.
Buerger, M. J.
Cochran, W.
Cottrell, A. H.
Darwin, C. G.
Mitchell, J. W.
Siegbahn, M.
Tolansky, S.
Wyckoff, R. W. G.

CYTOLOGY
Brachet, J. L. A.
Elkind, M. M.
Fell, H. B.
Mazia, D.
Metz, C. W.
Murray, R. G. E.
Potter, V. R.
Puck, T. T.
White, M. J. D.

ELECTRICAL AND ELECTRONIC ENGINEERING
Berkner, L. V.
Bush, V.
Busignies, H. G.
Eckert, J. P.
Essen, L.
Ginzton, E. L.
Goldmark, P. C.
Guillemin, E. A.
Hillier, J.
Kalman, R. E.
Ramo, S.
Whinnery, J. R.
Williams, F. C.

ENGINEERING
Berkner, L. V.
Brun, E. A.
Bush, V.
Busignies, H. G.
Danckwerts, P. V.
Dryden, H. L.
Eckert, J. P.
Essen, L.
Gaudin, A. M.
Ginzton, E. L.
Goldmark, P. C.
Goldstein, H.
Guillemin, E. A.
Hawthorne, W. R.
Hillier, J.
Hunt, F. V.
Kalman, R. E.
Kantrowitz, A. R.
Kavanagh, T. C.
Mehl, R. F.
Newitt, D. M.

ENGINEERING—*cont.*
Ramo, S.
Seamans, R. C.
Von Kármán, T.
Whinnery, J. R.
Wilhelm, R. H.
Williams, F. C.

ENTOMOLOGY
Dethier, V. G.
Knipling, E. F.
Lindauer, M.
Michener, C. D.
Roeder, K. D.
Williams, C. M.

EVOLUTION
Huxley, J. S.
Manton, S. M.
Mayr, E.
Moore, J. A.
Rensch, B.
Simpson, G. G.
Stebbins, G. L.
Waddington, C. H.
Wardlaw, C. W.

EXPERIMENTAL PSYCHOLOGY
Bartlett, F. C.
Carmichael, L.
Ditchburn, R. W.
Estes, W. K.
Galambos, R.
Guilford, J. P.
Hebb, D. O.
Konorski, J.
McFarland, R. A.
Miller, G. A.
Pfaffmann, C.
Piaget, J.
Richter, C. P.
Sperry, R. W.

GENETICS
Avery, O. T.
Benzer, S.
Brink, R. A.
Dunn, L. C.
Hotchkiss, R. D.
Huxley, J. S.
Kihara, H.
MacLeod, C. M.
Mather, K.
Metz, C. W.
Neel, J. V. G.
Pontecorvo, G.
Puck, T. T.
Sears, E. R.
Waddington, C. H.
White, M. J. D.
Yanofsky, C.
Zinder, N. D.

GEOLOGY
Anderson, C. A.
Bowen, N. L.
Buerger, M. J.

ORGANIC CHEMISTRY—*cont.*

Freudenberg, K. J.
Fuson, R. C.
Hammond, G. S.
Huisgen, R.
Leonard, N. J.
Long, F. A.
Nesmeyanov, A. N.
Prelog, V.
Roberts, J. D.
Ružička, L. S.
Sarett, L. H.
Sheehan, J. C.
Shemyakin, M. M.
Tarbell, D. S.
Tishler, M.
Tréfouël, J.
Westheimer, F. H.
Wintersteiner, O. P.
Wolfrom, M. L.

PALEONTOLOGY

Cooper, G. A.
Godwin, H.
Kellogg, A. R.
Newell, N. D.
Russell, L. S.
Sears, P. B.
Simpson, G. G.
Thomas, H. H.

PARASITOLOGY

Keilin, D.

PHARMACOLOGY

Burn, J. H.
Dale, H. H.
Djerassi, C.
Domagk, G.
Tishler, M.
Tréfouël, J.
Wintersteiner, O. P.

PHYSICAL ANTHROPOLOGY

Krogman, W. M.
Le Gros Clark, W. E.
Stewart, T. D.

PHYSICAL CHEMISTRY

Badger, R. M.
Baker, W. O.
Bartlett, N.
Cohn, W. E.
Cotton, F. A.
Coulson, C. A.
Drickamer, H. G.
Dubinin, M. M.
Eigen, M.
Emmett, P. H.
Friedlander, G.
Fuoss, R. M.
Hammond, G. S.
Herzfeld, K. F.
Hirschfelder, J. O.
Hornig, D. F.
Huizenga, J. R.

PHYSICAL CHEMISTRY—*cont.*

Kargin, V. A.
Kondratiev, V. N.
Lipscomb, W. N.
Long, F. A.
Longuet-Higgins, H. C.
McConnell, H. M.
Mehl, R. F.
Mitchell, J. W.
Neurath, H.
Pitzer, K. S.
Porter, G.
Rasmussen, J. O.
Rossini, F. D.
Smyth, C. P.
Spedding, F. H.
Strassmann, F.
Szwarc, M.
Thode, H. G.
Thompson, H. W.
Wall, F. T.
Walling, C. T.
Warner, J. C.
Westheimer, F. H.
Williams, J. W.
Wilson, E. B.

PHYSICS

Abelson, P. H.
Agnew, H. M.
Aigrain, P. R. R.
Andrade, E. N. da C.
Auger, P. V.
Batchelor, G. K.
Bates, L. F.
Beams, J. W.
Berkner, L. V.
Bernal, J. D.
Bleaney, B.
Bohr, A.
Brode, R. B.
Broglie, L. de
Brun, E. A.
Chew, G. F.
Cochran, W.
Condon, E. U.
Cottrell, A. H.
Dalitz, R. H.
Darwin, C. G.
Deutsch, M.
Dicke, R. H.
Ditchburn, R. W.
Dryden, H. L.
Duckworth, H. E.
Dyson, F. J.
Eckart, C.
Essen, L.
Fitch, V. L.
Forbush, S. E.
Franck, J.
Goldhaber, M.
Goldstein, H.
Gorter, C. J.
Herzberg, G.
Herzfeld, K. F.
Hillier, J.
Hirschfelder, J. O.
Houston, W. V.

PHYSICS—*cont.*

Hunt, F. V.
Jacquinot, P.
Kantrowitz, A. R.
Kastler, A.
Kemble, E. C.
London, H.
Maiman, T. H.
Marsden, E.
Marshak, R. E.
Martyn, D. F.
Meitner, L.
Mitchell, J. W.
Morse, P. M.
Néel, L. E. F.
Nier, A. O. C.
O'Brien, B.
Oppenheimer, J. R.
Peierls, R. E.
Pippard, A. B.
Pound, R. V.
Raman, C. V.
Ratcliffe, J. A.
Regge, T.
Sadron, C. L.
Seamans, R. C.
Sedov, L. I.
Seitz, F.
Sekera, Z.
Shoenberg, D.
Siegbahn, M.
Smith, C. S.
Stoner, E. C.
Teller, E.
Tolansky, S.
Van de Graaff, R. J.
Van Vleck, J. H.
Weisskopf, V. F.
Wheeler, J. A.
Wilkinson, D. H.

PHYSIOLOGY

Astwood, E. B.
Bremer, F.
Bronk, D. W.
Burwell, C. S.
Cole, K. S.
Courrier, R.
Dale, H. H.
Dragstedt, L. R.
Fenn, W. O.
Fessard, A. E.
Gerard, R. W.
Granit, R. A.
Harris, G. W.
Hartline, H. K.
Ingle, D. J.
Kety, S. S.
Konorski, J.
Landis, E. M.
Lim, R. K. S.
Loeb, R. F.
McFarland, R. A.
Moruzzi, G.
Pappenheimer, J. R.
Pfaffmann, C.
Pincus, G.
Pitts, R. F.

PHYSIOLOGY—*cont.*

Rushton, W. A. H.
Schmidt-Nielsen, K.
Visscher, M. B.
Warburg, O. H.
Weber, H. H.
Wilkins, R. W.
Young, J. Z.

PSYCHOLOGY

See Experimental
Psychology.

SOLID-STATE PHYSICS

Aigrain, P. R. R.
Bernal, J. D.
Cochran, W.
Cottrell, A. H.
Darwin, C. G.
Gorter, C. J.
London, H.
Maiman, T. H.
Mitchell, J. W.
Pippard, A. B.
Seitz, F.
Shoenberg, D.

STATISTICS

Cramér, H.

THEORETICAL AND
MATHEMATICAL
CHEMISTRY

Coulson, C. A.
Courant, R.

THEORETICAL AND
MATHEMATICAL
PHYSICS

Chew, G. F.
Dalitz, R. H.
Dicke, R. H.
Dyson, F. J.
Herzfeld, K. F.
Kemble, E. C.
Morse, P. M.
Peierls, R. E.
Regge, T.
Sedov, L. I.
Teller, E.
Van Vleck, J. H.
Weisskopf, V. F.
Wheeler, J. A.

VIROLOGY

Andrewes, C. H.
Cohen, S. S.
Dalldorf, G.
Meselson, M. S.
Williams, R. C.
Wyckoff, R. W. G.

ZOOLOGY

Dethier, V. G.
Dunn, L. C.
Fessard, A. E.